MANSHIP'S UK

CONCISE RARE SOUL 45RPM

Price Guide

*Includes: Northern Soul, Funk, Tamla Motown, Deep Soul,
60's through to 90's & much more.*

*RARE UK SOUL & TAMLA MOTOWN 45RPM
Over 30,000 titles compiled by John Manship.*

ACKNOWLEDGEMENTS

The author would like to thank the following friends and collectors for their invaluable help during this long project.

Neil Rushton, John Vincent, Keith Rylatt, Nick Haycock, Richard Yaxley, Glen Bellamy, Will Johnson and my staff Stella Morris, Karen Kemp, Julie Coley, Emma Coley and my partner Lisa Ruddy. Without these guys this 8 year project would maybe have been left unfinished.

FOREWORD

Somebody once told me my hobby of collecting Soul records must be "nice".

I was dumbfounded. Obsessive, maddening, satisfying, frustrating, selfish, expensive, silly – yes..but not something so humdrum could be defined as "nice"

In reality collecting rare and not so rare soul on vinyl is like a curable disease. You think you are all sorted and can relax and then when you do, something else appears on the horizon that you've just got to have

John Manship understands this, which is why I know this guide will be packed full of cold fact and red hot enthusiasm.

The thing I like about John is that he goes into trances. I don't know if he is aware of this or will appreciate me bringing it to the attention of the record collecting world but it's a fact. The first time he did it to me, we were listening to records – sorry masterpieces, made by Detroit's Pied Piper Production team. Since that time (and this is why this long awaited guide to British released soul singles will be so good) he has done it whilst looking at Northern Soul records released on UK labels. It could be caused by rarities like Ray Whitley on HMV, Darrell Banks on London, Hoagy Lands on Stateside or a Roy Hamilton on MGM. At other times they have not been rare at all, but still wonderful artefacts of soul music, recorded over there in America and released over here in UK at around the same time.

If those records had not been released in the UK they would not have been the catalyst that helped form and create the underground British Soul movement that started life with no name; became known as Rhythm n' Soul and turned into the monster that is the world recognised phase Northern Soul.

Yes this music is the music of Black America and we are all but mere customers of someone else's art. But the Northern Soul scene is also about 60's and 70's British teenagers who got turned on to this almost alien music and made it one of the cornerstones of their lives. With USA imports more or less inaccessible in the early years, these young enthusiasts had to rely on records licensed and released over here to get their hands on their chosen music. Which is why UK soul releases are so historic and important when considering Northern Soul.

As a young devotee I was privileged to be allowed to see the record collections of DJ Carl Dene and the iconic Midlands record collector Steve Glover. Rare USA label 45's from Richard Temple, Leon Haywood and Jackie Lee induced goose bumps, but it was the rows upon rows of the UK seven "inchers" that blew my mind. How come Gene Chandler's "Nothing Can stop Me" was on Stateside as well as Soul City? Why were the Coral "demo" labels a lovely blue, compared to the standard black label issues. Why were the Tamla Motown promo's red and white as well as green and white? Why did Atlantic have black label and red labels and yellow demo copies? How come the Los Angeles label Modern Records artist Jackie Day was released on Sue and stable mate Mary Love were issued on King and Stateside? Why was Doris Troy's "I'll Do Anything" released on Calla in the USA and Cameo Parkway in the UK. Why was Little Hank "Mr. Bang Bang Man" on both London American and UK Monument? What connections did Track have, that led them to releasing Revilot and Solid Hit recordings on Track and were releasing Ric Tic records in 1969 when Motown had bought the company in 1966, and could I have a copy of everything please!

To this day 45's like Formations "At The Top Of The Stairs" on UK MGM and Art Freeman's "Slipping Around" on UK Atlantic mean much more to me than the original releases on their respective USA labels. It probably doesn't seem logical to prefer Percy Millen on Stateside to the original Memphis Goldwax press and why would I sniff disdainfully when shown a Kim Weston 45 on Gordy, maybe because it doesn't compare with the Red & White promo's on Tamla Motown waiting at home. But that's the way it is and that's why many enthusiasts will be grateful for a guide to collecting British label releases.

I once spent a morning in Detroit surrounded by tens of thousands of Ric-Tic singles in the wonderful company of the former label's one time promotion man. Amongst those 45's I pulled out 100's of copies of one of my favourite recordings Edwin Starr's "I Have Faith In You" . Yet despite those treasured memories nothing can compare to my UK Polydor promo.

Don't get me wrong, I have also got the bug for USA soul releases, but for me, and many other "Old School" soul pioneers, our first love of British label releases will always be the most enduring. This book will help inform and sustain it.

Hopefully it will put you in a trance. Me I'm off to buy some records: Got any British mate?

Neil Rushton 2005

WE HAVE ALL BEING WAITING A LONG TIME

I would have probably got twenty years for murder, but that dark night in Mr M's almost 30 years ago I saw the lady I loved; "Wanting You" by April Stevens; we talked, we haggled, we unfolded huge sums of money but he would not sell – you could look but you couldn't touch!

This was a true virgin – unplayed UK rare vinyl, gorgeous pink adorned with a silver 'A'; this was almost the Mona Lisa. Weeks later another doll walked past – Nancy Ames "I don't want to talk about it"- Well she certainly didn't want to talk to me! And it went on and on, and then joy, bumping into Lynne Randell one night – total euphoria, the lady was for buying! So my love of the UK soul single started and in the days when a trip to Wigan meant you could hear Richard Searling play Nancy Wilson and Chapter Five and even stomp to "You got me where you want me" by Jon Ford when I played it in my set; the English soul single was by then well and truly established on the Northern Soul Scene.

Reading this book has reminded me that this fascination and deep devotion for these icons of soul vinyl still lives with me today, but above all when reading through the pages is my deep desire to consume as much information as possible, seeking out that missing number, the information which over the years has been so hard to come by! This then, is train spotting with a capitol 'T' this is the combined volume of all those elusive cuts issued in the UK, you can, if like me you were around at the time relive all those aural delights of these cherished discs, these were vinyl platters from our shores, this is VINYL HEAVEN, this is THE BOOK, read it, read it again, and yes I am a vinyl junkie.....................

John Vincent.
(Still searching)
Northern Soul DJ

THE AUTHOR'S VIEW

I wanted this guide to collecting UK release Soul 45's, to be more than a reference for values. Over the 40 years plus that Soul has been the first love for a large part of the British vinyl seeking fraternity, it is now an ideal opportunity to cover the history of UK Soul, which evolved into the world collecting phenomenon "Northern Soul", which is today the most collectable of all the different forms of vinyl 45 collectables. Britain in the early sixties, was the undisputed birthplace of Northern Soul.

The early sixties saw the all nightclubs around Britain filled with jazz enthusiasts. The UK jazz explosion started in the early 50's and carried on through the early 60's. With every university in the land having several young aspiring jazz groups and bands. Youngsters like John Mayall, Jimmy Powell, Graham Bond; Georgie Fame etc were gigging at such famous clubs as The Marquee, The Little Theatre, The Flamingo and many more. Jazz was the "in" sound, and the country's all night clubs were filled to the rafters with youngsters dancing and listening to those radical sounds.

But slowly it changed; R&B was getting vinyl release in the UK through Decca's London American, Top Rank, Vocalion etc. Jazz was getting too popular, too mainstream for the teenager looking for something exclusive, something hipper than his friend was listening to. Rock and Roll and teddy boys were so passé, The UK pop scene with the trend of a pop group being made up of 1 drummer, 3 guitarists and vocal of immature out of tune voices, hardly held the depth required for a more discerning ear. Probably a cutting and even blinkered viewpoint but I must say Brit-pop of the sixties always sounded empty to me, as it did to so many other youngsters.
From the well heeled middle class British teenagers who frequented jazz clubs, evolved the smartly dressed but working class R&B slanted teenager soon to be known as the "Mod"

1961 was a year of many R&B releases appeared on the release sheets, and review pages of the musical pop papers of the day. As USA music slowly broke through the years of black group harmony, rock and roll and pop vocals. A new sound was surfacing; it was a softer more melodic and happier Rhythm & Blues later to be termed "soul music". Across the USA music was changing; in New Orleans Ernie K. Doe, in Memphis provided Stax with it's first hit, in Chicago the raucous vocals of Etta James were being recorded, and all these records were to enjoy UK release. In every USA city there was a new sound being born and each city had a slightly different slant to it. Imagine a jazz club customer in 1961 first hearing The Mar-Keys "last night" it was a totally new experience. No jazz instrumental of the time could stand up to its infectious power, and pose the question was there any other music like this?

There sure was, a year later Booker T and his Memphis Group took the UK and the jazz artists by a storm. So much so that Georgie Fame started to play and seek out more R&B style music, at the famous all night sessions at the Flamingo Club in Wardour Street, London. Georgie switched from Jazz to his new found love R&B punching out "Green Onions" "Night Train" "Parchman Farm" "Work Song" and many more. Jazz as a night club music was fading.

With Tamla Motown providing EMI and Stateside with the UK's first soul number one the nation's youngsters were not only embracing a new sound, many were actively seeking it out by backtracking to 1960 and seeing what they had missed. As the more industrious vinyl fan turned up soul records by previously unknown artists by playing anything and everything in search of the "new". As word travelled, the race for the deletions boxes, market stalls and those independent record shops that ordered every 45 off the weekly release sheets, had begun. One of these sources may have a Nella Dodds, Sugar Pie DeSanto on Pye, a Lou Johnson, Round Robin, Rufus Thomas on London and if you didn't find any of them on your vinyl treasure hunt you still had the chance to discover a "soul" record you never knew before.

Soul was blooming, helped by UK groups like the Searchers who blandly covered The Drifters USA hits. The Hollies covered the Maurice Williams classic "Stay", the Rolling Stones exploded into the UK charts with Bobby and Cecil Womack's "It's All Over Now" to mention but a drop in the bucket. You couldn't escape the new wave of soul or soul style music. Soul was "the new kid on the block."

With the Mod scene now in full swing and various clubs up and down the country not only playing soul vinyl but also featuring UK live "soul" acts who were springing up everywhere. Jimmy James & the Vagabonds, Geno Washington & his Ram Jam Band, Alan Bown Set, the list was endless.

1965 and 1966 were the explosive years for "soul." . For the club DJ's it had to be R&B and Soul on the turntables, with the teenagers travelling to clubs that played USA soul. DJ's influenced the club scene so much, many clubs were excluding "white" music from their sets. Roger Eagle was the main DJ who everyone admired and copied. But Roger was well ahead of the competition and was spinning sounds that the punters had no idea where to get a copy from. Demand was mounting with clubs like The Esquire in Sheffield and The Twisted Wheel in Manchester playing very similar titles, demand for certain records was spreading and almost nationwide teenagers were searching for elusive, deleted and impossible 45's that only 6 months before may have been new releases.

Tamla Motown was racking up hit after hit, The Motown Revue had just toured the UK. EMI Stateside label's thirst for USA soul release seemed unquenchable. Dave Godin's Motown Appreciation Society fanzine and the New Musical Express were keeping the soul fan well informed, so it wasn't a lottery picking your selection of new releases to buy. But Mr. Eagle would always find a great tune everyone had overlooked.

The Mod following for the lifestyle and the music, just grew and grew, until it became a huge fashion and record collecting scene. To a Mod it was not just the clothes you wore, or how many wing mirrors your Vespa had. It was also a matter of musical knowledge, did you know who Felice Taylor was, or more importantly did you own a copy of here record. But you would always get the one-upmanship of "She's OK but how many Jackie Ross 45s do you own?"

By 1968 with clubs like The Nite Owl, Mojo, Beachcomber, Twisted Wheel, The Attic etc were not only playing soul music, but were presenting big USA acts like Billy Stewart, Ben E. King, Sam & Dave, Edwin Starr etc. The interest in the music was near epidemic. But that's when it happened Decca, EMI, Pye, etc had deleted their early soul 45 releases many years before but the club DJ's were still playing Alexander Patton, Chubby Checker, Round Robin, Roscoe Robinson, Major Lance. The demand for these titles was huge and the market in deleted soul 45's was booming, even though supply was very limited. So evolved the soul vinyl hound, I became one in 1969, before that I'd only heard tales at school of a guy on Birmingham market who had a Donnie Elbert "Little Piece Of Leather" for sale, or when Danny Reynold's older brother Tyrone was out on his Lambretta, we'd sneek a look at his 45 collection. We could mess around with those beautiful labels blue Stax, red Atlantic and that Sue label ..wow "Harlem Shuffle". When I left school in the summer of 1969, I had two quests. Get laid as many times as possible and to find as many soul 45's as possible. To be honest I'm not sure which was harder to come by, I would religiously scan release sheets every week, for anything that remotely resembled a soul release. Thinking I was somewhat unique I set about searching the cities of Leicester & Nottingham to add to my growing collection. But when in the autumn of 1969 I entered college in Leicester I realised why my task was mostly fruitless. Everyone in my class and years above were soul freaks.

I learnt more about club soul in the first month at college than I did in my previous 16 years. Cassette tapes with Mickey Lee Lane, Homer Banks, Hoagy Lands would blast out in the lunch breaks, I was spellbound and felt so inferior to these "city" kids who were just streets ahead in knowledge and accessibility.

That first year at college turned me into an addicted vinyl hound, but I had serious competition at the tuesday and thursday market stall ,I would have to beat Mick Stacy, Chris & Steve Frost, Peter Tierney and a host of others to get a chance of anything good. My heart sank one day, when a guy I'd not seen before, bought a Thrills on UK Capitol in front of my eyes. I'd never heard of the group but when it was spun on the stall holders portable player the hair on the back of my neck stood up, wow I must find one of them…just to underline the rarity of UK pressed soul in the 36 years since, I never have.

In Leicester like all major UK cities there were several sources for 45's A.T. Brown's had maybe 15,000 to 20,000 45's without sleeves all in long wooden boxes all in label order and all without sleeves to make looking at them a much slicker task. I'd wiz through them as quick as possible on my one hour lunch break, with every 45 making that zipping friction crunch as the 45 edge would slide over another 45's grooves. I was often not alone as many as 5 or 6 teenagers would stand shoulder to shoulder their fingers full of anxiety just in case the competition finds something before they do. On reflection the shop had been wiped clean of anything great years before, but I found my very first unknown there. Chapter Five's version of Maxine Brown's "One in a Million," Wand had just reissued Maxine's version so I knew the song, but not by these guys. If something "new" was played at the weekend at the Torch or The Junction on a UK release, there was a great chance that it would be there. Chris Frost found a few copies of Wayne Gibson's "Under My Thumb" the weekend after it was played at The Torch. But his major find was the copy of George Blackwell "Can't Lose My Head" in a small village at the edge of Leicester called Blaby. This looking for soul 45's was a damn exciting hobby and for some very financially rewarding.

By 1970 all the "Soul" clubs were playing unobtainable 45's, the trickle of USA imports that had started a few years earlier had turned into a torrent and the UK 45's were relegated to 2nd. Place. Even the most avid, UK collector on seeing the different vinyl and labels of the import, had been know to go home, to spend the whole evening pushing the small hole centres out of his 45's, or even drill holes through the labels as to resemble USA 45 cut outs. Or as in the case of Keith Rylatt whose family didn't own a drill, he used a heated knitting needle. Now you know why so many rare UK soul 45's have been defaced in some peculiar way.

For me the lure of the import was too much, I sold my whole collection for £18 to buy Jimmy Soul Clark's "Sweet Darling", Dick Jensen's "Groove With What You've Got" Tee Fletcher's "Thank You Baby" from Brian 45 Philips. The US bug had bit me, but it was 5 years before I could afford my first buying trip to the States after the Gas Board had sacked me as a hopeless case and a certified danger to the public.

By 1971 the Golden Torch in Stoke was a huge "Rare Soul" venue, with the Catacoombs in Wolverhampton, Magic Lantern in Market Harborough, and Up The Junction in Crewe these were just a few of the clubs that creating future foundations for collecting Soul.

1972 saw the greatest night ever in the history of UK soul when Chicago's Major Lance appeared live at The Torch on that memorable lock-out Saturday night on December 9th. 1972. Since then the Northern Soul scene has steadily mushroomed into what it is today: The world's most talked about, but misunderstood vinyl collecting obsession.

AN UNDERSTANDING

As it's a partially DJ driven hobby and prices can in some cases be dictated by its current club turntable exposure, I've tried to unravel some of the misconceptions of collecting UK soul.

All prices in this book are values John Manship Records would expect to sell the 45 for, in excellent plus condition throughout: It is totally unrealistic to quote the values of MINT unplayed records. MINT records in the year 2005 are extremely difficult to find, MINT copies of any 45 listed within these pages should carry a small premium to the value.

Vinyl in excellent plus condition: vinyl should retain much of it's "new" shine, but may have a small amount of very light marks, caused by sleeve or hand contact, it should NOT have any scratches caused by contact with grit or dirt, certainly no scratches that dull the overall newness of the vinyl and no scratches that are audible on the stylus.
Label in excellent plus condition: The label to be classed in this condition must be free of any writing, water stains, tears, sticker residue marks, drill holes, ring wear on the higher ridges of the label and most importantly retain its original centre. Note: Records that have had their original centre removed should be value at 1/3rd. of the value of a completely fault free excellent plus copy. This rule does not apply to companies who released the 45 with a clean "machine dinked" larger hole.

DJ COPY VS STOCK

Just recently some dealers / collector and self appointed "expert" have wrote and said some ridiculous things about the rarity and the value of UK Soul 45 promotional copies. Record Collector have even quoted a certain 45 to be rarer on a stock copy than a promo. Whether it be rarer or not, in 99% of cases of collecting UK Soul records the DJ copy will achieve a higher value, because they are infinitely more attractive and in 99% of cases infinitely harder to find.

There is a misconception that few people actually bought these 45's on release in the 60's, so the promo must be rarer. This is so far from the truth, that I'd like to offer the following points for your consideration.

Throughout the 60's UK record shops were in serious competition with each other. Many shops, in fact maybe more than one, to every major town and city would order at least one copy of everything from the weekly release sheet. Owners wanted to be seen as the shop, that could say yes to the customer without special ordering.
Ainley's in Leicester was "raided" for all their worthwhile soul releases from 1965 to 69 they had, like many shops up and down the country, unsold stock just filed on their shelves. When Nancy Ames "I Don't Want To Talk About It" was first played at the Blackpool Mecca in 1971. Steve Frost walked into Ainley's and got one straight off the back wall racks, everything filed by label and label number. This shop was not even slightly unusual, most larger shops had this policy but cash flow and the amount of customers through the door dictated to what degree this policy was followed. Famous shops with back catalogue 45's were discovered in Sandbach, Bristol, Galashiels, Derby, Sheffield and Bow in London. As late as the early and mid seventies there were still outlets absolutely crammed with everything a soul collector could wish for:

The Sandbach shop received a mention in Blues & Soul, a Klondyke Soul rush took place rendering the shop bare of soul 45's within days. The Bristol shop was allegedly Pete Widdison's personal Alladin's Cave for many years, but I still found hundreds of soul records there well into the late seventies.

The Galashiels shop was one of the major and most interesting stories to unfold. Dickie Watt went to University there, and passed the music shop daily on his way to class. One day passing the window he saw a Chess EP cover of Fontella Bass & Bobby McClure in the window. Pinching myself, he ventured over the threshold for the first time. A very polite Scottish lady asked if she could help, Dickie pointed to the EP in the window and promptly bought it. As he was about to turn and leave, the lady asked "anything else I can help you with, today?" Dickie thought awhile and then out popped the stupid question "Do you have anything on Stateside?". "Auch ey" the lady turned to the back wall of huge filing cabinets and pulled out a draw 2 foot long! Dickie was absolutely astonished, as the deep blue sleeves revealed themselves, gleaming in front of his eyes. Dickie looked at the lady and questioned "Are those are all Stateside's?" "Yes, and we have more in these two drawers also" pulling two identical drawers open. You can only imagine Dickie shouting Sue! Chess! Vocalion, Tamla Motown!

Many 50's & 60's record Shops had the attitude, of wanting to say yes to unusual requests. Violet May's record shop in Sheffield with a stock of over 20,000 45's allegedly could pull requested soul records off the shelves, like a magician with rabbits and doves.

The grand daddy shop of them all though, must have been the legendary shop in Bow, London. During the fifties and sixties the Jewish owner would order absolutely every release from the release sheets, sometimes multiple copies. The shop was a closely guarded secret, I heard later it was visited by Ian Clark and his brother and a selected few. They would come away with more or less any 45's they had requested.

In 1975 the Jewish owner sold his interest in the shop, when two young guys took over they started to list the 45's in Record Collector. I noticed an advert, with a solid run on the Fontana Label for auction. It was all there, Sandy Wynns "Touch of Venus", Johnny Carr, Jimmy Cliff etc, etc. I was straight on the phone begging to be allowed to view their stock. Eventually my persistence paid off as the reaction from the auction, disappointed the new retailers.

The shop was on the bustling street in Bow where the market stalls ran the whole length of the street, waiting outside for the shop to open, the anticipation was killing me. Once inside, I was lead down to a racked out cellar which held 1000's upon 1000's of 45's, all in the same condition as the day they were made. Rows and rows of orange Tamla Motown, olive Tamla Motown sleeves, the blue of Stateside, the yellow and white of the Oriole section. I didn't know where to start, the place was full to the rafters with neatly organised 45's all in label and number order. If I spent £300 they were a £1.00 each, less if I spent more. Spending £300 was easy but I'd only brought £500 with me. After running through the Orioles and coming up with The Valadiers, Mike & The Modifyers, Eddie Holland I was leaving Stevie Wonder and Marvin Gaye my money just would stretch any further as I had a box full of Stateside, United Artists, a few Sue's and all the 500 series Tamla Motown. This place was more than a dream, it was soul seekers utopia. After a couple of hours I'd run out of money.

A week later I was back, and finally the week after that. On the last week with less to search through, I started to investigate the cellar more thoroughly. I noticed some huge filing cabinets. Inside the small drawers were handwritten file cards for every 45 the old owner had ever bought. All noted with artist name A+B sides label distributor and full label number,number of copies ordered, amount re-ordered, and a note and date of every record sold. An absolutely astonishing archive that I found interesting, and spent about 30 minutes browsing it. Today it would have been the definitive file on all UK 60's releases and a constant reference guide. Inside I found order cards for Denis D'ell "Better Use Your Head" - ordered 1 copy sold 1 copy with note for the re-order, saying "deleted". Order cards included Garnett Mimms "Looking For You" ordered 8 copies sold 6 and I had found 2 copies. When I look back on those three visits, I recognised how little I knew about record dealing. Having run out of soul 45's, I purchased the entire run of the Apple label thinking they would be a great investment. Then as I was about to leave I asked if I could use the toilet. He led me to the far end of the cellar, pointing to a door. As I stood there relieving myself, I was realised I was leaning on floor to ceiling tower 3 foot long record boxes standing three abreast squeezed tight against the porcelain bowl and the wall. I estimated I had about 10,000 45's to look through. I pushed the door ajar and shouted "what's in these boxes?". The guy replied "it's all ska & reggae" sure enough the boxes were marked Coxone, Blue Beat, Doctor Bird, Black Swan, Bamboo and Ackee. He quickly added "you can have the lot for £100", I quickly retorted "Are you kidding, what do I want that crap for" Looking back I realise it's wasn't the first or last time I'd make a bad decision, whilst holding my dick!

DJ and STOCK COPY PRICES

The point of all these record hunting stories, is that the stock copies did leave the distributors because the shops were ordering them. But the demand a few years later outstripped supply, and were quickly sniffed out by the young soul vinyl pioneers searching for that elusive tune. In todays market every "Soul Sound" label bootleg is infinitely rarer than its Stateside, London or Cameo Parkway original counterpart. There were an estimated 200/250 "Soul Sounds" pressed, so we can estimate that from special orders and shop orders most of the rare 60's soul 45's sold at least 200 to 300 copies. That is a guess, but the maths stack up. When was the last time you even saw a 45 on the "Soul Sounds" label?

It was recently suggested in soul fanzine "Manifesto" that the promo's of 60's UK 45's must be commoner. This suggestion only validates the lack of understanding of the developing sixties British 45 market by those who arrived on the scene "late". But if you only joined the soul scene 15 years after its releasing peak, you can be excused for making the wrong assumption. The UK music market was not like that of the USA, in the states RCA could make and send out 10,000 promo 45's per title. There were after all, thousands of radio stations and I have seen as many as ten copies of the same promo in old radio station stock and there are almost as many music reviewers. The numbers start to add up, especially when you add the countless promo guys, rack jobbers, distributors etc. So the difference in rarity of a non-hit USA RCA stock copy to a DJ copy can be significant. Not so, in the UK where promo 45's were only posted to two principle areas, firstly, radio stations & TV stations in the UK, Europe, B.F.P.O., and Commonwealth countries and secondly music reviewers.

1. Radio stations in the sixties were limited to the BBC (remembering radio 1,2,3 & 4 were not born yet) and pirate radio or free radio as it was affectionately known were Radio London, Caroline North, Caroline South, Radio City, Radio Essex, Radio 355 / 227, Tower Radio, Radio Hauraki, Radio 390, Radio Veronica, Radio Scotland, Radio 270 and of course Radio Luxenbourg. These would all get promo 45's. Promo copies were certainly sent as far away as Singapore and often turned up in Europe. But it is universally agreed that maybe no more than 100, and even if the figures were larger, promo copies of UK 45's were scattered across the world. And many still remain in Radio Station libraries or in DJ's collections with the old commonwealth countries.

2. Music reviewers were certainly sent promo copies but the only significant find was in Sheffield. The local Sheffield pop reporter sold his whole hoard to a dealer in Nottingham, when the dealer asked where were the Beatles and Rolling Stones promo 45's the reviewer had given them away to various paperboys as Christmas tips!

3. UK promo soul singles are highly prized and are seriously hard to find. The numbers were limited, and have never been available at street level. I looked for UK soul 45's every spare minute I could during the late 60's and early 70's, in all that time I can never ever remember finding a red & white EMI promo of any significance. I thought at first I was just unlucky, but over the years many renowned collectors have confirmed the same frustration. Most promotion copies of these most desirable of 45's have surfaced over the years, through DJ's collections, music reviewer's clear-outs, and sometimes apparently finding the outside world, by leaving the building unlawfully via being pushed down the trouser fronts of radio station employees. One influx of promo 45's happened in the 90's when Granada TV sold off their vinyl library. I personally had two good hauls of promo 45's. One from Belgium and one from France. But as for the UK the classic soul 45 on a promo, it is still a most difficult piece to find and is correctly revered for its rarity and its design, and consequently its high price.

Collecting UK soul 45's is a difficult task, made harder by the limited numbers in circulation. But over the years the UK 45 has proved a profitable investment as the chances of any titles "turning up" in any quantities are virtually nil. There is certainly no chance of the "Danny Moore" syndrome happening to a UK release soul 45.

Good hunting

John Manship

HOW TO USE THIS GUIDE

Firstly this guide, is exactly that. The values quoted are the prices we would expect to achieve on set sale for excellent plus condition 45's, with no label defects.

Values in BOLD type are actual prices achieved on internet auction on www.raresoulman.co.uk weekly auctions.

All listings are in LABEL ORDER

YEAR OF RELEASE

First number indicates the year of release. All these years have been researched through Blues & Soul, Rock Rom, release sheets, and other reliable sources. In my research I found other price guides were consistently inaccurate when quoting year of release. And the date printed on the label more often than not, referred to the date of the publishing NOT the date release of the vinyl. Eg: Ike & Tina Turners "Dust My Broom" on HMV the label date reads 1966. This 45 was released both in the USA and the UK in 1967.

LABEL RELEASE NUMBER

All label numbers were taken wherever possible from the actual record. Again during research I found too many inaccurate releases numbers taken from other sources than the record itself.

DJ = promotional release press, not sold in the shops.

Unissued = schedule release did not happen. Acetate or test press may exist but   at the moment unconfirmed.

sh = small hole centre.

lh = large die cut centre.

Die cut = machine cut four pronged attached centre.

Ink = plastic screen printed label

Paper = A paper as apposed to the screen print method used on the same release.

Test press = in house press for quality control purposes.

A colour quoted after the number, is a variation of the LABEL colours.

A colour then the word VINYL, indicates different coloured vinyl

PS = release with a picture sleeve also.

sold subject to = EMI 45 releases during the 60's had the following printed on the center. "SOLD IN THE U.K. SUBJECT TO RESALE PRICE CONDITIONS SEE PRICE LIST". EMI ceased the practice in late 1969. But EMI continually repressed many classic titles using the same release number and same label design but omitted "sold subject to conditions"

NO sold subject = 70's EMI repress 45.

A-SIDE TITLE

The first title quoted is the most significant side for soul collectors, not necessarily the A-side it was released with. Flipside immediately follows this.

VALUE = estimated price that would be achieved at sale.

Remember this is a price guide not a pricing bible. But this guide, as with all MANSHIP'S PRICE GUIDES, 90% of values quoted are taken directly from recent sales or similar type sales, achieved from our own sales catalogues or website purchases. More UK soul 45's are sold from www.raresoulman.co.uk than any other single source in the world.

CONTENTS

Artiste listing indicating label release(s) .... page 1 – 16

Alphabetical label listing.

Artiste listings indicating label release(s)

? and the MYSTERIANS – see Q
100 PROOF - HOT WAX
100 PROOF AGED IN SOUL - HOT WAX
100% PURE POISON - EMI
1984 - BIG T
21ST. CREATION - MOTOWN UK
3 OUNCES OF LOVE - MOTOWN UK
4 SEASONS - PHILIPS
5 MILES OUT - ACTION
5 STAIRSTEPS - BUDDAH
5000 VOLTS - PHILIPS
5TH. DIMENSION – ABC, LIBERTY, MOTOWN UK
8TH. DAY - INVICTUS

A

A BAND OF ANGELS c/w JASON KNIGHT - SOUL SUPPLY
A TASTE OF HONEY - CAPITOL
ABBOTT, BILLY & the JEWELS - CAMEO PARKWAY
ABICAIR, SHIRLEY – PICCADILLY
A BROTHERS GUIDING LIGHT - SEVENS
ACE, BUDDY – VOCALION, ACTION
ACE, JOHNNY – VOCALION, VOGUE
ACKLIN, BARBARA – BRUNSWICK, MCA
ACT ONE - MERCURY
ACTION - PARLOPHONE
AD LIBS – BUDDAH, CHARLY, CONTEMPO RARIES, SOUL
    CITY, RED BIRD, DEEP SOUL, INFERNO
ADAMS APPLES - BRUNSWICK
ADAMS APPLES c/w JACKIE WILSON - KENT
ADAMS, ARTHUR - RCA
ADAMS, ARTHUR K. - BLUE HORIZON
ADAMS, BILLY - LONDON
ADAMS, GAYLE - EPIC
ADAMS, JOHNNY - SPECIAL AGENT, POLYDOR, ATLANTIC
ADAMS, JUNE - KING
ADDERLEY, CANNONBALL - CAPITOL
ADENO, BOBBY - VOCALION
ADLIBS - FONTANA
ADMIRATIONS - SOUL CITY
AFRICAN BEAVERS - RCA
AFRICAN MUSIC MACHINE – CONTEMPO, CONTEMPO
    RARIES, MOJO
AFRIQUE - PYE INTERNATIONAL
AFRO DIMENSIONS - JAY BOY
AGENTS – GRAPEVINE, WIGAN CASINO
AKENS, JEWEL - LONDON
AKENS, JEWELL - EMBER
AKKERMAN, JAN - ATLANTIC
ALAIMO, STEVE – HMV, PYE INTERNATIONAL, ATLANTIC
ALBINO GORILLA - EMBER
ALDO, STEVE - PARLOHPONE
ALDO, STEVE & the CHALLENGERS - DECCA
ALDRICH, RONNIE - DECCA
ALESHURE - PHOENIX
ALEXANDER, ARTHUR – BUDDAH, LONDON
ALEXANDER, GOLDIE - PROJECT
ALLEN GROUP, RANCE - STAX
ALLEN, L c/w WARD, HERB - SEVENS
ALLEN, PATRICK - K&B
ALLENS - MOWEST
ALLEY - JAY BOY
ALLNIGHT BAND - CASINO CLASSICS
AMAZING DANCING BAND - VERVE
AMBASSADORS - JOX
AMBELIQUE - GOLDSOUL
AMBOY DUKES - POLYDOR
AMBROSE, SAMMY - STATESIDE
AMERICAN BREED – STATESIDE, DOT
AMERICAN GYPSY - CBS
AMERICAN POETS - LONDON
AMERICAN YOUTH CHIOR - POLYDOR
AMES, NANCY - COLUMBIA
ANACOSTIA - CBS

ANDERSON BROS. - SEVENS
ANDERSON, CARL - EPIC
ANDERSON, CAROL – GRAPEVINE, GRAPEVINE 2000
ANDERSON, CAROL - SEVENS
ANDERSON, ERNESTINE - MERCURY, STATESIDE, SUE
ANDERSON, GENE - LONDON
ANDERSON, JAMES - ATLANTIC
ANDERSON, KIP - PRESIDENT
ANDERSON, ROSHELL - CONTEMPO
ANDERSON, ROSHELL - CONTEMPO
ANDERSON, UDELL T. - DIRECTION
ANDREWS, ERNIE - CAPITOL
ANDREWS, JOHN & the LONELY ONES - PARLOPHONE
ANDREWS, LEE – T.B. SUPER SOUL, WIGAN CASINO
ANDREWS, RUBY – ABC, SEVENS
ANGEL, MARION - COLUMBIA
ANGELS - PYE INTERNATIONAL, MERCURY, PHILIPS
ANGELS ONE FIVE - PYE
ANGLOS – FONTANA, ISLAND, SUE, BRIT
ANKA, PAUL - RCA
ANN, BEVERLEY – RCA, SOS,
ANNIS - GTO
ANTHONY & THE IMPERIALS - UNITED ARTISTS
ANTHONY, DAVE - MERCURY
ANTHONY, LITTLE WAYNE - JAY BOY
ANTHONY, RAY - MANGO MEDIA
ANTHONY, SHEILA - ROUTE
ANTIQUES c/w UTOPIAS - SEVENS
ANTOINETTE - PICCADILLY
ANTON, REY & the PEPPERMINT MEN - PARLOPHONE
APOLLO - MOTOWN UK
APPLEJACKS - CBS
APPRECIATIONS - SOUL CITY, DESTINY
AQUARIAN DREAM - BUDDAH
AREETY, COLIN - DERAM
ARMADA ORCHESTRA – CONTEMPO, CONTEMPO RARIES
ARMSTRONG, CHUCK – ACTION
ARMSTRONG , JIMMY - HORACES
ARNAU, B.J. - MOJO
ARNELL, GINNY - MGM
ARNIE'S LOVE - STREETWAVE
ARNOLD, BILLY BOY - CHARLY
ARNOLD, CALVIN - MGM
ARNOLD, P.P. – IMMEDIATE, POLYDOR, VIRGIN
ARPEGGIO - POLYDOR
ARROWS - PYE
ART WOODS - DECCA
ARTISTICS – BRUNSWICK, CORAL, MCA
ASHFORD & SIMPSON - WARNER BROS, CAPITOL
ASHFORD, JACK & SOUND OF NEW DETROIT - LONDON
ASHLEY, TYRONE - PYE INTERNATIONAL, TOMORROW
ASTORS - ATLANTIC
ATKINS - WARNER BROS
ATKINSON, SWEET PEA - ZE RECORDS
ATLANTA DISCO BAND - ARIOLA
ATLANTIC STARR - A&M
ATLANTIS - JAY BOY
ATMOSFEAR - MCA
AUGER TRINITY, BRIAN – COLUMBIA, MARMALADE
AUGER, BRIAN - COLUMBIA
AUGER'S OBLIVION EXPRESS, BRIA - CBS
AUSTIN, PATTI - CBS, EPIC, PROBE, QWEST, UNITED ARTISTS
AUGUST & DENEEN – ABC, MCA
AVERAGE WHITE BAND - ATLANTIC
AYERS UBIQUITY, ROY - POLYDOR
AYSHEA - POLYDOR
AZYMUTH – MILESTONE

B

BABE RUTH - CAPITOL
BACHARACH & his ORCHESTRA, BURT - LONDON
BAD WEATHER INC: - SOUL CITY
BAKER SELECTION, GEORGE - PENNY FARTHING

BAKER, ERNEST - GRAPEVINE 2000
BAKER, LAVERN - FLOORFILLERS, HORACES, LONDON
BAKER, SAM - MONUMENT
BAKER, YVONNE c/w PARIS, BOBBY - LONDON
BALDRY, LONG JOHN - UNITED ARTISTS
BALLAD, HANK - MOJO
BALLARD, FLORENCE - STATESIDE
BALLARD, HANK & the MIDNIGHTERS - PARLOPHONE
BALTIMORE & OHIO MARCHING BAND - STATESIDE
BALTIMORE FIRST CLASS - ALL PLATINUM
BAND OF ANGELS - GREEN LIGHT, PICCADILLY
BAND OF ANGELS c/w SOUL SISTERS - GREENLIGHT
BANDWAGON - DIRECTION
BANKS, BESSIE – CONTEMPO, RED BIRD, SOUL CITY, VERVE
BANKS, DARRELL – ATLANTIC, STAX, STATESIDE,
    CONTEMPO, LONDON, SEVENS
BANKS, HOMER - GREEN LIGHT, LIBERTY, MIDNIGHT HOUR,
    MINIT, UA MIDNIGHT HOUR, UNITED ARTISTS
BANKS, LARRY - STATESIDE
BANKS, ROSE - TAMLA MOTOWN
BANZAI - CONTEMPO
BARBARA & BRENDA - DIRECTION
BARKAN, MARK - STATESIDE
BAR-KAYS – ATLANTIC, STAX
BARKER, BUTCH - CREOLE
BARNES, BARNEY J. - DECCA
BARNES, DENA - GRAPEVINE
BARNES, J.J. – ACHIEVEMENT, CASINO CLASSICS ,
    CONTEMPO, HAYLEY, GROOVESVILLE, INFERNO, MOTOR
    CITY, MOTOWN, STAX, TAMLA MOTOWN
BARNES, J.J./BANKS, DARRELL - SEVENS
BARNES, SIDNEY - CHARLY
BARNUM, H.B. – CAPITOL, FONTANA, RCA
BARONS - JAY BOY
BARRETT, RITCHIE - LONDON
BARRETTO, RAY – LONDON, COLUMBIA
BARRINO BROTHERS - INVICTUS
BARRY LEN - BRUNSWICK, MCA
BARRY, LEN – BELL, BRUNSWICK, CAMEO PARKWAY, MCA,
    NOW, RCA
BARRY, SANDRA - PYE
BARTLEY, CHRIS - RIGHT ON, BELL, CAMEO PARKWAY
BASIC BLACK & PEARL - BUS STOP
BASIE, COUNT & his ORCHESTRA - FONTANA
BASS, BILLY - PAMA
BASS, FONTELLA – CHESS, CONTEMPO, MOJO
BASS, FONTELLA & BOBBY MCCLURE - CHESS
BASS, JEWELL - SPECIAL AGENT
BATAAN – EPIC, RCA
BATAAN, JOE - RCA
BATEMAN, JUNE/NOBLE WATTS BAND - SUE
BATES, JOHN - CBS
BATISTE, ROSE c/w GEORGE LEMONS - SEVENS
BATS - DECCA
BATTLE, JEAN - MOJO
BB + Q - COOL TEMPO
BEAN, CARL - MOTOWN UK
BEAS - PAMA
BEATSTALKERS - CBS
BEAUMONT, JIMMY - LONDON
BEAVERS, JACKEY – BUDDAH, JAY BOY
BEAZERS - DECCA
BEDFORD, CHUCK - ROCKFIELD
BEE, EDWIN - DECCA
BEGINNING OF THE END - ATLANTIC
BEL CANTOS - R&B
BELL BROTHERS - ACTION
BELL, ARCHIE & the DRELLS – ACHIEVEMENT, ARCHIVES,
    ATLANTIC, NIGHTMARE, PIR, PORTRAIT
BELL, MADELINE – COLUMBIA, HMV, PHILIPS,
BELL, WILLIAM – ATLANTIC, MERCURY, STAX
BELL, WILLIAM & CLAY, JUDY - STAX
BELLE, CADO - ANCHOR

BELLES – CONTEMPO, CONTEMPO RARIES, PRESIDENT
BENNETT, BOBBY – CBS, COLUMBIA, LONDON
BENNETT, BRIAN - FONTANA
BENNETT, CLIFF & the REBEL ROUSERS - PARLOPHONE
BENNY & TINA - MERCURY
BENSON, BARRY - PARLOPHONE
BENSON, GEORGE – CTI, WARNER BROS
BENTON, BROOK – ATLANTIC, MERCURY
BENTON, BUSTER – CHARLY, RONN
BERNARD, KENNY – CBS, PYE
BERNARD, KENNY – PYE DISCO DEMAND
BERNSTEIN, ELMER - MGM
BERRY STREET STATION - CRYSTAL
BERRY, CHUCK – CHESS, MERCURY, PYE INTERNATIONAL
BERRY, DAVE - DECCA
BERRY, RICHARD & the PHARAOHS - EMBER
BETTERS, HAROLD - SUE
BEVERLEY - DERAM
BEVERLY, FRANK & THE BUTLERS - INFERNO
BEVERLY, FRANK – CAPITOL, SEVENS
BIDDU ORCHESTRA - EPIC
BIG BORIS - RCA
BIG MAC - CHARLY
BIG MAYBELLE – CBS, DIRECTION, JOE BOY, LONDON
BILLUPS, EDDIE - GRAPEVINE 2000
BIRDLEGS & PAULINE - SUE
BIRDS - DECCA
BIRDS OF A FEATHER - PAGE ONE
BIRKIN, JANE & GAINSBOROUGH, SERGE- FONTANA,
    MAJOR MINOR
BISHOP, EDDIE - KENT
BLACK ABBOTS - EVOLUTION
BLACK BLOOD - BRADLEYS
BLACK HEAT - ATLANTIC
BLACK IVORY – KWANZA, POWER EXCHANGE
BLACK NASTY - GRAPEVINE
BLACK SATIN feat. FRED PARRIS - BUDDAH
BLACK STASH - SEVILLE
BLACK, BILL - LONDON
BLACK, CODY c/w JIMMY BURNS - TOP DOG
BLACK, JAY - UNITED ARTISTS
BLACK, MARTIN - 20TH. CENTURY
BLACKBYRDS - FANTASY
BLACKFOOT, J. - ALLEGIANCE
BLACKS COMBO, BILL - LONDON
BLACK'S COMBO, BILL - LONDON
BLACKWELL, GEORGE - WIGAN CASINO
BLAIR, LITTLE JOHNNY - PYE DISCO DEMAND
BLAKE, COREY - GRAPEVINE 2000
BLAND, BILLY – ATLANTIC, LONDON, VOGUE
BLAND, BOBBY – ABC, ACTION, KENT, SUE, VOGUE,
    VOCALION
BLENDELLS - REPRISE
BLINKY & EDWIN STARR - TAMLA MOTOWN
BLISS, MELVIN - CONTEMPO
BLOOD SWEAT AND TEARS - CBS
BLOODSTONE - DECCA
BLOSSOMS – MGM, MOJO, PAMA
BLOW MONKEYS with CURTIS MAYFIELD - RCA
BLUE CHIPS - PYE
BLUE MAGIC – ATLANTIC, STREETWAVE
BLUES BUSTERS – ISLAND, JAY BOY
BLUESOLOGY - FONTANA
BO STREET RUNNERS - COLUMBIA , DECCA , OAK
BO, EDDIE - ACTION
BOB & EARL BAND - JAY BOY
BOB & EARL. - B&C, CONTEMPO RARIES, ISLAND, JAY BOY,
    SUE, UNI, WARNER BROS
BOB AND EARL BAND - JAY BOY
BOB & FRED - SEVENS
BOBBETTES - ACTION
BOBBY M featuring JEAN CARN - GORDY
BO-BELLES - ARISTA
BOBO, WILLIE - VERVE
BOCKY AND THE VISIONS - ATLANTIC

BODDY, J.P. - COLUMBIA
BOHANNON, HAMILTON - BRUNSWICK
BOLAN, MARC & GLORIA JONES - EMI
BOMBERS - FLAMINGO
BOND ORGANISATION, GRAHAM – COLUMBIA, DECCA
    PAGE ONE
BOND, ISABEL - MAJOR MINOR
BOND, JACKI - COLUMBIA ,STRIKE
BOND, JOYCE – AIRBORNE, ISLAND, PAMA, UPFRONT
BOND, JOYCE & LITTLE JOHN - PAMA
BONDS, GARY (U.S.) - STATESIDE
BONDS, U.S. - TOP RANK
BONE, DRIZA - 4TH. + BROADWAY, JOE BOY, SOUL HQ
BONE, OLIVER and SOUNDS MAXIMUM - PARLOPHONE
BONNEY, GRAHAM – COLUMBIA, EMI
BONNIE & the TREASURES - LONDON
BOO, BETTY - GRAPEVINE
BOO, BETTY c/w BELLES - WIGAN CASINO
BOOGIE MAN ORCHESTRA - CONTEMPO
BOOKER T. & THE MG'S – ATLANTIC, LONDON, STAX
BOOKER, JAMES – VOGUE, VOCALION
BOOMERANGS - FONTANA
BOONE, JESSE – SEVENS
BOONE FAMILY - MOWEST
BOONES - TAMLA MOTOWN
BOOTSY'S RUBBER BAND - WARNER BROS
BOUNTY, JAMES - SEVENS
BOWEN, JIMMY - REPRISE
BOWENS, BOBBY - MOVE
BOWIE, JOHN - SEVENS
BOWN SET, ALAN - PYE
BOX TOPS – BELL, STATESIDE
BRADLEY, JAN - PYE INTERNATIONAL
BRADLEY, PATRICK – KENT
BRADY, BOB & the CON CHORDS - BELL
BRAGG, JOHNNY - INFERNO
BRAGGS, AL TNT - ACTION, VOCALION
BRAMLETT, DELANEY - VOCALION
BRANDON, BILL – KENT, MERCURY
BRANDON, CAL - GRAPEVINE 2000
BRASS CONSTRUCTION - UNITED ARTISTS
BRASSEAUR, ANDRE - CBS
BREEDLOVE, JIMMY - PYE DISCO DEMAND
BREMERS, BEVERLEY - WAND
BRENDA & THE TABULATIONS – ACTION, CBS, DIRECTION,
    EPIC, LONDON
BRIDGE - ATLANTIC
BRIDGER, BOBBY - BEACON
BRIGHTER SIDE OF DARKNESS - PYE INTERNATIONAL
BRIMMER, CHARLES - HAYLEY
BRINKLEY & PARKER - CONTEMPO
BRISCOE, JIMMY & the LITTLE BEAVERS - NEMS
BRISTOL, JOHNNY – ARIOLA , MGM, MOTOR CITY
MEL BRITT - SEVENS
BRITT, TINA - LONDON
BRITTEN, BUDDY & THE REGENTS – ORIOLE, PICCADILLY
BROCKINGTON, ALFREDA - P4DB
BROOKS & JERRY - DIRECTION
BROOKS, CHUCK - SOUL CITY
BROOKS, DALE - STATESIDE
BROOKS, ELKIE – DECCA, HMV
BROTHER TO BROTHER - PHILIPS
BROTHERHOOD OF MAN - DERAM
BROTHERS – PEOPLE, RCA
BROTHERS GRIMM – EMBER
BROTHERS GUIDING LIGHT - SEVENS
BROTHERS TWO - ACTION
BROWN, BEN - POLYDOR
BROWN, FRIDAY - FONTANA
BROWN, JAMES (& THE FAMOUS FLAMES)- EMBER,
    FONTANA, LONDON, MOJO, PARLOPHONE, PHILIPS,
    PEOPLE, POLYDOR, ,PYE INTERNATIONAL, SCOTTI BROS,
    SONET, SUE, URBAN
BROWN, JOE - PYE
BROWN, MATT - GRAPEVINE 2000

BROWN, MAXINE – AVCO, HMV, KENT, LONDON, MAJOR
    MINOR, PYE DISCO DEMAND, PYE INTERNATIONAL,
    STATESIDE
BROWN, MELVIN & JAMES MATTHEWS - GRAPEVINE 2000
BROWN, PETER - TK
BROWN, RANDY - PARACHUTE
BROWN, RUTH – BRUNSWICK , LONDON, PRESIDENT
BROWN, SEVERIN - MOWEST
BROWN, SHIRLEY – ARISTA, CONTEMPO RARIES, STAX
BROWN, VEDA - STAX
BROWN, VERNON - MOJO
BROWN, WATSON T. – BELL, PRESIDENT
BROWNE, FRIDAY - PARLOPHONE
BROWNE, WATSON T. – MAM, PYE, SEVEN SUN
BROWNER, DUKE - GRAPEVINE
BRUBECK QUARTET, DAVE - FONTANA
BRUCE, TOMMY and the BRUSERS - POLYDOR
BRUNO, TONY - CAPITOL
BRYANT TRIO, RAY - PYE INTERNATIONAL
BRYANT, ANITA - CBS
BRYANT, J.D. c/w PROPHETS - SOUL CITY
BRYANT, JAY DEE - ISLAND
BRYANT, SANDRA - MAJOR MINOR
BRYSON, PEABO – BANG
B.T.EXPRESS - PYE INTERNATIONAL
BUBBA LOU & THE HIGHBALLS – HIGHBALLS, STIFF
BUCHANAN BROTHERS - PAGE ONE
BUCKINGHAMS – CBS, STATESIDE
BUENA VISTAS - STATESIDE
BUGALOO BRASS - DECCA
BUNCH - CBS
BURCH, VERNON - UNITED ARTISTS
BURDICK, DONI - LOWTON
BURKE, KENI - RCA
BURKE, SOLOMON – ANCHOR, ATLANTIC, BELL, LONDON
BURNETT, FRANCES - CORAL
BURNETTE, DORSEY – CONTEMPO RARIES, LIBERTY, TAMLA
    MOTOWN
BURNS, BYRON - SPLASH
BURNS, JACKIE and the BO-BELLS - MGM
BURNS, JIMMY - GRAPEVINE
BURRAGE, HAROLD – PRESIDENT, SUE
BURTON, JEANNIE - SEVILLE
BUSH, ERNIE - CONTEMPO
BUTLER, BILLY – EPIC, SOUL CITY
BUTLER, JERRY – CHARLY, COLUMBIA, FONTANA, LONDON,
    MERCURY, MOTOWN UK, PIR, PRESIDENT, STATESIDE,
    SUE, TAMLA MOTOWN, TOP RANK
BUTLER, JERRY & BRENDA LEE EAGER - MERCURY
BUTTERCUPS - PAMA
BUTTERFLYS - RED BIRD
BYERS, ANN - GOLDMINE SOUL SUPPLY, GOLDMINE TEST
    PRESS, POWER EXCHANGE, SEVENS
BYNUM, JAMES - GRAPEVINE
BYRD, BOBBY – CONTEMPO, MOJO,,SEVILLE, WARNER
    BROS
BYRD, BOBBY c/w VICKI ANDERSON - MOJO
BYRD, DONALD - BLUE NOTE, UNITED ARTISTS, VERVE
BYRD, RUSSELL - SUE
BYRDE, ESTHER - SURVIVAL
BYSTANDERS – PICCADILLY

C

C, FANTASTIC JOHNNY – ACTION, ISLAND, LONDON
C, ROY – EMBER, ISLAND, MERCURY, UK
C.O.D'S - STATESIDE
CAIROS - SHRINE
CAIROS c/w CAUTIONS - SHRINE
CALDWELL, BOBBY - TK
CALENDER - ALL PLATINUM
CALIFORNIA IN CROWD - FONTANA
CALLIER, TERRY - ELEKTRA
CAMEL DRIVERS - PYE INTERNATIONAL
CAMEO - CASABLANCA
CAMEOS - TOAST

CAMERON, G.C. – ARDENT, FLAMINGO, MOTOR CITY TAMLA MOTOWN
CAMPBELL, ETHNA - MERCURY
CAMPBELL, JUNIOR - DERAM
CAMPBELL'S BIG BAND, CHOKER - TAMLA MOTOWN
CANDLEWICK GREEN - BUK
CANDY & THE KISSES - CAMEO PARKWAY, KENT
CANDY CHOIR - POLYDOR
CANNIBAL and the HEADHUNTERS - STATESIDE
CANNON, ACE - LONDON
CANNON, FREDDY - STATESIDE
CAPITALS– SEVENS, WHITE LABEL
CAPITOLS – ATLANTIC, CONTEMPO, CONTEMPO RARIES
CAPPS, AL - STATESIDE
CAPREEZ - GRAPEVINE
CARBON COPIES - GRAPEVINE 2000
CARGO feat: DAVE COLLINS - Z
CARLTON, CARL – 20TH. CENTURY, ABC, ACTION
CARLTON, EDDIE - CREAM
CARLTON, LITTLE CARL – ACTION, KENT
CARN, JEAN – MOTOWN, PIR
CARNABY – PICCADILLY, SOS
CARNE, JEAN - OMNI
CAROLINES - POLYDOR
CARR, JAMES - B&C, BELL, MOJO, STATESIDE
CARR, JOHNNY - FONTANA
CARR, JOHNNY and the CADILLACS - DECCA
CARR, LINDA - STATESIDE
CARR, ROMEY - COLUMBIA
CARROLL, BERNADETTE - STATESIDE
CARROLL, DINA - A&M
CARROLL, PAT - PYE INTERNATIONAL
CARROLL, VIVIAN - SEVENS
CARROLLS – CBS, POLYDOR
CARROLS - POLYDOR
CARSTAIRS – INFERNO, SOUL HQ
CARTER BROTHERS - CHARLY
CARTER, CAROLYN - LONDON
CARTER, CLARENCE – ATLANTIC, CERTAIN, TOUT ENSEMBLE, UNITED ARTISTS
CARTER, JEAN - STATESIDE
CARTER, JEAN & the CENTERPIECES - STATESIDE
CARTER, LYNDA - MOTOWN UK
CARTER, MEL – AIRWAVE, LIBERTY, PYE INTERNATIONAL
CARTER, RALPH - MERCURY
CARTER, SHELIA and the EPISODE SIX - PYE
CARTER, VALERIE - CBS
CASH, ALVIN - BRUNSWICK, CONTEMPO, PRESIDENT
CASH, ALVIN & the CRAWLERS - STATESIDE
CASH, ALVIN & the REGISTERS – PRESIDENT, STATESIDE
CASHMERE. - FOURTH & BROADWAY
CASHMERES - SOUL CITY
CASINOS - CONTEMPO RARIES, PRESIDENT
CASINO'S - EMBER
CASSIDY - UNITED ARTISTS
CASSIDY, TED - CAPITOL
CASTAWAYS - LONDON
CASTON & MAJORS - TAMLA MOTOWN
CASTOR, JIMMY – MERCURY, PHILIPS
CASUALEERS - PYE DISCO DEMAND
CASWELL, JOHNNY - KENT
CATCH - LONDON
CATE BROS. - ASYLUM
CATS EYES - DERAM
CERRONE - ATLANTIC
CHAIN REACTION - GULL
CHAIRMEN OF THE BOARD – INVICTUS, INFERNO
CHAKACHAS - POLYDOR
CHAMBER OF KOMMERCE - CLOUD ONE
CHAMBERS BROTHERS – CBS, DIRECTION, VOCALION
CHAMBERS, JIMMY - CUBE
CHAMPAIGN - CBS
CHAMPION, MICKIE – SEVENS, SOUL CITY
CHAMPS - PAMA
CHANCE, ROB and the CHANCES-R – CBS

CHANDELL, TIM - ORBITONE
CHANDELLE, DANY - COLUMBIA
CHANDLER, E.J. - DESTINY
CHANDLER, GENE – 20TH. CENTURY, ACTION, BLUE BIRD, BRUNSWICK, CHARLY, CHESS, CHI SOUND, COLUMBIA, CORAL, MCA, MERCURY, PRESIDENT, SEVENS, SOUL CITY, SOUL SOUNDS, STATESIDE
CHANDLER, GEORGE - RCA
CHANDLER, KENNY - STATESIDE
CHANDLER, LORRAINE - BLACK MAGIC, KENT
CHANDLERS - DEMAND
CHANGE - WEA
CHANGE. - WEA
CHANNEL, BRUCE – BELL, MERCURY ,STATESIDE
CHANNEL 3 - S.C.S.C.
CHANTELLES – BLACK MAGIC, CBS, DESTINY, EMIDISC, PARLOPHONE, POLYDOR
CHANTELS – CAPITOL, LONDON, ROULETTE
CHANTERS - CBS
CHANTS – CHIPPING NORTON, DECCA, FONTANA, PAGE ON, PYE, RCA
CHAPTER FIVE – CBS, SEVENS
CHAPTER THREE - PYE INTERNATIONAL
CHAQUITO - PHILIPS
CHARLENE - MOTOWN UK
CHARLES, DON – DECCA, PARLOPHONE
CHARLES, RAY – ATLANTIC, HMV, LONDON, SOS, STATESIDE
CHARLES, SONNY and the CHECKMATES - A&M, EMBER
CHARLES, TINA - CBS
CHARO and the SALSOUL ORCHESTRA – SALSOUL
CHAVEZ, FREDDIE - SEVENS
CHECKER, CHUBBY - B.J.D., BUDDAH, CAMEO PARKWAY, COLUMBIA, LONDON, PYE INTERNATIONAL, SOUL SOUNDS, TOP RANK
CHECKER, CHUBBY - KENT
CHECKERBOARD SQ. - SEVENS
CHECKERBOARD SQUARES - INFERNO
CHECKMATES LTD. - A&M, EMBER
CHEETAHS - PHILIPS
CHEETHAM, WILLIE - FEELGOOD
CHENIER, C. - ACTION
CHEQUERS - CREOLE
CHEROKEES - COLUMBIA
CHERRY PEOPLE - BLACK MAGIC, MGM
CHESTERFIELDS - GRAPEVINE 2000
CHESTNUT, MORRIS - GRAPEVINE
CHIFFONS – LONDON, STATESIDE
CHILDE, SONNY – DECCA, POLYDOR
CHI-LITES – BEACON, BRUNSWICK, CHI SOUND, MCA MERCURY
CHIMES - LONDON
CHOCOLATE BOYS - DECCA
CHOCOLATE MILK - RCA
CHOICE FOUR - RCA
CHOICE OF COLOUR - GRAPEVINE 2000
CHORDS FIVE - JAY BOY
CHOSEN FEW – ACTION, POLYDOR, PYE DISCO DEMAND
CHRISTIAN, LIZ - CBS
CHRISTIE, LOU - MGM
CHRISTIEN, DEREK - MAJOR MINOR
CHRISTOPHER, JORDAN - UNITED ARTISTS
CHUBUKOS - MAINSTREAM
CINDERELLAS - COLPIX
CITY OF WESTMINSTER STRING BAND - PYE
C-JAM BLUES - COLUMBIA
CLANTON, JIMMY - STATESIDE
CLARK, ALICE - ACTION
CLARK, ALICE - WARNER BROS
CLARK, CHRIS - TAMLA MOTOWN
CLARK, CLAUDINE - PYE INTERNATIONAL, SUE
CONNIE CLARK - SEVENS
CLARK, DEE – CHARLY, CHELSEA, COLUMBIA, LIBERTY, LONDON, STATESIDE, TOP RANK
CLARK, DUANE - SPARK
CLARK, JIMMEY SOUL - BLACK MAGIC, INFERNO, SEVENS

CLARK, JIMMY SOUL - SEVENS
CLARK, MICHEAL - LIBERTY
CLARK, PETULA - PYE
CLARK, ROSALIND - WARNER BROS
CLARKE, RICK – RCA, WA RECORDS
CLARKE, SHARON DEE - NIGHTMARE
CLARKE, STANLEY - EPIC
CLARKE, TONY – CHESS, PYE INTERNATIONAL
CLASSIC IV - LIBERTY
CLASSIC SULLIVANS - KWANZA
CLAY, CASSIUS - CBS
CLAY, JUDY – KENT, STAX
CLAY, JUDY & BELL, WILLIAM - STAX
CLAY, OTIS – ATLANTIC, LONDON, PRESIDENT
CLAY, TOM – MOWEST, TAMLA MOTOWN
CLAYTON, MERRY - A&M
CLAYTON, MERRY c/w FIVE SATINS - RCA
CLEFTONES - COLUMBIA
CLEMENTS, SOUL JOE - PLEXIUM
CLEMMONS, ANGELA - PORTRAIT
CLIFF, JIMMY – FONTANA, ISLAND, STATESIDE
CLIFFORD, LINDA – CRC, CURTOM, PARAMOUNT
CLINTON, GEORGE – ABC, CAPITOL
CLINTON, LARRY – GRAPEVINE, WIGAN CASINO
CLOUD - CHAMPAGNE
CLOUD ONE - CONTEMPO
CLOVERS - ATLANTIC
COASTERS – ATLANTIC, CBS, DIRECTION, LONDON, PARLOPHONE, STATESIDE
COATES, ODIA - UNITED ARTISTS
COBB, JIMMY - EXPANSION
COCO - ARIOLA
CODAY, BILL c/w SANDRA WRIGHT - GRAPEVINE 2000
COFFEE - DE-LITE
COFFEY, DENNIS - A&M, ATLANTIC, SUSSEX
COFFEY, DENNIS & the DETROIT GUITAR - A&M
COGNAC - RISE RECORDS
COGNAC feat: SALSOUL ORCHESTRA - ELECTRIC RECORD C
COIT, JAMES - DESTINY
COLD BLOOD - ATLANTIC
COLE, BILLY - POWER EXCHANGE
COLE, CINDY - COLUMBIA
COLE, DON & ALLEYNE - FONTANA
COLE, NAT KING - CAPITOL
COLE, NATALIE - CAPITOL
COLEMAN, BOBBY - PYE INTERNATIONAL
COLLIER, MITTY - PYE INTERNATIONAL
COLLINS SHOWBAND, DONIE - PYE
COLLINS, BOB c/w EMBERS - GOLDSOUL
COLLINS, GLENDA - HMV
COLLINS, KEANYA - GRAPEVINE
COLLINS, LYN – POLYDOR, MOJO
COLLINS, RODGER – FANTASY, VOCALION
COLLINS, ROMONA - SEVENS
COLLINS, TERRY - WARNER BROS
COLTON, TONY and the BIG BOSS BAND – PYE
COLLINS, WILL - SEVENS
COMMODORES – ATLANTIC, MOTOWN UK, TAMLA MOTOWN
COMPLETE CYCLE - JAY BOY
CON FUNK SHUN - CONTEMPO
CON-CHORDS - POLYDOR
CONLEY, ARTHUR – ATCO, ATLANTIC, CAPRICORN
CONLEY, ARTHUR c/w THOMAS, CARLA - ATLANTIC
CONNORS, NORMAN - ARISTA
CONNORS, NORMAN & the STARSHIP ORCH - BUDDAH
CONSTELLATIONS c/w JEWEL AKENS - SEVENS
CONTOURS - JOE BOY, MOTOR CITY, ORIOLE, STATESIDE, TAMLA MOTOWN
CONTRASTS - MONUMENT
CONTROLLERS – PRESIDENT, TK
CONWELL, JIMMY – CONTEMPO RARIES, JAY BOY,
COOK, LITTLE JOE – SONET, SUE, WIGAN CASINO
COOK, SAM - RCA
COOK, TONY and the PARTY PEOPLE - OSCEOLA
COOKE, SAM – HMV, LONDON, RCA

3

COOKE, SAM c/w DUANE EDDY - RCA
COOKE, SAMONA - MERCURY
COOKIES – COLPIX, LONDON
COOPER, EULA - GRAPEVINE
COOPER, GARNELL - LONDON
COOPER, LES & the SOUL ROCKERS - STATESIDE
COOPERETTES - BRUNSWICK
COPELAND, JOHNNY - ATLANTIC
CORDELL, PHIL - MOWEST
CORDETT, LOUISE - DECCA
CORNELIUS BROTHERS & SISTER ROSE - UNITED ARTISTS
CORNELIUS, EDDIE - GB RECORDS
CORTEZ, DAVE BABY – COLUMBIA, LONDON, PYE
INTERNATIONAL, ROULETTE
COSBY, BILL - WARNER BROS
COTTAGE - CRYSTAL
COTTON JAZZMEN, MIKE - COLUMBIA
COTTON SOUND, MIKE - MGM, POLYDOR
COULTER, PHIL - INFERNO
COUNT BASIE - REPRISE
COUNT FIVE - PYE INTERNATIONAL
COUNTS - JANUS
COURCEY, JOANN - SEVENS
COURTNEY, DEAN – KENT, RCA
COURTSHIPS - UK
COVAY, DON & THE GOODTIMERS - - ATLANTIC, CAMEO
PARKWAY, MERCURY, PHILIPS, PYE INTERNATIONAL
COVEY, JULIEN and the MACHINE - ISLAND
COX, WALLY – KENT, PYE DISCO DEMAND, VOGUE
CRAWFORD, CAROLYN - STATESIDE
CRAZY ELEPHANT - MAJOR MINOR
CREATION – ATLANTIC, BLACK MAGIC, DESTINY, PLANET,
STATESIDE
CREATIVE SOURCE – POLYDOR, SUSSEX
CRESTS - LONDON
CREWE GENERATION, BOB - STATESIDE
CROPPER, STEVE - STAX
CROW – INFERNO, RIGHT ON
CROWN HEIGHTS AFFAIR – CONTEMPO, POLYDOR
CROWNS - PAMA
CRUMLEY, RAY - MAGNET
CRUSADERS – ABC, BLUE THUMB
CRYSTAL GRASS - PHILIPS
CRYSTALS – LONDON, PARLOPHONE, PHIL SPECTOR
INT.,UNITED ARTISTS, WARNER SPECTOR
CUBA SEXTET, JOE - PYE INTERNATIONAL
CUNNINGHAM, GAYLE - BIG FISH
CUPIDS INSPIRATION – BELL, CBS, NEMS
CURRY, CLIFFORD – ACTION, PAMA
CURTIS, CLEM & the FOUNDATIONS - RIVERSIDE
CURTIS, GLEM - PYE
CURTIS, JOHNNY – MAJOR MINOR, PARLOPHONE
CYAN THREE - DECCA
CYMANDE – ALASKA, CONTEMPO

D

D, KIM - PYE
DACOSTA, RITA - CONTEMPO
DALE, GLEN - PAGE ONE
DALLON, MIKI - STRIKE
DAMARIS - CBS
DAN THE BANJO MAN - RARE EARTH
DANTE - CHRYSALIS
DARIN, BOBBY – ATLANTIC, CAPITOL
DARLETTES - PRESIDENT
DARNELL, JACKIE - PHILIPS
DARRELL, GUY – CBS, SANTA PONSA
DARREN, JENNIE & the SECOND CITY S. - MAJOR MINOR
DARREN, MAXINE - PYE
DARROW MOORE, JOHNNY – MAGNET
BOBBY DARIN - MOWEST
DATE WITH SOUL - STATESIDE
DAVID & THE GIANTS - CAPITOL
DAVIDSON, ALFIE – BOOT, SOS
DAVIDSON, DIANNE - JANUS

DAVIES, CYRIL - PYE INTERNATIONAL
DAVIES, TYRONE - ATLANTIC
DAVIS GROUP, SPENCER – FONTANA, ISLAND
DAVIS JR., SAMMY - BOOT, MOTOWN UK, REPRISE
DAVIS MONDAY BAND, WARREN - COLUMBIA
DAVIS, BILLIE – ABC, DECCA, PICCADILLY
DAVIS, BILLIE and the LeROYS - COLUMBIA
DAVIS, DARLEEN - SERIOUS RECORDS
DAVIS, JESSE - ATLANTIC
DAVIS, LARRY - KENT
DAVIS, MELVIN – ACTION, SEVENS
DAVIS, TYRONE – ATLANTIC, BRUNSWICK, CBS, STATESIDE
DAVISON, ALFIE – BOOT, PHILLY GROOVE, SOS
DAWKINS, JIMMY - MOJO
DAWN/THE DEE JAYS - RCA
DAWSON, LESLEY - MERCURY
DAY, BOBBY - SUE
DAY, JACKIE - SOUL SPIN, SUE
DAY, MURIEL – CBS, PAGE ONE, SOUL STOP
DAYBREAK – ISLAND, SEVENS
DAYE, EDDIE & 4 BARS – HORACES, SHRINE
DAYE, JOHNNY - STAX
DAYLIGHTERS - SUE
DE LORY, AL – CAPITOL, LONDON
DE LORY, AL & MANDANGO - CAPITOL
DE SANTO, SUGAR PIE – CHESS, PYE INTERNATIONAL
DEAL, BILL & the RHONDELS - MGM
DEAN & JEAN - STATESIDE
DEAN, SNOOPY - SEVILLE
DEANO - COLUMBIA
DEBONAIRES – TSEVENS, TRACK
DECISIONS - A&M
DEE, JAY - WARNER BROS
DEE, JEANIE - BEACON
DEE, KIKI – FONTANA, TAMLA MOTOWN
DEES, SAM – ATLANTIC, MAJOR MINOR, RCA, SEVENS,
SOUL CITY,
DEL CAPRIS - GRAPEVINE
DEL LARKS - SOUL SERIES
DELCOS - SOS
DELEGATION - STATE
DELFONICS - BELL, MOJO
DELFONICS - PHILLY GROOVE
DELICATO, PAUL - LONDON
DELIGHTS - SOUL CITY
DELIGHTS ORCHESTRA - ATCO
DE-LITES – DESTINY, GRAPEVINE, SEVENS, SOUL CITY
D'ELL, DENNIS - CBS
DEL-LARKS – SEVENS, SOUL SERIES
DELLS - 20TH. CENTURY, CADET, CHARLY, CHESS,
MERCURY, PYE, PRESIDENT, PYE INTERNATIONAL
DELORENZO, JOEY - FABULOUS
DELT, KENNIE and PRANA - MERCURY
DELTONES - COLUMBIA
DEMAIN, ARIN - SEVENS
DEODATO - CTI
DEREK & CYNDI - PIR
DEREK & RAY - RCA, SOS
DESANTO, SUGAR PIE – CHESS, PYE INTERNATIONAL
DESHANNON, JACKIE - LIBERTY
DESMOND, PAULA - FLAMINGO
DESTINATIONS - PYE INTERNATIONAL
DESTINY ORCHESTRA - DESTINY
DETOURS - CBS
DETROIT EMERALDS – ATLANTIC, JANUS, PHONOGRAM
PYE INTERNATIONAL, WESTBOUND
DETROIT EXECUTIVES - SEVENS
DETROIT SPINNERS – ATLANTIC, TAMLA MOTOWN
DETROIT with MITCH RYDER - PARAMOUNT
DEVASTATING AFFAIR - MOWEST
DEVAUGHN, WILLIAM – CHELSEA, EMI
DEVONNES - UK
DEVOTIONS – COLUMBIA, POLYDOR
DEXY'S MIDNIGHT RUNNERS - LATE NIGHT FEELINGS
DEY, TRACY - STATESIDE

DEZRO ORCHESTRA - ROUTE
DIAMOND, GREGG - TK
DIBANGO, MANU – DECCA, LONDON
DIDDLEY, BO – CHESS, PYE INTERNATIONAL, LONDON
DIJON, COBY - FONTANA
DILLARD, MOSES & JOSHUA – MOJO, STATESIDE
DILLARD, MOSES - BUDDAH, CONTEMPO
DIPLOMATS – DIRECTION, KENT
DIXIE CUPS – BUDDAH, CONTEMPO RARIES, HMV, PYE
INTERNATIONAL, RED BIRD
DIXIE DRIFTER - COLUMBIA
DIXON, ERROL – DECCA, DIRECT, FAB, ORIOLE, RAINBOW
,TRANSATLANTIC
DOBSON, DOBBY & the DELTAS – KING
DOCKER, ROY – DOMAIN, PAMA
DODDS, NELLA - PYE INTERNATIONAL
DOE, ERNIE K. – see K-DOE, ERNIE
DOGGETT, BILL – PARLOPHONE, WARNER BROS
DOMINO – EMI, EPIC
DOMINO, FATS – HMV, LIBERTY, LONDON, MERCURY,
REPRISE, SONET, UNITED ARTISTS
DON & DEWEY – CAMEO PARKWAY, LONDON, SUE
DON & JUAN - LONDON
DONALDSON, BO and the HEYWOODS - ABC
DONAYS - ORIOLE
DONNER, RAL - INFERNO
DONTELLS – FONTANA, PRESIDENT
DOOBIE BROTHERS - WARNER BROS
DORSETS - SUE
DORSEY ORCHESTRA, JACK - PYE
DORSEY ORCHESTRA, TOMMY - BRUNSWICK
DORSEY, LEE – BELL , CHARLY, MOJO, POLYDOR, STATESIDE,
SUE, TOP RANK
DORSEY, LEE & HARRIS, BETTY - BUFFALO
DOTTIE and MILLIE - KENT
DOUBLE EXPOSURE - SALSOUL
DOUBLE FEATURE - DERAM
DOUGLAS, CARL & the BIG STAMPEDE – CBS, GO, PYE,
UNITED ARTISTS
DOUGLAS, CAROL - RCA
DOUGLAS, CRAIG – PYE, TOP RANK
DOUGLAS, KARL - BLUE MOUNTAIN
DOVE, RONNIE - STATESIDE
DOVELLS - CAMEO PARKWAY, COLUMBIA
DOWNING, AL – CHESS, JANUS
DOWNING, BIG AL - SUE
DOWNING, DON - PEOPLE
DOWNLINERS SECT - COLUMBIA
DOYLEY BROTHERS - SAFARI
DOZIER, GENE & THE UNITED FRONT - MERCURY
DOZIER, LAMONT – ABC, CBS, DEMON, PROBE, WARNER
BROS
DR. BUZZARD'S ORIGINAL SAVANNA - RCA
DR. FEELGOOD and the INTERNS – CAPITOL, CBS, COLUMBIA
DRAIN, CHARLES - RCA
DRAMATICS – ABC, CAPITOL, STAX
DREAMS - JAY BOY
DREVAR, JOHN - POLYDOR
DREVAR'S EXPRESSION, JOHN - MGM
DREVARS, JOHN - DESTINY
DREW, PATTI - CAPITOL
DRIFTERS – ARISTA, ATLANTIC, BELL, LONDON
DRISCOLL, JULIE – COLUMBIA, MARMALADE, PARLOPHONE
DRISCOLL, JULIE & BRIAN AUGER - MARMALADE
DUBS - LONDON
DUCANE, DIANE - CONTACT
DU-ETTES - PRESIDENT
DUKE, DORIS – CONTEMPO, CONTEMPO RARIES,
MAINSTREAM, MOJO
DUKE, GEORGE - EPIC
DUKES - WEA
DUNCAN, LESLEY - MERCURY
DUNCAN, TOMMY - SUE
DUPARS feat. VENETTA FIELDS - CONTEMPO
DUPREES – LONDON, POLYDOR, STATE

DURHAM, JUDITH - COLUMBIA
DUTCH - PHILIPS
DYKE AND THE BLAZERS - PYE INTERNATIONAL
DYNAMIC CONCEPT – POWER EXCHANGE
DYNAMIC CORVETTES - CONTEMPO
DYNAMIC SUPERIORS - TAMLA MOTOWN
DYNAMICS – ATLANTIC, KING, LONDON, SEVENS
DYNATONES - PYE INTERNATIONAL, SOS
DYNELLS - ATCO
DYSON, RONNIE – ARDENT, CBS

E

EAGLE - PYE INTERNATIONAL
EMANONS ORCHESTRA - GOLDMINE SOUL SUPPLY
EARL-JEAN - COLPIX
EARLS - ATLANTIC, LONDON, STATESIDE
EARTH, WIND & FIRE – CBS, WARNER BROS
EAST COAST CONNECTION - OREOLE
EATON, KOOKIE - CONDOR
EBB TIDE - POLYDOR
EBONY RHYTHM FUNK CAMPAIGN - EMI
EBONY, IVORY & JADE - CBS
EBONYS - CBS
ECHOES - PHILIPS
ECKSTINE, BILLY - TAMLA MOTOWN
ECSTASY, PASSION & PAIN - PYE INTERNATIONAL
ECXCITERS - UNITED ARTISTS
EDDIE & ERNIE - UNITED ARTISTS
EDMUND JR., LADA - MCA
EDWARDS, CHUCK - SOUL CITY
EDWARDS, DEE c/w DONI BURDICK - WIGAN CASINO
EDWARDS, DENIS - SOUL CITY
EDWARDS, DENNIS - GORDY
EDWARDS, JACKIE – ALLADIN, DIRECTION, FONTANA,
   HORSE, ISLAND, SUE, TROJAN
EDWARDS, JACKIE and JIMMY CLIFF - ISLAND
EDWARDS, JOHN – COTILLION, KENT
EDWARDS, MILL - ACTION
EDWARDS, TYRONE - INVICTUS
EDWARDS, VINCE - UNITED ARTISTS
EL DORADOS - MOJO
ELBERT, DONNIE – AVCO, BRADLEYS, CBS, ECHO, EPIC, JAY
   BOY, JOE BOY, KLIK, LONDON, MOJO, NEW
   WAVE, PARLOPHONE, POLYDOR, RCA, SUE
EL CHICANO - MCA
ELDRED, LEE - MERCURY
ELECTRIC EXPRESS - GRAPEVINE 2000
ELECTRIC INDIAN - UNITED ARTISTS
ELEPHANT BAND - MOJO
ELEVENTH HOUR - 20TH. CENTURY, PYE INTERNATIONAL
ELGINS – GOLDSOUL, TAMLA MOTOWN
ELLIMAN, YVONNE - RSO
ELLINGTONS - GRAPEVINE
ELLIOTT, BERN - DECCA
ELLIOTT, BERN and the FENMEN - DECCA
ELLIS, ALTON - A&M
ELLIS, SHIRLEY – CBS, LONDON, SOUL SOUNDS.
ELLISON, LORRAINE – MERCURY, WARNER BROS
ELLISON, WILLIE JOHN - ARDENT
EMERALDS - DECCA
EMMANUEL, DAVID - WHITE LODGE
EMOTIONS - DEEP SOUL, STATESIDE, STAX
EMPERORS – PAMA, STATESIDE
EMPIRES - SEVENS
ENCHANTED FOREST - STATESIDE
ENCHANTERS - WARNER BROS
ENCHANTMENT - UNITED ARTISTS
ENCHANTMENTS c/w MARSHA GEE – JOKER
ENGLISH, BARBARA JEAN - CONTEMPO
ENGLISH, KIM - SUSU
ENTICERS - ATLANTIC
EPISODE SIX – PYE
EPITOME OF SOUND - SEVENS
EPPERSON, MINNIE - ACTION
EQUALS – MERCURY, PRESIDENT

ERIC & the VIKINGS - KOOL KAT
ERNIE & ED - JAY BOY
ERWIN, DEE - SIGNPOST
ESCORTS – ALASKA, COLUMBIA, CONTEMPO, FONTANA
ESQUIRES – ACTION, STATESIDE
ESSENCE - EPIC
ESSEX - COLUMBIA
ESSEX, DAVID - DECCA
ETTA & HARVEY - LONDON
EVANS, CHRISTINE - PHILIPS
EVANS, MAUREEN – CBS, ORIOLE
EVANS, MILL - KENT
EVANS, RUSSELL - ATLANTIC
EVERETT, BETTY – CHARLY, FONTANA, KING, LIBERTY, MCA,
   MCA SOUL BAG, PRESIDENT, STATESIDE, SUE, UNI
EVERETT, BETTY & BUTLER, JERRY – FONTANA, PRESIDENT,
   STATESIDE
EVERETT, VINCE - FONTANA
EVERGREEN BLUES - MERCURY
EXCELS - ATLANTIC
EXCITERS - 20TH. CENTURY, COLUMBIA, CONTEMPO,
   EMIDISC, JAY BOY, LONDON, MECCA, RCA, TOMORROW,
   UNITED ARTISTS
EXECUTIVE SUITE - CLOUD ONE, POLYDOR
EXECUITIVES - CBS
EXECUTIVE SUITE - CLOUD ONE
EXITS - SEVENS
EXOTICS - COLUMBIA
EXPRESSIONS - EMI
EYES OF BLUE – DERAM

F

FABULOUS COUNTS - MOJO
FABULOUS ECHOES – CONTEMPO
FABULOUS IMPACTS - KENT
FABULOUS JADES - SOUL CITY
FACTOTUMS - IMMEDIATE
FADING COLOURS - EMBER
FAIR, YVONNE - TAMLA MOTOWN
FAITH HOPE & CHARITY - CREWE
FAITH, GENE - POWER EXCHANGE
FAITH, HORACE - DJM
FALCONS - JOE BOY, LONDON
FAME, GEORGIE – CBS, COLUMBIA, ISLAND
FAME, GEORGIE & the BLUE FLAMES - COLUMBIA
FAMILY AFFAIR - CASINO CLASSICS, PYE
FAMILY PLANN - PRESIDENT
FANTASTIC FOUR - MOTOR CITY, TAMLA MOTOWN
FANTASTIC PUZZLES – INFERNO, RIGHT ON
FANTASTICS – BELL, BUS STOP, DERAM, MGM, MOJO
FARDON, DON - GOLDSOUL
FARLOWE, CHRIS - IMMEDIATE
FARRA, MARYANN & SATIN SOUL - BRUNSWICK
FASCINATIONS – MOJO, STATESIDE, SUE
FASHIONS – EVOLUTION, STATESIDE
FAT LARRY'S BAND - WMOT
FATBACK – ATLANTIC, SPRING
FATBACK BAND – POLYDOR, SPRING
FATHERS ANGELS - BLACK MAGIC, INFERNO, MGM
FATS DOMINO - LONDON
FAVOURITE SONS - MERCURY
FEARNS BRASS FOUNDRY - DECCA
FEATHERS - BELL
FEDERATION - 20TH. CENTURY
FELDER, WILTON feat. BOBBY WOMACK - MCA
FELDERS ORIOLES - PICCADILLY
FELICIANO - RCA
FELICIANO, JOSE - MOTOWN UK
FENWAYS - LIBERTY
FERGUSON, HELENA - LONDON
FERGUSON, JESSE LEE - PYE INTERNATIONAL
FERNICK, MAYA - PHILIPS
FERREZ, DIANE - COLUMBIA
FERRIS WHEEL - PYE
FESSOR FUNK - CHELSEA

FIDELS - DJM
FI-DELS - JAY BOY
FIELDS, RICHARD DIMPLES - EPIC
FIESTAS – ATLANTIC, LONDON
FIFTH ESTATE - STATESIDE
FINISHED TOUCH - MOTOWN UK
FINNIGAN, MIKE - CBS
FIRST BORN - ATLANTIC
FIRST CHOICE – BELL, PHILLY GROOVE, PYE
   INTERNATIONAL, SALSOUL, SERIOUS RECORDS
FIRST GEAR - PYE
FISHER, TONI - TOP RANK
FISHER, WILLIE - JAMA
FITZGERALD, ELLA – ATLANTIC, REPRISE, STATESIDE
FIVE & A PENNY - POLYDOR
FIVE CARD STUD - PHILIPS
FIVE DU-TONES – PRESIDENT, STATESIDE
FIVE EMPREES - STATESIDE
FIVE SPECIAL - ELEKTRA
FIVE STAIRSTEPS - BUDDAH
FIVE STAIRSTEPS & CUBIE – BUDDAH, PYE INTERNATIONAL
FIVE TOWNS - DIRECTION
FLACK, ROBERTA - ATLANTIC
FLAME N KING/BOLD ONES - GRAPEVINE
FLAMING EMBER – HDH, HOT WAX
FLAMING EMERALDS - GRAPEVINE
FLAMINGOS – PHILIPS, TOP RANK
FLAMINGOS c/w MITCH RYDER - PHILIPS
FLASH & the BOARD OF DIRECTORS - BELL
FLASHLIGHT – PHILLY GROOVE, SOUL HQ
FLAVOR – DIRECTION, MOTOWN UK
FLEETWOODS - LIBERTY
FLEMING, DEBBIE - BRADLEYS
FLEMING, JOY - PRIVATE STOCK
FLEMONS, WADE c/w HANK JACOBS - SEVENS
FLETCHER, DARROW - LONDON
FLETCHER, DON – VOCALION
FLETCHER, SAM -SEVENS
FLICK SOUND, VIC - CHAPTER ONE
FLINT-NIKS - PYE DISCO DEMAND
FLIRTATIONS – CASINO CLASSICS, DERAM, LONDON
   TRAFFIC, POLYDOR , RCA
FLOWER SHOPPE - POLYDOR
FLOWERS, PHIL - A&M
FLOYD, EDDIE – ATLANTIC, LONDON , POLYDOR, SPECIALITY,
   STAX
FONTANA, WAYNE – FONTANA, PHILIPS
FORD, DEE DEE – LONDON, SOUL CITY, STATESIDE
FORD, FRANKIE - SUE
FORD, JOHN - PHILIPS
FORD, JON - ZELLA RECORDS
FORD, SIR TED - BARAK
FOREHAND, EDDIE BUSTER - ACTION
FORK IN THE ROAD - EMBER
FORMATIONS – MGM, MOJO
FORTSON & SCOTT - GRAPEVINE 2000
ROBBY FORTSON - GRAPEVINE 2000
FORTUNE, RITA - CBS
FORUM - B&C, LONDON
FOSTER, DIANA - CASINO CLASSICS
FOSTER, EDDIE - SEVENS
FOSTER, GINA - RCA
FOUNDATIONS – MCA, PSYCHO, PYE, SUMMIT
FOUNTAIN, JAMES – CREAM, SEVENS
FOUR BELOW ZERO - BOOT
FOUR DYNAMICS - GRAPEVINE 2000
FOUR KENTS - RCA
FOUR PENNIES - STATESIDE
FOUR PERFECTIONS – CREAM, INFERNO, WIGAN CASINO
FOUR SEASONS – PHILIPS, STATESIDE
FOUR TOPS – ABC, CALIBRE, CASABLANCA, MOTOWN UK,
   PROBE, STATESIDE, TAMLA MOTOWN
FOUR TRACKS - SEVENS
FOUR VANDALS – BOARDWALK, SEVENS
FOUR VOICES - SEVENS

FOURMOST – CBS, PARLOPHONE
FOWLEY, KIM - ACTION
FOXX, CHARLIE & INEZ - SUE
FOXX, INEZ – STAX, SUE
FOXX, INEZ & CHARLIE – DIRECTION, LONDON,
  PYE INTERNATIONAL, STATESIDE, SUE, UNITED ARTISTS
FOXX, INEZ. - PYE INTERNATIONAL, SUE
FOXY - JAY BOY
FRANCIS, CONNIE - MGM
FRANK POPP ESSEMBLE - EXPANSION
FRANKIE & JOHNNY – DECCA, INFERNO
FRANKIE & THE CLASSICALS – PHILIPS, PYE DISCO DEMAND
FRANKLIN, ARETHA – ARISTA, ATLANTIC, CBS, FONTANA
FRANKLIN, CAROLYN - RCA
FRANKLIN, ERMA – JAY BOY, LONDON, MCA, SOUL CITY
FRANKLIN, MARIE - MGM
FRASER, JIMMY - EPIC
FRAZIER, BILLY - CHAMPAGNE
FRAZIER, JOE - CONTEMPO
FRED, JOHN and his PLAYBOY BAND – CBS,
  PYE INTERNATIONAL
FREDERICKS, BILL – POLYDOR, UNIGRAM
FREE - PHILIPS
FREE MOVEMENT - CBS
FREE SPIRIT – CHESS, COLUMBIA
FREEEZ - BEGGARS BANQUET
FREEMAN, ART - ATLANTIC
FREEMAN, BOBBY – LONDON, PARLOPHONE
  PYE INTERNATIONAL
FREEMAN, GEORGE - JAY BOY
FREEMAN, R.B. - AVCO
FRENCH, RAY - PYE
FRESH FLAVOR - BUDDAH
FRIDAY, CAROL - PARLOPHONE
FRIENDLY PERSUASION - RARE EARTH
FRIENDS OF DISTINCTION - RCA
FRISAURA, LORRAINE - RCA
FROG, WYNDER K. - ISLAND
FUGITIVES - PYE DISCO DEMAND
FULSOM, LOWELL - FONTANA, OUTASITE, POLYDOR, SUE
FUNKADELIC – JANUS, PYE INTERNATIONAL, WARNER BROS
FUNKEES - BLACK MAGIC, CONTEMPO
FURYS – INFERNO, JAY BOY, STATESIDE
FUTURES - BUDDAH
FUZZ – MOJO, PYE DISCO DEMAND

G

G., TOMMY and the CHARMS - LONDON
GABRIELI BRASS - POLYDOR
GABRIELLI BRASS - POLYDOR
GAGE, YVONNE - ATLANTIC
GAGNON, ANDRE - DECCA
GAINES, PEGGY - KENT
GALLA, TONY - SWAN
GALT, JAMES - PYE
GAME - DECCA
GAMMON, PATRICK - MOTOWN UK
GANDY, LITTLE JIMMY - ROULETTE
GANPOT, DAVID - OSCEOLA
GARDNER, DON - GRAPEVINE 2000, PEOPLE, SOUL CITY,
  STATESIDE
GARNER, REGGIE - CAPITOL
GARNETT, GALE - RCA
GARRETT, BOBBY - KENT
GARRETT, LEE - CHRYSALIS
GARRETT, VERNON – ACTION, STATESIDE
GARRICK, DAVID - PICCADILLY
GARVIN, REX - ATLANTIC
GARVIN, REX & the MIGHTY CRAVERS - ATLANTIC
GARY'S GANG - CBS
GATES, RAY – DECCA
GATURS - ATALANTIC
GAYE, FRANKIE - MOTOR CITY
GAYE, MARVIN – CBS, CHRIS KINGS, MOTOWN UK, ORIOLE
  STATESIDE, TAMLA MOTOWN

GAYE, MARVIN & TAMMI TERRELL - TAMLA MOTOWN
GAYE, MARVIN & WESTON, KIM – STATESIDE,
  TAMLA MOTOWN
GAYE, MARVIN c/w DIANA ROSS - TAMLA MOTOWN
GAYNOR, GLORIA – CBS, MGM, POLYDOR
GAYTEN, PAUL - LONDON
GAYTONES – ACTION
GAZ - SALSOUL
GEE, JUDY & the CLASSMATES - ROUTE
GEE, MARSHA - DEMAND
GENE & JERRY - MERCURY
GENERAL ASSEMBLY - DESTINY
GENERAL JOHNSON - ARISTA
GENTLE PERSUASION - PEOPLE
GENTLEMAN AND THEIR LADY - PYE INTERNATIONAL
GENTLEMEN & THEIR LADIES - CONTEMPO
GENTLEMEN & THEIR LADY - CONTEMPO
GENTRY, ART - MOJO
GENTRYS - STAX
GEORGE, BARBARA – LONDON, SUE
GERRARD, DONNY - ROCKET RECORD CO.
GHETTO CHILDREN - CBS
GIBSON, WAYNE – COLUMBIA, KINGDOM, PYE DISCO
  DEMAND
GIDIAN - COLUMBIA
GILES, EDDIE – CHARLY, HIT & RUN
GILLIES, CORRAINE - SOUL STOP
GILSTRAP, JIM - CHELSEA
GIRLFRIENDS - COLPIX
GIRLS FROM U.N.C.L.E. - JOE BOY
GLADIATORS - DIRECTION
GLASS HOUSE – HDH, INVICTUS
GLITTER BAND - BELL
GLOBETROTTERS - RCA
GLORIES - CBS , DIRECTION
GODFREY, RAY – GRAPEVINE, MERCURY
GOINS, HERBIE and the NIGHTIMERS - PARLOPHONE
GOLDE, FRANNIE - ATLANTIC
GOLDIE – DECCA, FONTANA, IMMEDIATE
GOLDIE and the GINGERBREADS - DECCA
GOLDSBORO, BOBBY - UNITED ARTISTS
GOLDSTEIN, WILLIAM & MAGIC DISCO - MOTOWN UK
GOLSON, BENNY - CBS
GONZALEZ – EMI, RAK
GOOD, LEMME B. - MERCURY
GOODEES - STAX
GOODHAND-TAIT, PHILIP - PARLOHPONE
GOODING, CUBA - MOTOWN UK
GOODISON, JOHNNY - DERAM
GORDON, RONNIE - R&B
GORDON, ROSCO – CHARLY, STATESIDE, TOP RANK
GORDON, ROSCOE – ISLAND, VOCALION
GORDON, SAMMY & the HIP HUGGERS - POLYDOR
GORE, LESLEY - MERCURY
GORME, EYDIE - CBS
GOSPEL CLASSICS - CHESS
GQ - ARISTA
GRACIE, CHARLIE - STATESIDE
GRAHAM CENTRAL STATION - WARNER BROS
GRAHAM, BILLY/ESCALATORS - ATLANTIC
GRAHAM, BOBBIE - FONTANA
GRAHAM, LARRY - WARNER BROS
GRAINER ORCHESTRA, RON - CASINO CLASSICS
GRANGER, GERRI - CASINO CLASSICS, LONDON
GRANGER, GERRI + 2 - CASINO CLASSICS
GRANT, EARL - BRUNSWICK
GRANT, JULIE - PYE
GRASS ROOTS – PROBE, RCA, STATESIDE DUNHILL
GRAVES, CARL - A&M, ARIOLA
GRAY ORCHESTRA, BARRY - PYE
GRAY, DOBIE – BLACK MAGIC, DECCA, DESTINY, INFERNO,
  INFINITY, LONDON, MCA, PYE INTERNATIONAL, SEVENS,
  SOUL SOUNDS
GRAY, OWEN – ALADDIN, ISLAND
GREAT EXPECTATIONS - POLYDOR

GREATEST LITTLE SOUL BAND IN THE WORLD - MCA
  SOUL BAG
GREAVES, R.B. – ATCO, ATLANTIC
GREEN, AL - FLASH BACKS, LONDON
GREEN, GARLAND – KENT, MCA, POLYDOR
GREEN, JESSE - EMI
GREEN, TOM - ACTION
GREENE, AL & the SOUL MATES – ACTION, BELL, STATESIDE
GREENE, JEANIE - ATLANTIC
GREENE, LAURA - GRAPEVINE
GREENWICH, ELLIE – BELL, UNITED ARTISTS
GREGORY, DON and the SOUL TRAINERS - PROBE
GREY & HANKS - RCA
GRIER, ROOSEVELT – ACTION, HORACES, PAMA
GRIFFIN, BILLY - MOTOR CITY
GRIFFIN, HERMAN - CONNOISSEURS
GRIFFIN, VIRGIL - JAY BOY
GRIFFITH INC., JOHNNY - RCA
GRIMES, CAROL & the RED PRICE BAND - B&C
GRINER, LINDA - BRETBY
GROUP WITH NO NAME - CASABLANCA
GUESS WHO - KING
GUESS, LENIS - ROUTE
GUEST, EARL - COLUMBIA
GUITAR CRUSHER - BLUE HORIZON
GUITAR RED - PYE INTERNATIONAL
GUNN, JON - DERAM
GUSTAFSON, JOHNNY - POLYDOR
GUY, BUDDY – ATLANTIC, CHESS, FONTANA
GUYS FROM UNCLE - SWAN
GYPSIES – CBS

H

HALL, BARBARA - EMI
HALL, DELORES - JAY BOY
HALL, GERRI - GRAPEVINE 2000, SUE
HALL'S ORCHESTRA, RENE - LONDON
HAMBRIC, BILLY - GRAPEVINE
HAMILTON, EDWARD & THE ARABIANS - GRAPEVINE
HAMILTON, LITTLE JOHNNY – HORACES, JOE BOY
HAMILTON, ROY - DEEP SOUL, FONTANA, MGM, RCA
HAMMER, JACK – POLYDOR,UNITED ARTISTS, YOUNGBLOOD
HAMMOND BROS. AND MAGGIE - LONDON
HAMMOND, CLAY - JAY BOY
HAMPTON, JOHNNY - GOLDMINE, GOLDMINE SOUL SUPPLY,
HANCOCK, HERBIE - BLUE NOTE, CBS, WARNER BROS
HANDY, JOHN - IMPULSE
HANNA, BOBBY - DECCA
HAPPY CATS - GRAPEVINE
HARDIE, CELESTE – LOWTON, SEVENS
HARDY, LAVELL - DIRECTION
HARLEM JOHNS RESHUFFLE - FONTANA
HARMONICA FATS – ACTION, STATESIDE
HARNER, BILLY - KAMA SUTRA
HARPER, BUD - VOCALION
HARPER, JEANETTE - SOUL STOP
HARPER, MIKE – CONCORD, RCA, RETREAT
HARPER, TONI - VOCALION
HARPO, SLIM - BLUE HORIZON, PRESIDENT, PYE
  INTERNATIONAL STATESIDE
HARRELL, ROCQ-E – ACHIEVEMENT, S.W.O.N.S, TWIRL
HARRIS & F.L.O. , RAHNI - MERCURY
HARRIS ORCHESTRA, JOHNNY - WARNER BROS
HARRIS, ANITA – CBS, PYE
HARRIS, BETTY – ACTION, CHARLY, LONDON, STATESIDE
HARRIS, BOBBY - LONDON
HARRIS, BRENDA JO - ROULETTE
HARRIS, DAMON - FANTASY
HARRIS, EDDIE – ATLANTIC
HARRIS, KURT - SEVENS
HARRIS, MAJOR – ATLANTIC, BUZZ INTERNATIONAL,
  LONDON
HARRIS, THURSTON - SUE
HARRISON, EARL - LONDON
HARRISON, WILBERT – ACTION, ISLAND, LONDON, SUE,

TOP RANK

HARVEY & JOKERS - SEVENS
HARVEY, ALEX & HIS SOUL BAND – FONTANA POLYDOR
HATCHER, ROGER - MINT
HATFIELD, BOBBY -VERVE
HATHAWAY, DONNY – ATCO, ATLANTIC
HAUSER, FAY - PHILIPS
HAVEN, ALAN - FONTANA
HAVENS, RICHIE - VERVE
HAWKINS, RONNIE - ATLANTIC
HAWKINS, SCREAMING JAY – COLUMBIA, DIRECTION, SUE
HAYES, ISAAC - STAX
HAYES MOVEMENT, ISAAC - ABC
HAYWOOD, JOE - ISLAND
HAYWOOD, LEON - 20TH. CENTURY, CAPITOL, FANTASY, MCA
    SOUL BAG, PYE INTERNATIONAL, SOUL SOUNDS,
    VOCALION
HEAD, ROY – LONDON, PYE INTERNATIONAL, STATESIDE,
    VOCALION
HEATH, WALTER - BUDDAH
HEATWAVE - GTO
HEAVEN 17 feat. JIMMY RUFFIN - VIRGIN
HEBB, BOBBY - PHILIPS
HEIGHT, DONALD – AVCO, JAY BOY, LONDON, SOUL SOUNDS.
HELMS, JIMMY – CAPITOL, CUBE, LONDON, PYE
HENDERSON, EDDIE - CAPITOL
HENDERSON, FINIS - MOTOWN UK
HENDERSON, MICHEAL - BUDDAH
HENDERSON, RON & CHOICE OF COLOUR - GRAPEVINE 2000
HENDERSON, WILLIE – CONTEMPO, CONTEMPO RARIES, MCA
    PYE INTERNATIONAL
HENDRICKS, BOBBY - SUE
HENDRIX, MARGIE - MERCURY
HENLEY, LARRY - HICKORY
HENRY III – RCA
HENRY, ANDREA – SEVENS
HENRY, BOB - PHILIPS
HENRY, ROBERT – PHILIPS
HENRY, VIRGIL - FABULOUS
HENSLEY, ROBERT HENRY - POLYDOR
HERMAN, WOODY - CHESS
HERVEY, PAT - PRESIDENT
HESITATIONS – KENT, LONDON, SOUL SERIES
HESTOR, TONY – GOLDMINE, SEVENS
HETHERINGTON - MOWEST
HI - NUMBERS - DECCA
HI TENSION - ISLAND
HIATT, JOHN - MCA
HICKORY - CBS
HICKS, JIMMY - LONDON
HICKS, MARVA - INFINITY
HIDEAWAYS – ACTION, JAY BOY
HIGH & MIGHTY - HMV
HIGH INERGY – GORDY, MOTOWN, MOTOWN UK
HIGH KEYES - LONDON
HIGHTOWER, ROZETTA – BADGER, CBS, PHILIPS, TOAST
HILL, BUNKER and the RAYMEN - STATESIDE
HILL, JESSIE - LONDON
HILL, LONNIE - 10
HILL, RONI - CREOLE
HILL, Z.Z. – ACTION, CBS, CONTEMPO, MOJO, R&B, SUE,
    UNITED ARTISTS
HILLERY, JANE - COLUMBIA
HINES, HINES & DAD - CBS
HINES, SONNY - KING
HINTON, JOE - VOCALION
HIPSTER IMAGE - DECCA
HIRT, AL - RCA
HIT PACK - TAMLA MOTOWN
HITSON, HERMAN - GRAPEVINE 2000, SPECIAL AGENT
HOBSON, GEORGE - GRAPEVINE 2000
HODGE, ARCHIE - GRAPEVINE 2000
HODGE, MARVA - POLYDOR
HODGES, JAMES, & SMITH – LONDON, PYE
HOGS - JAY BOY

HOLDER, MARK - ATLANTIC
HOLIDAY, JIMMY – LIBERTY, LONDON, MINIT, VOCALION
HOLIDAY, JIMMY & KING, CLYDIE - SOUL SOUNDS,
    UNITED ARTISTS
HOLIDAYS - POLYDOR
HOLLAND, BRIAN - HDH, INVICTUS
HOLLAND, EDDIE – ADVANCE, FONTANA, ORIOLE
HOLLAND, LYNN - EMBER
HOLLAND-DOZIER - INVICTUS
HOLLIDAY, JENIFFER - GEFFEN
HOLLIDAY, SUSAN - COLUMBIA
HOLLOWAY, BRENDA – ILLUSION, NIGHTMARE, STATESIDE,
    TAMLA MOTOWN, TMW
LOLEATTA HOLLOWAY – KENT, SALSOUL, UNITED ARTISTS
HOLLOWAY, PATRICE - CAPITOL
HOLMAN, EDDIE – ABC, ACTION, CAMEO PARKWAY,
    GRAPEVINE 2000, GSF, KENT, POLYDOR, GSF, SALSOUL,
    SEVENS, SOUL BEAT, S.W.O.N.S, STATESIDE, WIGAN
    CASINO
HOLMES, CHRISTINE - MERCURY
HOMESICK JAMES - SUE
HONEST MEN - TAMLA MOTOWN
HONEY & THE BEES – GOLDMINE, SEVENS
HONEY CONE - HOT WAX
HONEYEND - SPARK
HOOKER, EARL - BLUE HORIZON
HOOKER, FRANK & POSITIVE PEOPLE - DJM
HOOKER, JOHN LEE – ATLANTIC, CHARLY, CHESS,
    EMBER, POLYDOR, PRESIDENT, PYE INTERNATIONAL,
    RIVERSIDE, STATESIDE, SUE
HOOKER, JOHN LEE with GROUNDHOGS - PLANET
HOOPER, STIX - MCA
HOPKINS, LINDA - CORAL
HOPKINS, LINDA & JACKIE WILSON - CORAL
HOPKINS, NICKY - CBS
HORAN, EDDIE - LONDON
HORNE, JIMMY BO - RCA , TK
HORNE, LENA – STATESIDE, UNITED ARTISTS
HOT ICE - ATLANTIC
HOT ROCKS - BELL
HOUSTON, BOBBIE - ACTION
HOUSTON, CISSY – GLITTER, JANUS, MAJOR MINOR,
    PHONOGRAM, PRIVATE STOCK, PYE INTERNATIONAL,
HOUSTON, THELMA - MOTOWN UK, MOWEST, PROBE,
    STATESIDE, TAMLA MOTOWN
HOWARD BAND, JOHNNY - DECCA
HOWEEFEEL - CONTEMPO
HOWELL, REUBEN – MOWEST
HOWLIN' WOLF – CHESS, PYE INTERNATIONAL
HUDMON, R.B. - ATLANTIC
HUDSON, AL & THE SOUL PARTNER - ABC
HUDSON, DAVID - TK
HUDSON, JOHNNY - ARDENT
HUDSON, POOKIE - JOKER
HUES CORPORATION - RCA
HUEYS – LONDON
HUGHES, FRED – DJM, ,FONTANA
HUGHES, FRED - BRUNSWICK
HUGHES, JIMMY – ATLANTIC, CHARLY, LONDON, PYE
    INTERNATIONAL, STAX, SUE
HUMAN BEINZ – CAPITOL, SOUL SOUNDS.
HUMBUG - CBS
HUMPHREY, DELLA - ACTION
HUMPHREY, PAUL - ABC
HUNT, GERALDINE – CHAMPAGNE, EMI, ROULETTE
HUNT, MARSHA - ELECTRIC RECORD CO.
HUNT, TOMMY - CASINO CLASSICS, DIRECTION, HORACES,
    KENT, POLYDOR, PYE, RK, SPARK, TOP RANK, TRIDENT
    STUDIOS
HUNT, WILLIE AMOS - CAMP
HUNTER, DAVE - RCA
HURTT, PHIL - FANTASY
WILLIE HUTCH – ABC, KENT, MOTOWN UK, TAMLA
    MOTOWN
HUTCHINS, SAM – BELL

HUTSON, LEROY – CURTOM, WARNER BROS
HUTTON, BOBBY - ABC
HUTTON, BOBBY - SEVENS
HYLAND, BRIAN - PHILIPS
HYMAN, PHYLLIS – ARISTA, BUDDAH

I

I.G.'S - RCA
ICE - CREOLE
IFE, KRIS – MGM, MUSIC FACTORY
IKETTES – LIBERTY, LONDON, MOJO, POLYDOR, STATESIDE,
    SUE
IMPACT - ATLANTIC
IMPERIALS - POWER EXCHANGE, TAMMI RECORDS
IMPRESSIONS – ABC, BUDDAH, CURTOM, HMV, STATESIDE
    WARNER BROS
IN CROWD - PARLOPHONE
INCREDIBLES - CONTEMPO RARIES, STATESIDE
INDEPENDANTS - PYE INTERNATIONAL, WAND
INDEPENDENTS - PYE INTERNATIONAL
INGRAM, BRIMSTONE - GRAPEVINE
INGRAM, LUTHER – SEVENS, STAX
INNER CITY EXPRESS - EBONY
INNERSECTION - SEVENS
INSPIRATIONS - GOLDMINE ,POLYDOR, SEVENS
INSTANT FUNK - SALSOUL
INTENTSIONS - SUE
INTRIGUE - MUSIC POWER
INTRIGUES – JANUS, LONDON
INTRUDERS – ACTION, EMBER, LONDON, PIR
INVITATIONS - JAY BOY, MOJO, POLYDOR, SOUL SOUNDS,
    STATESIDE
IRWIN, BIG DEE – COLPIX, STATESIDE
IRWIN, DEE - MINIT
ISLEY BROTHERS – ATLANTIC, EPIC, MAJOR MINOR, RCA,
    STATESIDE, TAMLA MOTOWN, UNITED ARTISTS
IVORIES - SOUL CITY
IVORY, JACKIE - ATLANTIC
IVORYS – KENT

J

J.A.L.N. BAND - MAGNET
J.B.'S - MOJO
JACKSON & SMITH - POLYDOR
JACKSON 5 – LYNTONE, MOTOWN UK, RICE KRISPIES,
    TAMLA MOTOWN
JACKSON FIVE - TAMLA MOTOWN
JACKSON SISTERS - CBS, MUMS, URBAN
JACKSON, ALEXANDER - SUE
JACKSON, CHRIS – 444, SOUL CITY
JACKSON, CHUCK – ACHIEVEMENT, ALL 4U, ALL PLATINUM,
    DEBUT, KENT, MOTOR CITY, NIGHTMARE, PROBE, PYE
    DISCO DEMAND, PYE INTERNATIONAL, SOUL CITY, SOUL
    GALORE, STATESIDE, S.W.O.N.S, TAMLA MOTOWN, TOP
    RANK,
JACKSON, CHUCK and BROWN, MAXINE - PYE
    INTERNATIONAL
JACKSON, CLYDENE - SOUL HQ
JACKSON, DEON – ATLANTIC, CONTEMPO RARIES
JACKSON, EARL – ABC
JACKSON, GARY – BLACK MAGIC
JACKSON, GEORGE – CAPITOL, LONDON
JACKSON, J.J. –LONDON, MOJO, POLYDOR, STRIKE,
    WARNER BROS
JACKSON, JERMAINE – ARISTA, MOTOWN UK,
    TAMLA MOTOWN
JACKSON, JERRY – CAMEO PARKWAY, LONDON
JACKSON, LEVI - COLUMBIA
JACKSON, MICHEAL - TAMLA MOTOWN
JACKSON, MILLIE – MOJO, POLYDOR, SPRING
JACKSON, MILLIE - KENT
JACKSON, ROOT & JENNY - BEACON
JACKSON, SHAWNE – PYE ADVANCE PRESSING, RCA
JACKSON, SHIRLEY - DECCA
JACKSON, TONY - OPIUM

JACKSON, TONY & the VIBRATIONS - PYE
JACKSON, WALTER – ATLANTIC, BLUEBIRD, BRUNSWICK, COLUMBIA, TRENTHAM GARDENS, UNITED ARTISTS
JACKSONS - EPIC
JACOBS, HANK - SUE
JADES - GRAPEVINE 2000, SOUL CITY
JAM - POLYDOR
JAMES BOYS - DIRECTION
JAMES, BOBBY c/w LOVELITES - GRAPEVINE 2000
JAMES, ELMORE - SUE
JAMES, ELMORE & the BROOM DUSTERS - SUE
JAMES, ETTA – CHESS, LONDON, PYE INTERNATIONAL, SUE, WARNER BROS
JAMES, ETTA & SUGAR PIE DESANTO - CHESS
JAMES, GARY - POLYDOR
JAMES, JACKY - AQUARIUS
JAMES, JESSE – MOJO, SOUL CITY
JAMES, JESSE c/w PROPHETS - SOUL CITY
JAMES, JIMMY - BLACK SWAN, DICE, EMI, SKA BEAT, R&B, STATESIDE
JAMES, JIMMY & THE VAGABONDS – COLUMBIA, EMI, MIAMI, PICCADILLY, PYE, TROJAN, TROJAN DISCO PICK
JAMES, JOSIE - TPL
JAMES, MARK - LIBERTY
JAMES, PHILIP - ISLAND
JAMES, RICK – GORDY, MOTOWN, MOTOWN UK
JAMES, RUBY - FONTANA
JAMES, TOMMY & the SHONDELLS - MAJOR MINOR, ROULETTE
JAMESON, BOBBY - LONDON
JARMELS - TOP RANK
JARVIS, MARION - CHELSEA
JAVELLS - PYE DISCO DEMAND
JAVELLS feat. NOSMO KING – PYE, PYE DISCO DEMAND
JAY & THE AMERICANS - UNITED ARTISTS
JAY & THE TECHIQUES - MERCURY
JAY & THE TECHNIQUES – MERCURY, PHILIPS, POLYDOR
JAY DEE - WARNER BROS
JAY, PETER and the JAYWALKERS – DECCA, PICCADILLY
JAYBIRDS - SUE
JAYE, JERRY - LONDON
JAYNETTS - STATESIDE
JAYWALKERS - CREAM
JB's ALLSTARS - RCA
JEAN and the STATESIDERS - COLUMBIA
JEAN, SCHERRIE & LYNDA - MOTOR CITY
JEAN, NORMA - GRAPEVINE 2000
JEFFERSON, EDDIE - STATESIDE
JEFFREE – EXPANSION
JELLY BEANS - INFERNO, RIGHT ON, RED BIRD, PYE INTERNATIONAL
JENKINS, DIANE - CRYSTAL
JENNIFER - MOTOWN UK
JENSON, KRIS - HICKORY
JENSEN, DICK - EPIC
JEROME - DJM
JERRY O - JAY BOY , LONDON
JESS & JAMES - MGM
JESS & JAMES & the J.J. BAND - MGM
JESTERS - JAM
JEWELL, LEN - SOUL CITY
JEWELS - COLPIX
JEZEBELLES - PYE DISCO DEMAND
JIVE FIVE – PARLOPHONE, STATESIDE, UNITED ARTISTS
JO MAMA - ATLANTIC
JO, DAMITA - MERCURY
JOBELL & ORCHESTRA DE SALSA - PYE INTERNATIONAL
JOHN BULL BREED - POLYDOR
JOHN, LITTLE WILLIE - PARLOPHONE
JOHN, MABLE – ATLANTIC, STAX
JOHN, ROBERT - A&M, CBS
JOHN, SAMMIE - STATESIDE
JOHNNY & JOHN - POLYDOR
JOHNSON, AL - CBS
JOHNSON, BOBBY and the ATOMS - EMBER

JOHNSON, DEBRA - KENT
JOHNSON, GENERAL – ARISTA, HDH, INVICTUS
JOHNSON, HOWARD - JAY BOY
JOHNSON, JIMMY - SUE
JOHNSON, JOHNNY & the BANDWAGON - BELL DIRECTION,EMI, EPIC, STATESIDE
JOHNSON, JUDI - HMV
JOHNSON, JUDI and the PERFECTIONS - HMV
JOHNSON, L.J. – AVI, MERCURY, PHILIPS, TOMORROW
JOHNSON, L.V. - GRAPEVINE 2000, SEVENS
JOHNSON, LOU – GOLDMINE, LONDON
JOHNSON, MARV – LONDON, NIGHTMARE, TAMLA MOTOWN, UNITED ARTISTS
JOHNSON, MARV - TAMLA MOTOWN
JOHNSON, NORMAN & the SHOWMEN - ACTION
JOHNSON, ROY LEE - ACTION
JOHNSON, RUBY - STAX
JOHNSON, SYL – EMBER, GRAPEVINE 2000, LONDON
JOKER - PALADIN
JON and JEANNIE - BEACON
JON and the WEIRDEST - SEVENS
JONES BROS. - PYE INTERNATIONAL
JONES BROTHERS - GRAPEVINE 2000
JONES GIRLS - PIR
JONES, BEVERLY and the PRESTONS - PARLOPHONE
JONES, BRENDA LEE - UK
JONES, BRENDA with GROOVE HOLMES - RCA
JONES, BUSTER - SPRING
JONES, CHUCK AND CO - PYE DISCO DEMAND
JONES, DORIS - NEMS ,TOMORROW
JONES, GLORIA – CAPITOL, EMI, INFERNO, SIDEWALK, STATESIDE, TAMLA MOTOWN
JONES, JIMMY – COLUMBIA, STATESIDE
JONES, JOHNNY & the KING CASUALS - BRUNSWICK, CREAM, MCA
JONES, JUGGY - CONTEMPO
JONES, JUSTIN - LONDON
JONES, LINDA – LONDON, WARNER BROS
JONES, PALMER - DIRECTION
JONES, QUINCY - A&M
JONES, RONNIE – CBS, DECCA
JONES, RONNIE and the NIGHT-TIMERS - DECCA
JONES, SALENA - COLUMBIA
JONES, SALINA - POLYDOR
JONES, SAMANTHA - UNITED ARTISTS
JONES, SELENA - COLUMBIA, DJM
JONES, TAMIKO - ARISTA, CONTEMPO
JONES, THELMA - CBS, SOUL CITY, SUE
JONES, TOM - DECCA
JONESES - MERCURY
JORDAN, DICK - PICCADILLY
JORDAN, EARL - UNITED ARTISTS
JOSEPH, DAVID - ISLAND
JOSEPH, MARGIE – ATLANTIC, STAX
JOSEPH, MARGIE & BLUE MAGIC - ATLANTIC
JOSIE, MARVA - POLYDOR
JOY, RODDIE - RED BIRD
JUNOFF, LENA - OLGA
JUST BROTHERS – HAYLEY, INFERNO, SOUL CITY
JUSTE, SAMANTHA - GO
JUSTICE, JIMMY – DECCA, RCA
JUSTIN, JAY – COLUMBIA

K

K, KRISSI - PEOPLE
KADDO STRINGS - GRAPEVINE
KANE, EDEN - DECCA
KARIM, TY c/w J.D. BRYANT - LOWTON
KARMEN, STEVE - UNITED ARTISTS
KASENETZ-KATZ – BUDDAH, PYE INTERNATIONAL
KATE - CBS
KAY, BARBARA - PYE
KAY, CAROL – DESTINY
KAY, JUDY - DECCA
KAYE, LINDA - COLUMBIA

KC & THE SUNSHINE BAND - JAY BOY
K-DOE, ERNIE – LONDON, VOCALION
KEITH - MERCURY
KEITH & DARRELL - MOTOWN UK
KEITH, RON - A&M
KEITH. - MERCURY
KELLEY, PAT - GAS
KELLING, TONY - PYE
KELLY & THE SOUL EXPLOSIONS - DECCA
KELLY BROTHERS – BLUE HORIZON, PRESIDENT, SUE
KELLY, PAUL – ATLANTIC, PHILIPS, WARNER BROS
KELLY, ROBERTA - CONTEMPO
KEMP, WAYNE - ATLANTIC
KENDRICK, LINDA - POLYDOR
KENDRICK, LORRETTA - HAYLEY
KENDRICK, NAT and the SWANS - TOP RANK
KENDRICKS, EDDIE – MOTOWN UK, TAMLA MOTOWN
KENDRICKS, LINDA - POLYDOR
KENNER, CHRIS – LONDON, SUE
KENT STYLE, RICHARD – COLUMBIA, MCA, MERCURY
KENT, AL – MOJO,TAMLA MOTOWN, TRACK
KENWRIGHT, BILL and the RUNAWAYS – COLUMBIA
KENYATTA, ROBIN - ATLANTIC
KERR, PATRICK - DECCA
KEYES, CAROL - FONTANA
KEYES, EBONY – PARLOPHONE, PICCADILLY
KEYES, KAROL – COLUMBIA, FONTANA
KEYES, TROY - STATESIDE
KHAN SOUND ORCHESTRA, ALFIE - ATLANTIC
KHAN, CHAKA - WARNER BROS
KIDD, CHRISTINE - ANCHOR
KILGORE, THEOLA - SUE
KIMBLE, STEVE - DECCA
KING CURTIS – ATCO, ATLANTIC, CAPITOL, LONDON, SPECIALITY
KING FLOYD – ATLANTIC, CONTEMPO
KING GEORGE - RCA
KING SOUL BAND, RAY - PICCADILLY
KING, AL - SUE
KING, ALBERT – ATLANTIC, STAX
KING, ANNA & BOOBY BYRD - PHILIPS
KING, B.B. – BLUE HORIZON, EMBER, HMV, POLYDOR, PROBE, STATESIDE, SUE
KING, BEN E. – ATLANTIC, CBS, CREWE, LONDON ATLANTIC
KING, BOBBY & SILVER FOXX BAND - MOTOWN UK
KING, BOBBY feat: ALFIE SILAS - MOTOWN UK
KING, BOBBY. - MOTOWN
KING, CLYDIE – MINIT, UK
KING, CAROL – A&M
KING, DEE - PICCADILLY
KING, EVELYN - RCA
KING, EVELYN CHAMPAGNE - RCA
KING, FREDDIE – A&M, ATLANTIC, EMBER, PARLOPHONE, RSO
KING, FREDDY - SUE
KING, JAY W. - STATESIDE
KING, LOUIS - GRAPEVINE 2000
KING, MARTIN LUTHER - PAMA
KING, NOSMO - PYE
KING, RAMONA - WARNER BROS
KING, SOLOMAN - COLUMBIA
KING, SOLOMON – COLUMBIA
KINGFISH, JOEY - CONNOISSEURS
KINGSMEN - PYE INTERNATIONAL, WAND
KIRBY, KATHY - DECCA
KIRTON, LEW - EPIC
KISSOON, KATIE - COLUMBIA
KISSOON, MAC – BOULEVARD, YOUNGBLOOD
KISSOON, MAC and KATIE - YOUNGBLOOD
KLEEER - ATLANTIC
KLINT, PETE – ATLANTIC, MERCURY
KLYMAXX - SOLAR
KNICKERBOCKERS - LONDON
KNIGHT BROTHERS - CHESS

KNIGHT, FREDERICK - STAX
KNIGHT, GLADYS – BUDDAH, CBS
KNIGHT, GLADYS & The PIPS – BUDDAH, CBS, CONTEMPO, DJM, EMBER, MOTOWN UK, STATESIDE, SUE, TAMLA MOTOWN
KNIGHT, JASON - CASINO CLASSICS, PYE
KNIGHT, JEAN - STAX
KNIGHT, MARIE – FONTANA, KENT, SOUL CITY, STATESIDE
KNIGHT, PAULA - EMBER
KNIGHT, ROBERT – BELL, LONDON, MONUMENT, PRIVATE STOCK
KOFFIE - RED ROOSTER
KOFFMAN, MOE – CBS, KAMA SUTRA
KOLETTES – CHESS, PYE INTERNATIONAL
KOOBAS – COLUMBIA, PYE
KOOL & THE GANG – CONTEMPO, LONDON, MOJO, POLYDOR
KOOPER, AL - CBS
KOOPER, ALAN - MERCURY
KORDA, PAUL - COLUMBIA
KORNER, ALEXIS – CBS, FONTANA, KING, PARLOPHONE
KRAMER, SU - DECCA
KRYSTAL GENERATION - MERCURY
KUBAN, BOB & THE IN-MEN – BELL, STATESIDE
KUBAS – COLUMBIA

L

L.A.X. - EPIC
L.T.D. - A&M
LA VELLE - SIDEWALK
LABATT, VICKI - GRAPEVINE 2000
LABELLE, PATTI - ATLANTIC
LABELLE, PATTI & HER BLUEBELLES - CAMEO PARKWAY
LABELLE, PATTI & THE BLUEBELLES – ATLANTIC, SUE
LABELLE, PATTY & HER BLUEBELLES - ATLANTIC
LABELLE. - EPIC
LADY LEE - DECCA
LAINE, CLEO - PHILIPS
LAMBE, JEANNIE - CBS
LAMP SISTERS - SUE
LANCASTER, DIANE - POLYDOR
LANCE, MAJOR – ATLANTIC, BUDDAH, COLUMBIA, CONTEMPO, CONTEMPO RARIES, EPIC, MOTOWN UK, PYE, PYE INTERNATIONAL, SOS, SOUL CITY, SOUL SERIES, STAX, WARNER BROS
LANDON, NEIL - DECCA
LANDS, HOAGY – ACTION, STATESIDE, UK
LANE, MICKEY LEE - STATESIDE
LANE, PENNY - CBS
LANGLEY, PERTETUAL - PLANET
LARK, TOBI - KENT, SEVENS
LARKINS, PERCY - MOVE.
LARKS - PYE INTERNATIONAL
LARRY & TOMMY - POLYDOR
LARSON, NICOLETTE - WARNER BROS
LaRUE, D.C. - PYE INTERNATIONAL
LASALLE, DENISE - JANUS, MALACO, WESTBOUND
LASKY, EMANUEL - WIGAN CASINO
LAST WORD - POLYDOR
LATIMORE – PRESIDENT, TK
LATTER, GENE – CBS, DECCA, DIRECTION, PARLOPHONE, SPARK
LATTIMORE, CHARLES - JAY BOY
LAVERNE, CONNIE - DESTINY
LAVERNE, CONNIE - DESTINY
LAVETTE, BETTY – ATLANTIC, CHARLY, MOJO, PAMA, POLYDOR, STATESIDE
LAVETTE, BETTYE - MOTOWN UK
LAVETTE, TAMMI - S.W.O.N.S
LAWS, ELOISE - CBS, INVICTUS
LAWS, HUBERT - CTI
LAWS, RONNIE - BLUE NOTE, UNITED ARTISTS
ROBBY LAWSON - SEVENS
LAWSON, SHIRLEY - SOUL CITY
LAWTON, LOU – EMBER, SPECIALITY
LAWTON, LOU - GOLDSOUL

LEACH, JOHN - DESTINY
LEADERS - FONTANA
LEAPERS CREEPERS SLEEPERS - ISLAND
LEAR, KEVIN KING - PAGE ONE, POLYDOR, PYE, ROUTE
LEAVILL, OTIS – ATLANTIC, CONTEMPO
LEAVILLE, OTIS - ATLANTIC
LEE, BRENDA –BRUNSWICK
CURTIS LEE - KENT
LEE, CURTIS and the K.C.P.'s - CBS
LEE, DINAH – ALADDIN, BRIT
LEE, IAN - SOLENT
LEE, JACKIE – CONTEMPO, CONTEMPO RARIES, FONTANA, JAY BOY, KENT, LONDON
LEE, JACKIE & HALL, DOLORES – B&C, JAY BOY
LEE, LAURA – CHESS, HOT WAX, INVICTUS, TAMLA MOTOWN
LEE, NICKIE - DEEP SOUL
LEE, WARREN - PAMA
LEE'S GROUNDHOGS, JOHN - PLANET
LEFERVE, RAYMOND & HIS ORCHESTRA – BARCLAY, MAJOR MINOR
LEFT BANKE - PHILIPS
LEGEND, TOBI - RK
LEGRAND, MICHEAL - TAMLA MOTOWN
LENIOR, J.B. - SUE
LENTON, VAN - IMMEDIATE
LEONARD, CHARLES - JAY BOY
LEONIE - REAL SIDE
LEO'S SUNSHIPP - GRAPEVINE
LES CHANSONETTES - SHRINE
LESTER, KETTY – CAPITOL, CONTEMPO RARIES, LONDON, RCA
LESTER, LAZY - STATESIDE
LESTER, LONNIE - SEVENS
LEVEL 42 - POLYDOR
LEVINE, HANK - HMV
LEVON & THE HAWKS - ATLANTIC
LEWIS SISTERS - TAMLA MOTOWN
LEWIS TRIO, RAMSEY - CHESS
LEWIS, BARBARA – ATLANTIC, HORACES, LONDON, SOUL SOUNDS.
LEWIS, BARBARA – PARLOPHONE, STATESIDE
LEWIS, DIANE c/w J.J.BARNES - SEVENS
LEWIS, GARY & THE PLAYBOYS – LIBERTY, UNITED ARTISTS
LEWIS, HERMAN - GROOVESVILLE
LEWIS, JERRY LEE - PHILIPS
LEWIS, JIMMY - MINIT
LEWIS, LINDA – ARISTA, POLYDOR
LEWIS, MIA - PARLOPHONE
LEWIS, PAT – CONNOISSEURS, JOE BOY, TMW
LEWIS, PAT - SEVENS
LEWIS, PHILLIPPA – DECCA
LEWIS, RAMSEY – CBS, CHESS, COLUMBIA
LEWIS, STEVIE - MERCURY
LEWIS, TAMALA - DESTINY
LEWIS, TINA - INFERNO
LEWIS, WEBSTER - EPIC
LEYTON, JOHN E. & the LE ROYS - HMV
LIBERTY BELLES - JAY BOY
LIFE - PHILIPS
LIFESTYLE - MCA
LIGHT OF THE WORLD – EMI , ENSIGN
LIMMIE & THE FAMILY COOKIN' - AVCO
LINDA & THE FUNKY BOYS - SPARK
LINDH, JAYSON - ATLANTIC
LINDSEY, TERRY - PRESIDENT
LIQUID SMOKE - PYE INTERNATIONAL
LITTLE ANN - KENT
LITTLE ANN c/w O.C. TOLBERT - KENT
LITTLE ANTHONY - UNITED ARTISTS
LITTLE ANTHONY & the IMPERIALS – AVCO, GREENLIGHT, JANUS, LONDON, TOP RANK, UNITED ARTISTS
LITTLE ARCHIE - ATLANTIC
LITTLE BEAVER - PRESIDENT
LITTLE BEVERLEY - PAMA

LITTLE EVA – COLPIX, LONDON, OLD GOLD, STATESIDE
LITTLE HANK - GRAPEVINE 2000, LONDON, MONUMENT
LITTLE HELEN - DESTINY
LITTLE LUTHER - PYE INTERNATIONAL
LITTLE MAC & the BOSS SOUNDS - ATLANTIC
LITTLE MILTON – CHESS, PYE INTERNATIONAL, SEVILLE, SUE, STAX
LITTLE MR. LEE and the CHEROKEES - VOCALION
LITTLE RICHARD – ACTION, COLUMBIA, DECCA, FONTANA, LONDON, MCA, MERCURY, PRESIDENT, REPRISE, STATESIDE, SUE,VOCALION
LITTLE RICHIE - INFERNO
LITTLE SISTER. – ATLANTIC
LITTLE SONNY - SUE, TOP RANK
LITTLE TONY - DURIUM
LITTLE WALTER - LONDON, PYE INTERNATIONAL
LITTLES, HATTIE - NIGHTMARE
LLOYD QUARTET, CHARLES - ATLANTIC
LOCKETS - PYE INTERNATIONAL
LOCKSMITH - ARISTA
LOCOMOTIVE – DIRECTION, PARLOHPONE
LOLLIPOPS - ATLANTIC
LONG, SHORTY - TAMLA MOTOWN
LOPEZ, TRINI - REPRISE
LORELEI - CBS
LOS BRAVOS - DECCA
LOS CANARIOS – MAJOR MINOR
LOUISANA RED - COLUMBIA
LOUISIANA RED - SUE
LOVABLES - STATESIDE
LOVE COMMITTEE – ARIOLA, PIR, SALSOUL
LOVE UNLIMITED - 20TH. CENTURY, MCA, OLD GOLD, PYE INTERNATIONAL, UNI
LOVE UNLIMITED ORCHESTRA - PYE INTERNATIONAL, UNLIMITED GOLD
LOVE, C.P. - GRAPEVINE 2000
LOVE, DARLENE – LONDON, PHIL SPECTOR INTERNATIONAL, WARNER SPECTOR
LOVE, JILL BABY - BLACK MAGIC
LOVE, MARY - B.J.D., KENT, KING, STATESIDE
LOVE, MARY/IKETTES/ETTA JAMES - KENT
LOVE, MARY+ WILLIE HUTCH + SWEETHEA - KENT
LOVE, RONNIE – GRAPEVINE, LONDON
LOVEJOY, JOY - CHESS
LOVELITES - GRAPEVINE
LOVESMITH, MICHEAL – MOTOWN UK, TAMLA MOTOWN
LOVIN' SPOONFUL - KAMA SUTRA
LOVING KIND - PICCADILLY
LOWRELL - AVI
LOYD, MARK - PARLOPHONE
LUCAS - POLYDOR
LUCAS & THE MIKE COTTON SOUND – MGM, PYE
LULU - DECCA
LULU and the LUVERS - DECCA
LUMLEY, RUFUS – EMI, STATESIDE
LUNAR FUNK - BELL
LUTHER - COTILLION
LYNCH, ED E. - FONTANA
LYNCH, KENNY – HMV, COLUMBIA
LYNDELL, LINDA - STAX
LYNN, BARBARA – ATLANTIC, IMMEDIATE, LONDON, OVAL SOUL CITY, SUE
LYNN, BOBBI – BELL, STATESIDE
LYNN, BOBBY - STATESIDE
LYNN, CHERYL - CBS
LYNN, TAMI – ATLANTIC, CONTEMPO RARIES, MOJO, SOUL SOUNDS.
LYNNE, GLORIA - LONDON
LYNNE, SUE - RCA
LYNTON, JACKIE – COLUMBIA

M

M&M and the PEANUTS c/w CHARMAINES - KENT
M.G.'s - STAX
M.V.P.'S - BUDDAH
M.V.P's c/w BENNY TROY - BOOT
MABLEY, MOMS - MERCURY
MABON, WILLIE - SUE
MACEO & ALL THE KING'S MEN - PYE INTERNATIONAL
MACEO & THE MACKS - URBAN
MACHINE - RCA
MACK, JIMMY - SEVENS, SOUL BANDIT
MACK, LONNIE - PRESIDENT
MACK'S EXT. IN SOUNDS, FREDDIE - CONTEMPO
MAD DOG & THE PUPS - MAGIC CITY
MAD LADS - ATLANTIC
MAD LADS & CROSSFIRE BAND - CHAMPION
MADIGAN, BETTY – MGM
MAESTRO, JOHNNY - SOUL CITY
MAGIC DISCO MACHINE - TAMLA MOTOWN
MAGIC NIGHT - PYE INTERNATIONAL
MAGIC SAM – PYTHON, ROOSTER
MAGICIANS - KENT
MAGISTRATES - MGM
MAGNETICS - GRAPEVINE 2000
MAGNETICS feat: JOHNNY MCKINNEY - GRAPEVINE 2000
MAGNIFICENT MEN - CAPITOL
MAGNIFICENTS - SOUL CITY
MAHAL, TAJ - CBS, DIRECTION
MAHAVISHNU ORCHESTRA - CBS
MAHONEY, SKIP - UNDERWORLD
MAIN INGREDIENT - POWER EXCHANGE, RCA
MAJESTICS – CUBE
MAJESTICS – SEVENS, SOS
MAJORS – LIBERTY, LONDON
MAKEBA, MIRIAM – LONDON, REPRISE
MALTBY, RICHARD - COLUMBIA
MANCHA, STEVE – COLUMBIA, GROOVESVILLE, HAYLEY, RCA, SEVENS
MANCHESTER PLAYBOYS - FONTANA
MANDINGO - EMI
MANDRE – MOTOWN, MOTOWN UK
MANDRILL – ARISTA, POLYDOR
MANHATTAN TRANSFER - ATLANTIC
MANHATTANS – CARNIVAL, CBS, SUE
MANITOBA - RCA
MANN, BARRY - CAPITOL
MANN, CHARLES - PROBE
MANN, HERBIE - A&M, ATLANTIC
MARATHONS – PYE INTERNATIONAL, VOGUE
MARBOO - EMI
MARCELLE, LYDIA - SUE
MARCELS - PYE INTERNATIONAL
MARCH, PEGGY - RCA
MARCHAN, BOBBY – ACTION, ATLANTIC
MARCHAND, RAY - JOE BOY
MARDEN, JANIE - DECCA
MARDI GRAS - BELL
MARGO & the MARVETTES – PARLOPHONE, PICCADILLY, PYE
MARIE, TEENA - MOTOWN UK
MARIONETTES – DECCA, PARLOPHONE
MARKETTS - WARNER BROS
MAR-KEYS - ATLANTIC, LONDON, STAX
MARKHAM, PIGMEAT - CHESS
MARSDEN, BERYL – COLUMBIA, DECCA
MARTELL, LENA - DECCA
MARTELLS - DECCA
MARTHA & THE VANDELLAS – ORIOLE, STATESIDE, TAMLA MOTOWN
MARTIN & FINLEY - TAMLA MOTOWN
MARTIN, BOBBI - LONDON
MARTIN, DEREK – COLUMBIA, STAX, SUE
MARTIN, JEAN - DECCA
MARTIN, PAUL - SUE
MARTIN, RODGE - POLYDOR
MARTIN, SETH - PAGE ONE

MARTIN, SHANE - CBS
MARTIN, TONY – STATESIDE, TAMLA MOTOWN
MARTINO, AL - CAPITOL
MARVELETTES – FONTANA, ORIOLE, STATESIDE, TAMLA MOTOWN
MARVELOWS - HMV
MARVELS - COLUMBIA
MARVELS FIVE - HMV
MARVIN & TAMARA - EPIC
MASAI - CONTEMPO
MASEKELA, HUGH - UNI
MASKMAN & THE AGENTS - DIRECTION
MASON, BARBARA – ACTION, BUDDAH, DIRECTION, LONDON
MASQUERADERS – BELL, GRAPEVINE, NOW
MASS PRODUCTION - ATLANTIC
MASTERS, VALERIE - POLYDOR
MATATA - PRESIDENT
MATHIS, JODI - CAPITOL
MATHIS, JOHNNY - CBS
MATTHEWS INC., MILT - EMBER
MATTHEWS, AL - CBS
MATTHEWS, JOE - SOUL CITY, SUE
MATTHEWS, MILT - LONDON
MAUDS - MERCURY
MAUGHN, SUSAN - PHILIPS
MAURIAT ORCH., PAUL - PHILIPS
MAURICE & MAC – CHESS
MAYBERRY MOVEMENT - KENT
MAXEY, JOE S. - ACTION
MAXIMILIAN - LONDON
MAXWELL, HOLLY - BUDDAH
MAYER, NATHANIEL - HMV
MAYFIELD SINGERS - MAYFIELD
MAYFIELD, CURTIS – BUDDAH, FLASH BACKS, RSO
MAYFIELD, PERCY - HMV, SPECIALTY
MAZE feat. FRANK BEVERLY - - CAPITOL
McCALL, CASH - CHESS
McCALL, TOUSSAINT - PYE INTERNATIONAL
McCALLA, NOEL - DIRECTION
McCALLUM, DAVID - CAPITOL
McCANN LTD., LES - VOGUE
McCANN, LES – ATLANTIC, MERCURY
McCANTS, JUNIOR - KENT
McCARTHY, MARY - CBS
McCLAIN, ALTON and DESTINY - POLYDOR
McCLURE, BOBBY – CHESS, ISLAND
McCORMICK, GAYLE - PROBE
McCOY, VAN - BUDDAH
McCOY, VAN & the SOUL CITY SYMPHONY - AVCO
McCOYS – IMMEDIATE, LONDON
McCRACKLIN, JIMMY – CHESS, LIBERTY, LONDON, MINIT, OUTASITE, R&B, VOCALION, TOP RANK
McCRAE, GEORGE - JAY BOY, PRESIDENT
McCRAE, GWEN – ATLANTIC, FLAME RECORDS, PRESIDENT
McDANIELS, GENE – LIBERTY, LONDON
McDONALD, MIKE - RCA
McDUFF, BROTHER JACK – ATLANTIC, STATESIDE
McFARLAND, JIMMY - SEVENS
McGEE, DONNA - ANCHOR
McGLOIRY, MICHEAL - RECORD SHACK
McGRIFF, JIMMY – SUE, UNITED ARTISTS
McKAY, TONY - POLYDOR
McKEE, LONETTE - SUSSEX
McKENNA, VAL - CASINO CLASSICS, PICCADILLY, SPARK
McLOYD, EDDIE - BRUNSWICK
McNAIR, BARBARA - TAMLA MOTOWN
McNEELEY, BIG JAY - SUE, TOP RANK
McNEIL, AARON - ACTION
McNEIR, RONNIE – ALL 4U, ACHIEMENT, LONDON, SEVENS
McPHATTER, CLYDE – B&C, DERAM, EMBER, LONDON, MGM, MERCURY, PAMA, STATESIDE,
McRAE, CARMEN – ATLANTIC, FONTANA
McVAY SOUND, RAY – PHILIPS, PYE
MEGATONS - SUE
MEL & TIM – CONCORD, STAX

MELVIN, HAROLD & the BLUENOTES – ABC, CBS, PIR, ROUTE, SOURCE
MEMPHIS HORNS – ATLANTIC, RCA
MEMPHIS SLIM - SUMMIT
MERCER, BARBARA - CONNOISSEUR.
MERCURY, ERIC - CAPITOL
MERRELL, RAY - JAY BOY
METERS – CHARLY, DIRECTION, ISLAND, REPRISE, STATESIDE
METROPLOLIS - SALSOUL
METROS – JOKER, KENT
MEZA, LEE - STATESIDE
MFSB - PIR
MIAMI - JAY BOY
MICHAELS, CODY - GRAPEVINE
MICHAELS, LEE - A&M
MICHEALS, TONY - POLYDOR
MIDDLETON, TONY – GRAPEVINE, POLYDOR
MIDDLETON, TONY - JOKER
MIDNIGHT - ARIOLA
MIDNIGHT MOVERS – CONTEMPO, MOJO
MIDNIGHT MOVERS UNLTD. - CONTEMPO RARIES
MIDNITE - MAGNET
MIGHTY CLOUDS OF JOY – ABC, PHOENIX
MIGHTY DODOS - SPARK
MIGHTY MARVELOWS - PROBE
MIGHTY SAM - HIT & RUN, SOUL CITY, STATESIDE
MIGIL FIVE - PYE
MIKE & BILL - ARISTA
MIKE & THE MODIFIERS - ORIOLE
MILBURN JR., AMOS - LONDON
MILEM, PERCY – SOUL SERIES, STATESIDE
MILES EXPRESS, BUDDY - MERCURY
MILES, ARTHUR - FFRR
MILES, BUDDY – CBS, MERCURY
MILES, JOHN – DECCA, ORANGE
MILES, LENNY - TOP RANK
MILES, SHAN - JAY BOY
MILESTONES - BLACK MAGIC
MILLER, GLEN - DOCTOR BIRD, FABULOUS
MILLIE - FONTANA
MILLIONAIRES – ARDENT, GRAPEVINE, KENT, MERCURY
MILLS, BARBARA – HICKORY, INFERNO, LONDON
MILLS, STEPHANIE - 20TH. CENTURY, PARAMOUNT, TAMLA MOTOWN
MILSAP, RONNIE - PYE INTERNATIONAL, WAND
MILWAUKEE COASTERS - PAMA
MIMMS, GARNET (and the ENCHANTERS) - ARISTA, UNITED ARTISTS, VERVE
MIMS, GARNETT & TRUCKIN' CO. - ARISTA
MINNELLI, LIZA - CAPITOL
MIRACLES - FONTANA, LONDON, ORIOLE, STATESIDE, TAMLA MOTOWN
MIRETTES - CONTEMPO RARIES, JAY BOY, MCA SOUL BAG, UNI
MISS DEE DEE - DESTINY
MISS LAVELL - VOCALION
MISTURA feat. MICHEALS, LLOYD – ROUTE, PYE
MISTURA - PYE
MITCHELL, GROVER – LONDON, VANGUARD
MITCHELL, MCKINLEY - PRESIDENT
MITCHELL, PHILLIP - JAY BOY, LONDON
MITCHELL, STANLEY - GOLDMINE SOUL SUPPLY, SEVENS
MITCHELL, VALERIE - COLUMBIA
MITCHELL, WILLIE - CREAM, LONDON
MOB – MERCURY, MGM, POLYDOR, UK
MODERN REDCAPS - SWAN
MODS '79 - CASINO CLASSICS
MODULATIONS - BUDDAH
MOHAWKS – PAMA, SUPREME
MOJO MEN - PYE INTERNATIONAL, REPRISE
MOMENT OF TRUTH - PYE INTERNATIONAL
MOMENTS - ALL PLATINUM, LONDON
MONDAY, DANNY - KENT
MONEY, ZOOT - DECCA

MONEY'S BIG ROLL BAND, ZOOT – COLUMBIA, POLYDOR
MONITORS – ADVANCE, MOTOR CITY
MONOPOLY - POLYDOR
MONRO, MATT - CAPITOL
MONROE, BARRY - POLYDOR
MONTCLAIRS – CONTEMPO, GRAPEVINE 2000
MONTENEGRO, HUGO - ORIOLE
MONTENEGRO, HUGO and his ORCHESTRA - ORIOLE
MONTEZ, CHRIS – LONDON, PYE INTERNATIONAL
MONTGOMEREY, JACK/KNIGHT, MARI - KENT
MONTGOMERY, JACK - SOUL CITY
MOOD-MOSAIC – COLUMBIA, SOUL SUPPLY
MOONSHINE, MICKEY - DECCA
MOORE, BEN - DJM
MOORE, BOBBY - PYE INTERNATIONAL
MOORE, BOBBY & the RHYTHM ACES - CHESS
MOORE, CURLEY & KOOL ONES - PYE INTERNATIONAL
MOORE, DOROTHY – EPIC, CONTEMPO
MOORE, JACKIE – ATLANTIC, CBS, JAY BOY, RCA
MOORE, JOHNNY – BEE COOL, GRAPEVINE 2000
MOORE, JOSEPH - JOE BOY
MOORE, LEE - SOURCE
MOORE, MELBA – BUDDAH, EMI, FABULOUS, FLASH BACKS, HORACES, KENT
MOORE, SAM - EXPANSION
MORGAN, TONY/MUSCLE POWER BAND - BEACON
MORISETTE, JOHNNY - STATESIDE
MORRISON, DOROTHY - ELEKTRA
MORRISON, VAN - WARNER BROS
MORTIMER, AZIE - LONDON
MORTON COMBINATION, MIKE - PLEXIUM
MOSELY, ERNEST - SEVENS
MOSES & JOSHUA - BELL
MOSS, BILL - PAMA
MOTHER FREEDOM BAND - ALL PLATINUM
MOTOWN SPINNERS - TAMLA MOTOWN
MOULTRIE, MATTIE – CBS
MOUSIE & the TRAPS - JOE BOY
MOVING FINGER - MERCURY
MOVING VIOL.ATION - ATLANTIC
MR SOUL - TRENTHAM GARDENS
MR. BLOE – DJM, OLD GOLD
MR. DYNAMITE - SUE
MR. FLOOD PARTY – BULLDOG, EMBER
MR. FLOODS PARTY – EMBER, INFERNO, SOUL CITY
MR. SOUL, BOBO - LONDON
MSFB - PIR
MTUME - EPIC
MUNNINGS, RAY - TAMMI RECORDS
MURPHY, MARK - RIVERSIDE
MURPHY, WALTER & BIG APPLE BAND - PRIVATE STOCK
MURRAY, MICKEY - POLYDOR
MUSCLE SHOALS HORNS - LONDON
MUSIC & MYSTERY feat: GWEN McRAE - KTDA
MUSIC EXPLOSION – LONDON, STATESIDE, UK
MYERS, ALICIA - MCA
MYSTIC MERLIN – CAPITOL
MYSTIC MOODS – MINT, WARNER BROS

N

NABAY – GRAPEVINE
NASH, JOHNNY – CBS, CHESS, MAJOR MINOR, MGM, PYE INTERNATIONAL, RCA, REGAL ZONOPHONE, WARNER BROS
NATURAL BRIDGE BUNCH - ATLANTIC
NATURAL FOUR - CURTOM
NATURE'S DEVINE - INFINITY
NDUGU and the CHOCOLATE JAM COMPANY - EPIC
NEAL, TOMMY – SEVENS, VOCALION
NELSON, DAVID - PHILIPS
NELSON, EARL - LONDON
NERO, FRANCES – DEBUT, MOTOR CITY
NESBIT, SAM - RIGHT ON
NEVILLE, AARON - B&C, CONTEMPO RARIES, STATESIDE
NEW BREED - DECCA

NEW CENSATION - DJM
NEW EXPERIENCE - CONTEMPO
NEW FACES - PYE
NEW FORMULA – PICCADILLY
NEW FOUNDATIONS - ATLANTIC
NEW MONITORS - BUDDAH
NEW WANDERERS - GRAPEVINE
NEW YORK CITY - RCA
NEW YORK PORT AUTHORITY - INVICTUS
NEWBEATS – HICKORY, JAM, LONDON
NEWBY & JOHNSON - MERCURY
NEWCOMERS - STAX
NEWMAN, PAUL and the X'CALIBURS - MERCURY
NEWMAN, TONY – DECCA
BOBBY NEWTON - ATLANTIC
NEWS - DECCA
NEWSOME, BOBBY - MOJO
NICOL, JIMMY - PYE
NICOL, JIMMY and the SHUBDUBS - PYE
NICOLE with TIMMY THOMAS - PORTRAIT
NIGHTINGALE, MAXINE – PYE, UNITED ARTISTS
NIGHT-TIMERS - PARLOPHONE
NINO & APRIL – A&M
NITE PEOPLE - FONTANA
NITELITERS - RCA
NITE-LITERS - RCA
NIXON, MEL – ALASKA, PARLOPHONE
NOBLE, PATSY ANN - COLUMBIA
NOBLES, CLIFF & CO. – CBS, DIRECTION
NOMADS – SEVENS
NORMA JEAN - GRAPEVINE 2000
NORMAN, OLIVER - POLYDOR
NORTH, FREDDIE - CONTEMPO RARIES, MOJO
NORTHERN SOUL INC. - POLYDOR
NOTATIONS - CHAPTER ONE, CURTOM
NUNN, BOBBY - MOTOWN UK
NU-SOUND EXPRESS LTD - PYE INTERNATIONAL

O

OCEAN, BILLY - GTO
ODDJOB - LIGHTNING
ODOM, JOE - CAPITOL
ODYSSEY - RCA
O'HARA, JOHN/THE PLAYBOYS - FONTANA
OHIO PLAYERS – JANUS, MERCURY, SPECIAL AGENT
O'JAYS – BELL, CBS, LIBERTY, MOJO, NOW, PIR, POWER EXCHANGE, STATESIDE , UNITED ARTISTS,
O'KAYSIONS - STATESIDE
OKIN, EARL - CBS
OLLIE and the NIGHTINGALES - STAX
OLYMPIC RUNNERS - CHIPPING NORTON, LONDON
OLYMPICS – ACTION, COLUMBIA, CONTEMPO RARIES, FONTANA, HMV, JAY BOY, SUE, VOGUE POP, WARNER BROS
OMNI - R.B. RECORDS
ONE WAY - MCA
ONENESS OF JUJU - BUDDAH
OPEL, JACKIE – KING
ORIGINALS – BOOT, SOUL BEAT, TAMLA MOTOWN
ORLONS - CAMEO PARKWAY, COLUMBIA, JOKER, MOJO, PLANET
O.R.S. - SALSOUL
OSBOURNE, JEFFREY - A&M
OTHER BROTHERS - PAMA
OTIS SHOW, JOHNNY – BULLDOG, EMBER, EPIC, SONET
OTIS, JOHNNY – EMBER, VOCALION
OUTER LIMITS - DERAM
OUTRIDERS - DART
OUTSIDERS - CAPITOL
OWENS, GWEN – BIG TREE, CASABLANCA, SEVENS

P

PACIFIC GAS AND ELECTRIC - CBS
PACKERS - PYE INTERNATIONAL, SOUL CITY
PAC-KEYS – SPECIALITY

PADDED CELL - JOKER
PAGE, MALLY - PYE
PAIGE, RAY - RCA
PAIGE, SHARON - SOURCE
PAINTBOX - YOUNGBLOOD
PANTER, JAN - PYE
PAPER DOLLS - PYE
PARADOX - POLYDOR
PARAMOR, NORRIE - COLUMBIA
PARAMOUNTS - PARLOPHONE
PARFITT, PAULA - BEACON
PARIS - SEVENS
PARIS, BOBBY – CAPITOL, POLYDOR, SOS
PARIS, MICA and WILL DOWNING - 4TH. + BROADWAY
PARKER, BOBBY - BLUE HORIZON, LONDON, SUE
PARKER, CECIL - EMI
PARKER, EDDIE – GRAPEVINE, SEVENS, SOUL SERIES
PARKER, JUNIOR – CHARLY, VOCALION
PARKER, LITTLE JUNIOR - VOGUE
PARKER, RAYMOND - SUE
PARKER, ROBERT – CHARLY, CONTEMPO RARIES, ISLAND, REPLAY
PARKER, WILLIE – PRESIDENT
PARKER, WINFIELD - MOJO
PARLIAMENT – CASABLANCA, HDH, INVICTUS
PARLIAMENTS – SEVENS, TRACK
PARR, CATHERINE - DECCA
PARRISH, DEAN – RK, SOUL CITY, SOUL SOUNDS, STATESIDE, UK
PARSONS, MATT - SOS
PATRICK BIG SIX, BOBBY - DECCA
PATRON OF THE ARTS - PAGE ONE
PATTERSON, BOBBY & the MUSTANGS - ACTION, CHARLY, CONTEMPO, MOJO, PAMA
PATTI & THE EMBLEMS - GOLDMINE SOUL SUPPLY, SEVENS
PATTI and the PATETTES - UNITED ARTISTS
PATTO, MIKE – GOODEAR, COLUMBIA
PATTON, ALEXANDER - B.J.D., CAPITOL, SOUL SOUNDS.
PATTY & THE EMBLEMS - STATESIDE
PAUL, BILLY – EPIC, PIR
PAUL, CLARENCE - LONDON
PAUL, DARLENE - CAPITOL
PAUL, JOHN E. - DECCA
PAYNE, FREDA – ABC, HDM, HMV, INFERNO , INVICTUS
PAYNE, JACKIE - BARAK
PAYNE, SCHERRIE - MOTOWN UK
PAYNE, TAMMY - TALKIN LOUD
PAYTON, LAWRENCE - ABC
PEACHES & HERB – CBS, CONTEMPO, DIRECTION, EPIC, SOUL SOUNDS
PEANUT - PYE
PEARLS – BELL, PRIVATE STOCK
PEARSON BAND, BUSTER – ACTION
PEARSON, DOTTIE - BEECOOL
PEARSON ORCHESTRA, JOHNNY - COLUMBIA
PEASTON, DAVID - GEFFEN
PEDDLERS - PHILIPS
PEEBLES, ANN – HI, LONDON
PEELS – AUDIO FIDELITY, STATESIDE
PENDERGRASS, TEDDY - PIR
PENISTON, CE CE - A&M
PENNINGTON, BARBARA – NIGHTMARE, TOMORROW, UNITED ARTISTS, USA
PENTAGONS - KENT
PEOPLES CHOICE – LONDON, MOJO, PIR, SEVENS
PEPPERS - SPARK
PERFORMERS - ACTION
PERISHERS - FONTANA
PERKINS, GEORGE - HIT & RUN
PERKINS, JOE - MOJO
PERRY, BARBARA - PAMA
PERRY, GREG - CASABLANCA
PERRY, JEFF – ARISTA, SOS
PERSIANS – CAPITOL, PAMA
PERSUADERS - ATLANTIC

PERSUASIONS – COLUMBIA, MINIT
PETER'S FACES - PICCADILLY
PETERSON QUINTET, BOBBY - TOP RANK
PETERSON, BOBBY - SUE
PETERSON, PAUL - TAMLA MOTOWN
PHELPS, JAMES - PARAMOUNT
PHILADELPHIA ALL-STARS - PIR
PHILADELPHIA FLYERS - EMI, GM
PHILADELPHIA SOCIETY - GULL
PHILIPS, ESTHER – ATLANTIC, KUDU, ROULETTE, SUE
PHILIPS, LITLE ESTHER - EMBER
PHILLIPS, ESTHER – ATLANTIC, EMBER, KUDU, ROULETTE,
    STATESIDE
SANDRA PHILLIPS – RIGHT ON
PHILLY CREAM - WMOT
PHILLY DEVOTIONS - CBS
PHOENIX - PYE
PIC & BILL - PAGE ONE
PICKETT, WILSON - ATLANTIC, EMI, EMI AMERICA , LIBERTY
MGM, MOTOWN UK, PRESIDENT
PICKETT, WILSON & THE FALCONS - LONDON
PIGLETS – BELL
PIKE, DAVE - ATLANTIC
PINKY - POLYDOR
PIONEERS – ICE, MERCURY
PIPS - TOP RANK
PITNEY, GENE - PYE INTERNATIONAL, STATESIDE
PITTS, RICHIE - CONTEMPO, MAGNET
PLATINUM HOOK - MOTOWN UK
PLATTERS – CONTEMPO RARIES, GREENLIGHT, KENT,
    MERCURY, PYE INTERNATIONAL, STATESIDE
PLAYERS - ORIOLE
PLAYTHINGS – CASINO CLASSICS, PYE, PYE DISCO DEMAND
PLEASURE - FANTASY
PLEASURES - SUE
PLUM, JEAN - LONDON
POCKETS - CBS
POETS – IMMEDIATE, STRIKE COLA, UNITED ARTISTS
POINDEXTER BROTHERS - VERVE
POINTER SISTERS - BLUE THUMB
POINTER, BONNIE – MOTOWN UK
POLITICIANS - HOT WAX
POLK, FRANK - CAPITOL
POLLARD, RAY - HORACES , UNITED ARTISTS
PONDEROSA TWINS + ONE - LONDON
POOLE, BRIAN - CBS
POOLE, BRIAN and the TREMELOES - DECCA
POOLE, LOU & LAURA - JAY BOY
POOR SOULS – ALP, DECCA
POPPIES - COLUMBIA
POPULAR FIVE - MINIT
PORTER, DAVID - STAX
PORTER, N.F. - SOS
PORTER, NOLAN - PROBE
PORTER, ROBIE - MGM
POSEY, SANDY - MGM
POST COALITION, MIKE - WARNER BROS
POSTER, ADRIENNE - DECCA
POTION - CHAMPAGNE
POWELL, BOBBY - MOJO
POWELL, KEITH - PICCADILLY
POWELL, KEITH & BILLIE DAVIS - PICCADILLY
POWELL, MARILYN - CBS
POWER, DUFFY with PARAMOUNTS - PARLOPHONE
PRECISIONS – GRAPEVINE, TRACK
PRENOSILOVA, YVONNE – PYE
PRESENT - SOS
PRESIDENTS - A&M
PRESLEY, ELVIS - RCA
PRESSURE - MCA
PRESTON, BILLY - A&M, APPLE, CAPITOL, MOTOWN UK,
    PRESIDENT, SOUL CITY, SUE
PRETTY PURDIE - DIRECTION
PRICE SET, ALAN - DECCA
PRICE, LLOYD – GSF, HMV, WAND

PRIDE, LOU - SEVENS
PRIME MATES - ACTION
PRINCE & PRINCESS - ALADDIN
PRINCE HAROLD – MERCURY
PRISCILLA - STATESIDE
PROBY, P.J. - LIBERTY
PROCTOR, MIKE - COLUMBIA
PROFFESSIONALS – CONNOISSEURS, WIGAN CASINO
PROFFESOR LONGHAIR - SUE
PROFILES – SEVENS
PROMISED LAND - BLACK MAGIC, DESTINY
PROPHETS – MERCURY, SEVENS
PRYSOCK, ARTHUR – CBS, POLYDOR
PUFFS - JOE BOY
PURIFY, JAMES & BOBBY – BELL, MERCURY, MOJO,
    STATESIDE
PURPLE MUNDI - S.C.S.C.
PUTHLI, ASHA - CBS
PYRAMIDS – POLYDOR

Q

QUADRAPHONICS - CONTEMPO
QUAITE, CHRISTINE – ORIOLE, STATESIDE
QUAKERS - STUDIO 36
QUALLS, SIDNEY JOE – EXPANSION, S.C.S.C.
QUARTERMAN, JOE – GSF
? and the MYSTERIANS - CAMEO PARKWAY, LONDON
QUICKEST WAY OUT - WARNER BROS
QUIK – DERAM

R

RADCLIFFE, JIMMY – DJM, PYE INTERNATIONAL, RK,
    SEVENS STATESIDE,
RADIANTS - CHESS
RAELETS – HMV, TANGERINE, TRC
RAGLAND, LOU – INFERNO, WARNER BROS
RAIN with CHARITY BROWN - AXE
RAINBOW PEOPLE - CASINO CLASSICS, PYE
RAISINS - MAJOR MINOR
RALFI - ISLAND
RALLO, TONY & the MIDNITE BAND - CALIBRE
RAM JAM BAND - COLUMBIA
RANDAZZO, TEDDY and the DAZZLERS - HMV
RANDELL, LYNNE - CBS
RANDOLF, BARBARA - TAMLA MOTOWN
RARE EARTH – PRODIGAL, RARE EARTH, TAMLA MOTOWN
RARE PLEASURE - DJM
RASCALS - ATLANTIC
RATTLES - FONTANA
RAVELL, DAVID - SOUL TRAIN
RAWLS, LOU – BELL, CAPITOL, EPIC, MGM, PIR,
RAY, JAMES - PYE INTERNATIONAL
RAY, JOHNNIE - LONDON
RAY, RICARDO - ROULETTE
RAYE, ANTHONY - GRAPEVINE
RAYNOR, MARTIN & the SECRETS - COLUMBIA
RAZOR'S EDGE - STATESIDE
RAZZY - MGM
READING, WILMA (or WILMER) - PYE
REAL THING – PYE, PYE INTERNATIONAL
REALISTICS – EPIC, WARNER BROS
RED SQUARES - COLUMBIA
REDD, SHARON - EPIC
REDDING, GENE - CAPITOL
REDDING, OTIS - ATCO, ATLANTIC, LONDON, PYE
    INTERNATIONAL, REVOLUTION, STAX, SUE
REDDING, OTIS & THOMAS, CARLA - STAX
REDE, EMMA - COLUMBIA
REDMOND, ROY - WARNER BROS
REED ORCHESTRA, LES - CHAPTER ONE
REED, A.C. - SEVENS
REED, BOBBY – EXPANSION, SHRINE
REED, JIMMY – CHARLY, HMV, STATESIDE, SUE, TOP RANK
REED, LULA & FREDDIE KING - EMBER
REED, LULA & SYL JOHNSON - EMBER

REED, TAWNY - PYE
REED, VIVIAN – ATCO, CBS, DIRECTION, EPIC
REEGAN, VALA & THE VALARONS - ATLANTIC
REESE, DELLA – AVCO, HMV, PEOPLE, RCA, STATESIDE
REEVES, MARTHA – ARISTA, MCA, TAMLA MOTOWN
REEVES, MARTHA & the VANDELLAS - TAMLA MOTOWN
REFLECTIONS – CAPITOL, MCA, OYSTER, STATESIDE,
    TAMLA MOTOWN
REGAL DEWY – RCA
REGAN, EDDIE - ABC
REGAN, JOAN - CBS
REID, BERYL - HMV
REID, CLARENCE - ATLANTIC
RELF, BOB - BLACK MAGIC
RENAY, DIANE - STATESIDE
RENE COMBO, GOOGIE – ATLANTIC, LONDON
REPARATA & the DELRONS – BELL, DART, RCA,
    STATESIDE
RESONANCE - BRADLEYS
REVELATION - HANDSHAKE
REVERE, PAUL and the RAIDERS - JAY BOY, SUE
REVILL, CHICO - DESTINY
REX, ROBERTA - FONTANA
REYNOLDS, L.J. - CAPITOL
REYNOLDS, L.J. & CHOCOLATE SYRUP - AVCO
RHINOCEROS - ELEKTRA
RHYTHM HERITAGE - ABC
RHYTHM MAKERS - POLYDOR
RICE, GENE - RCA
RICE, MACK - ATLANTIC
RICE, SIR MACK - CONTEMPO
RICH, BOBBY - GRAPEVINE 2000
RICH, CHARLIE – LONDON, MERCURY, PHILIPS, RCA
RICHARDS, LISA - VOCALION
RICHARDSON, JOE GROUNDHOG - MAJOR MINOR
RICHARDSON, MONA - RCA
RICHIE, LIONEL – MOTOWN UK
RIDER, MITCH – see RYDER
RIDLEY, SHARON - PRESIDENT
RIGHTEOUS BROTHERS – LONDON, PYE INTERNATIONAL,SUE
    VERVE
RIGHTEOUS BROTHERS BAND - PHIL SPECTOR
    INTERNATIONAL
RIMSHOTS - ALL PLATINUM
RINGLEADERS - S.C.S.C.
RIOT SQUAD - PYE
RIPPERTON, MINNIE - EPIC
RIPPLE - SALSOUL
RITA & THE TIARAS – DESTINY, DORE, JOE BOY
RIVERA, HECTOR – HORACES, POLYDOR
RIVER HEAD BAND - MOWEST
RIVERS, JOHNNY - LIBERTY
RIVERS, MAVIS - REPRISE
RIVINGTONS – CBS, LIBERTY
ROBERTS, JOHN – ACTION, SUE
ROBERTS, KENNY - PYE
ROBERTS, LEA - UNITED ARTISTS
ROBIN, EDE - CRYSTAL
ROBINS, JIMMY - PRESIDENT
ROBINSON, ALVIN - PYE INTERNATIONAL, RED BIRD, STRIKE
ROBINSON, EDDIE - EMBER
ROBINSON, J.P. - ATLANTIC
ROBINSON, JACKIE - PYE INTERNATIONAL
ROBINSON, JOHNNY - S.C.S.C.
ROBINSON, ROSCO - CONTEMPO, GREENLIGHT , PYE
    INTERNATIONAL, WAND
ROBINSON, SMOKEY - MOTOWN UK, TAMLA MOTOWN
ROBINSON, SMOKEY & MIRACLES - TAMLA MOTOWN
ROBINSON, VICKIE SUE - RCA
ROCK FLOWERS - RCA
ROCKIN' BERRIES - PICCADILLY
ROCKITS - MOWEST
ROCKWELL - MOTOWN UK
ROCOMARS - KING
RODRIGUEZ, RECO - PAMA

ROE, TOMMY - STATESIDE
ROGERS, D.J. - CBS
ROGERS, LINCOLN - PHEONIX
ROGERS, TRACY - POLYDOR
ROLAND, CHERRY - DECCA
ROLLINS, BIRD - MOJO
ROMA, GLORIA - DECCA
ROMAN, LYN - BRUNSWICK
RONETTES – A&M, LONDON, PHIL SPECTOR INT.
RONNETTES – PHIL SPECTOR INTERNATIONAL
RONNIE & ROBYN - GRAPEVINE
RONSTADT, LINDA - ASYLUM
ROSE COLORED GLASS - PRESIDENT
ROSE ROYCE - WHITFIELD
ROSE, TIM - CBS
ROSIE - CORAL
ROSIE & THE ORIGINALS - LONDON
ROSS, DIANA – CAPITOL, EMI, MOTOWN UK, TAMLA
    MOTOWN
ROSS, DIANA & MARVIN GAYE - TAMLA MOTOWN
ROSS, DIANA & the SUPREMES - TAMLA MOTOWN
ROSS, DIANA SUPREMES +TEMPTATIONS –
    TAMLA MOTOWN
ROSS, JACKIE – CHESS, PYE INTERNATIONAL
ROSS, SONNY - MOJO
ROSSI, NITA - PICCADILLY
ROTARY CONNECTION - CHESS
ROULETTES - PARLOPHONE
ROUND ROBIN – LONDON, SOUL SOUNDS.
ROWE, NORMIE - POLYDOR
ROY, LEE - ISLAND
ROYAL GUARDSMEN - LONDON
ROYAL, BILLY JOE - ATLANTIC , CBS
ROYAL, JAMES – CBS, PARLOPHONE
ROYAL, JAMES & the HAWKS - PARLOPHONE
ROYAL, ROBBIE - MERCURY
ROYALETTES - BIG T, MGM
ROYAL PLAYBOYS - SEVENS
ROYCE, EARL & the OLYMPICS – COLUMBIA, PARLOPHONE
ROYE, LEE - MCA
ROZA, LITA - EMBER
ROZAA & WINE - RIGHT ON
RUBAIYATS - ACTION
RUBIN - MCA
RUBY & THE ROMANTICS - A&M, LONDON
RUFFIN & KENDRICK - RCA
RUFFIN, DAVID - MOTOWN UK, TAMLA MOTOWN
RUFFIN, JIMMY – EPIC, ERC, HAYLEY, MOJO, POLYDOR, RSO
    TAMLA MOTOWN
RUFUS - ABC
RUMBLERS – KING, LONDON
RUSH, OTIS - BLUE HORIZON, VOCALION
RUSHEN, PATRICE - ELEKTRA
RUSKIN, BARBARA - PICCADILLY
RUSS, LONNIE - FONTANA
RUSSELL, KEITH - PICCADILLY
RYAN, MARION - PHILIPS
RYDER CONGREGATION, JOHN & ANNE - MCA
RYDER, MITCH – AVCO, SOUL SOUNDS.
RYDER, MITCH & DETROIT WHEELS – DOT, PYE DISCO
    DEMAND, STATESIDE

S

S.S.O. - GULL
SABU, PAUL - PYE
SAGOE, SALLY - DART
SAIN, OLIVER – CONTEMPO, MOJO
SAINTS - GRAPEVINE 2000
SALES, SOUPY - HMV
SALVADORS - SEVENS
SAM & BILL - BRUNSWICK
SAM & KITTY - GRAPEVINE
SAM AND BILL - PYE INTERNATIONAL
SAM AND DAVE – ATLANTIC, CONTEMPO, KING, STAX
SAM THE SHAM & the PHAROAHS - MGM

SAM, ERV & TOM - DIRECTION
SAN REMO STRINGS - TAMLA MOTOWN
SAND PEBBLES - TRACK
SANDON, JOHNNY and the REMO FOUR - PYE
SANDPEBBLES - TOAST
SANDPIPERS - PYE INTERNATIONAL
SANDS, EVIE - A&M, CAMEO PARKWAY, RED BIRD
SANDS, TOMMY – CAPITOL, LIBERTY
SANTAMARIA, MONGO – CBS, DIRECTION, RIVERSIDE
SANTELLS - SUE
SANTOS, LARRY – CASABLANCA, SOUL CITY
SAPPHIRES – ABC, HMV, PROBE, SOUL SERIES, STATESIDE
SARI & the SHALIMARS - UNITED ARTISTS
SATIN BELLS – CBS, DECCA, PYE
SATTON, LON - CBS
SAUNDERS, LARRY - LONDON
SAVANNA - R&B RECORDS
SAVOY, RONNIE - MGM
SAX OF SOUL - CRYSTAL
SAYLES, JOHNNY – LIBERTY, SOUL CITY
SCAGGS, BOZ - CBS
SCALES, HARVEY & the 7 SOUND - ATLANTIC
SCEPTRES - SPARK
SCHIFRIN, LALO – 20TH. CENTURY, CTI, DOT, WARNER BROS
SCHROEDER ORCH., JOHN – ALASKA, PICCADILLY,
    PYE DISCO DEMAND
SCOTT, BRUCE – MERCURY, MGM
SCOTT, CINDY - GOLDMINE SOUL SUPPLY, HARTHON
SCOTT, CINDY - GOLDMINE SOUL SUPPLY
SCOTT, FREDDIE – COLPIX, JAY BOY, JOY, LONDON,
    ROULETTE, UPFRONT
SCOTT, GLORIA - CASABLANCA
SCOTT, JIMMY - MOVE
SCOTT, JUDI - PAGE ONE
SCOTT, LINDA - CBS
SCOTT, PEGGY – PINNACLE, POLYDOR
SCOTT, PEGGY & BENSON, JO JO – ATLANTIC, CHARLY,
    POLYDOR
SCOTT, SHARON – KENT
SCOTT, SHARON - KENT
SCOTT-HERON, GIL – ARISTA, CHAMPAGNE, INFERNO,
    PHILIPS
SEARCHERS - PYE
SECOND CITY SOUND - MAJOR MINOR
SEEDORF, RUDY - ISLAND
SEEDS - VOCALION
SEEDS OF THE EARTH - CONTEMPO
SEFTONS - CBS
SENATE - COLUMBIA
SENSATIONS – DECCA, PYE INTERNATIONAL
SENSATIONS feat. YVONNE - PYE INTERNATIONAL
SENYAH, JIMMY - ROKEL
SERVICEMEN - GRAPEVINE 2000
SEVENTH WONDER – CONTEMPO, GRAPEVINE
SEX - GRAPEVINE 2000
SEXTON, ANN - INFERNO
SHADES OF BLUE - SUE
SHADOWS OF KNIGHT – ATLANTIC, BUDDAH
SHAFTO, BOBBY - PARLOPHONE
SHAKERS – ABC, POLYDOR, PROBE
SHALAMAR - SOULTRAIN
SHAMROCKS - POLYDOR
SHA-NA-NETTS - PYE
SHANGRI-LAS – BUDDAH, CHARLY, RARIES, KAMA SUTRA,
    MERCURY, PHILIPS, RED BIRD
SHANNON, DEL - LIBERTY
SHAPIRO, HELEN – ARISTA, COLUMBIA, DJM, PARLOPHONE,
    PYE
SHA-RAE, BILLY - ACTION
SHARKS - RCA
SHARONETTES - BLACK MAGIC, DESTINY
SHARP GAMBLE, DEE DEE - PIR
SHARP, BOBBY - STATESIDE
SHARP, DEE DEE – ACTION, ATLANTIC, CAMEO PARKWAY,
    COLUMBIA, SOS

SHARPEES – PRESIDENT, SOUL SOUNDS, STATESIDE
SHAW, MARLENA - BLUE NOTE, CHESS, CBS, UNITED
    ARTISTS
SHAW, NINA - CBS
SHAW, SANDIE - PYE
SHAW, TIMMY - PYE INTERNATIONAL
SHAWN, DAMON - JANUS
SHED, HENRY – STATESIDE
SHEELER, CYNTHIA - GRAPEVINE 2000
SHEEN, BOBBY – CAPITOL, WARNER BROS
SHEEP – STATESIDE
SHELBY, ERNIE - MOJO
SHELDON, DOUG – DECCA, SUE
SHELDON, SANDI - EPIC
SHELLEY, LIZ - BRUNSWICK
SHELLY, ALAN - PHILIPS
SHELTON, ROSCOE - SUE
SHEPHERD SISTERS - LONDON
SHEPPARD, T.G. - MOWEST
SHEPPARDS - JAY BOY
SHERMAN, FLAMMA - SMB
SHERRYS – LONDON, SEVENS
SHERRY'S c/w LITTLE JOE COOK - SOUL CITY
SHIFRIN, SUSAN - DECCA
SHILLELAGH SISTERS - CBS
SHIRELLES – BRUNSWICK, LONDON, MERCURY, HMV,PYE
    INTERNATIONAL, TOP RANK, STATESIDE ,UNITED
    ARTISTS , WAND
SHIRLEY - LONDON
SHIRLEY & ALFRED - LIBERTY
SHIRLEY & COMPANY - ALL PLATINUM
SHIRLEY & LEE - ISLAND
SHIRLEY and the SHIRELLES - BELL
SHIRLEY, SUSAN - PHILIPS
SHIVEL, BUNNY - CAPITOL
SHORT KUTS - UNITED ARTISTS
SHORT KUTS feat. EDDIE HARRISON - UNITED ARTISTS
SHORT PEOPLE - INFERNO
SHOW STOPPERS - BEACON
SHOWMEN JOKER, LONDON, PAMA
SHOWSTOPPERS – BEACON, CREAM, INFERNO, MGM
SIDE EFFECT - FANTASY
SIDE EFFECT feat: JIM GILSTRAP - SOUL BROTHER RECORDS
SIDEKICKS - RCA
SIGHT & SOUND - FONTANA
SIGLER, BUNNY – CAMEO PARKWAY, EPIC, LONDON, PIR
SIGNS - DECCA
SILENT MAJORITY - HOT WAX
SILHOUETTES - PARLOPHONE
SILHOUETTES - SEVENS
SILVER BULLIT - PHILIPS
SILVER, ANDEE - FONTANA
SILVER, LORRAINE - CASINO CLASSICS, PYE
SILVERSPOON, DOOLEY - SEVILLE
SIMMONS, BEVERLEY – PAMA, PAMA SUPREME
SIMMONS, SIMTEC - CONTEMPO
SIMMS, JASON - DOMAIN
SIMON & GARFUNKEL - CBS
SIMON, CARLY c/w CHIC - WEA
SIMON, JOE – CHARLY, LONDON, MONUMENT, MOJO,
    POLYDOR, SPRING
SIMON, TONY - TRACK
SIMONE - KRP
SIMONE, NINA – CHARLY, COLPIX , PARLOPHONE, PHILIPS ,
    PYE INTERNATIONAL, RCA
SIMONE, SUGAR – GO, SUE
SIMPSON, PAUL feat. ANTHONY WHITE - COOLTEMPO
SIMPSON, VALERIE - TAMLA MOTOWN
SINGER, RAY - EMBER
SINGER, SUSAN - ORIOLE
SINGING PRINCIPAL - ACTION
SINGLETON, MAXINE - SYSTEM
SIR DOUGLAS QUINTET - LONDON
SISTER SLEDGE – ATLANTIC, COTILLION

SISTERS LOVE - A&M, MOTOR CITY, MOWEST, TAMLA MOTOWN
SKEL, BOBBY - LONDON
SKULL SNAPS - GSF
SKYY - SALSOUL
SLEDGE, PERCY – ATLANTIC, CAPRICORN
SLIK - ARISTA
SLIM HARPO - STATESIDE
SLOAN, SAMMI - COLUMBIA
SLY & THE FAMILY STONE – CBS, COLUMBIA, DIRECTION, EPIC
SMALL, KAREN - VOCALION
SMITH BROTHERS - GRAPEVINE
SMITH, BARRY – PEOPLE
SMITH, BOBBY - SEVENS
SMITH, BUDDY - CONNOISSEURS
SMITH, EDGEWOOD - SUE
SMITH, EFFIE – SUE
SMITH, GEORGE – BLUE HORIZON, SEVENS
SMITH, HUEY & the CLOWNS - SUE
SMITH, JIMMY - VERVE
SMITH, JIMMY & the BIG BAND - HMV
SMITH, KENNY & the NITELITERS - PRESIDENT
SMITH, LONNIE LITSON – CBS, RCA
SMITH, MARTHA - PYE
SMITH, MARVIN – CORAL, CONTEMPO
SMITH, MOSES - JOKER
SMITH, O.C. – CARIBOU, CBS
SMITH, STUART - POLYDOR
SMITH, TRULY - DECCA
SMITH, VERDELLE - CAPITOL
SMOKESTACK LIGHTNIN' - BELL
SMOKEY & the FABULOUS BLADES – ROUTE
SOBERS, ERROL - BEACON
SOCIALITES - WARNER BROS
SOFTONES - H&L
SONNY - ATLANTIC
SONNY & CHER – ATLANTIC, VOCALION
SONS & LOVERS - BEACON
SONS OF MOSES - MCA
SONS OF ROBIN STONE - ATLANTIC
SOUL AGENTS - PYE
SOUL BROS. - DECCA
SOUL BROS. INC - GOLDEN EYE
SOUL BROTHERS – MERCURY, PARLOPHONE
SOUL BROTHERS SIX - ATLANTIC
SOUL CHILDREN - STAX
SOUL CITY - CAMEO PARKWAY
SOUL CITY EXECUTIVES - SOUL CITY
SOUL CLAN - ATLANTIC
SOUL FOOD - POWER EXCHANGE
SOUL FOX ORCHESTRA - BLACK MAGIC
SOUL GENERATION – GRAPEVINE, STICKY
SOUL MERCHANTS - PRESIDENT
SOUL POTION - CONTEMPO
SOUL PURPOSE - ISLAND
SOUL SEARCHERS - SUSSEX
SOUL SISTERS – LONDON, SUE, UNITED ARTISTS
SOUL SURVIVORS – ATLANTIC, STATESIDE
SOUL TWINS – GRAPEVINE, SOUL CITY
SOUL, CINDY - INFERNO
SOUL, JIMMY - STATESIDE
SOUL, SHARON - STATESIDE
SOUL, SHARON - CONNOISSEURS
SOULE, GEORGE - UNITED ARTISTS
SOULFUL STRINGS - CHESS
SOULMATES - PARLOPHONE
SOULRUNNERS - POLYDOR
SOUND SYSTEM - ISLAND
SOUNDS INCORPED - COLUMBIA
SOUNDS OF LANCASHIRE - PYE DISCO DEMAND
SOUNDS ORCHESTRAL – COLUMBIA, PICCADILLY, PYE
SOUTH SHORE COMMISSION - PYE INTERNATIONAL
SOUTH SIDE MOVEMENT - PYE INTERNATIONAL
SOUTH, GLEN - DECCA

SOUTH, JOE – CAPITOL, MGM
SOUTHSIDE MOVEMENT - PYE INTERNATIONAL
SOUTHWEST F.O.B. - STAX
SOVEREIGNS - KING
SOXX, BOB B. , & THE BLUE JEANS - LONDON
SPAN, MIKE STUART - COLUMBIA
SPELLBINDERS – CBS, DIRECTION
SPELLMAN, BENNY - LONDON
SPENCER, EDDIE - POWER EXCHANGE
SPICE - UNITED ARTISTS
SPIDELLS - SUE
SPIDERS WEB - FANTASY
SPINNERS – ATLANTIC, COLUMBIA, TAMLA MOTOWN
SPIRAL STAIRCASE - CBS
SPOOKEY - DECCA
SPOTLIGHTS - PHILIPS
SPRINGERS - GRAPEVINE 2000
SPRINGFIELD, DUSTY - PHILIPS
SPUNKY ONION - CONTEMPO
SPYRO GYRA - INFINITY
ST. CLAIR, CHERYL - CBS
ST. JOHN, BARRY – COLUMBIA, DECCA
ST. JOHN, TAMMY – CASINO CLASSICS, PYE
ST. LOUIS UNION - DECCA
STAIRSTEPS – BUDDAH, DARK HORSE
STAMPLEY, JOE - DOT
STANBACK, JEAN - DEEP SOUL
STANLEY - ACTION
STAPLE SINGERS – COLUMBIA, RIVERSIDE, SOUL CITY, STAX
STAR, MARTHA - WIGAN CASINO
STARPOINT - ELEKTRA
STARR, EDWIN – 20TH. CENTURY, AVATAR, BRADLEYS, CAPITOL, CONNOISSEURS GTO, HIPPODROME, MOTOR CITY, MOTOWN, POLYDOR, SEVENS, TAMLA MOTOWN
STARR, STELLA - PICCADILLY
STATEN, PATRINELLE - SEVENS
STATON, CANDI – CAPITOL, UNITED ARTISTS, WARNER BROS
STEELERS – DIRECTION
STEINWAYS – KENT
STEMMONS EXPRESS - DEMAND
STEPHENSON SHOWBAND, STEVE - DECCA
STEREOS - MGM
STERLING - MOTOWN UK
STEVENS, APRIL - MGM
STEVENS, APRIL & NINO TEMPO - ATLANTIC
STEVENS, CONNIE - WARNER BROS
STEVENSON, MICKY - EMBER
STEWART, BILLY – CHESS, PYE INTERNATIONAL
STEWART, DARRYL - PYE
STONE CITY BAND - MOTOWN UK
STONE, CISSY - DECCA
STONE, GEORGE - STATESIDE
STONE, SLY - EPIC
STONEY & MEATLOAF – PRODIGAL, RARE EARTH
STORM - PLUM
STORMY MONDAY - CONTEMPO
STORYTELLERS - DECCA
STRANGE BROS. SHOW - POLYDOR
STRANGE, BILLY - VOCALION
STRANGELOVES – IMMEDIATE, LONDON, STATESIDE
STRAWBERRY JAM - PYE
STREET, JUDY – GRAPEVINE, SEVENS, SOUL STOP
STREISAND, BARBARA - CBS
STRONG, BARRETT – CAPITOL, LONDON, TAMLA MOTOWN
STRUNK, JUD - MOWEST
STRUTT - BRUNSWICK
STUDIO SIX - POLYDOR
STYLISTICS - AVCO
SUE & SUNNY – CBS, COLUMBIA
SUGAR - POWER EXCHANGE
SUGARLUMPS - JAY BOY
SUMMER, DONNA – GTO, PEOPLE
SUMMERS, BILL & SUMMERS HEAT - PRESTIGE
SUN – CAPITOL

SUNLINERS - LONDON
SUNNY & the SUNGLOWS – LONDON
SUPERBS - JOE BOY
SUPERLATIVES - SEVENS
SUPREMES - MOTOWN UK, STATESIDE, TAMLA MOTOWN
SURFARIS - PARAMOUNT
SUSPICIONS – INFERNO
SUZIE & BIG DEE IRWIN - POLYDOR
SWAMP DOGG – CONTEMPO, DJM, ISLAND
SWANN, BETTY - CBS
SWANN, BETTYE – ATLANTIC, CAPITOL, CBS, CONTEMPO RARIES, MOJO
SWANN, RUTH - SPARK
SWANS – DORE, STATESIDE
SWANSON, BENICE - CHESS
SWEET BLINDNESS - QUALITY
SWEET INSPIRATIONS - ATLANTIC
SWEET SENSATION - PYE
SWETE, ANTHONY - RCA
SWINGING MEDALLIONS - PHILIPS
SWINGING SOUL MACHINE - POLYDOR
SWISS MOVEMENT - GRAPEVINE 2000, RCA
SWITCH - MOTOWN UK
SYLVERS - GEFFEN
SYLVESTER - FANTASY
SYLVIA – LONDON, SOUL CITY
SYMBOLS - PRESIDENT
SYMPHONICS - POLYDOR
SYNDICATE OF SOUND - STATESIDE
SYREETA - MOTOWN UK, MOWEST, TAMLA MOTOWN
SYREETA & G.C.CAMERON - MOTOWN UK

T

T.V. and the TRIBESMEN - PYE ADVANCE PRESSING, PYE INTERNATIONAL
TABOU COMBO - DECCA
TAM, TIM & the TURNONS - ISLAND
TAMANGOES - GRAPEVINE
TAMS – ABC, CAPITOL, CASINO CLASSICS, HMV, PROBE, STATESIDE, VIRGIN
TANDY, SHARON – ATLANTIC, MERCURY, PYE
TAPP, DEMETRISS - CORAL
TARA - POLYDOR
TARHEEL SLIM & LITTLE ANN – CHARLY, SUE
TASHAN - DEF JAM
TATE, HOWARD - MAJOR MINOR, VERVE
TATE, RICHARD - ABC
TATE, TOMMY – COLUMBIA, GRAPEVINE 2000
TAVARES - CAPITOL
TAVARES with FREDA PAYNE - CAPITOL
TAVASCO - GRAPEVINE 2000
TAYLOR, ALEX - ATLANTIC
TAYLOR, BOBBY - EPIC
TAYLOR, BOBBY & the VANCOUVERS - TAMLA MOTOWN
TAYLOR, DEBBIE - ARISTA
TAYLOR, FELICE - PRESIDENT
TAYLOR, GLORIA - POLYDOR
TAYLOR, JOHNNIE – CBS, GOLDMINE SOUL SUPPLY, KENT, SEVENS, STAX
TAYLOR, KINGSIZE – DECCA, POLYDOR
TAYLOR, KO KO - CHESS
TAYLOR, LINDA - GPL
TAYLOR, LITTLE JOHNNY – CHARLY, CONTEMPO, MOJO, VOCALION
TAYLOR, R. DEAN – POLYDOR, RARE EARTH, TAMLA MOTOWN
TAYLOR, TED – CHARLY, CONTEMPO
T-CONNECTION – SEVILLE
TEARDROPS - KENT
TEE, WILLIE – ATLANTIC, CONTEMPO, GRAPEVINE 2000 MOJO
TEMPLE, RICHARD - CONTEMPO RARIES, JAY BOY
TEMPO, NINO & 5th. AVE. SAX - A&M
TEMPO, NINO & APRIL STEVENS – BELL, LONDON
TEMPOS - SOUL CITY

TEMPOS - SEVENS
TEMPREES – EPIC, STAX
TEMPTATIONS – EPIC, MOTOWN, MOTOWN UK, STATESIDE TAMLA MOTOWN
TEMPTATIONS feat: DENNIS EDWARDS - MOTOWN UK
TERRACE, PETE. - PYE INTERNATIONAL
TERRELL, PHIL - KENT
TERRELL, TAMMI - TAMLA MOTOWN
TERRY and JERRY - R&B
TEX, JOE – ATLANTIC, BOOT, EPIC, MERCURY, SOUL FIRE, SOUL FOOD, SUE,
THEMES - KENT
THIRD TIME AROUND - CONTEMPO
THOMAS AND TAYLOR - COOL TEMPO
THOMAS, ANNETTE - STAX
THOMAS, B.J. and the TRIUMPHS - HICKORY
THOMAS, CARLA – ATLANTIC, HORACES, KENT, LONDON, STAX
THOMAS, CHARLIE & the DRIFTERS - EMI
THOMAS, DON - DJM
THOMAS, ETTA - SANTA PONSA
THOMAS, EVELYN - 20TH. CENTURY, TOMORROW
THOMAS, IRMA – ATLANTIC, LIBERTY, POLO, SUE, UNITED ARTISTS
THOMAS, JAMO (& his PARTY BROTHERS) – CHESS, MOJO, POLYDOR
THOMAS, JIMMY - 20TH. CENTURY, CONTEMPO, CONTEMPO RARIES , JAY BOY, OSCEOLA, PARLOPHONE, SPARK
THOMAS, RUFUS – ATLANTIC, LONDON, STAX
THOMAS, TIMMY – MOJO, POLYDOR, TK
THOMPSON, JACKIE - DIRECTION
THOMPSON, ROY - COLUMBIA
THOMPSON, SUE - HICKORY
THOMPSON, SUE - HICKORY
THORNTON, WILLIE MAE - SUE
THREE BELLS - COLUMBIA
THREE CAPS – ATLANTIC
THREE DEGREES – MOJO, PIR, PYE INTERNATIONAL, STATESIDE
THREE PIECES - FANTASY
THRILLS – CAPITOL, GRAPEVINE
THUMANN, HARRY - DECCA
THUNDER, JOHNNY - STATESIDE
THUNDER, JOHNNY & RUBY WINTERS - STATESIDE
THUNDER, MARGO - CAPITOL
THUNDERBIRD SOUND - HAYLEY
THURSTON, BOBBY – EPIC, EXPANSION
TIFFANIES - CHESS
TIG, JIMMY & LOUISE - DEEP SOUL
TIKKI, TAKI, SUZI, LIES - UPC
TIMEBOX – DERAM, PICCADILLY
TIMMIE & THE PERSIONETTES - GOLDMINE TEST PRESS
TIP TOPS - CAMEO PARKWAY
TIPPIE and the CLOVERS - STATESIDE
TIPTON, LESTER - GRAPEVINE, WIGAN CASINO
TJADER, CAL - VERVE
TLC ORCHESTRA feat: LEON THOMAS - EMI
TOKAYS - SEVENS
TOLBERT, ISREAL (POPPER STOPPER) – STAX
TOLBERT, O.C. - KENT
TOM & JERRIO - HMV
TOMLIN, LEE - CBS
TOMORROW'S CHILDREN - EXPLOSION
TONER, ELEANOR – DECCA
TONEY JR., OSCAR – BELL, CAPRICORN, CONTEMPO,STATESIDE
TONY & TYRONE – ATLANTIC, EMBER
TONY AND TANDY - ATLANTIC
TOOTS & the MAYTALS - DRAGON
TOPSY, TINY – PARLOPHONE, PYE INTERNATIONAL
TOPSY, TINY and the CHARMS - PARLOPHONE
TORINO, AL - DECCA
TORME, MEL - LONDON
TORRENCE, GEORGE & the NATURALS - JAY BOY, LONDON

TOTT, TINA - PYE
TOUSSAINT, ALLEN – REPRISE, SOUL CITY
TOWER OF POWER – CBS, WARNER BROS
TOWNSEND, ED - WARNER BROS
TOYS – BELL, CASINO CLASSICS, PHILIPS, STATESIDE
TRACY, JEANNIE - SEVENS
TRADE WINDS - KAMA SUTRA, RED BIRD
TRAITS - PYE INTERNATIONAL
TRAMMELL, BOBBY LEE - SUE
TRAMMPS – ATLANTIC, BUDDAH, PIR
TREETOPS - COLUMBIA
TRENDS - PYE
TRENT, JACKIE – ORIOLE, PICCADILLY, PYE
TRENT, JACKIE - CASINO CLASSICS
TRIBE – POLYDOR, PROBE
TRIUMPHS - DEMAND
TROIS, CHUCK and the AMAZING MAZE – ACTION
TROY, DORIS – APPLE, ATLANTIC, CAMEO PARKWAY, LONDON, MOJO, PEOPLE, PYE INTERNATIONAL, TOAST
TRUE CONNECTION, ANDRE - BUDDAH
TRUE IMAGE - GRAPEVINE 2000
TUCKER, TOMMY – CHESS, LONDON, PYE INTERNATIONAL, RED LIGHTNIN
TURNER, BIG JOE – ATLANTIC, LONDON
TURNER, IKE – FLEETVILLE, UNITED ARTISTS
TURNER, IKE & KINGS OF RHYTHM - SUE
TURNER, IKE & TINA – A&M, HARVEST, HMV, LIBERTY, LONDON, MINIT, STATESIDE, SUE, UNITED ARTISTS, WARNER BROS
TURNER, SAMMY - LONDON
TURNER, SPYDER – KWANZA, MGM
TURNER, TITUS – BLUE BEAT, LONDON, ORIOLE, PARLOPHONE
TWIGGY - EMBER
TWILIGHTS - COLUMBIA
TWO OF CLUBS - PRESIDENT
TYLER, TERRY - PYE INTERNATIONAL
TYMES – CAMEO PARKWAY, DIRECTION, LONDON RCA
TYMES feat: GEORGE WILLIAMS - CBS
TYRONE & CARR – JAM

U

U.K. PLAYERS - A&M
U.S. T-BONES - LIBERTY
ULTRA HIGH FREQUENCY - PYE INTERNATIONAL
ULTRAFUNK - CONTEMPO
ULTRAFUNK feat: FREDDIE MACK - CONTEMPO
UNDERTAKERS - PYE
UNDISPUTED TRUTH - TAMLA MOTOWN, WHITFIELD
UNIFICS - LONDON
UNIQUES – CHARLY, PYE INTERNATIONAL
UPCHURCH COMBO, PHILIP – HMV, SUE, UNITED ARTISTS
UPCHURCH, ROBERT – PIR

V

V.I.P.'S - ISLAND
VALADIERS - ORIOLE
VALENS, RITCHIE - SUE
VALENTINE BROTHERS - ENERGY
VALENTINE, T.D. - EPIC
VALENTINO - GAIEE
VALENTINO, MARK - STATESIDE
VALENTINOS - POLYDOR, SOUL CITY, STATESIDE
VALLI, FRANKIE – MOWEST, PHILIPS
VALLI, FRANKIE & the FOUR SEASONS - MOWEST, TAMLA MOTOWN
VALUES - EMBER
VAN DYKE, EARL – NIGHTMARE, STATESIDE, TAMLA MOTOWN
VAN DYKES - STATESIDE
VAN, ILA – PATHEWAY, PYE DISCO DEMAND
VANDERBILT, LEE - UNITED ARTISTS
VANDROSS, LUTHER - EPIC
VANILLA FUDGE - ATLANTIC
VANN'S ORCHESTRA, TEDDY - CAPITOL

VARIATIONS - UK
VARNADO, LYNN - HAYLEY
VARNER, DON – DEMAND, SOUL CITY
VARTAN, SYLVIE - RCA
VAUGHAN, SARAH - MERCURY
VAUGHN, FRANKIE - PHILIPS
VAUGHN, MORRIS - FONTANA
VAUGHN, SARAH - MERCURY
VEGA, TATA - MOTOWN UK
VELEZ, MARTHA - BLUE HORIZON, LONDON
VELICIA - TIFFANY
VELOURS - MGM
VELVELETTES - MOTOWN UK, STATESIDE, TAMLA MOTOWN
VELVET HAMMER - BEE, SEVENS, R.B. RECORDS
VELVET LOVE - ALASKA
VEL-VETS - PYE DISCO DEMAND
VELVETTES - MERCURY
VENTURA, DAVE - MERCURY
VENTURES – LIBERTY,UNITED ARTISTS
VERA, BILLY - ATLANTIC
VERA, BILLY & JUDY CLAY - ATLANTIC
VERDELL, JACKIE - WEA
VERITY - POLYDOR
VERNADO, LYNN - SOUL CITY
VERNEE, YVONNE - GROOVEY GROOVES, SOUL CITY
VIBRATIONS – COLUMBIA, DIRECTION, LONDON, PYE INTERNATIONAL, SOS
VICKERS, MIKE - COLUMBIA
VICTORIA - ATLANTIC
VILLAGE SOUL CHOIR - DIRECTION
VINES - GRAPEVINE 2000
VIRGIL BROTHERS - PARLOPHONE
VIRGINIA WOLVES - STATESIDE
VOGUES – KING, LONDON
VOICES OF EAST HARLEM – ELEKTRA, SEVENS
VOLUMES – FONTANA, LONDON, PAMA
VONTASTICS – CHESS, STATESIDE

W

WADE, ADAM - COLUMBIA
WADE, MIKE - BEACON
WAITERS, L.J. & the ELECTRIFIERS - ROUTE
WALKER BROTHERS - PHILIPS
WALKER, ANNA & THE CROWNETTES - PAMA
WALKER, DAVID - RCA
WALKER, JR. - MOTOWN UK, TAMLA MOTOWN
WALKER, JR. & THE ALL STARS - MOTOWN UK, TAMLA MOTOWN
WALKER, RANDOLF - JAY BOY
WALKER, RONNIE – POLYDOR, STATESIDE
WALKER, T-BONE – LIBERTY
WALKER, WEE WILLIE - KENT
WALLACE BROTHERS - SUE
WALSH GYPSY BAND, JAMES - RCA
WALTER & THE ADMIRATIONS - SOUL CITY
WALTON JR., WILBUR - DEMAND
WALTON, DAVE - CBS
WALTON, RON - GULL
WAMMACK, TRAVIS – ATLANTIC, UNITED ARTISTS
WANDERERS – MGM, UNITED ARTISTS
WANSEL, DEXTER - PIR
WAR – ISLAND, LIBERTY, UNITED ARTISTS
WAR. - UNITED ARTISTS
WARD, CLARA – MGM, STATESIDE
WARM SENSATION - COLUMBIA
WARWICK, DEE DEE – ATCO, ATLANTIC, MERCURY, PRIVATE STOCK
WARWICK, DIONNE – ATLANTIC, PYE INTERNATIONAL, SCOOP, STATESIDE, WARNER BROS
WASH HOPSON SINGERS - ACTION
WASHINGTON JR, GROVER - MOTOWN
WASHINGTON, ALBERT - KENT
WASHINGTON, ALBERT and the KINGS - PRESIDENT
WASHINGTON, BABY – ATLANTIC, LONDON, PEOPLE, SUE, UNITED ARTISTS

WASHINGTON, BABY & DON GARDNER - PEOPLE
WASHINGTON, CECIL - WIGAN 25TH. ANNIVERS
WASHINGTON, DINAH – COLUMBIA,
WASHINGTON, ELLA - MONUMENT
WASHINGTON, GENO – DJM, PYE
WASHINGTON, GENO & RAM JAM BAND - FLASH BACKS,
    PICCADILLY, PYE,
WASHINGTON, JERRY - CONTEMPO
WASHINGTON, NORMAN T. - PAMA
WATERS, FREDDIE – BUDDAH, MINT
WATERS, MUDDY – CHESS, PYE INTERNATIONAL
WATKINS, LOVELACE - FONTANA
WATSON, JOHNNY GUITAR – DJM, FANTASY
WATTS 103rd. ST. RHYTHM BAND - JAY BOY, WARNER BROS
WATTS 103rd. STREET STRINGS – ARCHIVES, S.W.O.N.S,
WAYGOOD BAND, OTIS - DECCA
WAYNE, BOBBY - GRAPEVINE 2000
WEATHER GIRLS - CBS
WEATHERMEN - B&C
WEATHERS, OSCAR - MOJO
WEBB, JIM - CBS
WEBS - LONDON
WEE THREE - PEOPLE
WEE WILLIE & the WINNERS – ACTION, PEOPLE
WEISS, FRANK - STAX
WELCH, LENNY – LONDON, MAINSTREAM, MAJOR MINOR
WELLS, BOBBY – BEACON, GRAPEVINE
WELLS, BRANDI - WMOT
WELLS, JAMES - POLYDOR
WELLS, JEAN - MOJO
WELLS, JUNIOR - MERCURY
WELLS, KENNY - S.C.S.C.
WELLS, MARY – ATLANTIC, DIRECTION, ORIOLE, STATESIDE,
    TAMLA MOTOWN
WELLS, MARY and GAYE, MARVIN - STATESIDE
WELLS, TERI - LONDON
WES MINSTER FIVE - CARNIVAL
WESLEY, FRED & the J.B'S – MOJO, POLYDOR, RSO
WEST FIVE - HMV
WEST, DODIE – DECCA, PICCADILLY
WESTON, KIM - MAJOR MINOR, MGM, STATESIDE, STAX
    TAMLA MOTOWN
WESTSIDE - PEOPLE
WHIRLWIIND - PYE INTERNATIONAL
WHISPERS - JANUS
WHITE, ANTHONY – PIR, SALSOUL
WHITE, BARRY - 20TH. CENTURY, PRESIDENT, PYE
    INTERNATIONAL
WHITE, DANNY – MCA, SUE
WHITE, JEANETTE - A&M
WHITE, TAM - DECCA
WHITE, TONY JOE - MONUMENT
WHITING, LEONARD - PYE
WHITING, MARGARET - LONDON
WHITLEY, RAY - HMV
WHITNEY, MARVA – MOJO, POLYDOR
WIGANS OVATION - SPARK
WIGGINS, PERCY - ATLANTIC
WIGGINS, SPENCER – PAMA, SOUL SERIES, STATESIDE,
    TORCH
WILD HONEY – MAM, PRIVATE STOCK, RK
WILD MAGNOLIAS - BARCLAY
WILDWEEDS - CHESS
WILLIAMS ORCHESTRA, PAT - CAPITOL
WILLIAMS, AL - GRAPEVINE, SEVENS, T.B. SUPERSOUL,
    WIGAN CASINO
WILLIAMS, ANDY – LONDON
WILLIAMS, BERNIE – FLOORFILLERS
WILLIAMS, BOBBY – ACTION, CONTEMPO, CONTEMPO
    RARIES
WILLIAMS, CAROL - SALSOUL
WILLIAMS, DANNY – DERAM, ENSIGN, HMV
WILLIAMS, DENIECE - CBS
WILLIAMS, DOROTHY - KENT
WILLIAMS, ESTHER - RCA

WILLIAMS, JEANETTE - ACTION
WILLIAMS, JERRY - PYE DISCO DEMAND
WILLIAMS, JIMMY - ATLANTIC
WILLIAMS, JOANNE - ALASKA
WILLIAMS, JOHNNY – CONTEMPO, EPIC, POLYDOR
WILLIAMS, KENNY - DECCA
WILLIAMS, LARRY – DECCA, MGM, SUE
WILLIAMS, LARRY & JOHNNY WATSON – COLUMBIA, EPIC
WILLIAMS, LENNY – ABC, CRUSH MUSIC
WILLIAMS, LITTLE JERRY - CAMEO PARKWAY
WILLIAMS, LORETTA - ATLANTIC
WILLIAMS, MARY LOU - SUE
WILLIAMS, MASON - WARNER BROS
WILLIAMS, MAURICE and the ZODIACS - TOP RANK
WILLIAMS, MIKE - ATLANTIC
WILLIAMS, MOON - DJM
WILLIAMS, NATHAN - GRAPEVINE 2000
WILLIAMS, PAUL & ZOOT MONEY BAND - COLUMBIA
WILLIAMS, RONNIE - CHELSEA
WILLIAMS, SAM - GRAPEVINE
WILLIAMS, SAM c/w TOWANDA BARNES - GRAPEVINE
WILLIAMS, TONY - PHILIPS
WILLIAMSON, SONNY BOY - BLUE HORIZON, CHESS,
    PYE INTERNATIONAL, SUE
WILLIE & ANTHONY - JAY BOY
WILLINGHAM, DORIS - JAY BOY
WILLIS, BRUCE - MOTOWN UK
WILLIS, SLIM - R&B
WILLIS, TIMMY – EPIC, MIDNIGHT HOUR, SOUL HQ,
    UNITED ARTISTS
WILLS, VIOLA – ARIOLA, ARISTA, GOODEAR, PRESIDENT
WILMER & THE DUKES - ACTION
WILSON, AL – ARISTA, BELL, CASINO CLASSICS, LIBERTY,
    PYE DISCO DEMAND, SEVENS, SOUL CITY
WILSON, EDDIE - ACTION
WILSON, FRANK - ABBEY ROAD, BOOT, JOKER, TAMLA
    MOTOWN, TRACO
WILSON, JACKIE – BRUNSWICK, BRUNSWICK, EMBER, MCA,
    MCA SOUL BAG, SMP, TRENTHAM GARDENS, VOGUE
    CORAL
WILSON, JACKIE & FRANKLIN, ERMA - SOUL HQ
WILSON, JACKIE AND COUNT BASIE – MCA, MCA SOUL BAG
WILSON, JACKIE and HOPKINS, LINDA - CORAL
WILSON, JOE - PYE INTERNATIONAL
WILSON, MARI - COMPACT
WILSON, MARI and the IMAGINATIONS - GTO
WILSON, MARY - MOTOWN UK
WILSON, MAYNELL - CBM RECORDS
WILSON, NANCY - CAPITOL
WILSON, NICKY - CASINO CLASSICS
WILSON, PRECIOUS - JIVE
WILSON, REUBEN – CHESS, PEOPLE
WILSON, RUBY & the BLUE CHIPS - JAY BOY
WILSON, TIMOTHY - DECCA
WILSON, TONY - COLUMBIA
WILSON, VENICIA - SEVENS , TOP-TOP
WINDING, KAI - VERVE
WINNERS CIRCLE - WARNER BROS
WINSTONS - PYE INTERNATIONAL
WINTERS, ROBERT & FALL - BUDDAH
WINTERS, RUBY – CREOLE, STATESIDE
WINTERS, SHELLEY - INFERNO
WISHFUL THINKING - DECCA
WITCHES & the WARLOCK - PRESIDENT
WITHERS, BILL - A&M
WITHERSPOON, JIMMY – PROBE, STATESIDE, VERVE,
    VOCALION, VOGUE
WOMACK, BOBBY – ARISTA, CBS, JAY BOY, MINIT, MOTOWN
    UK , UNITED ARTISTS
WONDER WHO - PHILIPS
WONDER, LITTLE STEVIE – ORIOLE, STATESIDE, TAMLA
    MOTOWN
WONDER, STEVIE – MOTOWN UK, STATESIDE, TAMLA, TAMLA
    MOTOWN,
WOOD, ANITA - SUE

WOOD, BRENTON – EPIC, LIBERTY, MIDNIGHT HOUR,
    PHILIPS, PYE INTERNATIONAL, UNITED ARTISTS
WOOD, CHUCK – BIG T, MOJO, PRT, PYE DISCO DEMAND
WOODRUFF, STANLEY - GRAPEVINE
WOODS, BELITA c/w BANKS, DARRELL - KGH
WOODS, BILLY - SOUL CITY
WOODS, CAROL - 20TH. CENTURY, TOMORROW
WOODS, DANNY - INVICTUS
WOODS, DANNY- ACTION, SEVENS
WOODS, PEGGY - KENT
WORLD COLUMN - CAPITOL
WREN, JENNY - FONTANA
WRIGHT, BETTY – ATLANTIC, RCA
WRIGHT, CHARLES & WATTS 103rd. ST. - WARNER BROS
WRIGHT, EARL - CAPITOL
WRIGHT, MILTON - GRAPEVINE
WRIGHT, O.V. – ACTION, LONDON, SUE, VOCALION
WRIGHT, RITA – JET, TAMLA MOTOWN
WRIGHT, RUBEN - CAPITOL
WRIGHT, SAMUEL E. - PARAMOUNT
WYATT, JOHNNY – PRESIDENT, SOUL CITY
WYLIE, RICHARD (POPCORN) - COLUMBIA, GRAPEVINE,
    TAMLA MOTOWN
WYNNS, SANDY – FONTANA, INFERNO

Y

YOUNG & COMPANY - CALIBRE
YOUNG BLOOD - PYE
YOUNG FOLK - PRESIDENT
YOUNG HOLT TRIO - CORAL
YOUNG HOLT UNLIMITED - MCA
YOUNG RASCALS - ATLANTIC
YOUNG STRINGS, LEON – PYE, PYE DISCO DEMAND
YOUNG, BARRY – DOT
YOUNG, BILLY – ATLANTIC, JAY BOY
YOUNG, BILLY JOE - SURREY INTERNATIONAL
YOUNG, JOE E. and the TONIKS - TOAST
YOUNG, KAREN - MAJOR MINOR, MERCURY, PYE
YOUNG, RETTA - ALL PLATINUM
YOUNG, ROGER - COLUMBIA
YOUNG, TOMMIE - CONTEMPO
YOUNG, TOMMY - CONTEMPO
YOUNGHEARTS - 20TH. CENTURY, ABC
YOUNG-HOLT UNLTD. – MCA,
YURO, TIMI – LIBERTY, MERCURY
YURO, TIMI - LONDON
ZAGER BAND, MICHEAL - LONDON
ZAVARONI, LENA - PRESIDENT
ZEBERA - MINT
ZETTERBERG, SVEN - GOLDSOUL

16

Alphabetical label listings

10

86	87	FRANKIE KELLY	AIN'T THAT THE TRUTH	I LOVE YOU	6.00
86	111 PS	LONNIE HILL	GALVESTON BAY	MY SWEET LOVE	6.00
86	117 PS	LONNIE HILL	COULD THIS BE LOVE	STEP ON OUT	30.00

20TH. CENTURY

Distrubuted in the UK by Pye records, first release had the distinction of being a tailor made Northern Soul 45, with The Exciters being produced by Ian Levine.
Levine had numerous releases through 20th.Century with several reaching pop chart status.

75	1001	EXCITERS	LOVE YOU BABY	same: instrumental	5.00
75	1001 DJ	EXCITERS	LOVE YOU BABY	same: instrumental	6.00
75	1002	JIMMY THOMAS	BEAUTIFUL NIGHT	I CAN'T LIVE MY LIFE WITH YOU	5.00
75	1002 DJ	JIMMY THOMAS	BEAUTIFUL NIGHT	I CAN'T LIVE MY LIFE WITHOUT U	6.00
75	1003	MADAME	DO IT NOW	PRAY FOR THE PEOPLE	4.00
75	1003 DJ	MADAME	DO IT NOW	PRAY FOR THE PEOPLE	5.00
75	1005 blue logo	EXCITERS	REACHING FOR THE BEST	KEEP ON REACHIN'	6.00
75	1005 blue logo DJ	EXCITERS	REACHING FOR THE BEST	KEEP REACHING	15.00
75	1005 red logo	EXCITERS	REACHING FOR THE BEST	KEEP ON REACHIN'	6.00
75	1005 red logo DJ	EXCITERS	REACHING FOR THE BEST	KEEP ON REACHIN'	8.00
75	1006	MARTIN BLACK	SOONER OR LATER	IN THE COVERS OF DARKNESS	6.00
75	1006 DJ	MARTIN BLACK	SOONER OR LATER	IN THE COVERS OF DARKNESS	8.00
75	1013	EXCITERS	YOU'RE GONNA MAKE ME LOVE YOU	SOUL OVER THE HORIZON	4.00
75	1013 DJ	EXCITERS	YOU'RE GONNA MAKE ME LOVE YOU	SOUL OVER THE HORIZON	6.00
75	1014	EVELYN THOMAS	WEAK SPOT	DANCIN' IS MY WEAK SPOT	4.00
75	1014 DJ	EVELYN THOMAS	WEAK SPOT	DANCIN' IS MY WEAK SPOT	6.00
75	1015	EXCITERS	SUFFERING	SUFFERING: disco version	4.00
75	1015 DJ	EXCITERS	SUFFERING	SUFFERING: disco version	6.00
75	1017	EVELYN THOMAS	DOOMSDAY	THE DAY AFTER DOOMSDAY	4.00
75	1017 DJ	EVELYN THOMAS	DOOMSDAY	THE DAY AFTER DOOMSDAY	5.00
75	1018	CAROL WOODS	HEADING DOWN FOOLS ROAD	ONCE MORE DOWN FOOLD ROAD	5.00
75	1018 DJ	CAROL WOODS	HEADING DOWN FOOLS ROAD	ONCE MORE DOWN FOOLS ROAD	6.00
76	1019	EXCITERS	SWALLOW YOUR PRIDE	PRIDE COMES BEFORE A FALL	4.00
76	1019 DJ	EXCITERS	SWALLOW YOUR PRIDE	PRIDE COMES BEFORE A FALL	6.00
76	1023	FEDERATION	TWENTY FIVE MINUTES TO LOVE	HOOKED ON LOVE	5.00
76	1023 DJ	FEDERATION	TWENTY FIVE MINUTES TO LOVE	HOOKED ON LOVE	8.00
76	1027	EVELYN THOMAS	LOVE'S NOT JUST AN ILLUSION	THE CHICAGO HUSTLE	4.00
76	1027 DJ	EVELYN THOMAS	LOVE'S NOT JUST AN ILLUSION	THE CHICAGO HUSTLE	5.00
76	1028	CAROL WOODS	YOUR FACE KEEPS HAUNTING ME	HAUNTING MEMORY	4.00
76	1028 DJ	CAROL WOODS	YOUR FACE KEEPS HAUNTING ME	HAUNTING MEMORY	5.00
76	1029	EVELYN THOMAS	MY HEAD'S IN THE STARS	same: instrumental	4.00
76	1029 DJ	EVELYN THOMAS	MY HEAD'S IN THE STARS	same: instrumental	6.00
79	1040	GENE CHANDLER	GET DOWN	GREATEST LOVE EVER KNOWN	4.00
79	1040 DJ	GENE CHANDLER	GET DOWN	GREATEST LOVE EVER KNOWN	5.00
79	1041	BARRY WHITE	SHA LA LA MEANS I LOVE YOU	IT'S ONLY LOVE DOING IT'S THIN	4.00
79	1041 DJ	BARRY WHITE	SHA LA LA MEANS I LOVE YOU	IT'S ONLY LOVE DOING IT'S THIN	5.00
79	1045	BARRY WHITE	SEPTEMBER WHEN WE FIRST MET	EARLY YEARS	4.00
79	1045 DJ	BARRY WHITE	SEPTEMBER WHEN WE FIRST MET	EARLY YEARS	5.00
74	2130	YOUNGHEARTS	WAKE UP AND START STANDING	DEDICATE (MY LIFE TO YOU)	4.00
74	2130 DJ	YOUNGHEARTS	WAKE UP AND START STANDING	DEDICATE (MY LIFE TO YOU)	6.00
74	2133	BARRY WHITE	YOU'RE THE FIRST, THE LAST, MY EVERY	MORE THAN ANYTHING YOU'RE M EV	4.00
74	2133 DJ	BARRY WHITE	YOU'RE THE FIRST, THE LAST, MY EVERY	MORE THAN ANYTHING YOU'RE M EV	6.00
74	2149	LOVE UNLIMITED	IT MAY BE WINTER OUTSIDE	I LOVE YOU SDO NEVER LET YOU GO	4.00
74	2149 DJ	LOVE UNLIMITED	IT MAY BE WINTER OUTSIDE	I LOVE YOU SDO NEVER LET YOU GO	5.00
74	2146	LEON HAYWOOD	THE DAY I LAID EYES ON YOU	BELIEVE HALF OF WHAT YOU SEE	6.00
74	2146 DJ	LEON HAYWOOD	THE DAY I LAID EYES ON YOU	BELIEVE HALF OF WHAT YOU SEE	10.00
74	2150	LALO SCHIFRIN	APE SHUFFLE	THE HEART IS BUT SO STRONG	20.00
74	2150 DJ	LALO SCHIFRIN	APE SHUFFLE	THE HEART IS BUT SO STRONG	30.00
74	2168	LOVE UNLIMITED	ALWAYS THINKING OF YOU	SATIN SOUL	4.00
74	2168 DJ	LOVE UNLIMITED	ALWAYS THINKING OF YOU	SATIN SOUL	5.00
74	2177	BARRY WHITE	WHAT AM I GONNA DO	same: instrumental	4.00
74	2177 DJ	BARRY WHITE	WHAT AM I GONNA DO	same: instrumental	5.00
74	2178	LOVE UNLIMITED	I'M UNDER THE INFLUENCE OF LOVE	I BELONG TO YOU	4.00
74	2178 DJ	LOVE UNLIMITED	I'M UNDER THE INFLUENCE OF LOVE	I BELONG TO YOU	6.00
75	2203 unissued	R.B. GREAVES	MY PLACE OR YOURS	LET'S TRY IT AGAIN	UN
75	2203 DJ	R.B. GREAVES	MY PLACE OR YOURS	LET'S TRY IT AGAIN	50.00
75	2208	BARRY WHITE	FOR YOU I'LL BE ANYTING YOU WANT ME TO	FOR ANYTHING YOU WANT ME TO	4.00
75	2208 DJ	BARRY WHITE	FOR YOU I'LL BE ANYTING YOU WANT ME TO	FOR ANYTHING YOU WANT ME TO	5.00
75	2215	ELEVENTH HOUR	HOLLYWOOD HOT	same: instrumental	5.00
75	2215 DJ	ELEVENTH HOUR	HOLLYWOOD HOT	same: instrumental	8.00
75	2416	BARRY WHITE	I LOVE TO SING THE SONGS I SING	OH ME OH MY	3.00
75	2416 DJ	BARRY WHITE	I LOVE TO SING THE SONGS I SING	OH ME OH MY	4.00
75	2228	LEON HAYWOOD	I KNOW WHAT LOVE IS	I WANT TO DO SOMETHING FREAKY	4.00
75	2228 DJ	LEON HAYWOOD	I KNOW WHAT LOVE IS	I WANT TO DO SOMETHING FREAKY	5.00
75	2265	BARRY WHITE	LET THE MUSIC PLAY	same:instrumental	4.00
75	2265 DJ	BARRY WHITE	LET THE MUSIC PLAY	same: instrumental	5.00
76	2277	BARRY WHITE	YOU SEE THE TROUBLE WITH ME	I'M SO BLUE AND YOU ARE TOOQ	4.00

76	2277 DJ	BARRY WHITE	YOU SEE THE TROUBLE WITH ME	I'M SO BLUE AND YOU ARE TOOQ	4.00
76	2292	SAMMY DAVIS JR.	BARRETTA'S THEME	I HEARD A SONG	6.00
76	2292 DJ	SAMMY DAVIS JR.	BARRETTA'S THEME	I HEARD A SONG	8.00
76	2298	BARRY WHITE	BABY WE BETTER TRY TO GET IT	IF YOU KNOW WON'T YOU TELL ME	3.00
76	2298 DJ	BARRY WHITE	BABY WE BETTER TRY TO GET IT	IF YOU KNOW WON'T YOU TELL ME	4.00
76	2309	BARRY WHITE	DON'T MAKE ME WAIT TOO LONG	DON'T MAKE ME WAIT TOO LONG part 2	3.00
76	2309 DJ	BARRY WHITE	DON'T MAKE ME WAIT TOO LONG	DON'T MAKE ME WAIT TOO LONG part 2	4.00
77	2328	BARRY WHITE	I'M QUALIFIED TO SATISFY YOU	I'M QUALIFIED TO SATISFY YOU part 2	3.00
77	2328 DJ	BARRY WHITE	I'M QUALIFIED TO SATISFY YOU	I'M QUALIFIED TO SATISFY YOU part 2	4.00
77	2350	BARRY WHITE	IT'S ECSTASY WHEN YOU LAY DOWN NEXT TO ME	I NEVER THOUGH I'D FALL IN LOVE	3.00
77	2350 DJ	BARRY WHITE	IT'S ECSTASY WHEN YOU LAY DOWN NEXT TO ME	I NEVER THOUGH I'D FALL IN LOVE	3.00
78	2365	BARY WHITE	OH WHAT A NIGHT FOR DANCING	YOU'RE SO GOOD, YOU'RE SO BAD	3.00
78	2365 DJ	BARY WHITE	OH WHAT A NIGHT FOR DANCING	YOU'RE SO GOOD, YOU'RE SO BAD	4.00
78	2380	BARRY WHITE	JUST THE WAY YOU ARE	YOU SWEET IS MY WEAKNESS	4.00
78	2380 DJ	BARRY WHITE	JUST THE WAY YOU ARE	YOU SWEET IS MY WEAKNESS	5.00
78	2396	EDWIN STARR	CONTACT	DON'T WASTE YOR TIME	4.00
78	2396 DJ	EDWIN STARR	CONTACT	DON'T WASTE YOR TIME	6.00
79	2411	GENE CHANDLER	WHEN YOU'RE NUMBER 1	I'LL REMEMBER YOU	3.00
79	2411 DJ	GENE CHANDLER	WHEN YOU'RE NUMBER 1	I'LL REMEMBER YOU	5.00
79	2451	GENE CHANDLER	LET ME MAKE LOVE TO YOU	DOES SHE HAVE A FRIEND FOR ME	15.00
79	2451 DJ	GENE CHANDLER	LET ME MAKE LOVE TO YOU	DOES SHE HAVE A FRIEND FOR ME	20.00
79	2460	STEPHANIE MILLS	NEVER KNEW LOVE LIKE THIS BEFORE	STILL MINE	6.00
79	2460 DJ	STEPHANIE MILLS	NEVER KNEW LOVE LIKE THIS BEFORE	STILL MINE	8.00
79	2463	DELLS	ALL ABOUT THE PAPERS	I TOUCHED A DREAM	8.00
79	2463 DJ	DELLS	ALL ABOUT THE PAPERS	I TOUCHED A DREAM	10.00
81	2478	DELLS	YOUR SONG	LOOK AT US NOW	75.00
81	2478 DJ	DELLS	YOUR SONG	LOOK AT US NOW	85.00
81	2479	CHI-LITES	ALL I WANNA DO IS MAKE LOVE TO	LOVE SHOCK	5.00
81	2479 DJ	CHI-LITES	ALL I WANNA DO IS MAKE LOVE TO	LOVE SHOCK	6.00
81	2488	CARL CARLTON	THIS FEELING'S RATED X-TRA	SHE'S A BAD MAMA JAMA	5.00
81	2488 DJ	CARL CARLTON	THIS FEELING'S RATED X-TRA	SHE'S A BAD MAMA JAMA	5.00
81	2492	STEPHANIE MILLS	TWO HEARTS	I JUST WANNA SAY	6.00
81	2492 DJ	STEPHANIE MILLS	TWO HEARTS	I JUST WANNA SAY	6.00
81	2505	GENE CHANDLER	LOVE IS THE ANSWER	I'M ATTRACTED TO YOU	4.00
81	2505 DJ	GENE CHANDLER	LOVE IS THE ANSWER	I'M ATTRACTED TO YOU	5.00

444

70	acetate	CHRIS JACKSON	SINCE THERE'S NO DOUBT	WE WILL BE TOGETHER	1000.00

Only one known copy which is a full label studio acetate of the unissued Soul City 120.

4TH. + BROADWAY

85	022 PS	CASHMERE	WE NEED LOVE	KEEP ME UP	5.00
89	122 PS	MICA PARIS and WILL DOWNING	WHERE IS THE LOVE	SAME FEELING	4.00
91	223	DRIZA BONE	REAL LOVE	REAL LOVE (JAZZY)	10.00
91	223 PS	DRIZA BONE	REAL LOVE	REAL LOVE (JAZZY)	15.00
91	264	DRIZA BONE	PRESSURE	PRESSURE (nu solution mix)	30.00
91	264 PS	DRIZA BONE	PRESSURE	PRESSURE (nu solution mix)	**165.00**

A&M

This Herb Alpert and Jerry Moss owned Los Angeles label, started releasing 45s in the UK in 1968, although A&M had their own label in the USA way back in 1962. Mostly known as a "middle of the road" label, it was started with very little money by trumpet man Herb Alpert and Jerry Moss who built this label from nothing to become the world's largest independent label, which sold out to Polgram in 1989.

Herb Alpert was born March 31st. 1935 in Los Angles, California. At the age of 13 Herb started playing the trumpet; taught by Ben Klazkin first trumpeter of the San Francisco Symphony. With his honed talents a young 15-year-old Herb formed his own band, which won a local TV talent show. After time in national service, Herb became interested in the jazz greats changing direction in his style. After the army, a fateful meeting with an insurance man changed the course of Herb's life. Lou Adler was having a good day, having sold Mr. Alpert $10,000 worth of life insurance, he had time to chat. Lou confided his first love was poetry and from that day the writing team of Alpert and Adler began. Ironically for soul fans there first composition was published by Sam Cooke's Keen label. Then he had a hit with Sam Butera on Dot records, then using a royalty cheque, Herb set up a recording studio in his garage.

On a break from writing and recording, Herb went on vacation to Tijuana, Mexico. With a fresh mind he came up with the idea of tweaking a song called "Twinkle Star" adding an extra trumpet. Herb's new tune, re-titled by Jerry Moss as "Lonely Bull" was ready to go to vinyl in the late summer of 1962. In February 1963 "Lonely Bull" had hit the USA pop charts selling over 700,000 copies. The debut A&M label had got Alpert & Moss off to a spectacular start. Five years later they launched the A&M label in the UK.

The first label UK design is the brown with the white logo, later in the 70's moving to a redesigned silver background with a full label light brown A&M logo. 45 highlights on the label are few, but Jeanette White – "Music" – originally release on the small independent USA Vibration label, got national and UK release through A&M to become a Northern Soul classic. Robert John's – "Raindrops, love and Sunshine" – (so similar to another Northern Soul classic by Spiral Staircase – "More Today Than Yesterday") is still being played at Northern Soul venues in 2005 and is very difficult to find on its UK release. Ron Keith's 1976 soulful B-side – "Gotta Go By What You Tell Me" – is the most sought after soul 45 on the label. And if it wasn't for the Sex Pistols withdrawn A&M 7284 – "God Save The Queen" – it would be the most expensive 45 on the label, period. Ron Keith's 45 is also hard to find in the USA as a stock copy, it was a total flip, and all the promo copies are – "Party Music" – stereo and mono. Making the UK press even more sought after. Then recently Northern Soul DJs started to play the very individual sound of Nino Tempo & his 5th. Avenue Sax, which saw the price of –"Sister James" – A&M 7089 rocket from £5 to £50 almost overnight: Such is the power of Northern Soul exposure on the price of a 7" disc.

For soul fans the main proportion of the soul releases on this label in the UK came from the SUSSEX catalogue, which was issued in the UK through A&M. With an impressive listing of artists like Bill Withers, Dennis Coffey, and male group harmony bands like the highly respected Van McCoy produced Presidents, and the Mike Theodore and Dennis Coffey - Detroit produced Decisions. But the UK never saw any of those classic Northern Soul 45's by Towanda Barnes, Toni Basil, Collins & Collins etc, get a UK release. Bill Withers however did provide A&M with its largest soul sales in the UK before moving to Columbia Records.

83	101 PS	DINA CARROLL	WHY DID I LET YOU GO	SO CLOSE	6.00
83	101 DJ	DINA CARROLL	WHY DID I LET YOU GO	SO CLOSE	6.00
83	140	JEFFREY OSBOURNE	DON'T YOU GET SO MAD	SO MUCH LOVE	4.00
83	140 DJ	JEFFREY OSBOURNE	DON'T YOU GET SO MAD	SO MUCH LOVE	5.00

68	719	HERBIE MANN	UNCHAIN MY HEART	GLORY OF LOVE	10.00
68	719 DJ	HERBIE MANN	UNCHAIN MY HEART	GLORY OF LOVE	15.00
68	736	EVIE SANDS	UNTIL IT'S TIME FOR YOU TO GO	SHADOW OF THE EVENING	5.00
68	736 DJ	EVIE SANDS	UNTIL IT'S TIME FOR YOU TO GO	SHADOW OF THE EVENING	6.00
69	747	CHECKMATES LTD.	LOVE IS ALL I HAVE TO GIVE	I NEVER SHOULD HAVE LIED	8.00
69	747 DJ	CHECKMATES LTD.	LOVE IS ALL I HAVE TO GIVE	I NEVER SHOULD HAVE LIED	10.00
69	748	RONETTES	YOU CAME, YOU SAW, YO0U	I CAN HEAR MUSIC	8.00
69	748 DJ	RONETTES	YOU CAME, YOU SAW, YO0U	I CAN HEAR MUSIC	10.00
69	750	RUBY & THE ROMANTICS	HURTING EACH OTHER	BABY I COULD BE SO GOOD AT LOV	15.00
69	750 DJ	RUBY & THE ROMANTICS	HURTING EACH OTHER	BABY I COULD BE SO GOOD AT LOV	20.00
69	752	SONNYCHARLES & CHECKMATES	BLACK PEARL	LAZY SUSAN	8.00
69	752 DJ	SONNYCHARLES & CHECKMATES	BLACK PEARL	LAZY SUSAN	15.00
69	760	EVIE SANDS	ANY WAY THAT YOU WANT ME	I'LL NEVER BE ALONE AGAIN	5.00
69	760 DJ	EVIE SANDS	ANY WAY THAT YOU WANT ME	I'LL NEVER BE ALONE AGAIN	6.00
69	761 brown	JEANETTE WHITE	MUSIC	NO SUNSHINE	75.00
69	761 yellow DJ	JEANETTE WHITE	MUSIC	NO SUNSHINE	85.00
77	761 silver & brown	JEANETTE WHITE	MUSIC	NO SUNSHINE	25.00

Reissued using the original 1969 release #.The second press label has a silver background with a large light brown A&M logo.

69	766	PHIL FLOWERS	KEEP ON SOCKIN' IT CHILDREN	LIKE A ROLLING STONE	20.00
69	766 DJ	PHIL FLOWERS	KEEP ON SOCKIN' IT CHILDREN	LIKE A ROLLING STONE	25.00
69	769	CHECKMATES LTD.	PROUD MARY	SPANISH HARLEM	6.00
69	769 DJ	CHECKMATES LTD.	PROUD MARY	SPANISH HARLEM	8.00
69	772	SISTERS LOVE	FORGET IT, I'VE GOT IT	EYE TO EYE	30.00
69	772 DJ	SISTERS LOVE	FORGET IT, I'VE GOT IT	EYE TO EYE	40.00
69	780	SONNY CHARLES & CHECKMATES	I KEEP FORGETTING	DO YOU LOVE YOUR BABY	6.00
69	780 DJ	SONNY CHARLES & CHECKMATES	I KEEP FORGETTING	DO YOU LOVE YOUR BABY	8.00
70	781	QUINCY JONES	KILLER JOE	OH HAPPY DAY	4.00
70	781 DJ	QUINCY JONES	KILLER JOE	OH HAPPY DAY	5.00
70	781	EVIE SANDS	BUT YOU KNOW I LOVE YOU	MAYBE TOMORROW	6.00
70	781 DJ	EVIE SANDS	BUT YOU KNOW I LOVE YOU	MAYBE TOMORROW	8.00
70	783	IKE & TINA TURNER	EVERYDAY I HAVE TO CRY	MAKE 'EM WAIT	8.00
70	783 DJ	IKE & TINA TURNER	EVERYDAY I HAVE TO CRY	MAKE 'EM WAIT	10.00
70	784	PHIL FLOWERS	IF IT FEELS GOOD DO IT	EVERYDAY I HAVE TO CRY SOME	20.00
70	784 DJ	PHIL FLOWERS	IF IT FEELS GOOD DO IT	EVERYDAY I HAVE TO CRY SOME	25.00
70	787	SONNYCHARLES & CHECKMATES	IT TAKES A LITTLE LONGER	WELFARE MAN	6.00
70	787 DJ	SONNYCHARLES & CHECKMATES	IT TAKES A LITTLE LONGER	WELFARE MAN	8.00
70	802	MERRYCLAYTON	GIMME SHELTER	GOOD GIRLS	10.00
70	802 DJ	MERRYCLAYTON	GIMME SHELTER	GOOD GIRLS	15.00
70	808	SISTERS LOVE	THE BIGGER YOU LOVE (THE HARDER	PIECE OF MY HEART	5.00
70	808 DJ	SISTERS LOVE	THE BIGGER YOU LOVE (THE HARDER	PIECE OF MY HEART	8.00
71	829	IKE & TINA TURNER	OH BABY (THINGS AIN'T WHAT THEY	RIVER DEEP - MOUNTAIN HIGH	15.00
71	829 DJ	IKE & TINA TURNER	OH BABY (THINGS AIN'T WHAT THEY	RIVER DEEP - MOUNTAIN HIGH	22.00
71	835	ROBERT JOHN	RAINDROPS LOVE AND SUNSHINE	WHEN THE PARTY IS OVER	60.00
71	835 DJ	ROBERT JOHN	RAINDROPS LOVE AND SUNSHINE	WHEN THE PARTY IS OVER	100.00
71	843	PRESIDENTS	SWEET MAGIC	FIDDLE DE DE	10.00
71	843 DJ	PRESIDENTS	SWEET MAGIC	FIDDLE DE DE	15.00
71	844	DECISIONS	I CAN'T FORGET ABOUT YOU	IT'S LOVE THAT REALLY COUNTS	15.00
71	844 DJ	DECISIONS	I CAN'T FORGET ABOUT YOU	IT'S LOVE THAT REALLY COUNTS	20.00
71	845	BILLWITHERS	HARLEM	EVERYBODY'S TALKING	5.00
71	845 DJ	BILLWITHERS	HARLEM	EVERYBODY'S TALKING	6.00
71	849	CAROLE KING	I FEEL THE EARTH MOVE	IT'S TOO LATE	5.00
71	849 DJ	CAROLE KING	I FEEL THE EARTH MOVE	IT'S TOO LATE	10.00
71	856	PRESIDENTS	5-10-15-20 (25-30 YEARS OF LOVE)	TRIANGLE OF LOVE	8.00
71	856 DJ	PRESIDENTS	5-10-15-20 (25-30 YEARS OF LOVE)	TRIANGLE OF LOVE	10.00
71	858	BILLWITHERS	AIN'T NO SUNSHINE	HARLEM	6.00
71	858 DJ	BILLWITHERS	AIN'T NO SUNSHINE	HARLEM	8.00
71	875	DENNIS COFFEY	SCORPIO	SAD ANGEL	6.00
71	875 DJ	DENNIS COFFEY	SCORPIO	SAD ANGEL	8.00
72	882	MICHAELS, LEE	CAN I GET A WITNESS	YOU ARE WHAT YOU DO	5.00
72	882 DJ	MICHAELS, LEE	CAN I GET A WITNESS	YOU ARE WHAT YOU DO	6.00
72	7004	BILLWITHERS	LEAN ON ME	BETTER OFF DEAD	4.00
72	7004 DJ	BILLWITHERS	LEAN ON ME	BETTER OFF DEAD	5.00
72	7007	BILLY PRESTON	OUTA SPACE	THE BUS	6.00
72	7007 DJ	BILLY PRESTON	OUTA SPACE	THE BUS	7.00
72	7010	DENNIS COFFEY	GETTING IT ON	RIDE, SALLY RIDE	5.00
72	7010 DJ	DENNIS COFFEY	GETTING IT ON	RIDE, SALLY RIDE	6.00
72	7038	BILLWITHERS	USE ME	LET ME IN YOUR LIFE	5.00
72	7038 DJ	BILLWITHERS	USE ME	LET ME IN YOUR LIFE	6.00
72	7039	IKE & TINA TURNER	RIVER DEEP - MOUNTAIN HIGH	A LOVE LIKE YOURS + SAVE THE L	4.00
72	7039 DJ	IKE & TINA TURNER	RIVER DEEP - MOUNTAIN HIGH	A LOVE LIKE YOURS + SAVE THE L	6.00
72	7049	BILLY PRESTON	WILL IT GO ROUND IN CIRCLES	BLACKBIRD	5.00
72	7049 DJ	BILLY PRESTON	WILL IT GO ROUND IN CIRCLES	BLACKBIRD	6.00
73	7055	BILLWITHERS	KISSING MY LOVE	I DON'T KNOW	4.00
73	7055 DJ	BILLWITHERS	KISSING MY LOVE	I DON'T KNOW	5.00
73	7068	BILLWITHERS	LOOK WHAT I FOUND	THE LADY IS WAITING	5.00
73	7068 DJ	BILLWITHERS	LOOK WHAT I FOUND	THE LADY IS WAITING	6.00
73	7075	NINO & APRIL	PUT IT WHERE YOU WANT IT	I CAN'T GET OVER YOU BABY	6.00
73	7075 DJ	NINO & APRIL	PUT IT WHERE YOU WANT IT	I CAN'T GET OVER YOU BABY	8.00
73	7076	FREDDIE KING	WOMAN ACROSS THE RIVER	HELP ME THROUGH THE DAY	5.00

73	7076 DJ	FREDDIE KING	WOMAN ACROSS THE RIVER	HELP ME THROUGH THE DAY	6.00
73	7080	BILLWITHERS	AIN'T NO SUNSHINE	HARLEM + GRANDMA'S HANDS	5.00
73	7080 DJ	BILLWITHERS	AIN'T NO SUNSHINE	HARLEM + GRANDMA'S HANDS	8.00
73	7084	BILLY PRESTON	SPACE RACE	WE'RE GONNA MAKE IT	4.00
73	7084 DJ	BILLY PRESTON	SPACE RACE	WE'RE GONNA MAKE IT	5.00
73	7089	NINO TEMPO & 5th.AVE.SAX	SISTER JAMES	CLAIR DE LUNE (IN JAZZ)	40.00
73	7089 DJ	NINO TEMPO & 5th.AVE.SAX	SISTER JAMES	CLAIR DE LUNE (IN JAZZ)	55.00
73	7089 DJ + art sleeve	NINO TEMPO & 5th.AVE.SAX	SISTER JAMES	CLAIR DE LUNE (IN JAZZ)	75.00
73	7093	ALTON ELLIS	SHO-BE-DO-BE DO (I LOVE YOU)	I LOVE YOU TRUE	5.00
73	7093 DJ	ALTON ELLIS	SHO-BE-DO-BE DO (I LOVE YOU)	I LOVE YOU TRUE	6.00
73	7097	BILLY PRESTON	YOU'RE SO UNIQUE	HOW LONG HAS THAT TRAIN BEEN HERE	6.00
73	7097 DJ	BILLY PRESTON	YOU'RE SO UNIQUE	HOW LONG HAS THAT TRAIN BEEN HERE	8.00
73	7108	BILL WITHERS	THE SAME LOVE THAT MADE ME LAUGH	MAKE A SMILE FOR ME	4.00
73	7108 DJ	BILL WITHERS	THE SAME LOVE THAT MADE ME LAUGH	MAKE A SMILE FOR ME	5.00
74	7123	PERSUASIONS	GONNA KEEP ON TRYIN' TO WIN YOU'RE LOVE	OCCAPELLA	4.00
74	7123 DJ	PERSUASIONS	GONNA KEEP ON TRYIN' TO WIN YOU'RE LOVE	OCCAPELLA	5.00
74	7124	QUINCY JONES	SOUL SAGA	BODY HEAT	4.00
74	7124 DJ	QUINCY JONES	SOUL SAGA	BODY HEAT	5.00
74	7126	BILLY PRESTON	NOTHING FROM NOTHING	MY SOUL IS A WITNESS	4.00
74	7126 DJ	BILLY PRESTON	NOTHING FROM NOTHING	MY SOUL IS A WITNESS	5.00
74	7145	BILLY PRESTON	STRUTTIN'	YOU'RE SO BEAUTIFUL	4.00
74	7145 DJ	BILLY PRESTON	STRUTTIN'	YOU'RE SO BEAUTIFUL	5.00
74	7151	CARL GRAVES	BABY HANG UP THE PHONE	WALK SOFTLY	8.00
74	7151 DJ	CARL GRAVES	BABY HANG UP THE PHONE	WALK SOFTLY	10.00
75	7173	CHARITY BROWN	TAKE ME IN YOUR ARMS AND ROCK ME	OUR DAY WILL COME	8.00
75	7173 DJ	CHARITY BROWN	TAKE ME IN YOUR ARMS AND ROCK ME	OUR DAY WILL COME	10.00
75	7176	FREDDIE KING	GOIN' HOME	ME AND MY GUITAR	4.00
75	7176 DJ	FREDDIE KING	GOIN' HOME	ME AND MY GUITAR	5.00
75	7180	CARL GRAVES	THE NEXT BEST THING	BROWN SKIN LOVE	5.00
75	7180 DJ	CARL GRAVES	THE NEXT BEST THING	BROWN SKIN LOVE	6.00
75	7181	JOAN ARMATRADING	BACK TO THE NIGHT	SO GOOD	4.00
75	7181 DJ	JOAN ARMATRADING	BACK TO THE NIGHT	SO GOOD	5.00
75	7190	NINO TEMPO & 5th. AVE. SAX	COME SEE ME 'ROUND MIDNIGHT	HIGH ON MUSIC	4.00
75	7190 DJ	NINO TEMPO & 5th. AVE. SAX	COME SEE ME 'ROUND MIDNIGHT	HIGH ON MUSIC	5.00
75	7198	BILLY PRESTON	FANCY LADY	SONG OF JOY	4.00
75	7198 DJ	BILLY PRESTON	FANCY LADY	SONG OF JOY	5.00
76	7217	RON KEITH	GOTTA GO BY WHAT YOU TELL ME	PARTY MUSIC	150.00
76	7217 DJ	RON KEITH	GOTTA GO BY WHAT YOU TELL ME	PARTY MUSIC	200.00
76	7235	CARL GRAVES	MY WHOLE WORLD ENDED (THE MOMENT	BABY DON'T KNOCK	4.00
76	7235 DJ	CARL GRAVES	MY WHOLE WORLD ENDED (THE MOMENT	BABY DON'T KNOCK	5.00
76	7237	BROTHERS JOHNSON	GET THE FUNK OUT OF MY FACE	TOMORROW	4.00
76	7237 DJ	BROTHERS JOHNSON	GET THE FUNK OUT OF MY FACE	TOMORROW	5.00
76	7249	JOAN ARMATRADING	LOVE AND AFFECTION	HELP YOURSELF	4.00
76	7249 DJ	JOAN ARMATRADING	LOVE AND AFFECTION	HELP YOURSELF	5.00
76	7251	BROTHERS JOHNSON	GET THE FUNK OUT OF MY FACE	TOMORROW	4.00
76	7251 DJ	BROTHERS JOHNSON	GET THE FUNK OUT OF MY FACE	TOMORROW	5.00
76	7265	L.T.D.	LOVE BALLAD	LET THE MUSIC KEEP PLAYING	4.00
76	7265 DJ	L.T.D.	LOVE BALLAD	LET THE MUSIC KEEP PLAYING	5.00
77	7319	L.T.D.	BACK IN LOVE	MATERIAL THINGS	4.00
77	7319 DJ	L.T.D.	BACK IN LOVE	MATERIAL THINGS	5.00
78	7367	QUINCY JONES	STUFF LIKE THAT	THERE'S A TRAIN LEAVIN'	3.00
78	7367 DJ	QUINCY JONES	STUFF LIKE THAT	THERE'S A TRAIN LEAVIN'	4.00
81	8137 PS	U.K. PLAYERS	MIDNIGHT	EXIT	4.00
81	8137 DJ	U.K. PLAYERS	MIDNIGHT	EXIT	5.00
82	8218	ATLANTIC STARR	CIRCLES	DOES IT MATTER	10.00
82	8218 DJ	ATLANTIC STARR	CIRCLES	DOES IT MATTER	15.00

ABBEY ROAD

EMI owned North London's Abbey Road Studios, opened its doors in November 1931 and is perhaps the most famous recording studio in the world today.

79	acetate	FRANK WILSON	DO I LOVE YOU (INDEED I DO)	blank:	500.00

Fully labeled acetate with handwritten credits, two known copies

ABC

ABC stands for American Broadcasting Corporation formed in New York in 1955. As this corporation was part of American Broadcasting – Paramount Theatres, it came know as ABC – Paramount. This huge American music label, bought out many smaller labels throughout the 50s and the 60s. The two most important purchases that will interest soul fans; were Dunhill from Lou Adler (see the A&M label) and the iconic Houston, Texas based rhythm and blues group of labels Duke, Peacock and Sure Shot from Don Robey.

Already within its structure were such highly collectable labels, Ray Charles's Tangerine label being perhaps the finest. Jazz & Soul orientated Blue Thumb label who had such highly respected acts as Ike & Tina Turner, Crusaders etc, within its catalogue.

For many, many years the ABC USA label was released in the UK through EMI either on the HMV or Stateside labels. In 1974 the distribution was taken over by Anchor Records, who gave ABC its own label. Check out the Stateside and HMV label for ABC USA soul releases in the UK.

74	4002	SOLOMON BURKE	MIDNIGHT AND YOU	I HAVE A DREAM	5.00
74	4002 DJ	SOLOMON BURKE	MIDNIGHT AND YOU	I HAVE A DREAM	6.00
74	4003	LAMONT DOZIER	BREAKING OUT ALL OVER	FISH AIN'T BITING	6.00
74	4003 DJ	LAMONT DOZIER	BREAKING OUT ALL OVER	FISH AIN'T BITING	8.00
74	4005	B.B. KING	WHO ARE YOU	OH TO ME	4.00
74	4005 DJ	B.B. KING	WHO ARE YOU	OH TO ME	5.00
74	4005	TRIBE	TRIBE	LEARN TO LOVE	5.00
74	4005 DJ	TRIBE	TRIBE	LEARN TO LOVE	6.00

74	4008	RUFUS	TELL ME SOMETHING GOOD	OH TO ME		4.00
74	4008 DJ	RUFUS	TELL ME SOMETHING GOOD	OH TO ME		5.00
74	4011	MIGHTY CLOUDS OF JOY	TIME	LAUGH		10.00
74	4011 DJ	MIGHTY CLOUDS OF JOY	TIME	LAUGH		15.00
74	4012	EDDIE HOLMAN	HEY THERE LONELY GIRL	IT'S ALL IN THE GAME		4.00
74	4012 DJ	EDDIE HOLMAN	HEY THERE LONELY GIRL	IT'S ALL IN THE GAME		8.00
74	4013	FOUR TOPS	THE WELL IS DRY	MIDNIGHT FLOWER		4.00
74	4013 DJ	FOUR TOPS	THE WELL IS DRY	MIDNIGHT FLOWER		5.00
74	4014	BOBBYBLAND	AIN'T NO LOVE IN THE HEART OF THE CITY	TWENTY FOUR HOUR BLUES		4.00
74	4014 DJ	BOBBYBLAND	AIN'T NO LOVE IN THE HEART OF THE CITY	TWENTY FOUR HOUR BLUES		6.00
74	4017	B.B. KING	PHILADELPHIA	UP AT 5 PM		4.00
74	4017 DJ	B.B. KING	PHILADELPHIA	UP AT 5 PM		5.00
74	4018	SHAKERS	ONE WONDERFUL MOMENT	LOVE LOVE LOVE		6.00
74	4018 DJ	SHAKERS	ONE WONDERFUL MOMENT	LOVE LOVE LOVE		8.00
74	4020	TAMS	BE YOUNG BE FOOLISH BE HAPPY	HEY GIRL DON'T BOTHER ME		8.00
74	4020 DJ	TAMS	BE YOUNG BE FOOLISH BE HAPPY	HEY GIRL DON'T BOTHER ME		12.00
74	4021	LAWRENCE PAYTON	TELL ME YOU LOVE ME (LOVE SOUNDS)	I FOUND THE SPIRIT		40.00
74	4021 DJ	LAWRENCE PAYTON	TELL ME YOU LOVE ME (LOVE SOUNDS)	I FOUND THE SPIRIT		50.00
74	4022	RUFUS	YOU GOT THE LOVE	RAGS TO RUFUS		4.00
74	4022 DJ	RUFUS	YOU GOT THE LOVE	RAGS TO RUFUS		5.00
74	4025	CARL CARLTON	EVERLASTING LOVE	I WANNA BE YOUR MAIN SQUEEZE		5.00
74	4025 DJ	CARL CARLTON	EVERLASTING LOVE	I WANNA BE YOUR MAIN SQUEEZE		6.00
74	4026	DONALDSON, BO and the HEYWOODS	GIRL DON'T MAKE ME WAIT	THE HEARTBREAK KID		5.00
74	4026 DJ	DONALDSON, BO and the HEYWOODS	GIRL DON'T MAKE ME WAIT	THE HEARTBREAK KID		8.00
74	4027	FREDA PAYNE	IT'S YOURS TO HAVE	RUN FOR YOUR LOVE		4.00
74	4027 DJ	FREDA PAYNE	IT'S YOURS TO HAVE	RUN FOR YOUR LOVE		5.00
74	4030	BOBBY BLAND	AIN'T GONNA BE THE FIRST TO CRY	I WOULDN'T TREAT A DOG (THE WAY YOU TR		8.00
74	4030 DJ	BOBBY BLAND	AIN'T GONNA BE THE FIRST TO CRY	I WOULDN'T TREAT A DOG (THE WAY YOU TR		10.00
74	4032	EDDIE HOLMAN	SINCE I DON'T HAVE YOU	I LOVE YOU		4.00
74	4032 DJ	EDDIE HOLMAN	SINCE I DON'T HAVE YOU	I LOVE YOU		5.00
74	4033	LAMONT DOZIER	I WANNA BE WITH YOU	LET ME START TONITE		6.00
74	4033 DJ	LAMONT DOZIER	I WANNA BE WITH YOU	LET ME START TONITE		8.00
74	4036	MIGHTY CLOUDS OF JOY	CLOUDS OF JOY	EVERYTHING IS GOING UP		4.00
74	4036 DJ	MIGHTY CLOUDS OF JOY	CLOUDS OF JOY	EVERYTHING IS GOING UP		5.00
74	4037	CLARENCE CARTER	WARNING	ON YOUR WAY DOWN		4.00
74	4037 DJ	CLARENCE CARTER	WARNING	ON YOUR WAY DOWN		5.00
74	4038	RUFUS	STOP ON BY	RUFUSIZED		6.00
74	4038 DJ	RUFUS	STOP ON BY	RUFUSIZED		8.00
74	4040	CARL CARLTON	SMOKIN' ROOM	SIGNED, SEALED, DELIVERED, I'M		4.00
74	4040 DJ	CARL CARLTON	SMOKIN' ROOM	SIGNED, SEALED, DELIVERED, I'M		5.00
74	4046	PAUL HUMPHREY	COCHISE	WHAT'S THE NOISE P.K.		5.00
74	4046 DJ	PAUL HUMPHREY	COCHISE	WHAT'S THE NOISE P.K.		8.00
74	4046 multi coloured	PAUL HUMPHREY	COCHISE	WHAT'S THE NOISE P.K.		4.00
75	4048	POINTER SISTERS	LIVE YOUR LIFE BEFORE YOU DIE	SHAKEY FLAT BLUES		4.00
75	4048 DJ	POINTER SISTERS	LIVE YOUR LIFE BEFORE YOU DIE	SHAKEY FLAT BLUES		5.00
75	4051	CRUSADERS	STOMP AND BUCK DANCE	BALLAD FOR JOE		4.00
75	4051 DJ	CRUSADERS	STOMP AND BUCK DANCE	BALLAD FOR JOE		5.00
75	4052	DRAMATICS	TRYING TO GET OVER LOSING YOU	HOW DO YOU FEEL		4.00
75	4052 DJ	DRAMATICS	TRYING TO GET OVER LOSING YOU	HOW DO YOU FEEL		6.00
75	4053	GEORGE CLINTON	PLEASE DON'T RUN FROM ME	LIFE AND BREATH		10.00
75	4053 DJ	GEORGE CLINTON	PLEASE DON'T RUN FROM ME	LIFE AND BREATH		15.00
75	4055	RUFUS	ONCE YOU GET STARTED	RIGHT IS RIGHT		4.00
75	4055 PS	RUFUS	ONCE YOU GET STARTED	RIGHT IS RIGHT		5.00
75	4055 DJ	RUFUS	ONCE YOU GET STARTED	RIGHT IS RIGHT		6.00
75	4056	LAMONT DOZIER	ALL CRIED OUT	ROSE		6.00
75	4056 DJ	LAMONT DOZIER	ALL CRIED OUT	ROSE		8.00
75	4057	FOUR TOPS	SEVEN LONELY NIGHTS	I CAN'T HOLD ON MUCH LONGER		4.00
75	4057 DJ	FOUR TOPS	SEVEN LONELY NIGHTS	I CAN'T HOLD ON MUCH LONGER		6.00
75	4060	RON BANKS and the DRAMATICS	I CRIED ALL THE WAY HOME	E & MRS JONES		8.00
75	4060 DJ	RON BANKS and the DRAMATICS	I CRIED ALL THE WAY HOME	E & MRS JONES		10.00
75	4064	POINTER SISTERS	LET IT BE ME	STEAM BOAT		4.00
75	4064 DJ	POINTER SISTERS	LET IT BE ME	STEAM BOAT		5.00
75	4065	MIGHTY CLOUDS OF JOY	STONED WORLD	HEART FULL OF LOVE		4.00
75	4065 DJ	MIGHTY CLOUDS OF JOY	STONED WORLD	HEART FULL OF LOVE		5.00
75	4066	AMAZING RHYTHM ACES	3RD. RATE ROMANCE	MYSTERY TRAIN		3.00
75	4066 DJ	AMAZING RHYTHM ACES	3RD. RATE ROMANCE	MYSTERY TRAIN		4.00
75	4068	RUFUS	PARDON ME	SOMEBODYS WATCHING YOU		4.00
75	4068 DJ	RUFUS	PARDON ME	SOMEBODYS WATCHING YOU		5.00
75	4069	POINTER SISTERS	HOW LONG	EASY DAYS		4.00
75	4069 DJ	POINTER SISTERS	HOW LONG	EASY DAYS		5.00
75	4071	BILLIE DAVIS	THREE STEPS FROM TRUE LOVE	LIGHT A CANDLE		6.00
75	4071 DJ	BILLIE DAVIS	THREE STEPS FROM TRUE LOVE	LIGHT A CANDLE		8.00
75	4074	FRANKIE REDMOND	FIGHTING TO KEEP MY HEAD ABOVE WATER	YESTERDAY I BELIEVE I LIED		8.00
75	4074 DJ	FRANKIE REDMOND	FIGHTING TO KEEP MY HEAD ABOVE WATER	YESTERDAY I BELIEVE I LIED		10.00
75	4076	ISAAC HAYES	CHOCOLATE CHIP	same: instrumental		4.00
75	4076 DJ	ISAAC HAYES	CHOCOLATE CHIP	same: instrumental		5.00
75	4087	FREDA PAYNE	LOST IN LOVE	YOU		4.00
75	4087 DJ	FREDA PAYNE	LOST IN LOVE	YOU		5.00
75	4088	CRUSADERS	CREOLE	I FELT THE LOVE		4.00

75	4088 DJ	CRUSADERS	CREOLE	I FELT THE LOVE	5.00
75	4089	POINTER SISTERS	GOING DOWN SLOW	SLEEPING ALONE	4.00
75	4089 DJ	POINTER SISTERS	GOING DOWN SLOW	SLEEPING ALONE	5.00
75	4090	DRAMATICS	I'M GOING BY THE STARS IN YOUR EYES	ME MYSELF AND I	4.00
75	4090 DJ	DRAMATICS	I'M GOING BY THE STARS IN YOUR EYES	ME MYSELF AND I	5.00
75	4091	RUFUS & CHAKA KHAN	SWEET THING	CIRCLES	4.00
75	4091 DJ	RUFUS & CHAKA KHAN	SWEET THING	CIRCLES	5.00
75	4095	RHYTHM HERITAGE	THEME FROM S.W.A.T.	I WOULDN'T TREAT A DOG	4.00
75	4095 DJ	RHYTHM HERITAGE	THEME FROM S.W.A.T.	I WOULDN'T TREAT A DOG	5.00
76	4100	ISAAC HAYES MOVEMENT	DISCO CONNECTION	ST. THOMAS SQUARE	4.00
76	4100 DJ	ISAAC HAYES MOVEMENT	DISCO CONNECTION	ST. THOMAS SQUARE	6.00
76	4101	DRAMATICS	YOU'RE FOOLING YOU	I'LL MAKE IT SO GOOD	4.00
76	4101 DJ	DRAMATICS	YOU'RE FOOLING YOU	I'LL MAKE IT SO GOOD	5.00
76	4102	MIGTY CLOUDS OF JOY	MIGHTY HIGH	TOUCH MY SOUL	5.00
76	4f02 DJ	MIGTY CLOUDS OF JOY	MIGHTY HIGH	TOUCH MY SOUL	6.00
76	4109	LYDIA PENSE and COLD BLOOD	I GET OFF ON YOU	WE CAME DOWN HERE + COLD BLOOD SMOKING	4.00
76	4109 DJ	LYDIA PENSE and COLD BLOOD	I GET OFF ON YOU	WE CAME DOWN HERE + COLD BLOOD SMOKING	5.00
76	4110	EARL JACKSON	SOUL SELF SATISFACTION	LOOKING THRU THE EYES OF LOVE	15.00
76	4110 DJ	EARL JACKSON	SOUL SELF SATISFACTION	LOOKING THRU THE EYES OF LOVE	20.00
76	4112	MARILYN McCOO & BILLY DAVIS	I HOPE WE GOT TO LOVE IN TIME	THERE'S GOT TO BE AN HAPPY ENDING	4.00
76	4112 DJ	MARILYN McCOO & BILLY DAVIS	I HOPE WE GOT TO LOVE IN TIME	THERE'S GOT TO BE AN HAPPY ENDING	5.00
76	4114	RUFUS and CHAKA KHAN	DANCE WIT ME	EVERYBODY'S GOT AN AURA	4.00
76	4114 DJ	RUFUS and CHAKA KHAN	DANCE WIT ME	EVERYBODY'S GOT AN AURA	5.00
76	4117	RHYTHM HERITAGE	BARRETTA'S THEME	MY CHERIE AMOUR	4.00
76	4117 DJ	RHYTHM HERITAGE	BARRETTA'S THEME	MY CHERIE AMOUR	5.00
76	4118	5th DIMENSION	WILL YOU BE THERE	LOVE HANGOVER	6.00
76	4118 DJ	5th DIMENSION	WILL YOU BE THERE	LOVE HANGOVER	8.00
76	4122	CRUSADERS	KEEP THAT SAME OLD FEELING	TILL THE SUN SHINES	4.00
76	4122 DJ	CRUSADERS	KEEP THAT SAME OLD FEELING	TILL THE SUN SHINES	5.00
76	4127	BOBBYBLAND	IT AIN'T THE REAL THING	WHO'S FOOLING WHO	10.00
76	4127 DJ	BOBBYBLAND	IT AIN'T THE REAL THING	WHO'S FOOLING WHO	15.00
76	4135	RUFUS and CHAKA KHAN	JIVE TALKIN'	ON TIME	3.00
76	4135 DJ	RUFUS and CHAKA KHAN	JIVE TALKIN'	ON TIME	4.00
76	4136	ISAAC HAYES	JUICY FRUIT	JUICY FRUIT part 2	4.00
76	4136 DJ	ISAAC HAYES	JUICY FRUIT	JUICY FRUIT part 2	5.00
76	4141	CRUSADERS	PUT IT WHERE YOU WANT IT	DON'T LET IT GET YOU DOWN	4.00
76	4141 DJ	CRUSADERS	PUT IT WHERE YOU WANT IT	DON'T LET IT GET YOU DOWN	6.00
76	4143	FOUR TOPS	LOOK AT MY BABY	CATFISH	5.00
76	4143 DJ	FOUR TOPS	LOOK AT MY BABY	CATFISH	8.00
76	4148	IMPRESSIONS	YOU'VE BEEN CHEATIN'	AMEN	6.00
76	4148 DJ	IMPRESSIONS	YOU'VE BEEN CHEATIN'	AMEN	10.00
76	4156	RUBY ANDREWS	I GOT A BONE TO PICK WITH YOU	I DON'T KNOW HOW TO LOVE YOU	15.00
76	4156 DJ	RUBY ANDREWS	I GOT A BONE TO PICK WITH YOU	I DON'T KNOW HOW TO LOVE YO	20.00
76	4157	POINTER SISTERS	YOU'VE GOT TO BELIEVE	SHAKEY FLAT BLUES	3.00
76	4157 DJ	POINTER SISTERS	YOU'VE GOT TO BELIEVE	SHAKEY FLAT BLUES	4.00
77	4161	HAROLD MELVIN & the BLUENOTES	REACHING FOR THE WORLD	STAY TOGETHER	4.00
77	4161 DJ	HAROLD MELVIN & the BLUENOTES	REACHING FOR THE WORLD	STAY TOGETHER	6.00
77	4165	RUFUS and CHAKA KHAN	AT MIDNIGHT	BETTER DAYS	3.00
77	4165 DJ	RUFUS and CHAKA KHAN	AT MIDNIGHT	BETTER DAYS	4.00
77	4181	AUSTUST & DENEEN c/w RELECTIONS	WE GO TOGETHER	LIKE ADAM AND EVE	8.00
77	4181 DJ	AUSTUST & DENEEN c/w RELECTIONS	WE GO TOGETHER	LIKE ADAM AND EVE	UN

Stock copies of this Northern Soul back to back classic have a large black A on the label. Promo copies with" not for sale" the existence is unconfirmed also see MCA 4181

77	4186	BOBBYBLAND	THE SOUL OF A MAN	IF I WEREN'T A GAMBLER	4.00
77	4186 DJ	BOBBYBLAND	THE SOUL OF A MAN	IF I WEREN'T A GAMBLER	5.00
77	4192	YOUNGHEARTS	MAKE A LITTLE WISH	NUMBER ONE ATTRACTION	10.00
77	4192 DJ	YOUNGHEARTS	MAKE A LITTLE WISH	NUMBER ONE ATTRACTION	15.00
77	4194	LENNY WILLIAMS	SHOO DOO FU FU OOH!	PROBLEM SOLVER	6.00
77	4194 DJ	LENNY WILLIAMS	SHOO DOO FU FU OOH!	PROBLEM SOLVER	8.00
77	4198	LENNY WILLIAMS	CHOOING YOU	TRUST IN ME	6.00
77	4198 DJ	LENNY WILLIAMS	CHOOSING YOU	TRUST IN ME	8.00
77	4199	FOUR TOPS	FOR YOUR LOVE	YOU'LL NEVER FIND A BETTER MAN	4.00
77	4206	BOBBY HUTTON c/w WILLIE HUTCH	LEND A HAND	LOVE RUNS OUT	30.00
77	4206 DJ	BOBBY HUTTON c/w WILLIE HUTCH	LEND A HAND	LOVE RUNS OUT	UN

Stock copies of this Northern Soul back to back classic have a large black A on the label. Promo copies with" not for sale" the existence is unconfirmed

77	4209 blue vinyl	RUFUS	BLUE LOVE	TAKE TIME (instrumental)	5.00
78	4210	DRAMATICS	SHAKE IT WELL	SPACED OUT OVER YOU	4.00
78	4210 DJ	DRAMATICS	SHAKE IT WELL	SPACED OUT OVER YOU	5.00
78	4220	RICHARD TATE	FILL MY LIFE WITH LOVE	CRAZY BABY	10.00
78	4220 DJ	RICHARD TATE	FILL MY LIFE WITH LOVE	CRAZY BABY	15.00
78	4221 white	SAPPHIRES c/w EDDIE REGAN	GONNA BE A BIG THING	PLAYING HIDE AND SEEK	10.00
78	4221 DJ	SAPPHIRES c/w EDDIE REGAN	GONNA BE A BIG THING	PLAYING HIDE AND SEEK	UN

Stock copies of this Northern Soul back to back classic have a large black A on the label. Promo copies with" not for sale" the existence is unconfirmed

78	4221 yellow & orange	SAPPHIRES c/w EDDIE REGAN	GONNA BE A BIG THING	PLAYING HIDE AND SEEK	8.00
78	4222	GAYLE McCORMICK	RESCUE ME	IT'S A CRYING SHAME	8.00
78	4222 DJ	GAYLE McCORMICK	RESCUE ME	IT'S A CRYING SHAME	10.00
78	4227	STEPHANIE MILLS	MOVIN' IN THE RIGHT DIRECTION	YOU DO IT TO ME	5.00
78	4227 DJ	STEPHANIE MILLS	MOVIN' IN THE RIGHT DIRECTION	YOU DO IT TO ME	6.00
78	4228	LENNY WILLIAMS	YOU GOT ME RUNNING	COME REEP MY LOVE	6.00
78	4228 DJ	LENNY WILLIAMS	YOU GOT ME RUNNING	COME REEP MY LOVE	8.00

| 78 | 4238 | AL HUDSON AND THE SOUL PARTNERS | SPREAD LOVE | | LOVE ME FOREVER | 40.00 |
| 78 | 4238 DJ | AL HUDSON AND THE SOUL PARTNERS | SPREAD LOVE | | LOVE ME FOREVER | 50.00 |

ABSOLUTE
Part of Tout Ensemble

85	lute 1 PS	WILLIAM BELL	HEADLINE NEWS		THAT'S WHAT YOU GET	6.00
86	lute 2 PS	CLARENCE CARTER	MESSING UP MY MIND		I WAS IN THE NEIGHBOURHOOD	40.00
86	lute 3 PS	WILLIAM BELL	PASSION			6.00
96	501	ARIN DEMAIN c/w DONI BURDICK	SILENT TREATMENT		BARI TRACK	10.00

The above is not the same label as the William Bell. This was a limited press, originating in Nottingham, of two in-demand Northern Soul classics.

ACHIEVEMENT

99	10006	ROCQ-E HARRELL	MY HEART KEEPS BEATING FASTER		same: instrumental	6.00
99	10007	CHUCK JACKSON	ALL OVER THE WORLD		ALL OVER THE WORLD '99	5.00
99	10008	ARCHIE BELL & the DRELLS	LOOK BACK OVER YOUR SHOULDER		same: instrumental	10.00
99	10009	WATTS 103rd. STREET STRINGS	SOUL- A- GO- GO		CROSSOVER	5.00
99	10010	RONNIE McNEIR	LUCKY NUMBER		I'M DEDICATING MY LOVE	5.00
99	10011	J.J. BARNES	TALK OF THE GRAPEVINE		ON TOP OF THE WORLD	5.00

ACTION

One of the most important and influential, and certainly most attractive of 60s British labels: first became available, when the UK soul market was at its late 60s peak. Just as clubs like the Brit in Nottingham, Twisted Wheel in Manchester, the Nite Owl in Leicester, Mojo and Esquire in Sheffield and the George at Wilby, Northamptonshire and many other clubs, were opening their doors to droves of newly converted soul fans, mostly driven by the MOD culture which was largely based on American R&B.

B&C records launched the first label totally dedicated to USA release soul music; that label was aptly christened ACTION. Pulling material from various small independent labels from all over the USA: Arctic, Gamble & Swan from Philadelphia, Duke & Peacock from Houston, Sansu from New Orleans, Constellation from Chicago to quote only a few. This highly colourful label, like Sue did 3 or 4 years earlier, put in place a springboard for UK collectors and DJ's to advance from. As the USA soul invasion came thick and fast on the new release sheets, eagerly scanned by ever more enthusiastic collector, Action soon became a must order anything on this label, as the ACT45** prefix always indicated a soul 45. Only Tamla Motown and the previously mentioned Sue label had ever reached this "must buy" status. Unfortunately like Sue and other specialist labels before and after them, they could only justify their single-minded marketing area, if they had an occasional hit. After almost five years, the hits never came and towards the end a few non-soul releases made an appearance before B&C abandoned ship and ceased interest in the Action label and ultimately the soul market.

Today there are still many collectors trying to complete the run of this fabulous series: This label has got to be considered as important in soul collecting circles as Sue. Both labels took a brave purist approach releasing non-commercial 45s, to provide access to the collector for the then obscure recordings of some very small USA artists and labels.

Action did do promo copies, these were ink stamped with a full label sized "A" made up of two lines. These A's were put on by hand with a rubber stamp and an inkpad. So the A's are not usually in line with the label logo or credits, but it matters not, Action promo copies are highly desirable.

68	4500	WILMER & THE DUKES	GIVE ME ONE MORE CHANCE		GET IT	15.00
68	4500 DJ	WILMER & THE DUKES	GIVE ME ONE MORE CHANCE		GET IT	20.00
68	4501	LITTLE CARL CARLTON	COMPETITION AIN'T NOTHING		THREE WAY LOVE AFFAIR	40.00
68	4501 DJ	LITTLE CARL CARLTON	COMPETITION AIN'T NOTHING		THREE WAY LOVE	75.00
68	4502	ERNIE K. DOE	DANCING MAN		LATER FOR YOU	20.00
68	4502 DJ	ERNIE K. DOE	DANCING MAN		LATER FOR YOU	30.00
68	4503	MINNIE EPPERSON	GRAB YOUR CLOTHES (AND GET ON		NO LOVE AT ALL	45.00
68	4503 DJ	MINNIE EPPERSON	GRAB YOUR CLOTHES (AND GET ON		NO LOVE AT ALL	75.00
68	4504	BUDDY ACE	GOT TO GET MYSELF TOGETHER		DARLING DEPAND ON ME	15.00
68	4504 DJ	BUDDY ACE	GOT TO GET MYSELF TOGETHER		DARLING DEPAND ON ME	20.00
68	4505	O.V. WRIGHT	OH BABY MINE		WORKING YOUR GAME	25.00
68	4505 DJ	O.V. WRIGHT	OH BABY MINE		WORKING YOUR GAME	35.00
68	4506	AL TNT BRAGGS	EARTHQUAKE		HOW LONG (DO YOU HOLD ON)	15.00
68	4506 DJ	AL TNT BRAGGS	EARTHQUAKE		HOW LONG (DO YOU HOLD ON)	25.00
68	4507	HARMONICA FATS	TORE UP		I GET SO TIRED	15.00
68	4507 DJ	HARMONICA FATS	TORE UP		I GET SO TIRED'	25.00
68	4508	VERNON GARRETT	SHINE IT ON		THINGS ARE LOOKING BETTER	30.00
68	4508 DJ	VERNON GARRETT	SHINE IT ON		THINGS ARE LOOKING BETTER	45.00
68	4509	BOBBY WILLIAMS	BABY I NEED YOUR LOVE		TRY IT AGAIN	45.00
68	4509 DJ	BOBBY WILLIAMS	BABY I NEED YOUR LOVE		TRY IT AGAIN	70.00
68	4510	BELL BROTHERS	TELL HIM NO		THROW AWAY THE KEY	15.00
68	4510 DJ	BELL BROTHERS	TELL HIM NO		THROW AWAY THE KEY	25.00
68	4511	JOHN ROBERTS	I'LL FORGET YOU		BE MY BABY	20.00
68	4511 DJ	JOHN ROBERTS	I'LL FORGET YOU		BE MY BABY	30.00
68	4512	ERNIE K. DOE.	GOTTA PACK MY BAG		HOW SWEET YOU ARE	20.00
68	4512 DJ	ERNIE K. DOE	GOTTA PACK MY BAG		HOW SWEET YOU ARE	30.00
68	4513	BROTHERS TWO	HERE I AM, IN LOVE AGAIN		I'M TIRED OF YOU BABY	15.00
68	4513 DJ	BROTHERS TWO	HERE I AM, IN LOVE AGAIN		I'M TIRED OF YOU BABY	25.00
68	4514	LITTLE CARL CARLTON	WHY DON'T THEY LEAVE US ALONE		46 DRUMS, I GUITAR	15.00
68	4514 DJ	LITTLE CARL CARLTON	WHY DON'T THEY LEAVE US ALONE		46 DRUMS, I GUITAR	25.00
68	4515	ROOSEVELT GRIER	PEOPLE MAKE THE WORLD		HARD TO FORGET	15.00
68	4515 DJ	ROOSEVELT GRIER	PEOPLE MAKE THE WORLD		HARD TO FORGET	25.00
68	4516	RUBAIYATS	OMAR KHAYYAM		TOMORROW	60.00
68	4516 DJ	RUBAIYATS	OMAR KHAYYAM		TOMORROW	75.00
68	4517	CHUCK TROIS and the WOODSMEN	CALL ON YOU		WOODSMAN	15.00
68	4517 DJ	CHUCK TROIS and the WOODSMEN	CALL ON YOU		WOODSMAN	22.00
68	4518	ROY LEE JOHNSON	BOOGALOO No. 3		SO ANNA JUST LOVE ME	30.00
68	4518 DJ	ROY LEE JOHNSON	BOOGALOO No. 3		SO ANNA JUST LOVE ME	40.00
70	4518 black green	ROY LEE JOHNSON	BOOGALOO No..3		SO ANNA JUST LOVE ME	15.00
70	4518 black green DJ	ROY LEE JOHNSON	BOOGALOO No..3		SO ANNA JUST LOVE ME	20.00
69	4519	EDDIE BUSTER FOREHAND	YOUNG BOY BLUES		YOU WERE MEANT FOR ME	20.00
69	4519 DJ	EDDIE BUSTER FOREHAND	YOUNG BOY BLUES		YOU WERE MEANT FOR ME	25.00

69	4520	ALICE CLARK	YOU GOT A DEAL	SAY YOU'LL NEVER (NEVER LEAVE	20.00
69	4520 DJ	ALICE CLARK	YOU GOT A DEAL	SAY YOU'LL NEVER (NEVER LEAVE	30.00
69	4522	DEE DEE SHARP	WHAT KIND OF LADY	YOU'RE GONNA MISS ME (WHEN I'M	50.00
69	4522 DJ	DEE DEE SHARP	WHAT KIND OF LADY	YOU'RE GONNA MISS ME (WHEN I'M	**153.00**
69	4523	INTRUDERS	SLOW DRAG	SO GLAD I'M YOURS	15.00
69	4523 DJ	INTRUDERS	SLOW DRAG	SO GLAD I'M YOURS	25.00
69	4524	BOBBY BLAND	ROCKIN' THE SAME OLD BOAT	WOULDN'T YOU RATHER HAVE ME	15.00
69	4524 DJ	BOBBY BLAND	ROCKIN' THE SAME OLD BOAT	WOULDN'T YOU RATHER HAVE ME	25.00
69	4525	DELLA HUMPHREY	DON'T MAKE THE GOOD GIRLS GO BAD	YOUR LOVE IS ALL I NEED	20.00
69	4525 DJ	DELLA HUMPHREY	DON'T MAKE THE GOOD GIRLS GO BAD	YOUR LOVE IS ALL I NEED	30.00
69	4526	AL TNT BRAGGS	I'M A GOOD MAN	I LIKE WHAT YOU DO TO ME	15.00
69	4526 DJ	AL TNT BRAGGS	I'M A GOOD MAN	I LIKE WHAT YOU DO TO ME	25.00
69	4527	O.V. WRIGHT	I WANT EVERYONE TO KNOW	I'M GONNA FORGET ABOUT YOU	20.00
69	4527 DJ	O.V. WRIGHT	I WANT EVERYONE TO KNOW	I'M GONNA FORGET ABOUT YOU	30.00
69	4528	LITTLE RICHARD	BABY WHAT DO YOU WANT ME TO DO	same: part 2	20.00
69	4528 DJ	LITTLE RICHARD	BABY WHAT DO YOU WANT ME TO DO	same: part 2	25.00
69	4529	NORMAN JOHNSON	OUR LOVE WILL GROW	YOU'RE EVERYTHING	75.00
69	4529 DJ	NORMAN JOHNSON	OUR LOVE WILL GROW	YOU'RE EVERYTHING	125.00
69	4530	PRIME MATES	HOT TAMALES	HOT TAMALES part 2	20.00
69	4530 DJ	PRIME MATES	HOT TAMALES	HOT TAMALES part 2	30.00
69	4531	MELVIN DAVIS	THIS LOVE WAS MEANT TO BE	SAVE IT (NEVER TOO LATE)	30.00
69	4531 DJ	MELVIN DAVIS	THIS LOVE WAS MEANT TO BE	SAVE IT (NEVER TOO LATE)	45.00
69	4532	Z.Z. HILL	MAKE ME YOURS	WHAT AM I LIVING FOR	75.00
69	4532 DJ	Z.Z. HILL	MAKE ME YOURS	WHAT AM I LIVING FOR	100.00
69	4533	BOBBY MARCHAN	AIN'T NO REASON FOR GIRLS TO BE	same: instrumental	15.00
69	4533 DJ	BOBBY MARCHAN	AIN'T NO REASON FOR GIRLS TO BE	same: instrumental	25.00
69	4534	JEANETTE WILLIAMS	STUFF	YOU GOTTA COME THROUGH	15.00
69	4534 DJ	JEANETTE WILLIAMS	STUFF	YOU GOTTA COME THROUGH	25.00
69	4535	BETTY HARRIS	RIDE YOUR PONY	TROUBLE WITH MY LOVER	25.00
69	4535 DJ	BETTY HARRIS	RIDE YOUR PONY	TROUBLE WITH MY LOVER	35.00
69	4536	EDDIE WILSON	SHING-A-KING STROLL	DON'T KICK THE TEENAGER AROUND	22.00
69	4536 DJ	EDDIE WILSON	SHING-A-KING STROLL	DON'T KICK THE TEENAGER AROUND	35.00
69	4537	CARL CARLTON	BAD FOR EACH OTHER	LOOK AT MARY WONDER	15.00
69	4537 DJ	CARL CARLTON	BAD FOR EACH OTHER	LOOK AT MARY WONDER	25.00
69	4538	BOBBY BLAND	GOTTA GET TO KNOW YOU	BABY I'M ON MY WAY	20.00
69	4538 DJ	BOBBY BLAND	GOTTA GET TO KNOW YOU	BABY I'M ON MY WAY	30.00
69	4539	OLYMPICS	BABY DO THE PHILLY DOG	MINE EXCLUSIVELY	10.00
69	4539 DJ	OLYMPICS	BABY DO THE PHILLY DOG	MINE EXCLUSIVELY	20.00
69	4540	AL GREENE & the SOUL MATES	GET YOURSELF TOGETHER	DON'T HURT ME NO MORE	15.00
69	4540 DJ	AL GREENE & the SOUL MATES	GET YOURSELF TOGETHER	DON'T HURT ME NO MORE	25.00
69	4541	BRENDA & THE TABULATIONS	THAT'S IN THE PAST	I CAN'T GET OVER YOU	30.00
69	4541 DJ	BRENDA & THE TABULATIONS	THAT'S IN THE PAST	I CAN'T GET OVER YOU	50.00
69	4542	BARBARA MASON	HALF A LOVE	SLIPING AWAY	20.00
69	4542 DJ	BARBARA MASON	HALF A LOVE	SLIPING AWAY	30.00
69	4543	FANTASTIC JOHNNY C	IS THERE ANYTHING BETTER THAN MAKIN	NEW LOVE	20.00
69	4543 DJ	FANTASTIC JOHNNY C	IS THERE ANYTHING BETTER THAN MAKIN	NEW LOVE	30.00
69	4544	HIDEAWAYS	HIDE OUT	JOLLY JOE	15.00
69	4544 DJ	HIDEAWAYS	HIDE OUT	JOLLY JOE	20.00
70	4544 black green	HIDEAWAYS	HIDE OUT	JOLLY JOE	10.00
70	4544 black green DJ	HIDEAWAYS	HIDE OUT	JOLLY JOE	15.00
69	4545	NORMAN JOHNSON& the SHOWMEN	TAKE IT BABY	IN PARADISE	40.00
69	4545 DJ	NORMAN JOHNSON& the SHOWMEN	TAKE IT BABY	IN PARADISE	60.00
69	4546	WASH HOPSON SINGERS	HE'S GOT A BLESSING	ROCK IN A WEARY LAND	15.00
69	4546 DJ	WASH HOPSON SINGERS	HE'S GOT A BLESSING	ROCK IN A WEARY LAND	20.00
69	4547	EDDIE HOLMAN	I SURRENDER	I LOVE YOU	**155.00**
69	4547 DJ	EDDIE HOLMAN	I SURRENDER	I LOVE YOU	175.00
69	4548	BOBBY BLAND	HONEY CHILD	SHARE YOUR LOVE WITH ME	20.00
69	4548 DJ	BOBBY BLAND	HONEY CHILD	SHARE YOUR LOVE WITH ME	30.00
69	4549	CLIFFORD CURRY	SHE SHOT A HOLE IN MY SOUL	WE'RE GONNA HATE OURSELVES IN	15.00
69	4549 DJ	CLIFFORD CURRY	SHE SHOT A HOLE IN MY SOUL	WE'RE GONNA HATE OURSELVES IN	25.00

 # 4550 is the first release using the black label with the green logo. Earlier release numbers in this design are 1970 reissues

69	4550	C.CHENIER	FROG LEGS	BLACK GAL	10.00
69	4550 DJ	C.CHENIER	FROG LEGS	BLACK GAL	15.00
69	4551	GENE CHANDLER	I CAN TAKE CARE OF MYSELF	I CAN'T SAVE IT	75.00
69	4551 DJ	GENE CHANDLER	I CAN TAKE CARE OF MYSELF	I CAN'T SAVE IT	150.00
69	4552	PERFORMERS	I CAN'T STOP YOU	L.A.STOMP	20.00
69	4552 DJ	PERFORMERS	I CAN'T STOP YOU	L.A. STOMP	30.00
69	4553	BOBBY BLAND	CHAINS OF LOVE	ASK ME 'BOUT NOTHING BUT THE B	20.00
69	4553 DJ	BOBBY BLAND	CHAINS OF LOVE	ASK ME 'BOUT NOTHING BUT THE B	30.00
69	4554	unissued			
70	4555	EDDIE WILSON	GET OUT ON THE STREET	MUST BE LOVE	20.00
70	4555 DJ	EDDIE WILSON	GET OUT ON THE STREET	MUST BE LOVE	25.00
70	4556	OLYMPICS	THE SAME OLD THING	I'LL DO A LITTLE BIT MORE	25.00
70	4556 DJ	OLYMPICS	THE SAME OLD THING	I'LL DO A LITTLE BIT MORE	45.00
70	4557	JEANETTE WILLIAMS	I CAN FEEL A HEARTBREAK	HOUND DOG	10.00
70	4557 DJ	JEANETTE WILLIAMS	I CAN FEEL A HEARTBREAK	HOUND DOG	20.00
70	4558	unissued			
70	4601	NORMAN JOHNSON& the SHOWMEN	OUR LOVE WILL GROW	YOU'RE EVERYTHING	50.00
70	4601 DJ	NORMAN JOHNSON& the SHOWMEN	OUR LOVE WILL GROW	YOU'RE EVERYTHING	75.00

71	4602	BILLY SHA-RAE	CRYING CLOWN	DO IT	18.00
71	4602 DJ	BILLY SHA-RAE	CRYING CLOWN	DO IT	25.00
70	4603	BOBBETTES	THAT'S A BAD THING TO KNOW	ALL IN YOUR MIND	10.00
70	4603 DJ	BOBBETTES	THAT'S A BAD THING TO KNOW	ALL IN YOUR MIND	15.00
72	4604	BOBBY PATTERSON	I'M IN LOVE WITH YOU	MARRIED LADY	100.00
72	4604 DJ	BOBBY PATTERSON	I'M IN LOVE WITH YOU	MARRIED LADY	150.00
70	4605	HOAGY LANDS	WHY DIDN'T YOU LET ME KNOW	DO YOU KNOW WHAT LIFE IS ALL A	30.00
70	4605 DJ	HOAGY LANDS	WHY DIDN'T YOU LET ME KNOW	DO YOU KNOW WHAT LIFE IS ALL A	45.00
72	4606	KIM FOWLEY	BORN TO MAKE YOU CRY	THUNDER ROAD	10.00
72	4606 DJ	KIM FOWLEY	BORN TO MAKE YOU CRY	THUNDER ROAD	15.00
73	4607	JOE S. MAXEY	SIGN OF THE CRAB	MAY THE BEST MAN WIN	10.00
73	4607 DJ	JOE S. MAXEY	SIGN OF THE CRAB	MAY THE BEST MAN WIN	15.00
73	4608	SINGING PRINCIPAL	WOMAN'S LIB	THANK YOU BABY	75.00
73	4608 DJ	SINGING PRINCIPAL	WOMAN'S LIB	THANK YOU BABY	100.00
73	4609	EDDIE BO	CHECK YOUR BUCKET Part1	CHECK YOUR BUCKET Part2	25.00
73	4609 DJ	EDDIE BO	CHECK YOUR BUCKET Part1	CHECK YOUR BUCKET Part2	30.00
73	4610	GAYTONES	SOUL MAKOSSA	SOUL MAKOSSA part 2	10.00
73	4610 DJ	GAYTONES	SOUL MAKOSSA	SOUL MAKOSSA part 2	15.00
73	4611	JAMAICA BAND	STICKY FINGERS	STICKY FINGERS part 2	8.00
73	4612	BUSTER PEARSON BAND	PRETTY WOMAN	BIG FUNK	15.00
73	4612 DJ	BUSTER PEARSON BAND	PRETTY WOMAN	BIG FUNK	20.00
73	4613	WILBERT HARRISON	GET IT WHILE YOU CAN	same:	10.00
73	4613 DJ	WILBERT HARRISON	GET IT WHILE YOU CAN	same:	8.00
73	4614	5 MILES OUT	SUPER SWEET GIRL OF MINE	SET YOUR MIND FREE	20.00
73	4614 DJ	5 MILES OUT	SUPER SWEET GIRL OF MINE	SET YOUR MIND FREE	25.00
73	4615	STANLEY	I'LL GO DOWN AND GETCHA	same: t. 2	10.00
73	4615 DJ	STANLEY	I'LL GO DOWN AND GETCHA	same: t. 2	12.00
73	4616	BACKYARD HEAVIES	JUST KEEP ON TRUCKING	NEVER CAN SAY GOODBYE	8.00
73	4617	MILL EDWARDS	I FOUND MYSELF	DON'T FORGET ABOUT ME	20.00
73	4617 DJ	MILL EDWARDS	I FOUND MYSELF	DON'T FORGET ABOUT ME	25.00
73	4618	ESQUIRES	MY SWEET BABY	HENRY RALPH	45.00
73	4618 DJ	ESQUIRES	MY SWEET BABY	same:	75.00
73	4619	AARON McNEIL	SOUL OF A BLACK MAN	REAP WHAT YOU SOW	10.00
73	4619 DJ	AARON McNEIL	SOUL OF A BLACK MAN	REAP WHAT YOU SOW	15.00
73	4620	CHUCK ARMSTRONG	GOD BLESS THE CHILDREN	BLACK FOXY WOMAN	10.00
73	4620 DJ	CHUCK ARMSTRONG	GOD BLESS THE CHILDREN	BLACK FOXY WOMAN	15.00
73	4621	TOM GREEN	ROCK SPRINS RAILROAD STATION	ENDLESS CONFUSION	100.00
73	4621 DJ	TOM GREEN	ROCK SPRINS RAILROAD STATION	ENDLESS CONFUSION	150.00
73	4622	BOBBIE HOUSTON	I WANT TO MAKE IT WITH YOU	same: instrumental	10.00
73	4622 DJ	BOBBIE HOUSTON	I WANT TO MAKE IT WITH YOU	same: instrumental	15.00
74	4623	CHOSEN FEW	FUNKY BUTTER	WONDERING	20.00
74	4623 DJ	CHOSEN FEW	FUNKY BUTTER	WONDERING	30.00
74	4624	WEE WILLIE & the WINNERS	GET SOME	A PLAN FOR THE MAN	10.00
74	4624 DJ	WEE WILLIE & the WINNERS	GET SOME	A PLAN FOR THE MAN	15.00

ACTION

If I Quote the reverse of the EP cover review, you'll experience another piece in the jigsaw of the developing rare soul scene in UK. This special 1967 Sheffield University Rag week EP release was exclusively sold by Sheffield University students in and around Sheffield, to raise money for charity.

67	ACT 002 EP PS	VARIOUS ARTISTS	RAG GOES MAD AT THE MOJO	5 track EP with picture cover	100.00

Exact sleeve notes from the reverse of the picture sleeve.:

Nick Walsh recordings: Every One Was There. The place: The Mojo Club Sheffield. The date June 29th 1967. The occasion. The live recording of Rag record '67. The result, eighteen whole minutes of action-packed music played in an electric atmosphere, and featuring a line-up of no less than four top groups from the area. Mr. Pete Stringfellow, the boys to the stomping, cheering, hand-clapping audience; how much sweat was lost during this fanastic recording is a matter for conjecture. What is certain is that to relive the experience requires only the playing of this disc.

It's all here as it happened.

The scene is set in motion by the Tangerine Ayr Band with an interpretation of that great Herbie Goins number "The Incredible Miss Brown" Pete Manton combining his powerful vocal with the groups clever backing. Next on stage are those well-known favourites at the Mojo. The Pityful Souls with a meaty rendition of William Bell's, "Never Like this Before". With the audience still in full cry, up jumps the human dynamo Delroy, along with his Good Good Band, to put everything he's got into that chart-topping number, "Sweet Soul Music", a sound that really gets the fans moving.

Side Two bring you Sheffield's veritable King Of Soul, Mr. Joe Cocker and his Blues Band. Joe, complete with flower-power shirt and some excellent drums and guitar backing sings the, Impressions number, "I've Been Trying" as it should always be sung. To round off the evening, he breaks into that great Rock and Soul number "Saved". Just listen to the audience reaction to this one, but hey! – what about some of those words Joe !

That's Rag live at The Mojo. Play It. And You Live it.

Side 1.

Incredible Miss Brown – The Tangerine Ayr Band
Never Like This Before – The Pityful Souls
Sweet Soul Music – The Delroy Good Good Band

Side Two.

I've Been Trying – Joe Cocker Blues Band
Saved - Joe Cocker Blues Band

ADVANCE

82	102	EDDIE HOLLAND & the CHECKMATES	LONELY LOVER	blank:	5.00

This UK pressed bootleg taken from a cassette tape is actually Marvin Gaye – Lonely Lover @ 48rpm.

82	1	MONITORS	SUSPICION	blank:	6.00

This UK pressed bootleg taken from a cassette tape and wrongly credited to the The Monitors. The real artist credit should have been "The Originals".

AGR

86	5	RARE MOODS	I'VE GOT LOVE	CLOSER TO YOUR BHEART	15.00

AIRBORNE

67	11		JOYCE BOND	MRS. SOUL	IT'S ALRIGHT	40.00

AIRWAVE

84	7		MEL CARTER	LOVE TEST	LOVERS FIR THE NIGHT	10.00

ALADDIN

Distributed by Island Records this obscure UK label was a overlooked vehicle for Jamaican artists to release soul in the UK. Missing numbers as far as I know are not soul 45's, but every 45 on the label seems to be difficult to find. There are some fine cover versions of USA soul classics, with the best perhaps being Dinah Lee's version of Barbara Lynn's classic Atlantic recording and also her rendition of Shirley Ellis's "Nitty Gritty" all add to the labels credibility. Owen Gray does a furious and creditable version of a Marvin Gaye 1963 hit. Whilst Prince and Princess is the only recording that had a release in the USA on Bell # 625. Jackie Edwards release on #601 is considered to be a fine ballad.

65	601	JACKIE EDWARDS	HE'LL HAVE TO GO	GOTTA LEARN TO LOVE AGAIN	75.00
65	603	OWEN GRAY	GONNA WORK OUT FINE	DOLLY BABY	15.00
65	605	JACKIE EDWARDS	HUSH	I AM IN LOVE WITH YOU NO MORE	15.00
65	606	DINAH LEE	THE NITTY GRITTY	I'LL FORGIVE YOU, THEN FORGET	20.00
65	607	OWEN GRAY	CAN I GET A WITNESS	LINDA LU	15.00
65	608	DINAH LEE	PUSHIN' A GOOD THINN TOO FAR	I CAN'T BELIEVE WHAT YOU SAY	30.00
65	609	PRINCE & PRINCESS	READY STEADY GO	TAKE ME SERIOUS	50.00
65	611	JACKIE EDWARDS	THE SAME ONE	I DON'T KNOW	15.00

ALASKA

A Pye distributed label that caught the attention of soul collectors when for some unexplained reason, at the very height of Northern Soul when both Wigan Casino and Cleethorpes Pier were in full swing John Schroeder did an instrumental version of The Velours MGM classic "I'm Gonna Change". An artist already appreciated for his instrumentals on Pye, including a very creditable version of Edwin Starr's Detroit hit "Agent Double O soul". Mr. Schroeder obviously saw some mileage in trying to cash in on the booming all-niter scene, as he later issued an instrumental entitled "All night." Both instrumentals got a cold reception from a Northern Soul following who refused to be manipulated by "tailor Made" Northern Soul music.

This seemed to alert the rare soul pioneers to the label. Cleethorpes DJ Rick Scott, an enthusiastic seeker of previously undiscovered UK releases found several more 45's on the label, which had Northern Soul potential. Velvet Love, Joanne Williams, Bookham & Riskett all had a little exposure at Cleethorpes Pier and Winter Gardens but never took off to become in-demand titles. Other highlights included three releases from the collectable Funk band Cymande and one from sweet soul band The Escorts. But don't think Alaska was a soul driven label, it released all manner of material by many unheard of obscure artists of the era. Even releasing a 45 by Ronnie Barker!

73	4	CYMANDE	THE MESSAGE	ZION I	10.00
73	4 DJ	CYMANDE	THE MESSAGE	ZION I	15.00
73	10	CYMANDE	BRA	RAS TAFARIAN FOLK SONG	10.00
73	10 DJ	CYMANDE	BRA	RAS TAFARIAN FOLK SONG	15.00
75	20	MEL NIXON	PUT IT IN YOUR PIPE AND SMOKE IT	SOUL SLEEPER	4.00
75	20 DJ	MEL NIXON	PUT IT IN YOUR PIPE AND SMOKE IT	SOUL SLEEPER	5.00
75	26	MEL NIXON	EVERY BEAT OF YOUR HEART	SOUL SLEEPER	5.00
75	26 DJ	MEL NIXON	EVERY BEAT OF YOUR HEART	SOUL SLEEPER	6.00
75	1001	JOHN SCHROEDER ORCHESTRA	I'M GONNA CHANGE	FIRST LOVE	5.00
75	1001 DJ	JOHN SCHROEDER ORCHESTRA	I'M GONNA CHANGE	FIRST LOVE	6.00
75	1002	MAIN ATTRACTION	CAST YOUR FATE TO THE WIND	CITY GIRL	4.00
75	1002 DJ	MAIN ATTRACTION	CAST YOUR FATE TO THE WIND	CITY GIRL	5.00
75	1005	INTIMATE STRANGERS	LOVE SOUNDS	THE TRACK	4.00
75	1005 DJ	INTIMATE STRANGERS	LOVE SOUNDS	THE TRACK	5.00
75	1010	VELVET LOVE	SYMPHONY OF DREAMS	RIDING HIGH	6.00
75	1010 DJ	VELVET LOVE	SYMPHONY OF DREAMS	RIDING HIGH	8.00
75	1011	JOHN SCHROEDER ORCHESTRA	ALL NIGHT	same: instrumental	4.00
75	1011 DJ	JOHN SCHROEDER ORCHESTRA	ALL NIGHT	same: instrumental	5.00
75	1012	JOANNE WILLIAMS	JACK OF ALL TRADES	CAN'T WE GET BACK	6.00
75	1012 DJ	JOANNE WILLIAMS	JACK OF ALL TRADES	CAN'T WE GET BACK	8.00
75	1013	CLIFF BENNETT	GOT TO GET YOU INTO MY LIFE	WORKING MY WAY INTO YOUR HEART	5.00
75	1013 DJ	CLIFF BENNETT	GOT TO GET YOU INTO MY LIFE	WORKING MY WAY INTO YOUR HEART	6.00
76	1014	ESCORTS	DISRESPECT CAN WRECK	BAM-A-LAM-A BOOGIE	6.00
76	1014 DJ	ESCORTS	DISRESPECT CAN WRECK	BAM-A-LAM-A BOOGIE	8.00
76	1015	BOOKHAM & RISKETT	WE GOT A LOVE	BAM LAM A BOOGIE	8.00
76	1015 DJ	BOOKHAM & RISKETT	WE GOT A LOVE	BAM LAM A BOOGIE	10.00
76	1021	CYMANDE	FRIENDS	ONE MORE	8.00
76	1021 DJ	CYMANDE	FRIENDS	ONE MORE	10.00

ALL 4 U

98	1 DJ		RONNIE McNEIR c/w CHUCK JACKSON	LUCKY NUMBER	ALL OVER THE WORLD	8.00

white label test press with handwritten credits

ALL PLATINUM

75	6146301	SHIRLEY & COMPANY	SHAME, SHAME, SHAME	MORE SHAME	4.00
75	6146302	MOMENTS & WHATNAUTS	GIRLS	MORE GIRLS	4.00
75	6146303	RIMSHOTS	SOUL WALKING	WHO'S GOT THE MONSTER	8.00
75	6146304	RIMSHOTS	7-6-5-4-3-2-1 (BLOW YOUR WHISTLE	HARVEY WALL BANGER	5.00
75	6146305	RETTA YOUNG	(SENDING OUT AN) S.O.S.	MORE S.O.S.	4.00
75	6146306	MOMENTS	DOLLY MY LOVE	MORE DOLLY	4.00
75	6146307	unissued ?			
75	6146308	CALENDER	HYPERTENSION	HYPERTENSION PART2	5.00
75	6146309	MOMENTS	LOOK AT ME (I'M IN LOVE)	LOOK AT ME I'M IN LOVE (French	5.00
75	6146310	CHUCK JACKSON	I'VE GOT THE NEED	BEAUTIFUL WOMAN	10.00
75	6146311	BROOK BENTON	MR. BARTENDER	TAXI	4.00
75	6146312	unissued ?			
76	6146313	MOMENTS	NINE TIMES	WHEN THE MORNING COMES	5.00

76	6146314	RIMSHOTS	DO WHAT YOU FEEL	DO WHAT YOU FEEL PART2	5.00
75	6146315	BROOK BENTON	MY FUNNY VALENTINE	YOU WERE GONE	4.00
76	6146316	RIMSHOTS	SUPER DISCO	GROOVE BUS	6.00
76	6146317	SYLVIA	L.A. SUNSHINE	TAXI	4.00
76	6146318	MOMENTS	JACK IN THE BOX	LOVE ON A TWO WAY STREET	5.00
76	6146319	SYLVIA and CHUCK JACKSON	WE CAN'T HIDE IT ANYMORE	MR. BARTENDER	4.00
77	6146320	BALTIMORE FIRST CLASS	ME & MY GEMINI	THIS IS IT	15.00
77	6146321	DONNIE ELBERT	WILL YOU STILL LOVE ME TOMORROW	WHAT DO YOU DO	6.00
77	6146322	MOMENTS	IT DON'T RAIN IN MY BACK YARD	NEXT TIME I SEE YOU	15.00
77	6146323	unissued ?			
77	6146323	unissued ?			
77	6146325	MOMENTS	OH I COULD HAVE LOVED YOU	I DON'T WANNA GO	5.00
77	6146326	MOTHER FREEDOM BAND	BEAUTIFUL SUMMER DAY	FLICK OF THE WRIST	40.00

ALLEGIANCE

84	1	MARY WELLS	MY GUY	?	UN
84	2	J. BLACKFOOT	TAXI	WHERE IS LOVE	5.00
84	3	SPENCER DAVIS & DUSTY SPRINGFIELD	PRIVATE NUMBER	DON'T YOU WANT ME NO MORE	4.00
84	4	ANNE LESEAR	TAKE HIM BACK	TAKE HIM BACK version	4.00
84	5	MARY WELLS	YOU BEAT ME TO THE PUNCH	?	UN
84	6	J. BLACKFOOT	WHAT YOU DID TO ME LAST NIGHT	I STOOD ON THE SIDEWALK	5.00
84	7	RODNEY SAULSBERRY	I WONDER	HER SONG	5.00

ALP

66	595004	POOR SOULS	PLEASE DON'T CHANGE YOUR MIND	LOVE ME	50.00

ANCHOR

76	1033	CADO BELLE	GOT TO LOVE	PAPER IN THE RAIN	75.00
76	1033 DJ	CADO BELLE	GOT TO LOVE	PAPER IN THE RAIN	100.00
76	1050	CHRISTINE KIDD	LOVIN' YOU IS LIKE LOVIN' THE WIND	I'M YOURS	4.00
76	1050 DJ	CHRISTINE KIDD	LOVIN' YOU IS LIKE LOVIN' THE WIND	I'M YOURS	5.00
76	1061	DONNA Mc GEE	DO AS I DO	MR. BLINDMAN	8.00
76	1061 DJ	DONNA Mc GEE	DO AS I DO	MR. BLINDMAN	10.00

ANTIC

75	11518	JOY FLEMING	BRIDGE OF LOVE	DIVORCEE	10.00
75	11518 DJ	JOY FLEMING	BRIDGE OF LOVE	DIVORCEE	15.00

APPLE

I could right pages and pages about the Beatles owned EMI distributed Apple label. But this is a soul reference book, and most of the information on Apple will be of no interest to the soul collector. The two black artists on the label did very desirable recordings for other labels before being signed to Apple. The Beatles always had an appreciation of USA soul music, after all Mary Wells was their favorite girl artist. The 45s listed here are perhaps more sought after by rock collectors, than soul scholars, all recording are soft rock performed by soulful artists.

69	12	BILLY PRESTON	THAT'S THE WAY GOOD PLANNED	WHAT ABOUT YOU	8.00
69	12 DJ	BILLY PRESTON	THAT'S THE WAY GOOD PLANNED	WHAT ABOUT YOU	12.00
69	12 PS	BILLY PRESTON	THAT'S THE WAY GOOD PLANNED	WHAT ABOUT YOU	8.00
69	19	BILLY PRESTON	EVERYTHING'S ALRIGHT	I WANT TO THANK YOU	8.00
69	19 DJ	BILLY PRESTON	EVERYTHING'S ALRIGHT	I WANT TO THANK YOU	12.00
70	21	BILLY PRESTON	ALL THAT I'VE GOT (I'M GONNA GIVE)	AS I GET OLDER	5.00
70	21 DJ	BILLY PRESTON	ALL THAT I'VE GOT (I'M GONNA GIVE)	AS I GET OLDER	12.00
70	21 PS	BILLY PRESTON	ALL THAT I'VE GOT (I'M GONNA GIVE)	AS I GET OLDER	20.00
70	24	DORIS TROY	AIN'T THAT CUTE	VAYA CON DIOS	6.00
70	24 DJ	DORIS TROY	AIN'T THAT CUTE	VAYA CON DIOS	15.00
70	24 PS	DORIS TROY	AIN'T THAT CUTE	VAYA CON DIOS	15.00
70	28	DORIS TROY	JACOB'S LADDER	GET BACK	8.00
70	28 DJ	DORIS TROY	JACOB'S LADDER	GET BACK	12.00

AQUARIUS

76	4	JACKY JAMES	MOVING LIKE A SUPERSTAR	I NEED YOUR LOVE	5.00

ARDENT

89	9001	SIR TED FORD	DISCO MUSIC	I'VE GOT A GOAL	5.00
89	9002	G.C.CAMERON	WAIT UNTIL TOMORROW	SHADOWS	15.00
89	9003	MILLIONAIRES	THIS IS LOVE	DON'T MESS WITH MY LOVE	15.00
90	9004	JOHNNY HUDSON	BETTER LOVE	same: instrumental	15.00
90	9005	WILLIE JOHN ELLISON	I JUST ANT YOUR BODY	same: instrumental	5.00
90	9006	RONNIE DYSON	SEE THE CLOWN	SHINE (COME TOWARDS THE LIGHT)	15.00

ARIOLA

78	105	LOVE COMMITTEE	CAN'T WIN FOR LOSING	LOVE WINS EVERYTIME	10.00
78	105 DJ	LOVE COMMITTEE	CAN'T WIN FOR LOSING	LOVE WINS EVERYTIME	15.00
78	109	M.J. WILLIAMS	I FOUND LOVE DANCING ON THE DISCO FLOOR	LIFE	5.00
78	109 DJ	M.J. WILLIAMS	I FOUND LOVE DANCING ON THE DISCO FLOOR	LIFE	6.00

The above artist is Moon Williams, go to DJM section to see more of his titles.

78	113	CARL GRAVES	SAD GIRL	WALK WITH LOVE	4.00
78	113 DJ	CARL GRAVES	SAD GIRL	WALK WITH LOVE	6.00
78	501	COCO	SAVE ME	MONEY SONG	10.00
78	514	MIDNIGHT	KEEP ON WALKING BY	DON'T BOTHER TO KNOCK	60.00
78	514 DJ	MIDNIGHT	KEEP ON WALKING BY	DON'T BOTHER TO KNOCK	75.00

78	514 PS	MIDNIGHT	KEEP ON WALKING BY	DON'T BOTHER TO KNOCK	75.00
78	514 DJ PS	MIDNIGHT	KEEP ON WALKING BY	DON'T BOTHER TO KNOCK	100.00
79	546	VIOLA WILLS	GONNA GET ALONG WITHOUT YOU	YOUR LOVE	4.00
79	546 DJ	VIOLA WILLS	GONNA GET ALONG WITHOUT YOU	YOUR LOVE	5.00
80	557	VIOLA WILLS	SOMEBODY'S EYES	IF I COULD READ YOUR MIND	6.00
801	557 DJ	VIOLA WILLS	SOMEBODY'S EYES	IF I COULD READ YOUR MIND	8.00
80	567	JOHNNY BRISTOL	LOVE NO LONGER HAS A HOLD ON ME	TILL I SEE YOU AGAIN	15.00
80	567 DJ	JOHNNY BRISTOL	LOVE NO LONGER HAS A HOLD ON ME	TILL I SEE YOU AGAIN	25.00

ARISTA

75	6	TAMIKO JONES	TOUCH ME BABY	CREEPIN' ON MY DREAMS	5.00
75	6 DJ	TAMIKO JONES	TOUCH ME BABY	CREEPIN' ON MY DREAMS	6.00
75	14	BRECKER BROTHERS	SNEEKIN' UP BEHIND YOU	SPONGE	5.00
75	14 DJ	BRECKER BROTHERS	SNEEKIN' UP BEHIND YOU	SPONGE	6.00
75	17	LINDA LEWIS	IT'S IN HIS KISS	WALK ABOUT	4.00
75	17 PS	LINDA LEWIS	IT'S IN HIS KISS	WALK ABOUT	5.00
75	17 DJ	LINDA LEWIS	IT'S IN HIS KISS	WALK ABOUT	6.00
87	17 dup #	BOBBY WOMACK	HOW COULD YOU BREAK MY HEART	GIVE IT UP + THE ROOTS IN ME	15.00
87	17 PS	BOBBY WOMACK	HOW COULD YOU BREAK MY HEART	GIVE IT UP + THE ROOTS IN ME	20.00
87	17 DJ	BOBBY WOMACK	HOW COULD YOU BREAK MY HEART	GIVE IT UP + THE ROOTS IN ME	20.00
75	23	GIL SCOTT-HERON	JOHANNESBURG	FELL TOGETHER	5.00
75	23 DJ	GIL SCOTT-HERON	JOHANNESBURG	FELL TOGETHER	6.00
76	35	DE BLANC	OH NO NOT MY BABY	GUAVA JELLY	6.00
76	35 DJ	DE BLANC	OH NO NOT MY BABY	GUAVA JELLY	8.00
76	36	MARTHA REEVES	NOW THAT WE FOUND LOVE	HIGHER AND HIGHER	6.00
76	36 DJ	MARTHA REEVES	NOW THAT WE FOUND LOVE	HIGHER AND HIGHER	8.00
76	45	GENERAL JOHNSON	READY, WILLING AND ABLE	ALL IN THE FAMILY	6.00
76	45 DJ	GENERAL JOHNSON	READY, WILLING AND ABLE	ALL IN THE FAMILY	8.00
76	50	DEBBIE TAYLOR	JUST DON'T PAY	I DON'T WANT TO LEAVE YOU	25.00
76	50 DJ	DEBBIE TAYLOR	JUST DON'T PAY	I DON'T WANT TO LEAVE YOU	30.00
76	51	JEFF PERRY	LOVE DON'T COME NO STRONGER (THAN	I'VE GOT TO SEE YOU RIGHT AWAY	15.00
76	51 DJ	JEFF PERRY	LOVE DON'T COME NO STRONGER (THAN	I'VE GOT TO SEE YOU RIGHT AWAY	30.00
76	72	BO-BELLES	GIRL, DON'T MAKE ME WAIT	WOE IS ME	6.00
76	72 DJ	BO-BELLES	GIRL, DON'T MAKE ME WAIT	WOE IS ME	8.00
76	78	DRIFTERS	YOU'RE MORE THAN A NUMBER IN MY LITTLE RED BOOK	DO YOU HAVE TO GO NOW	3.00
76	78 DJ	DRIFTERS	YOU'RE MORE THAN A NUMBER IN MY LITTLE RED BOOK	DO YOU HAVE TO GO NOW	5.00
76	83	SLIK	THIS SIDE UP	DON'T TAKE YOUR LOVE AWAY	4.00
76	83 DJ	SLIK	THIS SIDE UP	DON'T TAKE YOUR LOVE AWAY	6.00
76	94	DRIFTERS	I'LL KNOW WHEN TRUE LOVE REALLY	A GOOD SONG NEVER DIES	30.00
76	94 DJ	DRIFTERS	I'LL KNOW WHEN TRUE LOVE REALLY	A GOOD SONG NEVER DIES	50.00
76	95	MIKE & BILL	THINGS WON'T BE THIS BAD ALWAY	same: instrumental	4.00
76	95 DJ	MIKE & BILL	THINGS WON'T BE THIS BAD ALWAY	same: instrumental	6.00
77	102	SHIRLEY BROWN	BLESSED IS THE WOMAN (WITH A MAN	LOWDOWN, DIRTY, GOOD LOVER	5.00
77	102 DJ	SHIRLEY BROWN	BLESSED IS THE WOMAN (WITH A MAN	LOWDOWN, DIRTY, GOOD LOVER	6.00
77	109	GARNETT MIMMS & TRUCKIN'	WHAT IT IS	WHAT IT IS (PART 2)	6.00
77	109 DJ	GARNETT MIMMS & TRUCKIN'	WHAT IT IS	WHAT IT IS (PART 2)	8.00
77	124	DRIFTERS	IT LOOKS LIKE I'M THE CLOWN AGAIN	I CAN'T BELIEVE IT'S OVER	20.00
77	124 DJ	DRIFTERS	IT LOOKS LIKE I'M THE CLOWN AGAIN	I CAN'T BELIEVE IT'S OVER	25.00
77	125	LINDA LEWIS	NEVER BEEN DONE BEFORE	COME BACK & FINISH WHAT YOU STARTED	10.00
77	151	VIOLA WILLS	LET'S LOVE NOW	LET'S LOVE NOW disco version	4.00
77	151 DJ	VIOLA WILLS	LET'S LOVE NOW	LET'S LOVE NOW disco version	5.00
78	164	MANDRILL	FUNKY MONKEY	CAN YOU GET IT	4.00
78	164 DJ	MANDRILL	FUNKY MONKEY	CAN YOU GET IT	5.00
78	169	GIL SCOTT-HERON	THE BOTTLE (live)	HELLO SUNDAY, HELLO ROAD	6.00
78	169 DJ	GIL SCOTT-HERON	THE BOTTLE (live)	HELLO SUNDAY, HELLO ROAD	6.00
78	178	HELEN SHAPIRO	EVERY LITTLE BIT HURTS	TOUCHIN' WOOD	8.00
78	178 DJ	HELEN SHAPIRO	EVERY LITTLE BIT HURTS	TOUCHIN' WOOD	10.00
78	183 PS	RAYDIO	HONEY I'M RICH	SPELL IT	4.00
78	202	DRIFTERS	CLOSELY GUARDED SECRET	I CAN'T BELIEVE IT'S OVER	15.00
78	202 DJ	DRIFTERS	CLOSELY GUARDED SECRET	I CAN'T BELIEVE IT'S OVER	25.00
78	231	MANDRILL	WHEN YOU SMILE	HOLIDAY	5.00
78	231 DJ	MANDRILL	WHEN YOU SMILE	HOLIDAY	6.00
78	237	GENERAL JOHNSON	CAN'T NOBODY LOVE ME LIKE YOU	LIES	6.00
78	237 DJ	GENERAL JOHNSON	CAN'T NOBODY LOVE ME LIKE YOU	LIES	8.00
79	263	GQ	MAKE MY DREAMS A REALITY	THIS HAPPY FEELING	8.00
79	263 DJ	GQ	MAKE MY DREAMS A REALITY	THIS HAPPY FEELING	10.00
79	284	BOBBY WOMACK	HOW COULD YOU BREAK MY HEART	I HONESTLY LOVE YOU	20.00
79	284 DJ	BOBBY WOMACK	HOW COULD YOU BREAK MY HEART	I HONESTLY LOVE YOU	25.00
79	303 PS	GQ	I DO LOVE YOU	SPIRIT	4.00
79	303 DJ	GQ	I DO LOVE YOU	SPIRIT	4.00
80	323	PHYLLIS HYMAN	YOU KNOW HOW TO LOVE ME	GIVE A LITTLE LOVE	10.00
80	323 DJ	PHYLLIS HYMAN	YOU KNOW HOW TO LOVE ME	GIVE A LITTLE LOVE	15.00
80	328	GQ	STANDING OVATION	REASONS FOR THE SEASONS	4.00
80	328 DJ	GQ	STANDING OVATION	REASONS FOR THE SEASONS	5.00
80	343	PHYLLIS HYMAN	UNDER YOUR SPELL	KISS YOU ALL OVER	10.00
80	343 DJ	PHYLLIS HYMAN	UNDER YOUR SPELL	KISS YOU ALL OVER	15.00
80	363	NORMAN CONNORS	TAKE IT TO THE LIMIT	BLACK COW	6.00
80	363 DJ	NORMAN CONNORS	TAKE IT TO THE LIMIT	BLACK COW	8.00
80	364	LOCKSMITH	UNLOCK THE FUNK	CHINESE FUNK SONG	5.00

80	364 DJ	LOCKSMITH	UNLOCK THE FUNK	CHINESE FUNK SONG	6.00
80	377	ARETHA FRANKLIN	WHAT A FOOL BELIEVES	SCHOOL DAYS	4.00
81	424 PS	PHYLLIS HYMAN	YOU SURE LOOK GOOD TO ME	THE SUNSHINE IN MY LIFE	6.00
81	424	PHYLLIS HYMAN	YOU SURE LOOK GOOD TO ME	THE SUNSHINE IN MY LIFE	5.00
86	669	PHYLLIS HYMAN	YOU KNOW HOW TO LOVE ME	WE SHOULD BE LOVERS	6.00
86	669 PS	PHYLLIS HYMAN	YOU KNOW HOW TO LOVE ME	WE SHOULD BE LOVERS	8.00
86	678	ARETHA FRANKLIN	INTREGRITY	JUMPIN' JACK FLASH	25.00
86	678 DJ	ARETHA FRANKLIN	INTREGRITY	JUMPIN' JACK FLASH	40.00
86	678 PS	ARETHA FRANKLIN	INTREGRITY	JUMPIN' JACK FLASH	30.00
75	1436	AL WILSON	THE SNAKE	WILLOUGHBY BROOK	6.00
75	1436 DJ	AL WILSON	THE SNAKE	WILLOUGHBY BROOK	8.00
86	22678	ARETHA FRANKLIN	INTEGRITY	2 x 45 double pack with cover	40.00
84	JK1PS	JERMAINE JACKSON	SWEETEST, SWEETEST	COME TO ME (ONE WAY OR ANOTHER	4.00

ASYLUM

75	550	LINDA RONSTADT	HEATWAVE	LOVE IS A ROSE	4.00
76	13062	CATE BROS.	WHERE CAN WE GO	START ALL OVER AGAIN	30.00
76	13062 DJ	CATE BROS.	WHERE CAN WE GO	START ALL OVER AGAIN	40.00

ATCO

Atco was part of Atlantic records, distributed in the UK by Polydor. The company had a policy in the late 60's early seventies of dinking out the small hole middles to reveal a large jukebox friendly hole. The majority of the releases had the larger style center hole. But as with all the Polydor distributed labels of the time some 45's escaped this process, the small hole releases are infinity more desirable. I have quoted values for both. A little quirk in the numbering system starting at the 209 series uses ATLANTIC numbering but was pressed with an ATCO label. Some price guides actually quote the label release as Atlantic; this is because Music Master listing actually refers to Atlantic as the release label. See the UK Atlantic listing which will reveal which 45's used Atlantic numbers but had an ATCO label. Only the last two 45 releases on the label were issued as promo copies, these were to promote forthcoming CD releases.

69	226001 lh	OTIS REDDING	LOVE MAN	THAT'S HOW STRONG MY LOVE IS	15.00
69	226001 sh	OTIS REDDING	LOVE MAN	THAT'S HOW STRONG MY LOVE IS	20.00
69	226002 lh	OTIS REDDING	(YOUR LOVE HAS LIFTED ME) HIGHER & HIGHER	FREE ME	6.00
69	226002 sh	OTIS REDDING	(YOUR LOVE HAS LIFTED ME) HIGHER & HIGHER	FREE ME	8.00
69	226004 lh	ARTHUR CONLEY	STAR REVIEW	LOVE SURE IS A POWERFUL THING	5.00
69	226004 sh	ARTHUR CONLEY	STAR REVIEW	LOVE SURE IS A POWERFUL THING	7.00
69	226005 lh	DELIGHTS ORCHESTRA	KING OF THE HORSE	DO THE THING	8.00
69	226005 sh	DELIGHTS ORCHESTRA	KING OF THE HORSE	DO THE THING	10.00
69	226007 lh	R.B.GREAVES	TAKE A LETTER MARIA	BIG BAD CITY	5.00
69	226007 sh	R.B.GREAVES	TAKE A LETTER MARIA	BIG BAD CITY	6.00
70	226009 lh	JOHNNY JENKINS	THE VOODOO IN YOU	BACKSIDE BLUES	5.00
70	226009 sh	JOHNNY JENKINS	THE VOODOO IN YOU	BACKSIDE BLUES	6.00
70	226010 lh	DONNY HATHAWAY	THE GHETTO	THE GHETTO part 2	10.00
70	226010 sh	DONNY HATHAWAY	THE GHETTO	THE GHETTO part 2	15.00
70	226011 lh	ARTHUR CONLEY	HURT	THEY CALL THE WIND MARIA	5.00
70	226011 sh	ARTHUR CONLEY	HURT	THEY CALL THE WIND MARIA	6.00
70	226012 lh	OTIS REDDING	LOOK AT THAT GIRL	THAT'S A GOOD IDEA	8.00
70	226012 sh	OTIS REDDING	LOOK AT THAT GIRL	THAT'S A GOOD IDEA	10.00
70	2091011 lh	DEE DEE WARWICK	SHE DIDN'T KNOW (SHE KEPT ON TALKIN)	MAKE LOVE TO ME	8.00
70	2091011 sh	DEE DEE WARWICK	SHE DIDN'T KNOW (SHE KEPT ON TALKIN)	MAKE LOVE TO ME	10.00
70	2091012 lh	KING CURTIS	SOULIN'	TEASIN'	10.00
70	2091012 sh	KING CURTIS	SOULIN'	TEASIN'	12.00
70	2091013 lh	R.B.GREAVES	FIRE AND RAIN	BALLAD OF LEROY	5.00
70	2091013 sh	R.B.GREAVES	FIRE AND RAIN	BALLAD OF LEROY	6.00
70	2091014 lh	LULU with the DIXIE FLYERS	HUM A SONG (FROM YOUR HEART)	MR. BOJANGLES	6.00
70	2091014 sh	LULU with the DIXIE FLYERS	HUM A SONG (FROM YOUR HEART)	MR. BOJANGLES	8.00
70	2091019	DOCTOR JOHN	WASH MAMA WASH	MAMA ROUX	6.00
70	2091037 lh	DEE DEE WARWICK	I'M ONLY HUMAN	IF THIS WAS THE LAST SONG	8.00
70	2091037 sh	DEE DEE WARWICK	I'M ONLY HUMAN	IF THIS WAS THE LAST SONG	10.00
03	67855 DJ promo only	BEN E. KING c/w BOBBY SHEEN	I CAN'T BREAK THE NEWS TO MYSELF	SOMETHING NEW TO DO	10.00
03	72855 DJ promo only	VIVIAN REED c/w DYNELLS	SAVE YOUR LOVE FOR ME	LET ME PROVE THAT I LOVE YOU	10.00

ATLANTIC

Hailed as one of the greatest independent labels in music history, Atlantic featured heavily in the development of black music across the world. Formed in New York City circa 1947 by Turkish born jazz & blues collector Ahmet Ertegun along with Brooklyn born jazz & blues fan Herb Abramson. Herb was to handle the production side, Ahmet the talent spotting and business side. It didn't take long before they had a reputation for being straightforward, honest and good payers. Musicians were very willing to work for, and even sign long contracts for Atlantic as Herb & Ahmet treated their employee not only fairly but very generously also. Although Atlantic recorded and released a whole spectrum of music, it was its fifties Rhythm & Blues and its sixties soul that Atlantic Records is really famous for.
The label being predominately black artist was mainly due to the President's and Vice-Presidents personal taste in music. Before 1953 Atlantic was really only a three person administered record label, with Herb's wife Miriam making up the trio. When Herb was drafted into the army, another helping hand was required. Another New Yorker with a passion for black music was Jerry Wexler; whilst working for Billboard magazine he coined the phrase Rhythm & Blues to replace the universally used term "race music" R&B is still the leading term to describe black music today.
Ahmet Ertegun certainly held no prejudices and was always on the look for new black talent.. When Swingtime records wanted to raise a little cash Ahmet was there to snap up the contract of Ray Charles. Ahmet was not, just a clever businessman, he also knew his music. After Ray Charles spent too long without a hit crooning ballads and softer R&B tunes, Ahmet came up with a change in direction for Ray's musical style. His self-penned "The Mess Around" a furious Rock Roll / R&B dance tune got Ray off the mark and in 1953 Ray got his first major hit.
In the early 50's USA white artists, and to some extent UK white artists started to do cover versions of R&B. This helped Atlantic sales, as the more discerning ear was willing to seek out the superior original versions. At this time the artist roster at Atlantic was becoming stronger and stronger. Billy Ward & The Dominoes had "gifted" the extraordinary talents of Clyde McPhatter to Mr. Ertegun as he was fired from the Dominoes. McPhatter soon pulled together a group, and called them The Drifters who after their first record in 1953 had fifteen more years of continually hitting the charts, with an ever-changing line up but always-strong material. With acts like Ray Charles, Drifters, Lavern Baker, Clyde McPhatter, Ruth Brown, Clovers, Bobbettes, Ivory Joe Hunter etc, Atlantic slipped through the fifties on a wave of R&B and Rock and Roll hits, into a period that every UK soul collector will cherish as he heard his first Sam & Dave 45 or added his first black Atlantic 45 to his collection.
After years of the Atlantic label being distributed by Decca in the UK and released on their prestigious London label, July 1964 saw the issue of the first UK Atlantic label 45, this was the start of one of the UK's most important and collectable labels.

With the 4000 series Decca used a similar format to the London label. Stock copies were black and silver with the promo copies adopting the attractive yellow label format. In April 1966 the black label series ceased to exist, as the Atlantic label switched distributors to UK Polydor.

In May 1966 Polydor issued its first Atlantic 45 on the now very famous red Atlantic series. Using the prefix 584 to start all release numbers the highly attractive and soon very familiar plain red and black label became very collectable. Every young music fan would trawl the record shop ex-chart and sale bins hoping to come across that Red Atlantic or that Blue Stax. Polydor were never as enthusiastic about promo 45's as much as Decca was. Atlantic demos are few and far between, even now it is not even clear whether every release had a pre-release promo label pressed. The Polydor promo 45's, were far less attractive than their predecessor's the red Atlantic promo in the 584 series had a small solid black "A" on the lower right hand side just below the year date on the label. I have not priced all the promo copies on the 584 series as collectors don't find them different enough from the stock copies for them to have a major price difference. Promo copies would perhaps attract a value of 25% more than the stock copies. Factory Sample stickers or Promo Sticker Not For Sale does not constitute a category of DEMO copy.

Information on missing numbers would be most helpful, but at the moment I am reasonably confident they were either unissued or did not have any soul connection. 4000 series Decca distributed black label with silver lettering design from 1964 to 1966, every 45 had promotional copies pressed, using the same yellow style label as the London label promo's of the same era. Yellow Atlantic promo copies are highly desirable. With the 85 there is a scattering of rock and pop, but as with UK Tamla Motown, Sue etc. I felt such important labels meant that many collectors try to run the whole series, I would list those non-soul releases also. Below is the complete Decca distributed UK black Atlantic 45 releases.

64	4001	DRIFTERS	UNDER THE BOARDWALK	I DON'T WANT TO GO ON WITHOUT	12.00
64	4001 DJ	DRIFTERS	UNDER THE BOARDWALK	I DON'T WANT TO GO ON WITHOUT	22.00
64	4002	BOBBY DARIN	MILORD	GOLDEN RINGS	10.00
64	4002 DJ	BOBBY DARIN	MILORD	GOLDEN RINGS	15.00
64	4003	SKA KINGS	OIL IN MY LAMP	JAMAICAN SKA	30.00
64	4003 DJ	SKA KINGS	OIL IN MY LAMP	JAMAICAN SKA	40.00
64	4004	SOLOMON BURKE	EVERYBODY NEEDS SOMEBODY TO LOVE	LOOKING FOR MY BABY	15.00
64	4004 DJ	SOLOMON BURKE	EVERYBODY NEEDS SOMEBODY TO LOVE	LOOKING FOR MY BABY	28.00
64	4005	CARLA THOMAS	I'VE GOT NOT TIME TO LOSE	A BOY NAMED TOM	20.00
64	4005 DJ	CARLA THOMAS	I'VE GOT NOT TIME TO LOSE	A BOY NAMED TOM	28.00
64	4006	DON COVAY & the GOODTIMERS	MERCY, MERCY	CAN'T STAY AWAY	10.00
64	4006 DJ	DON COVAY & the GOODTIMERS	MERCY, MERCY	CAN'T STAY AWAY	22.00
64	4007	BEN E. KING	LET THE WATER RUN DOWN	IT OVER OVER	15.00
64	4007 DJ	BEN E. KING	LET THE WATER RUN DOWN	IT OVER OVER	22.00
64	4008	DRIFTERS	I'VE GOT SAND IN MY SHOES	HE'S JUST A PLAYBOY	15.00
64	4008 DJ	DRIFTERS	I'VE GOT SAND IN MY SHOES	HE'S JUST A PLAYBOY	25.00
64	4009	RUFUS THOMAS	ALL NIGHT WORKER	JUMP BACK	15.00
64	4009 DJ	RUFUS THOMAS	ALL NIGHT WORKER	JUMP BACK	25.00
64	4010	ISLEY BROTHERS	THE LAST GIRL	LOOKING FOR A LOVE	25.00
64	4010 DJ	ISLEY BROTHERS	THE LAST GIRL	LOOKING FOR A LOVE	35.00
64	4011	DORIS TROY	WHAT'CHA GONNA DO ABOUT IT	TOMORROW IS ANOTHER DAY	15.00
64	4011 DJ	DORIS TROY	WHAT'CHA GONNA DO ABOUT IT	TOMORROW IS ANOTHER DAY	28.00
64	4012	DRIFTERS	SATURDAY NIGHT AT THE MOVIES	SPANISH LACE	20.00
64	4012 DJ	DRIFTERS	SATURDAY NIGHT AT THE MOVIES	SPANISH LACE	35.00
64	4013	BARBARA LEWIS	PUSHIN' A GOOD THING TOO FAR	COME HOME	25.00
64	4013 DJ	BARBARA LEWIS	PUSHIN' A GOOD THING TOO FAR	COME HOME	35.00
64	4014	SOLOMON BURKE	THE PRICE	MORE ROCKIN' SOUL	10.00
64	4014 DJ	SOLOMON BURKE	THE PRICE	MORE ROCKIN' SOUL	20.00
64	4015	JOE TEX	HOLD ONTO WHAT YOU'VE GOT	FRESH OUT OF TEARS	10.00
64	4015 DJ	JOE TEX	HOLD ONTO WHAT YOU'VE GOT	FRESH OUT OF TEARS	20.00
64	4016	DON COVAY	TAKE THIS HURT OFF ME	PLEASE DON'T LET ME KNOW	10.00
64	4016 DJ	DON COVAY	TAKE THIS HURT OFF ME	PLEASE DON'T LET ME KNOW	20.00
65	4017	TRAVIS WAMMACK	SCRATCHY	FIRE FLY	45.00
65	4017 DJ	TRAVIS WAMMACK	SCRATCHY	FIRE FLY	85.00
65	4018	BEN E. KING	SEVEN LETTERS	RIVER OF TEARS	15.00
65	4018 DJ	BEN E. KING	SEVEN LETTERS	RIVER OF TEARS	22.00
65	4019	DRIFTERS	AT THE CLUB	ANSWER THE PHONE	15.00
65	4019 DJ	DRIFTERS	AT THE CLUB	ANSWER THE PHONE	30.00
65	4020	DORIS TROY	ONE MORE CHANCE	PLEASE LITTLE ANGEL	15.00
65	4020 DJ	DORIS TROY	ONE MORE CHANCE	PLEASE LITTLE ANGEL	25.00
65	4021	JOE TEX	YOU BETTER GET IT	YOU GOT WHAT IT TAKES	10.00
65	4021 DJ	JOE TEX	YOU BETTER GET IT	YOU GOT WHAT IT TAKES	20.00
65	4022	SOLOMON BURKE	GOT TO GET YOU OFF MY MIND	PEEPIN'	15.00
65	4022 DJ	SOLOMON BURKE	GOT TO GET YOU OFF MY MIND	PEEPIN'	25.00
65	4023	DRIFTERS	COME ON OVER TO MY PLACE	CHAINS OF LOVE	15.00
65	4023 DJ	DRIFTERS	COME ON OVER TO MY PLACE	CHAINS OF LOVE	26.00
65	4024	OTIS REDDING	MR. PITIFUL	THAT'S HOW STRONG MY LOVE IS	15.00
65	4024 DJ	OTIS REDDING	MR. PITIFUL	THAT'S HOW STRONG MY LOVE IS	40.00
65	4025	BEN E. KING	THE RECORD (BABY, I LOVE YOU)	THE WAY YOU SHAKE IT	20.00
65	4025 DJ	BEN E. KING	THE RECORD (BABY, I LOVE YOU)	THE WAY YOU SHAKE IT	40.00
65	4026	BIG JOE TURNER	MIDNIGHT CANNONBALL	BABY I STILL WANT YOU	18.00
65	4026 DJ	BIG JOE TURNER	MIDNIGHT CANNONBALL	BABY I STILL WANT YOU	25.00
67	4027	JOE TEX	A WOMAN CAN CHANGE A MAN	DON'T LET YOUR LEFT HAND KNOW	10.00
67	4027 DJ	JOE TEX	A WOMAN CAN CHANGE A MAN	DON'T LET YOUR LEFT HAND KNOW	18.00
65	4028	ESTHER PHILLIPS	SHANGRI-LA	AND I LOVE HIM	10.00
65	4028 DJ	ESTHER PHILLIPS	SHANGRI-LA	AND I LOVE HIM	18.00
65	4029 DJ	OTIS REDDING	I'VE BEEN LOVING YOU TOO LONG	WINTER WONDERLAND	UN

unissued test presses may exist, but unconfirmed

65	4030	SOLOMON BURKE	MAGGIE'S FARM	TONIGHT'S THE NIGHT	15.00
65	4030 DJ	SOLOMON BURKE	MAGGIE'S FARM	TONIGHT'S THE NIGHT	25.00
65	4031	BARBARA LEWIS	BABY I'M YOURS	I SAY LOVE	10.00
65	4031 DJ	BARBARA LEWIS	BABY I'M YOURS	I SAY LOVE	20.00
65	4032	DORIS TROY	HEARTACHES	YOU'D BETTER STOP	10.00
65	4032 DJ	DORIS TROY	HEARTACHES	YOU'D BETTER STOP	18.00
65	4033	BOOKER T. & THE MG'S	BOOT-LEG	OUTRAGE	10.00

65	4033 DJ	BOOKER T. & THE MG'S	BOOT-LEG	OUTRAGE	18.00
65	4034	DRIFTERS	THE OUTSIDE WORLD	FOLLOW ME	15.00
65	4034 DJ	DRIFTERS	THE OUTSIDE WORLD	FOLLOW ME	25.00
65	4035	SONNY & CHER	I GOT YOU BABE	IT'S GONNA RAIN	8.00
65	4035 DJ	SONNY & CHER	I GOT YOU BABE	IT'S GONNA RAIN	15.00
65	4036	WILSON PICKETT	IN THE MIDNIGHT HOUR	I'M NOT TIRED YET	10.00
65	4036 DJ	WILSON PICKETT	IN THE MIDNIGHT HOUR	I'M NOT TIRED YET	20.00
65	4037	ASTORS	CANDY	I FOUND OUT	85.00
65	4037 DJ	ASTORS	CANDY	I FOUND OUT	150.00
65	4038	SONNY	LAUGH AT ME	TONY	5.00
65	4038 DJ	SONNY	LAUGH AT ME	TONY	10.00
65	4039	OTIS REDDING	RESPECT	I'VE BEEN LOVING YOU TOO LONG	15.00
65	4039 DJ	OTIS REDDING	RESPECT	I'VE BEEN LOVING YOU TOO LONG	25.00
65	4040	DRIFTERS	I'LL TAKE YOU WHERE THE MUSIC'S	FAR FROM THE MADDING CROWD	20.00
65	4040 DJ	DRIFTERS	I'LL TAKE YOU WHERE THE MUSIC'S	FAR FROM THE MADDING CROWD	28.00
65	4041	BARBARA LEWIS	MAKE ME YOUR BABY	LOVE TO BE LOVED	10.00
65	4041 DJ	BARBARA LEWIS	MAKE ME YOUR BABY	LOVE TO BE LOVED	18.00
65	4042	JIMMY WILLIAMS	WALKING ON AIR	I'M SO LOST	20.00
65	4042 DJ	JIMMY WILLIAMS	WALKING ON AIR	I'M SO LOST	30.00
65	4043	BEN E. KING	CRY NO MORE	(THERE'S) NO PLACE TO HIDE	50.00
65	4043 DJ	BEN E. KING	CRY NO MORE	(THERE'S) NO PLACE TO HIDE	75.00
65	4044	SOLOMON BURKE	SOMEONE IS WATCHING	DANCE, DANCE, DANCE	10.00
65	4044 DJ	SOLOMON BURKE	SOMEONE IS WATCHING	DANCE, DANCE, DANCE	20.00
65	4045	JOE TEX	I WANT TO (DO EVERYTHING FOR YOU)	FUNNY BONE	10.00
65	4045 DJ	JOE TEX	I WANT TO (DO EVERYTHING FOR YOU)	FUNNY BONE	18.00
65	4046	BOBBY DARIN	WE DIDN'T ASK TO BE BOUGHT HERE	FUNNY WHAT LOVE CAN DO	6.00
65	4046 DJ	BOBBY DARIN	WE DIDN'T ASK TO BE BOUGHT HERE	FUNNY WHAT LOVE CAN DO	10.00
65	4047	SONNY & CHER	BUT YOU'RE MINE	HELLO	8.00
65	4047 DJ	SONNY & CHER	BUT YOU'RE MINE	HELLO	10.00
65	4048	ESTHER PHILLIPS	LET ME KNOW WHEN IT'S OVER	I SAW ME	8.00
65	4048 DJ	ESTHER PHILLIPS	LET ME KNOW WHEN IT'S OVER	I SAW ME	10.00
65	4049	BOCKY AND THE VISIONS	I GO CRAZY	GOOD-GOOD LOVIN'	20.00
65	4049 DJ	BOCKY AND THE VISIONS	I GO CRAZY	GOOD-GOOD LOVIN'	28.00
65	4050	OTIS REDDING	MY GIRL	DOWN IN THE VALLEY	10.00
65	4050 DJ	OTIS REDDING	MY GIRL	DOWN IN THE VALLEY	50.00
65	4051	MAD LADS	DON'T HAVE TO SHOP AROUND	TEAR-MAKER	25.00
65	4051 DJ	MAD LADS	DON'T HAVE TO SHOP AROUND	TEAR-MAKER	35.00
65	4052	WILSON PICKETT	DON'T FIGHT IT	IT'S ALL OVER	10.00
65	4052 DJ	WILSON PICKETT	DON'T FIGHT IT	IT'S ALL OVER	20.00
65	4053	PAUL KELLY	CHILLS AND FEVER	ONLY YOUR LOVE	40.00
65	4053 DJ	PAUL KELLY	CHILLS AND FEVER	ONLY YOUR LOVE	75.00
65	4054	LEVON & THE HAWKS	THE STONES I THROW	HE DON'T LOVE YOU	30.00
65	4054 DJ	LEVON & THE HAWKS	THE STONES I THROW	HE DON'T LOVE YOU	40.00
65	4055	PATTY LABELLE & the BLUEBELLES	YOU FORGOT HOW TO LOVE	ALL OR NOTHING	20.00
65	4055 DJ	PATTY LABELLE & the BLUEBELLES	YOU FORGOT HOW TO LOVE	ALL OR NOTHING	40.00
65	4056	DON COVAY	SEESAW	I NEVER GET ENOUGH OF YOUR LOV	15.00
65	4056 DJ	DON COVAY	SEESAW	I NEVER GET ENOUGH OF YOUR LOV	28.00
65	4057	FRONT LINE	I DON'T CARE	GOT LOVE	40.00
65	4057 DJ	FRONT LINE	I DON'T CARE	GOT LOVE	50.00
65	4058	JOE TEX	A SWEET WOMAN LIKE YOU	CLOSE THE DOOR	10.00
65	4058 DJ	JOE TEX	A SWEET WOMAN LIKE YOU	CLOSE THE DOOR	18.00
65	4059	YOUNG RASCALS	I AIN'T GONNA EAT MY HEART OUT	SLOW DOWN	10.00
65	4059 DJ	YOUNG RASCALS	I AIN'T GONNA EAT MY HEART OUT	SLOW DOWN	18.00
65	4060	SONNY & SONNY'S GROUP	REVOLUTION KIND	GEORGIA AND JOHN QUETZAL	10.00
65	4060 DJ	SONNY & SONNY'S GROUP	REVOLUTION KIND	GEORGIA AND JOHN QUETZAL	15.00
65	4061	SOLOMON BURKE	ONLY LOVE (CAN SAVE ME NOW)	LITTLE GIRL THAT LOVES ME	15.00
65	4061 DJ	SOLOMON BURKE	ONLY LOVE (CAN SAVE ME NOW)	LITTLE GIRL THAT LOVES ME	30.00
65	4062	DRIFTERS	NYLON STOCKINGS	WE GOTTA SING	15.00
65	4062 DJ	DRIFTERS	NYLON STOCKINGS lt	WE GOTTA SING	30.00
65	4063	BOOKER T. & THE MG'S	RED BEANS AND RICE	BE MY LADY	10.00
65	4063 DJ	BOOKER T. & THE MG'S	RED BEANS AND RICE	BE MY LADY	20.00
65	4064	PATTY LABELLE & her BLUEBELLES	OVER THE RAINBOW	GROOVY KIND OF LOVE	10.00
65	4064 DJ	PATTY LABELLE & her BLUEBELLES	OVER THE RAINBOW	GROOVY KIND OF LOVE	18.00
65	4065	BEN E. KING	GOODNIGHT MY LOVE, PLEASANT DREAMS	TELL DADDY	10.00
65	4065 DJ	BEN E. KING	GOODNIGHT MY LOVE, PLEASANT DREAMS	TELL DADDY	18.00
66	4065 test press	BEN E. KING	I CAN'T BREAK THE NEWS TO MYSELF	GOODNIGHT MY LOVE, PLEASANT DREAMS	1500.00
66	4066	SAM and DAVE	YOU DON'T KNOW LIKE I KNOW	BLAME ME DON'T BLAME MY HEART	15.00
66	4066 DJ	SAM and DAVE	YOU DON'T KNOW LIKE I KNOW	BLAME ME DON'T BLAME MY HEART	45.00
66	4067	MARY WELLS	DEAR LOVER	CAN'T YOU SEE (YOU'RE LOSING ME)	30.00
66	4067 DJ	MARY WELLS	DEAR LOVER	CAN'T YOU SEE (YOU'RE LOSING ME)	70.00
66	4068	BARBARA LEWIS	DON'T FORGET ABOUT ME	IT'S MAGIC	15.00
66	4068 DJ	BARBARA LEWIS	DON'T FORGET ABOUT ME	IT'S MAGIC	30.00
66	4069	SONNY & CHER	WHAT NOW MY LOVE	I LOOK FOR YOU	10.00
66	4069 DJ	SONNY & CHER	WHAT NOW MY LOVE	I LOOK FOR YOU	15.00
66	4070	DEON JACKSON	LOVE MAKES THE WORLD GO ROUND	YOU SAID YOU LOVED ME	30.00
66	4070 DJ	DEON JACKSON	LOVE MAKES THE WORLD GO ROUND	YOU SAID YOU LOVED ME	60.00
66	4071	TAMI LYNN	I'M GONNA RUN AWAY FROM YOU	THE BOY NEXT DOOR	60.00
66	4071 DJ	TAMI LYNN	I'M GONNA RUN AWAY FROM YOU	THE BOY NEXT DOOR	**108.00**
66	4072	WILSON PICKETT	634-5789	THAT'S A MAN'S WAY	10.00

66	4072 DJ	WILSON PICKETT	634-5789	THAT'S A MAN'S WAY	28.00
66	4073	SOLOMON BURKE	(NO, NO) I CAN'T STOP LOVIN' YOU	BABY COME ON HOME	10.00
66	4073 DJ	SOLOMON BURKE	(NO, NO) I CAN'T STOP LOVIN' YOU	BABY COME ON HOME	20.00
66	4074	CARLA THOMAS	COMFORT ME	I'M FOR YOU	15.00
66	4074 DJ	CARLA THOMAS	COMFORT ME	I'M FOR YOU	25.00
66	4075	JACKIE IVORY	HI HEEL SNEAKERS	DO IT TO DEATH	15.00
66	4075 DJ	JACKIE IVORY	HI HEEL SNEAKERS	DO IT TO DEATH	28.00
66	4076	GOOGIE RENE COMBO	SMOKEY JOE'S LA LA	NEEDING YOU	40.00
66	4076 DJ	GOOGIE RENE COMBO	SMOKEY JOE'S LA LA	NEEDING YOU	75.00
66	4077	ESTHER PHILLIPS	JUST SAY GOODBYE	I COULD HAVE TOLD YOU	100.00
66	4077 DJ	ESTHER PHILLIPS	JUST SAY GOODBYE	I COULD HAVE TOLD YOU	**156.00**
66	4078	DON COVAY	SOOKIE SOOKIE	WATCHING THE LATE LATE SHOW	10.00
66	4078 DJ	DON COVAY	SOOKIE SOOKIE	WATCHING THE LATE LATE SHOW	25.00
66	4079	MAR-KEYS	PHILLY DOG	HONEY POT	15.00
66	4079 DJ	MAR-KEYS	PHILLY DOG	HONEY POT	30.00
66	4080	OTIS REDDING	(I CAN'T GET NO) SATISFACTION	ANY OLE WAY	15.00
66	4080 DJ	OTIS REDDING	(I CAN'T GET NO) SATISFACTION	ANY OLE WAY	28.00
66	4081	JOE TEX	IF SUGAR WAS AS SWEET AS YOU	THE LOVE YOU SAVE	10.00
66	4081 DJ	JOE TEX	IF SUGAR WAS AS SWEET AS YOU	THE LOVE YOU SAVE	18.00
66	4082	YOUNG RASCALS	GOOD LOVIN'	MUSTAMG SALLY	15.00
66	4082 DJ	YOUNG RASCALS	GOOD LOVIN'	MUSTAMG SALLY	22.00
66	4083	MAD LADS	I WANT SOMEONE	NOTHING CAN BREAK THROUGH	20.00
66	4083 DJ	MAD LADS	I WANT SOMEONE	NOTHING CAN BREAK THROUGH	28.00
66	4084	DRIFTERS	MEMORIES ARE MADE OF THIS	MY ISLAND IN THE SUN	15.00
66	4084 DJ	DRIFTERS	MEMORIES ARE MADE OF THIS	MY ISLAND IN THE SUN	28.00
66	4085	SHADOWS OF KNIGHT	GLORIA	DARK SIDE	40.00
66	4085 DJ	SHADOWS OF KNIGHT	GLORIA	DARK SIDE	40.00
80s	4432	OTIS REDDING	(SITTIN' ON) THE DOCK OF THE BAY	SWEET LORENE + HARD TO HANDLE	4.00

AET 6000 series EPs.

64	6001 EP PS	RUFUS THOMAS	DO THE DOG	1964 4 track EP with cover	45.00
64	6002 EP PS	BOOKER T. & THE MG'S	R&B WITH BOOKER T. VOL. 2	1964 4 track EP with cover	20.00
64	6003 EP PS	DRIFTERS	DRIFTIN' vol. 2	1964 4 track EP with cover	30.00
64	6004 EP PS	BEN E. KING	WHAT NOW MY LOVE	1964 4 track EP with cover	45.00
64	6007 EP PS	DORIS TROY	WHATCHA GONNA DO ABOUT IT	1964 4 track EP with cover	75.00
65	6008 EP PS	SOLOMON BURKE	ROCK N' SOUL	1965 4 track EP with cover	50.00
65	6009 EP PS	LAVERN BAKER	BEST OF LAVERN	1965 4 track EP with cover	60.00
65	6010 EP PS	JOHN LEE HOOKER	JOHN LEE HOOKER	1965 4 track EP with cover	30.00
65	6011 EP PS	RUFUS THOMAS	JUMP BACK WITH RUFUS	1965 4 track EP with cover	45.00
65	6012 EP PS	DRIFTERS	TONIGHT	1965 4 track EP with cover	30.00
65	6013 EP PS	BOBBY DARIN	MILORD	1965 4 track EP with cover	25.00
65	6015 EP PS	BARBARA LEWIS	SNAP YOUR FINGERS	1965 4 track EP with cover	75.00

1980 double artist 4 track Eps with special 45 sleeves.

80	ATM 1 EP	DON COVAY c/w BAR-KAYS,	SEE SAW + MERCY MERCY	LAST NIGHT + SOUL FINGER	6.00
80	ATM 2 EP	OTIS REDDING c/w ARETHA FRANKLIN	I CAN'T TURN YOU LOOSE + DOCK OF	RESPECT + THINK	5.00
80	ATM 3 EP	BEN E. KING c/w PERCY SLEDGE	STAND BY ME + WHAT IS SOUL	WARM & TENDER LOVE + WHEN A MA	5.00
80	ATM 4 EP	DORIS TROY c/w SHARON TANDY	JUST ONE LOOK + WHAT'CHA GONNA ABO	HOLD ON + STAY WITH ME BABY	6.00
80	ATM 5 EP	JOE TEX c/w OTIS & CARLA	SHOW ME + HOLD WHAT YOU'VE GOT	TRAMP + OOH OTIS OOH CARLA	5.00
80	ATM 6 EP	DRIFTERS c/w SOUL BROS 6 + CAPITOL	SAT THE CLUB + UNDER THE BOARDWALK	COOL JERK + SOME KIND OF WONDERFUL	6.00
80	ATM 7 EP	WILSON PICKETT c/w SAM and DAVE	LAND OF A 1000 DANCES + MIDNIGHT	SOUL MAN + YOU DON'T KNOW LIKE I KNOW	5.00
80	ATM 8 EP	ARTHUR CONLEY c/w CARLA THOMAS	SWEET SOUL MUSIC + FUNKY STREET	GEE WHIZ + B.A.B.Y.	5.00
80	ATM 9 EP	RUFUS THOMAS c/w SOLOMON BURKE	WALKING THE DOG + JUMP BACK	IF YOU NEED ME + EVERYBODY NEE	5.00
80	ATM 10 EP	BOOKER T. & the MG'S c/w REX GARVIN	GREEN ONIONS + CHINESE CHECKERS	SOCK IT TO EM JB + MEMPHIS SOU	5.00

9000 series

84	9361	BEN E KING c/w COASTERS	STAND BY ME	YAKETY YAK	3.00
85	9565	BRIDGE	BABY DON'T HOLD YOUR LOVE BACK	same: instrumental	15.00
84	9607	OTIS REDDING	SITTIN' ON THE DOCK OF THE BAY	SWEET LORENE	4.00
84	9666	DETROIT SPINNERS	I'LL BE AROUND	RIGHT OR WRONG	8.00
84	9713	MARGIE JOSEPH	MIDNIGHT LOVER	BIG STRONG MAN	4.00
79	9744	SISTER SLEDGE	WE ARE FAMILY	THINKING OF YOU	5.00
83	9891	DETROIT SPINNERS	I'LL BE AROUND	RIGHT OR WRONG	8.00
78	9951	GWEN McCRAE	KEEP THE FIRE BURNING	FUNKY SENSATION	15.00

10000 series

In 1972 Atlantic changed label distribution from Polydor to music conglomerate Kinney, all release numbers were preceded with the letter K. Label changed from the classic red design to a multi coloured label more in the style of the time. As the seventies labels became more colourful. All the 45's in series do exist on promo copies. Most are the coloured stock copy design with a large full label size "A", a few carried the same design but with a white background with a red "A". The missing numbers for this series were attributed to other Kinney owned and distributed 45's, ie, the Warner Bros UK releases with release numbers beginning with a K. As you can see from the listing below Kinney's first task was to re-release the most popular classics from Polydor's catalogue.

72	10011	WILSON PICKETT	DON'T KNOCK MY LOVE	DON'T KNOCK MY LOVE part 2	5.00
72	10011 DJ	WILSON PICKETT	DON'T KNOCK MY LOVE	DON'T KNOCK MY LOVE part 2	6.00
72	10021	BEGINNING OF THE END	FUNKY NASSAU	FUNKY NASSAU part 1	5.00
72	10021 DJ	BEGINNING OF THE END	FUNKY NASSAU	FUNKY NASSAU part 1	6.00
72	10026	OTIS REDDING	SITTIN ON THE DOCK OF THE BAY	RESPECT + MR. PITIFUL	5.00
72	10026 DJ	OTIS REDDING	SITTIN ON THE DOCK OF THE BAY	RESPECT + MR. PITIFUL	6.00
72	10051	OTIS REDDING	RESPECT	THESE ARMS OF MINE	5.00
72	10051 DJ	OTIS REDDING	RESPECT	THESE ARMS OF MINE	6.00
72	10082	BAR-KAYS	SOUL FINGER	KNUCKLEHEAD	6.00
72	10082 DJ	BAR-KAYS	SOUL FINGER	KNUCKLEHEAD	8.00
72	10104	PERCY SLEDGE	WHEN A MAN LOVES A WOMAN	LOVE ME LIKE YOU MEAN IT	4.00
72	10104 DJ	PERCY SLEDGE	WHEN A MAN LOVES A WOMAN	LOVE ME LIKE YOU MEAN IT	5.00

72	10105	REX GARVIN & the MIGHTY CRAVERS	SOCK IT TO 'EM J.B.	SOCK IT TO 'EM J.B. part 2	6.00
72	10105 DJ	REX GARVIN & the MIGHTY CRAVERS	SOCK IT TO 'EM J.B.	SOCK IT TO 'EM J.B. part 2	10.00
72	10108	ARTHUR CONLEY	SWEET SOUL MUSIC	LET'S GO STEADY	5.00
72	10108 DJ	ARTHUR CONLEY	SWEET SOUL MUSIC	LET'S GO STEADY	6.00
72	10109	BOOKER T. & THE MG'S	GREEN ONIONS	BOOT LEG	4.00
72	10109 DJ	BOOKER T. & THE MG'S	GREEN ONIONS	BOOT LEG	5.00
72	10109 PS	BOOKER T. & THE MG'S	GREEN ONIONS	BOOT LEG	5.00
72	10110	BEN E. KING	STAND BY ME	SAVE THE LAST DANCE FOR ME	5.00
72	10110 DJ	BEN E. KING	STAND BY ME	SAVE THE LAST DANCE FOR ME	6.00
72	10111	OTIS REDDING	MR. PITIFUL	MY GIRL	5.00
72	10111 DJ	OTIS REDDING	MR. PITIFUL	MY GIRL	6.00
72	10115	ARTHUR CONLEY	FUNKY STREET	PUT OUR LOVE TOGETHER	5.00
72	10115 DJ	ARTHUR CONLEY	FUNKY STREET	PUT OUR LOVE TOGETHER	6.00
72	10117	THREE CAPS	COOL JERK	HELLO STRANGER	5.00
72	10117 DJ	THREE CAPS	COOL JERK	HELLO STRANGER	6.00
72	10119	OTIS LEAVILLE	I LOVE YOU	I NEED YOU	5.00
72	10119 DJ	OTIS LEAVILLE	I LOVE YOU	I NEED YOU	6.00
72	10121	KING FLOYD	GROOVE ME	WHAT OUR LOVE NEEDS	5.00
72	10121 DJ	KING FLOYD	GROOVE ME	WHAT OUR LOVE NEEDS	5.00
72	10122	JACKIE MOORE	PRECIOUS, PRECIOUS	WILLPOWER	6.00
72	10122 DJ	JACKIE MOORE	PRECIOUS, PRECIOUS	WILLPOWER	8.00
72	10126	OTIS REDDING	(SITTIN' ON) THE DOCK OF THE BAY	RESPECT + MR.PITIFUL	5.00
72	10126 DJ	OTIS REDDING	(SITTIN' ON) THE DOCK OF THE BAY	RESPECT + MR.PITIFUL	6.00
72	10126 PS	OTIS REDDING	(SITTIN' ON) THE DOCK OF THE BAY	RESPECT + MR.PITIFUL	8.00
72	10128	BARBARA LEWIS	SOMEDAY WE'RE GONNA LOVE AGAIN	BABY, I'M YOURS	15.00
72	10128 DJ	BARBARA LEWIS	SOMEDAY WE'RE GONNA LOVE AGAIN	BABY, I'M YOURS	20.00
72	10129	WILSON PICKETT	IN THE MIDNIGHT HOUR	DANGER ZONE	5.00
72	10129 DJ	WILSON PICKETT	IN THE MIDNIGHT HOUR	DANGER ZONE	6.00
72	10143	BETTY WRIGHT	CLEAN UP WOMAN	I'LL LOVE YOU FOREVER	8.00
72	10143 DJ	BETTY WRIGHT	CLEAN UP WOMAN	I'LL LOVE YOU FOREVER	10.00
72	10144	PERCY SLEDGE	RAINBOW ROAD	STANDING ON THE MOUNTAIN	5.00
72	10144 DJ	PERCY SLEDGE	RAINBOW ROAD	STANDING ON THE MOUNTAIN	6.00
72	10145	ARTHUR CONLEY	FUNKY STREET	PUT OUR LOVE TOGETHER	5.00
72	10145 DJ	ARTHUR CONLEY	FUNKY STREET	PUT OUR LOVE TOGETHER	6.00
72	10148	DRIFTERS	SATURDAY NIGHT AT THE MOVIES	AT THE CLUB + MEMORIES ARE MAD	5.00
72	10148 DJ	DRIFTERS	SATURDAY NIGHT AT THE MOVIES	AT THE CLUB + MEMORIES ARE MAD	6.00
72	10149	J.P. ROBINSON	EORGE JACKSON	WALL TO WALL LOVE	8.00
72	10149 DJ	J.P. ROBINSON	EORGE JACKSON	WALL TO WALL LOVE	10.00
72	10154	ARETHA FRLANKLIN	DAY DREAMING	I'VE BEEN LOVING YOU TOO LONG	4.00
72	10154 DJ	ARETHA FRLANKLIN	DAY DREAMING	I'VE BEEN LOVING YOU TOO LONG	5.00
72	10161	ROBERTA FLACK	THE FIRST TIME EVER I FACE YOUR FACE	WILL YOU STILL LOVE ME TOMORROW	4.00
72	10161 DJ	ROBERTA FLACK	THE FIRST TIME EVER I FACE YOUR FACE	WILL YOU STILL LOVE ME TOMORROW	5.00
72	10162	KING FLOYD	EVERYBODY NEEDS SOMEBODY	WOMAN DON'T GO ASTRAY	4.00
72	10162 DJ	KING FLOYD	EVERYBODY NEEDS SOMEBODY	WOMAN DON'T GO ASTRAY	5.00
72	10164	JACKIE MOORE	TIME	DARLING BABY + COVER ME	5.00
72	10164 DJ	JACKIE MOORE	TIME	DARLING BABY + COVER ME	6.00
72	10165	PERCY SLEDGE	BABY, HELP ME + TAKE TIME TO KNOW	WARM AND TENDER LOVE	5.00
72	10165 DJ	PERCY SLEDGE	BABY, HELP ME + TAKE TIME TO KNOW	WARM AND TENDER LOVE	6.00
72	10166	WILSON PICKETT	ON'T LET THE GREEN GRASS FOOL YOU	COVERING THE SAME OLD GROUND	8.00
72	10166 DJ	WILSON PICKETT	ON'T LET THE GREEN GRASS FOOL YOU	COVERING THE SAME OLD GROUND	10.00
72	10167	IRMA THOMAS	FULL TIME WOMAN	SHE'S TAKEN MY PART	5.00
72	10167 DJ	IRMA THOMAS	FULL TIME WOMAN	SHE'S TAKEN MY PART	6.00
72	10168	ESTHER PHILLIPS	CATCH ME I'M FALLING	RELEASE ME	20.00
72	10168 DJ	ESTHER PHILLIPS	CATCH ME I'M FALLING	RELEASE ME	30.00
72	10172	QUINCY JONES	LISTEN TO THE MELODY	HOT ROCK THEME	3.00
72	10172 DJ	QUINCY JONES	LISTEN TO THE MELODY	HOT ROCK THEME	4.00
72	10174	BETTYE SWAN	VICTIM OF A FOOLISH HEART	COLD DAY (IN HELL)	8.00
72	10174 DJ	BETTYE SWAN	VICTIM OF A FOOLISH HEART	COLD DAY (IN HELL)	10.00
72	10179	HERBIE MANN	PHILLY DOG + MEMPHIS	IT'S A FUNKY THING	4.00
72	10179 DJ	HERBIE MANN	PHILLY DOG + MEMPHIS	IT'S A FUNKY THING	5.00
72	10180	SAM and DAVE	SOUL MAN	THANK YOU + SOOTHE ME	6.00
72	10180 DJ	SAM and DAVE	SOUL MAN	THANK YOU + SOOTHE ME	8.00
72	10181	WILSON PICKETT	FUNK FACTORY	ONE STEP AWAY	5.00
72	10181 DJ	WILSON PICKETT	FUNK FACTORY	ONE STEP AWAY	6.00
72	10182	FIRST BORN	IF THIS IS OUR LAST TIME	HEY CLOUD	4.00
72	10190 DJ	BETTY WRIGHT	IS IT YOU GIRL	CRYIN' IN MY SLEEP	6.00
72	10193	DONNY HATHAWAY	THE GHETTO part 1 & 2	LITTLE GHETTO BOY	10.00
72	10193 DJ	DONNY HATHAWAY	THE GHETTO part 1 & 2	LITTLE GHETTO BOY	15.00
72	10194	LITTLE SISTER	YOU'RE THE ONE	SOMEBODY'S WATCHING YOU	8.00
72	10194 DJ	LITTLE SISTER	YOU'RE THE ONE	SOMEBODY'S WATCHING YOU	10.00
72	10195	BUDDY GUY	HONEY DRIPPER	MAN OF MANY WORDS	8.00
72	10195 DJ	BUDDY GUY	HONEY DRIPPER	MAN OF MANY WORDS	10.00
72	10202	ROBERTA FLACK & DONNY HATHAWAY	WHERE IS THE LOVE	MOOD	4.00
72	10202 DJ	ROBERTA FLACK & DONNY HATHAWAY	WHERE IS THE LOVE	MOOD	5.00
72	10204	SOUL BROTHERS SIX	SOME KIND OF WONDERFUL	CHECK YOURSELF	6.00
72	10204 DJ	SOUL BROTHERS SIX	SOME KIND OF WONDERFUL	CHECK YOURSELF	8.00
72	10205	CAPITOLS	AIN'T THAT TERRIBLE	ZIG - ZAGGING	6.00
72	10205 DJ	CAPITOLS	AIN'T THAT TERRIBLE	ZIG - ZAGGING	8.00
72	10206	OTIS REDDING	WHITE CHRISTMAS	MERRY CHRISTMAS BABY	5.00

72	10206 DJ	OTIS REDDING	WHITE CHRISTMAS	MERRY CHRISTMAS BABY	6.00
72	10207	TYRONE DAVIS	CAN I CHANGE MY MIND + ONE WAY	TURN BACK THE HANDS OF TIME	8.00
72	10207 DJ	TYRONE DAVIS	CAN I CHANGE MY MIND + ONE WAY	TURN BACK THE HANDS OF TIME	10.00
72	10209	J.P. ROBINSON	WHAT CAN I TELL HER	PLEASE ACCEPT MY CALL	10.00
72	10209 DJ	J.P. ROBINSON	WHAT CAN I TELL HER	PLEASE ACCEPT MY CALL	15.00
72	10210	ARCHIE BELL & the DRELLS	HERE I GO AGAIN	A WORLD WITHOUT MUSIC	10.00
72	10210 DJ	ARCHIE BELL & the DRELLS	HERE I GO AGAIN	A WORLD WITHOUT MUSIC	20.00
72	10211	MAJOR LANCE	FOLLOW THE LEADER	SINCE YOU'VE BEEN GONE	5.00
72	10211 DJ	MAJOR LANCE	FOLLOW THE LEADER	SINCE YOU'VE BEEN GONE	8.00
72	10216	DRIFTERS	COME ON OVER TO MY PLACE	UP ON THE ROOF + I DON'T WANT	5.00
72	10216 DJ	DRIFTERS	COME ON OVER TO MY PLACE	UP ON THE ROOF + I DON'T WANT	8.00
72	10219	OTIS LEAVILLE	I LOVE YOU	I NEED YOU	6.00
72	10219 DJ	OTIS LEAVILLE	I LOVE YOU	I NEED YOU	8.00
72	10224	ARETHA FRANKLIN	ROCK STEADY	ALL THE KINGS HORSES	8.00
72	10224 DJ	ARETHA FRANKLIN	ROCK STEADY	ALL THE KINGS HORSES	10.00
72	10239	SAM & DAVE	SOUL SISTER BROWN SUGAR	I WASN'T GONN TELL NOBODDY + YOU GOT ME	5.00
72	10239 DJ	SAM & DAVE	SOUL SISTER BROWN SUGAR	I WASN'T GONN TELL NOBODDY + YOU GOT ME	6.00
72	10242	JOHNNY COPELAND	SUFFERIN CITY	IT'S MY OWN TEARS THAT'S BEING	10.00
72	10242 DJ	JOHNNY COPELAND	SUFFERIN CITY	IT'S MY OWN TEARS THAT'S BEING	15.00
72	10243	DETROIT SPINNERS	I'LL BE AROUND	HOW COULD I LET YOU GET AWAY	15.00
72	10243 DJ	DETROIT SPINNERS	I'LL BE AROUND	HOW COULD I LET YOU GET AWAY	25.00
72	10243 DJ	SPINNERS	I'LL BE AROUND	HOW COULD I LET YOU GET AWAY	25.00
72	10244	WILLIAM BELL	TRIBUTE TO A KING	NEVER LIKE THIS BEFORE + MARCHING OFF TO	5.00
72	10244 DJ	WILLIAM BELL	TRIBUTE TO A KING	NEVER LIKE THIS BEFORE + MARCHING OFF TO	6.00
72	10245	JOHNNY ADAMS	I WISH IT WOULD RAIN	YOU'RE A LADY	5.00
72	10245 DJ	JOHNNY ADAMS	I WISH IT WOULD RAIN	YOU'RE A LADY	6.00
72	10250	BETTY WRIGHT	BABY SITTER	OUTSIDE WOMAN	6.00
72	10250 DJ	BETTY WRIGHT	BABY SITTER	OUTSIDE WOMAN	8.00
72	10254	MARY WELLS	DEAR LOVER	CAN'T YOU SEE YOUR LOSING ME	15.00
72	10254 DJ	MARY WELLS	DEAR LOVER	CAN'T YOU SEE YOUR LOSING ME	20.00
72	10257	DONNY HATHAWAY	I LOVE YOU MORE THAN YOU'LL EVER KNOW	LORD HELP ME	5.00
72	10257 DJ	DONNY HATHAWAY	I LOVE YOU MORE THAN YOU'LL EVER KNOW	LORD HELP ME	6.00
72	10258	COASTERS	YACKETY YAK	SHOPPING FOR CLOTHES + POISON IVY	4.00
72	10258 DJ	COASTERS	YACKETY YAK	SHOPPING FOR CLOTHES + POISON IVY	5.00
72	10260	DRIFTERS	I'LL TAKE YOU HOME + HE'S JUST A PLAYBOY + I'VE GOT SAND IN MY SHOES		5.00
72	10260 DJ	DRIFTERS	I'LL TAKE YOU HOME + HE'S JUST A PLAYBOY + I'VE GOT SAND IN MY SHOES		6.00
72	10262	KING FLOYD	EVERYBODY NEEDS SOMEBODY	WOMAN DON'T GO ASTRAY	5.00
72	10262 DJ	KING FLOYD	EVERYBODY NEEDS SOMEBODY	WOMAN DON'T GO ASTRAY	6.00
72	10263	ARCHIE BELL & the DRELLS	(THERE'S GONNA BE) A SHOWDOWN	TIGHTEN UP	6.00
72	10263 DJ	ARCHIE BELL & the DRELLS	(THERE'S GONNA BE) A SHOWDOWN	TIGHTEN UP	10.00
72	10265	PERSUADERS	THIN LINE BETWEEN LOVE AND HATE	PEACE IN THE VALLEY	6.00
72	10265 DJ	PERSUADERS	THIN LINE BETWEEN LOVE AND HATE	PEACE IN THE VALLEY	8.00
72	10269	WILSON PICKETT	EVERYBODY NEEDS SOMEBODY	DON'T FIGHT IT + FIRE AND WATER	5.00
72	10269 DJ	WILSON PICKETT	EVERYBODY NEEDS SOMEBODY	DON'T FIGHT IT + FIRE AND WATER	6.00
72	10270	BLACK HEAT	STREET OF TEARS	CHIPS FUNK	8.00
72	10270 DJ	BLACK HEAT	STREET OF TEARS	CHIPS FUNK	10.00
72	10272	PAUL KELLY	CHILLS AND FEVER	ONLY YOUR LOVE	8.00
72	10272 DJ	PAUL KELLY	CHILLS AND FEVER	ONLY YOUR LOVE	10.00
72	10273	BETTYE SWANN	TODAY I STARTED LOVING YOU AGAIN	I'D RATHER GO BLIND	8.00
73	10273 DJ	BETTYE SWANN	TODAY I STARTED LOVING YOU AGAIN	I'D RATHER GO BLIND	10.00
73	10274	OTIS REDDING & CARLA THOMAS	TRAMP	KNOCK ON WOOD	5.00
73	10274 DJ	OTIS REDDING & CARLA THOMAS	TRAMP	KNOCK ON WOOD	6.00
73	10276	CLARENCE REID	GOOD OLD DAYS	TEN TONS OF DYNAMITE	5.00
73	10276 DJ	CLARENCE REID	GOOD OLD DAYS	TEN TONS OF DYNAMITE	6.00
73	10277	BILLY YOUNG	THE SLOOPY	SAME THING ALL OVER	10.00
73	10277 DJ	BILLY YOUNG	THE SLOOPY	SAME THING ALL OVER	15.00
73	10278	JOE TEX	SHOW ME	I WANT TO (DO EVERYTHING FOR Y	6.00
73	10278 DJ	JOE TEX	SHOW ME	I WANT TO (DO EVERYTHING FOR Y	8.00
73	10279	GATURS	COLD BEAR	THE BOOGIE MAN	15.00
73	10279 DJ	GATURS	COLD BEAR	THE BOOGIE MAN	20.00
73	10280	MARK HOLDER	WHATEVER'S FAIR	WHY DEAR LORD	15.00
73	10280 DJ	MARK HOLDER	WHATEVER'S FAIR	WHY DEAR LORD	20.00
73	10281	CLARENCE CARTER	LOOKING FOR A FOX	IT'S ALL IN YOUR MIND	8.00
73	10281 DJ	CLARENCE CARTER	LOOKING FOR A FOX	IT'S ALL IN YOUR MIND	10.00
73	10282	ROBERTA FLACK	KILLING ME SOFTLY WITH HIS SONG	JUST LIKE A WOMAN	4.00
73	10282 DJ	ROBERTA FLACK	KILLING ME SOFTLY WITH HIS SONG	JUST LIKE A WOMAN	5.00
73	10283	DETROIT SPINNERS	COULD IT BE I'M FALLING IN LOVE	JUST YOU AND ME BABY	5.00
73	10283 DJ	DETROIT SPINNERS	COULD IT BE I'M FALLING IN LOVE	JUST YOU AND ME BABY	6.00
73	10288	ARETHA FRANKLIN	MASTER OF EYES	MOODYS MOOD	8.00
73	10288 DJ	ARETHA FRANKLIN	MASTER OF EYES	MOODYS MOOD	10.00
73	10294	ARTHUR CONLEY	TAKE A STEP + PUT OUR LOVE TOGETHER	LOVE COMES AND GOES	5.00
73	10294 DJ	ARTHUR CONLEY	TAKE A STEP + PUT OUR LOVE TOGETHER	LOVE COMES AND GOES	6.00
73	10298	ROBIN KENYATTA	LAST TANGO IN PARIS	WEREWOLF	5.00
73	10298 DJ	ROBIN KENYATTA	LAST TANGO IN PARIS	WEREWOLF	6.00
73	10299	BETTY LAVETTE	YOUR TURN TO CRY	SOUL TAMBOURINE	15.00
73	10299 DJ	BETTY LAVETTE	YOUR TURN TO CRY	SOUL TAMBOURINE	20.00
73	10307	WILSON PICKETT	INTERNATIONAL PLAYBOY	COME RIGHT HERE	5.00
73	10307 DJ	WILSON PICKETT	INTERNATIONAL PLAYBOY	COME RIGHT HERE	6.00
73	10311	DETROIT SPINNERS	ONE OF A KIND (LOVE AFFAIR)	DON'T LET THE GREEN GRASS FOOL	4.00

73	10311 DJ	DETROIT SPINNERS	ONE OF A KIND LOVE AFFAIR	DON'T LET THE GREEN GRASS FOOL	5.00
73	10313	MARGIE JOSEPH	HOW DO YOU SPELL LOVE	LET'S STAY TOGETHER	6.00
73	10313 DJ	MARGIE JOSEPH	HOW DO YOU SPELL LOVE	LET'S STAY TOGETHER	8.00
73	10321	WILSON PICKETT	LAND OF A 1000 DANCES	IN THE MIDNIGHT HOUR	6.00
73	10321 DJ	WILSON PICKETT	LAND OF A 1000 DANCES	IN THE MIDNIGHT HOUR	8.00
73	10333	ARETHA FRANKLIN	SPANISH HARLEM	LEAN ON ME	5.00
73	10333 DJ	ARETHA FRANKLIN	SPANISH HARLEM	LEAN ON ME	6.00
73	10335	BETTY WRIGHT	CLEAN UP WOMAN	IT'S HARD TO STOP	5.00
73	10335 DJ	BETTY WRIGHT	CLEAN UP WOMAN	IT'S HARD TO STOP	6.00
73	10344	BOBBY NEWTON	THERE'S AN ISLAND	LITTLE BIT OF SOAP	6.00
73	10344 DJ	BOBBY NEWTON	THERE'S AN ISLAND	LITTLE BIT OF SOAP	8.00
73	10346	ARETHA FRANKLIN	ANGEL	SISTER FROM TEXAS	5.00
73	10346 DJ	ARETHA FRANKLIN	ANGEL	SISTER FROM TEXAS	6.00
73	10352	BLUE MAGIC	LOOK ME UP	WHAT'S COME OVER ME	5.00
73	10352 DJ	BLUE MAGIC	LOOK ME UP	WHAT'S COME OVER ME	6.00
73	10353	WILSON PICKETT	CALL MY NAME, I'LL BE THERE	WOMAN LET ME BE	6.00
73	10353 DJ	WILSON PICKETT	CALL MY NAME, I'LL BE THERE	WOMAN LET ME BE	8.00
73	10354	DONNY HATHAWAY	LOVE LOVE LOVE	SOMEDAY WE'LL BE FREE	6.00
73	10354 DJ	DONNY HATHAWAY	LOVE LOVE LOVE	SOMEDAY WE'LL BE FREE	8.00
73	10355	JACKIE MOORE	SWEET CHARLIE BABE	IF	15.00
73	10355 DJ	JACKIE MOORE	SWEET CHARLIE BABE	IF	20.00
73	10358	PERCY SLEDGE	SUNSHINE	UNCHANGING LOVE	5.00
73	10358 DJ	PERCY SLEDGE	SUNSHINE	UNCHANGING LOVE	6.00
73	10359	DETROIT SPINNERS	GHETTO CHILD	WE BELONG TOGETHER	5.00
73	10359 DJ	DETROIT SPINNERS	GHETTO CHILD	WE BELONG TOGETHER	6.00
73	10362	CLYDE BROWN	GHETTO COWBOY	YOU'VE GONE TO FAR	8.00
73	10362 DJ	CLYDE BROWN	GHETTO COWBOY	YOU'VE GONE TO FAR	10.00
73	10370	BETTY WRIGHT	LET ME BE YOUR LOVEMAKER	JEALOUS MAN	6.00
73	10370 DJ	BETTY WRIGHT	LET ME BE YOUR LOVEMAKER	JEALOUS MAN	8.00
73	10371	ROBERTA FLACK	WHEN YOU SMILE	CONVERSATION LOVE	5.00
73	10371 DJ	ROBERTA FLACK	WHEN YOU SMILE	CONVERSATION LOVE	6.00
73	10375	SISTER SLEDGE	NEITHER ONE OF US	MAMA NEVER TOLD ME	20.00
73	10375 DJ	SISTER SLEDGE	NEITHER ONE OF US	MAMA NEVER TOLD ME	25.00
73	10380	MARGIE JOSEPH	RIDIN' HIGH	COME LAY SOME LOVIN' ON ME	20.00
73	10380 DJ	MARGIE JOSEPH	RIDIN' HIGH	COME LAY SOME LOVIN' ON ME	28.00
73	10389	WILSON PICKETT	IN THE MIDNIGHT HOUR	LAND OF 1000 DANCES + FUNKY	5.00
73	10389 DJ	WILSON PICKETT	IN THE MIDNIGHT HOUR	LAND OF 1000 DANCES + FUNKY	6.00
73	10390	OTIS REDDING	SITTIN' ON THE DOCK OF THE BAY	I CAN'T TURN YOU LOSE + SATISF	5.00
73	10390 DJ	OTIS REDDING	SITTIN' ON THE DOCK OF THE BAY	I CAN'T TURN YOU LOSE + SATISF	6.00
73	10393	COASTERS	CHARLIE BROWN	SEARCHIN' + ALONG CAME JONES	4.00
73	10393 DJ	COASTERS	CHARLIE BROWN	SEARCHIN' + ALONG CAME JONES	5.00
73	10394	PERCY SLEDGE	BABY HELP ME	WHEN A MAN LOVES A WOMAN	6.00
73	10394 DJ	PERCY SLEDGE	BABY HELP ME	WHEN A MAN LOVES A WOMAN	8.00
74	10399	ARETHA FRANKLIN	UNTIL YOU COME BACK TO ME	IF YOU DON'T THINK	6.00
74	10399 DJ	ARETHA FRANKLIN	UNTIL YOU COME BACK TO ME	IF YOU DON'T THINK	8.00
74	10403	BLUE MAGIC	STOP TO START	WHERE HAVE YOU BEEN	5.00
74	10403 DJ	BLUE MAGIC	STOP TO START	WHERE HAVE YOU BEEN	6.00
74	10404	PERSUADERS	SOME GUYS HAVE ALL THE LUCK	LOVE ATTACK	5.00
74	10404 DJ	PERSUADERS	SOME GUYS HAVE ALL THE LUCK	LOVE ATTACK	6.00
74	10406	DONNY HATHAWAY	MAGDELENA	VALDEZ IN THE COUNTRY	4.00
74	10406 DJ	DONNY HATHAWAY	MAGDELENA	VALDEZ IN THE COUNTRY	6.00
74	10409	HERBIE MANN	SPINBALL	TURTLE BAY	5.00
74	10409 DJ	HERBIE MANN	SPINBALL	TURTLE BAY	6.00
74	10415	ROBERTA FLACK	JESSE	NO TEARS (IN THE END)	4.00
74	10415 DJ	ROBERTA FLACK	JESSE	NO TEARS (IN THE END)	5.00
74	10416	DETROIT EMERALDS	MIGHTY LOVE	MIGHTY LOVE part 2	4.00
74	10416 DJ	DETROIT EMERALDS	MIGHTY LOVE	MIGHTY LOVE part 2	5.00
74	10417	ELLA FITZGERALD	I'VE GOT YOU UNDER MY SKIN	C'EST MAGNIFIQUE	3.00
74	10417 DJ	ELLA FITZGERALD	I'VE GOT YOU UNDER MY SKIN	C'EST MAGNIFIQUE	4.00
74	10437	CREATION	IT'S GOTTA BE THAT WAY	IT'S GONNA BE ALRIGHT	5.00
74	10437 DJ	CREATION	IT'S GOTTA BE THAT WAY	IT'S GONNA BE ALRIGHT	6.00
74	10441	SONS OF ROBIN STONE	GOT TO GET YOU BACK	LOVE IS JUST AROUND THE CORNER	50.00
74	10441 DJ	SONS OF ROBIN STONE	GOT TO GET YOU BACK	LOVE IS JUST AROUND THE CORNER	60.00
74	10447	ARETHA FRANKLIN	I'M IN LOVE	OH BABY	5.00
74	10447 DJ	ARETHA FRANKLIN	I'M IN LOVE	OH BABY	6.00
74	10456	CLARENCE REID	FUNKY PARTY	WINTER MAN	5.00
74	10456 DJ	CLARENCE REID	FUNKY PARTY	WINTER MAN	6.00
74	10460	MARGIE JOSEPH	SWEET SURRENDER	MY LOVE	6.00
74	10460 DJ	MARGIE JOSEPH	SWEET SURRENDER	MY LOVE	8.00
74	10467	ROBERTA FLACK	FEEL LIKE MAKIN' LOVE	CONVERSATION LOVE	4.00
74	10467 DJ	ROBERTA FLACK	FEEL LIKE MAKIN' LOVE	CONVERSATION LOVE	5.00
74	10471	SOUL BROTHERS SIX	THANK YOU BABY FOR LOVING ME	SOMEBODY ELSE IS LOVING MY BAB	10.00
74	10471 DJ	SOUL BROTHERS SIX	THANK YOU BABY FOR LOVING ME	SOMEBODY ELSE IS LOVING MY BAB	15.00
74	10474	BETTY WRIGHT	SECRETARY	VALUE YOUR LOVE	5.00
74	10474 DJ	BETTY WRIGHT	SECRETARY	VALUE YOUR LOVE	6.00
74	10480	DETROIT SPINNERS	HE'LL NEVER LOVE YOU LIKE I DO	I'M COMING HOME	6.00
74	10480 DJ	DETROIT SPINNERS	HE'LL NEVER LOVE YOU LIKE I DO	I'M COMING HOME	8.00
74	10481	JACKIE MOORE	BOTH ENDS AGAINST THE MIDDLE	WILLPOWER	10.00
74	10481 DJ	JACKIE MOORE	BOTH ENDS AGAINST THE MIDDLE	WILLPOWER	15.00

74	10489	AVERAGE WHITE BAND	PICK UP THE PIECES	YOU GOT IT	6.00
74	10489 DJ	AVERAGE WHITE BAND	PICK UP THE PIECES	YOU GOT IT	8.00
74	10493	DRIFTERS	SATURDAY NIGHT AT THE MOVIES	I'LL TAKE YOU WHERE THE MUSIC'S PLAYING	5.00
74	10493 DJ	DRIFTERS	SATURDAY NIGHT AT THE MOVIES	I'LL TAKE YOU WHERE THE MUSIC'S PLAYING	6.00
74	10494	BLUE MAGIC	SIDESHOW	JUST DON'T WANT TO BE LONELY	5.00
74	10494 DJ	BLUE MAGIC	SIDESHOW	JUST DON'T WANT TO BE LONELY	6.00
74	10495	DIONNE WARWICKE & DETROIT SPINNERS	THEN CAME YOU	JUST AS LONG AS WE HAVE LOVE	5.00
74	10495 DJ	DIONNE WARWICKE & DETROIT SPINNERS	THEN CAME YOU	JUST AS LONG AS WE HAVE LOVE	6.00
74	10496	DEE DEE WARWICK	SUSPICIOUS MINDS	I'M GLAD I'M A WOMAN	5.00
74	10496 DJ	DEE DEE WARWICK	SUSPICIOUS MINDS	I'M GLAD I'M A WOMAN	6.00
74	10498	AVERAGE WHITE BAND	NOTHING I CAN DO	JUST CAN'T GIVE YOU UP	4.00
74	10498 DJ	AVERAGE WHITE BAND	NOTHING I CAN DO	JUST CAN'T GIVE YOU UP	5.00
74	10508	BEN E. KING	SPANISH HARLEM	FIRST TASTE OF LOVE	5.00
74	10508 DJ	BEN E. KING	SPANISH HARLEM	FIRST TASTE OF LOVE	6.00
74	10513	EDDIE HARRIS	IS IT IN	FUNKAROMA	8.00
74	10513 DJ	EDDIE HARRIS	IS IT IN	FUNKAROMA	10.00
74	10514	NATURAL ESSENCE	IT'S YOU I NEED	OUT OF THE DARKNESS	6.00
74	10514 DJ	NATURAL ESSENCE	IT'S YOU I NEED	OUT OF THE DARKNESS	8.00
74	10515	DON COVAY & the GOODTIMERS	SEESAW	MERCY MERCY	6.00
74	10515 DJ	DON COVAY & the GOODTIMERS	SEESAW	MERCY MERCY	8.00
74	10516	MOVING VIOL.ATION	WILD GOOSE CHASE	SPINNING TOP	25.00
74	10516 DJ	MOVING VIOL.ATION	WILD GOOSE CHASE	SPINNING TOP	30.00
74	10528	BLUE MAGIC	WELCOME TO THE CLUB	WHAT'S COME OVER TO ME	5.00
74	10528 DJ	BLUE MAGIC	WELCOME TO THE CLUB	WHAT'S COME OVER TO ME	6.00
74	10529	MAJOR HARRIS	EACH MORNING I WAKE UP	JUST A THING I DO	8.00
74	10529 DJ	MAJOR HARRIS	EACH MORNING I WAKE UP	JUST A THING I DO	10.00
74	10538	DRIFTERS	WHITE CHRISTMAS	THE BELLS OF ST. MARY'S	4.00
74	10538 DJ	DRIFTERS	WHITE CHRISTMAS	THE BELLS OF ST. MARY'S	5.00
74	10543	ARETHA FRANKLIN	WITHOUT LOVE	DON'T GO BREAKING MY HEART	4.00
74	10543 DJ	ARETHA FRANKLIN	WITHOUT LOVE	DON'T GO BREAKING MY HEART	5.00
74	10551	SISTER SLEDGE	LOVE DON'T YOU GO THROUGH NO CHANGES ON ME	DON'T YOU MISS HIM	20.00
74	10551 DJ	SISTER SLEDGE	LOVE DON'T YOU GO THROUGH NO CHANGES ON ME	DON'T YOU MISS HIM	30.00
74	10553	BLUE MAGIC	3 RING CIRCUS	SPELL	5.00
74	10553 DJ	BLUE MAGIC	3 RING CIRCUS	SPELL	6.00
74	10554	JIMMY CASTOR BUNCH	BERTHA BUTT BOOGIE	BERTHA BUTT BOOGIE part 2	3.00
74	10554 DJ	JIMMY CASTOR BUNCH	BERTHA BUTT BOOGIE	BERTHA BUTT BOOGIE part 2	4.00
74	10555	HOT ICE	BOOGIE JOOGIE	BOOGIE JOOGIE part 2	3.00
74	10555 DJ	HOT ICE	BOOGIE JOOGIE	BOOGIE JOOGIE part 2	4.00
75	10561	EDDIE HARRIS	I NEED SOME MONEY	DON'T WANT NOBODY	8.00
75	10561 DJ	EDDIE HARRIS	I NEED SOME MONEY	DON'T WANT NOBODY	10.00
75	10565	BEN E. KING	SUPERNATURAL THING	SUPERNATURAL THING part 2	4.00
75	10565 DJ	BEN E. KING	SUPERNATURAL THING	SUPERNATURAL THING part 2	5.00
75	10570	DETROIT SPINNERS	SITTING ON TOP OF THE WORLD	SMILE, WE HAVE EACH OTHER	5.00
75	10570 DJ	DETROIT SPINNERS	SITTING ON TOP OF THE WORLD	SMILE, WE HAVE EACH OTHER	6.00
75	10571	DETROIT SPINNERS	I'VE GOT TO MAKE IT ON MY OWN	LIVING A LITTLE, LAUGHING A LI	50.00
75	10571 DJ	DETROIT SPINNERS	I'VE GOT TO MAKE IT ON MY OWN	LIVING A LITTLE, LAUGHING A LI	75.00
75	10574	GENE PAGE	SATIN SOUL	CREAM CORNER	4.00
75	10574 DJ	GENE PAGE	SATIN SOUL	CREAM CORNER	5.00
75	10577	ARETHA FRANKLIN	WHEN YOU GET RIGHT DOWN TO IT	SING IT AGAIN SAY AGAIN	4.00
75	10577 DJ	ARETHA FRANKLIN	WHEN YOU GET RIGHT DOWN TO IT	SING IT AGAIN SAY AGAIN	5.00
75	10579	NEW FOUNDATIONS	DARLING	YOU TOOK MY LOVE	8.00
75	10579 DJ	NEW FOUNDATIONS	DARLING	YOU TOOK MY LOVE	10.00
75	10580	HERBIE MANN	HIJACK	ORIENT EXPRESS	5.00
75	10580 DJ	HERBIE MANN	HIJACK	ORIENT EXPRESS	6.00
75	10585	MAJOR HARRIS	LOVE WON'T LET ME WAIT	AFTER LOVING YOU	6.00
75	10585 DJ	MAJOR HARRIS	LOVE WON'T LET ME WAIT	AFTER LOVING YOU	8.00
81	10585 later lbl design	MAJOR HARRIS	LOVE WON'T LET ME WAIT	AFTER LOVING YOU	5.00
75	10587	JIMMY CASTOR BUNCH	E MAN BOOGIE	YOU MAKE ME FEEL A BRAND NEW MAN	3.00
75	10587 DJ	JIMMY CASTOR BUNCH	E MAN BOOGIE	YOU MAKE ME FEEL A BRAND NEW MAN	4.00
75	10588	BLUE MAGIC	LOVE HAS FOUND IT'S WAY TO ME	WHEN YA COMING HOME	5.00
75	10588 DJ	BLUE MAGIC	LOVE HAS FOUND IT'S WAY TO ME	WHEN YA COMING HOME	6.00
75	10594	SAM and DAVE	YOU DON'T KNOW LIKE I KNOW	SAID I WASN'T GONNA TELL NOBOD	6.00
75	10594 DJ	SAM and DAVE	YOU DON'T KNOW LIKE I KNOW	SAID I WASN'T GONNA TELL NOBOD	8.00
75	10596	RUFUS THOMAS	WILLY NILLY	SISTERS GOT A BOYFRIEND	5.00
75	10596 DJ	RUFUS THOMAS	WILLY NILLY	SISTERS GOT A BOYFRIEND	6.00
75	10599	DRIFTERS	BABY WHAT I MEAN	ANOTHER NIGHT WITH THE BOYS	6.00
75	10599 DJ	DRIFTERS	BABY WHAT I MEAN	ANOTHER NIGHT WITH THE BOYS	6.00
75	10600	DON COVAY	YOU PUT ME ON THE CRITICAL LIST	40 DAYS & 40 NIGHTS	6.00
75	10600 DJ	DON COVAY	YOU PUT ME ON THE CRITICAL LIST	40 DAYS & 40 NIGHTS	8.00
75	10601	OTIS REDDING	MY GIRL	HARD TO HANDLE + DOWN IN THE VALLEY	5.00
75	10601 DJ	OTIS REDDING	MY GIRL	HARD TO HANDLE + DOWN IN THE VALLEY	6.00
75	10601 art sleeve	OTIS REDDING	MY GIRL	HARD TO HANDLE + DOWN IN THE VALLEY	6.00
75	10602	JOE TEX	PAPA WAS TOO	HOLD ON TO WHAT YOU GOT	5.00
75	10602 DJ	JOE TEX	PAPA WAS TOO	HOLD ON TO WHAT YOU GOT	6.00
75	10605	AVERAGE WHITE BAND	CUT THE CAKE	PERSON TO PERSON	8.00
75	10605 DJ	AVERAGE WHITE BAND	CUT THE CAKE	PERSON TO PERSON	6.00
75	10612	BLACK HEAT	QUESTIONS AND CONCLUSIONS	DRIVE MY CAR	5.00
75	10612 DJ	BLACK HEAT	QUESTIONS AND CONCLUSIONS	DRIVE MY CAR	6.00
75	10614	CONSUMERS RAPPORT	EASE ON DOWN THE ROAD	GO ON WITH YOUR BAD SELF	4.00

75	10614 DJ	CONSUMERS RAPPORT	EASE ON DOWN THE ROAD	GO ON WITH YOUR BAD SELF	5.00
75	10617	TONY & TYRONE	PLEASE OPERATOR	APPLE OF MY EYE	10.00
75	10617 DJ	TONY & TYRONE	PLEASE OPERATOR	APPLE OF MY EYE	15.00
artist credits on # 10617 - Tony & Tyrone is printed TONY TYRONE					
75	10618	BEN E. KING	HAPPINESS IS WHERE YOU FIND IT	DROP MY HEART OFF (ON YOUR WAY	20.00
75	10618 DJ	BEN E. KING	HAPPINESS IS WHERE YOU FIND IT	DROP MY HEART OFF (ON YOUR WAY	25.00
75	10619	SISTER SLEDGE	NEITHER ONE OF US (WANTS TO BE THIS	MAMA NEVER TOLD ME	20.00
75	10619 DJ	SISTER SLEDGE	NEITHER ONE OF US (WANTS TO BE THIS	MAMA NEVER TOLD ME	25.00
75	10622	BETTYE SWANN	ALL THE WAY IN OR ALL THE WAY OUT	DOING FOR THE ONE I LOVE	6.00
75	10622 DJ	BETTYE SWANN	ALL THE WAY IN OR ALL THE WAY OUT	DOING FOR THE ONE I LOVE	8.00
75	10623	ROBERTA FLACK	FEELING THAT GLOW	GOSPEL ACCORDING TO ST. MATTHEW	4.00
75	10623 DJ	ROBERTA FLACK	FEELING THAT GLOW	GOSPEL ACCORDING TO ST. MATTHEW	5.00
75	10626	DETROIT SPINNERS	SADIE	LAZY SUSAN	5.00
75	10626 DJ	DETROIT SPINNERS	SADIE	LAZY SUSAN	6.00
75	10629 test press	PATTI & THE LOVE LITES	LOVE BANDIT	I'M THE ONE THAT YOU NEED	150.00
75	10632	BARRABAS	MAD LOVE	FUNKY BABY	5.00
75	10632 DJ	BARRABAS	MAD LOVE	FUNKY BABY	6.00
75	10636	BEN E. KING	DO IT IN THE NAME OF LOVE	IMAGINATION	5.00
75	10636 DJ	BEN E. KING	DO IT IN THE NAME OF LOVE	IMAGINATION	6.00
75	10638	BROOK BENTON	RAINY NIGHT IN GEORGIA	SHOES	5.00
75	10638 DJ	BROOK BENTON	RAINY NIGHT IN GEORGIA	SHOES	6.00
75	10645	JIMMY CASTOR BUNCH	POTENTIAL	DANIEL	3.00
75	10645 DJ	JIMMY CASTOR BUNCH	POTENTIAL	DANIEL	4.00
75	10646	MARGIE JOSEPH	I CAN'T MOVE NO MOUNTAIN	JUST AS SOON AS THE FEELING'S	20.00
75	10646 DJ	MARGIE JOSEPH	I CAN'T MOVE NO MOUNTAIN	JUST AS SOON AS THE FEELING'S	28.00
75	10649	MARGIE JOSEPH & BLUE MAGIC	WHAT'S COME OVER ME	YOU AND ME ()GOT A GOOD THING	5.00
75	10649 DJ	MARGIE JOSEPH & BLUE MAGIC	WHAT'S COME OVER ME	YOU AND ME ()GOT A GOOD THING	6.00
75	10659	DETROIT SPINNERS	GAMES PEOPLE PLAY	DON'T WANT TO LOSE YOU	4.00
75	10659 DJ	DETROIT SPINNERS	GAMES PEOPLE PLAY	DON'T WANT TO LOSE YOU	5.00
75	10664	TRAMMPS	HOOKED FOR LIFE	IT'S ALRIGHT	4.00
75	10664 DJ	TRAMMPS	HOOKED FOR LIFE	IT'S ALRIGHT	5.00
75	10669	ARETHA FRANKLIN	MR. DJ (5 FOR THE DJ)	AS LONG AS YOU ARE THERE	5.00
75	10669 DJ	ARETHA FRANKLIN	MR. DJ (5 FOR THE DJ)	AS LONG AS YOU ARE THERE	6.00
75	10670	MANHATTAN TRANSFER	TUXEDO JUNCTION	OPERATOR	3.00
75	10670 DJ	MANHATTAN TRANSFER	TUXEDO JUNCTION	OPERATOR	4.00
75	10675	JIMMY CASTOR BUNCH	KING KONG	KING KONG part 2	3.00
75	10675 DJ	JIMMY CASTOR BUNCH	KING KONG	KING KONG part 2	4.00
75	10676	SAM DEES	FRAGILE HANDLE WITH CARE	SAVE THE LOVE AT ANY COST	**127.00**
75	10676 DJ	SAM DEES	FRAGILE HANDLE WITH CARE	SAVE THE LOVE AT ANY COST	150.00
75	10683	SISTER SLEDGE	LOVE HAS FOUND ME	LOVE AIN'T EASY	5.00
75	10683 DJ	SISTER SLEDGE	LOVE HAS FOUND ME	LOVE AIN'T EASY	6.00
75	10689	BLUE MAGIC	MAGIC OF THE BLUE	STOP TO START	5.00
75	10689 DJ	BLUE MAGIC	MAGIC OF THE BLUE	STOP TO START	6.00
75	10691	DRIFTERS	UNDER THE BOARDWALK	ON BROADWAY	5.00
75	10691 DJ	DRIFTERS	UNDER THE BOARDWALK	ON BROADWAY	6.00
75	10700	DRIFTERS	YOU GOTTA PAY YOUR DUES	ONE WAY LOVE	15.00
75	10700 DJ	DRIFTERS	YOU GOTTA PAY YOUR DUES	ONE WAY LOVE	30.00
75	10703	TRAMMPS	THAT'S WERE HAPPY PEOPLE GO	same: long version	5.00
75	10703 DJ	TRAMMPS	THAT'S WERE HAPPY PEOPLE GO	same: long version	6.00
75	10708	BEN E. KING	WE GOT LOVE	I HAD A LOVE	10.00
75	10708 DJ	BEN E. KING	WE GOT LOVE	I HAD A LOVE	15.00
75	10710	DETROIT SPINNERS	LOVE OR LEAVE	YOU MADE A PROMISE TO ME	5.00
75	10710 DJ	DETROIT SPINNERS	LOVE OR LEAVE	YOU MADE A PROMISE TO ME	6.00
75	10711	ARETHA FRANKLIN	YOU	WITHOUT YOU	5.00
75	10711 DJ	ARETHA FRANKLIN	YOU	WITHOUT YOU	6.00
75	10714	SIMON SAID	SMILE	TELL ME	4.00
75	10714 DJ	SIMON SAID	SMILE	TELL ME	5.00
75	10715	STANLEY CLARKE	SILLY PUTTY	HELLO JEFF	3.00
75	10715 DJ	STANLEY CLARKE	SILLY PUTTY	HELLO JEFF	4.00
75	10716	BARRABAS	CHECKMATE	FOUR SEASON WOMAN	5.00
75	10716 DJ	BARRABAS	CHECKMATE	FOUR SEASON WOMAN	6.00
75	10719	SAM DEES & BETTYE SWANN	JUST AS SURE	STORYBOOK CHILDREN	50.00
75	10719 DJ	SAM DEES & BETTYE SWANN	JUST AS SURE	STORYBOOK CHILDREN	75.00
75	10720	JACKIE CARTER	TREAT ME LIKE A WOMAN	MAMA DON'T WAIT UP FOR ME	5.00
75	10720 DJ	JACKIE CARTER	TREAT ME LIKE A WOMAN	MAMA DON'T WAIT UP FOR ME	6.00
75	10723	SONS OF ROBIN STONE	GOT TO GET YOU BACK	LOVE IS JUST AROUND THE CORNER	30.00
75	10723 DJ	SONS OF ROBIN STONE	GOT TO GET YOU BACK	LOVE IS JUST AROUND THE CORNER	40.00
75	10724	DETROIT SPINNERS	ONE OF A KIND	medley	4.00
75	10724 DJ	DETROIT SPINNERS	ONE OF A KIND	medley	5.00
76	10727	GENE PAGE	WILD CHERRY	ESCAPE TO THE DISCO	3.00
76	10727 DJ	GENE PAGE	WILD CHERRY	ESCAPE TO THE DISCO	4.00
76	10728	JIMMY CASTOR BUNCH	SUPERBOUND	DRIFTING	3.00
76	10728 DJ	JIMMY CASTOR BUNCH	SUPERBOUND	DRIFTING	4.00
76	10737	FRANNIE GOLDE	SAVE ME (I'M FALLING IN LOVE AGAIN)	STOP (AND LOOK AROUND	8.00
76	10737 DJ	FRANNIE GOLDE	SAVE ME (I'M FALLING IN LOVE AGAIN)	STOP (AND LOOK AROUND	10.00
76	10741	EDDIE HARRIS	GET ON UP AND DANCE	WHY MUST WE PART	5.00
76	10741 DJ	EDDIE HARRIS	GET ON UP AND DANCE	WHY MUST WE PART	6.00
76	10742	R.B. HUDMON	HOW CAN I BE A WITNESS	IF YOU DON'T CHEAT ON ME	15.00
76	10742 DJ	R.B. HUDMON	HOW CAN I BE A WITNESS	IF YOU DON'T CHEAT ON ME	20.00

76	10765	ARETHA FRANKLIN	SOMETHING HE CAN FEEL	LOVING YOU BABY	4.00
76	10765 DJ	ARETHA FRANKLIN	SOMETHING HE CAN FEEL	LOVING YOU BABY	5.00
76	10773	SIMON SAID	YOU AND ME	PUT SOME MORE FLAVOUR IN IT	3.00
76	10773 DJ	SIMON SAID	YOU AND ME	PUT SOME MORE FLAVOUR IN IT	4.00
76	10780	IMPACT	HAPPY MAN	HAPPY MAN part 2	10.00
76	10780 DJ	IMPACT	HAPPY MAN	HAPPY MAN part 2	15.00
76	10782	JIMMY CASTOR BUNCH	BOOM BOOM	WHAT'S BEST?	3.00
76	10782 DJ	JIMMY CASTOR BUNCH	BOOM BOOM	WHAT'S BEST?	4.00
76	10796	BLUE MAGIC	FREAK-N-STIEN	STOP AND GET A HOLD OF YOURSEL	3.00
76	10796 DJ	BLUE MAGIC	FREAK-N-STIEN	STOP AND GET A HOLD OF YOURSEL	4.00
76	10797	TRAMMPS	SOUL SEARCHING TIME	LOVE IS A FUNNY THING	3.00
76	10797 DJ	TRAMMPS	SOUL SEARCHING TIME	LOVE IS A FUNNY THING	4.00
76	10799	DETROIT SPINNERS	WAKE UP SUSAN	IF YOU CAN'T BE IN LOVE	4.00
76	10799 DJ	DETROIT SPINNERS	WAKE UP SUSAN	IF YOU CAN'T BE IN LOVE	5.00
76	10801	GENE PAGE	INTO MY THING	ORGAN GRINDER	3.00
76	10801 DJ	GENE PAGE	INTO MY THING	ORGAN GRINDER	4.00
76	10807	DETROIT SPINNERS	THE RUBBERBAND MAN	THE RUBBERBAND MAN PART2	4.00
76	10807 DJ	DETROIT SPINNERS	THE RUBBERBAND MAN	THE RUBBERBAND MAN PART2	5.00
76	10824	L.T.G. EXCHANGE	YOU'LL NEVER LEARN (ABOUT LOVE)	HUDDLE	50.00
76	10824 DJ	L.T.G. EXCHANGE	YOU'LL NEVER LEARN (ABOUT LOVE)	HUDDLE	75.00
76	10829	JIMMY CASTOR BUNCH	E-MAN GROOVIN'	SUPERLOVE	3.00
76	10829 DJ	JIMMY CASTOR BUNCH	E-MAN GROOVIN'	SUPERLOVE	4.00
76	10830	MANHATTAN TRANSFER	HELPLESS	IT WOULDN'T HAVE MADE ANY DIFF	5.00
76	10830 DJ	MANHATTAN TRANSFER	HELPLESS	IT WOULDN'T HAVE MADE ANY DIFF	6.00
76	10843	CLARENCE CARTER	PATCHES	SNATCHIN' IT BACK	5.00
76	10843 DJ	CLARENCE CARTER	PATCHES	SNATCHIN' IT BACK	6.00
76	10846	TRAMMPS	HOOKED FOR LIFE	IT'S ALRIGHT	5.00
76	10846 DJ	TRAMMPS	HOOKED FOR LIFE	IT'S ALRIGHT	6.00
76	10845	ROBERTA FLACK	FIRST TIME EVER I SAW YOUR FACE	KILLING ME SOFTLY WITH HIS SONG	4.00
76	10845 DJ	ROBERTA FLACK	FIRST TIME EVER I SAW YOUR FACE	KILLING ME SOFTLY WITH HIS SONG	5.00
76	10851	BETTYE SWANN	HEADING IN THE RIGHT DIRECTION	BE STRONG ENOUGH TO HOLD ON	8.00
76	10851 DJ	BETTYE SWANN	HEADING IN THE RIGHT DIRECTION	BE STRONG ENOUGH TO HOLD ON	10.00
76	10879	DARRELL BANKS	ANGEL BABY (DON'T YOU EVER LEAVE	LOOK INTO THE EYES OF A FOOL	15.00
76	10879 DJ	DARRELL BANKS	ANGEL BABY (DON'T YOU EVER LEAVE	LOOK INTO THE EYES OF A FOOL	20.00
77	10894	ALFIE KHAN SOUND ORCHESTRA	LAW OF THE LAND	WOMAN	6.00
77	10894 DJ	ALFIE KHAN SOUND ORCHESTRA	LAW OF THE LAND	WOMAN	8.00
77	10895	CERRONE	LOVE IN C MINOR	BLACK IS BLACK	4.00
77	10895 DJ	CERRONE	LOVE IN C MINOR	BLACK IS BLACK	5.00
77	10935 EP PS	DETROIT SPINNERS	COULD IT BE I'M FALLING IN LOVE	4 tracks EP with picture cover	5.00
77	10945	DETROIT EMERALDS	FEEL THE NEED	LOVE HAS COME TO ME	4.00
77	10945 DJ	DETROIT EMERALDS	FEEL THE NEED	LOVE HAS COME TO ME	5.00
77	10982	TRAMMPS	I FEEL I'VE BEEN LIVIN' (ON THE DARK	DON'T BURN NO BRIDGES	4.00
77	10982 DJ	TRAMMPS	I FEEL I'VE BEEN LIVIN' (ON THE DARK	DON'T BURN NO BRIDGES	5.00
77	10991	DENNIS COFFEY	FREE SPIRIT	OUR LOVE GOES ON FOREVER	4.00
77	10991 DJ	DENNIS COFFEY	FREE SPIRIT	OUR LOVE GOES ON FOREVER	5.00
78	11180	KAREN YOUNG	HOT SHOT	same: instrumental	4.00
78	11180 DJ	KAREN YOUNG	HOT SHOT	same: instrumental	5.00
78	11131	JAN AKKERMAN	CRACKERS	ANGEL WATCH	4.00
78	11131 DJ	JAN AKKERMAN	CRACKERS	ANGEL WATCH	5.00
78	11198	BETTY LAVETTE	DOIN' THE BEST THAT I CAN	DOIN' THE BEST THAT I CAN part2	6.00
78	11198 DJ	BETTY LAVETTE	DOIN' THE BEST THAT I CAN	DOIN' THE BEST THAT I CAN part2	8.00
78	11238	ROBERTA FLACK	INDEPENDENT MAN	AND THE FEELINGS GOOD	15.00
79	11286	DETROIT SPINNERS	ARE YOU READY FOR LOVE	ONCE YOU FALL IN LOVE	5.00
79	11286 DJ	DETROIT SPINNERS	ARE YOU READY FOR LOVE	ONCE YOU FALL IN LOVE	6.00
79	11374	JAN AKKERMAN	SHE'S SO DEVINE	SKYDANCER	4.00
79	11374 DJ	JAN AKKERMAN	SHE'S SO DEVINE	SKYDANCER	5.00
79	11432	DETROIT SPINNERS	WORKING MY WAY BACK TO YOU	DISCO RIDE	4.00
79	11432 DJ	DETROIT SPINNERS	WORKING MY WAY BACK TO YOU	DISCO RIDE	6.00
79	11448	LITTLE MAC & the BOSS SPUNDS	YOU CAN'T LOVE ME (IN THE MIDNIGHT HOUR)	IN THE MIDNIGHT HOUR instru.	5.00
79	11448 DJ	LITTLE MAC & the BOSS SPUNDS	YOU CAN'T LOVE ME (IN THE MIDNIGHT HOUR)	IN THE MIDNIGHT HOUR instru.	6.00
79	11455	SISTER SLEDGE	EASY STREET	HOW TO LOVE	4.00
79	11455 DJ	SISTER SLEDGE	EASY STREET	HOW TO LOVE	5.00
79	11475	MASS PRODUCTION	SHANTE	YOUR LOVE	6.00
79	11475 DJ	MASS PRODUCTION	SHANTE	YOUR LOVE	8.00
79	11481	ROBERTA FLACK & DONNY HATHAWAY	BACK TOGETHER AGAIN	ONLY HEAVEN CAN WAIT	8.00
79	11481 DJ	ROBERTA FLACK & DONNY HATHAWAY	BACK TOGETHER AGAIN	ONLY HEAVEN CAN WAIT	10.00
80	11498	DETROIT SPINNERS	CUPID / I'VE LOVED YOU FOR A LONG	PIPEDREAM	4.00
80	11498 DJ	DETROIT SPINNERS	CUPID / I'VE LOVED YOU FOR A LONG	PIPEDREAM	5.00
80	11558	DETROIT SPINNERS	SPLIT DECISION	NOW THAT YOU'RE MINE AGAIN	8.00
80	11558 DJ	DETROIT SPINNERS	SPLIT DECISION	NOW THAT YOU'RE MINE AGAIN	10.00
80	11560	KLEEER	GET TOUGH	HYPNOTISED	3.00
80	11560 DJ	KLEEER	GET TOUGH	HYPNOTISED	4.00
80	11564	DETROIT SPINNERS	YESTERDAY ONCE MORE/NOTHING	BE MY LOVE	4.00
80	11564 DJ	DETROIT SPINNERS	YESTERDAY ONCE MORE/NOTHING	BE MY LOVE	5.00
80	11165	ROBERTA FLACK	IF EVER SEE YOU AGAIN	I'D LIKE TO BE BABY TO YOU	4.00
80	11165 DJ	ROBERTA FLACK	IF EVER SEE YOU AGAIN	I'D LIKE TO BE BABY TO YOU	5.00
80	11624	DETROIT SPINNERS	I JUST WANT TO FALL IN LOVE	LOVE TRIPPIN'	50.00
80	11624 DJ	DETROIT SPINNERS	I JUST WANT TO FALL IN LOVE	LOVE TRIPPIN'	60.00
81	11707	DETROIT SPINNERS	CAN'T SHAKE THIS FEELIN'	KNACK FOR ME	4.00

81	11707 DJ	DETROIT SPINNERS	CAN'T SHAKE THIS FEELIN'	KNACK FOR ME	5.00
81	11708	YVONNE GAGE	TONIGHT I WANNA LOVE YOU	GARDEN OF EVE	4.00
81	11708 DJ	YVONNE GAGE	TONIGHT I WANNA LOVE YOU	GARDEN OF EVE	5.00

584 series was Polydor distributed from May 1966 to March 1970. Promotional demos have a bold black "A" to the lower right hand side of the label just underneath the label date. I can only confirm the first 49 releases actually got pressed with promo labels, if anyone can confirm any releases after # 584049 with promo labels we'd be very pleased to receive any extra information. Promo 45s from release number 584050 onwards had the labels, either date stamped with the release date or had a "Not For Sale" white with red lettering sticker. Neither the date stamp nor the sticker promo should be treated any different to the stock copies in value. Towards the end of the 584 series more and more rock records were issued, I have added those titles in because Atlantic is a completists label and many collectors are trying to buy the whole series. You will also notice with the rock period numbers that we have no info for, we are presuming they were never issued. If you have any further information on these few blank spaces, this would be most welcome.

66	584001	PERCY SLEDGE	WHEN A MAN LOVES A WOMAN	LOVE ME LIKE YOU MEAN IT	8.00
66	584001 DJ	PERCY SLEDGE	WHEN A MAN LOVES A WOMAN	LOVE ME LIKE YOU MEAN IT	30.00
66	584002	BILLY JOE ROYAL	NEVER IN A HUNDRED YEARS	WE HAVEN'T A MOMENT TO LOSE	5.00
66	584002 DJ	BILLY JOE ROYAL	NEVER IN A HUNDRED YEARS	WE HAVEN'T A MOMENT TO LOSE	10.00
66	584003	SAM AND DAVE	HOLD ON! I'M A COMING	I GOT EVERYTHING I NEED	15.00
66	584003 DJ	SAM AND DAVE	HOLD ON! I'M A COMING	I GOT EVERYTHING I NEED	30.00
66	584004	CAPITOLS	COOL JERK	HELLO STRANGER	30.00
66	584004 DJ	CAPITOLS	COOL JERK	HELLO STRANGER	50.00
66	584004	THREE CAPS	COOL JERK	HELLO STRANGER	10.00
66	584004 DJ unconfirmed	THREE CAPS	COOL JERK	HELLO STRANGER	UN
66	584005	SOLOMON BURKE	I FEEL A SIN COMING ON	MOUNTAIN OF PRIDE	8.00
66	584005 DJ	SOLOMON BURKE	I FEEL A SIN COMING ON	MOUNTAIN OF PRIDE	15.00
66	584006	WAYNE KEMP	LITTLE HOME WRECKER	WATCH THAT FIRST LITTLE STEP	15.00
66	584006 DJ	WAYNE KEMP	LITTLE HOME WRECKER	WATCH THAT FIRST LITTLE STEP	25.00
66	584007	PATTI LABELLE & the BLUEBELLES	FAMILY MAN	PATTI'S PRAYER	10.00
66	584007 DJ	PATTI LABELLE & the BLUEBELLES	FAMILY MAN	PATTI'S PRAYER	25.00
66	584008	BEN E. KING	SO MUCH LOVE	DON'T DRIVE ME AWAY	10.00
66	584008 DJ	BEN E. KING	SO MUCH LOVE	DON'T DRIVE ME AWAY	25.00
66	584009	VALA REEGAN & the VALARONS	FIREMAN	LIVING IN THE PAST	200.00
66	584009 DJ	VALA REEGAN & the VALARONS	FIREMAN	LIVING IN THE PAST	**251.00**
66	584010	RUSSELL EVANS	THE BOLD	SEND ME SOME CORNBREAD	20.00
66	584010 DJ	RUSSELL EVANS	THE BOLD	SEND ME SOME CORNBREAD	40.00
66	584011	CARLA THOMAS	LET ME BE GOOD TO YOU	ANOTHER NIGHT WITHOUT MY MAN	8.00
66	584011 DJ	CARLA THOMAS	LET ME BE GOOD TO YOU	ANOTHER NIGHT WITHOUT MY MAN	20.00
66	584012	DEON JACKSON	LOVE TAKES A LONG TIME GROWING	HUSH LITTLE BABY	20.00
66	584012 DJ	DEON JACKSON	LOVE TAKES A LONG TIME GROWING	HUSH LITTLE BABY	40.00
66	584013	ESTHER PHILLIPS	WHEN A WOMAN LOVE A MAN	UPS AND DOWNS	8.00
66	584013 DJ	ESTHER PHILLIPS	WHEN A WOMAN LOVE A MAN	UPS AND DOWNS	15.00
66	584015	GOOGIE RENE COMBO	CHICA-BOO	MERCY, MERCY (TO MUCH FOR THE	20.00
66	584015 DJ	GOOGIE RENE COMBO	CHICA-BOO	MERCY, MERCY (TO MUCH FOR THE	30.00
66	584016	JOE TEX	S.Y.S.L.F.M. (THE LETTER SONG)	I'M A MAN	10.00
66	584016 DJ	JOE TEX	S.Y.S.L.F.M. (THE LETTER SONG)	I'M A MAN	30.00
66	584017	JIMMY HUGHES	NEIGHBOR, NEIGHBOR	IT'S A GOOD THING	20.00
66	584017 DJ	JIMMY HUGHES	NEIGHBOR, NEIGHBOR	IT'S A GOOD THING	30.00
66	584018	SONNY & CHER	HAVE I STAYED TOO LONG	LEAVE ME BE	5.00
66	584018 DJ	SONNY & CHER	HAVE I STAYED TOO LONG	LEAVE ME BE	10.00
66	584019	OTIS REDDING	MY LOVER'S PRAYER	DON'T MESS WITH CUPID	8.00
66	584019 DJ	OTIS REDDING	MY LOVER'S PRAYER	DON'T MESS WITH CUPID	20.00
66	584020	DRIFTERS	UP IN THE STREETS OF HARLEM	YOU CAN'T LOVE THEM ALL	8.00
66	584020 DJ	DRIFTERS	UP IN THE STREETS OF HARLEM	YOU CAN'T LOVE THEM ALL	20.00
66	584021	SHADOWS OF KNIGHT	OH YEAH	LIGHT BULB BLUES	25.00
66	584021 DJ	SHADOWS OF KNIGHT	OH YEAH	LIGHT BULB BLUES	40.00
66	584022	MABLE JOHN	IT'S CATCHING	YOUR GOOD THING (IS ABOUT TO END)	15.00
66	584022 DJ	MABLE JOHN	IT'S CATCHING	YOUR GOOD THING (IS ABOUT TO END)	25.00
66	584023	WILSON PICKETT	991/2 (WON'T DO)	DANGER ZONE	8.00
66	584023 DJ	WILSON PICKETT	991/2 (WON'T DO)	DANGER ZONE	20.00
66	584024	YOUNG RASCALS	YOU BETTER RUN	LOVE IS A BEAUTIFUL THING	15.00
66	584024 DJ	YOUNG RASCALS	YOU BETTER RUN	LOVE IS A BEAUTIFUL THING	25.00
66	584025	DON COVAY & THE GOODTIMERS	IRON OUT THE ROUGH SPOTS	YOU PUT SOMETHINGN ON ME	15.00
66	584025 DJ	DON COVAY & THE GOODTIMERS	IRON OUT THE ROUGH SPOTS	YOU PUT SOMETHINGN ON ME	25.00
66	584026	SOLOMON BURKE	KEEP LOOKIN'	SUDDENLY	15.00
66	584026 DJ	SOLOMON BURKE	KEEP LOOKIN'	SUDDENLY	30.00
66	584027	MIKE WILLIAMS	LONELY SOLDIER	IF THIS ISN'T LOVE	30.00
66	584027 DJ	MIKE WILLIAMS	LONELY SOLDIER	IF THIS ISN'T LOVE	50.00
66	584028	REX GARVIN & THE MIGHTY CRAVERS	SOCK IT TO 'EM JB	SOCK IT TO 'EM JB PART 2	20.00
66	584028 DJ	REX GARVIN & THE MIGHTY CRAVERS	SOCK IT TO 'EM JB	SOCK IT TO 'EM JB PART 2	60.00
66	584029	RUFUS THOMAS	WILLY NILLY	SHO' GONNA MESS HIM UP	10.00
66	584029 DJ	RUFUS THOMAS	WILLY NILLY	SHO' GONNA MESS HIM UP	25.00
66	584030	OTIS REDDING	I CAN'T TURN YOU LOOSE	JUST ONE MORE DAY	10.00
66	584030 DJ	OTIS REDDING	I CAN'T TURN YOU LOOSE	JUST ONE MORE DAY	30.00
66	584031	LITTLE MACK & THE BOSS SOUNDS	IN THE MIDNIGHT HOUR	YOU CAN'T LOVE ME IN THE MIDNI	15.00
66	584031 DJ	LITTLE MACK & THE BOSS SOUNDS	IN THE MIDNIGHT HOUR	YOU CAN'T LOVE ME IN THE MIDNI	30.00
66	584032	LORETTA WILLIAMS	BABY CAKES	I'M MISSING YOU	30.00
66	584032 DJ	LORETTA WILLIAMS	BABY CAKES	I'M MISSING YOU	60.00
66	584033	COASTERS	SHE'S A YUM YUM	SATURDAY NIGHT FISH FRY	8.00
66	584033 DJ	COASTERS	SHE'S A YUM YUM	SATURDAY NIGHT FISH FRY	15.00
66	584034	PERCY SLEDGE	WARM AND TENDER LOVE	SUGAR PUDDIN'	8.00
66	584034 DJ	PERCY SLEDGE	WARM AND TENDER LOVE	SUGAR PUDDIN'	25.00
66	584035	JOE TEX	YOU BETTER BELIEVE IT	I BELIEVE I'M GONNA MAKE IT	20.00

66	584035 DJ	JOE TEX	YOU BETTER BELIEVE IT	I BELIEVE I'M GONNA MAKE IT	40.00
66	584036	BROTHER JACK McDUFF	DOWN IN THE VALLEY	A CHANGE IS GONNA COME	10.00
66	584036 DJ	BROTHER JACK McDUFF	DOWN IN THE VALLEY	A CHANGE IS GONNA COME	20.00
66	584037	BARBARA LEWIS	MAKE ME BELONG TO YOU	GIRLS NEED LOVING CARE	15.00
66	584037 DJ	BARBARA LEWIS	MAKE ME BELONG TO YOU	GIRLS NEED LOVING CARE	30.00
66	584038	MAD LADS	SUGAR SUGAR	GET OUT OF MY LIFE WOMAN	15.00
66	584038 DJ	MAD LADS	SUGAR SUGAR	GET OUT OF MY LIFE WOMAN	20.00
66	584039	WILSON PICKETT	LAND OF 1,000 DANCES	YOU'RE SO FINE	10.00
66	584039 DJ	WILSON PICKETT	LAND OF 1,000 DANCES	YOU'RE SO FINE	30.00
66	584040	SONNY & CHER	LITTLE MAN	MONDAY	5.00
66	584041	EDDIE FLOYD	KNOCK ON WOOD	GOT TO MAKE A COMEBACK	10.00
66	584041 DJ	EDDIE FLOYD	KNOCK ON WOOD	GOT TO MAKE A COMEBACK	30.00
66	584042	CARLA THOMAS	B-A-B-Y	WHAT HAVE YOU GOT TO OFFER ME	10.00
66	584042 DJ	CARLA THOMAS	B-A-B-Y	WHAT HAVE YOU GOT TO OFFER ME	25.00
66	584043	THREE CAPS	I GOT TO HANDLE IT	ZIG - ZAGGING	15.00
66	584043 DJ	THREE CAPS	I GOT TO HANDLE IT	ZIG - ZAGGING	30.00
66	584044	BOOKER T. & THE MG'S	MY SWEET POTATO	BOOKER LOO	10.00
66	584044 DJ	BOOKER T. & THE MG'S	MY SWEET POTATO	BOOKER LOO	25.00
66	584045	SHADOWS OF KNIGHT	BAD LITTLE WOMAN	GOSPEL ZONE	20.00
66	584045 DJ	SHADOWS OF KNIGHT	BAD LITTLE WOMAN	GOSPEL ZONE	30.00
66	584046	BEN E. KING	I SWEAR BY THE STARS ABOVE	GET IN A HURRY	15.00
66	584046 DJ	BEN E. KING	I SWEAR BY THE STARS ABOVE	GET IN A HURRY	30.00
66	584047	SAM AND DAVE	SAID I WASN'T GONNA TELL YOU	IF YOU GOT THE LOVING (I GOT T	8.00
66	584047 DJ	SAM AND DAVE	SAID I WASN'T GONNA TELL YOU	IF YOU GOT THE LOVING (I GOT T	10.00
66	584048	NINO TEMPO & APRIL STEVENS	COLDEST NIGHT OF THE YEAR	OOH LA LA	6.00
66	584048 DJ	NINO TEMPO & APRIL STEVENS	COLDEST NIGHT OF THE YEAR	OOH LA LA	15.00
66	584049	OTIS REDDING	FA-FA-FA-FA-FA (SAD SONG)	GOOD TO ME	10.00
66	584049 DJ	OTIS REDDING	FA-FA-FA-FA-FA (SAD SONG)	GOOD TO ME	30.00
66	584050	YOUNG RASCALS	COME ON UP	WHAT IS THE REASON	15.00
66	584051	BOBBY DARIN	IF I WERE A CARPENTER	RAININ'	5.00
66	584052	HERBIE MANN c/w DAVE PIKE	PHILLY DOG	SUNNY	15.00
66	584053	ART FREEMAN	SLIPPING AROUND	CAN'T GET YOU OUT OF MY MIND	255.00
66	584054	MARY WELLS	SUCH A SWEET THING	ME AND MY BABY	20.00
66	584055	PERCY SLEDGE	HEART OF A CHILD	MY ADORABLE ONE	15.00
66	584056	DEE DEE SHARP	BYE BYE BABY	MY BEST FRIEND'S MAN	20.00
66	584057	SONNY & CHER	LIVING FOR YOU	TURN AROUND	5.00
66	584058	HERBIE MANN	LOVE THEME FROM PARIS BURNING	HAPPY BRASS	6.00
66	584059	DON COVAY & THE GOODTIMERS	SEE-SAW	SOMEBODY'S GOT TO LOVE YOU	15.00
66	584060	BOOKER T. & THE MG'S	JINGLE BELLS	WINTER WONDERLAND	8.00
67	584061	BARBARA LEWIS	I REMEMBER THE FEELING	BABY WHAT DO YOU WANT ME TO DO	60.00
67	584062	ESTHER PHILLIPS	SOMEONE ELSE IS TAKING MY PLACE	WHEN LOVE COMES TO THE HUMAN R	8.00
67	584063	BOBBY DARIN	THE GIRL THAT STOOD BESIDE ME	A REASON TO BELIEVE	5.00
67	584064	SAM AND DAVE	YOU GOT ME HUMMIN'	SLEEP GOOD TONIGHT	8.00
67	584065	DRIFTERS	BABY WHAT I MEAN	ARETHA	10.00
67	584066	WILSON PICKETT	MUSTANG SALLY	THREE TIME LOSER	10.00
67	584067	YOUNG RASCALS	TOO MANY FISH IN THE SEA	NO LOVE TO GIVE	8.00
67	584068	JOE TEX	PAPA WAS TOO	THE TRUEST WOMAN IN THE WORLD	8.00
67	584069	BEN E. KING	WHAT IS SOUL	THEY DON'T GIVE MEDALS TO YEST	8.00
67	584070	OTIS REDDING	TRY A LITTLE TENDERNESS	SICK Y'ALL	8.00
67	584071	PERCY SLEDGE	OH, HOW HAPPY	IT TEARS ME UP	15.00
67	584072	PATTI LABELLE	TAKE ME FOR A LITTLE WHILE	I DON'T WANT TO GO ON WITHOUT	8.00
67	584073	BILLY GRAHAM & ESCALATORS	OOH-POO-PAH-DOO	EAST 24TH. STREET	15.00
67	584074	MAR-KEYS	LAST NIGHT	NIGHT BEFORE	8.00
67	584075	BITTER END SINGERS	A TASTE OF YOUR LOVE	EVERYBODY KNOWS MY NAME	6.00
67	584076	WILLIAM BELL	NEVER LIKE THIS BEFORE	SOLDIER'S GOODBYE	10.00
67	584077	BUFFALO SPRINGFIELD	DO I HAVE THE RIGHT TO SAY	FOR WHAT IT'S WORTH	6.00
67	584078	SONNY & CHER	THE BEAT GOES ON	LOVE DON'T COME	6.00
67	584079	BOBBY DARIN	LOVIN' YOU	AMY	5.00
67	584080	PERCY SLEDGE	BABY, HELP ME	YOU'VE GOT THAT SOMETHING WOND	15.00
67	584081	YOUNG RASCALS	I'VE BEEN LONELY TOO LONG	IF YOU KNEW	10.00
67	584082	DON COVAY & THE GOODTIMERS	SHINGALING '67	I WAS THERE	10.00
67	584083	ARTHUR CONLEY	SWEET SOUL MUSIC	LET'S GO STEADY AGAIN	6.00
67	584084	ARETHA FRANKLIN	I NEVER LOVED A MAN (THE WAY I LOVE YOU)	DO TIGHHT WOMAN - DO RIGHT MAN	8.00
67	584085	YOUNG RASCALS	I AIN'T GOONA EAT MY HERART OUT	GOOD LOVIN'	6.00
67	584086	SAM AND DAVE	YOU DON'T KNOW LIKE I KNOW	BLAME ME DON'T BLAME MY HEART	8.00
67	584087	COASTERS	SEACHIN'	YAKETY YAK	6.00
67	584088	BOOKER T. & THE MG'S	GREEN ONIONS	BOOT LEG	8.00
67	584089	RUFUS THOMAS	JUMP BACK	WALKING THE DOG	8.00
66	584090	BEN E. KING and the DRIFTERS	SAVE THE LAST DANCE FOR ME	STAND BY ME	6.00
67	584091	OTIS REDDING	RESPECT	THESE ARMS OF MINE	8.00
67	584092	OTIS REDDING	MY GIRL	MR.PITIFUL	8.00
67	584093	RAY CHARLES	WHAT'D I SAY	I GOT A WOMAN	6.00
67	584094	DON COVAY & THE GOODTIMERS	SOOKIE SOOKIE	MERCY MERCY	8.00
67	584095	SONNY & CHER	I GOT YOU BABE	BUT YOU'RE MINE	5.00
67	584096	JOE TEX	HOLD WHAT YOU'VE GOT	A SWEET WOMAN LIKE YOU	8.00
67	584097	REX GARVIN & the MIGHTY CRAVERS	I GOTTA GO NOW (UP ON THE FLOOR)	BELIEVE IT OR NOT	20.00
67	584098	SHARON TANDY	TOE HOLD	I CAN'T GET OVER IT	15.00
67	584099	ALBERT KING	CROSSCUT SAW	DOWN DON'T BOTHER ME	15.00
67	584100	SOLOMON BURKE	KEEP A LIGHT BY THE WINDOW TILL I	TIME IA A THIEF	6.00

67	584101	WILSON PICKETT	NOTHING YOU CAN DO	EVERYBODY NEEDS SOMEBODY	15.00
67	584102	JOE TEX	SHOW ME	A WOMAN SEES A HARD TIME	8.00
67	584103	ESTHER PHILLIPS	AND I LOVE HIM	SHANGRI-LA	8.00
67	584104	MARY WELLS	(HEY YOU) SET MY SOUL ON FIRE	COMING HOME	15.00
67	584105	BOBBY DARIN	THE LADY CAME FROM BALTIMORE	I AM	8.00
67	584106	BEN E. KING	TEARS, TEARS, TEARS	A MAN WITHOUT A DREAM	15.00
67	584107	WILSON PICKETT	NEW ORLEANS	SOUL DANCE III	10.00
67	584108	PERCY SLEDGE	OUT OF LEFT FIELD	IT CAN'T BE STOPPED	8.00
67	584109	KING CURTIS	HOLD ON I'M A COMIN'	GOOD TO ME	8.00
67	584110	SONNY & CHER	PODUNK	A BEAUTIFUL STORY	6.00
67	584111	YOUNG RASCALS	GROOVIN'	SUENO	10.00
67	584112	HERBIE MANN	AND THE BEAT GOES ON	FREE FOR ALL	6.00
67	584113	PERCY WIGGINS	BOOK OF MEMORIES	CAN'T FIND NOBODY (TO TAKE YOUR PLACE)	20.00
67	584114	DON COVAY & THE GOODTIMERS	40 DAYS - 40 NIGHTS	THE USUAL PLACE	10.00
67	584115	ARETHA FRANKLIN	SAVE ME	RESPECT	10.00
66	584116	WILLIE TEE	WALKING UP A ONE WAY STREET	THANK YOU JOHN	45.00
67	584117	SWEET INSPIRATIONS	WHY (AM I TREATED SO BAD)	I DON'T WANT TO GO ON WITHOUT	8.00
67	584118	SOUL BROTHERS SIX	I'LL BE LOVING YOU	SOME KIND OF WONDEFUL	50.00
67	584119	JOE TEX	WOMAN LIKE THAT YEAH	I'M GOING AND GE IT	6.00
67	584120	DARRELL BANKS	ANGEL BABY (DON'T YOU LEAVE ME)	LOOK INTO THE EYES OF A FOOL	75.00
67	584121	ARTHUR CONLEY	SHAKE, RATTLE & ROLL	YOU DON'T HAVE TO SEE ME	6.00
67	584122	SOLOMON BURKE	TAKE ME (JUST AS I AM)	STAYED AWAY TOO LONG	8.00
67	584123	VANILLA FUDGE	YOU KEEP ME HANGING ON	TAKE ME FOR A LITTLE WHILE	6.00
67	584124	SHARON TANDY	STAY WITH ME	HOLD ON	20.00
67	584125	CHARLES LLOYD QUARTET	SOMBRERO SAM	SOMBRERO SAM pt 2	5.00
67	584126	ESTHER PHILLIPS	CHEATER MAN	I'M SORRY	20.00
67	584127	ARETHA FRANKLIN	BABY I LOVE YOU	GOING DOWN SLOW	6.00
67	584128	YOUNG RASCALS	A GIRL LIKE YOU	IT'S LOVE	8.00
67	584129	SONNY & CHER	IT'S THE LITTLE THINGS	PLASTIC MAN	6.00
67	584130	WILSON PICKETT	FUNKY BROADWAY	I'M SORRY ABOUT THAT	6.00
67	584131	SONNY	I TOLD MY GIRL TO GO AWAY	MISTY ROSES	6.00
67	584132	SWEET INSPIRATIONS	LET IT BE ME	WHEN SOMETHING IS WRONG WITH M	6.00
67	584133	EXCELS	CALIFORNIA ON MY MIND	THE ARRIVAL OF MARY	6.00
67	584134	KING CURTIS	MEMPHIS SOUL STEW	BLUE NOCTURNE	5.00
67	584135	JIMMY HUGHES	HI-HEEL SNEAKERS	TIME WILL BRING YOU BACK	15.00
67	584136	SHADOWS OF KNIGHT	SOMEONE LIKE ME	THREE FOR LOVE	20.00
67	584137	SHARON TANDY	OUR DAY WILL COME	LOOK AND FIND	15.00
67	584138	YOUNG RASCALS	HOW CAN I BE SURE	I DON'T LOVE YOU ANYMORE	6.00
67	584139	VANILLA FUDGE	ILLUSIONS OF MY CHILHOOD - ELEANOR	ELEANOR RIGBY part 2	5.00
67	584140	PERCY SLEDGE	PLEDGING MY LOVE	YOU DON'T MISS YOUR WATER	8.00
67	584141	ARETHA FRANKLIN	YOU MAKE ME FEEL LIKE A NATURAL	NEVER LET ME GO	8.00
67	584142	WILSON PICKETT	STAG-O-LEE	I'M IN LOVE	6.00
67	584143	ARTHUR CONLEY	WHOLE LOTTA WOMAN	LOVE COMES AND GOES	6.00
67	584144	JOE TEX	SKINNY LEGS AND ALL	WATCH THE ONE (THAT BRINGS THE	8.00
67	584145	BUFFALO SPRINGFIELD	A CHILD'S CLAIM TO FAME	ROCK 'N ROLL WOMAN	6.00
67	584146	HARVEY SCALES & the 7 SOUNDS	GET DOWN	LOVE-I-TIS	15.00
67	584147	BOBBY DARIN	AT THE CROSSROADS	SHE KNOWS	5.00
67	584148	DORIS TROY	JUST ONE LOOK	WHAT'CHA GONNA DO ABOUT IT	8.00
67	584149	BEN E. KING	SEVEN LETTERS	GOODNIGHT MY LOVE	8.00
68	584150	WILSON PICKETT	IN THE MIDNIGHT HOUR	DANGER ZONE	8.00
68	584151	APRIL STEVENS & NINO TEMPO	COLDEST NIGHT OF THE YEAR	OOH LA LA	8.00
68	584152	DRIFTERS	I'LL TAKE YOU WHERE THE MUSIC	ON BROADWAY	8.00
68	584153	BARBARA LEWIS	HELLO STRANGER	BABY I'M YOURS	10.00
68	584154	CLARENCE CARTER	THREAD THE NEEDLE	DON'T MAKE ME CRY	10.00
68	584155	BOBBY MARCHAN	GET DOWN WITH IT	HALF A MIND	10.00
68	584156	CARMEN McRAE & HERBIE MANN	LIVE FOR LIFE	COTTAGE FOR SALE	5.00
68	584157	ARETHA FRANKLIN	CHAIN OF FOOLS	(I CAN'T GET NO) SATISFACTION	10.00
68	584157 alt. title	ARETHA FRANKLIN	NIGHT LIFE	(I CAN'T GET NO) SATISFACTION	15.00
68	584158	FERRE GRIGNARD	YELLOW YOU, YELLOW ME	LA SI DO	8.00
68	584159	DEON JACKSON	OOH BABY	ALL ON A SUNNY DAY	40.00
68	584159 DJ	DEON JACKSON	OOH BABY	ALL ON A SUNNY DAY	60.00

The above is an exception to the rule, this 45 does exist with a solid bold A on the promo label.

68	584160	CLOVERS	YOUR CASH AIN'T NOTHING BUT TRASH	I'VE GOT MY EYES ON YOU	10.00
68	584161	YOUNG RASCALS	IT'S WONDERFUL	OF COARSE	8.00
68	584162	SONNY & CHER	GOOD COMBINATION	YOU AND ME	10.00
68	584163	ROSE GARDEN	THE NEXT PLANE TO LONDON	FLOWER TOWN	6.00
68	584164	BILLY VERA & JUDY CLAY	STORYBOOK CHILDREN	REALLY TOGETHER	5.00
68	584165	BUFFALO SPRINGFIELD	EXPECT TO FLY	EVERYDAYS	6.00
68	584166	SHARON TANDY	FOOL ON THE HILL	FOR NO ONE	20.00
68	584167	SWEET INSPIRATIONS	I'M BLUE	SWEET INSPIRATION	15.00
68	584168	SONNY & CHER	CIRCUS	I WOULD MARRY YOU TODAY	6.00
68	584169	BILLY VERA & JUDY CLAY	COUNTRY GIRL AND A CITY MAN	LET IT BE ME	5.00
68	584170	JOHNNY BROWN	YOU'RE TOO MUCH IN LOVE WITH Y'SELF	DON'T DILLY DALLY DOLLY	6.00
68	584171	JOE TEX	MEN ARE GETTING SCARCE	YOU'RE GONNA THANK ME WOMAN	5.00
68	584172	ARETHA FRANKLIN	(SWEET SWEET BABY) SINCE YOU'VE	AIN'T NO WAY	5.00
68	584173	WILSON PICKETT	THAT KIND OF LOVE	I'VE COME A LONG WAY	8.00
68	584174	BARBARA LEWIS	THANKFUL FOR WHAT I GOT	SHO-NUFF (IT'S GOT TO BE YOUR	15.00
68	584175	ARTHUR CONLEY	FUNKY STREET	PUT OUR LOVE TOGETHER	8.00
68	584176	CLARENCE CARTER	LOOKING FOR A FOX	I CAN'T SEE MYSELF (CRYING BOU	20.00

68	584177	PERCY SLEDGE	TAKE TIM TO KNOW HER	IT'S ALL WRONG BUT IT'S ALL RI	6.00
68	584178	CARMEN McCRAE	ELUSIVE BUTTERFLY	I'M ALWAYS DRUNK IN SAN FRANCISCO	6.00
68	584179	VANILLA FUDGE	WHERE IS MY MIND	THE LOOK OF LOVE	8.00
68	584180	SHELLY MANNE	DAKTARI	OUT ON A LIMB	8.00
68	584181	SHARON TANDY	HURRY HURRY CHOO-CHOO	LOVE IS NOT A SIMPLE AFFAIR	18.00
68	584182	RASCALS	A BEAUTIFUL MORNING	RAINY DAY	8.00
68	584183	WILSON PICKETT	SHE'S LOOKING GOOD	WE'VE GOT TO HAVE LOVE	8.00
68	584184	BEN E. KING	FORGIVE THIS FOOL	DON'T TAKE YOUR LOVE FROM ME	15.00
68	584185	ARCHIE BELL & the DRELLS	TIGHTEN UP	DOG EAT DOG	20.00
68	584186	ARETHA FRANKLIN	THINK	YOU SEND ME	8.00
68	584187	CLARENCE CARTER	FUNKY FEVER	SLIP AWAY	6.00
68	584188	IRON BUTTERFLY	POSSESSION	UNCONSCIOUS POWER	6.00
68	584189	BUFFALO SPRINGFIELD	UNO MUNDO	MERY GO ROUND	6.00
68	584190	JOHN HAMMOND	CROSSCUT SAW	BROWN EYED HANDSOME MAN	10.00
68	584191	SOLOMON BURKE	I WISH I KNEW (HOW IT WOULD FEEL TO	IT'S JUST A MATTER OF TIME	6.00
68	584192	SAM AND DAVE	YOU DON'T KNOW WHAT YOU MEAN TO	THIS IS YOUR WORLD	8.00
68	584193	FLEUR-DE-LYS	STOP CROSSING THE BRIDGE	BRICK BY BRICK (STONE BY STONE)	40.00
68	584194	SHARON TANDY	YOU GOTTA BELIEVE IT	BORDER TOWN	15.00
68	584195	DRIFTERS	STILL BURNING IN MY HEART	I NEED YOU NOW	8.00
68	584196	BILLY VERA	WITH PEN INBHAND	GOOD MORNING BLUES	5.00
68	584197	ARTHUR CONLEY	PEOPLE SURE ACT FUNNY	BURNING FIRE	5.00
68	584198	EAST OF EDEN	KING OF SIAM	BALLAD OF HAVEY KAYE	25.00
68	584199	OTIS REDDING	HARD TO HANDLE	AMEN	8.00
68	584200	JERRY JEFF WALKER	MR. BOJANGLES	ROUND AND ROUND	6.00
68	584201	ARIF MARDIN ORCHESTRA	ROSEMARY'S BABY (LULLABY)	THE BLUE BULL	6.00
68	584202	SOUL CLAN	SOUL MEETING	THAT'S HOW IT FEELS	10.00
68	584202 PS	SOUL CLAN	SOUL MEETING	THAT'S HOW IT FEELS	20.00

The Soul Clan was a group put together by Atlantic as an experiment, members were Arthur Conley, Solomon Burke, Ben E. King, Don Covay and Joe Tex

68	584203 lh	WILSON PICKETT	I'M A MIDNIGHT MOVER	DEBORAH	5.00
68	584203 sh	WILSON PICKETT	I'M A MIDNIGHT MOVER	DEBORAH	8.00
68	584204	SOLOMON BURKE	SAVE IT	MEET ME IN CHURCH	6.00
68	584205	BEN E. KING	IT'S AMAZING	WHERE'S THE GIRL	10.00
68	584206	ARETHA FRANKLIN	I SAY A LITTLE PRAYER	SEE-SAW	6.00
68	584207	CHOCOLATE FROG	BUTCHERS AND BAKERS	I'LL FORGIVE YOU	25.00
68	584208	PETE KLINT QUINTET	HEY DIDDLE DIDDLE	JUST HOLDING ON	20.00
68	584209	LITTLE ARCHIE	I NEED YOU	I AM A CARPET	30.00
68	584210	RASCALS	PEOPLE GOT TO BE FREE	MY WORLD	5.00
68	584211	SAM AND DAVE	CAN'T YOU FIND ANOTHER WAY	STILL IS THE NIGHT	10.00
68	584212	JOE TEX	GO HOME AND DO IT	KEEP THE ONE YOU GOT	6.00
68	584213	VAMP	FLOATIN'	THINKIN' TO MUCH	30.00
68	584214	SHARON TANDY	THE WAY SHE LOOKS AT YOU	HE'LL HURT ME	15.00
68	584215	SONNY & CHER	I GOT YOU BABE	YOU GOTTA HAVE A THING OF YOUR OWN	5.00
68	584216	BETTY WRIGHT	GIRLS CAN'T DO WHAT THE GUYS DO	SWEET LOVIN' DADDY	10.00
68	584217	ARCHIE BELL & the DRELLS	I CAN'T STOP DANCIN'	YOU'RE SUCH A BEAUTIFUL CHILD	15.00
68	584218	EDDIE HARRIS	LISTEN HERE	THEME IN SEARCH OF A MOVIE	22.00
68	584219	SHARON TANDY	HOLD ON	DAUGHTER OF THE SUN	25.00
68	584220	OTIS REDDING	CHAMPAGNE AND WINE	I'VE GOT DREAMS TO REMEMBER	8.00
68	584221	WILSON PICKETT	I FOUND TRUE LOVE	FOR BETTER OR WORSE	8.00
68	584222	BROOK BENTON	DO YOUR OUR THING	I JUST DON'T KNOW WHAT TO DO W	4.00
68	584223	CLARENCE CARTER	TOO WEAK TO FIGHT	LET ME COMFORT	6.00
68	584224	ARTHUR CONLEY	AUNT DORA'S LOVE SOUL SHACK	IS THAT YOU LOVE	8.00
68	584225	PERCY SLEDGE	COME SOFTLY TO ME	YOU'RE ALL AROUND ME	6.00
68	584226	JEANIE GREENE	SURE AS SIN	I'VE BEEN A LONG TIME LOVING Y	8.00
68	584227	STEVE ALAIMO	THE TRAINS GO BY	THANK YOU FOR THE SUNSHINE DAYS	6.00
68	584228	SAM AND DAVE	IF I DIDN'T HAVE A GIRL YOU	EVERYBODY GOT TO BELIEVE IN SO	8.00
68	584229	SIW MALMKVIST	THE MAN WHO TOOK VASALINE OFF THE FLOOR	SADIE THE CLEANING LADY	6.00
68	584230	RASPBERRY PIRATES	LOOKY LOOKY MY COOKIE'S GONE	GOOD MORNING BABY	8.00
69	584231	NATURAL BRIDGE BUNCH	PIG SNOOTS	PIG SNOOTS part 2	15.00
68	584232	EDDIE HARRIS	IT'S CRAZY	LIVE RIGHT NOW	10.00
68	584233	SWEET INSPIRATIONS	YOU REALLY DIDN'T MEAN IT	WHAT THE WORLD NEEDS NOW IS LO	6.00
68	584234	OTIS REDDING	PAPA'S GOT A BRAND NEW BAG	DIRECT ME	8.00
68	584235	FREDDIE KING	PLAY IT COOL	FUNKY	10.00
68	584236	WILSON PICKETT	HEY JUDE	NIGHT OWL	5.00
68	584237	SAM AND DAVE	SOUL SISTER, BROWN SUGAR	COME ON IN	4.00
68	584238	BEN E. KING	TILL I CAN'T TAKE IT ANYMORE	IT AIN'T FAIR	10.00
68	584239	ARETHA FRANKLIN	DON'T LET ME LOSE THIS DREAM	THE HOUSE THAT JACK BUILT	25.00
68	584240	CARTOONE	KNICK KNACK MAN	PENNY FOR THE SUN	8.00
69	584241	SWEET INSPIRATIONS	I'M BLUE	SWEET INSPIRATION	10.00
69	584242	SHARON TANDY	GOTTA GET ENOUGH TIME	SOMEBODY SPEAKS YOUR NAME	15.00
69	584243	FLEUR-DE-LEYS	YOU'RE JUST A LIAR	ONE GIRL CITY	100.00
69	584244	BAR-KAYS	SOUL FINGER	KNUCKLEHEAD	10.00
69	584244 DJ	BAR-KAYS	SOUL FINGER	KNUCKLEHEAD	15.00
69	584245 lh	ASTORS	CANDY	I FOUND OUT	10.00
69	584245 sh	ASTORS	CANDY	I FOUND OUT	15.00
69	584246	DRIFTERS	SATURDAY NIGHT AT THE MOVIES	UNDER THE BOARDWALK	5.00
69	584247	SAM and DAVE	HOLD ON I'M COMING	YOU DON'T KNOW LIKE I KNOW	8.00
69	584248	CLARENCE CARTER	MAKING LOVE (AT THE DARK END OF	SNATCXHIN' IT BACK	6.00
69	584249	OTIS REDDING	A LOVER'S QUESTION	YOU MADE A MAN OUT OF ME	8.00
69	584250	MACK RICE	LOVE'S A MOTHER BROTHER	COAL MAN	8.00

69	584251	THREE CAPS	COOL JERK	HELLO STRANGER	8.00
69	584251 DJ	THREE CAPS	COOL JERK	HELLO STRANGER	15.00
69	584252	ARETHA FRANKLIN	THE WEIGHT	THE TRACKS OF MY TEARS	6.00
69	584253	TYRONE DAVIS	CAN I CHANGE MY MIND	A WOMAN NEEDS TO BE LOVED	15.00
69	584254	IRON BUTTERFLY	SOUL EXPERIENCE	IN THE CROWDS	8.00
69	584255	RASCALS	HEAVEN	BABY I'M BLUE	5.00
69	584256	SOUL BROTHERS SIX	SHE'S SOME KIND OF WONDERFUL	SOMEBODY ELSE IS LOVING MY BAB	10.00
69	584257	VANILLA FUDGE	SHOTGUN	GOOD GOOD LOVIN'	6.00
69	584258	RALPH SOUL JACKSON	'CAUSE I LOVE YOU	SUNSHINE OF YOUR LOVE	10.00
69	584259	WILLIAM BELL	EVERYDAY WILL BE LIKE A HOLIDAY	AIN'T GOT NO GIRL	8.00
69	584260 sh	ACE KEFFORD AND STAND	FOR YOR LOVE	GRAVY BOOBY JAM	30.00
69	584260 lh	ACE KEFFORD AND STAND	FOR YOR LOVE	GRAVY BOOBY JAM	20.00
69	584261	WILSON PICKETT	MINI-SKIRT MINNIE	BACK IN YOUR ARMS	6.00
69	584262	TONY AND TANDY	THE BITTER AND THE SWEET	TWO CAN MAKE IT TOGETHER	25.00
69	584263	VAMP	GREEN PEA	WAKE UP AND TELL ME	100.00
69	584264	PERCY SLEDGE	THE ANGEL'S LISTENED IN	ANY DAY NOW (MY WILD BEAUTIFUL	10.00
69	584265 sh	TYRONE DAVIS	IS IT SOMETHING YOU'VE GOT	UNDYING LOVE	20.00
69	584265 lh	TYRONE DAVIS	IS IT SOMETHING YOU'VE GOT	UNDYING LOVE	15.00
69	584266	BROOK BENTON	SHE KNOWS WHAT TO DO FOR ME	TOUCH 'EM WITH LOVE	4.00
69	584267	BROOK BENTON	NOTHING TAKES THE PLACE OF YOU	WOMAN WITHOUT LOVE	6.00
69	584268	unissued pressed on the next # 584269			
69	584269	LED ZEPPLIN	COMMUNICATIO BREAKDOWN	GOOD TIMES, BAD TIMES	700.00
69	584270	DYNAMICS	THE LOVE THAT I NEED	ICE CREAM SONG	15.00
69	584271	C and the SHELLS	ON YOUR WAY HOME	GOOD MORNING STARSHINE	8.00
69	584272	CLARENCE CARTER	THE FEELING IS RIGHT	YOU CAN'T MISS WHAT YOU CAN'T	6.00
69	584273	COMMODORES	KEEP ON DANCING	RISE UP	45.00
69	584274	unissued ?			
69	584275	SOUL SURVIVORS	MAMA SOUL	TELL DADDY	40.00
69	584276	VANILLA FUDGE	SOME VELVET MORNING	THOUGHTS	6.00
69	584277	MAJOR LANCE	FOLLOW THE LEADER	SINCE YOU'VE BEEN GONE	15.00
69	584278	CHER	WALK ON GILDED SPLINTERS	TONIGHT I'LL BE STAYING HERE	6.00
69	584279	SWEET INSPIRATIONS	SWEETS FOR MY SWEET	GET A LITTLE ORDER	6.00
69	584280	YES	SWEETNESS	SOMETHING'S COMING	40.00
69	584281	WILSON PICKETT	HEY JOE	BORN TO BE WILD	5.00
69	584282	OTIS CLAY	BABY JANE	YOU HURT ME FOR THE LAST TIME	75.00
69	584283	CROBY, STILLS & NASH	MARRAKESH EXPRESS	HELPLESSLY HOPING	6.00
69	584284	LES McCANN	BURNIN' COAL	WITH THESE HANDS	15.00
69	584285	ARETHA FRANKLIN	SHARE YOUR LOVE WITH ME	PLEDGING MY LOVE / THE CLOCK	5.00
69	584286	PERCY SLEDGE	KIND WOMAN	WOMAN OF THE NIGHT	6.00
69	584287	KING CURTIS	LA JEANNE	LITTLE GREEN APPLES	6.00
69	584288	TYRONE DAVIS	ALL THE WAITING IS NOT IN VAIN	NEED YOUR LOVING EVERYDAY	10.00
69	584289	JOHN BROMLEY	KICK THE TIN CAN	WONDERFUL AVENUE U.S.A	8.00
69	584290	CLARENCE REID	NOBODY BUT YOU BABE	SEND ME BACK MY MONEY	10.00
	584291	unissued ?			
69	584292	unissued ?			
69	584293	BILLY & JUDY CLAY VERA	REACHING FOR THE MOON	TELL IT LIKE IT IS	6.00
69	584294	ROBERTA FLACK	COMPARED TO WHAT	HEY, THAT'S NO WAY TO SAY GOOD	5.00
69	584295	ARIF MARDIN ORCHESTRA	GLASS ONION	HOW CAN I BE SURE	5.00
69	584296	JOE TEX	WE CAN'T SIT DOWN NOW	IT AIN'T SANITARY	6.00
69	584297	HERBIE MANN	MEMPHIS UNDERGROUND	NEW ORLEANS	5.00
69	584298 unissued	YES c/w BIG BERTHA	LOOKING AROUND	EVERYDAYS	UN
69	584299	BABY WASHINGTON	I CAN'T AFFORD TO LOSE HIM	I DON'T KNOW	15.00
69	584300	PERCY SLEDGE	TRUE LOVE TRAVELS ON A GRAVEL	FAITHFUL AND TRUE	6.00
69	584301	CLARENCE REID	I'M GONNA TEAR YOU A NEW HEART	I'M A MAN OF MY WORLD	8.00
69	584302	MAJOR LANCE	SWEETER AS THE DAYS GO BY	SHADOWS OF A MEMORY	10.00
69	584303	SAM and DAVE	HOLDIN' ON	OOH, OOH, OOH	15.00
69	584304	CROBY, STILLS & NASH	SUITE: JUDY BLUE EYES	A LONG TIME GONE	6.00
69	584305	CONRAD CANNON	MY BUNNY	GOOD BOY	6.00
69	584306	ARETHA FRANKLIN	ELEANOR RIGBY	IT AIN'T FAIR	6.00
69	584307	unissued ?			
69	584308 lh	DELANY & BONNIE BRAMLETT	COMIN' HOME	GROUPIE	6.00
69	584308 sh	DELANY & BONNIE BRAMLETT	COMIN' HOME	GROUPIE	10.00
70	584309	CLARENCE CARTER	TAKE IT OFF HIM AND PUT IT ON ME	THE FEW TROUBLES I'VE HAD	6.00
70	584310	unissued ?			
70	584311	WALTER JACKSON	ANY WAY THAT YOU WANT ME	LIFE HAS IT'S UPS AND DOWNS	10.00
70	584312	SWEET INSPIRATIONS	(GOTTA FIND) A BRAND NE BABY	SAME: Part2	5.00
70	584313	WILSON PICKETT	YOU KEEP ME HANGING ON	NOW YOU SEE ME, NOW YOU DON'T	6.00
70	584314	unissued ?			
70	584315	BROOK BENTON	RAINY NIGHT IN GEORGIA	WHERE DO I GO FROM HERE	6.00
70	584316	BABY WASHINGTON	BREAKFAST IN BED	WHAT BECOMES OF A BROKEN HEART	10.00
70	584317	CARMEN McCRAE	I LOVE YOU MORE THAN YOU'LL EVER KNOW	JUST A DREAM AGO	5.00
70	584318	JOE TEX	YOU'RE ALRIGHT RAY CHARLES	EVERYTHING HAPPENS ON TIME	4.00
70	584319	COLD BLOOD	YOU GOT ME HUMMIN'	IF YOU WILL	6.00
70	584320	RONNIE HAWKINS	DOWN IN THE ALLEY	MATCHBOX	5.00
70	584321	SCREAMING LORD SUTCH	'CAUSE I LOVE YOU	THUMING BEAT	15.00
70	584322	ARETHA FRANKLIN	CALL ME	SON OF A PREACHER MAN	5.00
70	584323	YES	TIME AND A WORD	THE PROPHET	60.00
70	584324	SAM and DAVE	BABY BABY DON'T STOP NOW	I'M NOT AN INDIAN GIVER	8.00

209 Series from May 1970 to November 1971. Some numbers came out on the UK ATCO label. They are quoted in many guide and label listing as Atlantic releases. If anyone has them on the red Atlantic label we sure would appreciate a label scan. We have copies of these 45's pressed on Atco. During this period many of the Polydor distributed labels had the center pieces cleanly cut to make a large hole and inserted a plastic triangle spider piece. This was a cost cutting idea some executive came up with, with no regard for record collectors' standards. But some copies of almost every release escaped the "dinking" machine. Copies which retain their "small hole" status are much more desirable and are valued higher. sh = small hole, lh = large hole.

Atlantic were coming more and more rock music based, I've filled in the first thirty releases 2091001 to 2091030 you'll see more Rock 45's than soul. You can consider any missing numbers in the series after 2091030 are rock 45s. I've omitted these listings as this is essentially a soul price guide.

Year	Catalog	Artist	A-side	B-side	Price
70	2091001 lh	LITTLE SISTER	YOU'RE THE ONE	YOU'RE THE ONE part 2	8.00
70	2091001 sh	LITTLE SISTER	YOU'RE THE ONE	YOU'RE THE ONE part 2	10.00
70	2091002 lh	CROSBY, STILLS & NASH	TEACH YOUR CHILDREN	COUNTRY GIRL	5.00
70	2091002 sh	CROSBY, STILLS & NASH	TEACH YOUR CHILDREN	COUNTRY GIRL	8.00
70	2091003 lh	TYRONE DAVIS	TURN BACK THE HANDS OF TIME	I KEEP COMING BACK	12.00
70	2091003 sh	TYRONE DAVIS	TURN BACK THE HANDS OF TIME	I KEEP COMING BACK	15.00
70	2091005 lh	WILSON PICKETT	SUGAR, SUGAR	COLE, COOK & REDDING	5.00
70	2091005 sh	WILSON PICKETT	SUGAR, SUGAR	COLE, COOK & REDDING	6.00
70	2091006 lh	SCREAMING LORD SUTCH	CAUSE I LOVE YOU	THUMPING BEAT	10.00
70	2091006 sh	SCREAMING LORD SUTCH	CAUSE I LOVE YOU	THUMPING BEAT	15.00
70	2091007 lh	RONNIE HAWKINS	BITTER GREEN	FORTY DAYS	5.00
70	2091007 sh	RONNIE HAWKINS	BITTER GREEN	FORTY DAYS	6.00
70	2091008 lh	ARETHA FRANKLIN	LET IT BE	MY SONG	5.00
70	2091008 sh	ARETHA FRANKLIN	LET IT BE	MY SONG	6.00
70	2091009 lh	BLUES IMAGE	RIDE CAPTAIN RIDE	PAY MY DUES	5.00
70	2091009 sh	BLUES IMAGE	RIDE CAPTAIN RIDE	PAY MY DUES	6.00
70	2091010 lh	CROSBY, STILLS & NASH	WOODSTOCK	HELPLESS	5.00
70	2091010 sh	CROSBY, STILLS & NASH	WOODSTOCK	HELPLESS	6.00
70	2091011	released on ATCO same release #			
70	2091012	released on ATCO same release #			
70	2091013	released on ATCO same release #			
70	2091014	released on ATCO same release #			
70	2091015 lh	OTIS LEAVILL	I LOVE YOU	I NEED YOU	8.00
70	2091015 sh	OTIS LEAVILL	I LOVE YOU	I NEED YOU	15.00
70	2091016 lh	DELANY & BONNIE BRAMLETT	SOUL SHAKE	FREE THE PEOPLE	6.00
70	2091016 sh	DELANY & BONNIE BRAMLETT	SOUL SHAKE	FREE THE PEOPLE	8.00
70	2091017 lh	SCREAMING LORD SUTCH	ELECTION FEVER	ROCK THE ELECTION	10.00
70	2091017 sh	SCREAMING LORD SUTCH	ELECTION FEVER	ROCK THE ELECTION	15.00
70	2091018 lh	DON COVAY & THE GOODTIMERS	EVERYTHING I DO GOIN' BE FUNKY	KEY TO THE HIGHWAY	6.00
70	2091018 sh	DON COVAY & THE GOODTIMERS	EVERYTHING I DO GOIN' BE FUNKY	KEY TO THE HIGHWAY	8.00
70	2091019	released on ATCO same release #			
70	2091020 lh	OTIS REDDING	WONDERFUL WORLD	SECURITY	10.00
70	2091020 sh	OTIS REDDING	WONDERFUL WORLD	SECURITY	10.00
70	2091021 lh	SONNY & CHER	GET IT TOGETHER	HOLD YOU TIGHTER	4.00
70	2091021 sh	SONNY & CHER	GET IT TOGETHER	HOLD YOU TIGHTER	4.00
70	2091022 lh	ASSEMBLED MULTITUDE	OVERTURE FOR TOMMY	MUD	5.00
70	2091022 sh	ASSEMBLED MULTITUDE	OVERTURE FOR TOMMY	MUD	6.00
70	2091023 lh	CROSBY, STILLS & NASH	OHIO	FIND THE COST OF FREEDOM	5.00
70	2091023 Sh	CROSBY, STILLS & NASH	OHIO	FIND THE COST OF FREEDOM	6.00
70	2091024 lh	IRON BUTTERFLY	IN A GADA DA VIDA	TERMINATION	5.00
70	2091024 Sh	IRON BUTTERFLY	IN A GADA DA VIDA	TERMINATION	6.00
70	2091025 lh	ARTHUR CONLEY	GOD BLESS	ALL DAY SINGING	4.00
70	2091025 sh	ARTHUR CONLEY	GOD BLESS	ALL DAY SINGING	5.00
70	2091027 lh	ARETHA FRANKLIN	DON'T PLAY THAT SONG	THE THRILLIS GONE	5.00
70	2091027 sh	ARETHA FRANKLIN	DON'T PLAY THAT SONG	THE THRILLIS GONE	6.00
70	2091028 lh	BROOK BENTON	DON'T IT MAKE YOU WANT TO GO	I'VE GOTTA BE ME	4.00
70	2091028 sh	BROOK BENTON	DON'T IT MAKE YOU WANT TO GO	I'VE GOTTA BE ME	5.00
70	2091029	unissued ?			
70	2091030 lh	CLARENCE CARTER	PATCHES	I CAN'T LEAVE YOUR LOVE ALONE	4.00
70	2091030 sh	CLARENCE CARTER	PATCHES	I CAN'T LEAVE YOUR LOVE ALONE	5.00
70	2091032 lh	WILSON PICKETT	GET ME BACK ON TIME ENGINE NO.9	INTERNATIONAL PLAYBOY	5.00
70	2091032 sh	WILSON PICKETT	GET ME BACK ON TIME ENGINE NO.9	INTERNATIONAL PLAYBOY	6.00
70	2091033 lh	ROBERTA FLACK	REVEREND LEE	BUSINESS GOES ON AS USUAL	4.00
70	2091033 sh	ROBERTA FLACK	REVEREND LEE	BUSINESS GOES ON AS USUAL	5.00
70	2091035 lh	OTIS LEAVILLE	LOVE UPRISING	GLAD I MET YOU	10.00
70	2091035 sh	OTIS LEAVILLE	LOVE UPRISING	GLAD I MET YOU	15.00
70	2091037	released on ATCO same release #			
70	2091042 unissued	ARETHA FRANKLIN	BORDER SONG (HOLY MOSES)	YOU AND ME	UN
70	2091044 lh	ARETHA FRANKLIN	OH NO NOT MY BABY	YOU AND ME	8.00
70	2091044 sh	ARETHA FRANKLIN	OH NO NOT MY BABY	YOU AND ME	10.00
70	2091045 lh	CLARENCE CARTER	WILLIE AND LAURA MAE JONES	IT'S ALL IN THE MIND	5.00
70	2091045 sh	CLARENCE CARTER	WILLIE AND LAURA MAE JONES	IT'S ALL IN THE MIND	6.00
70	2091050 lh	BROOK BENTON	SHOES + RAINY NIGHT IN GEORGIA	MY WAY	4.00
70	2091050 sh	BROOK BENTON	SHOES + RAINY NIGHT IN GEORGIA	MY WAY	5.00
70	2091051 lh	KING FLOYD	GROOVE ME	WHAT OUR LOVE NEEDS	5.00
70	2091051 sh	KING FLOYD	GROOVE ME	WHAT OUR LOVE NEEDS	6.00
70	2091053 lh	LITTLE SISTER	SOMEBODY'S WATCHING YOU	STANGA	6.00
70	2091053 sh	LITTLE SISTER	SOMEBODY'S WATCHING YOU	STANGA	8.00
70	2091054 lh	JACKIE MOORE	PRECIOUS, PRECIOUS	WILLPOWER	5.00
70	2091054 sh	JACKIE MOORE	PRECIOUS, PRECIOUS	WILLPOWER	6.00
71	2091055 lh	JAMES ANDERSON	MAMA MAMA	MUSKATEL, MUSKATEL	5.00
71	2091055 sh	JAMES ANDERSON	MAMA MAMA	MUSKATEL, MUSKATEL	6.00

71	2091057 lh	DEE DEE WARWICK	COLD NIGHT IN GEORGIA	SEARCHING	5.00
71	2091057 sh	DEE DEE WARWICK	COLD NIGHT IN GEORGIA	SEARCHING	6.00
71	2091062 lh	OTIS REDDING	I'VE BEEN LOVING YOU TOO LONG	TRY A LITTLE TENDERNESS	6.00
71	2091062 sh	OTIS REDDING	I'VE BEEN LOVING YOU TOO LONG	TRY A LITTLE TENDERNESS	8.00
71	2091063 lh	ARETHA FRANKLIN	YOU'RE ALL I NEED TO GET BY	THE BORDER SONG	5.00
71	2091063 sh	ARETHA FRANKLIN	YOU'RE ALL I NEED TO GET BY	THE BORDER SONG	6.00
71	2091064 lh	DRIFTERS	A ROSE BY ANY OTHER NAME	BE MY LADY	5.00
71	2091064 sh	DRIFTERS	A ROSE BY ANY OTHER NAME	BE MY LADY	6.00
71	2091066 lh	PEGGY SCOTT & JO JO BENSON	I THANK YOU	SPREADIN' LOVE	6.00
71	2091066 sh	PEGGY SCOTT & JO JO BENSON	I THANK YOU	SPREADIN' LOVE	8.00
71	2091073 lh	SWEET INSPIRATIONS	EVIDENCE	CHANGE ME NOT	5.00
71	2091073 sh	SWEET INSPIRATIONS	EVIDENCE	CHANGE ME NOT	6.00
71	2091075 lh	TONY & TANDY	TWO CAN MAKE IT TOGETHER	LOOK AND FIND	10.00
71	2091075 sh	TONY & TANDY	TWO CAN MAKE IT TOGETHER	LOOK AND FIND	15.00
71	2091076 lh	JESSE DAVIS	EVERY NIGHT IS SATURDAY NIGHT	WASHITA LOVE CHILD	5.00
71	2091076 sh	JESSE DAVIS	EVERY NIGHT IS SATURDAY NIGHT	WASHITA LOVE CHILD	8.00
71	2091078 lh	TYRONE DAVIS	COULD I FORGET YOU	JUST MY WAY OF LOVING YOU	10.00
71	2091078 sh	TYRONE DAVIS	COULD I FORGET YOU	JUST MY WAY OF LOVING YOU	15.00
71	2091079 lh	KING FLOYD	BABY LET ME KIS YOU	PLEASE DON'T LEAVE ME LONELY	5.00
71	2091079 sh	KING FLOYD	BABY LET ME KIS YOU	PLEASE DON'T LEAVE ME LONELY	6.00
71	2091080 lh	MEMPHIS HORNS	I CAN'T TURN YOU LOOSE	WOOLY BULLY	10.00
71	2091080 lh	MEMPHIS HORNS	I CAN'T TURN YOU LOOSE	WOOLY BULLY	15.00
71	2091086 lh	WILSON PICKETT	FIRE AND WATER	DON'T LET THE GREEN GRASS FOOL	5.00
71	2091086 sh	WILSON PICKETT	FIRE AND WATER	DON'T LET THE GREEN GRASS FOOL	6.00
71	2091092 lh	DEE DEE WARWICK	I'M GLAD I'M A WOMAN	SUSPICIOUS MINDS	10.00
71	2091092 sh	DEE DEE WARWICK	I'M GLAD I'M A WOMAN	SUSPICIOUS MINDS	15.00
71	2091093 lh	CLARENCE CARTER	THE COURT ROOM	GETTING THE BILLS	5.00
71	2091093 sh	CLARENCE CARTER	THE COURT ROOM	GETTING THE BILLS	6.00
71	2091095 lh	JACKIE MOORE	WONDEFUL, MARVELOUS	SOMETIMES IT'S GOTTA RAIN	5.00
71	2091095 sh	JACKIE MOORE	WONDEFUL, MARVELOUS	SOMETIMES IT'S GOTTA RAIN	6.00
71	2091097 lh	BEGINNING OF THE END	FUNKY NASSAU	FUNKY NASSAU part 2	15.00
71	2091097 sh	BEGINNING OF THE END	FUNKY NASSAU	FUNKY NASSAU part 2	20.00
71	2091100 lh	BEN E. KING	TEARS, TEARS, TEARS	IT'S AMAZING	6.00
71	2091100 sh	BEN E. KING	TEARS, TEARS, TEARS	IT'S AMAZING	8.00
71	2091101 lh	DRIFTERS	WHEN MY LITTLE GIRL IS SMILING	SWEETS FOR MY SWEET	5.00
71	2091101 sh	DRIFTERS	WHEN MY LITTLE GIRL IS SMILING	SWEETS FOR MY SWEET	6.00
71	2091104 lh	DON COVAY & THE GOODTIMERS	SEESAW	MERCY MERCY	5.00
71	2091104 sh	DON COVAY & THE GOODTIMERS	SEESAW	MERCY MERCY	6.00
71	2091105 lh	THREE CAPS	COOL JERK	HELLO STRANGER	8.00
71	2091105 sh	THREE CAPS	COOL JERK	HELLO STRANGER	10.00
71	2091106 lh	ARTHUR CONLEY	SWEET SOUL MUSIC	SHAKE, RATTLE AND ROLL	4.00
71	2091106 sh	ARTHUR CONLEY	SWEET SOUL MUSIC	SHAKE, RATTLE AND ROLL	5.00
71	2091107 lh	R.B. GREAVES	PAPERBACK WRITER	OVER YOU NOW	6.00
71	2091107 sh	R.B. GREAVES	PAPERBACK WRITER	OVER YOU NOW	8.00
71	2091109 lh	EDDIE FLOYD	THINGS GET BETTER	KNOCK ON WOOD	5.00
71	2091109 sh	EDDIE FLOYD	THINGS GET BETTER	KNOCK ON WOOD	6.00
71	2091111 lh	ARETHA FRANKLIN	I SAY A LITTLE PRAYER	(I CAN'T GET NO) SATISFACTION	5.00
71	2091111 sh	ARETHA FRANKLIN	I SAY A LITTLE PRAYER	(I CAN'T GET NO) SATISFACTION	6.00
71	2091112 lh	OTIS REDDING	(SITTIN' ON) THE DOCK OF THE BAY	RESPECT + MR. PITIFUL	5.00
71	2091112 sh	OTIS REDDING	(SITTIN' ON) THE DOCK OF THE BAY	RESPECT + MR. PITIFUL	6.00
71	2091114 lh	LOLLIPOPS	I BELIEVE IN LOVE	NOTHING GONNA STOP OUR LOVE	15.00
71	2091114 sh	LOLLIPOPS	I BELIEVE IN LOVE	NOTHING GONNA STOP OUR LOVE	25.00
71	2091116 lh	ROBERTA FLACK	YOU'VE GOT A FRIEND	GONE AWAY	4.00
71	2091116 sh	ROBERTA FLACK	YOU'VE GOT A FRIEND	GONE AWAY	5.00
71	2091120 lh	ARTHUR CONLEY	I'M LIVING GOOD	I'M SO GLAD YOU'RE HERE	5.00
71	2091120 sh	ARTHUR CONLEY	I'M LIVING GOOD	I'M SO GLAD YOU'RE HERE	6.00
71	2091121 lh	FIESTAS	SO FINE	BROKEN HEART	5.00
71	2091121 sh	FIESTAS	SO FINE	BROKEN HEART	6.00
71	2091124 lh	WILSON PICKETT	DON'T KNOCK MY LOVE PART1	DON'T KNOCK MY LOVE PART2	5.00
71	2091124 sh	WILSON PICKETT	DON'T KNOCK MY LOVE PART1	DON'T KNOCK MY LOVE PART2	6.00
71	2091125 lh	ALEX TAYLOR	BABY RUTH	ALL IN LINE	5.00
71	2091125 sh	ALEX TAYLOR	BABY RUTH	ALL IN LINE	6.00
71	2091127 lh	ARETHA FRANKLIN	BRAND NEW ME	SPIRIT IN THE DARK	6.00
71	2091127 sh	ARETHA FRANKLIN	BRAND NEW ME	SPIRIT IN THE DARK	8.00
71	2091129 lh	EARLS	REMEMBER THEN	I BELIEVE	4.00
71	2091129 sh	EARLS	REMEMBER THEN	I BELIEVE	6.00
71	2091130 lh	BILLY BLAND	LET THE LITTLE GIRL DANCE	CHICKEN HOP	4.00
71	2091130 sh	BILLY BLAND	LET THE LITTLE GIRL DANCE	CHICKEN HOP	5.00
71	2091131 lh	TYRONE DAVIES	ONE WAY TICKET	WE GOT A LOVE	8.00
71	2091131 sh	TYRONE DAVIES	ONE WAY TICKET	WE GOT A LOVE	10.00
71	2091133 lh	BARBARA LYNN	TAKE YOUR LOVE AND RUN	(UNTIL THEN) I'LL SUFFER	15.00
71	2091133 sh	BARBARA LYNN	TAKE YOUR LOVE AND RUN	(UNTIL THEN) I'LL SUFFER	30.00
71	2091136 lh	ENTICERS	CALLING FOR YOUR LOVE	STORYTELLER	50.00
71	2091136 sh	ENTICERS	CALLING FOR YOUR LOVE	STORYTELLER	75.00
71	2091138 lh	ARETHA FRANKLIN	SPANISH HARLEM	LEAN ON ME	5.00
71	2091138 sh	ARETHA FRANKLIN	SPANISH HARLEM	LEAN ON ME	6.00
71	2091139 lh	CLARENCE CARTER	SLIPPED, TRIPPED AND FELL IN LOVE	I HATE TO LOVE AND RUN	6.00
71	2091139 sh	CLARENCE CARTER	SLIPPED, TRIPPED AND FELL IN LOVE	I HATE TO LOVE AND RUN	5.00
71	2091143 lh	BARBARA LEWIS	SOMEDAY WE'RE GONNA LOVE AGAIN	BABY, I'M YOURS	15.00

71	2091143 sh	BARBARA LEWIS	SOMEDAY WE'RE GONNA LOVE AGAIN	BABY, I'M YOURS	25.00
71	2091152 lh	RASPUTIN'S STASH	YOUR LOVE IS CERTIFIED	WHATS ON YOUR MIND	5.00
71	2091152 sh	RASPUTIN'S STASH	YOUR LOVE IS CERTIFIED	WHATS ON YOUR MIND	6.00
71	2091153 lh	WILSON PICKETT	CALL MY NAME I'LL BE THERE	WOMAN LET ME BE DOWN HOME	5.00
71	2091153 sh	WILSON PICKETT	CALL MY NAME I'LL BE THERE	WOMAN LET ME BE DOWN HOME	6.00
71	2091156 lh	ARCHIE BELL & the DRELLS	TIGHTEN UP + I CAN'T STOP DANCIN'	(THERE'S GONNA BE) A SHOWDOWN	6.00
71	2091156 sh	ARCHIE BELL & the DRELLS	TIGHTEN UP + I CAN'T STOP DANCIN'	(THERE'S GONNA BE) A SHOWDOWN	8.00
71	2091158 lh	KING CURTIS	WHOLE LOTTA LOVE + CHANGES Part 1	LA JEANNE	5.00
71	2091158 sh	KING CURTIS	WHOLE LOTTA LOVE + CHANGES Part 1	LA JEANNE	6.00
71	2091159 lh	JO MAMA	SMACK WATER JACK	BACK ON THE STREET AGAIN	5.00
71	2091159 sh	JO MAMA	SMACK WATER JACK	BACK ON THE STREET AGAIN	6.00
71	2091160 h	OTIS LEAVILL	I'M SO JEALOUS	THERE'S NOTHING BETTER	10.00
71	2091160 sh	OTIS LEAVILL	I'M SO JEALOUS	THERE'S NOTHING BETTER	15.00
71	2091163 lh	KING FLOYD	GOT TO HAVE YOUR LOVIN'	LET US BE	4.00
71	2091163 sh	KING FLOYD	GOT TO HAVE YOUR LOVIN'	LET US BE	5.00
71	2091062 lh	OTIS REDDING	I'VE BEEN LOVING TOO LONG	TRY A LITTLE TENDERNESS	4.00
71	2091062 sh	OTIS REDDING	I'VE BEEN LOVING TOO LONG	TRY A LITTLE TENDERNESS	5.00
71	2091164 lh	PERSUADERS	THIN LINE BETWEEN LOVE AND HATE	THIGH SPY	8.00
71	2091164 sh	PERSUADERS	THIN LINE BETWEEN LOVE AND HATE	THIGH SPY	8.00
71	2091165 lh	ELECTRIC EXPRESS	IT'S THE REAL THING	IT'S THE REAL THING part 2	6.00
71	2091165 sh	ELECTRIC EXPRESS	IT'S THE REAL THING	IT'S THE REAL THING part 2	8.00
71	2091166 lh	BEGINNING OF THE END	MONKEY TAMARIND	HEY PRETTY GIRL	8.00
71	2091166 sh	BEGINNING OF THE END	MONKEY TAMARIND	HEY PRETTY GIRL	10.00
71	2091168 lh	ARETHA FRANKLIN	ROCK STEADY	OH ME OH MY (I'M A FOOL FOR YO	10.00
71	2091168 sh	ARETHA FRANKLIN	ROCK STEADY	OH ME OH MY (I'M A FOOL FOR YO	15.00
71	2091170 lh	R.B. GREAVES	PAPERBACK WRITER	OVER YOU NOW	4.00
71	2091170 sh	R.B. GREAVES	PAPERBACK WRITER	OVER YOU NOW	5.00

Some later releases outside the obvious label sequences.

82	FLAM 1	GWEN McCRAE	KEEP THE FIRE BURNING	FUNKY SENSATION	8.00
87	96	PERCY SLEDGE	WHEN A MAN LOVES AS WOMAN	WARM AND TENDER LOVE	3.00
87	118 PS	BEN E. KING	SPANISH HARLEM	FIRST TASTE OF LOVE	4.00
04	504671685	REX GARVIN b/w KING CURTIS	SOCK IT TO EM JB part 1	MEMPHIS SOUL STEW	10.00
04	504676251 DJ	ARCHIE BELL & the DRELLS	A THOUSAND WONDERS	HERE I GO AGAIN	15.00

AUDIO FIDELITY

66	527	PEELS	TIME MARCHES ON	SCROEY MOOEY	50.00
66	527 DJ	PEELS	TIME MARCHES ON	SCROEY MOOEY	75.00

AVATAR

83	2	EDWIN STARR	I WANNA TAKE YOU HOME	YOU HIT THE NAIL ON THE HEAD	10.00

AVCO / EMBASSY

Distributed by Philips Phonogram a label dedicated to USA soul and disco related music. As with all Phonogram 70s releases, after starting with a very attractive paper label, they adopted the cheaper to produce and more ecomonical to recycle ink screen print plastic injection moulded labels. Some of the earlier releases were released with paper labels then repressed with the "ink" labels as the back catalogue was kept available. The paper labels are so much more desirable and collectable. Paper labels seemed to have ceased production on and around release 6105039

71	6105001	MITCH RYDER	JENNY TAKE A RIDE	I NEVER HAD IT BETTER	6.00
71	6105004	STYLISTICS	STOP, LOOK LISTEN (TO YOUR HEART)	IF I LOVE YOU	5.00
71	6105004 ink label	STYLISTICS	STOP, LOOK LISTEN (TO YOUR HEART)	IF I LOVE YOU	4.00
71	6105005	DONALD HEIGHT	RAGS TO RICHES TO RAGS	DANCING TO THE MUSIC OF LOVE	100.00
71	6105007	STYLISTICS	YOU ARE EVERYTHING	YOU'RE A BIG GIRL NOW	6.00
71	6105007 ink label	STYLISTICS	YOU ARE EVERYTHING	YOU'RE A BIG GIRL NOW	4.00
72	6105009	DONNIE ELBERT	I CAN'T HELP MYSELF	LOVE IS HERE AND NOW YOU'RE GO	5.00
72	6105009 ink label	DONNIE ELBERT	I CAN'T HELP MYSELF	LOVE IS HERE AND NOW YOU'RE GO	4.00
72	6105010	DELLA REESE	IF IT FEELS GOOD, DO IT	GOOD LOVIN' (MAKES IT RIGHT)	10.00
72	6105010 ink label	DELLA REESE	IF IT FEELS GOOD, DO IT	GOOD LOVIN' (MAKES IT RIGHT)	6.00
72	6105011	STYLISTICS	BETCHA BY GOLLY WOW	EBONY EYES	4.00
72	6105011 ink label	STYLISTICS	BETCHA BY GOLLY WOW	EBONY EYES	4.00
72	6105013	DONNIE ELBERT	OOO BABY BABY	TELL HER FOR ME	4.00
72	6105014	L.J. REYNOLDS & CHOCOLATE SYRUP	THE PENGUIN BREAKDOWN	OO LA WE (YOUNGHEARTS)	6.00
72	6105014 ink label	L.J. REYNOLDS & CHOCOLATE SYRUP	THE PENGUIN BREAKDOWN	OO LA WE	5.00
72	6105015	STYLISTICS	I'M STONE IN LOVE WITH YOU	THE POINT OF NO RETURN	6.00
72	6105015 ink label	STYLISTICS	I'M STONE IN LOVE WITH YOU	THE POINT OF NO RETURN	6.00
73	6105019	LIMMIE and the FAMILY COOKIN'	YOU CAN DO MAGIC	SPIDER	4.00
73	6105019 ink label	LIMMIE and the FAMILY COOKIN'	YOU CAN DO MAGIC	SPIDER	5.00
73	6105020	STYLISTICS	BREAK UP TO MAKE UP	YOU AND ME	4.00
73	6105020 ink label	STYLISTICS	BREAK UP TO MAKE UP	YOU AND ME	3.00
73	6105022	MAXINE BROWN	PICKED UP, PACKED UP AND PUT AWAY	BELLA MIA	20.00
73	6105022 ink label	MAXINE BROWN	PICKED UP, PACKED UP AND PUT AWAY	BELLA MIA	15.00
73	6105023	STYLISTICS	PEEK A BOO	IF YOU DON'T WATCH OUT	4.00
73	6105023 ink label	STYLISTICS	PEEK A BOO	IF YOU DON'T WATCH OUT	3.00
73	6105025	LIMMIE and the FAMILY COOKIN'	DREAMBOAT	MADE IN HEAVEN	4.00
73	6105025 ink label	LIMMIE and the FAMILY COOKIN'	DREAMBOAT	MADE IN HEAVEN	4.00
73	6105026	STYLISTICS	ROCKIN' ROLL BABY	MAKE IT LAST	4.00
73	6105026 ink label	STYLISTICS	ROCKIN' ROLL BABY	MAKE IT LAST	4.00
74	6105027	LIMMIE and the FAMILY COOKIN'	WALKIN' MIRACLE	HERE'S TOMORROW	5.00
74	6105027 ink label	LIMMIE and the FAMILY COOKIN'	WALKIN' MIRACLE	HERE'S TOMORROW	4.00
74	6105028	STYLISTICS	YOU MAKE ME FEEL BRAND NEW	ONLY FOR THE CHILDREN	5.00
74	6105028 ink label	STYLISTICS	YOU MAKE ME FEEL BRAND NEW	ONLY FOR THE CHILDREN	4.00

74	6105029	LIMMIE and the FAMILY COOKIN'	SAXOPHONE JONES	I'LL BE YOUR SONG	4.00
74	6105029 ink label	LIMMIE and the FAMILY COOKIN'	SAXOPHONE JONES	I'LL BE YOUR SONG	3.00
74	6105030	VAN McCOY	LOVE IS THE ANSWER	KILING ME SOFTLY	4.00
74	6105030 ink label	VAN McCOY	LOVE IS THE ANSWER	KILING ME SOFTLY	3.00
74	6105031	LITTLE ANTHONY & the IMPERIALS	LA LA LA AT THE END	I DON'T HAVE TIME TO WORRY	5.00
74	6105031 ink label	LITTLE ANTHONY & the IMPERIALS	LA LA LA AT THE END	I DON'T HAVE TIME TO WORRY	4.00
74	6105032	STYLISTICS	LET'S PUT IT ALL TOGETHER	I TAKE IT OUT ON YOU	4.00
75	6105035	STYLISTICS	STAR ON A TV SHOW	HEY GIRL, COME AND GET IT	3.00
75	6105036	STYLISTICS	SING BABY SING	THANK YOU BABY	4.00
75	6105037	VAN McCOY & the SOUL CITY	THE HUSTLE	GET DANCIN	6.00
75	6105038	VAN McCOY & the SOUL CITY	THE HUSTLE	HEY GIRL, COME AND GET IT	5.00
75	6105038 ink label	VAN McCOY & the SOUL CITY	THE HUSTLE	HEY GIRL, COME AND GET IT	3.00
75	6105039	STYLISTICS	I CAN'T GIVE YOU ANYTHING	I'D RATHER BE LOVED BY YOU	4.00
75	6105040	R.B. FREEMAN	I'M SHAFT (YOU AIN'T SHAFT)	same: instrumental	8.00
75	6105040 ink label	R.B. FREEMAN	I'M SHAFT (YOU AIN'T SHAFT)	same: instrumental	5.00
75	6105041	STYLISTICS	NA-NA IS THE SADDEST WORD	TO SAVE MY ROCK N' ROLL SOUL	4.00
75	6105041 ink label	STYLISTICS	NA-NA IS THE SADDEST WORD	TO SAVE MY ROCK N' ROLL SOUL	4.00
75	6105042	VAN McCOY & the SOUL CITY	CHANGE WITH THE TIMES	GOOD NIGHT BABY	4.00
76	6105044	STYLISTICS	FUNKY WEEKEND	IF YOU ARE THERE	4.00
76	6105045	SOFTONES	THAT OLD BLACK MAGIC	WHY WHY BABY	4.00
76	6105061	VAN McCOY & the SOUL CITY	PARTY	LOVE IS THE ANSWER	4.00
76	6105059	STYLISTICS	SIXTEEN BARS	I WILL LOVE YOU ALWAYS	3.00
77	6105073	STYLISTICS	$7000 AND YOU	THAT DON'T SHAKE ME	4.00
77	6105078	SOFTONES	LOVE STORY	LAUNDROMAT	4.00
78	6105086	STYLISTICS	WONDER WOMAN	LUCKY ME	3.00
79	6105092 PS	VAN McCOY & the SOUL CITY	THE HUSTLE	LOVE IS THE ANSWER	4.00

AVI

79	107	L.J. JOHNSON	24 HOURS A DAY	YOUR MAGIC PUT A SPELL ON ME	4.00
79	107 DJ	L.J. JOHNSON	24 HOURS A DAY	YOUR MAGIC PUT A SPELL ON ME	6.00
79	108	LOWRELL	MELLOW, MELLOW RIGHT ON	YOU'RE PLAYING DIRTY	10.00
79	108 DJ	LOWRELL	MELLOW, MELLOW RIGHT ON	YOU'RE PLAYING DIRTY	15.00
80	109	EL COCO	LET'S GET IT TOGETHER	LOCO MOTION '79	4.00
80	109 DJ	EL COCO	LET'S GET IT TOGETHER	LOCO MOTION '79	5.00

AXE

77	43 large hole center	RAIN with CHARITY BROWN	OUT OF MY MIND	HERE WITH YOU	8.00
77	43 solid center	RAIN with CHARITY BROWN	OUT OF MY MIND	HERE WITH YOU	10.00

B&C

B&C Records Limited, 37 Soho Square, London W1

After the demise of their Action label venture into soul. B&C's first seven releases were still aimed at the soul market, perhaps because they still had contractual commitments to certain USA labels. But these releases were met with much the same response. The soul fans bought the 45s from music paper reviews and release sheets, but not in enough quantities to encourage B&C to continue as they did the previous two years, releasing all manner of material from small USA labels. After disappointing sales figures, B&C veered away from the soul market to concentrate on releasing rock and pop this did achieve some measure of success with groups like Atomic Rooster, Steeleye Span, and in 1971 a Shakin' Stevens LP called "Rock & Roll Party" was released so the disenchantment with soul was complete. B&C continued releasing vinyl for another eight years without another soul release.

71	2 DJ	CAROL GRIMES & the RED PRICE	I DON'T WANT TO DISCUSS IT	I'M WALKING	15.00

special promo only release to promote "The Battle Of The Bands" LP. UK only version of Little Richard's Northern Soul classic

69	101	JAMES CARR	FREEDOM TRAIN	THAT'S THE WAY LOVE TURNED OUT	10.00
69	101 DJ	JAMES CARR	FREEDOM TRAIN	THAT'S THE WAY LOVE TURNED OUT	15.00
69	102	BOB AND EARL	DANCIN' EVERYWHERE	BABY IT'S OVER	6.00
69	102 DJ	BOB AND EARL	DANCIN' EVERYWHERE	BABY IT'S OVER	8.00
69	104	HORACE FAITH	SPINNING WHEEL	LIKE I USED TO DO	5.00
69	104 DJ	HORACE FAITH	SPINNING WHEEL	LIKE I USED TO DO	6.00
69	105	JACKIE LEE & DELORES HALL	WHETHER IT'S RIGHT OR WRONG	BABY I'M SATISFIED	10.00
69	105 DJ	JACKIE LEE & DELORES HALL	WHETHER IT'S RIGHT OR WRONG	BABY I'M SATISFIED	15.00
69	106	CLYDE McPHATTER	DENVER	TELL ME	15.00
69	106 DJ	CLYDE McPHATTER	DENVER	TELL ME	20.00
69	107	AARON NEVILLE	TELL IT LIKE IT IS	WHY WORRY	8.00
69	107 DJ	AARON NEVILLE	TELL IT LIKE IT IS	WHY WORRY	10.00
69	110	DON FOX	YOU BELONG TO MY HEART	ONCE IN A WHILE	5.00
69	110 DJ	DON FOX	YOU BELONG TO MY HEART	ONCE IN A WHILE	6.00
70	119	FORUM	THE RIVER IS WIDE	I FALL IN LOVE (ALL OVER AGAIN	6.00
70	119 DJ	FORUM	THE RIVER IS WIDE	I FALL IN LOVE (ALL OVER AGAIN	8.00
71	147	WEATHERMEN	HONEY BEE (KEEP ON STINGING ME)	ANARCHY ROCK	5.00
71	147 DJ	WEATHERMEN	HONEY BEE (KEEP ON STINGING ME)	ANARCHY ROCK	6.00

BADGER

This obscure mid-seventies label only soul related 45 was by ex-Orlons vocalist Rozetta Hightower with a good cover version of Ike & Tina Turner's classic.

75	3	ROZETTA HIGHTOWER	RIVER DEEP MOUNTAIN HIGH	FRIENDSHIP TRAIN	8.00

BANG

76	02	MUSCLE SHOALS HORNS	BREAKDOWN	GET IT UP	4.00
76	03	McCOYS	HANG ON SLOOPY	FEVER	4.00
77	04	BRICK	DAZZ	DAZZ part 2	4.00
77	05	MUSCLE SHOALS HORNS	WHERE I'M COMING FROM	BUMP DE BUMP DE BOODIE	4.00
77	07	MICHEAL ZAGER EVANS BAND	DO IT WITH FEELING		4.00
77	08	BRICK	MUSIC MATIC	CAN'T WAIT	4.00

77	010	PEABO BRYSON	SMILE	I CAN MAKE IT BETTER	5.00
78	012	BRICK	DUSIC	HAPPY	4.00
78	013	BOILING POINT	LET'S GET FUNKTIFIED	LET'S GET FUNKTIFIED part 2	4.00
79	016	BRICK	DANCIN' MAN	WE'LL LOVE	4.00

BARAK

Small 70s label which had only had five releases, only two of them were soul. Both release were from Southern Soul stalwarts were ignored at the time but in recent years have become very collectable. Both 45s are extremely difficult to find.

77	3	SIR TED FORD	I WANNA BE NEAR YOU	RIDIN' TOO HIGH	50.00
77	4	JACKIE PAYNE	I FOUND MYSELF	IT'S GONNA BE ALRIGHT	30.00

BARCLAY

75	29	RAYMOND LEFERVE & HIS ORCH. SOUL COAXING		EMANUEL	6.00
75	29 DJ	RAYMOND LEFERVE & HIS ORCH. SOUL COAXING		EMMANUELLE	6.00
75	30	WILD MAGNOLIAS	SMOKE MY PEACE PIPE (SMOKE IT	HANDA WANDA	6.00
75	34	WILD MAGNOLIAS	THEY CALL US WILD	JUMALAKA BOOM BOOM	5.00

BEACON

331-333, High Road, London NW 10

After a short stint of leasing his material to other labels, producer Milton Samuels launched the Beacon label in 1968 which was distributed by EMI. With his first release by the Show Stoppers going straight into the charts, Milton had the funds to sign up numerous writers and producers including the later highly successful Biddu; Micki Dallon and even Donnie Elbert produced for Beacon: Together they released some of the most collectable Brit Soul around. Home grown talent like Root & Jenny Jackson, Jon and Jeannie, Paula Parfitt were released along side Philadelphia Soul Soul artists the Showstoppers and Bobby Wells; even including an obscure Chi-lites recording before they were ever known in the UK. Milton was not afraid of releasing obscure artists from the USA or producing young talented artists from the UK. It all added up to a very interesting label that released a wide range of music genres. The label has several design and colour changes but promo copies only seem to have been pressed on the first release. After almost ninety releases the label sadly ceased making 45's.

68	100 red swirl	SHOW STOPPERS	WHAT CAN A MAN DO	AIN'T NOTHING BUT A HOUSE PARTY	20.00
68	100 red swirl DJ	SHOW STOPPERS	WHAT CAN A MAN DO	AIN'T NOTHING BUT A HOUSE PARTY	75.00
68	100 yellow	SHOW STOPPERS	WHAT CAN A MAN DO	AIN'T NOTHING BUT A HOUSE PARTY	25.00
69	100 orange	SHOW STOPPERS	WHAT CAN A MAN DO	AIN'T NOTHING BUT A HOUSE PARTY	20.00
70	100 green	SHOW STOPPERS	WHAT CAN A MAN DO	AIN'T NOTHING BUT A HOUSE PARTY	10.00
68	101 yellow	SONS & LOVERS	FEEL ALRIGHT	HELP ME	10.00
68	102 yellow	BOBBY WELLS	LET'S COPP A GROOVE	RECIPE FOR LOVE	40.00
69	102 white	BOBBY WELLS	LET'S COPP A GROOVE	RECIPE FOR LOVE	15.00
70	102 green	BOBBY WELLS	LET'S COPP A GROOVE	RECIPE FOR LOVE	10.00
68	104 yellow	MIKE WADE	LOVERS	TWO THREE FOUR	10.00
68	105 yellow	JON and JEANNIE	LOVER'S HOLIDAY	SOMETHING YOU GOT	15.00
68	106 yellow	SHOWSTOPPERS	HEARTBREAKER	SHAKE YOUR MINI	50.00
68	108 yellow	RAM JAM HOLDER	I JUST CAME TO SEE MY BABY	YES I DO	10.00
69	110 yellow	ROOT & JENNY JACKSON	LEAN ON ME	PLEASE COME HOME	10.00
69	110 white	ROOT & JENNY JACKSON	LEAN ON ME	PLEASE COME HOME	5.00
69	110 dup. #	SHOWSTOPPERS	DON'T LEAVE ME STANDING IN THE RAIN	DO YOU NEED MY LOVE	10.00
69	111	CINNAMON	YOU WON'T SEE ME LEAVING	LEAVES OF LOVE	10.00
68	113 white	JON and JEANNIE	DON'T SIGN THE PAPERS	WE GOT LOVIN'	15.00
68	114	BARRY DAVIS	I WISH IT WOULD RAIN	STRANGE DAYS	5.00
69	115	JEANNIE DEE	COME INTO MY ARMS	SUN SHINE ON ME	6.00
69	119	CHI-LITES	PRETTY GIRL	LOVE BANDIT	75.00
69	125	TONY RITCHIE	GRAB A BIT OF MY HEART	LINDYLINDY	5.00
69	130	SHOWSTOPPERS	SCHOOL PROM.	JUST A LITTLE BIT OF LOVIN'	40.00
69	135	PAULA PARFITT	LOVE IS WONDERFUL	I'M GONNA GIVE YOU BACK YOUR RING	150.00

The above 45 by Paula Parfitt were bootlegged using the original UK label design. The authentic original has the serrated anti-slip raised edge around the labels circumference.

69	136	ROOT & JENNY JACKSON	LET'S GO SOMEWHERE	IF I DON'T LOVE YOU	10.00
69	142	JEANIE DEE	COME SEE ABOUT ME	DON'T GO HOME MY LITTLE DARLIN	20.00
70	149	BOBBY BRIDGER	WHY DO I LOVE YOU	THE WORLD IS TURNING ON	5.00
70	156	SUGAR SIMONE	I KEEP ON TRYING	ONLY THE LONELY	6.00
70	158	ROOT & JENNY JACKSON	SO FAR AWAY	same: instrumental	15.00
70	159	BOBBY BRIDGER	YOU'RE IN LOVE	SUGAR SHAKER	15.00
70	159	ERROL SOBERS	YOU'RE IN LOVE	SUGAR SHAKER	18.00
70	173	TONY RITCHIE	ANYBODY AT THE PARTY SEEN JENNY	YOU CAN'T WIN	5.00
70	174	SUGAR SIMONE	WHY CAN'T I TOUGH YOU	GOTTA GET IT OFF MY MIND	5.00
71	177	SHOWSTOPPERS	REACH IN THE GOODY BAG	HOW DO YOU FEEL	4.00
71	182	SHOWSTOPPERS	ACTION SPEAKS LOUDER THAN WORDS	PICK UP YOUR SMILE	10.00
71	188	TONY MORGAN & MUSCLE BAND	BLACK SKIN BLUE EYED BOYS	WHY BUILD A MOUNTAIN	5.00

BEE

79	477	VELVET HAMMER	HAPPY	KEYS TO THE CITY (OMNI)	8.00

BEECOOL

01	100 EP PS	VARIOUS ARTISTS	THE IN CROWD: COOL 4	jacky beavers - I need my baby	15.00
03	101 DJ	JOHNNY MOORE c/w DOTTIE PEARSON	CAN'T LIVE WITHOUT YOUR LOVE	HELLO BABY	10.00

BEGGARS BANQUET

81	51	FREEEZ	SOUTHERN FREEEZ	same: lp version	5.00

BELL

Part of Columbia pictures: The USA Bell, Amy, and Mala are a well respected group of labels, that carry literally 100's of highly collectable soul 45's. Distributed by EMI before 1968 the USA recordings gained UK release through the Stateside label. In 1968 Bell's huge catalogue was rewarded with it very own label. Below, are the releases in the UK between 1968 and 1976, the label went through changes in design and colour, please note several Northern Soul classics were released and repressed using the same release number, but different label designs, these are noted and priced accordingly. Bell had some wonderful labels within it's control these included Philly Groove, A.G.P, Chariot, Vando, Dynovoice etc. Up until 1970 every soul release on the label was a USA production, later in the 70s a few Brit Soul artists broke through with some interesting releases. In 1974 Bell became Arista.

68	1001	BOX TOPS	CRY LIKE A BABY	THE DOOR YOU CLOSED TO ME	8.00
68	1001 DJ	BOX TOPS	CRY LIKE A BABY	THE DOOR YOU CLOSED TO ME	10.00
68	1002	REPARATA & the DELRONS	CAPTAIN OF YOUR SHIP	TOOM TOOM IS A LITTLE BOY	6.00
68	1002 DJ	REPARATA & the DELRONS	CAPTAIN OF YOUR SHIP	TOOM TOOM IS A LITTLE BOY	10.00
68	1003	OSCAR TONEY JR.	WITHOUT LOVE (THERE IS NOTHING	A LOVE THAT NEVER GROWS COLD	8.00
68	1003 DJ	OSCAR TONEY JR.	WITHOUT LOVE (THERE IS NOTHING	A LOVE THAT NEVER GROWS COLD	12.00
68	1004	JAMES CARR	A MAN NEEDS A WOMAN	STRONGER THAN LOVE	10.00
68	1004 DJ	JAMES CARR	A MAN NEEDS A WOMAN	STRONGER THAN LOVE	15.00
68	1005	DELFONICS	LA LA MEANS I LOVE YOU	CAN'T GET OVER LOSING YOU	8.00
68	1005 DJ	DELFONICS	LA LA MEANS I LOVE YOU	CAN'T GET OVER LOSING YOU	10.00
68	1006	LEE DORSEY	CAN YOU HEAR ME	CYNTHIA	6.00
68	1006 DJ	LEE DORSEY	CAN YOU HEAR ME	CYNTHIA	8.00
68	1007	FLASH & the BOARD OF DIRECTORS	BUSY SIGNAL	LOVE AIN'T EASY	15.00
68	1007 DJ	FLASH & the BOARD OF DIRECTORS	BUSY SIGNAL	LOVE AIN'T EASY	20.00
68	1008	JAMES & BOBBY PURIFY	I WAS BORN TO LOSE OUT	I CAN'T REMEMBER	8.00
68	1008 DJ	JAMES & BOBBY PURIFY	I WAS BORN TO LOSE OUT	I CAN'T REMEMBER	10.00
68	1010	BRUCE CHANNEL	KEEP ON	BARBARA ALLEN	4.00
68	1010 DJ	BRUCE CHANNEL	KEEP ON	BARBARA ALLEN	8.00
68	1011	OSCAR TONEY JR.	NO SAD SONG	NEVER GET ENOUGH OF YOUR LOVE	8.00
68	1011 DJ	OSCAR TONEY JR.	NO SAD SONG	NEVER GET ENOUGH OF YOUR LOVE	12.00
68	1014	REPARATA & the DELRONS	PANIC	SATURDAY NIGHT DIDN'T HAPPEN	30.00
68	1014 DJ	REPARATA & the DELRONS	PANIC	SATURDAY NIGHT DIDN'T HAPPEN	60.00
68	1016	DELFONICS	I'M SORRY	YOU'RE GONE	8.00
68	1016 DJ	DELFONICS	I'M SORRY	YOU'RE GONE	12.00
68	1017	BOX TOPS	CHOO CHOO TRAIN	FIELDS OF CLOVER	5.00
68	1017 DJ	BOX TOPS	CHOO CHOO TRAIN	FIELDS OF CLOVER	6.00
68	1018	MOSES & JOSHUA	GET OUT OF MY HEART	THEY DON'T WANT US TOGETHER	20.00
68	1018 DJ	MOSES & JOSHUA	GET OUT OF MY HEART	THEY DON'T WANT US TOGETHER	40.00
68	1020	O'JAYS	I'M SO GLAD I FOUND YOU	LOOK OVER YOUR SHOULDER	40.00
68	1020 DJ	O'JAYS	I'M SO GLAD I FOUND YOU	LOOK OVER YOUR SHOULDER	75.00
68	1021	REPARATA & the DELRONS	WEATHER FORECAST	YOU CAN'T CHANGE A YOUNG BOY'S	8.00
68	1021 DJ	REPARATA & the DELRONS	WEATHER FORECAST	YOU CAN'T CHANGE A YOUNG BOY'S	10.00
68	1022	LEN BARRY	4 - 5 - 6 NOW I'M ALONE	FUNKY NIGHT	5.00
68	1022 DJ	LEN BARRY	4 - 5 - 6 NOW I'M ALONE	FUNKY NIGHT	8.00
68	1023	MASQUERADERS	I AIN'T GOT TO LOVE NOBODY ELSE	I GOT IT	15.00
68	1023 DJ	MASQUERADERS	I AIN'T GOT TO LOVE NOBODY ELSE	I GOT IT	22.00
68	1024	JAMES & BOBBY PURIFY	HELP YOURSELF TO ALL MY LOVIN'	LAST PIECE OF LOVE	10.00
68	1024 DJ	JAMES & BOBBY PURIFY	HELP YOURSELF TO ALL MY LOVIN'	LAST PIECE OF LOVE	15.00
68	1025 silver bells	BOB BRADY & the CONCORDS	EVERYBODY'S GOIN' TO THE LOVE-IN	IT'S BEEN A LONG TIME BETWEEN	30.00
68	1025 DJ green	BOB BRADY & the CONCORDS	EVERYBODY'S GOIN' TO THE LOVE-IN	IT'S BEEN A LONG TIME BETWEEN	**81.00**
68	1025 black	BOB BRADY & the CONCORDS	EVERYBODY'S GOIN' TO THE LOVE-IN	IT'S BEEN A LONG TIME BETWEEN	20.00
70	1025 DJ black	BOB BRADY & the CONCORDS	EVERYBODY'S GOIN' TO THE LOVE-IN	IT'S BEEN A LONG TIME BETWEEN	30.00
71	1025 plain silver	BOB BRADY & the CONCORDS	EVERYBODY'S GOIN' TO THE LOVE-IN	IT'S BEEN A LONG TIME BETWEEN	15.00
71	1025 DJ plain silver	BOB BRADY & the CONCORDS	EVERYBODY'S GOIN' TO THE LOVE-IN	IT'S BEEN A LONG TIME BETWEEN	25.00
68	1027 silver bells	BOB KUBAN & THE IN-MEN	THE CHEATER	TRY ME BABY	15.00
68	1027 DJ green	BOB KUBAN & THE IN-MEN	THE CHEATER	TRY ME BABY	25.00
70	1027 black	BOB KUBAN & THE IN-MEN	THE CHEATER	TRY ME BABY	15.00
70	1027 DJ black	BOB KUBAN & THE IN-MEN	THE CHEATER	TRY ME BABY	22.00
71	1027 silver	BOB KUBAN & THE IN-MEN	THE CHEATER	TRY ME BABY	10.00
71	1027 DJ silver	BOB KUBAN & THE IN-MEN	THE CHEATER	TRY ME BABY	15.00
68	1028	DELFONICS	BREAK YOUR PROMISE	ALFIE	6.00
68	1028 DJ	DELFONICS	BREAK YOUR PROMISE	ALFIE	8.00
68	1029	ROBERT KNIGHT	ISN'T IT LONELY TOGETHER	WE'D BETTER STOP	8.00
68	1029 DJ	ROBERT KNIGHT	ISN'T IT LONELY TOGETHER	WE'D BETTER STOP	10.00
68	1031	CHRIS BARTLEY	I FOUND A GOODIE	BE MINE FOREVER	25.00
68	1031 DJ	CHRIS BARTLEY	I FOUND A GOODIE	BE MINE FOREVER	40.00
68	1032	MASQUERADERS	I AIN'T GOT TO LOVE NOBODY ELSE	I GOT IT	20.00
68	1032 DJ	MASQUERADERS	I AIN'T GOT TO LOVE NOBODY ELSE	I GOT IT	28.00
68	1033	O'JAYS	THE CHOICE	GOING GOING GONE	10.00
68	1033 DJ	O'JAYS	THE CHOICE	GOING GOING GONE	15.00
68	1035	BOX TOPS	I MET HER IN CHURCH	PEOPLE GONNA TALK	5.00
68	1035 DJ	BOX TOPS	I MET HER IN CHURCH	PEOPLE GONNA TALK	6.00
68	1038	BRUCE CHANNEL	MR. BUS DRIVER	TROUBLE WITH SAM	10.00
68	1038 DJ	BRUCE CHANNEL	MR. BUS DRIVER	TROUBLE WITH SAM	15.00
69	1042	DELFONICS	READY OR NOT HERE I COME	SOMEBODY LOVES YOU	6.00
69	1042 DJ	DELFONICS	READY OR NOT HERE I COME	SOMEBODY LOVES YOU	10.00
69	1043	JAMES & BOBBY PURIFY	UNTIE ME	WE'RE FINALLY GONNA MAKE IT	10.00
69	1043 DJ	JAMES & BOBBY PURIFY	UNTIE ME	WE'RE FINALLY GONNA MAKE IT	15.00
69	1044	SAM HUTCHINS	DANG ME	I'M TIRED OF PRETENDING	15.00
69	1044 DJ	SAM HUTCHINS	DANG ME	I'M TIRED OF PRETENDING	20.00
69	1046	SMOKESTACK LIGHTNIN'	LIGHT IN MY WINDOW	LONG STEMMED EYES	8.00
69	1046 DJ	SMOKESTACK LIGHTNIN'	LIGHT IN MY WINDOW	LONG STEMMED EYES	10.00
69	1047	SOLOMON BURKE	UP TIGHT GOOD WOMAN	I CAN STOP	8.00
69	1047 DJ	SOLOMON BURKE	UP TIGHT GOOD WOMAN	I CAN STOP	10.00
69	1049 silver bells	SHIRLEY and the SHIRELLES	LOOK WHAT YOU'VE DONE TO MY HEART	A MOS UNUSUAL BOY	22.00
69	1049 DJ green	SHIRLEY and the SHIRELLES	LOOK WHAT YOU'VE DONE TO MY HEART	A MOS UNUSUAL BOY	40.00
70	1049 black	SHIRLEY and the SHIRELLES	LOOK WHAT YOU'VE DONE TO MY HEART	A MOS UNUSUAL BOY	15.00
70	1049 DJ black	SHIRLEY and the SHIRELLES	LOOK WHAT YOU'VE DONE TO MY HEART	A MOS UNUSUAL BOY	22.00
71	1049 silver	SHIRLEY and the SHIRELLES	LOOK WHAT YOU'VE DONE TO MY HEART	A MOS UNUSUAL BOY	10.00

71	1049 DJ silver	SHIRLEY and the SHIRELLES	LOOK WHAT YOU'VE DONE TO MY HEART	A MOS UNUSUAL BOY	15.00
69	1051	LEE DORSEY	I'M GONNA SIT RIGHT DOWN AND	LITTLE BABY	6.00
69	1051 DJ	LEE DORSEY	I'M GONNA SIT RIGHT DOWN AND	LITTLE BABY	8.00
69	1053	TOYS	A LOVER'S CONCERTO	BABY TOYS	6.00
69	1053 DJ	TOYS	A LOVER'SD CONCERTO	BABY TOYS	10.00
69	1056 silver bells	JAMES & BOBBY PURIFY	SHAKE A TAIL FEATHER	LET LOVE COME BETWEEN US	15.00
69	1056 DJ green	JAMES & BOBBY PURIFY	SHAKE A TAIL FEATHER	LET LOVE COME BETWEEN US	25.00
72	1056 silver	JAMES & BOBBY PURIFY	SHAKE A TAIL FEATHER	LET LOVE COME BETWEEN US	10.00
72	1056 DJ silver	JAMES & BOBBY PURIFY	SHAKE A TAIL FEATHER	LET LOVE COME BETWEEN US	15.00
69	1057	OSCAR TONEY JR.	DOWN IN TEXAS	JUST FOR YOU	10.00
69	1057 DJ	OSCAR TONEY JR.	DOWN IN TEXAS	JUST FOR YOU	15.00
69	1060	LEE DORSEY	RIDE YOUR PONY	GET OUT OF MY LIFE WOMAN	6.00
69	1060 DJ	LEE DORSEY	RIDE YOUR PONY	GET OUT OF MY LIFE WOMAN	10.00
69	1062	SOLOMON BURKE	PROUD MARY	WHAT AM I LIVING FOR	6.00
69	1062 DJ	SOLOMON BURKE	PROUD MARY	WHAT AM I LIVING FOR	8.00
69	1065	SHIRLEY and the SHIRELLES	PLAYTHINGS	LOOKING GLASS	6.00
69	1065 DJ	SHIRLEY and the SHIRELLES	PLAYTHINGS	LOOKING GLASS	8.00
69	1066	DELFONICS	YOU CAN'T BE LOVING HIM	LET IT BE ME	15.00
69	1066 DJ	DELFONICS	YOU CAN'T BE LOVING HIM	LET IT BE ME	20.00
69	1067	JAMES & BOBBY PURIFY	DO UNTO ME	WISH YOU DIDN'T HAVE TO GO	10.00
69	1067 DJ	JAMES & BOBBY PURIFY	DO UNTO ME	WISH YOU DIDN'T HAVE TO GO	15.00
69	1068	BOX TOPS	SOUL DEEP	THE HAPPY SONG	6.00
69	1068 DJ	BOX TOPS	SOUL DEEP	THE HAPPY SONG	10.00
69	1069	CUPIDS INSPIRATION	THE SAD THING	LOOK AT ME	5.00
69	1069 DJ	CUPIDS INSPIRATION	THE SAD THING	LOOK AT ME	6.00
69	1073	DELFONICS	FUNNY FEELING	YOU GOT YOURS I'LL GET MINE	6.00
69	1073 DJ	DELFONICS	FUNNY FEELING	YOU GOT YOURS I'LL GET MINE	10.00
69	1074	LEE DORSEY	EVERYTHING I DO GONH BE FUNKY	THERE SHOULD BE A BOOK	6.00
69	1074 DJ	LEE DORSEY	EVERYTHING I DO GONH BE FUNKY	THERE SHOULD BE A BOOK	8.00
69	1087	NINO TEMPO & APRIL STEVENS	SEA OF LOVE / SITTIN ON THE DOCK OF BAY	TWILIGHT TIME	4.00
69	1087 DJ	NINO TEMPO & APRIL STEVENS	SEA OF LOVE / SITTIN ON THE DOCK OF BAY	TWILIGHT TIME	5.00

Bell changes it's label to black with silver lettering

70	1099	DELFONICS	DIDN'T I (BLOW YOUR MIND THIS TIME)	DOWN IS UP, UP IS DOWN	6.00
70	1099 DJ	DELFONICS	DIDN'T I (BLOW YOUR MIND THIS TIME)	DOWN IS UP, UP IS DOWN	10.00
70	1105	ELLIE GREENWICH	AIN'T THAT PECULIAR	I DON'T WANNA BE LEFT OUTSIDE	8.00
70	1105 DJ	ELLIE GREENWICH	AIN'T THAT PECULIAR	I DON'T WANNA BE LEFT OUTSIDE	10.00
70	1109	WATSON T. BROWN	WILL YOU STILL LOVE ME TOMORROW	SAVE THE LAST DANCE FOR ME	5.00
70	1109 DJ	WATSON T. BROWN	WILL YOU STILL LOVE ME TOMORROW	SAVE THE LAST DANCE FOR ME	6.00
70	1111	JOHNNY JOHNSON & the BANDWAGON	SWEET INSPIRATION	PRIDE COMES BEFORE A FALL	5.00
70	1111 DJ	JOHNNY JOHNSON & the BANDWAGON	SWEET INSPIRATION	PRIDE COMES BEFORE A FALL	6.00
70	1114	BOB BRADY & the CONCORDS	EVERYBODY'S GOIN' TO THE LOVE-IN	IT'S BEEN A LONG TIME BETWEEN	10.00
70	1114 DJ	BOB BRADY & the CONCORDS	EVERYBODY'S GOIN' TO THE LOVE-IN	IT'S BEEN A LONG TIME BETWEEN	15.00
70	1116	DELFONICS	TRYING TO MAKE A FOOL OF ME	BABY I LOVE YOU	6.00
70	1116 DJ	DELFONICS	TRYING TO MAKE A FOOL OF ME	BABY I LOVE YOU	8.00
70	1122	5TH. DIMENSION	ON THE BEACH	THIS IS YOUR LIFE	3.00
70	1122 DJ	5TH. DIMENSION	ON THE BEACH	THIS IS YOUR LIFE	4.00
70	1123	FIVE FLIGHTS UP	DO WHAT YOU WANNA DO	BLACK CAT	6.00
70	1123 DJ	FIVE FLIGHTS UP	DO WHAT YOU WANNA DO	BLACK CAT	8.00
70	1127	DELFONICS	WHEN YOU GET RIGHT DOWN TO IT	THINK ABOUT ME	6.00
70	1127 DJ	DELFONICS	WHEN YOU GET RIGHT DOWN TO IT	THINK ABOUT ME	10.00
70	1128	JOHNNY JOHNSON & the BANDWAGON	(BLAME IT) ON THE PONY EXPRESS	NEVER LET YOU GO	5.00
70	1128	JOHNNY JOHNSON & the BANDWAGON	(BLAME IT) ON THE PONY EXPRESS	NEVER LET YOU GO	6.00

From number 1135 the Bell label changes colour to silver with black lettering. Number before 1135 that are silver and black are company represses.

71	1135	PHIL FLOWERS	THE MAN THE WIFE AND THE LITTLE BABY DAUGHTER	NOTHING LASTS FOREVER	6.00
71	1135 DJ	PHIL FLOWERS	THE MAN THE WIFE AND THE LITTLE BABY DAUGHTER	NOTHING LASTS FOREVER	10.00
71	1137	5TH. DIMENSION	ONE LESS BELL TO ANSWER	FEELING ALRIGHT	4.00
71	1137 DJ	5TH. DIMENSION	ONE LESS BELL TO ANSWER	FEELING ALRIGHT	5.00
71	1141	FANTASTICS	SOMETHING OLD, SOMETHING NEW	HIGH AND DRY	3.00
71	1141 DJ	FANTASTICS	SOMETHING OLD, SOMETHING NEW	HIGH AND DRY	5.00
71	1154	JOHNNY JOHNSON & the BANDWAGON	SOUL SAHARA	MR. TAMBOURINE MAN	15.00
71	1154 DJ	JOHNNY JOHNSON & the BANDWAGON	SOUL SAHARA	MR. TAMBOURINE MAN	20.00
71	1161	5TH. DIMENSION	LIGHT SINGS	LOVES, LINES, ANGLES AND RHYMES	3.00
71	1161 DJ	5TH. DIMENSION	LIGHT SINGS	LOVES, LINES, ANGLES AND RHYMES	4.00
71	1162	FANTASTICS	SOMETHING WONDERFUL	MAN MADE WORLD	3.00
71	1162 DJ	FANTASTICS	SOMETHING WONDERFUL	MAN MADE WORLD	4.00
71	1165	DELFONICS	LA - LA MEANS I LOVE YOU	CAN'T GET OVER LOSING YOU	5.00
71	1165 DJ	DELFONICS	LA - LA MEANS I LOVE YOU	CAN'T GET OVER LOSING YOU	10.00
71	1168	BOBBI LYNN	EARTHQUAKE	OPPORTUNITY STREET	15.00
71	1168 DJ	BOBBI LYNN	EARTHQUAKE	OPPORTUNITY STREET	22.00
71	1175	DELFONICS	READY OR NOT HERE I COME	SOMEBODY LOVES YOU	6.00
71	1175 DJ	DELFONICS	READY OR NOT HERE I COME	SOMEBODY LOVES YOU	8.00
71	1185	JOHNNY JOHNSON & the BANDWAGON	SALLY PUT YOUR RED SHOES ON	CASOLINE ALLEY BRED	4.00
71	1185 DJ	JOHNNY JOHNSON & the BANDWAGON	SALLY PUT YOUR RED SHOES ON	CASOLINE ALLEY BRED	5.00
71	1188	AL GREENE & the SOUL MATES	DON'T LEAVE ME	BACK UP TRAIN	15.00
71	1188 DJ	AL GREENE & the SOUL MATES	DON'T LEAVE ME	BACK UP TRAIN	20.00
71	1198	5TH. DIMENSION	THE DECLARATION	A CHANGE IS GONNA COME + PEOPLE GOTTA BE	3.00
71	1198 DJ	5TH. DIMENSION	THE DECLARATION	A CHANGE IS GONNA COME + PEOPLE GOTTA BE	4.00
71	1202	FANTASTICS	LOVE ME LOVE THE LIFE I LEAD	OLD RAGS AND TATTERS	4.00
71	1202 DJ	FANTASTICS	LOVE ME LOVE THE LIFE I LEAD	OLD RAGS AND TATTERS	5.00

71	1207	5TH. DIMENSION	TOGETHER LET'S FIND LOVE	NEVER MY LOVE	3.00
71	1207 DJ	5TH. DIMENSION	TOGETHER LET'S FIND LOVE	NEVER MY LOVE	4.00
72	1215	DELFONICS	TRYTIN' TO MAKE A FOOL OF ME	BABY I LOVE YOU	6.00
72	1215 DJ	DELFONICS	TRYTIN' TO MAKE A FOOL OF ME	BABY I LOVE YOU	10.00
72	1217	PEARLS	THIRD FINGER, LEFT HAND	LITTLE LADY LOVE ME	4.00
72	1217 DJ	PEARLS	THIRD FINGER, LEFT HAND	LITTLE LADY LOVE ME	5.00
72	1221	JOHNNY JOHNSON & the BANDWAGON	HIGH AND DRY	NEVER SET ME FREE	4.00
72	1221 DJ	JOHNNY JOHNSON & the BANDWAGON	HIGH AND DRY	NEVER SET ME FREE	5.00
72	1223	5TH. DIMENSION	I DIDN'T GET TO SLEEP AT ALL LAST NIGHT	RIVER WITCH	3.00
72	1223 DJ	5TH. DIMENSION	I DIDN'T GET TO SLEEP AT ALL LAST NIGHT	RIVER WITCH	4.00
72	1225	LUNAR FUNK	MR. PENGUIN	MR. PENGUIN PART2	8.00
72	1225 DJ	LUNAR FUNK	MR. PENGUIN	MR. PENGUIN PART2	10.00
72	1226	MARDI GRAS	TOO BUSY THINKING ABOUT MY BABY	LETTER OF RECOMMENDATION	4.00
72	1226 DJ	MARDI GRAS	TOO BUSY THINKING ABOUT MY BABY	LETTER OF RECOMMENDATION	5.00
72	1227	PIGLETS	BABY LOVE	MY FAULT	4.00
72	1227 DJ	PIGLETS	BABY LOVE	MY FAULT	5.00
72	1232	REAL THING	VICIOUS CIRCLES	VICIOUS CIRCLES part 2	5.00
72	1232 DJ	REAL THING	VICIOUS CIRCLES	VICIOUS CIRCLES part 2	6.00
72	1251	SHIRLEY and the SHIRELLES	LOOK WHAT YOU'VE DONE TO MY HEART	A MOST USUAL BOY	8.00
72	1251 DJ	SHIRLEY and the SHIRELLES	LOOK WHAT YOU'VE DONE TO MY HEART	A MOST USUAL BOY	10.00
72	1252	REPARATA & the DELRONS	CAPTAIN OF YOUR SHIP	TOOM TOOM IS A LITTLE BOY	4.00
72	1252 DJ	REPARATA & the DELRONS	CAPTAIN OF YOUR SHIP	TOOM TOOM IS A LITTLE BOY	5.00
72	1254	PEARLS	YOU CAME YOU SAW	SING OUT TO ME	4.00
72	1254 DJ	PEARLS	YOU CAME YOU SAW	SING OUT TO ME	5.00
72	1264	HOT ROCKS	PUT IT WHERE YOU WANT IT	CAN'T GET IT THROUGH MY HEAD	5.00
72	1264 DJ	HOT ROCKS	PUT IT WHERE YOU WANT IT	CAN'T GET IT THROUGH MY HEAD	6.00
73	1266	FANTASTICS	THE BEST OF STRANGERS NOW	SOMETHING TO REMEMBER ME BY	4.00
73	1266 DJ	FANTASTICS	THE BEST OF STRANGERS NOW	SOMETHING TO REMEMBER ME BY	5.00
73	1269	DRIFTERS	EVERY NIGHT	SOMETHING TELLS ME	4.00
73	1269 DJ	DRIFTERS	EVERY NIGHT	SOMETHING TELLS ME	5.00
73	1284	PEARLS	YOU ARE EVERYTHING	SHE SAY HE SAY	3.00
73	1284 DJ	PEARLS	YOU ARE EVERYTHING	SHE SAY HE SAY	4.00
73	1285	DELFONICS	WHEN YOU GET RIGHT DOWN TO IT	BREAK YOUR PROMISE	6.00
73	1285 DJ	DELFONICS	WHEN YOU GET RIGHT DOWN TO IT	BREAK YOUR PROMISE	8.00
73	1297	FIRST CHOICE	ARMED AND EXTREMELY DANGEROUS	GONNA KEEP ON LOVIN' HIM	5.00
73	1297 DJ	FIRST CHOICE	ARMED AND EXTREMELY DANGEROUS	GONNA KEEP ON LOVIN' HIM	6.00
73	1298	5TH. DIMENSION	LIVING TOGETHER GROWING TOGETHER	LOVE ALL AROUND	3.00
73	1298 DJ	5TH. DIMENSION	LIVING TOGETHER GROWING TOGETHER	LOVE ALL AROUND	4.00
73	1300	FANTASTICS	BY THE TIME THE SUN GOES DOWN	SOFT LIGHTS SWEET SOUL MUSIC	4.00
73	1300 DJ	FANTASTICS	BY THE TIME THE SUN GOES DOWN	SOFT LIGHTS SWEET SOUL MUSIC	5.00
73	1313	DRIFTERS	LIKE SISTER AND BROTHER	THE SONG WE USED TO SING	3.00
73	1313 DJ	DRIFTERS	LIKE SISTER AND BROTHER	THE SONG WE USED TO SING	5.00
73	1324	FIRST CHOICE	ONE STEP AWAY	SMARTY PANTS	8.00
73	1324 DJ	FIRST CHOICE	ONE STEP AWAY	SMARTY PANTS	10.00
73	1330	AL WILSON	SHOW AND TELL	LISTEN TO ME	6.00
73	1330 DJ	AL WILSON	SHOW AND TELL	LISTEN TO ME	10.00
73	1339	DRIFTERS	I'M FREE	SAY GOODBYE TO ANGELA	3.00
73	1339 DJ	DRIFTERS	I'M FREE	SAY GOODBYE TO ANGELA	4.00
73	1351	B.J. ARNAU	STEP IN THE RIGHT DIRECTION	SUPERMAN	10.00
73	1351 DJ	B.J. ARNAU	STEP IN THE RIGHT DIRECTION	SUPERMAN	15.00
73	1352	PEARLS	GUILTY	I'LL SAY IT OVER AGAIN	4.00
73	1352 DJ	PEARLS	GUILTY	I'LL SAY IT OVER AGAIN	5.00
74	1353	DELFONICS	I TOLD YOU SO	SEVENTEEN (AND IN LOVE)	15.00
74	1353 DJ	DELFONICS	I TOLD YOU SO	SEVENTEEN (AND IN LOVE)	20.00
74	1358	DRIFTERS	KISSING IN THE BACK ROW OF THE MOVIES	I'M FEELING SAD	3.00
74	1358 DJ	DRIFTERS	KISSING IN THE BACK ROW OF THE MOVIES	I'M FEELING SAD	5.00
74	1376	FIRST CHOICE	THE PLAYER	THE PLAYER part 2	10.00
74	1376 DJ	FIRST CHOICE	THE PLAYER	THE PLAYER part 2	15.00
74	1378	CHUCK BEDFORD	WHEN I SEE YOU SMILE	DON'T MAKE ME HISTORY	20.00
74	1378 DJ	CHUCK BEDFORD	WHEN I SEE YOU SMILE	DON'T MAKE ME HISTORY	28.00
74	1381	DRIFTERS	DOWN ON THE BEACH TONIGHT	SAY GOODBYE TO ANGELA	4.00
74	1381 DJ	DRIFTERS	DOWN ON THE BEACH TONIGHT	SAY GOODBYE TO ANGELA	5.00
74	1389	AL WILSON	LA LA PEACE SONG	KEEP ON LOVIN' YOU	5.00
74	1389 DJ	AL WILSON	LA LA PEACE SONG	KEEP ON LOVIN' YOU	6.00
74	1390	LOU RAWLS	SHE'S GONE	HOURGLASS	4.00
74	1390 DJ	LOU RAWLS	SHE'S GONE	HOURGLASS	5.00
74	1394	PEARLS	DOCTOR LOVE	PASS IT ON	4.00
74	1394 DJ	PEARLS	DOCTOR LOVE	PASS IT ON	5.00
75	1396	DRIFTERS	LOVE GAMES	THE CUT IS DEEP	4.00
75	1396 DJ	DRIFTERS	LOVE GAMES	THE CUT IS DEEP	5.00
75	1402	FANTASTICS	IS THERE A DOCTOR IN THE HOUSE	TEAR DOWN SATURDAY NIGHT	3.00
75	1402 DJ	FANTASTICS	IS THERE A DOCTOR IN THE HOUSE	TEAR DOWN SATURDAY NIGHT	4.00
75	1405	LINDA LEWIS	REMEMBER THE DAYS OF THE SCHOOL YARD	CORDON BLUES	3.00
75	1405 DJ	LINDA LEWIS	REMEMBER THE DAYS OF THE SCHOOL YARD	CORDON BLUES	4.00
75	1436	AL WILSON	THE SNAKE	WILLOUGHBY BROOK	8.00
75	1436 DJ	AL WILSON	THE SNAKE	WILLOUGHBY BROOK	10.00
75	1454	DELFONICS	DIDN'T I BLOW YOUR MIND THIS TIME	DOWN IS UP AND UP IS DOWN	4.00
75	1454 DJ	DELFONICS	DIDN'T I BLOW YOUR MIND THIS TIME	DOWN IS UP AND UP IS DOWN	5.00
76	1462	DRIFTERS	CAN I TAKE YOU HOME LITTLE GIRL	PLEASE HELP ME DOWN	4.00

76	1462 DJ	DRIFTERS	CAN I TAKE YOU HOME LITTLE GIRL		PLEASE HELP ME DOWN	5.00
76	1467	DELFONICS	WITH THESE HANDS		LET IT BE ME	4.00
76	1467 DJ	DELFONICS	WITH THESE HANDS		LET IT BE ME	5.00
76	1469	DRIFTERS	HELLO HAPPINESS		I CAN'T GET AWAY FROM YOU BABY	4.00
76	1469 DJ	DRIFTERS	HELLO HAPPINESS		I CAN'T GET AWAY FROM YOU BABY	5.00
76	1471	GLITTER BAND	MAKES YOU BLIND		PEOPLE LIKE YOU AND PEOPLE LIK	6.00
76	1471 DJ	GLITTER BAND	MAKES YOU BLIND		PEOPLE LIKE YOU AND PEOPLE LIK	10.00
76	1491	DRIFTERS	EVERY NIGHT IS A SATURDAY NIGHT WITH YOU		I'LL GET TO KNOW YOU ALONG THE WAY	3.00
76	1491 DJ	DRIFTERS	EVERY NIGHT IS A SATURDAY NIGHT WITH YOU		I'LL GET TO KNOW YOU ALONG THE WAY	4.00
76	1494	FEATHERS	LOST SUMMER LOVE		same: instrumental	5.00
76	1494 DJ	FEATHERS	LOST SUMMER LOVE		same: instrumental	6.00

BIG FISH

3		GAYLE CUNNINGHAM	PICK UP THE PHONE		LITTLE CHILD	30.00

BIG T

67	104	CHUCK WOOD	SEVEN DAYS TOO LONG		SOUL SHING-A-LING	30.00
67	106	ROYALETTES	RIVER OF TEARS		SOMETHING WONDERFUL	20.00
68	107	CHUCK WOOD	BABY YOU WIN		I'VE GOT MY LOVELIGHT SHINING	15.00
70	120	1984	I'VE GOT TO HAVE YOUR LOVE		HERE WE ARE	10.00

BIG TREE

11	335	GWEN OWENS	I DON'T WANT TO DANCE NO MORE		HOLD ME LIKE YOU NEVER HAD ME	4.00

B.J.D.

Late 60's UK repro label, perhaps from the same source as the Soul Sounds 45's. This label is just as sought after, circa 1969 pressed in high quality vinyl similar to the Jay Boy vinyl and made to resemble a USA import. It was very fashionable in the late sixties to own imports rather than the UK releases.

69	101	ALEXANDER PATTON c/w INEZ & CHARLIE FOXX	A LIL LOVIN' SOMETIMES		TIGHTROPE	20.00
69	102	CHUBBYCHECKER	DISCOTHEQUE		CU MA LA BESTA	15.00
69	103	MARY LOVE	YOU TURNED MY BITTER INTO SWEET		LAY THIS BURDEN DOWN	20.00

BLACK MAGIC

In the late 1960s, early 1970s a record shop on Arkwright Street, Nottingham became a famous shrine for soul fans. Handy for soul collectors far and wide, being only a short stroll from Nottingham's train station. Once through the door of the small shop front, we'd hurry past the rock & pop upstairs counter, that never seemed busy. We'd eagerly scramble down the narrow wooden stairs, to a small, but welcoming cellar. What delights will Bill have behind that bare wooden counter, today? Bill always had delights, in fact very special delights, always tons of 45's we had previously never heard of. When you were only 17 and you'd never seen an Okeh 45 before, the cellar at Select-a-disc was the stepping stone to your USA soul apprenticeship.

And then when Bill dropped the needle on Sam & Kitty – "I've Got Something Good" - Who was Sam? Who was Kitty? How good was this! An astounding thumping' soul tune, just bouncing off the four walls of that deep cellar, ricocheting off the low ceiling, directly entering the ear and straight to your heart. I hadn't felt a feeling like this, since an encounter with Lucy Stevens in the Sarson High School bike shed. Bill knew what he was doing, he'd just nearly caused a stampede of 20 or more salivating soul disciples that Saturday morning at Select-a-Disc.

Selecta, as it was affectionately known, was a weekly pilgrimage into the wondrous world of music we couldn't hear on the radio. 45's couldn't buy in any other shop, it was a life changing experience every trip. Once I bought a copy of Rufus Lumley on Stateside for £10, when my weekly gas fitting wage was less than £8.00 a week. I treasured that Rufus Lumley 45, even after my flat mate pushed the middle out, cut it into a triangle for a makeshift plectrum for his guitar. Sadly Select-A-Disc moved from Arkwright Street, then I discovered Brian 45 Philips and those Saturday mornings were no more. But Select-a-disc did have one last say in the rare soul market of the UK, in 1975 they launched their short lived Black Magic label then after 16 releases they moved on to other things and would never again serve the UK teenager with mind blowing tunes from heaven.

75	101	BOB RELF	BLOWING MY MIND TO PIECES		Female Version by Paula Rousse	8.00
75	101 DJ	BOB RELF	BLOWING MY MIND TO PIECES		Female Version by Paula Rousse	12.00
75	102	SHARONETTES	PAPA OOH MOW MOW		same: instrumental	4.00
75	102 DJ	SHARONETTES	PAPA OOH MOW MOW		same: instrumental	6.00
75	103	FATHERS ANGELS	BOK TO BACH		DISCO TRUCKING	8.00
75	103 DJ	FATHERS ANGELS	BOK TO BACH		DISCO TRUCKING	12.00
75	104	SHARONETTES	GOING TO A GO GO		same: instrumental	4.00
75	104 DJ	SHARONETTES	GOING TO A GO GO		same: instrumental	6.00
75	105	LORRAINE CHANDLER	WHAT CAN I DO		LOVE YOU BABY	8.00
75	105 DJ	LORRAINE CHANDLER	WHAT CAN I DO		LOVE YOU BABY	15.00
75	106	SOUL FOX ORCHESTRA	THUMB A RIDE		AIN'T NO SOUL	4.00
75	106 DJ	SOUL FOX ORCHESTRA	THUMB A RIDE		AIN'T NO SOUL	6.00
75	107	DOBIE GRAY	OUT ON THE FLOOR		BE A MAN	8.00
75	107 DJ	DOBIE GRAY	OUT ON THE FLOOR		BE A MAN	20.00
75	108	CHANTELLES	RUNAWAY		same: instrumental	5.00
75	108 DJ	CHANTELLES	RUNAWAY		same: instrumental	10.00
75	109	CREATION c/w PROMISED LAND	I GET THE FEVER		PROMISED LAND	8.00
75	109 DJ	CREATION c/w PROMISED LAND	I GOT THE FEVER		PROMISED LAND	10.00
75	110	CHANTELLES c/w GARY JACKSON	SUGAR DUMPLING		SUGAR DUMPLING	8.00
75	110 DJ	CHANTELLES c/w GARY JACKSON	SUGAR DUMPLING		SUGAR DUMPLING	10.00
75	111	MILESTONES	THE JOKER		JUCIE BRUCIE	8.00
75	111 DJ	MILESTONES	THE JOKER		JUCIE BRUCIE	12.00
75	112	CHERRY PEOPLE	AND SUDDENLY		IMAGINATION	6.00
75	112 DJ	CHERRY PEOPLE	AND SUDDENLY		IMAGINATION	10.00
75	113	SHARONETTES	BROKEN-HEARTED MELODY		BROKEN-HEARTED MELODY part 2	6.00
75	113 DJ	SHARONETTES	BROKEN-HEARTED MELODY		BROKEN-HEARTED MELODY part 2	8.00
75	114	FUNKEES	ABRAKA		OLE	5.00
75	114 DJ	FUNKEES	ABRAKA		OLE	8.00
76	115	JIMMY SOUL CLARK	SWEET DARLIN'		same: Instrumental	10.00
76	115 DJ	JIMMY SOUL CLARK	SWEET DARLIN'		same: instrumental	20.00
75	116	JILL BABY LOVE	MY WAY OR THE HIGHWAY		same: instrumental	5.00

| 75 | 116 DJ | JILL BABY LOVE | MY WAY OR THE HIGHWAY | same: instrumental | 8.00 |

BLACK SWAN

| 64 | 437 | JIMMY JAMES | THINKING OF YOU | SHIRLEY | 30.00 |

BLUE BIRD

| 84 | 10 | GENE CHANDLER | I'LL MAKE THE LIVING IF YOU MAKE | TIME IS A THIEF | 6.00 |

BLUE HORIZON

One of the most collectable labels ever to be released in the UK, I've only listed those 45's which will have any interest to the Soul or Northern Soul collectors. Primarily a blues orientated label.

65	1002	GEORGE HARMONICA SMITH	BLUES IN THE DARK	TELEPHONE BLUES	80.00
65	1002 DJ	GEORGE HARMONICA SMITH	BLUES IN THE DARK	TELEPHONE BLUES	100.00
66	1008	SONNY BOY WILLIAMSON	FROM THE BOTTOM	EMPTY BEDROOM	70.00
66	1008 DJ	SONNY BOY WILLIAMSON	FROM THE BOTTOM	EMPTY BEDROOM	85.00
68	57-3136	ARTHUR K. ADAMS	SHE DRIVES ME OUT OF MY MIND	GIMME SOME OF YOUR LOVIN'	20.00
68	57-3136 DJ	ARTHUR K. ADAMS	SHE DRIVES ME OUT OF MY MIND	GIMME SOME OF YOUR LOVIN'	25.00
68	57-3144	B.B. KING	THE WOMAN I LOVE	BLUES FOR ME	18.00
68	57-3144 DJ	B.B. KING	THE WOMAN I LOVE	BLUES FOR ME	25.00
68	57-3149	GUITAR CRUSHER	SINCE MY BABY HIT THE NUMBERS	HAMBONE BLUES	20.00
68	57-3149 DJ	GUITAR CRUSHER	SINCE MY BABY HIT THE NUMBERS	HAMBONE BLUES	25.00
68	57-3151	BOBBY PARKER	IT'S HARD BUT IT'S FAIR	I COULDN'T QUIT MY BABY	25.00
68	57-3151 DJ	BOBBY PARKER	IT'S HARD BUT IT'S FAIR	I COULDN'T QUIT MY BABY	30.00
69	57-3159	OTIS RUSH	ALL YOUR LOVE	DOUBLE TROUBLE	20.00
69	57-3159 DJ	OTIS RUSH	ALL YOUR LOVE	DOUBLE TROUBLE	28.00
69	57-3161	B.B. KING	EVERYDAY I HAVE THE BLUES	FIVE LONG YEARS	18.00
69	57-3161 DJ	B.B. KING	EVERYDAY I HAVE THE BLUES	FIVE LONG YEARS	22.00
69	57-3166	EARL HOOKER	BOOGIE DON'T BLOT	FUNKY BLUES	20.00
69	57-3166 DJ	EARL HOOKER	BOOGIE DON'T BLOT	FUNKY BLUES	25.00
70	57-3175	SLIM HARPO	FOLSOM PRISON BLUES	MUTUAL FRIEND	20.00
70	57-3175 DJ	SLIM HARPO	FOLSOM PRISON BLUES	MUTUAL FRIEND	25.00
70	57-3177	KELLY BROTHERS	THAT'S WHAT YOU MEAN TO ME	COMIN' ON IN	25.00
70	57-3177 DJ	KELLY BROTHERS	THAT'S WHAT YOU MEAN TO ME	COMIN' ON IN	40.00
70	57-3178	GEORGE SMITH	SOMEDAY YOU'RE GONNA LEARN	BEFORE YOU DO YOUR THING	10.00
70	57-3178 DJ	GEORGE SMITH	SOMEDAY YOU'RE GONNA LEARN	BEFORE YOU DO YOUR THING	15.00
70	57-3181	BACON FAT	EVIL	BLUES FEELING	20.00
70	57-3181 DJ	BACON FAT	EVIL	BLUES FEELING	25.00
71	2096002	MARSHALL HOOKS	I WANT THE SAME THING TOMORROW	HOOKIN' IT	20.00
71	2096002 DJ	MARSHALL HOOKS	I WANT THE SAME THING TOMORROW	HOOKIN' IT	25.00
71	2096005	FUGI	RED MOON	RED MOON part 2	20.00
71	2096005 DJ	FUGI	RED MOON	RED MOON part 2	25.00
72	2096010	MARTHA VELEZ	BOOGIE KITCHEN	TWO BRIDGES	15.00
72	2096010 DJ	MARTHA VELEZ	BOOGIE KITCHEN	TWO BRIDGES	20.00

BLUE MOUNTAIN

| 72 | 1007 | KARL DOUGLAS | SOMEBODY STOP THIS MADNESS | AIN'T NO USE | 5.00 |

BLUE JEAN

| 74 | 702 | SOUL RESPONSE | LOVING ON THE LOSING SIDE | SIGN OF THE TIMES | 8.00 |
| 74 | 702 DJ | SOUL RESPONSE | LOVING ON THE LOSING SIDE | SIGN OF THE TIMES | 10.00 |

BLUE NOTE

75	7001	DONALD BYRD	BLACK BIRD	SLOP JAR BLUES	8.00
75	7001 DJ	DONALD BYRD	BLACK BIRD	SLOP JAR BLUES	10.00
75	7002	CARMEN McCRAE	WHO GAVE YOU PERMISSION	THE TROUBLE WITH HELLO IS GOODBYE	5.00
75	7002 DJ	CARMEN McCRAE	WHO GAVE YOU PERMISSION	THE TROUBLE WITH HELLO IS GOODBYE	6.00
76	7003	DONALD BYRD	CHANGES MAKE YOU WANNA HUSTLE	CHANGES MAKE YOU WANNA HUSTLE part 2	8.00
76	7003 SJ	DONALD BYRD	CHANGES MAKE YOU WANNA HUSTLE	CHANGES MAKE YOU WANNA HUSTLE part 2	10.00
76	7004	RONNIE LAWS	ALWAYS THERE	TIDAL WAVE	6.00
76	7004 DJ	RONNIE LAWS	ALWAYS THERE	TIDAL WAVE	8.00
63	1887	HERBIE HANCOCK	BLIND MAN, BLIND MAN	BLIND MAN, BLIND MAN part 2	10.00
69	1956	LOU DONALDSON	EVERYTHING I DO GOTTA BE FUNKY	MINOR BASH	10.00
76	36125	MARLENA SHAW	IT'S BETTER THAN WALKING	BE FOR REAL	8.00
76	36125 DJ	MARLENA SHAW	IT'S BETTER THAN WALKING OUT	BE FOR REAL	10.00
77	36163	MARLENA SHAW	LOVE HAS GONE AWAY	NO HIDING PLACE	6.00
77	36163 DJ	MARLENA SHAW	LOVE HAS GONE AWAY	NO HIDING PLACE	8.00
78	36251	EARL KLUGH	I HEARD IT THROUGH THE GRAPEVINE	KIKO	5.00
78	36251 DJ	EARL KLUGH	I HEARD IT THROUGH THE GRAPEVINE	KIKO	5.00
79	36497	RONNIE LAWS	ALWAYS THERE	TIDAL WAVE	4.00
79	36497 DJ	RONNIE LAWS	ALWAYS THERE	TIDAL WAVE	5.00

BLUE THUMB

| 72 | 6143 | CRUSADERS | PUT IT WHERE YOU WANT IT | MOSADI (WOMAN) | 8.00 |
| 73 | 6171 | POINTER SISTERS | YES WE CAN CAN | JADA | 5.00 |

BLUEBIRD

| 84 | 11 | WALTER JACKSON | TOUCHING IN THE DARK | IT'S COOL | 8.00 |

BOOT

A mid-eighties label, aimed at the Northern Soul and Mod collectors market. The label named with a little tongue in cheek humour.

	1	M.V.P's c/w BENNY TROY	TURNING MY HEARTBEAT UP	I WANNA GIVE YOU TOMORROW	6.00
	2	JOE TEX c/w THE ORIGINALS	UNDER YOUR POWERFUL LOVE	SUSPICION	8.00
	3	ALFIE DAVIDSON c/w SAMMY DAVIS JR.	LOVE IS A SERIOUS BUSINESS	YOU CAN COUNT ON ME (HAWAII 5-	8.00
	4	FOUR BELOW ZERO c/w FRANK WILSON	MY BABY'S GOT E.S.P.	DO I LOVE YOU (INDEED I DO)	8.00

BOULEVARD

68	101	MAC KISSOON	WEAR IT ON YOUR FACE	IN A DREAM	15.00

BRADLEY'S

This attractive mid-seventies label, was unfortunately not noted for it's contribution to soul: Within it's artist roster were performers like John Cleese, Bill Odie, The Goodies, Stephanie DeSykes which only strengthen it's identity as a pop and novelty label. Although two fine 45s from Edwin Starr's USA Granite sessions saw release in 1975 but failed to sell significant copies. Bradley's also had enough insight to release a current all-nighter play of the era from Canadian artist Debbie Fleming, these are the highlights of an otherwise disappointing 45 catalogue.

74	7410	RESONANCE	O.K. CHICAGO	YELLOW TRAIN	15.00
74	7415	FASCINATIONS	MOMA'S BOY	STAY WITH ME	5.00
75	7501	DONNIE ELBERT	YOU'RE GONNA CRY WHEN I'M GONE	ANOTHER TEAR WILL TAKE IT'S PLACE	5.00
75	7502	SWEET DREAMS	THE BEST OF EVERYTHING	ONLY YOU CAN TOUCH ME	5.00
75	7519	DEBBIE FLEMING	LONG GONE	ALL ABOUT YOU	8.00
75	7606	LOVE MACHINE	POOR SIDE OF TOWN	SHOOT YOU BEST SHOT	4.00
75	7510	ENDEAVOURS	BABY'S COMING HOME	1st PRIZE WINNER	4.00
75	7512	FASCINATIONS	SHOT DOWN IN ACTION	I BELIEVE YOU BABY	5.00
75	7518	BLACK BLOOD	AIE BWANA	MARIE THERESA	3.00
75	7519	DEBBIE FLEMING	LONG GONE	ALL ABOUT YOU	8.00
75	7520	EDWIN STARR	STAY WITH ME	I'LL NEVER FORGET YOU	15.00
75	7531	EDWIN STARR	PAIN	PARTY	15.00

BRETBY

A white label test press, that was actually brought to the soul night at Bretby nr. Burton On Trent when Linda Griner performed live. On early USA Motown promotion material she was credited as being Linda Glyner. This 45 was a straight white label repro of her highly sought after USA Motown 45 # 1037. This was a very limited press, suggestions of as little as a 100 were made, but maybe the truth is there was nearer 250. Anyhow they have long disappeared and are now hard to find. The 45 is a white label test press with handwritten credits.#

99	43467	LINDA GRINER	GOODBYE CRUEL LOVE	A SHE'S GOT YOU	20.00

BRIT

Distributed by Island records the release numbers run up to 1008 these are the only 45s of interest to soul collectors

65	1002	MILLIE	MY STREET	MIXED UP, FICKLE, SELF CENTERED BOY	15.00
65	1004	ANGLOS	INCENSE	YOU'RE FOOLOING ME	40.00
65	1005 unissued	DINAH LEE	PUSHIN' A GOOD THING TOO FAR	I CAN'T BELIEVE WHAT YOU SAY	UN

BRUNSWICK

Brunswick label was founded in 1923 in New York City. UK Decca aquired all the UK releasing rights in 1934. USA, Decca & Coral recordings were released in the UK on Brunswick, a label that Decca terminated production on in 1967. The USA Chicago based soul recordings on Brunswick 45's ie: Jackie Wilson, Artistics etc, were released in the UK on a Brunswick subsiduary Coral and later on MCA. Then in 1972 Decca did give the Chicago based soul label its own identity by releasing a series of 45's under the Brunswick logo.

Brunswick signed Jackie Wilson in 1957, Jackie soon became Brunswick's most prolific recording artist, in fact it has been quote that Jackie Wilson "WAS" the Brunswick label, although Northern Soul scholars would perhaps disagree with this sweeping statement. But it was qualified when in 1964 Brunswick were desperate to resign Jackie to the label, so desperate in fact they gave his manager Nat Tarnopool 50% of the label! Then in 1965 Tarnapool brought in Carl Davis to produce......see the Coral label for the rest of the story.........

58	05746	SHIRELLES	I MET HIM ON A SUNDAY	I WANT YOU TO BE MY BOYFRIEND	70.00
59	05757 tri	TOMMY DORSEY ORCHESTRA	MY BABY JUST CARES FOR ME	TEA FOTR TWO CHA CHA	8.00
60	05824 tri	EARL GRANT	HOUSE OF BAMBOO	TWO LOVES HAVE I	25.00
64	05904	RUTH BROWN	WHAT HAPPENED TO YOU	YES SIR, THAT'S MY BABY	25.00
64	05904 DJ	RUTH BROWN	WHAT HAPPENED TO YOU	YES SIR, THAT'S MY BABY	35.00
65	05940	LIZ SHELLEY	MAKE ME YOUR BABY	YOU MADE MADE ME HURT	15.00
65	05940 DJ	LIZ SHELLEY	MAKE ME YOUR BABY	YOU MADE MADE ME HURT	25.00
65	05942	LEN BARRY	1 – 2 – 3	BULLSEYE	6.00
65	05942 DJ	LEN BARRY	1 – 2 – 3	BULLSEYE	30.00
65	05945	EARL GRANT	STAND BY ME	AFTER HOURS	6.00
65	05945 DJ	EARL GRANT	STAND BY ME	AFTER HOURS	10.00
65	05949	LEN BARRY	LIKE A BABY	HAPPINESS (IS A GIRL LIKE YOU)	5.00
65	05949 DJ	LEN BARRY	LIKE A BABY	HAPPINESS (IS A GIRL LIKE YOU)	25.00
66	05953	LIZ SHELLEY	I CAN'T FIND YOU	NO MORE LOVE	15.00
66	05953 DJ	LIZ SHELLEY	I CAN'T FIND YOU	NO MORE LOVE	22.00
66	05955	LEN BARRY	SOMEWHERE	IT'S A CRYING SHAME	6.00
66	05955 DJ	LEN BARRY	SOMEWHERE	IT'S A CRYING SHAME	20.00
66	05957	BRENDA LEE	TIME AND TIME AGAIN	TOO LITTLE TIME	45.00
66	05957 DJ	BRENDA LEE	TIME AND TIME AGAIN	TOO LITTLE TIME	60.00
66	05962	LEN BARRY	IT'S THAT TIME OF THE YEAR	HAPPILY EVER AFTER	6.00
66	05962 DJ	LEN BARRY	IT'S THAT TIME OF THE YEAR	HAPPILY EVER AFTER	25.00
66	05963	BRENDA LEE	AIN'T GONNA CRY NO MORE	IT TAKES ONE TO KNOW ONE	15.00
66	05963 DJ	BRENDA LEE	AIN'T GONNA CRY NO MORE	IT TAKES ONE TO KNOW ONE	25.00
66	05966	LEN BARRY	I STRUCK IT RICH	LOVE IS	8.00
66	05966 DJ	LEN BARRY	I STRUCK IT RICH	LOVE IS	22.00
66	05967 DJ	BRENDA LEE	COMING ON STRONG	YOU KEEP COMING BACK TO ME	15.00
66	05967 DJ	BRENDA LEE	COMING ON STRONG	YOU KEEP COMING BACK TO ME	25.00
67	05973	SAM & BILL	I'LL TRY	I FEEL LIKE CRYIN'	45.00
67	05973 DJ	SAM & BILL	I'LL TRY	I FEEL LIKE CRYIN'	75.00

67	05976	BRENDA LEE	WHERE'S THE MELODY	BORN TO BE BY YOUR SIDE	20.00
67	05976 DJ	BRENDA LEE	WHERE'S THE MELODY	BORN TO BE BY YOUR SIDE	28.00

With a gap of five years Decca reactivated the UK Brunswick label pulling from the catalogue of the highly successful Chicago parent label of the same name.

72	1	CHI-LITES	LIVING IN THE FOOTSTEPS OF ANOTHER	WE NEED ORDER	15.00
72	1 DJ	CHI-LITES	LIVING IN THE FOOTSTEPS OF ANOTHER	WE NEED ORDER	20.00
72	2	CHI-LITES	A LETTER TO MYSELF	.SALLY	4.00
72	2 DJ	CHI-LITES	A LETTER TO MYSELF	SALLY	6.00
72	3	JACKIE WILSON	WHAT'CHA GONNA DO ABOUT LOVE	BEAUTIFUL DAY	15.00
72	3 DJ	JACKIE WILSON	WHAT'CHA GONNA DO ABOUT LOVE	BEAUTIFUL DAY	25.00
73	4	TYRONE DAVIS	WITHOUT YOU IN MY LIFE	HOW COULD I FORGET YOU	7.00
73	4 DJ	TYRONE DAVIS	WITHOUT YOU IN MY LIFE	HOW COULD I FORGET YOU	5.00
73	5	WALTER JACKSON	EASY EVIL	I NEVER HAD IT SO GOOD	8.00
73	5 DJ	WALTER JACKSON	EASY EVIL	I NEVER HAD IT SO GOOD	10.00
73	6	TYRONE DAVIS	THERE IT IS	YOU WOULDN'T BELIEVE	8.00
73	6 DJ	TYRONE DAVIS	THERE IT IS	YOU WOULDN'T BELIEVE	10.00
73	7	CHI-LITES	STONED OF MY MIND	SOMEONE ELE'S ARMS	4.00
73	7 DJ	CHI-LITES	STONED OF MY MIND	SOMEONE ELE'S ARMS	6.00
73	8	BARBARA ACKLIN	I'LL BAKE ME A MAN	I CALL IT TROUBLE	8.00
73	8 DJ	BARBARA ACKLIN	I'LL BAKE ME A MAN	I CALL IT TROUBLE	10.00
73	9	CHI-LITES	HOMELY GIRL	I NEVER HAD IT SO GOOD	4.00
73	9 DJ	CHI-LITES	HOMELY GIRL	I NEVER HAD IT SO GOOD	6.00
74	10	TYRONE DAVIS	I WISH IT WAS ME	YOU DON'T HAVE TO BEG TO STAY	8.00
74	10 DJ	TYRONE DAVIS	I WISH IT WAS ME	YOU DON'T HAVE TO BEG TO STAY	10.00
75	11	LYN ROMAN	STOP, I DON'T NEED NO SYMPATHY	WHERE DO YOU GO	8.00
75	11 DJ	LYN ROMAN	STOP, I DON'T NEED NO SYMPATHY	WHERE DO YOU GO	15.00
75	12	CHI-LITES	I FOUND SUNSHINE	MY HEART JUST KEEPS ON BREAKIN	4.00
75	12 DJ	CHI-LITES	I FOUND SUNSHINE	MY HEART JUST KEEPS ON BREAKIN	6.00
75	13	CHI-LITES	TOO GOOD TO BE FORGOTTEN	THERE WILL NEVER BE ANY PEACE	4.00
75	13 DJ	CHI-LITES	TOO GOOD TO BE FORGOTTEN	THERE WILL NEVER BE ANY PEACE	6.00
75	14	HAMILTON BOHANNON	KEEP ON DANCING	KEEP ON DANCING	4.00
75	14 DJ	HAMILTON BOHANNON	KEEP ON DANCING	KEEP ON DANCING	5.00
75	15	CHI-LITES	TOBY	THAT'S HOW LONG	4.00
75	15 DJ	CHI-LITES	TOBY	THAT'S HOW LONG	6.00
75	16	HAMILTON BOHANNON	SOUTH AFRICAN MAN	HAVE A GOOD DAY	4.00
75	16 DJ	HAMILTON BOHANNON	SOUTH AFRICAN MAN	HAVE A GOOD DAY	5.00
75	17	CHI-LITES	I LIED	I FORGOT TO SAY I LOVE YOU TIL	4.00
75	17 DJ	CHI-LITES	I LIED	I FORGOT TO SAY I LOVE YOU TIL	6.00
75	18	JACKIE WILSON	I GET THE SWEETEST FEELING	HIGHER AND HIGHER	6.00
75	18 DJ	JACKIE WILSON	I GET THE SWEETEST FEELING	HIGHER AND HIGHER	10.00
75	19	HAMILTON BOHANNON	DISCO STOMP	RUN IT DOWN MR. DJ	4.00
75	19 DJ	HAMILTON BOHANNON	DISCO STOMP	same:	5.00
75	20	CHI-LITES	HAVE YOU SEEN HER?	OH GIRL	4.00
75	20 DJ	CHI-LITES	HAVE YOU SEEN HER?	OH GIRL	8.00
75	21	HAMILTON BOHANNON	FOOT STOMPIN' MUSIC	DANCE WITH YOUR PARNO	4.00
75	21 DJ	HAMILTON BOHANNON	FOOT STOMPIN' MUSIC	DANCE WITH YOUR PARNO	6.00
75	22	COOPERETTES	SHING-A-LING	DON'T TRUST ME	15.00
75	22 DJ	COOPERETTES	SHING-A-LING	DON'T TRUST HIM	25.00
75	23	JACKIE WILSON	WHISPERS (GETTIN' LOUDER)	REET PETITE	5.00
75	23 DJ	JACKIE WILSON	WHISPERS (GETTIN' LOUDER)	REET PETITE	10.00
75	24	HAMILTON BOHANNON	HAPPY FEELING	TRUCK STOP	4.00
75	24 DJ	HAMILTON BOHANNON	HAPPY FEELING	TRUCK STOP	6.00
75	25	CHI-LITES	THE COLDEST DAYS OF MY LIFE	IT'S TIME FOR LOVE	4.00
75	25 DJ	CHI-LITES	THE COLDEST DAYS OF MY LIFE	IT'S TIME FOR LOVE	6.00
75	26	BARBARA ACKLIN	LOVE MAKES A WOMAN	AM I THE SAME GIRL	6.00
75	26 DJ	BARBARA ACKLIN	LOVE MAKES A WOMAN	AM I THE SAME GIRL	10.00
75	27	EDDIE McLOYD	ONCE YOU FALL IN LOVE	BABY GET DOWN	20.00
75	27 DJ	EDDIE McLOYD	ONCE YOU FALL IN LOVE	BABY GET DOWN	28.00
75	28	JACKIE WILSON & CHI-LITES	DON'T BURN NO BRIDGES	same: instrumental	5.00
75	28 DJ	JACKIE WILSON & CHI-LITES	DON'T BURN NO BRIDGES	same: instrumental	6.00
75	29	CHI-LITES	I NEVER HAD IT SO GOOD (AND FELT SO	HERE I AM	4.00
75	29 DJ	CHI-LITES	I NEVER HAD IT SO GOOD (AND FELT SO	HERE I AM	5.00
76	30	GENE CHANDLER & BARBARA ACKLIN	FROM THE TEACHER TO THE PREACHER	LITTLE GREEN APPLES	6.00
76	30 DJ	GENE CHANDLER & BARBARA ACKLIN	FROM THE TEACHER TO THE PREACHER	LITTLE GREEN APPLES	10.00
76	31	TYRONE DAVIS	TURNING POINT	DON'T LET IT BE TOO LATE	8.00
76	31 DJ	TYRONE DAVIS	TURNING POINT	DON'T LET IT BE TOO LATE	6.00
76	32	CHI-LITES	I'M NOT A GAMBLER	THE DEVIL IS DOING HIS WORK	4.00
76	32 DJ	CHI-LITES	I'M NOT A GAMBLER	THE DEVIL IS DOING HIS WORK	6.00
76	33	HAMILTON BOHANNON	BOHANNONS BEAT	GENTLE BREEZE	4.00
76	33 DJ	HAMILTON BOHANNON	BOHANNONS BEAT	same:	4.00
76	34	CHI-LITES	YOU DON'T HAVE TO GO	same: instrumental	4.00
76	34 DJ	CHI-LITES	YOU DON'T HAVE TO GO	same: instrumental	5.00
76	35	STRUTT	FRONT ROW ROMEO	TIME MOVES ON	5.00
76	35 DJ	STRUTT	FRONT ROW ROMEO	TIME MOVES ON	6.00
76	36	HAMILTON BOHANNON	DANCE YOUR ASS OFF	STOP AND GO	4.00
76	36 DJ	HAMILTON BOHANNON	DANCE YOUR ASS OFF	same:	4.00
76	37	FRED HUGHESc/w JOHNNY JONES	BABY BOY	PURPLE HAZE	10.00
76	37 DJ	FRED HUGHESc/w JOHNNY JONES	BABY BOY	PURPLE HAZE	15.00
76	38	MARYANN FARRA & SATIN	LIVING IN THE FOOTSTEPS OF ANOTHER	STONED OUT OF MY MIND	20.00
76	38 DJ	MARYANN FARRA & SATIN	LIVING IN THE FOOTSTEPS OF ANOTHER	STONED OUT OF MY MIND	28.00

76	39	GENE CHANDLER c/w ARTISTICS	THERE WAS A TIME	I'M GONNA MISS YOU	10.00
76	39 DJ	GENE CHANDLER c/w ARTISTICS	THERE WAS A TIME	I'M GONNA MISS YOU	15.00
77	40	TYRONE DAVIS	EVER LOVIN' GIRL	FOREVER	4.00
77	40 DJ	TYRONE DAVIS	EVER LOVIN' GIRL	FOREVER	5.00
77	41	ALVIN CASH	ALI SHUFFLE	DOING THE FEELING	4.00
77	41 DJ	ALVIN CASH	ALI SHUFFLE	DOING THE FEELING	5.00
77	42	ADAMS APPLES	DON'T TAKE IT OUT ON THIS WORLD	DON'T YOU WANT ME HOME	15.00
77	42 DJ	ADAMS APPLES	DON'T TAKE IT OUT ON THIS WORLD	DON'T YOU WANT ME HOME	25.00
77	43	JACKIE WILSON	IT ONLY HAPPENS WHEN I LOOK AT YOU	JUST AS SOON AS THE FEELINGS	**87.00**
77	43 DJ	JACKIE WILSON	IT ONLY HAPPENS WHEN I LOOK AT YOU	JUST AS SOON AS THE FEELINGS	**179.00**

BUDDAH

Formed in the USA in 1967, the Buddah label was distributed in the USA by themselves. Launched in the UK in 1968 and distributed by Polydor using 2010 prefix. In 1974 Buddah changed distributors to Pye using the 400 prefix. USA Buddah also had many subsidiaries including, Brut, Curtom, National General, Super K, Sussex, and later Kama Sutra.

400 series

74	401	GLADYS KNIGHT & The PIPS	ON AND ON	THE MAKINGS OF YOU	3.00
74	401 DJ	GLADYS KNIGHT & The PIPS	ON AND ON	THE MAKINGS OF YOU	4.00
74	402	CURTIS MAYFIELD	KUNG FU	RIGHT ON FOR THE DARKNESS	4.00
74	402 DJ	CURTIS MAYFIELD	KUNG FU	RIGHT ON FOR THE DARKNESS	5.00
74	403	IMPRESSIONS	I'LL ALWAYS BE THERE	FINALLY GOT MYSELF TOGETHER	10.00
74	403 DJ	IMPRESSIONS	I'LL ALWAYS BE THERE	FINALLY GOT MYSELF TOGETHER	15.00
74	405	TRAMMPS	PENGUIN AT THE BIG APPLE	ZING WENT THE STRINGS OF MY HE	6.00
74	405 DJ	TRAMMPS	PENGUIN AT THE BIG APPLE	ZING WENT THE STRINGS OF MY HE	8.00
74	406	MODULATIONS	I CAN'T FIGHT YOUR LOVE	YOUR LOVE HAS ME LOCKED UP	15.00
74	406 DJ	MODULATIONS	I CAN'T FIGHT YOUR LOVE	YOUR LOVE HAS ME LOCKED UP	20.00
74	410	CURTIS MAYFIELD	MOVE ON UP	GIVE IT UP	6.00
74	410 DJ	CURTIS MAYFIELD	MOVE ON UP	GIVE IT UP	8.00
74	413	GLADYS KNIGHT & The PIPS	I FEEL A SONG	DON'T BURN DOWN THE BRIDGE	3.00
74	413 DJ	GLADYS KNIGHT & The PIPS	I FEEL A SONG	DON'T BURN DOWN THE BRIDGE	4.00
75	415	TRAMMPS	SCRUB BOARD	SIXTY MINUTE MAN	6.00
75	415 DJ	TRAMMPS	SCRUB BOARD	SIXTY MINUTE MAN	8.00
75	418	VAN McCOY	SOUL IMPROVISATIONS	SOUL IMPROVISATIONS PART2	8.00
75	418 DJ	VAN McCOY	SOUL IMPROVISATIONS	SOUL IMPROVISATIONS PART2	10.00
75	419	WALTER HEATH	SOUL MATE	I AM YOUR LEADER	3.00
75	419 DJ	WALTER HEATH	SOUL MATE	I AM YOUR LEADER	4.00
75	423	JACKEY BEAVERS	SOMEBODY HELP THE BEGGAR MAN	MR. BUMP MAN	5.00
75	423 DJ	JACKEY BEAVERS	SOMEBODY HELP THE BEGGAR MAN	MR. BUMP MAN	6.00
75	425	BARBARA MASON	FROM HIS WOMAN TO YOU	WHEN YOU WAKE UP IN GEORGIA	4.00
75	425 DJ	BARBARA MASON	FROM HIS WOMAN TO YOU	WHEN YOU WAKE UP IN GEORGIA	5.00
75	426	CURTIS MAYFIELD	MOTHER'S SON	LOVE ME RIGHT IN THE POCKET	4.00
75	426 DJ	CURTIS MAYFIELD	MOTHER'S SON	LOVE ME RIGHT IN THE POCKET	5.00
75	427	FRESH FLAVOR	WITHOUT YOU BABY, I'M A LOSER	TREAT HER LIKE A LADY	10.00
75	427 DJ	FRESH FLAVOR	WITHOUT YOU BABY, I'M A LOSER	TREAT HER LIKE A LADY	15.00
75	428	GLADYS KNIGHT & The PIPS	THE WAY WE WERE	LOVE FINDS IT'S OWN WAY	4.00
75	428 DJ	GLADYS KNIGHT & The PIPS	THE WAY WE WERE	LOVE FINDS IT'S OWN WAY	5.00
75	429	FIVE STAIRSTEPS	O-O-H CHILD	BECAUSE I LOVE YOU	5.00
75	429 DJ	FIVE STAIRSTEPS	O-O-H CHILD	BECAUSE I LOVE YOU	6.00
75	430	FUTURES	YOU BETTER BE CERTAIN	NO ONE COULD COMPARE	15.00
75	430 DJ	FUTURES	YOU BETTER BE CERTAIN	NO ONE COULD COMPARE	20.00
75	432	GLADYS KNIGHT & The PIPS	BEST THING THAT EVER HAPPENED TO	DON'T BURN DOWN THE BRIDGE	3.00
75	432 DJ	GLADYS KNIGHT & The PIPS	BEST THING THAT EVER HAPPENED TO	DON'T BURN DOWN THE BRIDGE	5.00
75	434	NEW BIRTH	DREAM MERCHANT	WHY DID I	4.00
75	434 DJ	NEW BIRTH	DREAM MERCHANT	WHY DID I	5.00
75	435	GLADYS KNIGHT & The PIPS	PART-TIME LOVE	STREET BROTHER	3.00
75	435 DJ	GLADYS KNIGHT & The PIPS	PART-TIME LOVE	STREET BROTHER	4.00
75	437	TRAMMPS	HOLD BACK THE NIGHT	TOM'S SONG	6.00
75	437 DJ	TRAMMPS	HOLD BACK THE NIGHT	TOM'S SONG	10.00
75	438	GLADYS KNIGHT & The PIPS	PART TIME LOVER	STREET BROTHER	3.00
75	438 DJ	GLADYS KNIGHT & The PIPS	PART TIME LOVER	STREET BROTHER	4.00
76	439	ARTHUR ALEXANDER	EVERY DAY I HAVE TO CRY	EVERYBODY NEEDS SOMEBODY TO LO	6.00
76	439 DJ	ARTHUR ALEXANDER	EVERY DAY I HAVE TO CRY	EVERYBODY NEEDS SOMEBODY TO LO	8.00
76	440	TRAMMPS	RUBBER BAND	RUBBER BAND (lp version)	6.00
76	440 DJ	TRAMMPS	RUBBER BAND	RUBBER BAND (lp version)	8.00
76	441	GLADYS KNIGHT & The PIPS	SILENT NIGHT	DO YOU HEAR WHAT I HEAR	3.00
76	441 DJ	GLADYS KNIGHT & The PIPS	SILENT NIGHT	DO YOU HEAR WHAT I HEAR	4.00
76	442	ANDRE TRUE CONNECTION	MORE, MORE, MORE	MORE, MORE, MORE part 2	4.00
76	442 DJ	ANDRE TRUE CONNECTION	MORE, MORE, MORE	MORE, MORE, MORE part 2	6.00
76	443	MELBA MOORE	THIS IS IT	STAY AWHILE	4.00
76	443 DJ	MELBA MOORE	THIS IS IT	STAY AWHILE	6.00
76	444	GLADYS KNIGHT & The PIPS	MIDNIGHT TRAIN TO GEORGIA	WINDOW RAISING GRANNY	3.00
76	444 DJ	GLADYS KNIGHT & The PIPS	MIDNIGHT TRAIN TO GEORGIA	WINDOW RAISING GRANNY	5.00
76	445	ANDREA TRUE CONNECTION	PARTY LINE	same: disco version	3.00
76	445 DJ	ANDREA TRUE CONNECTION	PARTY LINE	same: disco version	4.00
76	446	MELBA MOORE	LEAN ON ME	BRAND NEW	3.00
76	446 DJ	MELBA MOORE	LEAN ON ME	BRAND NEW	4.00
76	447	GLADYS KNIGHT & The PIPS	MAKE YOURS A HAPPY HOME	TENDERNESS IS HIS WAY	4.00
76	447 DJ	GLADYS KNIGHT & The PIPS	MAKE YOURS A HAPPY HOME	TENDERNESS IS HIS WAY	5.00
76	448	GLADYS KNIGHT & The PIPS	SO SAD IS THE SONG	SO SAD IS THE SONG part 2	3.00

76	448 DJ	GLADYS KNIGHT & The PIPS	SO SAD IS THE SONG	SO SAD IS THE SONG part 2	4.00
77	449	NORMAN CONNORS	YOU ARE MY STARSHIP	BUBBLES	5.00
77	449 DJ	NORMAN CONNORS	YOU ARE MY STARSHIP	BUBBLES	6.00
77	450	GLADYS KNIGHT & The PIPS	I FEEL A SONG (IN MY HEART AGAIN)	STREET BROTHER	3.00
77	450 DJ	GLADYS KNIGHT & The PIPS	I FEEL A SONG (IN MY HEART AGAIN)	STREET BROTHER	4.00
77	451	GLADYS KNIGHT & The PIPS	PIPE DREAMS	NOBODY BUT YOU	3.00
77	451 DJ	GLADYS KNIGHT & The PIPS	PIPE DREAMS	NOBODY BUT YOU	4.00
77	452	BLACK SATIN feat. FRED	TEARS, TEARS, TEARS	same: long version	4.00
77	452 DJ	BLACK SATIN feat. FRED	TEARS, TEARS, TEARS	same: long version	5.00
77	453	MELBA MOORE	GREATEST FEELING	LONG AND WINDING ROAD	4.00
77	453 DJ	MELBA MOORE	GREATEST FEELING	LONG AND WINDING ROAD	5.00
77	454	ANDRE TRUE CONNECTION	YOU GOT ME DANCING	KEEP IT UP LONGER	4.00
77	454 DJ	ANDRE TRUE CONNECTION	YOU GOT ME DANCING	KEEP IT UP LONGER	5.00
77	455	AQUARIAN DREAM	PHEONIX	ONCE AGAIN	5.00
77	455 DJ	AQUARIAN DREAM	PHEONIX	ONCE AGAIN	6.00
77	457	PHYLLIS HYMAN	LOVING YOU - LOSING YOU	same: long version	3.00
77	457 DJ	PHYLLIS HYMAN	LOVING YOU - LOSING YOU	same: long version	4.00
77	458	GLADYS KNIGHT & The PIPS	BABY DON'T CHANGE YOUR MIND	I LOVE TO FEEL THAT FEELING	4.00
77	458 DJ	GLADYS KNIGHT & The PIPS	BABY DON'T CHANGE YOUR MIND	I LOVE TO FEEL THAT FEELING	6.00
77	460	GLADYS KNIGHT & The PIPS	HOME IS WHERE THE HEART IS	YOU PUT A NEW LIFE IN MY BODY	3.00
77	460 DJ	GLADYS KNIGHT & The PIPS	HOME IS WHERE THE HEART IS	YOU PUT A NEW LIFE IN MY BODY	4.00
77	462	MICHEAL HENDERSON	I CAN'T HELP IT	MAKE ME FEEL BETTER	6.00
77	462 DJ	MICHEAL HENDERSON	I CAN'T HELP IT	MAKE ME FEEL BETTER	8.00
77	463	EDWIN HAWKINS SINGERS	OH HAPPY DAY	JESUS LOVER OF MY SOUL	3.00
77	463 DJ	EDWIN HAWKINS SINGERS	OH HAPPY DAY	JESUS LOVER OF MY SOUL	4.00
78	464	MELBA MOORE	STANDING RIGHT HERE	LIVING FREE	8.00
78	464 DJ	MELBA MOORE	STANDING RIGHT HERE	LIVING FREE	10.00
78	465	CLIFFORD CURRY	MOVIN' IN THE SAME CIRCLES	LONLINESS (IT'S KILLING ME)	4.00
78	465 DJ	CLIFFORD CURRY	MOVIN' IN THE SAME CIRCLES	LONLINESS (IT'S KILLING ME)	5.00
78	467	ANDRE TRUE CONNECTION	WHAT'S YOUR NAME WHAT'S YOUR NUMBER	FILL ME UP	4.00
78	467 DJ	ANDRE TRUE CONNECTION	WHAT'S YOUR NAME WHAT'S YOUR NUMBER	FILL ME UP	5.00
78	469	M.V.P.'S	TURNIN' MY HEARTBEAT UP	EVERY MAN FOR HERSELF	15.00
78	469 DJ	M.V.P.'S	TURNIN' MY HEARTBEAT UP	EVERY MAN FOR HERSELF	20.00
78	470	GLADYS KNIGHT & The PIPS	THE ONE AND ONLY	TO MAKE A LONG STORY SHORT	4.00
78	470 DJ	GLADYS KNIGHT & The PIPS	THE ONE AND ONLY	TO MAKE A LONG STORY SHORT	5.00
78	473	GLADYS KNIGHT & The PIPS	COME BACK AND FINISH WHAT YOU	IT'S UP TO YOU	4.00
78	473 DJ	GLADYS KNIGHT & The PIPS	COME BACK AND FINISH WHAT YOU	IT'S UP TO YOU	6.00
78	476	NORMAN CONNORS	SAY YOU LOVE ME	CAPTAIN CONNORS	5.00
78	476 DJ	NORMAN CONNORS	SAY YOU LOVE ME	CAPTAIN CONNORS	6.00
78	477	MICHAEL HENDERSON	TAKE ME I'M YOURS	LET ME LOVE YOU	8.00
78	477 DJ	MICHAEL HENDERSON	TAKE ME I'M YOURS	LET ME LOVE YOU	10.00
78	478	GLADYS KNIGHT & The PIPS	IT'S A BETTER THAN GOOD TIME	SAVED BY THE GRAE OF YOUR LOVE	4.00
78	478 DJ	GLADYS KNIGHT & The PIPS	IT'S A BETTER THAN GOOD TIME	SAVED BY THE GRAE OF YOUR LOVE	5.00
78	480	GLADYS KNIGHT & The PIPS	DO YOU HEAR WHAT I HEAR	GOSPEL MEDLEY	3.00
78	480 DJ	GLADYS KNIGHT & The PIPS	DO YOU HEAR WHAT I HEAR	GOSPEL MEDLEY	4.00
79	483	GLADYS KNIGHT & The PIPS	I'LL TAKE A MELODY	THE WAY IT WAS	4.00
79	483 DJ	GLADYS KNIGHT & The PIPS	I'LL TAKE A MELODY	THE WAY IT WAS	5.00
79	485	GLADYS KNIGHT & The PIPS	WE DON'T MAKE EACH OTHER LAUGH	LOVE GIVES YOU THE POWER	3.00
79	485 DJ	GLADYS KNIGHT & The PIPS	WE DON'T MAKE EACH OTHER LAUGH	LOVE GIVES YOU THE POWER	4.00
79	487	PHYLISS HYMAN	LIVING INSIDE YOUR LOVE	LOVE IS FREE	5.00
79	487 DJ	PHYLISS HYMAN	LIVING INSIDE YOUR LOVE	LOVE IS FREE	6.00
79	488	AQUARIAN DREAM	PHEONIX	EAST 6TH. STREET	5.00
79	488 DJ	AQUARIAN DREAM	PHEONIX	EAST 6TH. STREET	6.00
79	489	GLADYS KNIGHT & The PIPS	TRY TO REMEMBER / THE WAY WE WERE	I'M STILL CAUGHT UP WITH YOU	3.00
79	489 DJ	GLADYS KNIGHT & The PIPS	TRY TO REMEMBER / THE WAY WE WERE	I'M STILL CAUGHT UP WITH YOU	4.00
79	493	PHYLISS HYMAN	EVERY WAY BUT LOOSE	MAKE A CHANGE	5.00
79	493 DJ	PHYLISS HYMAN	EVERY WAY BUT LOOSE	MAKE A CHANGE	6.00
79	494	MICHEAL HENDERSON	I CAN'T HELP IT	WIDE RECEIVER	6.00
79	494 DJ	MICHEAL HENDERSON	I CAN'T HELP IT	WIDE RECEIVER	8.00
79	496	ROBERT WINTERS & FALL	MAGIC MAN	FACE THE MUSIC	4.00
79	496 DJ	ROBERT WINTERS & FALL	MAGIC MAN	FACE THE MUSIC	5.00
81	497	ONENESS OF JUJU	EVERY WAY BUT LOOSE	(FAMILY TREE) MAKE A CHANGE	5.00
81	497 DJ	ONENESS OF JUJU	EVERY WAY BUT LOOSE	(FAMILY TREE) MAKE A CHANGE	6.00

Missing numbers in the above series of 45's are NOT soul or soul related releases.

201000 series

68	201021 lh	IMPRESSIONS	FOOL FOR YOU	I'M LOVING NOTHING	8.00
68	201021 sh	IMPRESSIONS	FOOL FOR YOU	I'M LOVING NOTHING	10.00
69	201022 lh	KASENETZ-KATZ	QUICK JOEY SMALL (RUN JOEY RUN)	RUMBLE '69	5.00
69	201022 sh	KASENETZ-KATZ	QUICK JOEY SMALL (RUN JOEY RUN)	RUMBLE '69	6.00
69	201024 lh	SHADOWS OF KNIGHT	SHAKE	FROM WAY OUT TO WAY UNDER	25.00
69	201024 sh	SHADOWS OF KNIGHT	SHAKE	FROM WAY OUT TO WAY UNDER	30.00
69	201026 lh	FIVE STAIRSTEPS & CUBIE	STAY CLOSE TO ME	I MADE A MISTAKE	15.00
69	201026 sh	FIVE STAIRSTEPS & CUBIE	STAY CLOSE TO ME	I MADE A MISTAKE	20.00
69	201029 lh	BROOKLYN BRIDGE	THE WORST THAT COULD HAPPEN	YOUR KITE MY KITE	8.00
69	201029 sh	BROOKLYN BRIDGE	THE WORST THAT COULD HAPPEN	YOUR KITE MY KITE	10.00
69	201045 lh	CHUBBY CHECKER	BACK IN THE U.S.S.R.	WINDY CREAM	3.00
69	201045 sh	CHUBBY CHECKER	BACK IN THE U.S.S.R.	WINDY CREAM	4.00
69	201046 lh	MAJOR LANCE	GYPSY WOMAN	I MADE A MISTAKE	15.00
69	201046 sh	MAJOR LANCE	GYPSY WOMAN	I MADE A MISTAKE	20.00

69	201056 lh	HOLLY MAXWELL	SUFFER	ON ONE ELSE	6.00
69	201056 sh	HOLLY MAXWELL	SUFFER	ON ONE ELSE	8.00
69	201062 lh	IMPRESSIONS	CHOICE OF COLORS	MIGHTY MIGHTY SPADE AND WHITEY	6.00
69	201062 sh	IMPRESSIONS	CHOICE OF COLORS	MIGHTY MIGHTY SPADE AND WHITEY	8.00
70	201070 lh	FIVE STAIRSTEPS	LITTLE YOUNG LOVER	WE MUST BE IN LOVE	15.00
70	201070 sh	FIVE STAIRSTEPS	LITTLE YOUNG LOVER	WE MUST BE IN LOVE	20.00
70	201083 lh	FIVE STAIRSTEPS	O-O-H CHILD	DEAR PRUDENCE	10.00
70	201083 sh	FIVE STAIRSTEPS	O-O-H CHILD	DEAR PRUDENCE	12.00
70	2011030 lh	IMPRESSIONS	CAN'T YOU SEE	CHECK OUT YOUR MIND	6.00
70	2011030 sh	IMPRESSIONS	CAN'T YOU SEE	CHECK OUT YOUR MIND	8.00
70	2011036 lh	FIVE STAIRSTEPS	O-O-H CHILD	WHO DO YOU BELONG TO?	8.00
70	2011036 sh	FIVE STAIRSTEPS	O-O-H CHILD	WHO DO YOU BELONG TO?	10.00
70	2011042 lh	EDWIN HAWKINS SINGERS	IN MY FATHERS HOUSE	BLOWIN IN THE WIND	3.00
70	2011042 sh	EDWIN HAWKINS SINGERS	IN MY FATHERS HOUSE	BLOWIN IN THE WIND	4.00
70	2011045 lh	IMPRESSIONS	(BABY) TURN ON TO ME	SOULFUL LOVE	6.00
70	2011045 sh	IMPRESSIONS	(BABY) TURN ON TO ME	SOULFUL LOVE	8.00
70	2011046 lh	MAJOR LANCE	GYPSY WOMAN	STAY AWAY FROM ME	15.00
70	2011046 sh	MAJOR LANCE	GYPSY WOMAN	STAY AWAY FROM ME	20.00
70	2011053 lh	FIVE STAIRSTEPS	BECAUSE I LOVE YOU	AMERICA - STANDING	5.00
70	2011053 sh	FIVE STAIRSTEPS	BECAUSE I LOVE YOU	AMERICA - STANDING	6.00
70	2011055 lh	CURTIS MAYFIELD	IF THERE'S A HELL BELOW WE'RE ALL	THE MAKINGS OF YOU	4.00
70	2011055 sh	CURTIS MAYFIELD	IF THERE'S A HELL BELOW WE'RE ALL	THE MAKINGS OF YOU	5.00
70	2011059 lh	FREDDIE WATERS	SINGING A NEW SONG	I LOVE YOU, I LOVE YOU	15.00
70	2011059 sh	FREDDIE WATERS	SINGING A NEW SONG	I LOVE YOU, I LOVE YOU	20.00
71	2011066 lh	IMPRESSIONS	AIN'T GOT TIME	I'M SO PROUD	6.00
71	2011066 sh	IMPRESSIONS	AIN'T GOT TIME	I'M SO PROUD	8.00
71	2011069 lh	IMPRESSIONS	I'M SO PROUD	AIN'T GOT TIME	6.00
71	2011069 sh	IMPRESSIONS	I'M SO PROUD	AIN'T GOT TIME	8.00
71	2011075 lh	EDWIN HAWKINS SINGERS	THERE'S A PLACE FOR US	GET TOGETHER CHILDREN	3.00
71	2011075 sh	EDWIN HAWKINS SINGERS	THERE'S A PLACE FOR US	GET TOGETHER CHILDREN	4.00
71	2011079 lh	DIXIE CUPS	CHAPEL OF LOVE	PEOPLE SAY	4.00
71	2011079 sh	DIXIE CUPS	CHAPEL OF LOVE	PEOPLE SAY	5.00
71	2011080 multi sh	CURTIS MAYFIELD	MOVE ON UP	GIVE IT UP / BEAUTIFUL BROTHER OF MINE	22.00
71	2011080 multi lh	CURTIS MAYFIELD	MOVE ON UP	GIVE IT UP / BEAUTIFUL BROTHER OF MINE	15.00
71	2011080 black sh	CURTIS MAYFIELD	MOVE ON UP	GIVE IT UP / BEAUTIFUL BROTHER OF MINE	15.00
71	2011080 black lh	CURTIS MAYFIELD	MOVE ON UP	GIVE IT UP / BEAUTIFUL BROTHER OF MINE	12.00
71	2011080 ink	CURTIS MAYFIELD	MOVE ON UP	GIVE IT UP / BEAUTIFUL BROTHER OF MINE	6.00
71	2011083 lh	CHE CHE and PEPPY	I KNOW I'M IN LOVE	MY LOVE WILL NEVER FADE AWAY	10.00
71	2011083 sh	CHE CHE and PEPPY	I KNOW I'M IN LOVE	MY LOVE WILL NEVER FADE AWAY	15.00
71	2011085 lh	LOVE'S CHILDREN	SOUL IS LOVE	THIS IS THE END	3.00
71	2011085 sh	LOVE'S CHILDREN	SOUL IS LOVE	THIS IS THE END	4.00
71	2011087 lh	IMPRESSIONS	LOVE ME	DO YOU WEANT ME TO WIN	10.00
71	2011087 sh	IMPRESSIONS	LOVE ME	DO YOU WEANT ME TO WIN	15.00
71	2011089 lh	MOSES DILLARD & TEX TOWN	OUR LOVE IS TRUE	THANK GOD FOR THIS THING CALLE	12.00
71	2011089 sh	MOSES DILLARD & TEX TOWN	OUR LOVE IS TRUE	THANK GOD FOR THIS THING CALLE	15.00
71	2011092 lh	STAIRSTEPS	STAY CLOSE TO ME	I MADE A MISTAKE	15.00
71	2011092 sh	STAIRSTEPS	STAY CLOSE TO ME	I MADE A MISTAKE	20.00
71	2011099 lh	IMPRESSIONS	INNER CITY BLUES	AMEN + KEEP ON PUSHIN'	6.00
71	2011099 sh	IMPRESSIONS	INNER CITY BLUES	AMEN + KEEP ON PUSHIN'	8.00
71	2011101 lh	CURTIS MAYFIELD	PEOPLE GET READY	WE GOT TO HAVE PEACE	5.00
71	2011101 sh	CURTIS MAYFIELD	PEOPLE GET READY	WE GOT TO HAVE PEACE	6.00
71	2011108 lh	SANDRA RICHARDSON	I FEEL A SONG IN MY HEART	THE RING	5.00
71	2011108 sh	SANDRA RICHARDSON	I FEEL A SONG IN MY HEART	THE RING	6.00
71	2011118 lh	NEW MONITORS	FENCE AROUND YOUR HEART	HAVE YOU SEEN	30.00
71	2011118 sh	NEW MONITORS	FENCE AROUND YOUR HEART	HAVE YOU SEEN	45.00
72	2011119 lh	CURTIS MAYFIELD	KEEP ON KEEPING ON	STONE JUNKIE	4.00
72	2011119 sh	CURTIS MAYFIELD	KEEP ON KEEPING ON	STONE JUNKIE	5.00
72	2011124 lh	IMPRESSIONS	OUR LOVE GOES ON AND ON	THIS LOVES REAL	5.00
72	2011124 sh	IMPRESSIONS	OUR LOVE GOES ON AND ON	THIS LOVES REAL	6.00
72	2011133 lh	BARBARA MASON	BED AND BOARD	YES, IT'S YOU	8.00
72	2011133 sh	BARBARA MASON	BED AND BOARD	YES, IT'S YOU	10.00
72	2011134 lh	DONNY HATHAWAY & JUNE CONQUEST	JUST ANOTHER REASON	I THANK YOU	10.00
72	2011134 sh	DONNY HATHAWAY & JUNE CONQUEST	JUST ANOTHER REASON	I THANK YOU	15.00
72	2011140 multi sh	TRAMMPS	PENGUIN AT THE BIG APPLE	ZING WENT THE STRING OF M Y HE	10.00
72	2011140 black lh	TRAMMPS	PENGUIN AT THE BIG APPLE	ZING WENT THE STRING OF M Y HE	6.00
72	2011140 black sh	TRAMMPS	PENGUIN AT THE BIG APPLE	ZING WENT THE STRING OF M Y HE	8.00
75	2011140 ink	TRAMMPS	PENGUIN AT THE BIG APPLE	ZING WENT THE STRINGS TO MY HE	4.00
72	2011141 lh	CURTIS MAYFIELD	FREDDIE'S DEAD	UNDERGROUND	5.00
72	2011141 sh	CURTIS MAYFIELD	FREDDIE'S DEAD	UNDERGROUND	6.00
73	2011154 lh	BARBARA MASON	GIVE ME YOUR LOVE (LOVE SONG)	YOU CAN BE WITH THE ONE YOU	5.00
73	2011154 sh	BARBARA MASON	GIVE ME YOUR LOVE (LOVE SONG)	YOU CAN BE WITH THE ONE YOU	6.00
73	2011156 lh	CURTIS MAYFIELD	SUPERFLY	GIVE ME YOUR LOVE (LOVE SONG)	6.00
73	2011156 sh	CURTIS MAYFIELD	SUPERFLY	GIVE ME YOUR LOVE (LOVE SONG)	8.00
73	2011164 lh	SHANGRI-LAS c/w AD LIBS	GIVE HIM A GREAT BIG KISS	THE BOY FROM NEW YORK CITY	5.00
73	2011164 sh	SHANGRI-LAS c/w AD LIBS	GIVE HIM A GREAT BIG KISS	THE BOY FROM NEW YORK CITY	6.00
73	2011167 lh	IMPRESSIONS	THIN LINE	I'M LOVING YOU	6.00
73	2011167 sh	IMPRESSIONS	THIN LINE	I'M LOVING YOU	8.00
73	2011170 lh	GLADYS KNIGHT & The PIPS	WERE PEACEFUL WATERS FLOW	A PERFECT LOVE	3.00
73	2011170 sh	GLADYS KNIGHT & The PIPS	WERE PEACEFUL WATERS FLOW	A PERFECT LOVE	4.00

73	2011181 lh	GLADYS KNIGHT & The PIPS	MIDNIGHT TRAIN TO GEORGIA	WINDOW RAISING GRANNY	5.00
73	2011181 sh	GLADYS KNIGHT & The PIPS	MIDNIGHT TRAIN TO GEORGIA	WINDOW RAISING GRANNY	6.00
73	2011185 lh	GLADYS KNIGHT & The PIPS	MIDNIGHT TRAIN TO GEORGIA	WINDOW RAISIN' GRANNY	3.00
73	2011185 sh	GLADYS KNIGHT & The PIPS	MIDNIGHT TRAIN TO GEORGIA	WINDOW RAISIN' GRANNY	4.00
73	2011187 lh	CURTIS MAYFIELD	BACK TO THE WORLD	THE OTHER SIDE OF TOWN	4.00
73	2011187 sh	CURTIS MAYFIELD	BACK TO THE WORLD	THE OTHER SIDE OF TOWN	5.00
73	2011208 lh	GLADYS KNIGHT & The PIPS	I'VE GOT TO USE MY IMAGINATION	STORMS OF TROUBLED TIMES	4.00
73	2011208 sh	GLADYS KNIGHT & The PIPS	I'VE GOT TO USE MY IMAGINATION	STORMS OF TROUBLED TIMES	5.00

BUFFALO

69	1001	JUSTIN	RIGHT NOW	A PLACE WHERE SORROW HIDES	50.00
69	1002	LEE DORSEY & BETTY HARRIS	LOVE LOTS OF LOVIN'	TAKE CARE OF OUR LOVE	10.00

BUK

75	3019	CANDLEWICK GREEN	THINGS THAT WE SAID	LAST BUS HOME	10.00

BULLDOG

75	2	JOHNNY OTIS SHOW	WILLIE AND THE HAND JIVE	HARLEM NOCTURNE	5.00
75	6	MR. FLOOD PARTY	COMPARED TO WHAT	UNBREAKABLE TOY	15.00

BUS STOP

75	1029	RICHIE PITTS	DON'T TAKE THE NAME OF LOVE IN VAIN	SCUSE ME MA'AM	4.00
75	1029 DJ	RICHIE PITTS	DON'T TAKE THE NAME OF LOVE IN VAIN	SCUSE ME MA'AM	5.00
75	1030	BASIC BLACK & PEARL	THERE'LL COME A TIME, THERE'LL COME	RIGHT ON BABY	45.00
75	1030 DJ	BASIC BLACK & PEARL	THERE'LL COME A TIME, THERE'LL COME	RIGHT ON BABY	60.00
75	1032	FANTASTICS	10 MINUTES THAT CHANGED THE WORLD	TAKE AWAY THAT FEELING	4.00
75	1032 DJ	FANTASTICS	10 MINUTES THAT CHANGED THE WORLD	TAKE AWAY THAT FEELING	5.00
75	1038	RICHIE PITTS	THEY'RE COMING	PALLISADES INN	4.00
75	1038 DJ	RICHIE PITTS	THEY'RE COMING	PALLISADES INN	5.00
76	1040	FANTASTICS	BRING A LITTLE SMILE	LEFT RIGHT OUT OF MY LIFE	6.00
76	1040 DJ	FANTASTICS	BRING A LITTLE SMILE	LEFT RIGHT OUT OF MY LIFE	8.00
76	1051	FANTASTICS	SAME OLD FEELING	TAKE AWAY THAT FEELING	4.00
76	1051 DJ	FANTASTICS	SAME OLD FEELING	TAKE AWAY THAT FEELING	5.00

BUZZ INTERNATIONAL

	1	MAJOR HARRIS	I WANT YOUR LOVE	I WANT YOUR LOVE (club mix)	5.00

CADET

Special limited presss 4 track EP in company cover. Pressed to coincide with their only UK performance at Trentham Gardens, Stoke On Trent in 1999

99	1999 DJ EP	DELLS	RUN FOR COVER + WEAR IT ON OUR	THERE IS + MAKE SURE	15.00

CALIBRE

84	124 PS	FOUR TOPS	YOUR SONG	I'M HERE AGAIN	10.00
80	501	TONY RALLO & the MIDNITE	HOLDIN' ON	BURNIN' LOVE	6.00
80	501 dup #	YOUNG & COMPANY	I LIKE (WHAT YOU'RE DOING TO ME)	same: instrumental	4.00

CAMEO PARKWAY

USA Philadelphia based Cameo – Parkway label was apparently the first USA record company to be quoted on Wall Street. With runaway successes like Chubby Checker and teen idol Bobby Rydell investors had no hesitation investing in a successful recording company. Cameo started releasing 45's in 1957. Parkway followed by releasing 45's in 1959. The first record to be released from the Cameo Parklway catalogue in the UK was handled by London: The Rays – "Silhouette" – which is now a Doo-Wop classic. Then in 1961 UK Columbia handled the UK distribution releasing 45's by Chubby Checker inc: monster hit – "Let's Twist Again" – plus Len Barry's group The Dovells and top Philly girl group The Orlons. By late 1962 Pye had taken over the UK distribution: Pye had a policy of retaining the original USA release number. The letter "P" precedes Parkway recordings; likewise Cameo recording had the letter "C" prefix before the release number. This policy did cause a little confusion later in the 60's. When a mail order for collectable 45's, listed a stock copy of Cameo C-382 Dee Dee Sharp – "There Ain't Nothing I wouldn't Do For You" – Since then UK soul collectors have been searching for the UK release, as yet I've never seen a copy. I do believe the 45 quoted was a USA import but in those days import 45's were rare and everyone supposed it was a UK copy, perhaps even the dealer listing it. To this date, the UK copy is still unconfirmed. As is the Tymes P-933, which I believe suffers from the same scenario. Pye also used this release numbering system for UK Colpix, Hickory, Red Bird, Warner Bros etc. making it difficult for an avid collector to follow the release numbers and never be sure when he had completed a particular label.

Cameo Parkway lasted just over ten years and seems to have stopped pressing 45's in the USA by the end of 1967. We have tried to list not just soul related 45s, but all the UK releases as many collectors are trying to complete this most attractive of UK labels.

65	C-100	LITTLE JERRY WILLIAMS	JUST WHAT DO YOU PLAN TO DO ABOUT	BABY YOU'RE MY EVERYTHING	85.00
65	C-100 DJ	LITTLE JERRY WILLIAMS	JUST WHAT DO YOU PLAN TO DO ABOUT	BABY YOU'RE MY EVERYTHING	120.00
65	C-101	DORIS TROY	I'LL DO ANYTHING (HE WANTS ME TO DO)	BUT I LOVE HIM	150.00
65	C-101 DJ	DORIS TROY	I'LL DO ANYTHING (HE WANTS ME TO DO)	BUT I LOVE HIM	250.00
65	C-102	TERRY KNIGHT and the PACK	I (WHO HAVE NOTHING)	NUMBERS	75.00
65	C-102 DJ	TERRY KNIGHT and the PACK	I (WHO HAVE NOTHING)	NUMBERS	100.00
65	C-103	SOUL CITY	EVERYBODY DANCE NOW	WHO KNOWS	85.00
65	C-103 DJ	SOUL CITY	EVERYBODY DANCE NOW	WHO KNOWS	125.00
62	C-108	BOBBY RYDELL	FORGET HIM	HEY EV'RYONE	6.00
62	C-108 PS	BOBBY RYDELL	FORGET HIM	HEY EV'RYONE	10.00
62	C-108 DJ	BOBBY RYDELL	FORGET HIM	HEY EV'RYONE	10.00
62	C-129	BOBBY RYDELL	IT'S TIME WE PARTED	TOO MUCH TOO SOON	6.00
62	C-129 DJ	BOBBY RYDELL	IT'S TIME WE PARTED	TOO MUCH TOO SOON	10.00
63	C-228	BOBB RYDELL	THE CHA CHA CHA	THE BEST MAN CRIED	6.00
63	C-228 DJ	BOBB RYDELL	THE CHA CHA CHA	THE BEST MAN CRIED	10.00
62	C-230	DEE DEE SHARP	NIGHT	RIDE	40.00
62	C-230 DJ	DEE DEE SHARP	NIGHT	RIDE	75.00
62	C-231	ORLONS	DON'T HANG UP	THE CONSERVATIVE	15.00
62	C-231 DJ	ORLONS	DON'T HANG UP	THE CONSERVATIVE	30.00

62	C-237	JO ANN CAMPBELL	MR. FIXIT MAN	LET ME DO IT MY WAY	10.00
62	C-237 DJ	JO ANN CAMPBELL	MR. FIXIT MAN	LET ME DO IT MY WAY	15.00
62	C-239	DON COVAY	THE POPEYE WADDLE	ONE LITTLE BOY HAD MONEY	20.00
62	C-239 DJ	DON COVAY	THE POPEYE WADDLE	ONE LITTLE BOY HAD MONEY	28.00
62	C-242	BOBBY RYDELL	BUTTERFLY BABY	LOVE IS BLIND	6.00
62	C-242 DJ	BOBBY RYDELL	BUTTERFLY BABY	LOVE IS BLIND	10.00
63	C-243	ORLONS	SOUTH STREET	THEM TERRIBLE BOOTS	15.00
63	C-243 DJ	ORLONS	SOUTH STREET	THEM TERRIBLE BOOTS	28.00
63	C-244	DEE DEE SHARP	DO THE BIRD	LOVER BOY	20.00
63	C-244 DJ	DEE DEE SHARP	DO THE BIRD	LOVER BOY	28.00
63	C-249	JO ANN CAMPBELL	MOTHER PLEASE	WAITNG FOR LOVE	10.00
63	C-249 DJ	JO ANN CAMPBELL	MOTHER PLEASE	WAITNG FOR LOVE	15.00
63	C-257	ORLONS	NOT ME	MY BEST FRIENDS	20.00
63	C-257 DJ	ORLONS	NOT ME	MY BEST FRIENDS	30.00
63	C-260	DEE DEE SHARP	ROCK ME IN THE CRADLE OF LOVE	YOU'LL BE MINE	20.00
63	C-260 DJ	DEE DEE SHARP	ROCK ME IN THE CRADLE OF LOVE	YOU'LL BE MINE	30.00
63	C-272	BOBBY RYDELL	SINCE WE FELL IN LOVE	CHILDHOOD SWEETHEART	6.00
63	C-272 DJ	BOBBY RYDELL	SINCE WE FELL IN LOVE	CHILDHOOD SWEETHEART	10.00
63	C-273	ORLONS	IT'S NO BIG THING	CROSSFIRE	15.00
63	C-273 DJ	ORLONS	IT'S NO BIG THING	CROSSFIRE	28.00
63	C-274	DEE DEE SHARP	WILD	WHY DON'CHA ASK ME	20.00
63	C-274 DJ	DEE DEE SHARP	WILD	WHY DON'CHA ASK ME	28.00
63	C-287	ORLONS	DON'T THROW YOUR LOVE AWAY	BON DOO WAH	20.00
63	C-287 DJ	ORLONS	DON'T THROW YOUR LOVE AWAY	BON DOO WAH	30.00
63	C-290	LOS SENORS	AMAPOLA	ACCAPULCO	6.00
63	C-290 DJ	LOS SENORS	AMAPOLA	ACCAPULCO	10.00
63	C-295	ORLONS	SHIMMY SHIMMY	EVERYTHING'S NICE	15.00
63	C-295	ORLONS	SHIMMY SHIMMY	EVERYTHING'S NICE	22.00
64	C-302	SWANS	THE BOY WITH THE BEATLE HAIR CUT	PLEASE HURRY HOME	25.00
64	C-302 DJ	SWANS	THE BOY WITH THE BEATLE HAIR CUT	PLEASE HURRY HOME	35.00
64	C-309	BOBBY RYDELL	MAKE ME FORGET	DARLING JENNY	6.00
64	C-309 DJ	BOBBY RYDELL	MAKE ME FORGET	DARLING JENNY	10.00
64	C-319	ORLONS	RULES OF LOVE	HEARTBREAK HOTEL	15.00
64	C-319 DJ	ORLONS	RULES OF LOVE	HEARTBREAK HOTEL	20.00
64	C-332	ORLONS	KNOCK KNOCK (WHO'S THERE)	GOIN' PLACES	15.00
64	C-332 DJ	ORLONS	KNOCK KNOCK (WHO'S THERE)	GOIN' PLACES	25.00
65	C-336	CANDY & THE KISSES	THE 81	TWO HAPPY PEOPLE	100.00
65	C-336 DJ	CANDY & THE KISSES	THE 81	TWO HAPPY PEROPLE	**151.00**
65	C-361	BOBBY RYDELL	CIAO CIAO, BAMBINO	VOCE DE LA NOTRE	5.00
65	C-361 DJ	BOBBY RYDELL	CIAO CIAO, BAMBINO	VOCE DE LA NOTRE	8.00
65	C-375	DEE DEE SHARP	STANDING IN THE NEED OF LOVE	I REALLY LOVE YOU	100.00
65	C-375 DJ	DEE DEE SHARP	STANDING IN THE NEED OF LOVE	I REALLY LOVE YOU	140.00
65	C-382 unconfirmed	DEE DEE SHARP	THERE AIN'T NOTHING I WOULDN'T DO	IT'S A FUNNY SITUATION	UN
65	C-382 DJ	DEE DEE SHARP	THERE AIN'T NOTHING I WOULDN'T DO	IT'S A FUNNY SITUATION	150.00
66	C-413	EVIE SANDS	PICTURE ME GONE	IT MAKES ME LAUGH	100.00
66	C-413 DJ	EVIE SANDS	PICTURE ME GONE	IT MAKES ME LAUGH	150.00
66	C-428	? and the MYSTERIANS	96 TEARS	MIDNIGHT HOUR	30.00
66	C-428 DJ	? and the MYSTERIANS	96 TEARS	MIDNIGHT HOUR	50.00
66	C-441	? and the MYSTERIANS	I NEED SOMEBODY	8 TEEN	35.00
66	C-441 DJ	? and the MYSTERIANS	I NEED SOMEBODY	8 TEEN	50.00
66	C-461	HERMOINE GINGOLD	DOES YOUR CHEWING GUM LOSE IT'S FLAVOR	I'VE GOT THOSE RUDY VALLE BLUES	5.00
66	C-461 DJ	HERMOINE GINGOLD	DOES YOUR CHEWING GUM LOSE IT'S FLAVOR	I'VE GOT THOSE RUDY VALLE BLUES	8.00
67	C-467	? and the MYSTERIANS	CAN'T GET ENOUGH OF YOU, BASBY	SMOKES	20.00
67	C-467 DJ	? and the MYSTERIANS	CAN'T GET ENOUGH OF YOU, BASBY	SMOKES	28.00
67	C-479	? and the MYSTERIANS	GIRL (YOU CAPTIVATE ME)	GOT TO	20.00
67	C-479 DJ	? and the MYSTERIANS	GIRL (YOU CAPTIVATE ME)	GOT TO	28.00
67	C-496	? and the MYSTERIANS	DO SOMETHING TO ME	LOVE ME BABY	20.00
67	C-496 DJ	? and the MYSTERIANS	DO SOMETHING TO ME	LOVE ME BABY	28.00
63	552 EP PS	VARIOUS ARTISTS	CAMEO BIG FOUR	1963 4 track EP with cover Orlons, Checker, Dovells etc	15.00
64	556 EP PS	LEN BARRY	HAVIN' A GOOD TIME	1964 4 track EP with cover	20.00
66	CP-601	BOBBY RYDELL	UNTIL I MET YOU	NEW LOVE	6.00
66	CP-601 DJ	BOBBY RYDELL	UNTIL I MET YOU	NEW LOVE	10.00
66	CP-750	DON & DEWEY	SOUL MOTION	STRETCHIN' OUT	15.00
66	CP-750 DJ	DON & DEWEY	SOUL MOTION	STRETCHIN' OUT	25.00
66	CP-751	CHRIS PAGE	WAIT AND SEE	MINE MINE MINE	10.00
66	CP-751	CHRIS PAGE	WAIT AND SEE	MINE MINE MINE	15.00
65	P-100	JERRY JACKSON	I'M GONNA PAINT ME A PICTURE	IT'S ROUGH OUT THERE	**257.00**
65	P-100 DJ	JERRY JACKSON	I'M GONNA PAINT ME A PICTURE	IT'S ROUGH OUT THERE	300.00
65	P-101	CHRIS BARTLEY	SWEETEST THING THIS SIDE OF HE	LOVE ME BABY	75.00
65	P-101 DJ	CHRIS BARTLEY	SWEETEST THING THIS SIDE OF HE	LOVE ME BABY	100.00
67	P-153	BUNNY SIGLER	LET THE GOOD TIMES ROLL	THERE'S NO LOVE LEFT	20.00
67	P-153 DJ	BUNNY SIGLER	LET THE GOOD TIMES ROLL	THERE'S NO LOVE LEFT	75.00
62	P-127	EVERETT McKINLEY & BOBBY SENATOR	WILD THING	WILD THING part 2	10.00
62	P-127 DJ	EVERETT McKINLEY & BOBBY SENATOR	WILD THING	WILD THING part 2	15.00
62	P-806	CHUBBYCHECKER	WHAT DO YOU SAY	SOMETHING TO SHOUT ABOUT	8.00
62	P-806 DJ	CHUBBYCHECKER	WHAT DO YOU SAY	SOMETHING TO SHOUT ABOUT	15.00
62	P-824	CHUBBY CHECKER	LET'S TWIST AGAIN	THE TWIST	6.00
62	P-824 DJ	CHUBBY CHECKER	LET'S TWIST AGAIN	THE TWIST	10.00
62	P-845	DOVELLS	HULLY GULLY BABY	YOUR LAST CHANCE	8.00

62	P-845 DJ	DOVELLS	HULLY GULLY BABY	YOUR LAST CHANCE	12.00
62	P-849	CHUBBYCHECKER	LIMBO ROCK	POPEYE (THE HITCH-HIKER)	8.00
62	P-849 DJ	CHUBBYCHECKER	LIMBO ROCK	POPEYE (THE HITCH-HIKER)	12.00
63	P-861	DOVELLS	YOU CAN'T RUN AWAY FROM YOURSELF	SAVE ME BABY	8.00
63	P-861 DJ	DOVELLS	YOU CAN'T RUN AWAY FROM YOURSELF	SAVE ME BABY	12.00
63	P-862	CHUBBYCHECKER	LET'S LIMBO SOME MORE	TWENTY MILES	8.00
63	P-862 DJ	CHUBBYCHECKER	LET'S LIMBO SOME MORE	TWENTY MILES	15.00
63	P-863	REGGIE HARRISON and the HIPPIES	A LONELY PIANO	MEMORY LANE	15.00
63	P-863 DJ	REGGIE HARRISON and the HIPPIES	A LONELY PIANO	MEMORY LANE	20.00
63	P-867	DOVELLS	YOU CAN'T SIT DOWN	STOMPIN' EVERYWHERE	10.00
63	P-867 DJ	DOVELLS	YOU CAN'T SIT DOWN	STOMPIN' EVERYWHERE	20.00
63	P-868	TIP TOPS	HE'S BRAGGIN'	OO-KOOK-A-BOO	20.00
63	P-868 DJ	TIP TOPS	HE'S BRAGGIN'	OO-KOOK-A-BOO	30.00
63	P-871	TYMES	SO MUCH IN LOVE	ROSCOE JAMES MCCLAIN	10.00
63	P-871 DJ	TYMES	SO MUCH IN LOVE	ROSCOE JAMES MCCLAIN	20.00
63	P-873	CHUBBYCHECKER	BIRDLAND	BLACK CLOUD	8.00
63	P-873 DJ	CHUBBYCHECKER	BIRDLAND	BLACK CLOUD	15.00
63	P-874	BILLY ABBOTT & the JEWELS	GROOVY BABY	COME ON AND DANCE WITH ME	15.00
63	P-874 DJ	BILLY ABBOTT & the JEWELS	GROOVY BABY	COME ON AND DANCE WITH ME	22.00
63	P-879	CHUBBYCHECKER	TWIST IT UP	SURF PARTY	8.00
63	P-879	CHUBBYCHECKER	TWIST IT UP	SURF PARTY	12.00
63	P-882	DOVELLS	BETTY IN BERMUDAS	DANCE THE FROG	10.00
63	P-882 DJ	DOVELLS	BETTY IN BERMUDAS	DANCE THE FROG	15.00
63	P-884	TYMES	WONDERFUL! WONDERFUL	COME WITH ME TO THE SEA	10.00
63	P-884 DJ	TYMES	WONDERFUL ! WONDERFUL !	COME WITH ME TO THE SEA	15.00
63	P-884 PS	TYMES	WONDERFUL ! WONDERFUL !	COME WITH ME TO THE SEA	20.00
64	P-890	CHUBBYCHECKER	LODDY LO	HOOKA TOOKA	8.00
64	P-890 DJ	CHUBBYCHECKER	LODDY LO	HOOKA TOOKA	12.00
64	P-891	TYMES	SOMEWHERE	VIEW FROM MY WINDOW	15.00
64	P-891 DJ	TYMES	SOMEWHERE	VIEW FROM MY WINDOW	25.00
63	P-901	DOVELLS	BE MY GIRL	DRAGSTER ON THE PROWL	15.00
63	P-901 DJ	DOVELLS	BE MY GIRL	DRAGSTER ON THE PROWL	25.00
64	P-907	CHUBBYCHECKER	HEY, BOBBA NEEDLE	SPREAD JOY	8.00
64	P-907 DJ	CHUBBYCHECKER	HEY, BOBBA NEEDLE	SPREAD JOY	15.00
64	P-908	TYMES	TO EACH HIS OWN	WONDERLAND OF LOVE	15.00
64	P-908 DJ	TYMES	TO EACH HIS OWN	WONDERLAND OF LOVE	22.00
64	P-919	TYMES	THE MAGIC OF OUR SUMMER LOVE	WITH ALL MY HEART	15.00
64	P-919 DJ	TYMES	THE MAGIC OF OUR SUMMER LOVE	WITH ALL MY HEART	22.00
64	P-920	CHUBBYCHECKER	LAZY ELSIE MOLLY	ROSIE	8.00
64	P-920 DJ	CHUBBYCHECKER	LAZY ELSIE MOLLY	ROSIE	15.00
64	P-921	RAG DOLLS and the CALIENT COMBO	SOCIETY GIRL	RAGEN	10.00
64	P-921 DJ	RAG DOLLS and the CALIENT COMBO	SOCIETY GIRL	RAGEN	15.00
64	P-922	CHUBBY CHECKER	YOU BETTER BELIEVE IT BABY	SHE WANTS TO SWIM	25.00
64	P-922 DJ	CHUBBY CHECKER	YOU BETTER BELIEVE IT BABY	SHE WANTS TO SWIM	35.00
64	P-924	TYMES	HERE SHE COMES	MALIBU	**195.00**
64	P-924 DJ	TYMES	HERE SHE COMES	MALIBU	275.00
65	P-933 unconfirmed	MALIBUS	HERE SHE COMES	THE TWELVE OF NEVER	UN
65	P-935	PATTI LABELLE & HER BLUEBELLES	DANNY BOY	I BELIEVE	15.00
65	P-935 DJ	PATTI LABELLE & HER BLUEBELLES	DANNY BOY	I BELIEVE	25.00
65	P-936	CHUBBY CHECKER	THE WEEKEND'S HERE	LOVELY, LOVELY	40.00
65	P-936 DJ	CHUBBY CHECKER	THE WEEKEND'S HERE	LOVELY, LOVELY	60.00
65	P-949	CHUBBY CHECKER	(AT THE) DISCOTHEQUE	DO THE FREDDIE	50.00
65	P-949 DJ	CHUBBY CHECKER	(AT THE) DISCOTHEQUE	DO THE FREDDIE	150.00
65	P-959	CHUBBY CHECKER	EVERYTHINGS WRONG	CU MA LA BE - STAY	30.00
65	P-959 DJ	CHUBBY CHECKER	EVERYTHING'S WRONG	CU MA LA BE-STAY	70.00
65	P-960	EDDIE HOLMAN	THIS CAN'T BE TRUE	FREE COUNTRY	50.00
65	P-960 DJ	EDDIE HOLMAN	THIS CAN'T BE TRUE	FREE COUNTRY	85.00
65	P-965	CHUBBY CHECKER	YOU JUST DON'T KNOW (WHAT YOU DO TO ME)	TWO HEARTS MAKE ONE LOVE	200.00
65	P-965 DJ	CHUBBY CHECKER	YOU JUST DON'T KNOW (WHAT YOU DO TO ME)	TWO HEARTS MAKE ONE LOVE	400.00
65	P-969	LEN BARRY	HEARTS ARE TRUMP	LITTLE WHITE HOUSE	20.00
65	P-969 DJ	LEN BARRY	HEARTS ARE TRUMP	LITTLE WHITE HOUSE	30.00
65	P-989	CHUBBY CHECKER	HEY YOU ! LITTLE BOO-GA-LOO	PUSSY CAT	30.00
65	P-989 DJ	CHUBBY CHECKER	HEY YOU ! LITTLE BOO-GA-LOO	PUSSY CAT	50.00

CAMP

67	602003	WILLIE AMOS HUNT	WOULD YOU BELIEVE	MY BABY WANTS TO DANCE	75.00

CAPITOL

Think of Capitol Records and we all think of Capitol's Los Angeles Tower building on Vine Street, built in 1955, it is almost as famous as the Statue of Liberty. Songwriter Johnny Mercer created the company during the midst of the Second World War in Hollywood. With Los Angeles record store owner Glenn Wallich as a partner, and Buddy De Sylva as the financial muscle. The trio set about forming a world force in music. In their thirteenth year in business UK music giants EMI stepped in and paid $8.5 million for the company. Many fine Los Angeles recorded soul tunes came out in the UK, the likes of Alexander Patton, Bobby Sheen, H.B.Barnum all of which were released to very disappointing sales and quick deletion from their catalogue. Saved from obscurity by enterprising soul club DJ's working at clubs like the Twisted Wheel, Mojo, Nite Owl, Beachcomber etc. But EMI did appreciate that their was an underground club scene emerging, and even did a series of soul 45's with the phrase DISCOTHEQUE SERIES '66 or 67, as did EMI with their SOUL SUPPLY logo on the labels of Liberty etc. And still the records failed to sell.

Perhaps the vocals and productions of the likes of Alexander Patton were too different to be appreciated at the time. I know when I was first played the Patton disc in a collectors shop in Leicester around 1969, my young untrained ear didn't think much to it, mainly because I'd never heard anything even vaguely similar. Today, the 45 is rated by all rare soul collectors, as one of the greatest Northern Soul recordings ever made. The mid-sixties EMI label did release some wonderful soul 45's on those famous black labels with bright silver lettering.

78	101 DJ EP	NATALIE COLE	PARTY LIGHTS + INSEPARABLE	THIS WILL BE + SOPHISTICATED LADY	8.00
81	211	MAZE feat. FRANK BEVERLY	JOY AND PAIN	HAPPY FEELIN'S	4.00
81	216	ERIC MERCURY	GIMME A CALL SOMETIME	INCLUDE ME OUT	5.00
82	232	SHEREE BROWN	IT'S A PLEASURE	STRAIGT AHEAD	6.00
82	234 PS	DIANA ROSS	MIRROR MIRROR	SWEET NOTHINGS	3.00
82	252	DRAMATICS	I CAN'T STAND IT	IT'S DRAMATIC MUSIC	8.00
82	256 PS	DIANA ROSS	IT'S NEVER TOO LATE	SWEET SURRENDER	3.00
82	260	L.J. REYNOLDS	KEY TO THE WORLD	SPECIAL EFFECTS	75.00
83	271 PS	GEORGE CLINTON	LOOPZILLA	POT SHARING TOTS	4.00
83	298 PS	DIANA ROSS	PIECES OF ICE	STILL IN LOVE	3.00
84	337 PS	DIANA ROSS	TOUCH BY TOUCH	FIGHT FOR IT	3.00
84	355 PS	ASHFORD & SIMPSON	BABIES	OUTTA THE WORLD	3.00
84	357	A TASTE OF HONEY	BOOGIE OOGIE OOGIE ('84)	BOOGIE OOGIE OOGIE original	3.00
85	372 PS	DIANA ROSS	EATEN ALIVE	I'M WATCHING YOU	3.00
86	400 PS	DIANA ROSS	EXPERIENCE	OH TEACHER	3.00
86	402 PS	GEORGE CLINTON	DO FRIES GO WITH THAT SHAKE	PLEASURES OF EXHAUSTION	5.00
86	421 PS	MAZE feat. FRANK BEVERLY	I WANNA BE WITH YOU	same: instrumental	4.00
57	14781	TOMMY SANDS	LET ME BE LOVED	FANTASTICALLY FOOLISH	5.00
58	14902	PEGGY LEE	FEVER	YOU DON'T KNOW	10.00
62	15270	NAT KING COLE	THE GOOD TIMES	RAMBLIN' ROSE	10.00
62	15270 DJ	NAT KING COLE	THE GOOD TIMES	RAMBLIN' ROSE	20.00
62	15280	NAT KING COLE	WHO'S NEXT IN LINE	DEAR LONELY HEARTS	20.00
62	15280 DJ	NAT KING COLE	WHO'S NEXT IN LINE	DEAR LONELY HEARTS	30.00
62	15297	CHANTELS	SWAMP WATER	ETERNALLY	10.00
62	15297 DJ	CHANTELS	SWAMP WATER	ETERNALLY	15.00
63	15306	BOBBY DARIN	NOT FOR ME	EIGHTEEN YELLOW ROSES	20.00
63	15306 DJ	BOBBY DARIN	NOT FOR ME	EIGHTEEN YELLOW ROSES	30.00
64	15343	NANCY WILSON	THE BEST IS YET TO COME	NEVER LET ME GO	5.00
64	15343 DJ	NANCY WILSON	THE BEST IS YET TO COME	NEVER LET ME GO	8.00
64	15344	DARLENE PAUL	ACT LIKE NOTHING HAPPENED	LITTLE BIT OF HEAVEN	25.00
64	15344 DJ	DARLENE PAUL	ACT LIKE NOTHING HAPPENED	LITTLE BIT OF HEAVEN	40.00
64	15346	KING CURTIS	SOUL SERENADE	MORE SOUL	15.00
64	15346 DJ	KING CURTIS	SOUL SERENADE	MORE SOUL	22.00
64	15352	NANCY WILSON	(YOU DON'T KNOW) HOW GLAD I AM	NEVER LESS THAN YESTERDAY	6.00
64	15352 DJ	NANCY WILSON	(YOU DON'T KNOW) HOW GLAD I AM	NEVER LESS THAN YESTERDAY	10.00
65	15378	NANCY WILSON	DON'T COME RUNNING BACK TO ME	LOVE HAS MANY FACES	12.00
65	15378 DJ	NANCY WILSON	DON'T COME RUNNING BACK TO ME	LOVE HAS MANY FACES	20.00
65	15389	FRANK POLK	TRYING TO KEEP UP WITH THE JONESES	WELCOME HOME, BABY	75.00
65	15389 DJ	FRANK POLK	TRYING TO KEEP UP WITH THE JONESES	WELCOME HOME, BABY	100.00
65	15391	H.B. BARNUM	THE RECORD (BABY I LOVE YOU)	I'M A MAN	45.00
65	15391 DJ	H.B. BARNUM	THE RECORD (BABY I LOVE YOU)	I'M A MAN	75.00
65	15398	LOU RAWLS	NOTHING REALLY FEELS THE SAME	THREE O'CLOCK IN THE MORNING	6.00
65	15398 DJ	LOU RAWLS	NOTHING REALLY FEELS THE SAME	THREE O'CLOCK IN THE MORNING	10.00
65	15407	ERNIE ANDREWS	WHERE WERE YOU (WHEN I NEEDED	WHAT DO I SEE IN THE GIRL	25.00
65	15407 DJ	ERNIE ANDREWS	WHERE WERE YOU (WHEN I NEEDED	WHAT DO I SEE IN THE GIRL	35.00
65	15412	NANCY WILSON	WHERE DOES THAT LEAVE ME	GENTLE IS LOVE	25.00
65	15412 DJ	NANCY WILSON	WHERE DOES THAT LEAVE ME	GENTLE IS MY LOVE	45.00
65	15423	TED CASSIDY	THE LURCH	WESLEY	25.00
65	15423 DJ	TED CASSIDY	THE LURCH	WESLEY	40.00
65	15427	KETTY LESTER	WEST COAST	I'LL BE LOOKING BACK	50.00
65	15427 DJ	KETTY LESTER	WEST COAST	I'LL BE LOOKING BACK	75.00
65	15429	GLORIA JONES	HEARTBEAT - part 1	HEARTBEAT - part 2	30.00
65	15429 DJ	GLORIA JONES	HEARTBEAT - part 1	HEARTBEAT - part 2	60.00
66	15434	VERDELLE SMITH	LIKE A MAN	IN MY ROOM	10.00
66	15434 DJ	VERDELLE SMITH	LIKE A MAN	IN MY ROOM	22.00
66	15435	OUTSIDERS	TIME WON'T LET ME	WAS IT REALLY REAL	30.00
66	15435 DJ	OUTSIDERS	TIME WON'T LET ME	WAS IT REALLY REAL	75.00
66	15439	DAVID McCALLUM	COMMUNICATION	MY CAROUSEL	8.00
66	15439 DJ	DAVID McCALLUM	COMMUNICATION	MY CAROUSEL	12.00
66	15440	SCOTT ENGEL & JOHN STEWART	GREENS	I ONLY CAME TO DANCE YOU	40.00
66	15440 DJ	SCOTT ENGEL & JOHN STEWART	GREENS	I ONLY CAME TO DANCE YOU	50.00
66	15443	NANCY WILSON	POWER OF LOVE	RAIN SOMETIMES	6.00
66	15443 DJ	NANCY WILSON	POWER OF LOVE	RAIN SOMETIMES	10.00
66	15447	KETTY LESTER	WHAN A MAN LOVES A WOMAN	WE'LL BE TOGETHER AGAIN	8.00
66	15447 DJ	KETTY LESTER	WHAN A MAN LOVES A WOMAN	WE'LL BE TOGETHER AGAIN	10.00
66	15448	MATT MONRO	HONEY ON THE VINE	blank:	10.00
66	15448 DJ	MATT MONRO	HONEY ON THE VINE	blank:	20.00
66	15450	OUTSIDERS	GIRL IN LOVE	WHAT MAKES YOU SO BAD	15.00
66	15450 DJ	OUTSIDERS	GIRL IN LOVE	WHAT MAKES YOU SO BAD	25.00
66	15455	BOBBY SHEEN	DR. LOVE	SWEET SWEET LOVE	100.00
66	15455 DJ	BOBBY SHEEN	DR. LOVE	SWEET SWEET LOVE	200.00
66	15455 test press	BOBBY SHEEN	DR. LOVE	SWEET, SWEET LOVE	**131.00**
66	15456	VERDELLE SMITH	A PIECE OF THE SKY	TAR & CEMENT	20.00
66	15456 DJ	VERDELLE SMITH	A PIECE OF THE SKY	TAR & CEMENT	35.00
66	15458	BILLY PRESTON	IN THE MIDNIGHT HOUR	ADVICE	25.00
66	15458 DJ	BILLY PRESTON	IN THE MIDNIGHT HOUR	ADVICE	40.00
66	15460	RUBEN WRIGHT	I'M WALKING OUT ON YOU	HEY GIRL	40.00
66	15460 DJ	RUBEN WRIGHT	I'M WALKING OUT ON YOU	HEY GIRL	60.00
66	15461	ALEXANDER PATTON	A LIL LOVING SOMETIMES	NO MORE DREAMS	**325.00**

66	15461 DJ	ALEXANDER PATTON	A LIL LOVIN' SOMETIMES	NO MORE DREAMS	**350.00**
66	15462	MAGNIFICENT MEN	ALL YOUR LOVIN' GONE TO MY HEAD	PEACE OF MIND	40.00
66	15462 DJ	MAGNIFICENT MEN	ALL YOUR LOVIN' GONE TO MY HEAD	PEACE OF MIND	50.00
66	15463	BARRY MANN	LOOKING AT TOMORROW	ANGELICA	15.00
66	15463 DJ	BARRY MANN	LOOKING AT TOMORROW	ANGELICA	20.00
66	15465	LOU RAWLS	LOVE IS A HURTIN' THING	MEMORY LANE	20.00
66	15465 DJ	LOU RAWLS	LOVE IS A HURTIN' THING	MEMORY LANE	30.00
66	15466	NANCY WILSON	UPTIGHT (EVERYTHING'S ALRIGHT)	YOU'VE GOT YOUR TROUBLES	20.00
66	15466 DJ	NANCY WILSON	UPTIGHT (EVERYTHING'S ALRIGHT)	YOU'VE GOT YOUR TROUBLES	30.00
66	15468	OUTSIDERS	LOST IN MY WORLD	RESPECTABLE	20.00
66	15468 DJ	OUTSIDERS	LOST IN MY WORLD	RESPECTABLE	28.00
66	15469	THRILLS	WHAT CAN GO WRONG	NO ONE	100.00
66	15469 DJ	THRILLS	WHAT CAN GO WRONG	NO ONE	150.00
66	15471	BILLY PRESTON	LET THE MUSIC PLAY	SUNNY	18.00
66	15471 DJ	BILLY PRESTON	LET THE MUSIC PLAY	SUNNY	28.00
66	15480	OUTSIDERS	HELP ME GIRL	YOU GOTTA LOOK	15.00
66	15480 DJ	OUTSIDERS	HELP ME GIRL	YOU GOTTA LOOK	22.00
66	15481	VERDELLE SMITH	IF YOU CAN'T SAY ANYTHING NICE	I DON'T NEED ANYTHING	15.00
66	15481 DJ	VERDELLE SMITH	IF YOU CAN'T SAY ANYTHING NICE	I DON'T NEED ANYTHING	25.00
66	15483	LIZA MINNELLI	THE MIDDLE OF THE STREET	I (WHO HAVE NOTHING)	15.00
66	15483 DJ	LIZA MINNELLI	THE MIDDLE OF THE STREET	I (WHO HAVE NOTHING)	25.00
66	15484	PATRICE HOLLOWAY	LOVE AND DESIRE	ECSTASY	150.00
66	15484 DJ	PATRICE HOLLOWAY	LOVE AND DESIRE	ECSTASY	**266.00**
66	15485	NANCY WILSON	THAT SPECIAL WAY	GO AWAY	12.00
66	15485 DJ	NANCY WILSON	THAT SPECIAL WAY	GO AWAY	20.00
67	15487	BUNNY SHIVEL	YOU'LL NEVER FIND A LOVE LIKE	THE SLIDE	25.00
67	15487 DJ	BUNNY SHIVEL	YOU'LL NEVER FIND A LOVE LIKE	THE SLIDE	40.00
67	15488	LOU RAWLS	YOU CAN BRING ME ALL YOUR	A WOMAN WHO'S A WOMAN	20.00
67	15488 DJ	LOU RAWLS	YOU CAN BRING ME ALL YOUR	A WOMAN WHO'S WOMAN	40.00
67	15489	CANNONBALL ADDERLEY	MERCY MERCY MERCY	GAMES	6.00
67	15489 DJ	CANNONBALL ADDERLEY	MERCY MERCY MERCY	GAMES	10.00
67	15495	OUTSIDERS	I'LL GIVE YOU TIME	I'M NOT TRYIN' TO HURT YOU	20.00
67	15495 DJ	OUTSIDERS	I'LL GIVE YOU TIME	I'M NOT TRYIN' TO HURT YOU	28.00
67	15499	LOU RAWLS	DEAD END STREET	YES IT HURTS DOESN'T IT	15.00
67	15499 DJ	LOU RAWLS	DEAD END STREET	YES IT HURTS DOESN'T IT	25.00
67	15500	CANNONBALL ADDERLEY	WHY (AM I TREATED SO BAD)	I'M ON MY WAY	10.00
67	15500 DJ	CANNONBALL ADDERLEY	WHY (AM I TREATED SO BAD)	I'M ON MY WAY	15.00

 # 15500 was the last soul release where the promotional copies were white with a large red "A". #15507 was the first soul promotional 45 on this label to be green with a large white "A"

67	15507	LOU RAWLS	WHEN LOVE GOES WRONG	SHOW BUSINESS	20.00
67	15507 DJ	LOU RAWLS	WHEN LOVE GOES WRONG	SHOW BUSINESS	40.00
67	15508	NANCY WILSON	DON'T LOOK OVER YOUR SHOULDER	MERCY, MERCY, MERCY	10.00
67	15508 DJ	NANCY WILSON	DON'T LOOK OVER YOUR SHOULDER	MERCY, MERCY, MERCY	20.00
67	15509	SCOTT MacKENZIE	LOOK IN YOUR EYES	ALL I WANT IS YOU	20.00
67	15509 DJ	SCOTT MacKENZIE	LOOK IN YOUR EYES	ALL I WANT IS YOU	30.00
67	15514	VERDELLE SMITH	BABY BABY	THERE'S SO MUCH LOVE AROUND ME	20.00
67	15514 DJ	VERDELLE SMITH	BABY BABY	THERE'S SO MUCH LOVE AROUND ME	28.00
67	15515	LOU RAWLS	(HOW DO YOU SAY)I DON'T LOVE YOU	HARD TO GET THING CALLED LOVE	10.00
67	15515 DJ	LOU RAWLS	(HOW DO YOU SAY)I DON'T LOVE YOU	HARD TO GET THING CALLED LOVE	15.00
67	15516	AL MARTINO	MORE THAN THE EYE CAN SEE	RED IS RED	25.00
67	15516 DJ	AL MARTINO	MORE THAN THE EYE CAN SEE	RED IS RED	30.00
67	15515	LOU RAWLS	(HOW DO YOU SAY) I DON'T LOVE YOU	HARD TO GET THING CALLED LOVE	12.00
67	15515 DJ	LOU RAWLS	(HOW DO YOU SAY) I DON'T LOVE YOU	HARD TO GET THING CALLED LOVE	20.00
67	15522	LOU RAWLS	LITTLE DRUMMER BOY	CHILD WITH A TOY	4.00
67	15522 DJ	LOU RAWLS	LITTLE DRUMMER BOY	CHILD WITH A TOY	5.00
68	15529 silver logo	HUMAN BEINZ	NOBODY BUT YOU	SUENO	40.00
68	15529 DJ green	HUMAN BEINZ	NOBODY BUT YOU	SUENO	85.00
68	15529 blk/white logo	HUMAN BEINZ	NOBODY BUT ME	SUENO	6.00
68	15529 DJ black	HUMAN BEINZ	NOBODY BUT ME	SUENO	10.00

EMI reissue # 15529 using the same release number first press was the 1968 SILVER logo design. Second press in 1976 the CAPITOL was in black on top of a white background surrounded   by a silver box. Release date on this label is 1968 also.

68	15530	MAGNIFICENT MEN	SWEET SOUL MEDLEY part 1	SWEET SOUL MUSIC part 2	8.00
68	15530 DJ	MAGNIFICENT MEN	SWEET SOUL MEDLEY part 1	SWEET SOUL MUSIC part 2	15.00
68	15533	LOU RAWLS	EVIL WOMAN	MY ANCESTORS	6.00
68	15533 DJ	LOU RAWLS	EVIL WOMAN	MY ANCESTORS	8.00
68	15534	TONY BRUNO	SMALL TOWN, BRING DOWN	WHAT'S YESTERDAY	50.00
68	15534 DJ	TONY BRUNO	SMALL TOWN, BRING DOWN	WHAT'S YESTERDAY	75.00
68	15536	NANCY WILSON	YOU DON'T KNOW ME	ODE TO BILLY JOE	5.00
68	15536 DJ	NANCY WILSON	YOU DON'T KNOW ME	ODE TO BILLY JOE	8.00
68	15542	HUMAN BEINZ	TURN ON YOUR LOVELIGHT	IT'S FUN TO BE CLEAN	15.00
68	15542 DJ	HUMAN BEINZ	TURN ON YOUR LOVELIGHT	IT'S FUN TO BE CLEAN	20.00
68	15547 silver logo	NANCY WILSON	THE END OF OUR LOVE	FACE IT, GIRL IT'S OVER	75.00
68	15547 DJ green	NANCY WILSON	THE END OF OUR LOVE	FACE IT, GIRL IT'S OVER	100.00
76	15547 blk/white logo	NANCY WILSON	THE END OF OUR LOVE	FACE IT, GIRL IT'S OVER	10.00
76	15547 DJ black	NANCY WILSON	THE END OF OUR LOVE	FACE IT, GIRL, IT'S OVER	15.00

EMI reissue # 15547 using the same release number first press was the 1968 SILVER logo design. Second press in 1976 the CAPITOL was in black on top of a white background surrounded by a silver box. Release date on this label is 1968 also.

68	15548	LOU RAWLS	SOUL SERENADE	YOU'RE GOOD FOR ME	10.00
68	15548 DJ	LOU RAWLS	SOUL SERENADE	YOU'RE GOOD FOR ME	15.00
68	15557	PATTI DREW	WORKNG ON A GROOVY THING	WITHOUT A DOUBT	15.00

68	15557 DJ	PATTI DREW	WORKNG ON A GROOVY THING	WITHOUT A DOUBT	25.00
68	15560	LOU RAWLS	DOWN HERE ON THE GROUND	I'M SATISFIED	5.00
68	15560 DJ	LOU RAWLS	DOWN HERE ON THE GROUND	I'M SATISFIED	6.00
68	15569	DR. FEELGOOD and the INTERNS	SUGAR BEE	YOU'RE SO USED TO IT	15.00
68	15569 DJ	DR. FEELGOOD and the INTERNS	SUGAR BEE	YOU'RE SO USED TO IT	22.00
68	15570	MAGNIFICENT MEN	SAVE THE COUNTRY	SO MUCH LOVE WAITING	6.00
68	15570 DJ	MAGNIFICENT MEN	SAVE THE COUNTRY	SO MUCH LOVE WAITING	8.00
68	15575	PATTI DREW	JUST CAN'T FORGET ABOUT YOU	HARD TO HANDLE	20.00
68	15575 DJ	PATTI DREW	JUST CAN'T FORGET ABOUT YOU	HARD TO HANDLE	28.00
68	15583	LOU RAWLS	IT'S YOU	SWEET CHARITY	12.00
68	15583 DJ	LOU RAWLS	IT'S YOU	SWEET CHARITY	20.00
68	15586	BETTYE SWANN	(MY HEART IS) CLOSED FOR THE SEASON	DON'T TOUCH ME	20.00
68	15586 DJ	BETTYE SWANN	(MY HEART IS) CLOSED FOR THE SEASON	DON'T TOUCH ME	30.00
68	15600	JOE ODOM	IT'S IN YOUR POWER	BIG LOVE	15.00
68	15600 DJ	JOE ODOM	IT'S IN YOUR POWER	BIG LOVE	25.00
68	15601	CANDI STATON	I'D RATHER BE AN OLD MAN'S SWEETHEART	FOR YOU	8.00
68	15601 DJ	CANDI STATON	I'D RATHER BE AN OLD MAN'S SWEETHEART	FOR YOU	10.00
68	15605	GEORGE JACKSON	FIND 'EM, FOOL 'EM AND FORGET	MY DESIRES ARE GETTING THE BES	15.00
68	15605 DJ	GEORGE JACKSON	FIND 'EM, FOOL 'EM AND FORGET	MY DESIRES ARE GETTING THE BES	22.00
69	15608	JOE SOUTH	HEARTS DESIRE	DON'T IT MAKE YOU WANT TO	12.00
69	15608 DJ	JOE SOUTH	HEARTS DESIRE	DON'T IT MAKE YOU WANT TO	20.00
69	15611	LOU RAWLS	YOUR GOOD THING (IS ABOUT TO END)	SEASON OF THE WITCH	6.00
69	15611 DJ	LOU RAWLS	YOUR GOOD THING (IS ABOUT TO END)	SEASON OF THE WITCH	8.00
69	15620	CANDI STATON	HEART ON A STRING	I'M JUST A PRISONER	8.00
69	15620 DJ	CANDI STATON	HEART ON A STRING	I'M JUST A PRISONER	10.00
69	15624	NANCY WILSON	CAN'T TAKE MY EYES OFF YOU	DO YOU KNOW WHY	4.00
69	15624 DJ	NANCY WILSON	CAN'T TAKE MY EYES OFF YOU	DO YOU KNOW WHY	5.00
70	15630	LOU RAWLS	YOU'VE MADE ME SO VERY HAPPY	LET'S BURN DOWN THE CORNFIELD	5.00
70	15630 DJ	LOU RAWLS	YOU'VE MADE ME SO VERY HAPPY	LET'S BURN DOWN THE CORNFIELD	6.00
70	15634	LEON HAYWOOD	I WANNA THANK YOU	I WAS SENT TO LOVE YOU	15.00
70	15634 DJ	LEON HAYWOOD	I WANNA THANK YOU	I WAS SENT TO LOVE YOU	20.00
70	15646	CANDI STATON	SWEET FEELING	EVIDENCE	6.00
70	15646 DJ	CANDI STATON	SWEET FEELING	EVIDENCE	8.00
70	15650	TAMS	TOO MUCH FOOLIN' AROUND	HOW LONG LOVE	10.00
70	15650 DJ	TAMS	TOO MUCH FOOLIN' AROUND	HOW LONG LOVE	15.00
70	15658	CANDI STATON	STAND BY YOUR MAN	HOW CAN I PUT OUT THE FLAME	6.00
70	15658 DJ	CANDI STATON	STAND BY YOUR MAN	HOW CAN I PUT OUT THE FLAME	8.00
72	15713	BOBBY SHEEN	DR. LOVE	SWEET SWEET LOVE	20.00
72	15713 DJ	BOBBY SHEEN	DR. LOVE	SWEET SWEET LOVE	30.00
72	15726	PERSIANS	BABY COME BACK HOME	I WANT TO GO HOME	10.00
72	15726 DJ	PERSIANS	BABY COME BACK HOME	I WANT TO GO HOME	15.00
73	15762	JIMMY HELMS	MY LITTLE DEVIL	MAGNIFICENT SANCTUARY BAND	15.00
73	15762 DJ	JIMMY HELMS	MY LITTLE DEVIL	MAGNIFICENT SANCTUARY BAND	20.00
74	15792	GENE REDDING	ONCE A FOOL	BLOOD BROTHERS	6.00
74	15792 DJ	GENE REDDING	ONCE A FOOL	BLOOD BROTHERS	8.00
74	15795	TAVARES	SHE'S GONE	TO LOVE YOU	4.00
74	15795 DJ	TAVARES	SHE'S GONE	TO LOVE YOU	5.00
74	15796	NANCY WILSON	OCEAN OF LOVE	STREETRUNNER	20.00
74	15796 DJ	NANCY WILSON	OCEAN OF LOVE	STREETRUNNER	25.00
74	15797	PAT WILLIAMS ORCHESTRA	THEM FROM "POLICE STORY"	THEME FROM "THE MAGICIAN"	15.00
74	15797 DJ	PAT WILLIAMS ORCHESTRA	THEM FROM "POLICE STORY"	THEME FROM "THE MAGICIAN"	20.00
75	15807	BARBARA ACKLIN	SPECIAL LOVING	YOU GIVE HIM EVERYTHING BUT I GIVE HIM	6.00
75	15807 DJ	BARBARA ACKLIN	SPECIAL LOVING	YOU GIVE HIM EVERYTHING BUT I GIVE HIM	8.00
75	15808	MARGO THUNDER	EXPRESSWAY TO YOUR HEART	HUSH YOUR MOUTH	15.00
75	15808 DJ	MARGO THUNDER	EXPRESSWAY TO YOUR HEART	HUSH UP YOUR MOUTH	20.00
75	15809	TAVARES	MY SHIP	REMEMBER WHAT I TOLD YOU TO FO	6.00
75	15809 DJ	TAVARES	MY SHIP	REMEMBER WHAT I TOLD YOU TO FO	8.00
75	15810	NANCY WILSON	THERE'LL ALWAYS BE FOREVER	YOU'RE AS RIGHT AS RAIN	6.00
75	15810 DJ	NANCY WILSON	THERE'LL ALWAYS BE FOREVER	YOU'RE AS RIGHT AS RAIN	10.00
75	15825	EARL WRIGHT	THUMB A RIDE	LIKE A ROLLING STONE	10.00
75	15825 DJ	EARL WRIGHT	THUMB A RIDE	LIKE A ROLLING STONE	15.00
75	15826	REFLECTIONS	THREE STEPS FROM TRUE LOVE	HOW COULD WE LET THE LOVE GET	6.00
75	15826 DJ	REFLECTIONS	THREE STEPS FROM TRUE LOVE	HOW COULD WE LET THE LOVE GET	8.00
75	15827	JODI MATHIS	DON'T YOU CARE ANYMORE	MAMA	8.00
75	15827 DJ	JODI MATHIS	DON'T YOU CARE ANYMORE	MAMA	20.00
75	15832	TAVARES	IT ONLY TAKES A MINUTE	I HOPE SHE CHOOSES ME	5.00
75	15832 DJ	TAVARES	IT ONLY TAKES A MINUTE	I HOPE SHE CHOOSES ME	8.00
75	15834	NATALIE COLE	THIS WILL BE	JOEY	4.00
75	15834 DJ	NATALIE COLE	THIS WILL BE	JOEY	5.00
75	15842	REFLECTIONS	ONE INTO ONE	LOVE DELIVERY	5.00
75	15842 DJ	REFLECTIONS	ONE INTO ONE	LOVE DELIVERY	6.00
75	15844	PAT WILLIAMS ORCHESTRA	THEME FROM POLICE STORY	THE MAGICIAN	10.00
75	15844 DJ	PAT WILLIAMS ORCHESTRA	THEME FROM POLICE STORY	THE MAGICIAN	15.00
75	15848	TAVARES	FREE RIDE	IN THE EYES OF LOVE	4.00
75	15848 DJ	TAVARES	FREE RIDE	IN THE EYES OF LOVE	5.00
76	15851	H.B. BARNUM	HEARTBREAKER	SEARCHIN' FOR MY SOUL	10.00
76	15851 DJ	H.B. BARNUM	HEARTBREAKER	SEARCHIN' FOR MY SOUL	15.00
76	15852	WORLD COLUMN	SO IS THE SUN	IT'S NOT ALRIGHT	10.00
76	15852 DJ	WORLD COLUMN	SO IS THE SUN	IT'S NOT RIGHT	10.00

CAMEO PARKWAY

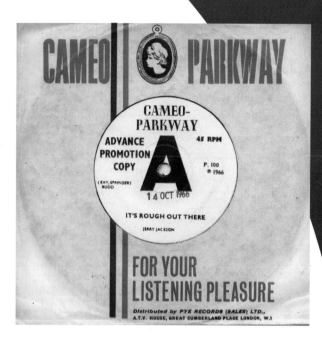

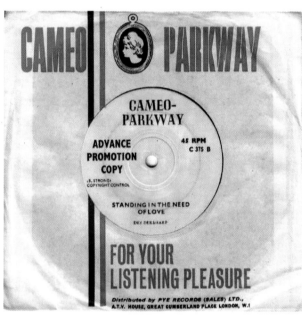

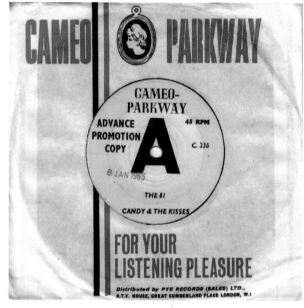

Action – Pama - Soul City – Domain - Plexium

Action – Deep Soul - Soul City – Parlophone - MGM - Evolution

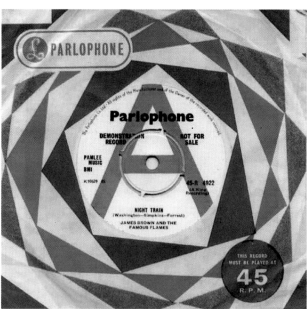

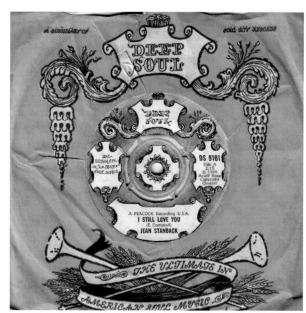

Extended-*Plays*

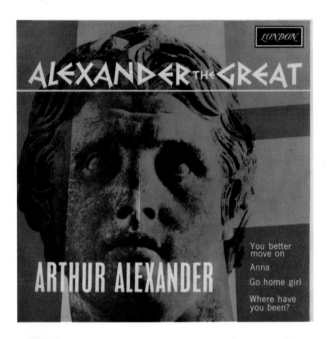

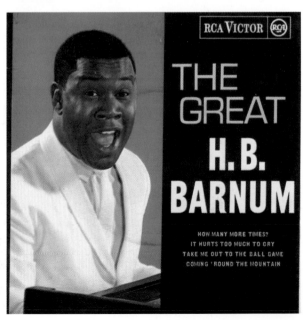

CAPITOL

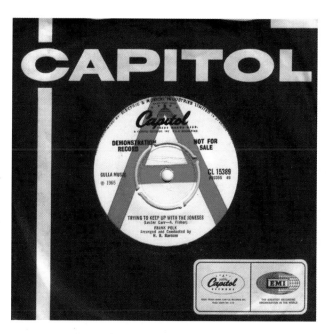

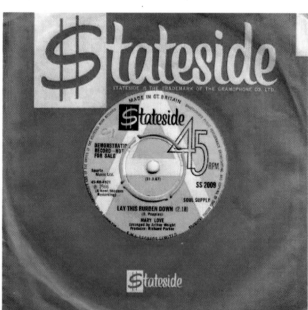 

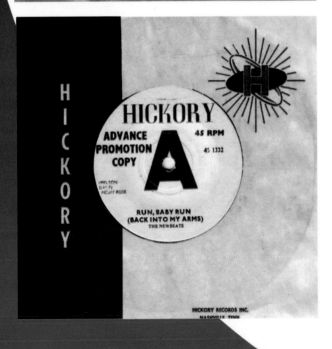

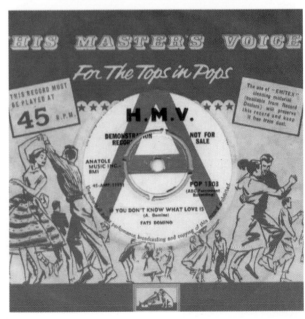

76	15852 with sticker	WORLD COLUMN	SO IS THE SUN	IT'S NOT RIGHT	25.00

Complete with special commemorative Cleethorpes Pier anniversary sticker on label. Perhaps the very first on the door giveaway Northern Soul 45. Free @ the 1976 Anniversary .

76	15864	BARRETT STRONG	MAN UP IN THE SKY	GONNA MAKE IT RIGHT	50.00
76	15864 DJ	BARRETT STRONG	MAN UP IN THE SKY	GONNA MAKE IT RIGHT	60.00
76	15867	TAVARES	THE LOVE I NEVER HAD	IN THE CITY	4.00
76	15867 DJ	TAVARES	THE LOVE I NEVER HAD	IN THE CITY	5.00
76	15869	BABE RUTH	ELUSIVE	SAY NO MORE	6.00
76	15869 DJ	BABE RUTH	ELUSIVE	SAY NO MORE	10.00
76	15873	ERNIE ANDREWS	FINE YOUNG GIRL	THEN I'LL KNOW	6.00
76	15873 DJ	ERNIE ANDREWS	FINE YOUNG GIRL	THEN I'LL KNOW	8.00
76	15874	REGGIE GARNER	HOT LINE	BLESSED BE THE NAME OF MY BABY	6.00
76	15874 DJ	REGGIE GARNER	HOT LINE	BLESSED BE THE NAME (OF MY BAB	15.00
76	15876	TAVARES	HEAVEN MUST BE MISSING AN ANGEL	same: part 2	4.00
76	15876 DJ	TAVARES	HEAVEN MUST BE MISSING AN ANGEL	same: part 2	8.00
76	15886	TAVARES	DON'T TAKE AWAY THE MUSIC	same: part 2	5.00
76	15886 DJ	TAVARES	DON'T TAKE AWAY THE MUSIC	same: part 2	8.00
76	15892	SYLVERS	HOT LINE	THAT'S WHAT LOVE IS MADE OF	3.00
76	15892 DJ	SYLVERS	HOT LINE	THAT'S WHAT LOVE IS MADE OF	4.00
76	15905 EP	TAVARES	THE MIGHTY POWER OF LOVE + MY SHIP	STRANGERS IN DARK CORNERS + 1	6.00
76	15905 EP DJ	TAVARES	THE MIGHTY POWER OF LOVE + MY SHIP	STRANGERS IN DARK CORNERS + 1	8.00
77	15911	AL DE LORY & MANDANGO	RIGHT ON	JESUS CHRISTO	6.00
77	15911 DJ	AL DE LORY & MANDANGO	RIGHT ON	JESUS CHRISTO	10.00
77	15914	TAVARES	WHODUNIT	FOOL OF THE YEAR	3.00
77	15914 DJ	TAVARES	WHODUNIT	FOOL OF THE YEAR	4.00
77	15915	DAVID & THE GIANTS	TEN MILES HIGH	SUPERLOVE	8.00
77	15915 DJ	DAVID & THE GIANTS	TEN MILES HIGH	SUPERLOVE	15.00
77	15922	MAZE	COLOR BLIND	WHILE I'M ALONE	15.00
77	15922 DJ	MAZE	COLOR BLIND	WHILE I'M ALONE	20.00
77	15930	TAVARES	ONE STEP AWAY	OUT OF THE PICTURE	4.00
77	15930 DJ	TAVARES	ONE STEP AWAY	OUT OF THE PICTURE	5.00
77	15937	EDDIE HENDERSON	THE FUNK SURGEON	SAY YOU WILL	4.00
77	15937 DJ	EDDIE HENDERSON	THE FUNK SURGEON	SAY YOU WILL	5.00
77	15945	TAVARES with FREDA PAYNE	I WANNA SEE YOU AGAIN	KEEP IN TOUCH	4.00
77	15945 DJ	TAVARES with FREDA PAYNE	I WANNA SEE YOU AGAIN	KEEP IN TOUCH	5.00
78	15968	TAVARES	BEIN' WITH YOU	THE GHOST OF LOVE	8.00
78	15968 PS green vinyl	TAVARES	BEIN' WITH YOU	THE GHOST OF LOVE	10.00
78	15968 DJ	TAVARES	BEIN' WITH YOU	THE GHOST OF LOVE	10.00
78	15977	TAVARES	MORE THAN A WOMAN	WE'RE BOTH READY FOR LOVE	3.00
78	15977 DJ	TAVARES	MORE THAN A WOMAN	WE'RE BOTH READY FOR LOVE	4.00
78	15978	MAZE	WORKIN' TOGETHER	TRAVELIN' MAN	4.00
78	15978 DJ	MAZE	WORKIN' TOGETHER	TRAVELIN' MAN	5.00
78	15979	SUN	SUN IS HERE	DANCE (DO WHAT YOU WANNA)	5.00
78	15979 DJ	SUN	SUN IS HERE	DANCE (DO WHAT YOU WANNA)	5.00
78	15987	NATALIE COLE	ANNIE MAE	OUR LOVE	8.00
78	15987 DJ	NATALIE COLE	ANNIE MAE	OUR LOVE	10.00
78	15988	A TASTE OF HONEY	BOOGIE OOGIE OOGIE	WORLD SPIN	3.00
78	15988 DJ	A TASTE OF HONEY	BOOGIE OOGIE OOGIE	WORLD SPIN	4.00
78	15996	TAVARES	SLOW TRAIN TO PARADISE	TIMBER	3.00
78	15996 DJ	TAVARES	SLOW TRAIN TO PARADISE	TIMBER	4.00
78	16012	TEDDY VANN'S ORCHESTRA	THEME FROM COLOUREDMAN	INTRODUCTION TO THE ADVENTURES	6.00
78	16012 DJ	TEDDY VANN'S ORCHESTRA	THEME FROM COLOREDMAN	AVENTURES OF:	10.00
78	16015	EDDIE HENDERSON	PRANCE ON	SAY YOU WILL	3.00
78	16015 DJ	EDDIE HENDERSON	PRANCE ON	SAY YOU WILL	4.00
78	16017	MAZE	GOLDEN TIME OF DAY	TRAVELIN' MAN	4.00
78	16017 DJ	MAZE	GOLDEN TIME OF DAY	TRAVELIN' MAN	5.00
78	16019	SUN	WANNA MAKE LOVE	BOGGIE BOPPER	4.00
78	16019 DJ	SUN	WANNA MAKE LOVE	BOGGIE BOPPER	5.00
78	16032	TAVARES	NEVER HAD A LOVE LIKE THIS BEFORE	POSITIVE FORCES	5.00
78	16032 DJ	TAVARES	NEVER HAD A LOVE LIKE THIS BEFORE	POSITIVE FORCES	6.00
79	16067	BOBBY PARIS c/w H.B. BARNUM	I WALKED AWAY	HEARTBREAKER	15.00
79	16067 DJ	BOBBY PARIS c/w H.B. BARNUM	I WALKED AWAY	HEARTBREAKER	20.00
79	16081	TAVARES	LET ME HEAL THE BRUISES	STRAIGHT FROM THE HEART	4.00
79	16081 DJ	TAVARES	LET ME HEAL THE BRUISES	STRAIGHT FROM THE HEART	6.00
80	16133	MYSTIC MERLIN	JUST CAN'T GIVE YOU UP	BURNED TO LEARN	8.00
80	16133 DJ	MYSTIC MERLIN	JUST CAN'T GIVE YOU UP	BURNED TO LEARN	10.00
81	16190	MYSTIC MERLIN	60 THRILLS A MINUTE	GOT TO MAKE IT BETTER	4.00
81	16190 DJ	MYSTIC MERLIN	60 THRILLS A MINUTE	GOT TO MAKE IT BETTER	5.00
81	16194	A TASTE OF HONEY	SUKIYKKI	DON'T YOU LEAD ME ON	3.00
81	16194 DJ	A TASTE OF HONEY	SUKIYKKI	DON'T YOU LEAD ME ON	4.00
62	20604 EP PS	NANCY WILSON	SECOND TIME AROUND	1962 4 track EP with cover	10.00
63	20646 EP PS	LOU RAWLS	LOST AND LOOKIN'	1963 4 track EP with cover	20.00
64	2082 EP PS	NANCY WILSON	TODAY, TOMORROW, FOREVER	1964 4 track EP with cover	15.00

CAPRICORN

72	17505	OSCAR TONEY JR.	THANK YOU, HONEY CHILE	I DO WHAT YOU WISH	8.00
72	17506	ARTHUR CONLEY	RITA	MORE SWEET SOUL MUSIC	6.00
74	2089009	PERCY SLEDGE	I'LL BE YOUR EVERYTHING	WALKIN' IN THE SUN	5.00
74	2089017	DOBIE GRAY	WHAT A LADY	IF LOVE MUST GO	3.00
74	2089024	ELVIN BISHOP	I FOOLED AROUND AND FELL IN LOVE	SLICK TICKY BOOM	3.00
74	2089033	DEXTER REDDING	LOVE IS BIOGGER THAN A BASEBALL	GOD BLESS	3.00

CARIBOU

76	4910	O.C. SMITH	JUST COULDN'T HELP MYSELF	TOGETHER	10.00
76	4910 DJ	O.C. SMITH	JUST COULDN'T HELP MYSELF	TOGETHER	15.00
77	5327	O.C. SMITH	SIMPLE LIFE	I FOUND THE SECRET	5.00
77	5327 DJ	O.C. SMITH	SIMPLE LIFE	I FOUND THE SECRET	6.00

CARNIVAL

Carnival Records, 24 Branford Place, Newark, New Jersey, USA
In 1966 Polydor tried to launch the USA iconic soul label Carnival in the UK, but after only two UK releases, both from their top recording male group the Manhattans, Polydor ceased to market the label. The UK public was not quite ready for male group harmony soul, and neither 45 took off and went into obscurity almost as soon as they were issued. It's a pity Polydor didn't persevere with the Carnival catalogue; Carnival USA is now considered at the top of collectable USA soul labels. Imagine Harry Caldwell, Lee Williams, the Topics, Lovettes, the Pets, Phil Terrell on UK releases.
The Wes Minster Five release was a UK only 1965 recording and had no association with the Newark based soul label.

66	100	MANHATTANS	BABY I NEED YOU	TEACH ME (THE PHILLY DOG)	20.00
66	101	MANHATTANS	CAN I	THAT NEW GIRL	15.00
65	7019	WES MINSTER FIVE	MICKEY'S MONKEY	STICKS AND STONES	15.00

CASABLANCA

77	103	PARLIAMENT	GIVE UP THE FUNK	DR. FUNKENSTEIN + P.FUNK	5.00
77	103 PS	PARLIAMENT	GIVE UP THE FUNK	DR. FUNKENSTEIN + P.FUNK	8.00
77	103 DJ	PARLIAMENT	GIVE UP THE FUNK	DR. FUNKENSTEIN + P.FUNK	6.00
77	106	CAMEO	POST MORTEM	RIGOR MORTIS	4.00
77	106 DJ	CAMEO	POST MORTEM	RIGOR MORTIS	5.00
77	112	CAMEO	FUNK FUNK	GOOD TIMES	4.00
77	112 DJ	CAMEO	FUNK FUNK	GOOD TIMES	5.00
78	115	PARLIAMENT	BOP GUN	I'VE BEEN WATCHING YOU	5.00
78	115 DJ	PARLIAMENT	BOP GUN	I'VE BEEN WATCHING YOU	6.00
78	121	CAMEO	IT'S SERIOUS	INFLATION	5.00
78	121 DJ	CAMEO	IT'S SERIOUS	INFLATION	6.00
78	123	PARLIAMENT	FLASH LIGHT	SWING DOWN, SWEET CHARIOT	5.00
78	123 DJ	PARLIAMENT	FLASH LIGHT	SWING DOWN, SWEET CHARIOT	6.00
78	136	PARLIAMENT	AQUA BOOGIE	(YOU'RE A FISH AND I'M A)WATER	5.00
78	136 DJ	PARLIAMENT	AQUA BOOGIE	(YOU'RE A FISH AND I'M A)WATER	6.00
79	143	CAMEO	INSANE	I WANT YOU	5.00
79	143 DJ	CAMEO	INSANE	I WANT YOU	6.00
79	154	PARLIAMENT	DEEP	FLASHLIGHT	5.00
79	154 DJ	PARLIAMENT	DEEP	FLASHLIGHT	6.00
79	166	CAMEO	FIND MY WAY	IT'S SERIOUS	10.00
79	166 DJ	CAMEO	FIND MY WAY	IT'S SERIOUS	15.00
80	188	PARLIAMENT	THEME FROM THE BLACK HOLE	BIG BANG THEORY	5.00
80	188 DJ	PARLIAMENT	THEME FROM THE BLACK HOLE	BIG BANG THEORY	6.00
80	204	CAMEO	WE'RE GOING OUT TONIGHT	SPARKLE	4.00
80	204 DJ	CAMEO	WE'RE GOING OUT TONIGHT	SPARKLE	5.00
81	223	PARLIAMENT	AGONY OF DeFEET	THE FREEZE	5.00
81	223 DJ	PARLIAMENT	AGONY OF DeFEET	THE FREEZE	6.00
75	505	PARLIAMENT	UP FOR THE DOWN STROKE	PRESENCE OF A BRAIN	5.00
75	505 DJ	PARLIAMENT	UP FOR THE DOWN STROKE	PRESENCE OF A BRAIN	6.00
75	509 DJ	GWEN OWENS	YOU BETTER WATCH OUT	EVERYBODY NEEDS LOVE	10.00
75	511	GREG PERRY	THE BOOGIE MAN	WILL SHE MEET THE TRAIN IN THE	5.00
75	511 DJ	GREG PERRY	THE BOOGIE MAN	WILL SHE MEET THE TRAIN IN THE	6.00
75	512	GLORIA SCOTT	JUST AS LONG AS WE'RE TOGETHER	THERE WILL NEVER BE ANOTHER	15.00
75	512 DJ	GLORIA SCOTT	JUST AS LONG AS WE'RE TOGETHER	THERE WILL NEVER BE ANOTHER	20.00
75	513	BUDDY MILES	ROCKIN & ROLLIN ON THE STREETS OF HOLLYWOOD	LIVIN IN THE RIGHT SPACE	3.00
75	513 DJ	BUDDY MILES	ROCKIN & ROLLIN ON THE STREETS OF HOLLYWOOD	LIVIN IN THE RIGHT SPACE	4.00
75	515	LARRY SANTOS	CAN'T GET YOU OFF MY MIND	WE CAN'T HIDE IT NO MORE	10.00
75	515 DJ	LARRY SANTOS	CAN'T GET YOU OFF MY MIND	WE CAN'T HIDE IT ANYMORE	15.00
76	518	PARLIAMENT	TEAR THE ROOF OFF THE SUCKER	P.FUNK	5.00
76	518 DJ	PARLIAMENT	TEAR THE ROOF OFF THE SUCKER	P.FUNK	6.00
76	520	JAMES & BOBBY PURIFY	DO YOUR THING	WHY LOVE	5.00
76	520 DJ	JAMES & BOBBY PURIFY	DO YOUR THING	WHY LOVE	6.00
76	521	GROUP WITH NO NAME	BABY LOVE (HOW COULD YOU LEAVE	ALL I NEED	5.00
76	521 DJ	GROUP WITH NO NAME	BABY LOVE (HOW COULD YOU LEAVE	ALL I NEED	6.00
81	1004	CAMEO	DON'T BE SO COOL	SOUND TABLE	4.00
81	1005	FOUR TOPS	WHEN WHE WAS MY GIRL	SOMETHING TO REMEMBER	5.00
81	1006	FOUR TOPS	DON'T WALK AWAY	I'LL NEVER EVER LEAVE AGAIN	4.00
80	2222	PARLIAMENT	PARTY PEOPLE	PARTY PEOPLE (REPRISE)	5.00

CASINO CLASSICS

You will see as you read through this book, many labels that dedicated themselves to releasing Northern Soul & rare soul releases. It's interesting to note that those labels that cheapened themselves by doing cover versions and releasing pop records generally are not so collectable as the ones who stuck to real soul 45's. If today you compare the Casino Classics catalogue launched in 1978, compared to the Grapevine label launched around the same period. The value differences of their product is quite staggering.
Distributed and promoted, to cash in on the growing music cult of Northern Soul, and the influence the country's most popular all-niter was having on the record buying public.
Non of the releases are particularly collectable although some came in neat art sleeves that can now be considered as rare memorabilia, as most sleeves were thought of as expendable. Mint sleeves for releases # 3 & # 6 are very difficult to find. Casino Classic never really had a catalogue depth of soul releases to pull from and consequently relied on such non-soul artists. Their first release indicated that future releases could be weak, as they released the infamous Lenny Gamble, aka Tony Blackburn's LP version of Doris Troy's Classic –"I'll Do Anything" - . Then followed with artists's like Ron Grainer (of Dr. Who theme tune fame), an awful remake of The Mylestones – "The Joker" – by the crassly named All Night Band, which turned Casino Classics into a bit of a Joker itself. Releases from Diana Foster & Nicky Wilson did nothing to rescue its decline in credibility. After seventeen releases and the decline of the Northern Soul boom in late 1980 the label ceased. An interesting label for the fact of its Wigan Casino association; but not for the soul quality of the releases.

Year	Cat#	Artist	A-side	B-side	Price
78	1	FLIRTATIONS c/w LENNY GAMBLE	LITTLE DARLING (I NEED YOU)	I'LL DO ANYTHING (she wants me to do)	6.00
78	1 DJ	FLIRTATIONS c/w LENNY GAMBLE	LITTLE DARLING (I NEED YOU)	I'LL DO ANYTHING (she wants me to do)	8.00
78	2	LORRAINE SILVER	LOST SUMMER LOVE	I KNOW THAT YOU'LL BE THERE	8.00
78	2 DJ	LORRAINE SILVER	LOST SUMMER LOVE	I KNOW THAT YOU'LL BE THERE	10.00
78	3 without sleeve	GERRI GRANGER	I GO TO PIECES (EVERYTIME..)	SHAKE A TAIL FEATHER + PANIC	8.00
78	3 DJ	GERRI GRANGER	I GO TO PIECES (EVERYTIME..)	SHAKE A TAIL FEATHER + PANIC	15.00
78	3 special sleeve	GERRI GRANGER	I GO TO PIECES (EVERYTIME..)	SHAKE A TAIL FEATHER + PANIC	15.00

This release had a special "Wigan Casino" design blue and white sleeve listing the three artists 1. Gerri Granger 2. James and Bobby Purify 3. Reparata & the Delrons

Year	Cat#	Artist	A-side	B-side	Price
78	4	JACKIE TRENTc/w FAMILY AFFAIR	YOU BABY + SEND HER AWAY	LOVE HUSTLE	5.00
78	4 DJ	JACKIE TRENTc/w FAMILY AFFAIR	YOU BABY + SEND HER AWAY	LOVE HUSTLE	5.00
78	5	RON GRAINER ORCHESTRA	A TOUCH OF VELVET - A STING OF BRASS	JOE 90	6.00
78	5 blue vinyl	RON GRAINER ORCHESTRA	A TOUCH OF VELVET - A STING OF BRASS	JOE 90	8.00
78	5 DJ	RON GRAINER ORCHESTRA	A TOUCH OF VELVET - A STING OF BRASS	JOE 90	8.00
79	6	ALLNIGHT BAND	THE JOKER (THE WIGAN JOKER)	SIX BY SIX	5.00
79	6 special sleeve	ALLNIGHT BAND	THE JOKER (THE WIGAN JOKER)	SIX BY SIX	4.00
79	7	DIANA FOSTER	I'M GONNA SHARE IT WITH YOU	TIME OUT	5.00
79	7 DJ	DIANA FOSTER	I'M GONNA SHARE IT WITH YOU	TIME OUT	6.00
79	7 white vinyl	DIANA FOSTER	I'M GONNA SHARE IT WITH YOU	TIME OUT	6.00
79	8	NICKY WILSON	STONE SOUL LOVING	CRY LIKE A CHILD	4.00
79	8 red vinyl	NICKY WILSON	STONE SOUL LOVING	CRY LIKE A CHILD	5.00
79	8 DJ	NICKY WILSON	STONE SOUL LOVING	CRY LIKE A CHILD	5.00
79	9	J.J. BARNES	HOW LONG	I CAN'T SEEM YTO HOLD YOU	6.00
79	9 DJ	J.J. BARNES	HOW LONG	I CAN'T SEEM YTO HOLD YOU	8.00
79	10	RON GRAINER ORCHESTRA	WHEN LOVE GROWS COLD	PLAYING IT COOL	4.00
79	10 DJ	RON GRAINER ORCHESTRA	WHEN LOVE GROWS COLD	PLAYING IT COOL	5.00
79	11	TOMMY HUNT c/w JASON KNIGHT	LOVING ON THE LOSING SIDE	LOVE IS GETTING STRONGER / STOP	5.00
79	11 DJ	TOMMY HUNT c/w JASON KNIGHT	LOVING ON THE LOSING SIDE	LOVE IS GETTING STRONGER / STOP	8.00
79	12	PLAYTHINGS c/w VAL McKENNA	SURROUNDED BY A RAY OF SUNSHINE	LOVE FEELING	6.00
79	12 DJ	PLAYTHINGS c/w VAL McKENNA	SURROUNDED BY A RAY OF SUNSHINE	I'M YOUR NUMBER ONE	4.00
79	13	MODS '79	GREEN ONIONS	HIGH ON YOUR LOVE	8.00
79	13 DJ	MODS '79	GREEN ONIONS	HIGH ON YOUR LOVE	10.00
79	14	RAINBOW PEOPLE c/w TAMMY ST. JOHN	LIVING IN A DREAMWORLD	NOBODY KNOWS WHAT'S GOING ON I	5.00
79	14 DJ	RAINBOW PEOPLE c/w TAMMY ST. JOHN	LIVING IN A DREAMWORLD	NOBODY KNOWS WHATS GOING ON IN	8.00
79	15	TOMMY HUNT	NEVER CAN SAY GOODBYE	SIGN ON THE DOTTED LINE + YOU	5.00
79	15 DJ	TOMMY HUNT	NEVER CAN SAY GOODBYE	SIGN ON THE DOTTED LINE + YOU	6.00
80	16	AL WILSON c/w THE TOYS	THE SNAKE	A LOVERS CONCERTO	8.00
80	16 DJ	AL WILSON c/w THE TOYS	THE SNAKE	A LOVERS CONCERTO	10.00
80	17	TAMS c/w JASON KNIGHT	HEY GIRL DON'T BOTHER ME	OUR LOVE IS GETTING STRONGER	8.00
80	17 DJ	TAMS c/w JASON KNIGHT	HEY GIRL DON'T BOTHER ME	OUR LOVE IS GETTING STRONGER	10.00

CBM RECORDS

Year	Cat#	Artist	A-side	B-side	Price
67	001	MAYNELL WILSON	MOTOWN FEELING	MEAN OLE WORLD	8.00

CBS

The UK subsidiary of USA media conglomerate Columbia Broadcasting Systems (CBS) for short. One of the longest surviving record companies in the world started trading way back in 1899; today CBS is owned by Sony.

Just before the Second World War Columbia was rivaling RCA for top spot as largest record label and broadcasting company in the USA.

It was not until the early 60's the CBS label was launched in the UK. CBS did show a commitment to the emerging popularity of soul in the UK. Some CBS UK releases soul 45's had a *SOUL SOUNDS* logo on the label, a cleverly designed "flower power" pop art influence. Most probably this is where the later 60's "Bootleg" label by the same name, got the idea to christen their abruptly halted project. In 1967 with discotheques almost exclusively playing black popular music, CBS UK launched the Direction label, which is also documented in this guide. The Direction label did take the bulk of the soul releases from late 1967, leaving the CBS listing of collectable soul in the period a little sparse. But there was a stable full of UK artists ready to fill the gap left. There are some home grown artists who were to record for CBS, that made future legendary 45's. Chapter Five, Kenny Bernard, Detours, Gene Latter etc, kept the CBS catalogue filled with future collectables. British born, Australian citizen Lynne Randell had two releases on CBS one mediocre forgettable up tempo hipshaker. But her version of The Cookies – "Stranger In My Arms" – is rated a masterpiece of Northern Soul. Relegated to the B-side upon release, it's a fine example of those early soul junkshop pioneers finding a future Northern Soul classic. You will notice duplicate release numbers, numbers that don't follow in years. CBS did have the most complicated catalogue numbers of all the UK labels. Check out CBS subsidiaries Direction, Philadelphia International etc, you'll see a baffling numbering system that I've long given up trying to understand. But the simple conclusion I've come to is that CBS release numbers covered ALL there owned labels, so when you see labels listed separately there doesn't seem to be any continuity to it.

Year	Cat#	Artist	A-side	B-side	Price
63	170	EYDIE GORME	EVERYBODY GO HOME	THE MESSAGE	15.00
64	190	CASSIUS CLAY	STAND BY ME	I AM THE GREATEST	30.00
72	1014	O'JAYS	992 ARGUMENTS	LISTEN TO THE CLOCK ON THE WAL	4.00
72	1014 DJ	O'JAYS	992 ARGUMENTS	LISTEN TO THE CLOCK ON THE WAL	5.00
81	1046	CHAMPAIGN	HOW 'BOUT US	SPINNIN'	4.00
81	1046 DJ	CHAMPAIGN	HOW 'BOUT US	SPINNIN'	5.00
68	1150	O.C. SMITH	THE SON OF HICKORY HOLLER'S TRAMP	FRIEND, LOVER, WOMAN, WIFE	4.00
68	1150 DJ	O.C. SMITH	THE SON OF HICKORY HOLLER'S TRAMP	FRIEND, LOVER, WOMAN, WIFE	6.00
74	1181	O'JAYS	LOVE TRAIN	WHO AM I	5.00
74	1181 DJ	O'JAYS	LOVE TRAIN	WHO AM I	8.00
77	1223	BENNY GOLSON	THE NEW KILLER JOE	WALKIN' AND STALKIN'	8.00
77	1223 DJ	BENNY GOLSON	THE NEW KILLER JOE	WALKIN' AND STALKIN'	10.00
81	1235	LAMONT DOZIER	COOL ME OUT	STARTING OVER (WE'VE MADE THE	8.00
81	1235 DJ	LAMONT DOZIER	COOL ME OUT	STARTING OVER (WE'VE MADE THE	10.00
81	1381	CHAMPAIGN	CAN YOU FIND THE TIME	WHIPLASH	6.00
81	1381 DJ	CHAMPAIGN	CAN YOU FIND THE TIME	WHIPLASH	8.00
73	1444	BRIAN AUGER'S OBLIVION EXP.	INNER CITY BLUES	LIGHT ON THE PATH	8.00
73	1444 DJ	BRIAN AUGER'S OBLIVION EXP.	INNER CITY BLUES	LIGHT ON THE PATH	10.00
73	1450	GHETTO CHILDREN	JUST GOTTA FIND SOMEONE TO ME	RAT-A-TAT-TAT	30.00
73	1450 DJ	GHETTO CHILDREN	JUST GOTTA FIND SOMEONE TO ME	RAT-A-TAT-TAT	45.00

81	1535	DENIECE WILLIAMS	SILLY	MY MELODY	4.00
81	1535 DJ	DENIECE WILLIAMS	SILLY	MY MELODY	5.00
73	1546	O'JAYS	TIME TO GET DOWN	SHIFTLESS, SHADY JEALOUS KIND	4.00
73	1546 DJ	O'JAYS	TIME TO GET DOWN	SHIFTLESS, SHADY JEALOUS KIND	5.00
73	1792	EARTH, WIND & FIRE	EVIL	CLOVER	4.00
73	1792 DJ	EARTH, WIND & FIRE	EVIL	CLOVER	5.00
73	1835	GLORIA GAYNOR	HONEY BEE	ALL IT TOOK BOY WAS LOSING YOU	5.00
73	1835 DJ	GLORIA GAYNOR	HONEY BEE	ALL IT TOOK BOY WAS LOSING YOU	6.00
73	1959	MANHATTANS	YOU'D BETTER BELIEVE IT	IT'S SO HARD LOVING YOU	4.00
73	1959 DJ	MANHATTANS	YOU'D BETTER BELIEVE IT	IT'S SO HARD LOVING YOU	5.00
73	1992	JOHNNY NASH	LOVING YOU	GONNA OPEN UP MY HEART AGAIN	4.00
73	1992 DJ	JOHNNY NASH	LOVING YOU	GONNA OPEN UP MY HEART AGAIN	5.00
74	2016	LON SATTON	THE LOVE I SEE IN YOUR EYES	DO YOU NEED MY LOVE TO GET BET	15.00
74	2016 DJ	LON SATTON	THE LOVE I SEE IN YOUR EYES	DO YOU NEED MY LOVE TO GET BET	20.00
74	2026	JOHNNY MATHIS	LIFE IS A SONG WORTH SINGING	I JUST WANTED TO BE ME	8.00
74	2026 DJ	JOHNNY MATHIS	LIFE IS A SONG WORTH SINGING	I JUST WANTED TO BE ME	10.00
74	2033	EARTH, WIND & FIRE	KEEP YOUR HEAD TO THE SKY	BUILD YOUR NEST	4.00
74	2033 DJ	EARTH, WIND & FIRE	KEEP YOUR HEAD TO THE SKY	BUILD YOUR NEST	5.00
74	2048	LORELEI	S.T.O.P. (STOP)	I'LL NEVER LET YOU DOWN	10.00
72	2048 DJ	LORELEI	S.T.O.P. (STOP)	I'LL NEVER LET YOU DOWN	15.00
81	2075	GLADYS KNIGHT & The PIPS	I WILL FIGHT	REACH HIGH	4.00
81	2075 DJ	GLADYS KNIGHT & The PIPS	I WILL FIGHT	REACH HIGH	5.00
74	2117	MANHATTANS	I'M NOT A RUN AROUND	SOUL TRAIN	3.00
74	2117 DJ	MANHATTANS	I'M NOT A RUN AROUND	SOUL TRAIN	4.00
74	2221	O.C. SMITH	LA LA PEACE SONG	WHEN MORNING COMES	5.00
74	2221 DJ	O.C. SMITH	LA LA PEACE SONG	WHEN MORNING COMES	8.00
74	2284	EARTH, WIND & FIRE	MIGHTY MIGHTY	DRUM SONG	4.00
74	2284 DJ	EARTH, WIND & FIRE	MIGHTY MIGHTY	DRUM SONG	5.00
74	2321	BOZ SCAGGS	YOU MAKE IT SO HARD (TO SAY NO)	THERE IS SOMEONE ELSE	5.00
74	2321 DJ	BOZ SCAGGS	YOU MAKE IT SO HARD (TO SAY NO)	THERE IS SOMEONE ELSE	6.00
74	2329	HERBIE HANCOCK	CHAMELEON	VEIN MELTER	4.00
74	2329 DJ	HERBIE HANCOCK	CHAMELEON	VEIN MELTER	5.00
74	2415	ASHA PUTHLI	ONE NIGHT AFFAIR	SALLY GO ROUND THE ROSES	8.00
74	2415 DJ	ASHA PUTHLI	ONE NIGHT AFFAIR	SALLY GO ROUND THE ROSES	10.00
74	2430	RONNIE DYSON	WE CAN MAKE IT LAST FOREVER	JUST A LITTLE LOVE FROM ME	10.00
74	2430 DJ	RONNIE DYSON	WE CAN MAKE IT LAST FOREVER long vers	WE CAN MAKE IT LAST FOREVER short vers	22.00
74	2462	BLOOD SWEAT & TEARS	TELL ME THAT IM WRONG	ROCK REPRISE	10.00
74	2462 DJ	·BLOOD SWEAT & TEARS	TELL ME THAT IM WRONG	ROCK REPRISE	15.00
74	2557	ANDRE BRASSEAUR	THE KID	HOLIDAY	8.00
74	2557 DJ	ANDRE BRASSEAUR	THE KID	HOLIDAY	10.00
74	2594	BLOOD SWEAT AND TEARS	LOVE LOOKS GOOD ON YOU (YOU'RE	ARE YOU SATISFIED	6.00
74	2594 DJ	BLOOD SWEAT AND TEARS	LOVE LOOKS GOOD ON YOU (YOU'RE	ARE YOU SATISFIED	8.00
74	2603	RITA FORTUNE	SISTERS AND BROTHERS	same: instrumental	6.00
74	2603 DJ	RITA FORTUNE	SISTERS AND BROTHERS	same: instrumental	8.00
67	2640	BUCKINGHAMS	DON'T YOU CARE	WHY DON'T YOU LOVE ME	25.00
67	2640 DJ	BUCKINGHAMS	DON'T YOU CARE	WHY DON'T YOU LOVE ME	35.00
67	2640 DJ PS	BUCKINGHAMS	DON'T YOU CARE	WHY DON'T YOU LOVE ME	75.00
67	2657	JOAN REGAN	A LOVE SO FINE	NO-ONE BESIDE ME	25.00
67	2657 DJ	JOAN REGAN	A LOVE SO FINE	NO-ONE BESIDE ME	30.00
67	2696	CHAPTER FIVE	ONE IN A MILLION	HEY HEY	UN
67	2696 DJ	CHAPTER FIVE	ONE IN A MILLION	HEY HEY	150.00
67	2699	RONNIE JONES	PUT YOUR TEARS AWAY	LITTLE BITTY PRETTY ONE	20.00
67	2699 DJ	RONNIE JONES	PUT YOUR TEARS AWAY	LITTLE BITTY PRETTY ONE	28.00
67	2711	PEACHES & HERB	CLOSE YOUR EYES	I WILL WATCH OVER YOU	8.00
67	2711 DJ	PEACHES & HERB	CLOSE YOUR EYES	I WILL WATCH OVER YOU	10.00
74	2712	JOHNNY NASH	YOU CAN'T GO HALFWAY	THE VERY FIRST TIME	3.00
74	2712 DJ	JOHNNY NASH	YOU CAN'T GO HALFWAY	THE VERY FIRST TIME	4.00
74	2713	BUDDY MILES	WE GOT LOVE	PAIN	4.00
74	2713 DJ	BUDDY MILES	WE GOT LOVE	PAIN	5.00
67	2717	CURTIS LEE and the K.C.P.'s	EVERYBODY'S GOING WILD	GET MY BAG	60.00
67	2717 DJ	CURTIS LEE and the K.C.P.'s	EVERYBODY'S GOING WILD	GET MY BAG	85.00
67	2731	JEANNIE LAMBE	DAY AFTER DAY AFTER DAY	CITY AT NIGHT	10.00
67	2731 DJ	JEANNIE LAMBE	DAY AFTER DAY AFTER DAY	CITY AT NIGHT	15.00
67	2732	BEATSTALKERS	AIN'T NO SOUL (LEFT IN THESE OLE SHOES)	MY ONE CHANCE TO MAKE IT	30.00
67	2732 DJ	BEATSTALKERS	AIN'T NO SOUL (LEFT IN THESE OLE SHOES)	MY ONE CHANCE TO MAKE IT	40.00
67	2735	BIG MAYBELLE	I CAN'T WAIT NO LONGER	TURN THE WORLD AROUND THE OTHE	75.00
67	2735 DJ	BIG MAYBELLE	I CAN'T WAIT NO LONGER	TURN THE WORLD AROUND THE OTHE	**109.00**
67	2740	BUNCH	DON'T COME BACK TO ME	YOU CAN'T DO THIS	30.00
67	2740 DJ	BUNCH	DON'T COME BACK TO ME	YOU CAN'T DO THIS	40.00
67	2749	COASTERS	DOWN HOME GIRL	SOUL PAD	15.00
67	2749 DJ	COASTERS	DOWN HOME GIRL	SOUL PAD	18.00
67	2776	SPELLBINDERS	SINCE I DON'T HAVE YOU	I BELIEVE	10.00
67	2776 DJ	SPELLBINDERS	SINCE I DON'T HAVE YOU	I BELIEVE	15.00
67	2777	CHANTELLES	THE MAN I LOVE	BLUE MOOD	20.00
67	2777 DJ	CHANTELLES	THE MAN I LOVE	BLUE MOOD	28.00
74	2782	EARTH, WIND & FIRE	KALIMBA STORY	THE NINE CHEE BIT	4.00
74	2782 DJ	EARTH, WIND & FIRE	KALIMBA STORY	THE NINE CHEE BIT	5.00
67	2786	GLORIES	I STAND ACCUSED (OF LOVING YOU)	WISH THEY COULD WRITE A SONG	30.00
67	2786 DJ	GLORIES	I STAND ACCUSED (OF LOVING YOU)	WISH THEY COULD WRITE A SONG	45.00

67	2807	DONNIE ELBERT	ALONG CAME PRIDE	GET READY	25.00
67	2807 DJ	DONNIE ELBERT	ALONG CAME PRIDE	GET READY	40.00
67	2817	SHIRLEY ELLIS	SUGAR, LET'S SHING-A-LING	HOW LONELY IS LONELY	10.00
67	2817 DJ	SHIRLEY ELLIS	SUGAR, LET'S SHING-A-LING	HOW LONELY IS LONELY	15.00
67	2832	MARY McCARTHY	THE FOLK I LOVE	YOU KNOW HE DID	10.00
67	2832 DJ	MARY McCARTHY	THE FOLK I LOVE	YOU KNOW HE DID	15.00
67	2843	GENE LATTER	FUNNY FACE GIRL	A LITTLE PIECE OF LEATHER	40.00
67	2843 DJ	GENE LATTER	FUNNY FACE GIRL	A LITTLE PIECE OF LEATHER	50.00
67	2847	LYNNE RANDELL	STRANGER IN MY ARMS	CIAO BABY	175.00
67	2847 DJ	LYNNE RANDELL	STRANGER IN MY ARMS	CIAO BABY	250.00
82	2855 PS	MARVIN GAYE	(SEXUAL) HEALING	same: instrumental	4.00
82	2855 DJ	MARVIN GAYE	(SEXUAL) HEALING	same: instrumental	6.00
67	2858	ROBERT PLANT	I'VE GOT A SECRET	LONG TIME COMING	300.00
67	2858 DJ	ROBERT PLANT	I'VE GOT A SECRET	LONG TIME COMING	400.00
67	2859	BUCKINGHAMS	YOU ARE GONE	MERCY, MERCY, MERCY	6.00
67	2859 DJ	BUCKINGHAMS	YOU ARE GONE	MERCY, MERCY, MERCY	8.00
67	2866	PEACHES & HERB	I NEED YOUR LOVE SO DESPERATELY	FOR YOUR LOVE	15.00
67	2866 DJ	PEACHES & HERB	I NEED YOUR LOVE SO DESPERATELY	FOR YOUR LOVE	22.00
67	2894	SHANE MARTIN	I NEED YOU	YOU'RE SO YOUNG	**250.00**
67	2894 DJ	SHANE MARTIN	I NEED YOU	YOU'RE SO YOUNG	300.00
75	2896	JACKSON SISTERS	BOY YOU'RE DYNAMITE	SHAKE HERE LOOSE	5.00
75	2896 DJ	JACKSON SISTERS	BOY YOU'RE DYNAMITE	SHAKE HERE LOOSE	6.00
67	2911	SIMON & GARFUNKEL	YOU DON'T KNOW WHERE YOUR INTEREST	LIES FAKIN' IT	15.00
67	2911 DJ	SIMON & GARFUNKEL	YOU DON'T KNOW WHERE YOUR INTEREST	LIES FAKIN' IT	25.00
83	2924	WEATHER GIRLS	IT'S RAINING MEN	same: instrumental	3.00
83	2924 DJ	WEATHER GIRLS	IT'S RAINING MEN	same: instrumental	4.00
67	2926	BIG MAYBELLE	MAMA (HE TREATS YOUR DAUGHTER	KEEP THAT MAN	20.00
67	2926 DJ	BIG MAYBELLE	MAMA (HE TREATS YOUR DAUGHTER	KEEP THAT MAN	28.00
67	2927	LYNNE RANDELL	THAT'S A HOW DOWN	I NEED YOU BABY	15.00
67	2927 DJ	LYNNE RANDELL	THAT'S A HOW DOWN	I NEED YOU BABY	20.00
67	2936 DJ	KENNY BERNARD	PITY MY FEET	SOMEBODY	75.00
67	2936 DJ	KENNY BERNARD	PITY MY FEET	SOMEBODY	100.00
67	2942	BETTY SWANN	MAKE ME YOURS	I WILL NOT CRY	85.00
67	2942 DJ	BETTYE SWANN	MAKE ME YOURS	I WILL NOT CRY	**145.00**
67	2942 DJ PS	BETTYE SWANN	MAKE ME YOURS	I WILL NOT CRY	200.00
67	2986	GENE LATTER	WITH A CHILD'S HEART	WAYS	18.00
67	2986 DJ	GENE LATTER	WITH A CHILD'S HEART	WAYS	25.00
67	2991	ANITA HARRIS	THE PLAYGROUND	B-A-D FOR ME	10.00
67	2991 DJ	ANITA HARRIS	THE PLAYGROUND	B-A-D FOR ME	15.00
67	3005	BRIAN POOLE	JUST HOW LOUD	THE OTHER SIDE OF THE SKY	20.00
67	3005 DJ	BRIAN POOLE	JUST HOW LOUD	THE OTHER SIDE OF THE SKY	28.00
75	3007	MAHAVISHNU ORCHESTRA	CAN'T STAND YOUR FUNK	ETERNITY'S BREATH part 1	5.00
75	3007 DJ	MAHAVISHNU ORCHESTRA	CAN'T STAND YOUR FUNK	ETERNITY'S BREATH part 1	6.00
75	3042	PHILLY DEVOTIONS	I JUST CAN'T SAY GOODBYE	same: instrumental	8.00
75	3042 DJ	PHILLY DEVOTIONS	I JUST CAN'T SAY GOODBYE	same: instrumental	10.00
67	3044	BILLY JOE ROYAL	HUSH	WATCHING FROM THE BANDSTAND	8.00
67	3044 DJ	BILLY JOE ROYAL	HUSH	WATCHING FROM THE BANDSTAND	10.00
83	3048 PS	MARVIN GAYE	MY LOVE IS WAITING	ROCKIN' AFTER MIDNIGHT	4.00
83	3048 DJ	MARVIN GAYE	MY LOVE IS WAITING	ROCKIN' AFTER MIDNIGHT	5.00
75	3059	HERBIE HANCOCK	PALM GREASE	BUTTERFLY	4.00
75	3059 DJ	HERBIE HANCOCK	PALM GREASE	BUTTERFLY	5.00
67	3059	ARETHA FRANKLIN	TAKE A LOOK	LEE CROSS	10.00
67	3059 DJ	ARETHA FRANKLIN	TAKE A LOOK	LEE CROSS	15.00
67	3067	EXECUITIVES	I'LL ALWAYS LOVE YOU	THE GINZA STRIP	15.00
67	3067 DJ	EXECUITIVES	I'LL ALWAYS LOVE YOU	THE GINZA STRIP	22.00
67	3130	ROB CHANCE and the CHANES R	I'VE GOT THE POWER	AT THE END OF THE DAY	15.00
67	3130 DJ	ROB CHANCE and the CHANES R	I'VE GOT THE POWER	AT THE END OF THE DAY	22.00
68	3213	DETOURS	RUN TO ME	HANGIN' ON	30.00
68	3213 DJ	DETOURS	RUN TO ME	HANGIN' ON	40.00
75	3220	JOHNNY NASH	TEARS ON MY PILLOW (I CAN'T TAKE IT)	BEAUTIFUL BABY	4.00
75	3220 DJ	JOHNNY NASH	TEARS ON MY PILLOW (I CAN'T TAKE IT)	BEAUTIFUL BABY	5.00
68	3239	NINA SHAW	LOVE SO FINE	WOVEN IN MY SOUL	20.00
68	3239 DJ	NINA SHAW	LOVE SO FINE	WOVEN IN MY SOUL	28.00
68	3277	TIM ROSE	I GOT A LONELINESS	LONG TIME MAN	40.00
68	3277 DJ	TIM ROSE	I GOT A LONELINESS	LONG TIME MAN	60.00
68	3310	PAUL REVERE and the RAIDERS	TOO MUCH TALK	HAPPENING '68	15.00
68	3310 DJ	PAUL REVERE and the RAIDERS	TOO MUCH TALK	HAPPENING '68	25.00
68	3343	O.C. SMITH	THE SON OF HICKORY HOLLER'S TRAMP	ON A CLEAR DAY YOU CAN SEE FOR	4.00
68	3343 DJ	O.C. SMITH	THE SON OF HICKORY HOLLER'S TRAMP	ON A CLEAR DAY YOU CAN SEE FOR	8.00
68	3363	BARBARA STREISAND	OUR CORNER OF THE NIGHT	HE COULD SHOW ME	20.00
68	3363 DJ	BARBARA STREISAND	OUR CORNER OF THE NIGHT	HE COULD SHOW ME	28.00
68	3401	DETOURS	WHOLE LOT OF LOVIN'	PIECES OF YOU	75.00
68	3401 DJ	DETOURS	WHOLE LOT OF LOVIN'	PIECES OF YOU	100.00
75	3429	AL MATTHEWS	FOOL	DON'T RUN FROM MY LOVE	6.00
75	3429 DJ	AL MATTHEWS	FOOL	DON'T RUN FROM MY LOVE	8.00
68	3436	ROBERT JOHN	IF YOU DON'T WANT MY LOVE	DON'T	25.00
68	3436 DJ	ROBERT JOHN	IF YOU DON'T WANT MY LOVE	DON'T	40.00
68	3450	JAMES ROYAL	HEY LITTLE BOY	THRU THE LOVE	35.00
68	3450 DJ	JAMES ROYAL	HEY LITTLE BOY	THRU THE LOVE	45.00

75	3453	PHILLY DEVOTIONS	I WAS A LONELY MAN	WE'RE GONNA MAKE IT	6.00
75	3453 DJ	PHILLY DEVOTIONS	I WAS A LONELY MAN	WE'RE GONNA MAKE IT	8.00
68	3475	JOHN FRED and his PLAYBOY BAND	HI HEEL SNEAKERS	SHIRLEY	10.00
68	3475 DJ	JOHN FRED and his PLAYBOY BAND	HI HEEL SNEAKERS	SHIRLEY	15.00
68	3507	SPIRAL STAIRCASE	BABY WHAT I MEAN	MAKIN' MY MIND UP	25.00
68	3507 DJ	SPIRAL STAIRCASE	BABY WHAT I MEAN	MAKIN' MY MIND UP	40.00
76	3518	CLIFF NOBLES & CO.	THE HORSE	LOVE IS ALRIGHT	6.00
76	3518 DJ	CLIFF NOBLES & CO.	THE HORSE	LOVE IS ALRIGHT	10.00
76	3519	EARTH, WIND & FIRE	THAT'S THE WAY OF THE WORLD	AFRICANO	4.00
76	3519 DJ	EARTH, WIND & FIRE	THAT'S THE WAY OF THE WORLD	same:	5.00
76	3520	ALEXIS KORNER	GET OFF MY CLOUD	STRANGE N' DERANGED	10.00
76	3520 DJ	ALEXIS KORNER	GET OFF MY CLOUD	STRANGE N' DERANGED	12.00
68	3544	MOE KOFFMAN	MIGHTY PECULIAR	ARCHIE BUCKLE UP	8.00
68	3544 DJ	MOE KOFFMAN	MIGHTY PECULIAR	ARCHIE BUCKLE UP	10.00
77	3599	EBONY, IVORY & JADE	SAMSON	SAD FACES	4.00
77	3599 DJ	EBONY, IVORY & JADE	SAMSON	same:	5.00
68	3667	HINES, HINES & DAD	SOMETHING EXTRA	HAMBONE	5.00
68	3667 DJ	HINES, HINES & DAD	SOMETHING EXTRA	HAMBONE	6.00
68	3672	JIM WEBB	I NEED YOU	I KEEP IT HID	40.00
68	3672 DJ	JIM WEBB	I NEED YOU	I KEEP IT HID	50.00
68	3710	CARROLLS	COME ON	EVER SINCE	20.00
68	3710 DJ	CARROLLS	COME ON	EVER SINCE	30.00
68	3713	GARY PUCKETT & the UNION GAP	OVER YOU	IF THE DAY WOULD COME	20.00
68	3713 DJ	GARY PUCKETT & the UNION GAP	OVER YOU	IF THE DAY WOULD COME	25.00
75	3742	ANACOSTIA	ALL I NEED	ONE LESS MORNING	8.00
75	3742 DJ	ANACOSTIA	ALL I NEED	ONE LESS MORNING	10.00
68	3814	FOURMOST	APPLERS, PEACHES, PUMPKIN PIE	HE COULD NEVER	30.00
68	3814 DJ	FOURMOST	APPLERS, PEACHES, PUMPKIN PIE	HE COULD NEVER	45.00
75	3847	EARTH, WIND & FIRE	HAPPY FEELIN'	SHINING STAR	6.00
75	3847 DJ	EARTH, WIND & FIRE	HAPPY FEELIN'	SHINING STAR	8.00
68	3860	KENNY BERNARD	A CHANGE IS GONNA COME	VICTIM OF PERFUME AND LACE	10.00
68	3860 DJ	KENNY BERNARD	A CHANGE IS GONNA COME	VICTIM OF PERFUME AND LACE	15.00
68	3874	SUE & SUNNY	LITTLE BLACK BOOK	THE SHOW MUST GO ON	10.00
68	3874 DJ	SUE & SUNNY	LITTLE BLACK BOOK	THE SHOW MUST GO ON	15.00
76	3877	ALEXIS KORNER	AIN'T THAT PECULIAR	TREE TOP FEVER	10.00
76	3877 DJ	ALEXIS KORNER	AIN'T THAT PECULIAR	TREE TOP FEVER	15.00
68	3918	O.C. SMITH	ISN'T IT LONELY TOGETHER	I AIN'T THE WORRYIN' KIND	6.00
68	3918 DJ	O.C. SMITH	ISN'T IT LONELY TOGETHER	I AIN'T THE WORRYIN' KIND	8.00
69	3963	HICKORY	GREEN LIGHT	THE KEY	25.00
69	3963 DJ	HICKORY	GREEN LIGHT	THE KEY	30.00
69	4056	ELOISE LAWS	TO KNOW HIM IS TO LOVE HIM	I'D DO IT ALL AGAIN	5.00
69	4056 DJ	ELOISE LAWS	TO KNOW HIM IS TO LOVE HIM	I'D DO IT ALL AGAIN	8.00
69	4115	MURIEL DAY	WAGES OF LOVE	THINKING OF YOU	15.00
69	4115 DJ	MURIEL DAY	WAGES OF LOVE	THINKING OF YOU	22.00
69	4123	KATE	SWEET LITTLE THING	SHOUT IT	25.00
69	4123 DJ	KATE	SWEET LITTLE THING	SHOUT IT	40.00
69	4160	AL KOOPER	HEY WESTERN UNION MAN	I STAND ALONE	8.00
69	4160 DJ	AL KOOPER	HEY WESTERN UNION MAN	I STAND ALONE	10.00
83	4172	DAMARIS	WHAT ABOUT MY LOVE?	HOORAY FOR LOVE	20.00
83	4172 DJ	DAMARIS	WHAT ABOUT MY LOVE?	HOORAY FOR LOVE	30.00
69	4187	SPIRAL STAIRCASE	MORE TODAY THAN YESTERDAY	BROKEN-HEARTED MAN	75.00
69	4187 DJ	SPIRAL STAIRCASE	MORE TODAY THAN YESTERDAY	BROKEN-HEARTED MAN	**154.00**
69	4217	SHILLELAGH SISTERS	GIVE ME MY FREEDOM	TEASIN' CHEATIN' MAN	6.00
69	4217 DJ	SHILLELAGH SISTERS	GIVE ME MY FREEDOM	TEASIN' CHEATIN' MAN	8.00
69	4401 orange	CARROLLS	WE'RE IN THIS THING TOGETHER	WE KNOW BETTER	10.00
69	4401 DJ	CARROLLS	WE'RE IN THIS THING TOGETHER	WE KNOW BETTER	20.00
69	4401 ornge/yellw fade	CARROLLS	WE'RE IN THIS THING TOGETHER	WE KNOW BETTER	5.00
69	4440	MARILYN POWELL	HAVE ANOTHER DREAM ON ME	AFRAID TO LOVE YOU	15.00
69	4440 DJ	MARILYN POWELL	HAVE ANOTHER DREAM ON ME	AFRAID TO LOVE YOU	22.00
76	4462	RONNIE DYSON	YOU AND ME	THE MORE YOU DO IT	10.00
76	4462 DJ	RONNIE DYSON	YOU AND ME	THE MORE YOU DO IT	6.00
69	4463	JAMES ROYAL	I'VE LOST YOU	SEND OUT LOVE	50.00
69	4463 DJ	JAMES ROYAL	I'VE LOST YOU	SEND OUT LOVE	75.00
69	4470	BILLY JOE ROYAL	CHERRY HILL PARK	HELPING HAND	5.00
69	4470 DJ	BILLY JOE ROYAL	CHERRY HILL PARK	HELPING HAND	6.00
69	4495	EARL OKIN	STOP AND YOU'LL BECOME AWARE	YOU'RE NOT THERE AT ALL	22.00
69	4495 DJ	EARL OKIN	STOP AND YOU'LL BECOME AWARE	YOU'RE NOT THERE AT ALL	30.00
69	4524	SPIRAL STAIRCASE	NO ONE FOR ME TO TURN TO	SWEET LITTLE THING	30.00
69	4524 DJ	SPIRAL STAIRCASE	NO ONE FOR ME TO TURN TO	SWEET LITTLE THING	50.00
69	4528	LINDA SCOTT	YOU MADE A FOOL OUT OF ME	THE COMPOSER	15.00
69	4528 DJ	LINDA SCOTT	YOU MADE A FOOL OUT OF ME	THE COMPOSER	22.00
76	4562	MANHATTANS	HURT	WE'LL HAVE FOREVER TO LOVE	4.00
76	4562 DJ	MANHATTANS	HURT	WE'LL HAVE FOREVER TO LOVE	6.00
76	4563	BOZ SCAGGS	LOWDOWN	JUMP STREET	10.00
76	4563 DJ	BOZ SCAGGS	LOWDOWN	JUMP STREET	15.00
69	4584	ROZETTA HIGHTOWER	ONE HEART FOR SALE	WHAT DO I DO	4.00
69	4584 DJ	ROZETTA HIGHTOWER	ONE HEART FOR SALE	WHAT DO I DO	5.00
76	4675	TOWER OF POWER	YOU OUGHT TO BE HAVIN' FUN	WHILE WE WENT TO THE MOON	15.00
76	4675 DJ	TOWER OF POWER	YOU OUGHT TO BE HAVIN' FUN	WHILE WE WENT TO THE MOON	20.00

76	4711	THELMA JONES	SALTY TEARS	YOU'RE THE SONG	20.00
76	4711 DJ	THELMA JONES	SALTY TEARS	YOU'RE THE SONG	25.00
70	4722	CUPIDS INSPIRATION	WITHOUT YOUR LOVE	DIFFERENT GUY	4.00
70	4722 DJ	CUPIDS INSPIRATION	WITHOUT YOUR LOVE	DIFFERENT GUY	5.00
70	4758	ROZETTA HIGHTOWER	APRIL FOOLS	I'LL HOLD OUT MY HAND	5.00
70	4758 DJ	ROZETTA HIGHTOWER	APRIL FOOLS	I'LL HOLD OUT MY HAND	6.00
70	4811	HUMBUG	GROOVIN' WITH MR. BLOE	MARIANNA	10.00
70	4811 DJ	HUMBUG	GROOVIN' WITH MR. BLOE	MARIANNA	15.00
76	4827	BOBBY WOMACK	HOME IS WHERE THE HEART IS	WE'VE ONLY JUST BEGUN	30.00
76	4827 DJ	BOBBY WOMACK	HOME IS WHERE THE HEART IS	WE'VE ONLY JUST BEGUN	40.00
76	4869	BOZ SCAGGS	WHAT CAN I SAY	HARBOR LIGHTS	5.00
76	4869 DJ	BOZ SCAGGS	WHAT CAN I SAY	HARBOR LIGHTS	8.00
70	4885	AL KOOPER	THE MONKEY TIME	BENDED KNEES (PLEASE DON'T LET	10.00
70	4885 DJ	AL KOOPER	THE MONKEY TIME	BENDED KNEES (PLEASE DON'T LET	15.00
76	4886	JOHNNIE TAYLOR	SOMEBODY'S GETTIN' IT	DISCO LADY	4.00
76	4886 blue vinyl	JOHNNIE TAYLOR	SOMEBODY'S GETTIN' IT	DISCO LADY	5.00
85	4894 dbl pack PS	MARVIN GAYE	SANCTIFIED LADY vocal + instrumental	SEXUAL HEALING + ROCKIN' AFTER	6.00
76	4901 black vinyl	SHIRLEY ELLIS	SOUL TIME	WAITIN'	5.00
76	4901 blue vinyl	SHIRLEY ELLIS	SOUL TIME	WAITIN'	10.00
76	4901 DJ	SHIRLEY ELLIS	SOUL TIME	WAITIN'	15.00
70	4988	ROZETTA HIGHTOWER	PERSUADER	COME TOGETHER	4.00
70	4988 DJ	ROZETTA HIGHTOWER	PERSUADER	COME TOGETHER	5.00
70	4990	ELOISE LAWS	YOU MAKE ME FEEL LIKE SOMEONE	THE ONLY BOY IN MY LIFE	5.00
70	4990 DJ	ELOISE LAWS	YOU MAKE ME FEEL LIKE SOMEONE	THE ONLY BOY IN MY LIFE	6.00
70	4994	CUPIDS INSPIRATION	ARE YOU GROWING TIRED OF MY LOVE	SUNSHINE	5.00
70	4994 DJ	CUPIDS INSPIRATION	ARE YOU GROWING TIRED OF MY LOVE	SUNSHINE	6.00
69	5035	GEORGIE FAME	SOMEBODY STOLE MY THUNDER	ENTERTAINING Mr. SLOANE	**84.00**
69	5035 DJ	GEORGIE FAME	SOMEBODY STOLE MY THUNDER	ENTERTAINING Mr. SLOANE	100.00
70	5039	PACIFIC GAS AND ELECTRIC	ARE YOU READY?	STAGGOLEE	10.00
70	5039 DJ	PACIFIC GAS AND ELECTRIC	ARE YOU READY?	STAGGOLEE	15.00
70	5054	SLY & THE FAMILY STONE	I WANT TO TAKE YOU HIGHER	YOU CAN MAKE IF YOU TRY	8.00
70	5054 DJ	SLY & THE FAMILY STONE	I WANT TO TAKE YOU HIGHER	YOU CAN MAKE IF YOU TRY	10.00
77	5093	MANHATTANS	IT'S YOU	MIND YOUR BUSINESS	8.00
77	5093 DJ	MANHATTANS	IT'S YOU	MIND YOUR BUSINESS	10.00
77	5108	VALERIE CARTER	OOH CHILD	HEARTACHE	5.00
77	5108 DJ	VALERIE CARTER	OOH CHILD	HEARTACHE	6.00
78	5198	EARTH, WIND & FIRE	BIYO	SINGASONG	5.00
78	5198 DJ	EARTH, WIND & FIRE	BIYO	SINGASONG	8.00
70	5203	O.C. SMITH	BABY, I NEED YOUR LOVING	SAN FRANCISCO IS A LONELY TOWN	10.00
70	5203 DJ	O.C. SMITH	BABY, I NEED YOUR LOVING	SAN FRANCISCO IS A LONELY TOWN	15.00
70	5208	HUMBUG	I GOT A FEELING	same: instrumental	10.00
70	5208 DJ	HUMBUG	I GOT A FEELING	same: instrumental	15.00
71	5246	MARLENA SHAW	PICTURES AND MEMORIES	NO DEPOSIT, NO RETURN	6.00
71	5246 DJ	MARLENA SHAW	PICTURES AND MEMORIES	NO DEPOSIT, NO RETURN	8.00
71	5249	PEACHES & HERB	SOOTHE ME WITH YOUR LOVE	WE'RE SO MUCH IN LOVE	5.00
71	5249 DJ	PEACHES & HERB	SOOTHE ME WITH YOUR LOVE	WE'RE SO MUCH IN LOVE	8.00
71	5285	RONNIE DYSON	I DON'T WANNA CRY	SHE'S GONE	8.00
71	5285 DJ	RONNIE DYSON	I DON'T WANNA CRY	SHE'S GONE	10.00
71	5309	WORTH	SHOOT 'EM UP BABY	TAKE THE WORLD IN YOUR HANDS	15.00
71	5309 DJ	WORTH	SHOOT 'EM UP BABY	TAKE THE WORLD IN YOUR HANDS	20.00
71	5311	PENNY LANE	ROCK ME IN THE CRADLE (OF YOUR	I'M FREE	8.00
71	5311 DJ	PENNY LANE	ROCK ME IN THE CRADLE (OF YOUR	I'M FREE	10.00
71	5389	CHAMBERS BROTHERS	FUNKY	LOVE, PEACE AND HAPPINESS	5.00
71	5389 DJ	CHAMBERS BROTHERS	FUNKY	LOVE, PEACE AND HAPPINESS	6.00
71	5415	TINA CHARLES	I'LL BE YOUR LIGHT	FALLIN' IN LOVE	8.00
71	5415 DJ	TINA CHARLES	I'LL BE YOUR LIGHT	FALLIN' IN LOVE	10.00
71	5422	VIVIAN REED	LEAN ON ME	MISSING YOU	5.00
71	5422 DJ	VIVIAN REED	LEAN ON ME	MISSING YOU	6.00
72	5432	DENIECE WILLIAMS	THAT'S WHAT FRIENDS ARE FOR	WATCHING OVER	4.00
72	5432 DJ	DENIECE WILLIAMS	THAT'S WHAT FRIENDS ARE FOR	WATCHING OVER	5.00
72	5445	TYRONE DAVIS	THIS I SWEAR	GIVIN' MYSELF TO YOU	8.00
72	5445 DJ	TYRONE DAVIS	THIS I SWEAR	GIVIN' MYSELF TO YOU	10.00
77	5550	MARLENA SHAW	GO AWAY LITTLE BOY	YU-MA GO AWAY LITTLE BOY	5.00
77	5550 DJ	MARLENA SHAW	GO AWAY LITTLE BOY	YU-MA GO AWAY LITTLE BOY	6.00
77	5553	Z.Z. HILL	LOVE IS SO GOOD WHEN YOU'RE	NEED YOU BY MY SIDE	5.00
77	5553	Z.Z. HILL	LOVE IS SO GOOD WHEN YOU'RE	NEED YOU BY MY SIDE	6.00
78	6056	EARTH, WIND & FIRE	FANTASY	BE EVER WONDERFUL	4.00
78	6056 DJ	EARTH, WIND & FIRE	FANTASY	BE EVER WONDERFUL	5.00
66	6076 EP PS	ARTHUR PRYSOCK	AGAIN	4 track EP with cover	25.00
78	6120 DJ	POCKETS	IN THE POCKET	DOIN' THE DO	10.00
78	6220	MARLENA SHAW	DON'T ASK TO STAY UNTIL TOMORROW	WRITINGS ON THE WALL	4.00
78	6220 DJ	MARLENA SHAW	DON'T ASK TO STAY UNTIL TOMORROW	WRITINGS ON THE WALL	5.00
78	6318	TOWER OF POWER	AM I A FOOL	LOVIN' YOU IS GONNA SEE ME THR	4.00
67	6363 EP PS	GEORGIE FAME	KNOCK ON WOOD	1967 4 track EP with cover	15.00
78	6516	JOHNNIE TAYLOR	HEY MISTER MELODY MAKER	GIVE ME MY BABY	3.00
78	6516 DJ	JOHNNIE TAYLOR	HEY MISTER MELODY MAKER	GIVE ME MY BABY	4.00
78	6530	HERBIE HANCOCK	I THOUGHT IT WAS YOU	NO MEANS YES	4.00
78	6530 DJ	HERBIE HANCOCK	I THOUGHT IT WAS YOU	NO MEANS YES	5.00
78	6656	MIKE FINNIGAN	JUST ONE MINUTE MORE	BLOOD IS THICKER THAN WATER	15.00

78	6656 DJ	MIKE FINNIGAN	JUST ONE MINUTE MORE	BLOOD IS THICKER THAN WATER	20.00
78	6664 DJ	D.J. ROGERS	LOVE BROUGHT ME BACK	same: part 2	8.00
71	7027	AMERICAN GYPSY	GYPSY QUEEN part 1	DEAD & GONE	8.00
71	7027 DJ	AMERICAN GYPSY	GYPSY QUEEN part 1	DEAD & GONE	10.00
71	7068	ROZETTA HIGHTOWER	GO PRAY FOR TOMORROW	GIVE ME JUST A LITTLE LINE	5.00
71	7068 DJ	ROZETTA HIGHTOWER	GO PRAY FOR TOMORROW	GIVE ME JUST A LITTLE LINE	6.00
71	7101	CARL DOUGLAS	DO YOU NEED MY LOVE (TO GET	LEAN ON ME	40.00
71	7101 DJ	CARL DOUGLAS	DO YOU NEED MY LOVE (TO GET	LEAN ON ME	50.00
79	7109	GARY'S GANG	KEEP ON DANCIN'	DO IT AT THE DISCO	4.00
79	7109 DJ	GARY'S GANG	KEEP ON DANCIN'	DO IT AT THE DISCO	5.00
80	7173	GLADYS KNIGHT & The PIPS	AM I TOO LATE	IT'S THE SAME OLD SONG	3.00
80	7173 DJ	GLADYS KNIGHT & The PIPS	AM I TOO LATE	IT'S THE SAME OLD SONG	4.00
71	7180	PATTI AUSTIN	ARE WE READY FOR LOVE	NOW THAT I KNOW WHAT LONELINES	20.00
71	7180 DJ	PATTI AUSTIN	ARE WE READY FOR LOVE	NOW THAT I KNOW WHAT LONELINES	30.00
71	7220	SATIN BELLS	THE BELLE TELEPHONE SONG	LOSING YOU	5.00
71	7220 DJ	SATIN BELLS	THE BELLE TELEPHONE SONG	LOSING YOU	6.00
71	7250	TYMES feat: GEORGE WILLIAMS	SOMEONE TO WATCH OVER ME	SHE'S GONE	8.00
71	7250 DJ	TYMES feat: GEORGE WILLIAMS	SOMEONE TO WATCH OVER ME	SHE'S GONE	10.00
71	7279	BRENDA & THE TABULATIONS	ALWAYS AND FOREVER	RIGHT ON THE TIP OF MY TONGUE	8.00
71	7279 DJ	BRENDA & THE TABULATIONS	ALWAYS AND FOREVER	RIGHT ON THE TIP OF MY TONGUE	10.00
71	7291	PEACHES & HERB	THE TWO OF US	THE SOUND OF SILENCE	5.00
71	7291 DJ	PEACHES & HERB	THE TWO OF US	THE SOUND OF SILENCE	6.00
71	7318	CHERYL LYNN	STAR LOVE	YOU'RE THE ONE	4.00
71	7318 DJ	CHERYL LYNN	STAR LOVE	YOU'RE THE ONE	5.00
71	7384	EBONYS	SEXY WAYS	YOU'RE THE REASON	6.00
71	7384 DJ	EBONYS	SEXY WAYS	YOU'RE THE REASON	8.00
71	7397	BEN E. KING	WHITE MOON	ALL OF YOUR SORROWS	6.00
71	7397 DJ	BEN E. KING	WHITE MOON	ALL OF YOUR SORROWS	8.00
71	7413	TAJ MAHAL	DIVING DUCK BLUES	FISHIN' BLUES	5.00
71	7413 DJ	TAJ MAHAL	DIVING DUCK BLUES	FISHIN' BLUES	6.00
79	7445	GLADYS KNIGHT & The PIPS	YOU BRING OUT THE BEST IN ME	YOU LOVED AWAY THE PAIN	6.00
79	7445 DJ	GLADYS KNIGHT & The PIPS	YOU BRING OUT THE BEST IN ME	YOU LOVED AWAY THE PAIN	6.00
71	7449	RONNIE DYSON	WHEN YOU GET RIGHT DOWN TO IT	SLEEPING SUN	4.00
71	7449 DJ	RONNIE DYSON	WHEN YOU GET RIGHT DOWN TO IT	SLEEPING SUN	6.00
71	7463 orange	SHIRLEY ELLIS	SOUL TIME	WAITIN'	20.00
71	7463 DJ orange A	SHIRLEY ELLIS	SOUL TIME	WAITIN'	30.00
75	7463 orange/yellow fade	SHIRLEY ELLIS	SOUL TIME	WAITIN'	8.00
75	7463 DJ 2line A	SHIRLEY ELLIS	SOUL TIME	WAITIN'	15.00
71	7689	CHAMBERS BROTHERS	(BY THE HAIR ON) MY CHINNY CHIN	HEAVEN	4.00
71	7689 DJ	CHAMBERS BROTHERS	(BY THE HAIR ON) MY CHINNY CHIN	HEAVEN	5.00
71	7691	EBONYS	DETERMINATION	DO IT	6.00
71	7691 DJ	EBONYS	DETERMINATION	DO IT	8.00
79	7722	JACKIE MOORE	THIS TIME BABY	LET'S GO SOMEWHERE AND MAKE LOVE	5.00
79	7722 DJ	JACKIE MOORE	THIS TIME BABY	LET'S GO SOMEWHERE AND MAKE LOVE	6.00
72	7768	FREE MOVEMENT	THE HARDER I TRY (THE BLUER I GET)	COMIN' HOME	5.00
72	7768 DJ	FREE MOVEMENT	THE HARDER I TRY (THE BLUER I GET)	COMIN' HOME	6.00
72	7785	BEN E. KING	TAKE ME TO THE PILOT	I GUESS IT'S GOODBYE	6.00
72	7785 DJ	BEN E. KING	TAKE ME TO THE PILOT	I GUESS IT'S GOODBYE	8.00
79	7858	DENIECE WILLIAMS	I FOUND LOVE	ARE YOU THINKING	3.00
79	7858 DJ	DENIECE WILLIAMS	I FOUND LOVE	ARE YOU THINKING	4.00
79	7876	GLADYS KNIGHT & The PIPS	YOU DON'T HAVE TO SAY I LOVE YOU	I JUST WANT TO BE WITH YOU	4.00
79	7876 DJ	GLADYS KNIGHT & The PIPS	YOU DON'T HAVE TO SAY I LOVE YOU	I JUST WANT TO BE WITH YOU	5.00
72	8084	AL KOOPER	THE MONKEY TIME	BENDED KNEES	8.00
72	8084 DJ	AL KOOPER	THE MONKEY TIME	BENDED KNEES	10.00
72	8270	O'JAYS	BACK STABBERS	SUNSHINE	6.00
72	8270 DJ	O'JAYS	BACK STABBERS	SUNSHINE	10.00
72	8280	RAMSEY LEWIS	SLIPPIN' INTO DARKNESS	COLLAGE	5.00
72	8280	RAMSEY LEWIS	SLIPPIN' INTO DARKNESS	COLLAGE	6.00
72	8291 DJ	HAROLD MELVIN the BLUENOTES	I MISS YOU	MISS YOU part 2	5.00
72	8291 DJ	HAROLD MELVIN the BLUENOTES	I MISS YOU	MISS YOU part 2	8.00
72	8496	HAROLD MELVIN the BLUENOTES	IF YOU DON'T KNOW ME BY NOW	LET ME INTO YOUR WORLD	4.00
72	8496 DJ	HAROLD MELVIN the BLUENOTES	IF YOU DON'T KNOW ME BY NOW	LET ME INTO YOUR WORLD	8.00
80	8542	GLADYS KNIGHT & The PIPS	LANDLORD	WE NEED HEARTS	5.00
80	8542 DJ	GLADYS KNIGHT & The PIPS	LANDLORD	WE NEED HEARTS	6.00
80	8545	AL JOHNSON	I'M BACK FOR MORE	YOU ARE MY PERSONAL ANGEL	8.00
80	8545 DJ	AL JOHNSON	I'M BACK FOR MORE	YOU ARE MY PERSONAL ANGEL	10.00
80	8660	LONNIE LISTON SMITH	GIVE PEACE A CHANCE (MAKE LOVE	SUNBURST	4.00
80	8660 DJ	LONNIE LISTON SMITH	GIVE PEACE A CHANCE (MAKE LOVE	SUNBURST	5.00
80	8890	GLADYS KNIGHT & The PIPS	TASTE A BITTER LOVE	ADD IT UP	8.00
80	8890 DJ	GLADYS KNIGHT & The PIPS	TASTE A BITTER LOVE	ADD IT UP	10.00
80	9081	GLADYS KNIGHT & The PIPS	BOURGIE, BOURGIE	GET THE LOVE	8.00
80	9081 DJ	GLADYS KNIGHT & The PIPS	BOURGIE, BOURGIE	GET THE LOVE	10.00
81	9496	GLADYS KNIGHT & The PIPS	STILL SUCH A THING	WE NEED HEARTS	3.00
81	9496 DJ	GLADYS KNIGHT & The PIPS	STILL SUCH A THING	WE NEED HEARTS	4.00
65	201732	ARETHA FRANKLIN	CAN'T YOU SEE ME	YOU LITTLE MISS RAGEDY ANNE	15.00
65	201732 DJ	ARETHA FRANKLIN	CAN'T YOU SEE ME	YOU LITTLE MISS RAGEDY ANNE	22.00
65	201752	MAUREEN EVANS	NEVER LET HIM GO	POCO SOLE	30.00
65	201752 DJ	MAUREEN EVANS	NEVER LET HIM GO	POCO SOLE	45.00
65	201766	MONGO SANTAMARIA	EL PUSSYCAT	BLACK EYED PEAS AND RICE	25.00

65	201766 DJ	MONGO SANTAMARIA	EL PUSSYCAT	BLACK EYED PEAS AND RICE	40.00
65	201785	GYPSIES	JERK IT	DIAMONDS, RUBIES, GOLD AND FAM	50.00
65	201785 DJ	GYPSIES	JERK IT	DIAMONDS, RUBIES, GOLD AND FAM	70.00
65	201818	JON BATES	WHERE WERE YOU LAST NIGHT	IF ANYTHING GOES WRONG	15.00
65	201818 DJ	JON BATES	WHERE WERE YOU LAST NIGHT	IF ANYTHING GOES WRONG	20.00
65	201820	ARTHUR PRYSOCK	IT'S TOO LATE, BABY TOO LATE	MY SPECIAL PRAYER	15.00
65	201820 DJ	ARTHUR PRYSOCK	IT'S TOO LATE, BABY TOO LATE	MY SPECIAL PRAYER	20.00
65	202026	ANITA BRYANT	MY MINDS PLAYING TRICKS ON ME	ANOTHER YEAR, ANOTHER LOVE	50.00
65	202026 DJ	ANITA BRYANT	MY MINDS PLAYING TRICKS ON ME	ANOTHER YEAR, ANOTHER LOVE	70.00
66	202041	CHERYL ST. CLAIR	MY HEART'S NOT IN IT	WE WANT LOVE	15.00
66	202041 DJ	CHERYL ST. CLAIR	MY HEART'S NOT IN IT	WE WANT LOVE	22.00
66	202055	NICKY HOPKINS	MR. BIG	JENNI	20.00
66	202055 DJ	NICKY HOPKINS	MR. BIG	JENNI	30.00
66	202057	DAVE WALTON	TELL ME A LIE	LOVE AIN'T WHAT IT USED TO BE	15.00
66	202057 DJ	DAVE WALTON	TELL ME A LIE	LOVE AIN'T WHAT IT USED TO BE	20.00
66	202082	GUY DARRELL	I'VE BEEN HURT	BLESSED	25.00
66	202082 DJ	GUY DARRELL	I'VE BEEN HURT	BLESSED	75.00
66	202087	BILLY JOE ROYAL	HEART'S DESIRE	EVERYBODY'S GOTTA CRY	65.00
66	202087 DJ	BILLY JOE ROYAL	HEART'S DESIRE	EVERYBODY'S GOTTA CRY	85.00
66	202088	RIVINGTONS	ROSE GROWING IN THE RUINS	TEND TO BUSINESS	75.00
66	202088 DJ	RIVINGTONS	ROSE GROWING IN THE RUINS	TEND TO BUSINESS	100.00
66	202098	DAVE WALTON	EVERY WINDOW IN THE CITY	I'VE LEFT THE TROUBLED GROUND	30.00
66	202098 DJ	DAVE WALTON	EVERY WINDOW IN THE CITY	I'VE LEFT THE TROUBLED GROUND	40.00
66	202099	DR. FEELGOOD and the INTERNS	DON'T TELL ME NO DIRTY	WHERE DID YOU GO	15.00
66	202099 DJ	DR. FEELGOOD and the INTERNS	DON'T TELL ME NO DIRTY	WHERE DID YOU GO	20.00
66	202100	JOAN REGAN	DON'T TALK TO ME ABOUT LOVE	I'M NO TOY	75.00
66	202100 DJ	JOAN REGAN	DON'T TALK TO ME ABOUT LOVE	I'M NO TOY	85.00
66	202190	CASSIUS CLAY	STAND BY ME	I AM THE GREATEST	20.00
66	202190 DJ	CASSIUS CLAY	STAND BY ME	I AM THE GREATEST	30.00
66	202349	BRIAN POOLE	EVERYTHING I TOUCH TURNS TO TEARS	I NEED HER TONIGHT	15.00
66	202349 DJ	BRIAN POOLE	EVERYTHING I TOUCH TURNS TO TEARS	I NEED HER TONIGHT	25.00
66	202395	CHAPTER FIVE	YOU CAN'T MEAN IT	ANYTHING YOU DO IS ALRIGHT	**677.00**
66	202395 DJ	CHAPTER FIVE	YOU CAN'T MEAN IT	ANYTHING YOU DO IS ALRIGHT	**580.00**
66	202453	SPELLBINDERS	HELP ME (GET MYSELF BACK TOGETHER	DANNY BOY	50.00
66	202453 DJ	SPELLBINDERS	HELP ME (GET MYSELF BACK TOGETHER	DANNY BOY	100.00
66	202455	LEE TOMLIN	SWEET SWEET LOVIN'	SAVE ME	25.00
66	202455 DJ	LEE TOMLIN	SWEET SWEET LOVIN'	SAVE ME	30.00
67	202468	ARETHA FRANKLIN	CRY LIKE A BABY	SWANEE	10.00
67	202468 DJ	ARETHA FRANKLIN	CRY LIKE A BABY	SWANEE	15.00
67	202470	EYDIE GORME	EVERYBODY GO HOME	THE MESSAGE	8.00
67	202470 DJ	EYDIE GORME	EVERYBODY GO HOME	THE MESSAGE	10.00
67	202483	GENE LATTER	SOMETHING INSIDE ME DIED	DON'T GO	6.00
67	202483 DJ	GENE LATTER	SOMETHING INSIDE ME DIED	DON'T GO	8.00
66	202491	SEFTONS	I CAN SEE THROUGH YOU	HERE TODAY	30.00
66	202491 DJ	SEFTONS	I CAN SEE THROUGH YOU	HERE TODAY	40.00
67	202508	DAVE WALTON	AFTER YOU THERE CAN BE NOTHING	CAN I GET IT FROM YOU	25.00
67	202508 DJ	DAVE WALTON	AFTER YOU THERE CAN BE NOTHING	CAN I GET IT FROM YOU	30.00
67	202509	PEACHES & HERB	WE'RE IN THIS THING TOGETHER	LET'S FALL IN LOVE	40.00
67	202509 DJ	PEACHES & HERB	WE'RE IN THIS THING TOGETHER	LET'S FALL IN LOVE	60.00
67	202511	BOBBY BENNETT	SHE BELIEVE IN ME	JUST SAY GOODBYE	20.00
67	202511 DJ	BOBBY BENNETT	SHE BELIEVE IN ME	JUST SAY GOODBYE	25.00
67	202520	LIZ CHRISTIAN	SUDDENLY YOU FIND LOVE	MAKE IT WORK OUT	**207.00**
67	202520 DJ	LIZ CHRISTIAN	SUDDENLY YOU FIND LOVE	MAKE IT WORK OUT	250.00
67	202525	JAMES ROYAL	CALL MY NAME	WHEN IT COMES TO MY BABY	15.00
67	202525 DJ	JAMES ROYAL	CALL MY NAME	WHEN IT COMES TO MY BABY	22.00
67	202547	MATTIE MOULTRIE	THAT'S HOW STRONG MY LOVE IS	THE SADDEST STORY EVER TILD	40.00
67	202547 DJ	MATTIE MOULTRIE	THAT'S HOW STRONG MY LOVE IS	THE SADDEST STORY EVER TILD	50.00
67	202548	BILLY JOE ROYAL	YO YO	WE TRIED	10.00
67	202548 DJ	BILLY JOE ROYAL	YO YO	WE TRIED	15.00
67	202557	ANDRE BRASSEAUR	THE KID	HOLIDAY	15.00
67	202557 DJ	ANDRE BRASSEAUR	THE KID	HOLIDAY	30.00
67	202565	CHAMBERS BROTHERS	FALLING IN LOVE	ALL STRUNG OUT OVER YOU	10.00
67	202565 DJ	CHAMBERS BROTHERS	FALLING IN LOVE	ALL STRUNG OUT OVER YOU	12.00
67	202587	GEORGIE FAME	BECAUSE I LOVE YOU	BIDIN' MY TIME	8.00
67	202587 PS	GEORGIE FAME	BECAUSE I LOVE YOU	BIDIN' MY TIME	10.00
67	202587 DJ	GEORGIE FAME	BECAUSE I LOVE YOU	BIDIN' MY TIME	12.00
67	202591	JOHNNIE LEE	LOVE NO LONGER SOUNDS	KISS TOMORROW GOODBYE	15.00
67	202591 DJ	JOHNNIE LEE	LOVE NO LONGER SOUNDS	KISS TOMORROW GOODBYE	22.00
67	202605	DENNIS D'ELL	BETTER USE YOUR HEAD	IT BREAKS MY HEART	500.00
67	202605 DJ	DENNIS D'ELL	BETTER USE YOUR HEAD	IT BREAKS MY HEART	**350.00**
67	202606	SHIRLEY ELLIS	SOUL TIME	WAITIN'	45.00
67	202606 DJ	SHIRLEY ELLIS	SOUL TIME	WAITIN'	**183.00**
67	202615	APPLEJACKS	YO'VE BEEN CHEATING	LOVE WAS IN MY EYES	25.00
67	202615 DJ	APPLEJACKS	YO'VE BEEN CHEATING	LOVE WAS IN MY EYES	40.00
67	202616	CHANTERS	YOU CAN'T FOOL ME	ALL DAY LONG	10.00
67	202616 DJ	CHANTERS	YOU CAN'T FOOL ME	ALL DAY LONG	15.00
67	202621	MAUREEN EVANS	SOMEWHERE THERE'S LOVE	IT TAKES A LITTLE TIME	10.00
67	202621 DJ	MAUREEN EVANS	SOMEWHERE THERE'S LOVE	IT TAKES A LITTLE TIME	15.00
67	202622	SPELLBINDERS	CHAIN REACTION	FOR YOU	40.00

67	202622 DJ	SPELLBINDERS	CHAIN REACTION	FOR YOU	60.00
67	202642	GUY DARRELL	DIDN'T I	CRYSTAL BALL	6.00
67	202642 DJ	GUY DARRELL	DIDN'T I	CRYSTAL BALL	8.00
67	202655	GENE LATTER	ALWAYS	A WOMAN CALLED SORROW	10.00
67	202655 DJ	GENE LATTER	ALWAYS	A WOMAN CALLED SORROW	15.00
67	202818	JOHN BATES	WHERE WERE YOU LAST NIGHT	IF ANYTHING GOES WRONG	10.00
67	202818 DJ	JOHN BATES	WHERE WERE YOU LAST NIGHT	IF ANYTHING GOES WRONG	15.00

CERTAIN

85	1	CLARENCE CARTER	MESSIN' WITH MY MIND	IT AIN'T WHAT YOU DO	40.00
85	1 PS	CLARENCE CARTER	MESSIN' WITH MY MIND	IT AIN'T WHAT YOU DO	50.00

CHAMPAGNE

81	302	GIL SCOTT-HERON	THE BOTTLE	THE BOTTLE drunk mix	5.00
80	501	GERALDINE HUNT	CAN'T FAKE THE FEELING	LOOK ALL AROUND	4.00
80	503	BILLY FRAZIER	BILLY WHO?	BILLY WHO? Part 2	8.00
81	funk 1	CLOUD	TAKE IT TO THE TOP	ALL NIGHT LONG remix	5.00
81	funk 5	POTION	CATCH THE FEELIN' (SHOWSTOPPER)	SHOWSTOPPER	6.00

CHAMPION

3		MAD LADS & CROSSFIRE BAND	YOU BLEW IT	TRYING TO FORGET ABOUT YOU	10.00

CHAPTER ONE

70	123	BLACK ABBOTS	SHE LOOKED MY WAY	I DON'T MIND	4.00
70	123 DJ	BLACK ABBOTS	SHE LOOKED MY WAY	I DON'T MIND	5.00
70	126	LES REED ORCHESTRA	MAN OF ACTION	MADRID	15.00
70	126 DJ	LES REED ORCHESTRA	MAN OF ACTION	MADRID	20.00
70	136	VIC FLICK SOUND	HANG ON	WONDERFUL WORLD	15.00
70	136 DJ	VIC FLICK SOUND	HANG ON	WONDERFUL WORLD	20.00
72	174	NOTATIONS	NEED YOUR LOVE	JUST NOTHING LEFT TO GIVE	30.00
72	174 DJ	NOTATIONS	NEED YOUR LOVE	JUST NOTHING LEFT TO GIVE	40.00
72	189	LES REED ORCHESTRA	MAN OF ACTION	LEST WE FORGET	10.00
72	189 DJ	LES REED ORCHESTRA	MAN OF ACTION	LEST WE FORGET	15.00

CHARLY

	CEP 101 EP PS	LEROY HUTSON	BEAR CAT	4 track EP with picture sleeve	6.00
80	106	JOHN LEE HOOKER	DIMPLES	BOOM BOMM + ONIONS	6.00
80	107	BETTY LAVETTE	EASIER TO SAY (THAN DO)	LET ME DOWN EASY + PIECE OF MY HEART	5.00
80	107 PS	BETTY LAVETTE	EASIER TO SAY (THAN DO)	LET ME DOWN EASY + PIECE OF MY HEART	5.00
80	109 EP PS	JOE SIMON	BRING IT ON TO ME	WHEN I'M GONE + LET'S DO IT OV	8.00
80	112	NINA SIMONE	MY BABY JUST CARES FOR ME	LOVE ME OR LEAVE ME	3.00
87	121	ROBERT PARKER	BAREFOOTIN'	LET'S GO BABY (WHERE THE ACTIO	5.00
87	121 PS	ROBERT PARKER	BAREFOOTIN'	LET'S GO BABY WHERE THE ACTION	8.00
87	123 PS	NINA SIMONE	LITTLE GIRL BLUE	I LOVES YOU, PORGY	4.00
80	1007	SIDNEY BARNES	I HURT ON THE OTHER SIDE	GOOD LOVIN'	20.00
78	1041 PS	SHANGRI-LAS c/w AD LIBS	LEADER OF THE PACK	THE BOY FROM NEW YORK CITY	4.00
80	CTD 101 EP PS	LEE DORSEY	HOLY COW + WORKING IN A COAL MINE	CAN YOU HEAR ME	8.00
80	CTD 102 EP PS	BETTY HARRIS	RIDE YOUR PONY + NEARER TO YOU	TROUBLE WITH MY LOVER	8.00
80	CTD 103 EP PS	JIMMY HUGHES	NEIGHBOR NEIGHBOR + TRY ME	A SHOT OF RHYTHM & BLUES	8.00
80	CTD 104 EP PS	BETTY EVERETT	GETTING MIGHTY CROWDED	YOU'RE NO GOOD + THE SHOOP SHO	8.00
80	CTD 105 EP PS	JIMMY REED	SHAME, SHAME, SHAME	BIG BOSS MAN + BRIGHT LIGHTS	8.00
80	CTD 106 EP PS	JOHN LEE HOOKER	BOOM BOOM	DIMPLES + ONIONS	8.00
80	CTD 107 EP PS	BETTY LAVETTE	EASIER TO SAY (THAN DO) + LET ME	PIECE OF MY HEART	8.00
80	CTD 108 EP PS	PEGGY SCOTT & JO JO BENSON	PICKING WILD MOUNTAIN BERRIES	LOVER'S HOLIDAY + SOUL SHAKE	8.00
80	CTD 109 EP PS	JOE SIMON	BRING IT ON HOME TO ME	WHEN I'M GONE + LET'S DO IT OV	8.00
80	CTD 110 EP PS	DELLS	STAY IN MY CORNER	OH WHAT A NITE + LOOKS LIKE IT	8.00
80	CTD 111 EP PS	TED TAYLOR	I NEED YOU LOVE SO BAD	IT'S TOO LATE + ONLY THE LONEL	8.00
80	CTD 111 EP PS	TED TAYLOR	IT'S TOO LATE + ONLY THE LONELY	I NEED YOUR LOVE SO BAD	8.00
80	CTD 112 EP PS	BOBBY PATTERSON	SHE DON'T HAVE TO SEE YOU	HOW DO YOU SPELL LOVE + I'M IN	8.00
80	CTD 113 EP PS	METERS	LOOK - KA PY PY	TIPPI TOSES + CISSY STRUT	8.00
80	CTD 114 EP PS	JERRY BUTLER	HE WILL BREAK YOUR HEART + I STAND	MAKE IT EASY ON YOURSELF	8.00
80	CTD 115 EP PS	DEE CLARK	HEY LITTLE GIRL	RAINDROPS + YOUR FRIENDS	8.00
80	CTD 116 EP PS	GENE CHANDLER	NOTHING CAN STOP ME + JUST BE TRUE	YOU THREW A LUCKY PUNCH	8.00
80	CTD 117 EP PS	BILLY BOY ARNOLD	I WISH YOU WOULD + ROCKINITIS	I AIN'T GOT YOU	8.00
80	CTD 118 EP PS	LITTLE JOHNNY TAYLOR	AS LONG AS I DON'T SEE YOU	MY SPECIAL ROSE + HOW CAN A STRONG MAN	8.00
80	CTD 119 EP PS	BENTON, BUSTER	SWEET 94 + SPIDER IN MY STEW	DO IT IN THE RAIN	8.00
80	CTD 120 EP PS	CARTER BROTHERS	SOUTHERN COUNTRY BOY	BOOZE IN THE BOTTLE + 1	8.00
80	CTD 121 EP PS	UNIQUES	ALL THESE THINGS + IT'S ALL OVER	YOU DON'T MISS YOUR WATER	8.00
80	CTD 122 EP PS	ROSCO GORDON	JUST A LITTLE BIT	YOU CAN MAKE IT IF YOU TRY	8.00
80	CTD 123 EP PS	ROBERT PARKER	BAREFOOTIN'	TROPICAL + I SHOT THE SHERRIFF	8.00
80	CTD 124 EP PS	EDDIE GILES	THAT'S HOW STRONG MY LOVE IS	TELL IT LIKE IT IS + 1	8.00
80	CTD 125 EP PS	BIG MAC c/w TARHEEL SLIM &	ROUGH DRIED WOMAN parts 1 & 2	NUMBER 9 TRAIN	8.00
81	CTD 126 EP PS	ELMORE JAMES	DUST MY BROOM	DONE SOMEBODY WRONG + PICKIN' THE BLUES	8.00
81	CTD 127 EP PS	TARHEEL SLIM	WILDCAT TAMER + LOOKOUT MABEL	DAVY CROCKETT + DID YOU EVER	8.00
81	CTD 128 EP PS	JOHN HAMILTON c/w DORIS ALLEN	THEM CHANGES + HOW MUCH CAN A MAN TAKE	DID YOU EVER	8.00
81	CTD 129 EP PS	LEE DORSEY	GET OUT OF MY LIFE WOMAN	AY-LA-AY + PEAOPLE SURE ACT FUNNY	8.00
81	CTD 130 EP PS	PROFESSOR LONGHAIR c/w EDDIE DANIELS	GOING TO THE MARDI GRAS + I WANNA KNOW + GOING TO THE MARDI GRAS		8.00

CHELSEA

74	2005002	WILLIAM DEVAUGHN	BE THANKFUL FOR WHAT YOU GOT	BE THANKFUL FOR WHAT YOU GOT part 2	6.00
74	2005008	NEW YORK CITY	HAPPINESS IS	SANITY	5.00
74	2005011	WILLIAM DEVAUGHN	BLOOD S THICKER THAN WATER	BLOOD S THICKER THAN WATER diFf mix	5.00
75	2005018	RONNIE WILLIAMS	DREAMIN'	AIN'T NO SIN TO LIE	5.00
75	2005021	JIM GILSTRAP	SWING YOUR DADDY	SWING YOUR DADDY part 2	4.00
75	2005025	LINDA CARR & the LOVE SQUAD	HIGH WIRE	MOTHER'S LITTLE CORNER OF THE WORLD	5.00
75	2005029	RONNIE WILLIAMS	MR. ME, MRS. YOU	AIN'T NO SIN TO LIE	5.00
75	2005032	JIM GILSTRAP	HOUSE OF STRANGERS	TAKE YOUR DADDY FOR A RIDE	4.00
75	2005037	DEE CLARK	RIDE A WILD HORSE	RIDE A WILD HORSE part 2	4.00
75	2005038	MARION JARVIS	A PENNY FOR YOUR THOUGHTS	A GOOD MAN TO WAKE UP TO	50.00
75	2005044	LINDA CARR & the LOVE SQUAD	DIAL L FOR THE LOVE SQUAD	LOST AND FOUND	5.00
75	2005050	JIM GILSTRAP	I'M ON FIRE	I'M ON FIRE part 2	6.00
76	2005057	STUFF N' RAMJETT	IT'S BEEN A LONG LONG TIME	TIME	6.00
76	2005061	UJIMA	STILL HOOKED ON YOU	KEEP ON ROLLIN'	10.00
76	2005063	FESSOR FUNK	I DIG YOU GIRL	I DIG YOU GIRL part 2	5.00
76	2005064	HONEY BEES	DREAM EXPRESS	same: insatrumental	4.00
76	2005071	JIM GILSTRAP	MOVE ME	MOVE ME part 2	4.00

CHERRY RED

82	39	MARC BOLAN	THE WIZARD	BEYOND THE RISIN' SUN	5.00
82	39 PS	MARC BOLAN	THE WIZARD	BEYOND THE RISIN' SUN	6.00

CHESS

Many consider Chicago's Chess label, to have done more to bring American black music to audiences and music enthusiasts worldwide than any other label. The label started life as ARISTOCRAT in Chicago 1947. The two elder sons of 1920's European immigrants the Chez family Leonard & Philip Chess (they changed their name slightly to become more westernized) were heavily involved in the Southside nightclub scene. A natural progression into running a record label for the acts that performed in their clubs seemed an obvious route. Leonard joined the team at Aristocrat Records, whilst Philips continued to run the night clubs. Over the next three years, slowly and surely Leonard bought out partners, to take full control and in 1950, when the name change took place and CHESS RECORDS was born. With Chicago's black community being the second largest in the USA and still growing with the migration of blacks from the blues birthplace the Mississippi Delta states: the Chess brothers had plenty of local talent to pull from. They soon had the largest number of blues artists in the country under their control. Including such blues giants as Sonny Boy Williamson, Muddy Waters, Little Walter, Sunnyland Slim, Buddy Guy, Bo Diddley, Willie Mabon and of course Chuck Berry to name but a few.
 The soul giants began to emerge in the very early 60's, with R&B performers like Etta James being produced with a "softer" approach, so Chicago R&B was slowly turning into SOUL with each release becoming less R&B and more soulful. As the soul sound grabbed the American buying public imagination.
Through the 50's Chess Records was distributed by Decca in the UK. The catalogue contained some of the most highly collectable Blues and Rock & Roll 45's & EP's, LP's being released on their London label.
In 1961 Pye got the distributing rights, to launch an era of black music that was the birth of the Chicago soul sound. If you check the Pye International listing you'll see many blues recordings on Pye, with many emerging soul artists scattered within. With the runaway success of Motown in the arch rival city of Detroit: the Chess brothers (Philip had now joined Leonard at the helm) saw the need to create a similar sound in Chicago, as the Motown sound was capturing sales in both the black and the white markets. Artists like Jackie Ross were soon performing songs in the style of Mary Well's Motown smash hits. Not forgetting Tony Clarke's Marvin Gaye impression with furious "Ain't Love Good – Ain't Love Proud". The Radiants doing the soulful male harmony upbeat dance tunes, but The Vontastics sounded more like the Temptations than any other group in the country. One Chicago icon within the Chess soul team, was Billy Stewart, he retained his own unique style throughout his career and today after his untimely death, is heralded as one of the all time greats of Chicago soul.
 You couldn't do a few lines on the Chess label without mentioning the world's finest male soul harmony group The Dells, the only real hit the 60's Chess label has in the UK was unusual – "I Can Sing A Rainbow" / "Love Is Blue" medley. It may be true to say, this most fabulous of soul groups was not fully appreciated in the UK until the Northern Soul scene, driven by "Wear It On Your Face" & "There Is." Discovered 45's like "Make Sure", "Run For Cover," "Thinking Of You", all of which failed to get released on these shores, the full Dells recording talents began to unfold. They are now heralded as a soul group in a class of their own, and as a live band, absolutely unequalled.
For the more adventurous early 60's UK soul fan to discover such talents as the above, a gateway was ajar to see what else was being quietly issued in the UK. Chess went a long way to developing the interest in soul music within the UK. Imagine first hearing the vocals of Billy Stewart after being fed a radio diet of Cliff Richard, Billy J. Kramer etc. Or if the best harmonies you'd heard were the Beatles or Freddie and the Dreamers, then you drop the needle on a Dells or a Radiants 45. The UK soul tsunami was about to make its first ripple. Chicago soul was being heard in the UK for the very first time.
Chess, Pye International releases were receiving such good reviews in teen pop magazines, where there was a small but dedicated movement following the soul releases. Artists like Sugar Pie DeSanto, Tommy Tucker, Little Milton, Johnny Nash were soon becoming talked about artists in youth clubs and record get-togethers in teenager's bedrooms. Where the hippest thing to do, was to bring along a 45 by an artist nobody had ever heard of. What effect did the vocal chords of Sugar Pie have on a young Brit in 1964 in the confines of the bedroom away from Pat Boone orientated parents.
After the summer of 1964 Pye decided to give Chess it's long overdue, own label. The Chess label covered releases not only from the USA Chess parent label, but also released material from Cadet, Checker, KR, and St. Lawrence, all Chicago distributed Chess labels.

E.P.'s 4 track extended plays with picture covers.

65	6000 EP PS	JOHN LEE HOOKER	DOWN AT THE LANDING	4 track EP with cover	25.00
65	6001 EP PS	SONNY BOY WILLIAMSON	HELP ME	1965 4 track EP with cover	40.00
65	6002 EP PS	CHUCK BERRY	PROMISED LAND	1965 4 track EP with cover	25.00
65	6004 EP PS	BUDDY GUY	CRAZY MUSIC	1965 4 track ep with sleeve	28.00
65	6005 EP PS	CHUCK BERRY	COME ON	1965 4 track ep with cover	25.00
65	6006 EP PS	MUDDY WATERS	I'M READY	1965 4 track EP with cover	70.00
66	6007 EP PS	JOHN LEE HOOKER	WALKING THE BOOGIE	1966 4 track EP with cover	25.00
66	6008 EP PS	BO DIDDLEY	I'M A MAN	1966 4 track ep with cover	30.00
66	6009 EP PS	VARIOUS ARTISTS	WITH THE BLUES	1966 4 track EP with cover	40.00
66	6010 EP PS	VARIOUS ARTISTS	IN CROWD	1966 4 track EP with cover	30.00
66	6011 EP PS	VARIOUS ARTISTS	THE BLUES vol. 2	1966 4 track EP with cover	30.00
66	6012 EP PS	CHUCK BERRY	I GOT A BOOKING	1966 4 track EP with cover	25.00
66	6013 EP PS	SONNY BOY WILLIAMSON	IN MEMORIAM	1966 4 track EP with cover	30.00
66	6014 EP PS	JOHN LEE HOOKER	THE JOURNEY	1966 4 track EP with cover	25.00
66	6015 EP PS	FONTELLA BASS	FONTELLA'S HITS	1966 4 track EP with cover inc: rescue me	30.00
66	6016 EP PS	unissued?			
66	6017 EP PS	HOWLIN' WOLF	REAL FOLK BLUES	1966 4 track EP with cover	30.00
66	6018 EP PS	SONNY BOY WILLIAMSON	REAL FOLK BLUES vol. 2	1966 4 track EP with cover	30.00
66	6019 EP PS	RAMSEY LEWIS TRIO	A HARD DAY'S NIGHT	1966 4 track EP with cover	20.00

66	6020 EP PS	FONTELLA BASS	I CAN'T REST		1966 4 track EP with cover	50.00
66	6021 EP PS	JOHN LEE HOOKER	REAL FOLK BLUE vol. 3		1966 4 track EP with cover	25.00
66	6022 EP PS	MUDDY WATERS	THE REAL FOLK BLUES		1966 4 track EP with cover	50.00
66	6023 EP PS	BO DIDDLEY	ROOSTER STEW		1966 4 track EP with cover	30.00
67	6024 EP PS	BILLY STEWART	I DO LOVE YOU		1967 4 track EP with cover	30.00
67	6025 EP PS	FONTELLA BASS & BOBBY McCLURE	FONTELLA & BOBBY		1967 4 track EP with cover	50.00
68	6026 EP PS	VARIOUS ARTISTS	YOUR CHESS REQUESTS		1968 4 track EP with cover	30.00

In the autumn of 1964 Pye International gave Chicago based Checker / Chess label their own label which ran for over 100 releases to become one of the most sought after collectable UK Soul labels. Promo copies looked like all the PYE distributed labels. But for the early stock copy releases they chose a Gold logo and lettering for the label, which was neatly presented inside a unique individual Chess logo'd company sleeve. Gold lettering was unusual for the era and considered a little out of fashion. But now Gold logo UK Chess have pride of place in all UK Soul collections. The last 45 on UK Chess to have a Gold lettering and logo was Ramsey Lewis's Jazz dance classic and Northern Soul oldies nite anthem # 8041. After that release # Pye switch the lettering and logo from gold to silver.

64	8000	BO DIDDLEY	HEY GOOD LOOKIN'	YOU AIN'T BAD (AS YOU CLAIM TO		10.00
64	8000 DJ	BO DIDDLEY	HEY GOOD LOOKIN'	YOU AIN'T BAD (AS YOU CLAIM TO		15.00
64	8001	MUDDY WATERS	SHORT DRESS WOMAN	MY JOHN THE CONQUER ROOT		25.00
64	8001 DJ	MUDDY WATERS	SHORT DRESS WOMAN	MY JOHN THE CONQUER ROOT		35.00
64	8002	RADIANTS	VOICE YOUR CHOICE	IF I ONLY HAD YOU		25.00
64	8002 DJ	RADIANTS	VOICE YOUR CHOICE	IF I ONLY HAD YOU		50.00
64	8003	JACKIE ROSS	NEW LOVER	JERK AND TWINE		40.00
64	8003 DJ	JACKIE ROSS	NEW LOVER	JERK AND TWINE		70.00
64	8004	BUDDY GUY	LET ME LOVE YOU BABY	TEN YEARS AGO		15.00
64	8004 DJ	BUDDY GUY	LET ME LOVE YOU BABY	TEN YEARS AGO		22.00
64	8005	JOHNNY NASH	STRANGE FEELING	RAININ' IN MY HEART		20.00
64	8005 DJ	JOHNNY NASH	STRANGE FEELING	RAININ' IN MY HEART		30.00
64	8006	unissued				

Unissued number possibilities. Chess # 8005 was USA release Argo 5492, if UK Pye had followed the USA Argo catalogue for it's next release of # 8006. Possibilities were for two 1. Etta James – Seven Day Fool Argo 5402 2. Herb Ward – Strange Change Argo 5410 the next Argo release in the UK was Chess 8025 which was released in the USA on Argo 5519. Only assumption, but studio test presses or acetate most probably exist for this blank in the series.

65	8007	FONTELLA BASS & BOBBY McCLURE	DON'T MESS UP A GOOD THING	JERK LOOSE (Oliver Sain)		20.00
65	8007 DJ	FONTELLA BASS & BOBBY McCLURE	DON'T MESS UP A GOOD THING	JERK LOOSE		40.00
65	8008	BENICE SWANSON	LYING AWAKE	BABY I'M YOURS		40.00
65	8008 DJ	BENICE SWANSON	LYING AWAKE	BABY I'M YOURS		60.00
65	8009	BILLY STEWART	I DO LOVE YOU	KEEP LOVING		20.00
65	8009 DJ	BILLY STEWART	I DO LOVE YOU	KEEP LOVING		30.00
65	8010	HOWLIN' WOLF	KILLING FLOOR	LOUISE		15.00
65	8010 DJ	HOWLIN' WOLF	KILLING FLOOR	LOUISE		25.00
65	8011	TONY CLARKE	THE ENTERTAINER	THIS HEART OF MINE		25.00
65	8011 DJ	TONY CLARKE	THE ENTERTAINER	THIS HEART OF MINE		60.00
65	8012	CHUCK BERRY	DEAR DAD	MY LITTLE LOVELIGHT		15.00
65	8012 DJ	CHUCK BERRY	DEAR DAD	MY LITTLE LOVELIGHT		22.00
65	8013	LITTLE MILTON	WE'RE GONNA MAKE IT	CAN'T HOLD BACK THE TEARS		20.00
65	8013 DJ	LITTLE MILTON	WE'RE GONNA MAKE IT	CAN'T HOLD BACK THE TEARS		30.00
65	8014	BO DIDDLEY	SOMEBODY BEAT ME	MUSH MOUTH MILLIE		10.00
65	8014 DJ	BO DIDDLEY	SOMEBODY BEAT ME	MUSH MOUTH MILLIE		15.00
65	8015	KNIGHT BROTHERS	TEMPTATION 'BOUT TO GET ME	SINKING LOW		25.00
65	8015 DJ	KNIGHT BROTHERS	TEMPTATION 'BOUT TO GET ME	SINKING LOW		45.00
65	8016	HOWLIN' WOLF	OOH BABY	TELL ME WHAT I'VE DONE		15.00
65	8016 DJ	HOWLIN' WOLF	OOH BABY	TELL ME WHAT I'VE DONE		25.00
65	8017 gold logo	BILLY STEWART	SITTING IN THE PARK	ONCE AGAIN		28.00
65	8017 DJ white	BILLY STEWART	SITTING IN THE PARK	ONCE AGAIN		45.00
68	8017 silver logo	BILLY STEWART	SITTING IN THE PARK	ONCE AGAIN		18.00
68	8017 DJ yellow	BILLY STEWART	SITTING IN THE PARK	ONCE AGAIN		30.00
65	8018	LITTLE MILTON	WHO'S CHEATING WHO?	AIN'T NO BIG DEAL ON YOU		20.00
65	8018 DJ	LITTLE MILTON	WHO'S CHEATING WHO	AIN'T NO BIG DEAL ON YOU		30.00
65	8019	MUDDY WATERS	I GOT A RICH MAN'S WOMAN	MY DOG CAN'T BARK		20.00
65	8019 DJ	MUDDY WATERS	I GOT A RICH MAN'S WOMAN	MY DOG CAN'T BARK		30.00
65	8020	RAMSEY LEWIS TRIO	THE IN CROWD	SINCE I FEEL FOR YOU		10.00
65	8020 DJ	RAMSEY LEWIS TRIO	THE IN CROWD	SINCE I FEEL FOR YOU		25.00
65	8021	BO DIDDLEY	LET THE KIDS DANCE	LET ME PASS		10.00
65	8021 DJ	BO DIDDLEY	LET THE KIDS DANCE	LET ME PASS		15.00
65	8022	CHUCK BERRY	IT WASN'T ME	IT'S MY OWN BUSINESS		15.00
65	8022 DJ	CHUCK BERRY	IT WASN'T ME	IT'S MY OWN BUSINESS		22.00
65	8023	FONTELLA BASS	RESCUE ME	SOUL OF A MAN		10.00
65	8023 DJ	FONTELLA BASS	RESCUE ME	SOUL OF A MAN		70.00
65	8024	RAMSEY LEWIS TRIO	HANG ON SLOOPY	MOVIN' EASY		10.00
65	8024 DJ	RAMSEY LEWIS TRIO	HANG ON SLOOPY	MOVIN' EASY		18.00
65	8025	ETTA JAMES & SUGAR PIE DeSANTO	DO I MAKE MYSELF CLEAR	SOMEWHERE DOWN THE LINE		30.00
65	8025 DJ	ETTA JAMES & SUGAR PIE DeSANTO	DO I MAKE MYSELF CLEAR	SOMEWHERE DOWN THE LINE		60.00
66	8026	BO DIDDLEY	500% MORE MAN	STOP MY MONKEY		10.00
66	8026 DJ	BO DIDDLEY	500% MORE MAN	STOP MY MONKEY		18.00
66	8027	FONTELLA BASS	RECOVERY	LEAVE IT IN THE HANDS OF LOVE		15.00
66	8027 DJ	FONTELLA BASS	RECOVERY	LEAVE IT IN THE HANDS OF LOVE		45.00
66	8028	BILLY STEWART	BECAUSE I LOVE YOU	MOUNTAIN OF LOVE		20.00
66	8028 DJ	BILLY STEWART	BECAUSE I LOVE YOU	MOUNTAIN OF LOVE		40.00
66	8029	RAMSEY LEWIS TRIO	A HARD DAYS NIGHT	'TOUT A DOUBT		10.00
66	8029 DJ	RAMSEY LEWIS TRIO	A HARD DAYS NIGHT	'TOUT A DOUBT		15.00
66	8030	SONNY BOY WILLIAMSON	BRING IT ON HOME	DOWN CHILD		15.00
66	8030 DJ	SONNY BOY WILLIAMSON	BRING IT ON HOME	DOWN CHILD		25.00
66	8031	RAMSEY LEWIS TRIO	HI-HEEL SNEAKERS	HI-HEEL SNEAKERS part 2		10.00

66	8031 DJ	RAMSEY LEWIS TRIO	HI-HEEL SNEAKERS	HI-HEEL SNEAKERS part 2	25.00
66	8032	FONTELLA BASS	I CAN'T REST	I SURRENDER	20.00
66	8032 DJ	FONTELLA BASS	I CAN'T REST	I SURRENDER	50.00
66	8033	BOBBY MOORE & the RHYTHM ACES	HEY, MR. D.J.	SEARCHING FOR MY LOVE	22.00
66	8033 DJ	BOBBY MOORE & the RHYTHM ACES	HEY, MR. D.J.	SEARCHING FOR MY LOVE	45.00
66	8034	SUGAR PIE DeSANTO & ETTA JAMES	THERE'S GONNA BE TROUBLE	IN THE BASEMENT	30.00
66	8034 DJ	SUGAR PIE DeSANTO & ETTA JAMES	THERE'S GONNA BE TROUBLE	IN THE BASEMENT	50.00
66	8035	KO KO TAYLOR	WANG DANG DOODLE	BLUES BLUES HEAVEN	30.00
66	8035 DJ	KO KO TAYLOR	WANG DANG DOODLE	BLUES BLUES HEAVEN	60.00
66	8036	BO DIDDLEY	WE'RE GONNA GET MARRIED	EASY	10.00
66	8036 DJ	BO DIDDLEY	WE'RE GONNA GET MARRIED	EASY	18.00
66	8037	CHUCK BERRY	RAMONA SAYS	LONELY SCHOOL DAYS	10.00
66	8037 DJ	CHUCK BERRY	RAMONA SAYS	LONELY SCHOOL DAYS	15.00
66	8038	BILLY STEWART	LOVE ME	WHY AM I LONELY	15.00
66	8038 DJ	BILLY STEWART	LOVE ME	WHY AM I LONELY	30.00
66	8039	JOHN LEE HOOKER	LET'S GO OUT TONIGHT	IN THE MOOD	15.00
66	8039 DJ	JOHN LEE HOOKER	LET'S GO OUT TONIGHT	IN THE MOOD	25.00
66	8040	BILLY STEWART	SUMMERTIME	TO LOVE TO LOVE	20.00
66	8040 DJ	BILLY STEWART	SUMMERTIME	TO LOVE TO LOVE	40.00
66	8041 gold logo	RAMSEY LEWIS	WADE IN THE WATER	AIN'T THAT PECULIAR	40.00
66	8041 DJ white	RAMSEY LEWIS	WADE IN THE WATER	AIN'T THAT PECULIAR	**235.00**
68	8041 silver logo	RAMSEY LEWIS	WADE IN THE WATER	AIN'T THAT PECULIAR	20.00
68	8041 DJ yellow	RAMSEY LEWIS	WADE IN THE WATER	AIN'T THAT PECULIAR	40.00

Pye changes the Chess logo lettering from GOLD to SILVER

66	8042	FONTELLA BASS	SAFE AND SOUND	YOU'LL NEVER EVER KNOW	20.00
66	8042 DJ	FONTELLA BASS	SAFE AND SOUND	YOU'LL NEVER EVER KNOW	50.00
66	8043	VONTASTICS	MY BABY	DAY TRIPPER	30.00
66	8043 DJ	VONTASTICS	MY BABY	DAY TRIPPER	50.00
66	8044	RAMSEY LEWIS	UP TIGHT (EVERYTHING'S ALRIGHT)	MONEY IN THE POCKET	10.00
66	8044 DJ	RAMSEY LEWIS	UP TIGHT (EVERYTHING'S ALRIGHT)	MONEY IN THE POCKET	20.00
66	8045	BILLY STEWART	LOOK BACK AND SMILE	SECRET LOVE	20.00
66	8045 DJ	BILLY STEWART	LOOK BACK AND SMILE	SECRET LOVE	45.00
66	8046	KNIGHT BROTHERS	SHE'S A - 1	THAT'LL GET IT	25.00
66	8046 DJ	KNIGHT BROTHERS	SHE'S A - 1	THAT'LL GET IT	45.00
66	8047 DJ	GENE CHANDLER	SUCH A PRETTY THING	I FOOLED YOU THIS TIME	60.00
66	8047 DJ	GENE CHANDLER	SUCH A PRETTY THING	I FOOLED YOU THIS TIME	**105.00**
66	8048	BOBBY McCLURE	YOU GOT ME BABY	PEAK OF LOVE	60.00
66	8048 DJ	BOBBY McCLURE	YOU GOT ME BABY	PEAK OF LOVE	85.00
66	8049	unissued			

Unissued number possibilities. Chess # 8049 and 8051 were unissued in the UK. The USA schedule for these releases was perhaps the finest period for Northern Soul collectors of the UK Chess label. USA 45s that could have been lined up for release on these two numbers included. Valeninos – "Sweeter Than The Day Before" – USA Chess #1977. Billy Stewart UK Chess # 8045 release, was USA Chess release # 1978. Tony Clarke's – "Landslide" – was issued on Chess #1979. Johnny Williams – "My Baby's Good" – Chess #1976 . Barbara Carr's – "Don't Knock Love" – Chess # 1985. Also Gene Chandler's – "After the laughter" – on USA Checker 1163 was released in USA within the same time frame. The possibilities are mind boggling, on what the UK soul public missed out on. These are only assumptions, but studio test presses or acetates most probably exist for this two unissued UK numbers in the series. What they were at this time nobody seems to know for sure.

After release # 8048 promotional copies change from a White label with a black A to a Yellow label with a two line A

67	8050	BILLY STEWART	OL' MAN RIVER	EVERY DAY (I HAVE THE BLUES)	20.00
67	8050 DJ	BILLY STEWART	OL' MAN RIVER	EVERY DAY (I HAVE THE BLUES)	40.00
67	8051	unissued			
67	8052	ETTA JAMES	I PREFER YOU	I'M SO GLAD (I FOUND LOVE IN YOU)	15.00
67	8052 DJ	ETTA JAMES	I PREFER YOU	I'M SO GLAD (I FOUND LOVE IN YOU)	22.00
67	8053	BO DIDDLEY	OOH BABY	BACK TO SCHOOL	15.00
67	8053 DJ	BO DIDDLEY	OOH BABY	BACK TO SCHOOL	25.00
67	8054	MARLENA SHAW	MERCY, MERCY, MERCY	GO AWAY LITTLE BOY	15.00
67	8054 DJ	MARLENA SHAW	MERCY, MERCY, MERCY	GO AWAY LITTLE BOY	25.00
67	8055	RAMSEY LEWIS	1 - 2 - 3	DOWN BY THE RIVERSIDE	10.00
67	8055 DJ	RAMSEY LEWIS	1 - 2 - 3	DOWN BY THE RIVERSIDE	15.00
67	8056	CASH McCALL	IT WONDERFUL (TO BE IN LOVE)	LET'S TRY IT OVER	10.00
67	8056 DJ	CASH McCALL	IT'S WONDERFUL (TO BE IN LOVE)	LET'S TRY IT OVER	18.00
67	8057	BO DIDDLEY	WRECKING MY LOVE LIFE	BOO-GA-LOO BEFORE YOU GO	10.00
67	8057 DJ	BO DIDDLEY	WRECKING MY LOVE LIFE	BOO-GA-LOO BEFORE YOU GO	15.00
67	8058	RAMSEY LEWIS	FUNCTION AT THE JUNCTION	HEY, MRS JONES	22.00
67	8058 DJ	RAMSEY LEWIS	FUNCTION AT THE JUNCTION	HEY, MRS JONES	15.00
67	8059	TIFFANIES	IT'S GOT TO BE A GREAT SONG	HE'S GOOD FOR ME	100.00
67	8059 DJ	TIFFANIES	IT'S GOT TO BE A GREAT SONG	HE'S GOOD FOR ME	**181.00**
67	8060	RAMSEY LEWIS	SATURDAY NIGHT AT THE MOVIES	CHINA GATE	8.00
67	8060 DJ	RAMSEY LEWIS	SATURDAY NIGHT AT THE MOVIES	CHINA GATE	10.00
67	8061	RAMSEY LEWIS	GIRL TALK	DANCING IN THE STREET	8.00
67	8061 DJ	RAMSEY LEWIS	GIRL TALK	DANCING IN THE STREET	12.00
67	8062	LAURA LEE	DIRTY MAN	IT'S MIGHTY HARD	15.00
67	8062 DJ	LAURA LEE	DIRTY MAN	IT'S MIGHTY HARD	22.00
67	8063	ETTA JAMES	TELL MAMA	I'D RATHER GO BLIND	15.00
67	8063 DJ	ETTA JAMES	TELL MAMA	I'D RATHER GO BLIND	25.00
67	8064	RAMSEY LEWIS	SOUL MAN	STRUTTIN' LIGHTLY	10.00
67	8064 DJ	RAMSEY LEWIS	SOUL MAN	STRUTTIN' LIGHTLY	18.00
67	8065	WILDWEEDS	IT WAS FUN (WHILE IT LASTED)	SORROW'S ANTHEM	15.00
67	8065 DJ	WILDWEEDS	IT WAS FUN (WHILE IT LASTED)	SORROW'S ANTHEM	25.00
67	8066	DELLS	THERE IS	0-0 I LOVE YOU	20.00
67	8066 DJ	DELLS	THERE IS	0-0 I LOVE YOU	35.00

67	8067	BILLY STEWART	CROSS MY HEART	WHY (DO I LOVE YOU SO)	15.00
67	8067 DJ	BILLY STEWART	CROSS MY HEART	WHY (DO I LOVE YOU SO)	28.00
67	8068	SOULFUL STRINGS	BURNING SPEAR	WITHIN YOU, WITHOUT YOU	40.00
67	8068 DJ	SOULFUL STRINGS	BURNING SPEAR	WITHIN YOU, WITHOUT YOU	60.00
67	8069	ETTA JAMES	SECURITY	I'M GONNA TAKE WHAT HE'S GOT	10.00
67	8069 DJ	ETTA JAMES	SECURITY	I'M GONNA TAKE WHAT HE'S GOT	18.00
68	8070	LAURA LEE	AS LONG AS I GOT YOU	A MAN WITH SOME BACKBONE	10.00
68	8070 DJ	LAURA LEE	AS LONG AS I GOT YOU	A MAN WITH SOME BACKBONE	15.00
68	8071	DELLS	WEAR IT ON OUR FACE	PLEASE DON'T CHANGE ME NOW	15.00
68	8071 DJ	DELLS	WEAR IT ON OUR FACE	PLEASE DON'T CHANGE ME NOW	40.00
68	8072	ROTARY CONNECTION	SOUL MAN	RUBY TUESDAY	6.00
68	8072 DJ	ROTARY CONNECTION	SOUL MAN	RUBY TUESDAY	10.00
68	8073	RADIANTS	HOLD ON	I'M GLAD I'M THE LOSER	20.00
68	8073 DJ	RADIANTS	HOLD ON	I'M GLAD I'M THE LOSER	50.00
68	8074	MAURICE & MAC	YOU LEFT THE WATER RUNNING	YOU'RE THE ONE	15.00
68	8074 DJ	MAURICE & MAC	YOU LEFT THE WATER RUNNING	YOU'RE THE ONE	28.00
68	8075	CHUCK BERRY	JOHNNY B. GOODE	SWEET LITTLE SIXTEEN	10.00
68	8075 DJ	CHUCK BERRY	JOHNNY B. GOODE	SWEET LITTLE SIXTEEN	15.00
68	8076	ETTA JAMES	I GOT YOU BABE	I WORSHIP THE GROUND YOU WALK	10.00
68	8076 DJ	ETTA JAMES	I GOT YOU BABE	I WORSHIP THE GROUND YOU WALK	15.00
68	8077	PIGMEAT MARKHAM	HERE COME THE JUDGE	THE TRAIL	8.00
68	8077 DJ	PIGMEAT MARKHAM	HERE COME THE JUDGE	THE TRAIL	15.00
68	8078	BO DIDDLEY	ANOTHER SUGAR DADDY	I'M HIGH AGAIN	10.00
68	8078 DJ	BO DIDDLEY	ANOTHER SUGAR DADDY	I'M HIGH AGAIN	15.00
68	8079	DELLS	STAY IN MY CORNER	LOVE IS SO SIMPLE	8.00
68	8079 DJ	DELLS	STAY IN MY CORNER	LOVE IS SO SIMPLE	10.00
68	8080	GOSPEL CLASSICS	MORE LOVE, THAT'S WHAT WE NEED	YOU NEED FAITH	100.00
68	8080 DJ	GOSPEL CLASSICS	MORE LOVE, THAT'S WHAT WE NEED	YOPU NEED FAITH	150.00
68	8081	MAURICE & MAC	WHY DON'T YOU TRY ME	LEAN ON ME	10.00
68	8081 DJ	MAURICE & MAC	WHY DON'T YOU TRY ME	LEAN ON ME	18.00
68	8082	ETTA JAMES	FIRE	YOU GOT IT	20.00
68	8082 DJ	ETTA JAMES	FIRE	YOU GOT IT	30.00
69	8083	MUDDY WATERS	LET'S SPEND THE NIGHT TOGETHER	I'M A MAN	12.00
69	8083 DJ	MUDDY WATERS	LET'S SPEND THE NIGHT TOGETHER	I'M A MAN	18.00
68	8084	DELLS	ALWAYS TOGETHER	I WANT MY MOMMA	8.00
68	8084 DJ	DELLS	ALWAYS TOGETHER	I WANT MY MOMMA	10.00
69	8085	PIGMEAT MARKHAM	SOCK IT TO 'EM JUDGE	THE HIP JUDGE	10.00
69	8085 DJ	PIGMEAT MARKHAM	SOCK IT TO 'EM JUDGE	THE HIP JUDGE	15.00
69	8086	TOMMY TUCKER	HI-HEEL SNEAKERS	I DON'T WANT 'CHA	10.00
69	8086 DJ	TOMMY TUCKER	HI-HEEL SNEAKERS	I DON'T WANT 'CHA	18.00
69	8087	LITTLE MILTON	GRITS AIN'T GROCERIES	I CAN'T QUIT YOU BABY	20.00
69	8087 DJ	LITTLE MILTON	GRITS AIN'T GROCERIES	I CAN'T QUIT YOU BABY	50.00
69	8088	BO DIDDLEY	BO DIDDLEY 1969	SOUL TRAIN	10.00
69	8088 DJ	BO DIDDLEY	BO DIDDLEY 1969	SOUL TRAIN	15.00
69	8089	CHUCK BERRY	NO PARTICULAR PLACE TO GO	IT WASN'T ME	8.00
69	8089 DJ	CHUCK BERRY	NO PARTICULAR PLACE TO GO	IT WASN'T ME	10.00
69	8090	FONTELLA BASS	I CAN'T REST	RESCUE ME	10.00
69	8090 DJ	FONTELLA BASS	I CAN'T REST	RESCUE ME	20.00
69	8091	TONY CLARKE	THE ENTERTAINER	AIN'T LOVE GOOD, AIN'T LOVE PR	10.00
69	8091 DJ	TONY CLARKE	THE ENTERTAINER	AIN'T LOVE GOOD, AIN'T LOVE PR	20.00
69	8092	BILLY STEWART	SUMMERTIME	I DO LOVE YOU	15.00
69	8092 DJ	BILLY STEWART	SUMMERTIME	I DO LOVE YOU	20.00
69	8093	SUGAR PIE DE SANTO	SOULFUL DRESS	THERE'S GONNA BE TROUBLE	15.00
69	8093 DJ	SUGAR PIE DE SANTO	SOULFUL DRESS	THERE'S GONNA BE TROUBLE	25.00
69	8094	SOULFUL STRINGS	LISTEN HERE	I WISH IT WOULD RAIN	15.00
69	8094 DJ	SOULFUL STRINGS	LISTEN HERE	I WISH IT WOULD RAIN	25.00
69	8095	WOODY HERMAN	LIGHT MY FIRE	HUSH	10.00
69	8095 DJ	WOODY HERMAN	LIGHT MY FIRE	HUSH	18.00
69	8096	RAMSEY LEWIS	WADE IN THE WATER	CRY BABY CRY	15.00
69	8096 DJ	RAMSEY LEWIS	WADE IN THE WATER	CRY BABY CRY	25.00
69	8097	HOWLIN' WOLF	EVIL	TAIL DAGGER	10.00
69	8097 DJ	HOWLIN' WOLF	EVIL	TAIL DAGGER	15.00
69	8098	JAMO THOMAS	I'LL BE YOUR FOOL	JAMO SOUL	15.00
69	8098 DJ	JAMO THOMAS	I'LL BE YOUR FOOL	JAMO SOUL	25.00
69	8099	DELLS	SING A RAINBOW/LOVE IS BLUE:MEDLEY	HALLELUJAH BABY	6.00
69	8099 DJ	DELLS	SING A RAINBOW/LOVE IS BLUE:MEDLEY	HALLELUJAH BABY	20.00
69	8100	LITTLE MILTON	LET'S GET TOGETHER	I'LL ALWAYS LOVE YOU	15.00
69	8100 DJ	LITTLE MILTON	LET'S GET TOGETHER	I'LL ALWAYS LOVE YOU	22.00
69	8101	HAROLD SMITH'S MAJESTIC CHIOR	WHY AM I TREATED SO BAD	WE CAN ALL WALK A LITTLE PROUDER	10.00
69	8101 DJ	HAROLD SMITH'S MAJESTIC CHIOR	WHY AM I TREATED SO BAD	WE CAN ALL WALK A LITTLE PROUDER	15.00
69	8102	DELLS	OH, WHAT A NIGHT	BELIEVE ME	6.00
69	8102 DJ	DELLS	OH, WHAT A NIGHT	BELIEVE ME	10.00
69	8103	ROTARY CONNECTION	THE WEIGHT	RESPECT	8.00
69	8103 DJ	ROTARY CONNECTION	THE WEIGHT	RESPECT	12.00
70	8104	RAMSEY LEWIS	JULIA	DO WHAT YOU WANNA	8.00
70	8104 DJ	RAMSEY LEWIS	JULIA	DO WHAT YOU WANNA	10.00
70	8105	DELLS	SITTING ON THE DOCK OF THE BAY	WHEN I'M IN YOUR ARMS	8.00
70	8105 DJ	DELLS	SITTING ON THE DOCK OF THE BAY	WHEN I'M IN YOUR ARMS	12.00
70	8106	ROTARY CONNECTION	I WANT TO KNOW	MEMORY BAND	8.00

70	8106 DJ	ROTARY CONNECTION	I WANT TO KNOW	MEMORY BAND	12.00
70	8107	DELLS	OH WHAT A DAY	THE CHANGE WE GO THROUGH (FOR	6.00
70	8107 DJ	DELLS	OH WHAT A DAY	THE CHANGE WE GO THROUGH (FOR	10.00

 # 8107 was the last black label release by PYE distributed label. UK distribution was taken over by PHONOGRAM, label changed to a light blue fade colour, this came inside a redesigned Chess sleeve. Later issues after # 6145021 and represses of the best selling titles were ink screen print injection moulded design labels inside a Phonogram sleeve, these are denoted by the word "ink". The word "paper"after the release # = the normal paper label design.

71	6145001	DELLS	THE LOVE WE HAD (STAYS ON MY MIND)	FREEDOM MEANS	6.00
72	6145002	BO DIDDLEY	I SAID SHUT UP WOMAN	I LOVE YOU MORE THAN YOU'LL EV	6.00
72	6145004 paper	RAMSEY LEWIS	WADE IN THE WATER	AIN'T THAT PECULIAR	8.00
74	6145004 ink	RAMSEY LEWIS	WADE IN THE WATER	AIN'T THAT PECULIAR	5.00
72	6145008	DELLS	IT'S ALL UP TO YOU	OH MY DEAR	30.00
72	6145009 paper	FONTELLA BASS	RESCUE ME	SOUL OF A MAN	8.00
74	6145009 ink	FONTELLA BASS	RESCUE ME	SOUL OF THE MAN	6.00
72	6145010 paper	JOY LOVEJOY	IN ORBIT	UM HUM	15.00
74	6145010 ink	JOY LOVEJOY	IN ORBIT	UH HUM	8.00
72	6145013	RAMSEY LEWIS	THE "IN" CROWD	SOUL MAN	5.00
72	6145016	ETTA JAMES	TELL MAMA + I FOUND LOVE	I'D RATHER GO BLIND	8.00
72	6145017	BILLY STEWART	SITTING IN THE PARK	SUMMERTIME	6.00
72	6145018	KO KO TAYLOR	WANG DANG DOODLE	THE EGG OR THE HEN + VIOLENT L	8.00
72	6145019 ink	CHUCK BERRY	MY DING-A-LING	LET'S BOOGIE	3.00
72	6145019 paper	CHUCK BERRY	MY DING-A-LING	LET'S BOOGIE	3.00
72	6145020	CHUCK BERRY	REELIN' & ROCKIN'	I WILL NOT LET YOU GO	3.00
72	6145021	KOLETTES	WHO'S THAT GUY	JUST HOW MUCH (CAN ONE HEART T	8.00

all 45's after number 6145021 were made with screen print ink injection moulded design label

73	6145022	DELLS	RUN FOR COVER	GIVE YOUR BABY A STANDING OVATION	30.00
73	6145027	CHUCK BERRY	SOUTH OF THE BORDER	BIO	3.00
73	6145029	DELLS	I MISS YOU	DON'T MAKE ME A STORY TELLER	8.00
74	6145030	TONY CLARKE	LANDSLIDE	THE ENTERTAINER	10.00
74	6145033	ETTA JAMES	OUT ON THE STREETS AGAIN	COME A LITTLE CLOSER	6.00
74	6145035	FREE SPIRIT	LOVE YOU JUST AS LONG AS I CAN	AS LONG AS I CAN	10.00
74	6145036	AL DOWNING	I'LL BE HOLDING ON	same: disco version	6.00
74	6145037	DELLS	BRING BACK THE LOVE OF YESTERDAY	LEARNING TO LOVE YOU WAS EASY	8.00
76	6078700	REUBEN WILSON	GOT TO GET YOUR OWN	GOT TO GET YOUR OWN part 2	10.00
84	101 PRT	RAMSEY LEWIS	WADE IN THE WATER	THE IN CROWD	6.00

CHI SOUND see 20th. Century

CHIPPING NORTON

76	2	CHANTS	I'VE BEEN TRYING	LUCKY OLD ME	40.00
76	3	OLYMPIC RUNNERS	DON'T LET UP	PERSONAL THANG	8.00

CHRIS KINGS

Free 45 given away on the door Chris King's 40th. Birthday party.

81156 DJ	MARVIN GAYE	THIS LOVE STARVED HEART OF MINE	same	20.00

CHRYSALIS

76	2087	LEE GARRETT	LOVE ENOUGH FOR TWO	YOU ARE MY EVERYTHING	5.00
76	2101	LEE GARRETT	HEART BE STILL	BROKEN DOWN DJ	6.00
85	2897 PS	DANTE	SO LONG	LOVIN' EYES	8.00

CLOUD ONE

75	1	EXECUTIVE SUITE	WHEN THE FUEL RUNS OUT	YOU GOT IT	8.00
75	2	CHAMBER OF KOMMERCE	FREE TO LIVE	THE MONOCLE	4.00
75	3	EXECUITIVE SUITE	YOU BELIEVED IN ME	YOU BELIEVED IN ME part 2	6.00
75	4	EARTHQUAKE	FRIDAY ON MY MIND	MADNESS	4.00

COLPIX

Another Pye Distributed 60's label that has the same release numbers as the corresponding USA release. Promo copies are either the light lilac label similar to some earlier Cameo Parkway demonstration copies or they are an attractive white, both shades of label have a solid black A in the center of the label.
There are some solid soul collectable recordings from Freddie Scott & Earl-Jean. Girl sound collectors appreciate the Little Eva & The Jewells releases. With the highlight of the label being the rare Cinderellas release which is a very elusive 45 both sides of the Atlantic. The releases from Big Dee Irwin were mostly soul novelty recordings, but he was later to become a mini Northern Soul icon with his Stateside label release.

63	200	NINA SIMONE	YOU CAN HAVE HIM	RETURN HOME	6.00
63	200 DJ	NINA SIMONE	YOU CAN HAVE HIM	RETURN HOME	10.00
64	303 EP PS	NINA SIMONE	FINE AND MELLOW	1964 4 track EP with cover	15.00
66	306 EP PS	NINA SIMONE	JUST SAY I LOVE HIM	1966 4 track EP with cover: inc: Work Song	15.00
66	307 EP PS	NINA SIMONE	I LOVE TO LOVE	1966 4 track EP with cover	15.00
63	692	FREDDIE SCOTT	HEY, GIRL	THE SLIDE	20.00
63	692 DJ	FREDDIE SCOTT	HEY, GIRL	THE SLIDE	30.00
63	709	FREDDIE SCOTT	BRAND NEW WORLD	I GOT A WOMAN	15.00
63	709 DJ	FREDDIE SCOTT	BRAND NEW WORLD	I GOT A WOMAN	25.00
63	712	GIRLFRIENDS	MY ONE AND ONLY, JIMMY BOY	FOR MY SAKE	20.00
63	712 DJ	GIRLFRIENDS	MY ONE AND ONLY, JIMMY BOY	FOR MY SAKE	28.00
64	729	EARL-JEAN	I'M INTO SOMETHING WRONG	WE LOVE AND LEARN	20.00
64	729 DJ	EARL-JEAN	I'M INTO SOMETHING WRONG	WE LOVE AND LEARN	30.00
64	748	EARL-JEAN	RANDY	THEY'RE JEALOUS OF ME	20.00
64	748 DJ	EARL-JEAN	RANDY	THEY'RE JEALOUS OF ME	30.00
64	771	VINCE EDWARDS	SEE THAT GIRL	NO NOT MUCH	20.00
64	771 DJ	VINCE EDWARDS	SEE THAT GIRL	NO NOT MUCH	28.00

64	799	NINA SIMONE	EXACTLY LIKE YOU	THE OTHER WOMAN	6.00
64	799 DJ	NINA SIMONE	EXACTLY LIKE YOU	THE OTHER WOMAN	8.00
63	11010	BIG DEE IRWIN& LITTLE EVA	SWINGING ON A STAR	ANOTHER NIGHT WITH THE BOYS	4.00
63	11010 DJ	BIG DEE IRWIN& LITTLE EVA	SWINGING ON A STAR	ANOTHER NIGHT WITH THE BOYS	6.00
63	11012	COOKIES	WILL POWER	I WANT A BOY FOR MY BIRTHDAY	15.00
63	11012 DJ	COOKIES	WILL POWER	I WANT A BOY FOR MY BIRTHDAY	22.00
63	11013	LITTLE EVA	THE TROUBLE WITH BOYS	WHAT I GOTTA DO (TO MAKE YOU J	15.00
63	11013 DJ	LITTLE EVA	THE TROUBLE WITH BOYS	WHAT I GOTTA DO (TO MAKE YOU J	22.00
63	11019	LITTLE EVA	PLEASE HURT ME	LET'S START THE PARTY AGAIN	10.00
63	11019 DJ	LITTLE EVA	PLEASE HURT ME	LET'S START THE PARTY AGAIN	15.00
64	11020	COOKIES	GIRLS GROW UP FASTER THAN BOYS	ONLY TO OTHER PEOPLE	15.00
64	11020 DJ	COOKIES	GIRLS GROW UP FASTER THAN BOYS	ONLY TO OTHER PEOPLE	22.00
64	11021	BIG DEE IRWIN & LITTLE EVA	I WISH YOU A MERRY CHRISTMAS	CHRISTMAS SONG	5.00
64	11021 DJ	BIG DEE IRWIN & LITTLE EVA	I WISH YOU A MERRY CHRISTMAS	CHRISTMAS SONG	6.00
64	11026	CINDERELLAS	BABY, BABY (I STILL LOVE YOU)	PLEASE DON'T WAKE ME	85.00
64	11026 DJ	CINDERELLAS	BABY, BABY (I STILL LOVE YOU)	PLEASE DON'T WAKE ME	120.00
64	11034	JEWELS	GOTTA FIND A WAY	OPPORTUNITY	30.00
64	11034 DJ	JEWELS	GOTTA FIND A WAY	OPPORTUNITY	45.00
64	11035	LITTLE EVA	RUN TO HER	MAKING WITH THE MAGILLA	10.00
64	11035 DJ	LITTLE EVA	RUN TO HER	MAKING WITH THE MAGILLA	15.00
64	11040	BIG DEE IRWIN	HEIGHO-HO	IT'S MY BIRTHDAY	5.00
64	11040 DJ	BIG DEE IRWIN	HEIGHO-HO	IT'S MY BIRTHDAY	6.00
64	11048	JEWELS	BUT I DO	SMOKEY JOE	15.00
64	11048 DJ	JEWELS	BUT I DO	SMOKEY JOE	25.00
64	11050	BIG DEE IRWIN	PERSONALITY	IT'S ONLY PAPER MOON	5.00
64	11050 DJ	BIG DEE IRWIN	PERSONALITY	IT'S ONLY PAPER MOON	6.00

COLUMBIA

59	4346	OLYMPICS	PRIVATE EYE (BABY)	HULLY GULLY	20.00
59	4346 DJ	OLYMPICS	PRIVATE EYE (BABY)	HULLY GULLY	28.00
59	4377	JOHNNY WELLS	LONELY MOON	THE ONE AND ONLY ONE	40.00
59	4377 DJ	JOHNNY WELLS	LONELY MOON	THE ONE AND ONLY ONE	50.00
60	4404	DAVE BABY CORTEZ	PIANO SHUFFLE	DAVE'S SPECIAL	10.00
60	4404 DJ	DAVE BABY CORTEZ	PIANO SHUFFLE	DAVE'S SPECIAL	15.00
60	4412	RONNIE HAWKINS	STOLEN LOVE	LOVE ME LIKE YOU CAN	50.00
60	4412 DJ	RONNIE HAWKINS	STOLEN LOVE	LOVE ME LIKE YOU CAN	75.00
60	4503	CHUBBY CHECKER	THE TWIST	TOOT	8.00
60	4503 DJ	CHUBBY CHECKER	THE TWIST	TOOT	15.00
60	4541	CHUBBY CHECKER	THE HUCKLEBUCK	WHOLE LOTTA SHAKIN' GOIN' ON	10.00
60	4541 DJ	CHUBBY CHECKER	THE HUCKLEBUCK	WHOLE LOTTA SHAKIN' GOIN' ON	15.00
61	4591	CHUBBY CHECKER	PONY TIME	OH SUSANNAH	6.00
61	4591 DJ	CHUBBY CHECKER	PONY TIME	OH SUSANNAH	10.00
61	4606	RICHARD MALTBY	THE RAT RACE	WALKIE TALKIE	15.00
61	4606 DJ	RICHARD MALTBY	THE RAT RACE	WALKIE TALKIE	25.00
61	4652	CHUBBY CHECKER	GOOD GOOD LOVING	MESS AROUND	8.00
61	4652 DJ	CHUBBY CHECKER	GOOD GOOD LOVING	MESS AROUND	10.00
61	4678	CLEFTONES	HEART AND SOUL	HOW DO YOU FEEL	150.00
61	4678 DJ	CLEFTONES	HEART AND SOUL	HOW DO YOU FEEL	175.00
61	4691	CHUBBY CHECKER	EVERYTHING'S GONNA BE ALRIGHT	LET'S TWIST AGAIN	4.00
61	4691 DJ	CHUBBY CHECKER	EVERYTHING'S GONNA BE ALRIGHT	LET'S TWIST AGAIN	8.00
61	4693	SPINNERS	THAT'S WHAT LITTLE GIRLS ARE MADE	HEEBIE JEEBIES	150.00
61	4693 DJ	SPINNERS	THAT'S WHAT LITTLE GIRLS ARE MADE	HEEBIE JEEBIES	200.00
61	4718	DOVELLS	THE BRISTOL STOMP	OUT IN THE COLD AGAIN	15.00
61	4718 DJ	DOVELLS	THE BRISTOL STOMP	OUT IN THE COLD AGAIN	20.00
61	4719	CARL and the COMMANDERS	FARMER JOHN	CLEANIN' UP	15.00
61	4719 DJ	CARL and the COMMANDERS	FARMER JOHN	CLEANIN' UP	22.00
61	4720	CLEFTONES	(I LOVE YOU) FOR SENTIMENTAL	DEED I DO	75.00
61	4720 DJ	CLEFTONES	(I LOVE YOU) FOR SENTIMENTAL	DEED I DO	100.00
61	4728	CHUBBY CHECKER	THE FLY	THAT'S THE WAY IT GOES	8.00
61	4728 DJ	CHUBBY CHECKER	THE FLY	THAT'S THE WAY IT GOES	10.00
61	4743	JERRY BUTLER	AWARE OF LOVE	MOON RIVER	25.00
61	4743 DJ	JERRY BUTLER	AWARE OF LOVE	MOON RIVER	30.00
62	4768	DEE CLARK	DON'T WALK AWAY FROM ME	YOU'RE TELLING OUR SECRETS	25.00
62	4768 DJ	DEE CLARK	DON'T WALK AWAY FROM ME	YOU'RE TELLING OUR SECRETS	35.00
62	4782	HELEN SHAPIRO	TELL ME WHAT HE SAID	I APOLOGISE	6.00
62	4782 DJ	HELEN SHAPIRO	TELL ME WHAT HE SAID	I APOLOGISE	15.00
62	4793	GENE CHANDLER	DUKE OF EARL	KISSIN' IN THE KITCHEN	15.00
62	4793 DJ	GENE CHANDLER	DUKE OF EARL	KISSIN' IN THE KITCHEN	25.00
62	4808	CHUBBY CHECKER	SLOW TWISTIN'	LOSE YOUR INHIBITIONS AND TWIS	6.00
62	4808 DJ	CHUBBY CHECKER	SLOW TWISTIN'	LOSE YOUR INHIBITIONS AND TWIS	10.00
62	4810	DOVELLS	DO THE NEW CONTINENTAL	MOPITTY MOPE STOMP	15.00
62	4810 DJ	DOVELLS	DO THE NEW CONTINENTAL	MOPITTY MOPE STOMP	20.00
62	4818	DEE DEE SHARP	SET MY HEART AT EASE	MASHED POTATO TIME	20.00
62	4818 DJ	DEE DEE SHARP	SET MY HEART AT EASE	MASHED POTATO TIME	30.00
62	4838	DR. FEELGOOD and the INTERNS	DR. FEELGOOD	MISTER MOONLIGHT	15.00
62	4838 DJ	DR. FEELGOOD and the INTERNS	DR. FEELGOOD	MISTER MOONLIGHT	20.00
62	4865	ORLONS	THE WAH WATUSI	HOLIDAY HILL	40.00
62	4865 DJ	ORLONS	THE WAH WATUSI	HOLIDAY HILL	70.00
62	4874	DEE DEE SHARP	BABY CAKES	GRAVY (FOR MY MASHED POTATOES)	20.00

62	4874 DJ	DEE DEE SHARP	BABY CAKES	GRAVY (FOR MY MASHED POTATOES)	30.00
62	4876	CHUBBY CHECKER	DANCIN' PARTY	GOTTA GET MYSELF TOGETHER	5.00
62	4876 DJ	CHUBBY CHECKER	DANCIN' PARTY	GOTTA GET MYSELF TOGETHER	8.00
62	4877	DOVELLS	BRISTOL TWISTIN' ANNIE	THE ACTOR	15.00
62	4877 DJ	DOVELLS	BRISTOL TWISTIN' ANNIE	THE ACTOR	20.00
62	4891	ADAM WADE	I'M CLIMBIN' (THE WALL)	THEY DON'T BELIEVE ME	20.00
62	4891 DJ	ADAM WADE	I'M CLIMBIN' (THE WALL)	THEY DON'T BELIEVE ME	28.00
62	4905	JOEY DEE & the STARLIGHTERS	WHAT KIND OF LOVE IS THIS	WING DING	30.00
62	4905 DJ	JOEY DEE & the STARLIGHTERS	WHAT KIND OF LOVE IS THIS	WING DING	40.00
62	4954	TONY ORLANDO	THE LONELIEST	BEAUTIFUL DREAMER	22.00
62	4954 DJ	TONY ORLANDO	THE LONELIEST	BEAUTIFUL DREAMER	32.00
63	4966	HELEN SHAPIRO	QUEEN FOR TONIGHT	DADDY COULDN'T GET ME ONE OF T	20.00
63	4966 DJ	HELEN SHAPIRO	QUEEN FOR TONIGHT	DADDY COULDN'T GET ME ONE OF T	30.00
63	4986	ADAM WADE	RAIN FROM THE SKIES	DON'T LET ME CROSS OVER	100.00
63	4986 DJ	ADAM WADE	RAIN FROM THE SKIES	DON'T LET ME CROSS OVER	150.00
63	4988	CLEFTONES	THERE SHE GOES	LOVER COME BACK TO ME	100.00
63	4988 DJ	CLEFTONES	THERE SHE GOES	LOVER COME BACK TO ME	150.00
63	7012	RICHARD WYLIE	BRAND NEW MAN	SO MUCH LOVE IN MY HEART	20.00
63	7012 DJ	RICHARD WYLIE	BRAND NEW MAN	SO MUCH LOVE IN MY HEART	30.00
63	7029	MIKE COTTON JAZZMEN	SWING THAT HAMMER	HEARTACHES	10.00
63	7029 DJ	MIKE COTTON JAZZMEN	SWING THAT HAMMER	HEARTACHES	15.00
63	7049	DINAH WASHINGTON	SOULVILLE	LET ME BE THE FIRST TOKNOW	10.00
63	7049 DJ	DINAH WASHINGTON	SOULVILLE	LET ME BE THE FIRST TOKNOW	15.00
63	7051	RAY BARRETTO	EL WATUSI	RITMO SABROSO	30.00
63	7051 DJ	RAY BARRETTO	EL WATUSI	RITMO SABROSO	45.00
63	7077	ESSEX	EASIER SAID THAN DONE	ARE YOU GOING MY WAY	15.00
63	7077 DJ	ESSEX	EASIER SAID THAN DONE	ARE YOU GOING MY WAY	25.00
63	7088	PATSY ANN NOBLE	HE TELLS ME WITH HIS EYES	ACCIDENTS WILL HAPPEN	15.00
63	7088 DJ	PATSY ANN NOBLE	HE TELLS ME WITH HIS EYES	ACCIDENTS WILL HAPPEN	20.00
63	7099	MAJOR LANCE	THE MONKEY TIME	MAMA DIDN'T KNOW	30.00
63	7099 DJ	MAJOR LANCE	THE MONKEY TIME	MAMA DIDN'T KNOW	75.00
63	7118	JULIE DRISCOLL	TAKE ME BY THE HAND	STAY AWAY FROM ME	25.00
63	7118 DJ	JULIE DRISCOLL	TAKE ME BY THE HAND	STAY AWAY FROM ME	30.00
63	7122	ESSEX	A WALKIN' MIRACLE	WHAT I DFON'T KNOW WON'T HURT	15.00
63	7122 DJ	ESSEX	A WALKIN' MIRACLE	WHAT I DFON'T KNOW WON'T HURT	25.00
63	7168	MAJOR LANCE	HEY LITTLE GIRL	CRYING IN THE RAIN	30.00
63	7168 DJ	MAJOR LANCE	HEY LITTLE GIRL	CRYING IN THE RAIN	70.00
63	7178	ESSEX	SHE'S GOT EVERYTHING	OUT OF SIGHT OUT OF MIND	15.00
63	7178 DJ	ESSEX	SHE'S GOT EVERYTHING	OUT OF SIGHT OUT OF MIND	20.00
64	7190	HELEN SHAPIRO	FEVER	OLE FATHER TIME	15.00
64	7190 DJ	HELEN SHAPIRO	FEVER	OLE FATHER TIME	20.00
64	7193	GEORGIE FAME & the BLUE FLAMES	DO THE DOG	SHOP AROUND	18.00
64	7193 DJ	GEORGIE FAME & the BLUE FLAMES	DO THE DOG	SHOP AROUND	25.00
64	7205	MAJOR LANCE	UM, UM, UM, UM, UM, UM	SWEET MUSIC	15.00
64	7205 DJ	MAJOR LANCE	UM, UM, UM, UM, UM, UM	SWEET MUSIC	70.00
64	7212	EARL GUEST	FOXY	BEGIN THE BEGUINE	25.00
64	7212 DJ	EARL GUEST	FOXY	BEGIN THE BEGUINE	35.00
64	7228	DR. FEELGOOD and the INTERNS	THE DOCTOR'S BOOGIE	BLANG DANG	15.00
64	7228 DJ	DR. FEELGOOD and the INTERNS	THE DOCTOR'S BOOGIE	BLANG DANG	20.00
64	7239	SOUNDS INCORPATED	DETROIT	THE SPARTANS	15.00
64	7239 DJ	SOUNDS INCORPATED	DETROIT	THE SPARTANS	20.00
64	7255	GEORGIE FAME & the BLUE FLAMES	GREEN ONIONS	DO-RE-MI	15.00
64	7255 DJ	GEORGIE FAME & the BLUE FLAMES	GREEN ONIONS	DO-RE-MI	25.00
64	7256	DEVOTIONS	RIP VAN WINKLE	I LOVE YOU FOR SENTIMENTAL REA	40.00
64	7256 DJ	DEVOTIONS	RIP VAN WINKLE	I LOVE YOU FOR SENTIMENTAL REA	50.00
64	7257	MADELINE BELL	DON'T CROSS OVER TO MY SIDE OF THE	YOU DON'T LOVE ME NO MORE	20.00
64	7257 DJ	MADELINE BELL	DON'T CROSS OVER TO MY SIDE OF THE	YOU DON'T LOVE ME NO MORE	28.00
64	7266	HELEN SHAPIRO	LOOK OVER YOU SHOULDER	YOU WON'T COME HOME	30.00
64	7266 DJ	HELEN SHAPIRO	LOOK OVER YOU SHOULDER	YOU WON'T COME HOME	40.00
64	7270	LOUISANA RED	KEEP YOUR HANDS OFF MY WOMAN	DON'T CRY	20.00
64	7270 DJ	LOUISANA RED	KEEP YOUR HANDS OFF MY WOMAN	DON'T CRY	28.00
64	7271	MAJOR LANCE	THE MATADOR	GONNA GET MARRIED	30.00
64	7271 DJ	MAJOR LANCE	THE MATADOR	GONNA GET MARRIED	70.00
64	7287	JEAN and the STATESIDERS	ONE FINE DAY	PUTTY IN YOUR HANDS	15.00
64	7287 DJ	JEAN and the STATESIDERS	ONE FINE DAY	PUTTY IN YOUR HANDS	20.00
64	7288	TONY ORLANDO	SHE DOESN'T KNOW IT	TELL ME WHAT I CAN DO	30.00
64	7288 DJ	TONY ORLANDO	SHE DOESN'T KNOW IT	TELL ME WHAT I CAN DO	45.00
64	7300	DOWNLINERS SECT	BABY WHAT'S WRONG	BE A SECT MANIAC	25.00
64	7300 DJ	DOWNLINERS SECT	BABY WHAT'S WRONG	BE A SECT MANIAC	30.00
64	7321	SOUNDS ORCHESTRAL	RINKY DINK	SPANISH HARLEM	10.00
64	7321 DJ	SOUNDS ORCHESTRAL	RINKY DINK	SPANISH HARLEM	15.00
64	7328	GEORGIE FAME & the BLUE FLAMES	BEND A LITTLE	I'M IN LOVE WITH YOU	10.00
64	7328 DJ	GEORGIE FAME & the BLUE FLAMES	BEND A LITTLE	I'M IN LOVE WITH YOU	15.00
64	7340	HELEN SHAPIRO	HE KNOWS HOW TO LOVE ME	SHOP AROUND	100.00
64	7340 DJ	HELEN SHAPIRO	HE KNOWS HOW TO LOVE ME	SHOP AROUND	200.00
64	7346	BILLIE DAVIS and the LeROYS	WHATCHA' GONNA DO	EVERYBODY KNOWS	15.00
64	7346 DJ	BILLIE DAVIS and the LeROYS	WHATCHA' GONNA DO	EVERYBODY KNOWS	25.00
64	7365	MAJOR LANCE	RHYTHM	PLEASE DON'T SAY NO MORE	30.00
64	7365 DJ	MAJOR LANCE	RHYTHM	PLEASE DON'T SAY NO MORE	85.00

64	7399	THREE BELLS	HE DOESN'T LOVE ME	SOFTLY IN THE NIGHT	15.00
64	7399 DJ	THREE BELLS	HE DOESN'T LOVE ME	SOFTLY IN THE NIGHT	20.00
64	7403	SUSAN HOLLIDAY	ANY DAY NOW	DON'T COME KNOCKING AT MY DOOR	10.00
64	7403 DJ	SUSAN HOLLIDAY	ANY DAY NOW	DON'T COME KNOCKING AT MY DOOR	15.00
64	7428	GEORGIE FAME & the BLUE FLAMES	YEAH, YEAH	PREACH AND TEACH	5.00
64	7428 DJ	GEORGIE FAME & the BLUE FLAMES	YEAH, YEAH	PREACH AND TEACH	15.00
64	7428 DJ PS	GEORGIE FAME & the BLUE FLAMES	YEH YEH	PREACH AND TEACH	75.00
64	7433	EARL ROYCE & the OLYMPICS	QUE SERA SERA	I REALLY DO	20.00
64	7433 DJ	EARL ROYCE & the OLYMPICS	QUE SERA SERA	I REALLY DO	25.00
64	7439	JEAN and the STATESIDERS	YOU WON'T FORGET ME	COLD, COLD WINTER	15.00
64	7439 DJ	JEAN and the STATESIDERS	YOU WON'T FORGET ME	COLD, COLD WINTER	20.00
65	7450	DANY CHANDELLE	LYING AWAKE	LOVE YOU	30.00
65	7450 DJ	DANY CHANDELLE	LYING AWAKE	LOVE YOU	45.00
65	7451	KUBAS	MAGIC POTION	I LOVE HER	30.00
65	7451 DJ	KUBAS	MAGIC POTION	I LOVE HER	40.00
65	7460	SCREAMING JAY HAWKINS	THE WHAMMY	STRANGE	20.00
65	7460 DJ	SCREAMING JAY HAWKINS	THE WHAMMY	STRANGE	30.00
65	7463	MAJOR LANCE	I'M SO LOST	SOMETIMES I WONDER	25.00
65	7463 DJ	MAJOR LANCE	I'M SO LOST	SOMETIMES I WONDER	60.00
65	7471	GRAHAM BOND ORGANISATION	WADE IN THE WATER	TAMMY	30.00
65	7471 DJ	GRAHAM BOND ORGANISATION	WADE IN THE WATER	TAMMY	45.00
65	7479	EXCITERS	TONIGHT, TONIGHT	I WANT YOU TO BE MY BOY	15.00
65	7479 DJ	EXCITERS	TONIGHT, TONIGHT	I WANT YOU TO BE MY BOY	20.00
65	7488	BO STREET RUNNERS	TELL ME WHAT YOU'RE GONNA DO	AND I DO JUST WHAT I WANT	75.00
65	7488 DJ	BO STREET RUNNERS	TELL ME WHAT YOU'RE GONNA DO	AND I DO JUST WHAT I WANT	85.00
65	7494	GEORGIE FAME & the BLUE FLAMES	IN THE MEANTIME	TELEGRAM	8.00
65	7494 DJ	GEORGIE FAME & the BLUE FLAMES	IN THE MEANTIME	TELEGRAM	10.00
65	7512	MADELINE BELL	DAYTIME	DON'T CRY MY HEART	5.00
65	7512 DJ	MADELINE BELL	DAYTIME	DON'T CRY MY HEART	8.00
65	7518	ZOOT MONEY'S BIG ROLL BAND	GOOD	BRING IT HOME TO ME	20.00
65	7518 DJ	ZOOT MONEY'S BIG ROLL BAND	GOOD	BRING IT HOME TO ME	28.00
65	7519	CINDY COLE	A LOVE LIKE YOURS	HE'S SURE THE BOY I LOVE	10.00
65	7519 DJ	CINDY COLE	A LOVE LIKE YOURS	HE'S SURE THE BOY I LOVE	15.00
65	7527	MAJOR LANCE	COME SEE	YOU BELONG TO ME MY LOVE	25.00
65	7527 DJ	MAJOR LANCE	COME SEE	YOU BELONG TO ME MY LOVE	60.00
65	7528	GRAHAM BOND ORGANISATION	TELL ME (I'M GONNA LOVE AGAIN)	LOVE COME SHINING THROUGH	30.00
65	7528 DJ	GRAHAM BOND ORGANISATION	TELL ME (I'M GONNA LOVE AGAIN)	LOVE COME SHINING THROUGH	40.00
65	7537	MARION ANGEL	IT'S GONNA BE ALRIGHT	TOMORROW'S FOOL	30.00
65	7537 DJ	MARION ANGEL	IT'S GONNA BE ALRIGHT	TOMORROW'S FOOL	40.00
65	7544	EXCITERS	JUST NOT READY	ARE YOU SATISFIED	15.00
65	7544 DJ	EXCITERS	JUST NOT READY	ARE YOU SATISFIED	20.00
65	7563	MARTIN RAYNOR & the SECRETS	CANDY TO ME	YOU'RE A WONDEFUL ONE	50.00
65	7563 DJ	MARTIN RAYNOR & the SECRETS	CANDY TO ME	YOU'RE A WONDEFUL ONE	70.00
65	7570	THREE BELLS	SOMEONE TO LOVE	OVER AND OVER AGAIN	10.00
65	7570 DJ	THREE BELLS	SOMEONE TO LOVE	OVER AND OVER AGAIN	15.00
65	7590	BRIAN AUGER TRINITY	FOOL KILLER	LET'S DO IT TONIGHT	30.00
65	7590 DJ	BRIAN AUGER TRINITY	FOOL KILLER	LET'S DO IT TONIGHT	45.00
65	7592	JIMMY JONES	WALKIN'	PARDON ME	70.00
65	7592 DJ	JIMMY JONES	WALKIN'	PARDON ME	85.00
65	7600	ZOOT MONEY'S BIG ROLL BAND	PLEASE STAY	YOU KNOW YOU'LL CRY	20.00
65	7600 DJ	ZOOT MONEY'S BIG ROLL BAND	PLEASE STAY	YOU KNOW YOU'LL CRY	28.00
65	7606	EXCITERS	RUN MASCARA	MY FATHER	15.00
65	7606 DJ	EXCITERS	RUN MASCARA	MY FATHER	25.00
65	7609	MAJOR LANCE	I'M THE ONE	PRIDE AND JOY	40.00
65	7609 DJ	MAJOR LANCE	I'M THE ONE	PRIDE AND JOY	85.00
65	7616	SUSAN HOLLIDAY	SOMETIMES	LONG HAIRED BOY	15.00
65	7616 DJ	SUSAN HOLLIDAY	SOMETIMES	LONG HAIRED BOY	25.00
65	7620	WALTER JACKSON	BLOWIN' IN THE WIND	WELCOME HOME	40.00
65	7620 DJ	WALTER JACKSON	BLOWIN' IN THE WIND	WELCOME HOME	75.00
65	7621	RAM JAM BAND	SHAKE SHAKE SHAKE	AKINIA	15.00
65	7621 DJ	RAM JAM BAND	SHAKE SHAKE SHAKE	AKINIA	20.00
65	7633	GEORGIE FAME & the BLUE FLAMES	LIKE WE USED TO BE	IT AIN'T RIGHT	6.00
65	7633 DJ	GEORGIE FAME & the BLUE FLAMES	LIKE WE USED TO BE	IT AIN'T RIGHT	8.00
65	7640	BO STREET RUNNERS	BABY NEVER SAY GOODBYE	GET OUT OF MY WAY	75.00
65	7640 DJ	BO STREET RUNNERS	BABY NEVER SAY GOODBYE	GET OUT OF MY WAY	85.00
65	7645	JANE MORGAN	MAYBE	WALKING THE STREETS IN THE RAIN	20.00
65	7645 DJ	JANE MORGAN	MAYBE	WALKING THE STREETS IN THE RAIN	30.00
65	7647	GRAHAM BOND ORGANISATION	LEASE ON LOVE	HEART'S IN LITTLE PIECES	25.00
65	7647 DJ	GRAHAM BOND ORGANISATION	LEASE ON LOVE	HEART'S IN LITTLE PIECES	30.00
65	7651	JEAN and the STATESIDERS	MAMA DIDN'T LIE	JUST LET ME CRY	25.00
65	7651 DJ	JEAN and the STATESIDERS	MAMA DIDN'T LIE	JUST LET ME CRY	30.00
65	7653	JIMMY JAMES & the VAGABONDS	SOO BE DOO YOU'RE MINE	WE'LL NEVER STOP LOVING YOU	15.00
65	7653 DJ	JIMMY JAMES & the VAGABONDS	SOO BE DOO YOU'RE MINE	WE'LL NEVER STOP LOVING YOU	20.00
65	7657	MIKE VICKERS	ON THE BRINK	THE PUFF ADDER	**102.00**
65	7657 DJ	MIKE VICKERS	ON THE BRINK	THE PUFF ADDER	150.00
65	7676	SOUNDS INCORPATED	MY LITTLE RED BOOK	JUSTICE NEDDI	15.00
65	7676 DJ	SOUNDS INCORPATED	MY LITTLE RED BOOK	JUSTICE NEDDI	20.00
65	7684	RAY BARRETTO	EL WATUSI	SWINGIN' SHEPHERD BLUES	25.00
65	7684 DJ	RAY BARRETTO	EL WATUSI	SWINGING SHEPHERD BLUES	40.00

65	7688	MAJOR LANCE	DARK AND LONELY	TOO HOT TO HOLD	30.00
65	7688 DJ	MAJOR LANCE	DARK AND LONELY	TOO HOT TO HOLD	75.00
65	7694	DEREK MARTIN	YOU BETTER GO	YOU KNOW	30.00
65	7694 DJ	DEREK MARTIN	YOU BETTER GO	YOU KNOW	45.00
65	7697	ZOOT MONEY'S BIG ROLL BAND	STUBBORN KIND OF FELLOW	SOMETHING IS WORRYING ME	25.00
65	7697 DJ	ZOOT MONEY'S BIG ROLL BAND	STUBBORN KIND OF FELLOW	SOMETHING IS WORRYING ME	30.00
65	7710	DIXIE DRIFTER	SOUL HEAVEN	THREE CHAIRS THEME	15.00
65	7710 DJ	DIXIE DRIFTER	SOUL HEAVEN	THREE CHAIRS THEME	20.00
65	7715	BRIAN AUGER TRINITY	GREEN ONIONS	KIKO	30.00
65	7715 DJ	BRIAN AUGER TRINITY	GREEN ONIONS	KIKO	40.00
65	7718	BERYL MARSDEN	GONNA MAKE HIM MY BABY	WHO YOU GONNA HURT?	15.00
65	7718 DJ	BERYL MARSDEN	GONNA MAKE HIM MY BABY	WHO YOU GONNA HURT?	20.00
65	7719	JACKI BOND	MY SISTER'S BOY	NOW I KNOW	8.00
65	7719 DJ	JACKI BOND	MY SISTER'S BOY	NOW I KNOW	12.00
65	7727	GEORGIE FAME & the BLUE FLAMES	OUTRAGE	SOMETHING	8.00
65	7727 DJ	GEORGIE FAME & the BLUE FLAMES	OUTRAGE	SOMETHING	15.00
65	7737	SOUNDS INCORPATED	ON THE BRINK	I'M COMING THROUGH	30.00
65	7737 DJ	SOUNDS INCORPATED	ON THE BRINK	I'M COMING THROUGH	40.00
65	7748	SUE & SUNNY	EVERY OUNCE OF STRENGTH	SO REMEMBER	8.00
65	7748 DJ	SUE & SUNNY	EVERY OUNCE OF STRENGTH	SO REMEMBER	10.00
65	7768	PAUL & ZOOT WILLIAMS	JUMP BACK	THE MANY FACES OF LOVE	20.00
65	7768 DJ	PAUL & ZOOT WILLIAMS	JUMP BACK	THE MANY FACES OF LOVE	28.00
65	7783	BARRY ST. JOHN	GOTTA BRAND NEW MAN	COME AWAY MELINDA	10.00
65	7783 DJ	BARRY ST. JOHN	GOTTA BRAND NEW MAN	COME AWAY MELINDA	15.00
65	7787	MAJOR LANCE	EVERYBODY LOVES A GOOD TIME	I JUST CAN'T HELP IT	45.00
65	7787 DJ	MAJOR LANCE	EVERYBODY LOVES A GOOD TIME	I JUST CAN'T HELP IT	85.00
65	7797	BERYL MARSDEN	BREAK-A-WAY	MUSIC TALK	15.00
65	7797 DJ	BERYL MARSDEN	BREAK-A-WAY	MUSIC TALK	25.00
66	7801	MOOD-MOSAIC	A TOUCH OF VELVET - A STING OF BRASS	BOND STREET P.M.	40.00
66	7801 DJ	MOOD-MOSAIC	A TOUCH OF VELVET - A STING OF BRASS	BOND STREET P.M.	**79.00**
65	7809	NANCY AMES	FRIENDS AND LOVERS FOREVER	I'VE GOT A LOT OF LOVE	10.00
65	7809 DJ	NANCY AMES	FRIENDS AND LOVERS FOREVER	I'VE GOT A LOT OF LOVE	15.00
65	7822	CHEROKEES	LAND OF A 1000 DANCES	EVERYBODY'S NEEDS	10.00
65	7822 DJ	CHEROKEES	LAND OF A 1000 DANCES	EVERYBODY'S NEEDS	15.00
66	7824	DIANE FERREZ	ME AND YOU	DON'T PRETEND	10.00
66	7824 DJ	DIANE FERREZ	ME AND YOU	DON'T PRETEND	15.00
66	7826	GIDIAN	THERE ISN'T ANYTHING	TRY ME OUT	20.00
66	7826 DJ	GIDIAN	THERE ISN'T ANYTHING	TRY ME OUT	30.00
66	7838	GRAHAM BOND ORGANISATION	ST. JAMES INFIRMARY	SOUL TANGO	30.00
66	7838 DJ	GRAHAM BOND ORGANISATION	ST. JAMES INFIRMARY	SOUL TANGO	40.00
66	7843	GRAHAM BONNEY	SUPER GIRL	HILL OF LOVIN'	15.00
66	7843 DJ	GRAHAM BONNEY	SUPER GIRL	HILL OF LOVIN'	50.00
66	7851	JOHNNY PEARSON ORCHESTRA	THE RAT CATCHERS THEME	WEAVER'S GREEN THEME	15.00
66	7851 DJ	JOHNNY PEARSON ORCHESTRA	THE RAT CATCHERS THEME	WEAVER'S GREEN THEME	20.00
66	7859	PERSUASIONS	LA, LA, LA, LA, LA	OPPORTUNITY	20.00
66	7859 DJ	PERSUASIONS	LA, LA, LA, LA, LA	OPPORTUNITY	28.00
66	7868	BARRY ST. JOHN	EVERYTHING I TOUCH TURNS TO TEARS	SOUNDS LIKE MY BABY	85.00
66	7868 DJ	BARRY ST. JOHN	EVERYTHING I TOUCH TURNS TO TEARS	SOUNDS LIKE MY BABY	120.00
66	7869	ROGER YOUNG	SWEET SWEET MORNING	WHATCHA GONNA GIVE ME	25.00
66	7869 DJ	ROGER YOUNG	SWEET SWEET MORNING	WHATCHA GONNA GIVE ME	30.00
66	7876	ZOOT MONEY'S BIG ROLL BAND	LET'S RUN FOR COVER	SELF-DISCIPLINE	20.00
66	7876 DJ	ZOOT MONEY'S BIG ROLL BAND	LET'S RUN FOR COVER	SELF-DISCIPLINE	28.00
66	7879	POPPIES	LULLABY OF LOVE	I WONDER WHY	30.00
66	7879 DJ	POPPIES	LULLABY OF LOVE	I WONDER WHY	50.00
66	7888	BERYL MARSDEN	LET'S GO SOMEWHERE	WHAT'S SHE GOT	15.00
66	7888 DJ	BERYL MARSDEN	LET'S GO SOMEWHERE	WHAT'S SHE GOT	20.00
66	7895	VIBRATIONS	CANADIAN SUNSET	THE STORY OF A STARRY NIGHT	20.00
66	7895 DJ	VIBRATIONS	CANADIAN SUNSET	THE STORY OF A STARRY NIGHT	30.00
66	7898	DEANO	I'M SO HAPPY	STARLIGHT, STARBRIGHT	20.00
66	7898 DJ	DEANO	I'M SO HAPPY	STARLIGHT, STARBRIGHT	28.00
66	7899	KAROL KEYES	THE GOOD LOVE, THE BAD LOVE	A FOOL IN LOVE	15.00
66	7899 DJ	KAROL KEYES	THE GOOD LOVE, THE BAD LOVE	A FOOL IN LOVE	20.00
66	7901	BO STREET RUNNERS	DRIVE MY CAR	SO VERY WOMAN	40.00
66	7901 DJ	BO STREET RUNNERS	DRIVE MY CAR	SO VERY WOMAN	45.00
66	7911	WAYNE GIBSON	UNDER MY THUMB	IT ALWAYS HAPPENS SAME LBL	45.00
66	7911 DJ	WAYNE GIBSON	UNDER MY THUMB	IT ALWAYS HAPPENS SAME LBL	100.00
66	7915	LINDA KAYE	I CAN'T STOP THINKING ABOUT YOU	WHEN WE MEET AGAIN	20.00
66	7915 DJ	LINDA KAYE	I CAN'T STOP THINKING ABOUT YOU	WHEN WE MEET AGAIN	30.00
66	7915	LINDA KAYE	I CAN'T STOP THINKING ABOUT YOU	WHEN WE MEET AGAIN	45.00
66	7918 DJ	JANE HILLERY	YOU'VE GOT THAT HOLD ON ME	TAKE ME AWAY	60.00
66	7946	GEORGIE FAME & the BLUE FLAMES	GETAWAY	EL BANDIDO	8.00
66	7946	GEORGIE FAME & the BLUE FLAMES	GETAWAY	EL BANDIDO	15.00
66	7949	WALTER JACKSON	IT'S AN UP HILL CLIMB TO THE BOTTOM	TEAR FOR TEAR	100.00
66	7949 DJ	WALTER JACKSON	IT'S AN UP HILL CLIMB TO THE BOTTOM	TEAR FOR TEAR	**234.00**
66	7964	RICHARD KENT STYLE	GO, GO CHILDREN	NO MATTER WHAT YOU DO	150.00
66	7964 DJ	RICHARD KENT STYLE	GO, GO CHILDREN	NO MATTER WHAT YOU DO	200.00
66	7967	MAJOR LANCE	INVESTIGATE	LITTLE YOUNG LOVER	75.00
66	7967 DJ	MAJOR LANCE	INVESTIGATE	LITTLE YOUNG LOVER	150.00
66	7973	CINDY COLE	JUST BEING YOU BABY (TURNS ME ON)	LONELY CITY BLUE BOY	30.00

66	7973 DJ	CINDY COLE	JUST BEING YOU BABY (TURNS ME ON)	LONELY CITY BLUE BOY	40.00
66	7974	LITTLE RICHARD	POOR DOG (WHO CAN'T WAG HIS OWN	WELL	30.00
66	7974 DJ	LITTLE RICHARD	POOR DOG (WHO CAN'T WAG HIS OWN	WELL	50.00
66	7975	ZOOT MONEY'S BIG ROLL BAND	BIG TIME OPERATOR	ZOOT'S SERMON	25.00
66	7975 DJ	ZOOT MONEY'S BIG ROLL BAND	BIG TIME OPERATOR	ZOOT'S SERMON	50.00
66	7980	THREE BELLS	CRY NO MORE	HE DOESN'T WANT YOU	40.00
66	7980 DJ	THREE BELLS	CRY NO MORE	HE DOESN'T WANT YOU	60.00
66	7988	KOOBAS	SWEET MUSIC	FACE	45.00
66	7988 DJ	KOOBAS	SWEET MUSIC	FACE	60.00
66	7991	SALENA JONES	I AM YOURS (mon credo)	I ONLY KNOW I LOVE YOU	5.00
66	7991 DJ	SALENA JONES	I AM YOURS (mon credo)	I ONLY KNOW I LOVE YOU	8.00
66	7994	PAUL KORDA	JUST COME CLOSER TO ME	GO ON HOME	60.00
66	7994 DJ	PAUL KORDA	JUST COME CLOSER TO ME	GO ON HOME	85.00
66	8001	KAROL KEYES	ONE IN A MILLION	DON'T JUMP	100.00
66	8001 DJ	KAROL KEYES	ONE IN A MILLION	DON'T JUMP	140.00
66	8005	GRAHAM BONNEY	MIXED UP BABY GIRL	NO ONE KNOWS	10.00
66	8005 DJ	GRAHAM BONNEY	MIXED UP BABY GIRL	NO ONE KNOWS	15.00
66	8015	GEORGIE FAME	SUNNY	DON'T MAKE PROMISES	8.00
66	8015 DJ	GEORGIE FAME	SUNNY	DON'T MAKE PROMISES	10.00
66	8039	NANCY AMES	I DON'T WANT TO TALK ABOUT IT	CRY SOFTLY	300.00
66	8039 DJ	NANCY AMES	I DON'T WANT TO TALK ABOUT IT	CRY SOFTLY	**293.00**

stock copy of this 45 is much rarer than the DJ

66	8046	TOMMY TATE	A LOVER'S REWARD	BIG BLUE DIAMONDS	100.00
66	8046 DJ	TOMMY TATE	A LOVER'S REWARD	BIG BLUE DIAMONDS	120.00
66	8051	RICHARD KENT STYLE	YOU PUT ME DOWN	ALL GOOD THINGS	50.00
66	8051 DJ	RICHARD KENT STYLE	YOU PUT ME DOWN	ALL GOOD THINGS	70.00
66	8054	WALTER JACKSON	NOT YOU	A CORNER IN THE SUN	30.00
66	8054 DJ	WALTER JACKSON	NOT YOU	A CORNER IN THE SUN	50.00
66	8058	LITTLE RICHARD	I NEED LOVE	THE COMMANDMENTS OF LOVE	25.00
66	8058 DJ	LITTLE RICHARD	I NEED LOVE	THE COMMANDMENTS OF LOVE	40.00
66	8061	ESCORTS	FROM HEAD TO TOE	NIGHT TIME	25.00
66	8061 DJ	ESCORTS	FROM HEAD TO TOE	NIGHT TIME	30.00
66	8064	C-JAM BLUES	CANDY	STAY AT HOME GIRL	25.00
66	8064 DJ	C-JAM BLUES	CANDY	STAY AT HOME GIRL	40.00
66	8065	TWILIGHTS	NEEDLE IN A HAYSTACK	I DON'T KNOW WHERE THE WIND WI	22.00
66	8065 DJ	TWILIGHTS	NEEDLE IN A HAYSTACK	I DON'T KNOW WHERE THE WIND WI	30.00
66	8090	ZOOT MONEY'S BIG ROLL BAND	THE MOUND MOVES	THE STAR OF THE SHOW	15.00
66	8090 DJ	ZOOT MONEY'S BIG ROLL BAND	THE MOUND MOVES	THE STAR OF THE SHOW	20.00
66	8091	MIKE PATTO	CAN'T STOP TALKING ABOUT MY BABY	LOVE	85.00
66	8091 DJ	MIKE PATTO	CAN'T STOP TALKING ABOUT MY BABY	LOVE	100.00
66	8096	GEORGIE FAME & the BLUE FLAMES	SITTING IN THE PARK	MANY HAPPY RETURNS	8.00
66	8096 DJ	GEORGIE FAME & the BLUE FLAMES	SITTING IN THE PARK	MANY HAPPY RETURNS	15.00
66	8097	JACKIE LYNTON	HE'LL HAVE TO GO	ONLY YOU	25.00
66	8097 DJ	JACKIE LYNTON	HE'LL HAVE TO GO	ONLY YOU	30.00
66	8099	SUE & SUNNY	YOU CAN'T BY PASS LOVE	I LIKE YOUR STYLE	20.00
66	8099 DJ	SUE & SUNNY	YOU CAN'T BY PASS LOVE	I LIKE YOUR STYLE	28.00
66	8108	ROY THOMPSON	SOOKIE SOOKIE	LOVE SAY SAY	25.00
66	8108 DJ	ROY THOMPSON	SOOKIE SOOKIE	LOVE SAY SAY	40.00
66	8110	SENATE	CAN'T STOP	AIN'T AS SWEET AS YOU	20.00
66	8110 DJ	SENATE	CAN'T STOP	AIN'T AS SWEET AS YOU	28.00
66	8116	LITTLE RICHARD	GET DOWN WITH IT	ROSE MARY	20.00
66	8116 DJ	LITTLE RICHARD	GET DOWN WITH IT	ROSE MARY	30.00
67	8122	MAJOR LANCE	AIN'T NO SOUL (LEFT IN THESE OLD SHOES)	YOU'LL WANT ME BACK	50.00
67	8122 DJ	MAJOR LANCE	AIN'T NO SOUL (LEFT IN THESE OLD SHOES)	YOU'LL WANT ME BACK	100.00
67	8136	EMMA REDE	I GOTTA BE WITH YOU	JUST LIKE A MAN	30.00
67	8136 DJ	EMMA REDE	I GOTTA BE WITH YOU	JUST LIKE A MAN	40.00
67	8140	LARRY WILLIAMS & JOHNNY WILLIAMS	A QUITTER NEVER WINS	MERCY, MERCY, MERCY	75.00
67	8140 DJ	LARRY WILLIAMS & JOHNNY WILLIAMS	A QUITTER NEVER WINS	MERCY, MERCY, MERCY	120.00
67	8149	MOOD-MOSAIC	CHINESE CHEQUERS	THE REAL MR. SMITH	10.00
67	8149 DJ	MOOD-MOSAIC	CHINESE CHEQUERS	THE REAL MR. SMITH	15.00
67	8153	TONY WILSON	CAN'T WASTE A GOOD THING	WHAT DID I DO	20.00
67	8153 DJ	TONY WILSON	CAN'T WASTE A GOOD THING	WHAT DID I DO	28.00
67	8154	WALTER JACKSON	SPEAK HER NAME	THEY DON'T GIVE MEDALS TO YEST	30.00
67	8154 DJ	WALTER JACKSON	SPEAK HER NAME	THEY DON'T GIVE MEDALS TO YEST	45.00
67	8160	RED SQUARES	PITY ME	MOUNTAIN'S HIGH	15.00
67	8160 DJ	RED SQUARES	PITY ME	MOUNTAIN'S HIGH	20.00
67	8163	BRIAN AUGER	TIGER	OH BABY, WON'T YOU COME TO CRO	30.00
67	8163 DJ	BRIAN AUGER	TIGER	OH BABY, WON'T YOU COME TO CRO	40.00
67	8172	ZOOT MONEY'S BIG ROLL BAND	NICK KNACK	I REALLY LEARNT HOW TO CRY	30.00
67	8172 DJ	ZOOT MONEY'S BIG ROLL BAND	NICK KNACK	I REALLY LEARNT HOW TO CRY	40.00
67	8175	VIBRATIONS	YOU BETTER BEWARE	PICK ME	25.00
67	8175 DJ	VIBRATIONS	YOU BETTER BEWARE	PICK ME	45.00
67	8182	RICHARD KENT STYLE	I'M OUT	MARCHING OFF TO WAR	75.00
67	8182 DJ	RICHARD KENT STYLE	I'M OUT	MARCHING OFF TO WAR	100.00
67	8186	VALERIE MITCHELL	LOVE CAN BE THE SWEETEST THING	I'M SORRY	10.00
67	8186 DJ	VALERIE MITCHELL	LOVE CAN BE THE SWEETEST THING	I'M SORRY	15.00
67	8190	WARREN DAVIS MONDAY BAND	WAIT FOR ME	I DON'T WANNA HURT YOU	15.00
67	8190 DJ	WARREN DAVIS MONDAY BAND	WAIT FOR ME	I DON'T WANNA HURT YOU	20.00
67	8206	MIKE STUART SPAN	INVITATION	DEAR	20.00

67	8206 DJ	MIKE STUART SPAN	INVITATION	DEAR	30.00
67	8212	SELENA JONES	RESPECT	WHEN I TELL YOU (THAT I LOVE Y	8.00
67	8212 DJ	SELENA JONES	RESPECT	WHEN I TELL YOU (THAT I LOVE Y	10.00
67	8225	JONNY ROSS	FORGET ABOUT HIM	TOO MUCH LOVE	10.00
67	8225 DJ	JONNY ROSS	FORGET ABOUT HIM	TOO MUCH LOVE	15.00
67	8233	DEANO	BABY, LET ME BE YOUR BABY	WHAT'S THE MATTTER WITH THE MA	10.00
67	8233 DJ	DEANO	BABY, LET ME BE YOUR BABY	WHAT'S THE MATTTER WITH THE MA	15.00
67	8239	BILL KENWRIGHT and the RUNAWAYS	I WANT TO GO BACK THERE AGAIN	WALK THROUGH DREAMS	10.00
67	8239 DJ	BILL KENWRIGHT and the RUNAWAYS	I WANT TO GO BACK THERE AGAIN	WALK THROUGH DREAMS	15.00
66	8240	LITTLE RICHARD	A LITTLE BIT OF SOMETHING	MONEY	50.00
66	8240 DJ	LITTLE RICHARD	A LITTLE BIT OF SOMETHING	MONEY	85.00
67	8254	MIKE PROCTOR	MR. COMMUTER	SUNDAY, SUNDAY, SUNDAY	50.00
67	8254 DJ	MIKE PROCTOR	MR. COMMUTER	SUNDAY, SUNDAY, SUNDAY	75.00
67	8256	HELEN SHAPIRO	STOP AND YOU'LL BECOME AWARE	SHE NEEDS COMPANY	125.00
67	8256 DJ	HELEN SHAPIRO	STOP AND YOU'LL BECOME AWARE	SHE NEEDS COMPANY	169.00
67	8263	LITTLE RICHARD	I DON'T WANT TO DISCUSS IT	HURRY SUNDOWN	50.00
67	8263 DJ	LITTLE RICHARD	I DON'T WANT TO DISCUSS IT	HURRY SUNDOWN	100.00
67	8270	WARREN DAVIS MONDAY BAND	LOVE IS A HURTING THING	WITHOUT FEAR	15.00
67	8270 DJ	WARREN DAVIS MONDAY BAND	LOVE IS A HURTING THING	WITHOUT FEAR	20.00
67	8290	JUDITH DURHAM	AGAIN AND AGAIN	MEMORIES	28.00
67	8290 DJ	JUDITH DURHAM	AGAIN AND AGAIN	MEMORIES	40.00
67	8292	STAPLE SINGERS	FOR WHAT IT'S WORTH	ARE YOU SURE?	20.00
67	8292 DJ	STAPLE SINGERS	FOR WHAT IT'S WORTH	ARE YOU SURE?	30.00
67	8318	VIBRATIONS	TALKIN' 'BOUT LOVE	ONE MINT JULEP	25.00
64	8318 EP PS	MAJOR LANCE	UM UM UM UM UM UM	6 track EP inc: hitch hike, monkey time Delilah + 3	75.00
67	8325	SOLOMON KING	SHE WEARS MY RING	I GET THAT FEELING OVER YOU	4.00
67	8325 DJ	SOLOMON KING	SHE WEARS MY RING	I GET THAT FEELING OVER YOU	6.00
64	8334 EP PS	GEORGIE FAME & the BLUE FLAMES	RHYTHM AND BLUEBEAT	1964 4 track EP with cover	30.00
68	8341	MARVELS	KEEP ON SEARCHING	HEARTACHE	100.00
68	8341 DJ	MARVELS	KEEP ON SEARCHING	HEARTACHE	130.00
68	8369	SLY & THE FAMILY STONE	DANCE TO THE MUSIC	LET ME HEAR IT FROM YOU	60.00
68	8369	SLY & THE FAMILY STONE	DANCE TO THE MUSIC	LET ME HEAR IT FROM YOU	85.00
64	8382 EP PS	GEORGIE FAME & the BLUE FLAMES	RHYTHM & BLUES AT THE FLAMINGO	night train, parchman farm + 2	30.00
64	8393 EP PS	GEORGIE FAME & the BLUE FLAMES	FAME AT LAST	1964 4 track EP with cover	15.00
65	8406 EP PS	GEORGIE FAME & the BLUE FLAMES	FATS FOR FAME	1965 4 track EP with cover	20.00
68	8418	EXOTICS	DON'T LEAD ME ON	YOU CAN TRY	22.00
68	8418 DJ	EXOTICS	DON'T LEAD ME ON	YOU CAN TRY	30.00
68	8430	NORRIE PARAMOR	SOUL COAXING	AUTUMN IN LONDON TOWN	10.00
68	8430 DJ	NORRIE PARAMOR	SOUL COAXING	AUTUMN IN LONDON TOWN	15.00
68	8439	JAY JUSTIN	REMINISCING	I SELL SUMMERTIME	10.00
68	8439 DJ	JAY JUSTIN	REMINISCING	I SELL SUMMERTIME	15.00
65	8454 EP PS	GEORGIE FAME & the BLUE FLAMES	MOVE IT ON OVER	1965 4 track EP with cover	20.00
68	8480	SAMMI SLOAN	BE HIS GIRL	YES I WOULD	30.00
68	8480 DJ	SAMMI SLOAN	BE HIS GIRL	YES I WOULD	50.00
66	8518 EP PS	GEORGIE FAME & the BLUE FLAMES	GETAWAY	1966 4 track EP with cover	20.00
69	8525	KATIE KISSOON	DON'T LET IT RAIN	WILL I NEVER SEE THE SUN	6.00
69	8525 DJ	KATIE KISSOON	DON'T LET IT RAIN	WILL I NEVER SEE THE SUN	8.00
69	8531	GRAHAM BONNEY	GET READY	FLY ME HIGH LORELEI	20.00
69	8531 DJ	GRAHAM BONNEY	GET READY	FLY ME HIGH LORELEI	28.00
69	8532	BOBBY BENNETT	YOU'RE READY NOW	MUSIC MOTHER MADE	50.00
69	8532 DJ	BOBBY BENNETT	YOU'RE READY NOW	MUSIC MOTHER MADE	75.00
69	8568	WARM SENSATION	I'LL BE PROUD OF YOU	THE CLOWN	15.00
69	8568 DJ	WARM SENSATION	I'LL BE PROUD OF YOU	THE CLOWN	20.00
69	8599	KENNY LYNCH	THE DRIFTER	DID I STAY TOO LONG?	25.00
69	8599 DJ	KENNY LYNCH	THE DRIFTER	DID I STAY TOO LONG?	35.00
69	8618	MOOD-MOSAIC	A TOUCH OF VELVET - A STING OF BRASS	BOND STREET P.M.	15.00
69	8618 DJ	MOOD-MOSAIC	A TOUCH OF VELVET - A STING OF BRASS	BOND STREET P.M.	25.00
69	8648	GRAHAM BONNEY	SIGN ON THE DOTTED LINE	WORDS WE SAID	15.00
69	8648 DJ	GRAHAM BONNEY	SIGN ON THE DOTTED LINE	WORDS WE SAID	25.00
70	8676	SOLOMAN KING	THIS BEAUTIFUL DAY	SAY A PRAYER	**156.00**
70	8676 DJ	SOLOMAN KING	THIS BEAUTIFUL DAY	SAY A PRAYER	175.00
70	8703	KENNY LYNCH	LOVING YOU IS SWEETER THAN EVER	IN OLD KENTUCKY	10.00
70	8703 DJ	KENNY LYNCH	LOVING YOU IS SWEETER THAN EVER	IN OLD KENTUCKY	15.00
70	8710	ROMEY CARR	THESE THINS WILL KEEP LOVING YOU	STAND UP AND FIGHT	40.00
70	8710 DJ	ROMEY CARR	THESE THINS WILL KEEP LOVING YOU	STAND UP AND FIGHT	60.00
70	8719	DELTONES	GIMME SOME LOVIN'	HAVE A LITTLE TALK WITH MYSELF	20.00
70	8719 DJ	DELTONES	GIMME SOME LOVIN'	HAVE A LITTLE TALK WITH MYSELF	28.00
71	8799	TREETOPS	WITHOUT THE ONE YOU LOVE	SO HERE I GO AGAIN	15.00
71	8799 DJ	TREETOPS	WITHOUT THE ONE YOU LOVE	SO HERE I GO AGAIN	22.00
71	8807	LEVI JACKSON	THIS BEAUTIFUL DAY	DON'T BE A SINNER	200.00
71	8807 DJ	LEVI JACKSON	THIS BEAUTIFUL DAY	DON'T BE A SINNER	**184.00**
71	8799	TREETOPS	WITHOUT THE ONE YOU LOVE	SO HERE I GO AGAIN	15.00
71	8799 DJ	TREETOPS	WITHOUT THE ONE YOU LOVE	SO HERE I GO AGAIN	20.00
73	8954	WANDA ARLETTY	COUNTING EACH MINUTE	MOTOR CAR	15.00
73	8954 DJ	WANDA ARLETTY	COUNTING EACH MINUTE	MOTOR CAR	22.00
73	8989	J.P. BODDY	STOP ME SPINNING (LIKE A TOP)	SONG WITHOUT A WORD	15.00
73	8989 DJ	J.P. BODDY	STOP ME SPINNING (LIKE A TOP)	SONG WITHOUT A WORD	20.00
91	9138 PS	STEVE MANCHA	IT'S ALL OVER THE GRAPEVINE	same: instrumental	6.00

COMPACT

82	1 PS	MARI WILSON	DANCE CARD	SHE'S HAD ENOUGH OF YOU	5.00
82	2 PS	MARI WILSON	BEAT THE BEAT	GLAMOURPUSS	4.00
82	3 PS	MARI WILSON	BABY IT'S TRUE	YOU LOOK SO GOOD	4.00
82	4 PS	MARI WILSON	JUST WHAT I ALWAYS WANTED	WOE, WOE, WOE	4.00
82	5 PS + postcard	MARI WILSON	A BEWARE BOYFRIEND	IT'S HAPPENING	5.00
83	6 PS	MARI WILSON	CRY ME A RIVER	RAVE (live)	4.00
83	7 PS	MARI WILSON	WONDERFUL	I MAY BE WRONG	4.00
84	9 PS	MARI WILSON	LET'S MAKE IT LAST	LET'S MAKE IT LAST shift mix	4.00

CONCORD

69	4 multi coloured swirl	MEL & TIM	BACKFIELD IN MOTION	DO RIGHT BABY	12.00
70	4 pink	MEL & TIM	BACKFIELD IN MOTION	DO RIGHT BABY	8.00
74	4 fried egg logo	MEL & TIM	BACKFIELD IN MOTION	DO RIGHT BABY	5.00
75	26 fried egg logo	MIKE HARPER	YOU GOT TOO MUCH GOING FOR YOU	THIS TIME	20.00
75	26 DJ	MIKE HARPER	YOU GOT TOO MUCH GOING FOR YOU	THIS TIME	25.00

CONDOR

68	1002	KOOKIE EATON	CREAM MACHINE	JOKE B SIDE	5.00
68	1002 DJ	KOOKIE EATON	CREAM MACHINE	JOKE B SIDE	8.00

CONNOISSEURS

96	101	PAT LEWIS	GENIE	NO ONE TO LOVE	15.00
96	102	BUDDY SMITH c/w JOEY KINGFISH	WHEN YOU LOSE THE ONE YOU LOVE	I WON'T HURT YOU NO MORE	20.00
96	103	EDWIN STARR c/w PROFESSIONALS	YOU GOT TO BE FOOLIN'	THAT'S WHY I LOVE YOU	15.00
97	104	EDWIN STARR c/w HERMAN GRIFFIN	HAS IT HAPPENED TO YOU YET	I NEED YOU LIKE A BABY	15.00
97	105	SHARON SOUL c/w BARBARA MERCER	GIRL CRAZY	HAPPINESS IS HERE	10.00

CONTACT

79	2	DIANE DUCANE	BETTER LATE THAN NEVER	ONE DAY (WE'RE GONNA DO IT AGA	15.00
79	3	RAISIN	THE MAN THAT I LOVE	I WANNA GO DANCINGQ	4.00
79	5	ALL NIGHT BAND	LOVELY LADIES	IT'S MY LIFE	40.00
79	5 DJ	ALL NIGHT BAND	LOVELY LADIES	IT'S MY LIFE	50.00
79	7	FRIDAY ROBINSON	KEEP OF THE GRASS	A ZOO	4.00

CONTEMPO

Founded in 1973 by John Abbey. The Contempo label was part of the "Blues & Soul" family. At the time Blues & Soul was the world's largest magazine for soul music. In the early seventies Blues & Soul was a fortnightly "Bible" for all soul enthusiasts, religiously bought by all Soul, Northern Soul & Funk fans. Even though it had Blues & Soul behind it, Contempo has never received the respect it deserves. You"ll discover within this listing there are some marvelous examples of early Southern Soul releases. 1973 John Abbey secured the UK distribution rights to Shreveport, Louisiana based Jewel / Ronn group of labels. From this catalogue Contempo released a series of, obscure soul 45s which maybe the British public would not have had easy access to if it were not for the efforts of John. Contempo also kept a close eye on emerging two scenes of club soul, up north the Northern Soul scene was becoming stronger they tried to cash in on it with the Armada Orchestra recording all manner of instrumentals none of which really had any measure of success. The London based "down south" scene which was more funk orientated was tapped into with recordings by Ultra Funk and current USA funk releases. Records made in the UK like Ultra Funk are starting to become collectable in countries like Japan, as they are now difficult to find.

Unfortunately Contempo never became regarded by collectors as a "must have the series" label that it promised to be, as releases like Napoleon Hatfield – Knees Up Mother Brown - spoilt the flow of successive soul releases. The choice of releases at the time was considered wise, but in hindsight when you consider Bashie, Canyon, Jewel, Mankind, Paula, Ronn, Soul Power, Sunburst, to name biut a few were all labels the company could have pulled from you can only imagine the release listing if you were to choose the titles today.

One major feather in the cap of Con tempo's short five years life, was it released 45s by Major Lance, Oscar Toney Jr. Jimmy Thomas that were UK recorded and to my knowledge not issued in any other country. Oscar Toney Jr. deep soul sessions are yet to receive the recognition they deserve. But Major Lance's releases are now extremely sought after, fitting perfectly into the Northern Soul crossover/modern scene. Contempo was distributed in the UK from 1973 to 1978 by Decca, Pye, and lastly WEA before ceasing trading in 1978.

73	1	MAJOR LANCE	THE RIGHT TRACK	UM UM UM UM UM UM	6.00
73	1 DJ	MAJOR LANCE	THE RIGHT TRACK	UM UM UM UM UM UM	10.00
73	2	FABULOUS ECHOES	DON'T YOUKNOW I LOVE YOU	IF YOU MOVE IT, YOU LOSE IT	6.00
73	2 DJ	FABULOUS ECHOES	DON'T YOUKNOW I LOVE YOU	IF YOU MOVE IT, YOU LOSE IT	8.00
73	3	RICHIE PITTS	EVERY COUPLE'S NOT A PAIR	I REFUSE TO KNOW YOUR NAME	5.00
73	3 DJ	RICHIE PITTS	EVERY COUPLE'S NOT A PAIR	I REFUSE TO KNOW YOUR NAME	6.00
73	4	BOB and EARL	HARLEM SHUFFLE remix	same: instrumental	4.00
73	4 DJ	BOB and EARL	HARLEM SHUFFLE remix	same: instrumental	5.00
73	5	JACKIE LEE	THE DUCK PART1	THE DUCK PART2	5.00
73	5 DJ	JACKIE LEE	THE DUCK PART1	THE DUCK PART2	6.00
73	6	OSCAR TONEY JR.	EVERYTHING I OWN	KENTUCKY BLUEBIRD (A MESSAGE TO MARTHA)	5.00
73	6 DJ	OSCAR TONEY JR.	EVERYTHING I OWN	KENTUCKY BLUEBIRD (A MESSAGE TO MARTHA)	6.00
73	7	MIDNIGHT MOVERS	FOLLOW THE WIND	FOLLOW THE WIND part 2	8.00
73	7 DJ	MIDNIGHT MOVERS	FOLLOW THE WIND	FOLLOW THE WIND part 2	10.00
73	8	JIMMY THOMAS	ALL GOD'S CHILDREN	THE WEAK-END IS MINE	3.00
73	8 DJ	JIMMY THOMAS	ALL GOD'S CHILDREN	THE WEAK-END IS MINE	4.00
73	9	MAJOR LANCE	AIN'T NO SOUL (LEFT IN THESE OLE	INVESTIGATE (Live at Torch) lt	5.00
73	9 DJ	MAJOR LANCE	AIN'T NO SOUL (LEFT IN THESE OLE	INVESTIGATE (Live at Torch) lt	8.00
73	10	GI-GI	DADDY LOVE	DADDY LOVE part 2	15.00
73	10 DJ	GI-GI	DADDY LOVE	DADDY LOVE part 2	20.00
73	11	JOHN FRED and his PLAYBOY BAND	JUDY IN DISGUISE (WTH GLASSES)	WHEN THE LIGHTS GO OUT	4.00
73	11 DJ	JOHN FRED and his PLAYBOY BAND	JUDY IN DISGUISE (WTH GLASSES)	WHEN THE LIGHTS GO OUT	5.00
73	12	TOMMIE YOUNG	EVERYBODY'S GOT A LITTLE DEVIL IN	DO YOU STILL FEEL THE SAME WAY	10.00
73	12 DJ	TOMMIE YOUNG	EVERYBODY'S GOT A LITTLE DEVIL IN	DO YOU STILL FEEL THE SAME WAY	15.00
73	13	AFRICAN MUSIC MACHINE	TROPICAL	A GIRL IN FRANCE	10.00

73	13 DJ	AFRICAN MUSIC MACHINE	TROPICAL	A GIRL IN FRANCE	12.00
73	14	FONTELLA BASS	IT SURE IS GOOD	I'M LEAVING IT UP TO YOU	5.00
73	14 DJ	FONTELLA BASS	IT SURE IS GOOD	I'M LEAVING IT UP TO YOU	6.00
76	CX14	ULTRAFUNK	GOTHAM CITY BOOGIE	SUNRISE	5.00
76	CX14 DJ	ULTRAFUNK	GOTHAM CITY BOOGIE	SUNRISE	6.00
73	15	LITTLE JOHNNY TAYLOR	AS LONG AS I DON'T HAVE TO SEE YOU	STRANGE BED WITH A STRANGE HEA	5.00
73	15 DJ	LITTLE JOHNNY TAYLOR	AS LONG AS I DON'T HAVE TO SEE YOU	STRANGE BED WITH A STRANGE HEA	6.00
73	16	ROSCOE ROBINSON	WE GOT A GOOD THING GOING	WE'RE LOSING IT BABY	8.00
73	16 DJ	ROSCOE ROBINSON	WE GOT A GOOD THING GOING	WE'RE LOSING IT BABY	10.00
73	17	BOBBY WILLIAMS	LET'S JAM	YOU'RE MY BABY	15.00
73	17 DJ	BOBBY WILLIAMS	LET'S JAM	YOU'RE MY BABY	20.00
73	18	WILLIE HENDERSON	THE DANCE MASTER	THE DANCE MASTER part 2	5.00
73	18 DJ	WILLIE HENDERSON	THE DANCE MASTER	THE DANCE MASTER part 2	6.00
73	19	TED TAYLOR	I WANT TO BE PART OF YOU GIRL	GOING IN THE HOLE	10.00
73	19 DJ	TED TAYLOR	I WANT TO BE PART OF YOU GIRL	GOING IN THE HOLE	15.00
73	20	JOHNNY WILLIAMS	JUST A LITTLE MISUNDERSTANDING	YOUR LOVE CONTROLS MY MIND	20.00
73	20 DJ	JOHNNY WILLIAMS	JUST A LITTLE MISUNDERSTANDING	YOUR LOVE CONTROLS MY MIND	25.00
73	21	FREDDIE MACK'S EXT. IN SOUNDS	PEOPLE PART1	PEOPLE PART2	8.00
73	21 DJ	FREDDIE MACK'S EXT. IN SOUNDS	PEOPLE PART1	PEOPLE PART2	10.00
73	22	JIMMY THOMAS	YOUNG, WILLING AND ABLE	TIME	4.00
73	22 DJ	JIMMY THOMAS	YOUNG, WILLING AND ABLE	TIME	5.00
73	23	TOMMIE YOUNG	SHE DON'T HAVE TO SEE YOU	THAT'S ALL A PART OF LOVING HI	8.00
73	23 DJ	TOMMIE YOUNG	SHE DON'T HAVE TO SEE YOU	THAT'S ALL A PART OF LOVING HI	10.00
73	24	OSCAR TONEY JR.	LOVE'S GONNA TEAR YOUR PLAYHOUSE DOWN	EVERYBODY'S NEEDED	5.00
73	24 DJ	OSCAR TONEY JR.	LOVE'S GONNA TEAR YOUR PLAYHOUSE DOWN	EVERYBODY'S NEEDED	6.00
73	25	AFRICAN MUSIC MACHINE	DAPP	NEVER NAME A BABY	10.00
73	25 DJ	AFRICAN MUSIC MACHINE	DAPP	NEVER NAME A BABY	12.00
73	26	MAJOR LANCE	DARK AND LONELY	MY GIRL	50.00
73	26 DJ	MAJOR LANCE	DARK AND LONELY	MY GIRL	60.00
73	27	NAPOLEON HATFIELFD	KNEES UP MOTHER BROWN	WHO ME	2.00
73	27 DJ	NAPOLEON HATFIELFD	KNEES UP MOTHER BROWN	WHO ME	3.00
76	1001	KOOL & THE GANG	SUPER BAD	OPEN SESAME	4.00
76	1001 DJ	KOOL & THE GANG	SUPER BAD	OPEN SESAME	5.00
76	1002	CROWN HEIGHTS AFFAIR	DANCIN'	LOVE ME	4.00
76	1002 DJ	CROWN HEIGHTS AFFAIR	DANCIN'	LOVE ME	5.00
74	2001	ULTRAFUNK	LIVING FOR THE CITY	WHO IS SHE AND WHAT IS HE TO Y	10.00
74	2001 DJ	ULTRAFUNK	LIVING FOR THE CITY	WHO IS SHE AND WHAT IS HE TO Y	15.00
74	2002	OSCAR TONEY JR.	IS IT BECAUSE I'M BLACK	MAKE IT EASY ON YOURSELF	10.00
74	2002 DJ	OSCAR TONEY JR.	IS IT BECAUSE I'M BLACK	MAKE IT EASY ON YOURSELF	15.00
74	2003	ARMADA ORCHESTRA	DO ME RIGHT	WON'T YOU CONSIDER	4.00
74	2003 DJ	ARMADA ORCHESTRA	DO ME RIGHT	WON'T YOU CONSIDER	5.00
74	2004	FONTELLA BASS	NOW THAT I'VE FOUND A GOOD THING	HOME WRECKER	5.00
74	2004 DJ	FONTELLA BASS	NOW THAT I'VE FOUND A GOOD THING	HOME WRECKER	6.00
74	2005	LOUIS BOND	TELL ME WHEN	INVITING YOU ALL	5.00
74	2005 DJ	LOUIS BOND	TELL ME WHEN	INVITING YOU ALL	6.00
74	2006	SPUNKY ONION	COOKIE MAN	COOKIE MAN part 2	50.00
74	2006 DJ	SPUNKY ONION	COOKIE MAN	COOKIE MAN part 2	60.00
74	2007	MASAI	ACROSS THE TRACKS	ACROSS THE TRACKS part 2	200.00
74	2007 DJ	MASAI	ACROSS THE TRACKS	ACROSS THE TRACKS part 2	220.00
74	2008	MONTCLAIRS	MAKE UP FOR LOST TIME	HOW CAN ONE MAN LIVE	8.00
74	2008 DJ	MONTCLAIRS	MAKE UP FOR LOST TIME	HOW CAN ONE MAN LIVE	10.00
74	2009	J.J. BARNES	TO AN EARLY GRAVE	Same: instrumental	6.00
74	2009 DJ	J.J. BARNES	TO AN EARLY GRAVE	Same: instrumental	8.00
74	2010	EXCITERS	LOVER'S QUESTION	LIVIN' FOR TOMORROW	4.00
74	2010 DJ	EXCITERS	LOVER'S QUESTION	LIVIN' FOR TOMORROW	5.00
74	2011	NEW EXPERIENCE	I DON'T WANT NOBODY (TO WASTE MY TIME)	NEW EXPERIENCE	8.00
74	2011 DJ	NEW EXPERIENCE	I DON'T WANT NOBODY (TO WASTE MY TIME)	NEW EXPERIENCE	10.00
74	2012	BRINKLEY & PARKER	(DON'T GET FOOLED BY) PANDER MAN	PANDER MAN (INSTRU.)	6.00
74	2012 DJ	BRINKLEY & PARKER	(DON'T GET FOOLED BY) PANDER MAN	PANDER MAN (INSTRU.)	8.00
74	2013	MELVIN BLISS	SYNTHETIC SUBSTITUTION	REWARD	75.00
74	2013 DJ	MELVIN BLISS	SYNTHETIC SUBSTITUTION	REWARD	100.00
74	2014	ROSHELL ANDERSON	NO PARTICULAR ONE	KNOW WHAT YOU'RE DOING WHEN YO	8.00
74	2014 DJ	ROSHELL ANDERSON	NO PARTICULAR ONE	KNOW WHAT YOU'RE DOING WHEN YO	10.00
74	2015	SOUL POTION	SOUL BABY	CIRCLE FULL OF LOVE	8.00
74	2015 DJ	SOUL POTION	SOUL BABY	CIRCLE FULL OF LOVE	10.00
74	2016	unissued ?			
74	2017	MAJOR LANCE	HOW CAN YOU SAY GOODBYE	GIMME A LITTLE SIGN	15.00
74	2017 DJ	MAJOR LANCE	HOW CAN YOU SAY GOODBYE	GIMME A LITTLE SIGN	20.00
74	2018	OSCAR TONEY JR.	THE THRILL IS GONE	MY GIRL	5.00
74	2018 DJ	OSCAR TONEY JR.	THE THRILL IS GONE	MY GIRL	6.00
74	2019	CYMANDE	BROTHERS ON THE SLIDE	PON DE DUNGLE	12.00
74	2019 DJ	CYMANDE	BROTHERS ON THE SLIDE	PON DE DUNGLE	15.00
74	2020	ULTRAFUNK	SWEET F.A. (FUNKY AL)	USE ME	8.00
74	2020 DJ	ULTRAFUNK	SWEET F.A. (FUNKY AL)	USE ME	10.00
74	2021	GLADYS KNIGHT & The PIPS	MAYBE MAYBE BABY	WHY DON'T YOU LOVE ME	5.00
74	2021 DJ	GLADYS KNIGHT & The PIPS	MAYBE MAYBE BABY	WHY DON'T YOU LOVE ME	6.00
74	2022	JOE FRAZIER	TRY IT AGAIN	KNOCK ON WOOD	10.00
74	2022 DJ	JOE FRAZIER	TRY IT AGAIN	KNOCK ON WOOD	15.00
74	2023	ULTRAFUNK feat. FREDDIE MACK	KUNG FU MAN	same: instrumental	3.00

74	2023 DJ	ULTRAFUNK feat. FREDDIE MACK	KUNG FU MAN	same: instrumental	4.00
74	2024	ARMADA ORCHESTRA	IT'S THE SAME OLD SONG	TO CHICAGO WITH LOVE	4.00
74	2024 DJ	ARMADA ORCHESTRA	IT'S THE SAME OLD SONG	TO CHICAGO WITH LOVE	5.00
74	2025	AFRICAN MUSIC MACHINE	CAMEL TIME	MR. BROWN	15.00
74	2025 DJ	AFRICAN MUSIC MACHINE	CAMEL TIME	MR. BROWN	20.00
74	2026	OLIVER SAIN	BUS STOP	NIGHTIME	8.00
74	2026 DJ	OLIVER SAIN	BUS STOP	NIGHTIME	10.00
74	2027	CON-FUNK-SHUN	CLIQUE	NOW & FOREVER	5.00
74	2027 DJ	CON-FUNK-SHUN	CLIQUE	NOW & FOREVER	6.00
74	2028	STORMY MONDAY	BOOGIE CHILDREN LET'S GET DOWN	same: instrumental	4.00
74	2028 DJ	STORMY MONDAY	BOOGIE CHILDREN LET'S GET DOWN	same: instrumental	5.00
74	2029	ESCORTS	LET'S MAKE LOVE (AT HOME	DIRESPECT CAN WRECK	6.00
74	2029 DJ	ESCORTS	LET'S MAKE LOVE (AT HOME	DIRESPECT CAN WRECK	8.00
74	2030	GENTLEMEN & THEIR LADIES	PARTY BUMP	PARTY BUMP part 2	4.00
74	2030 DJ	GENTLEMEN & THEIR LADIES	PARTY BUMP	PARTY BUMP part 2	5.00
74	2031	BARBARA JEAN ENGLISH	BREAKIN' UP A HAPPY HOME	GUESS WHO	6.00
74	2031 DJ	BARBARA JEAN ENGLISH	BREAKIN' UP A HAPPY HOME	GUESS WHO	8.00
74	2032	FONTELLA BASS	IT'S HARD TO GET BACK IN	TAKING ASBOUT FREEDOM	6.00
74	2032 DJ	FONTELLA BASS	IT'S HARD TO GET BACK IN	TAKING ASBOUT FREEDOM	8.00
74	2033	EXCITERS	BLOWING UP MY MIND	same: instrumental	5.00
74	2033 DJ	EXCITERS	BLOWING UP MY MIND	same: instrumental	6.00
74	2034	MARVIN SMITH	LET THE GOOD TIMES ROLL	AIN'T THAT A SHAME	4.00
74	2034 DJ	MARVIN SMITH	LET THE GOOD TIMES ROLL	AIN'T THAT A SHAME	5.00
74	2035	ROSHELL ANDERSON	THE GRAPEVINE WILL LIE SOMETIMES	SUCH A BEAUTIFUL THING	6.00
74	2035 DJ	ROSHELL ANDERSON	THE GRAPEVINE WILL LIE SOMETIMES	SUCH A BEAUTIFUL THING	8.00
75	2036	MONTCLAIRS	HUNG UP ON YOUR LOVE	I NEED YOU MORE THAN EVER	40.00
75	2036 DJ	MONTCLAIRS	HUNG UP ON YOUR LOVE	I NEED YOU MORE THAN EVER	85.00
75	2037	DORIS DUKE	GRASSHOPPER	PLEASE COME BACK	6.00
75	2037 DJ	DORIS DUKE	GRASSHOPPER	PLEASE COME BACK	5.00
75	2038	GENTLEMEN & THEIR LADY	LOOSE BOOTY	NOW GENERATION	10.00
75	2038 DJ	GENTLEMEN & THEIR LADY	LOOSE BOOTY	NOW GENERATION	10.00
75	2039	Z.Z.HILL	FAITHFUL AND TRUE	SECOND CHANCE	5.00
75	2039 DJ	Z.Z.HILL	FAITHFUL AND TRUE	SECOND CHANCE	6.00
75	2040	JERRY WASHINGTON	RIGHT HERE IS WHERE YOU BELONG	IN MY LIFE I HAVED LOVED	10.00
75	2040 DJ	JERRY WASHINGTON	RIGHT HERE IS WHERE YOU BELONG	IN MY LIFE I HAVED LOVED	15.00
75	2041	SEVENTH WONDER	FOR THE GOOD TIMES part 1	FOR THE GOOD TIMES part 2	5.00
75	2041 DJ	SEVENTH WONDER	FOR THE GOOD TIMES part 1	FOR THE GOOD TIMES part 2	6.00
75	2042	OLIVER SAIN	THE DOUBLE BUMP	CALIFORNIA SUNSET	5.00
75	2042 DJ	OLIVER SAIN	THE DOUBLE BUMP	CALIFORNIA SUNSET	6.00
75	2043	OSCAR TONEY JR.	I'VE BEEN LOVIN' YOU TOO LONG	FOR YOUR PRECIOUS LOVE	10.00
75	2043 DJ	OSCAR TONEY JR.	I'VE BEEN LOVIN' YOU TOO LONG	FOR YOUR PRECIOUS LOVE	15.00
75	2044	ROBERTA KELLY	KUNG FU'S BACK AGAIN	same: instrumental	4.00
75	2044 DJ	ROBERTA KELLY	KUNG FU'S BACK AGAIN	same: instrumental	5.00
75	2045	MAJOR LANCE	DON'T YOU KNOW I LOVE YOU	same: instrumental	15.00
75	2045 DJ	MAJOR LANCE	DON'T YOU KNOW I LOVE YOU	same: instrumental	20.00
75	2046	SWAMP DOGG	TOTAL DESTRUCTION TO YOUR MIND	REDNECK	4.00
75	2046 DJ	SWAMP DOGG	TOTAL DESTRUCTION TO YOUR MIND	REDNECK	5.00
75	2047	DORIS DUKE	A LITTLE BIT OF LOVIN'	HEY LADY	8.00
75	2047 DJ	DORIS DUKE	A LITTLE BIT OF LOVIN'	HEY LADY	10.00
75	2048	J.J. BARNES	SWEET SHERRY	CHAINS OF LOVE	5.00
75	2048 DJ	J.J. BARNES	SWEET SHERRY	CHAINS OF LOVE	6.00
75	2049	CON FUNK SHUN	BUMPSUMBOODY	MR. TAMBOURINE MAN	15.00
75	2049 DJ	CON FUNK SHUN	BUMPSUMBOODY	MR. TAMBOURINE MAN	20.00
75	2050	GENTLEMEN & THEIR LADIES	ONE MORE TIME part 2	YOU'RE GONNA NEED ME	4.00
75	2050 DJ	GENTLEMEN & THEIR LADIES	ONE MORE TIME part 2	YOU'RE GONNA NEED ME	5.00
75	2051	ARMADA ORCHESTRA	COCHISE	SUNRISE ON THE ARMADA	4.00
75	2051 DJ	ARMADA ORCHESTRA	COCHISE	SUNRISE ON THE ARMADA	5.00
75	2052	SEEDS OF THE EARTH	PLANTING SEEDS	BROTHER BAD	75.00
75	2052 DJ	SEEDS OF THE EARTH	PLANTING SEEDS	BROTHER BAD	100.00
75	2053	SIMTEC SIMMONS	SOME OTHER TIME	CLASSIFIED CRAZY MAN	4.00
75	2054	QUADRAPHONICS	BETCHA IF YOU CHECK IT OUT	PROVE MY LOVE TO YOU	8.00
75	2055	PEACHES & HERB	DOWN WHERE IT'S AT	same: instrumental	4.00
75	2056	MOSES DILLARD	WHAT YOU SEE IN ME	THEME FROM LOVEJOY	4.00
75	2057	OLIVER SAIN	LONDON EXPRESS	BLOWING FOR LOVE	8.00
75	2058	FUNKEES	TOO-LAY	COOL IT DOWN	20.00
75	2059	DYNAMIC CORVETTES	FUNKY MUSIC IS THE THING	FUNKY MUSIC IS THE THING part 2	15.00
75	2060	ERNIE BUSH	BREAKAWAY	Same: Instrumental	8.00
75	2061	RITA DACOSTA	DON'T BRING ME DOWN	NO! NO! NO!	15.00
75	2062	BARBARA JEAN ENGLISH	KEY IN THE MAILBOX	I'M LIVING A LIE	8.00
75	2063	J.J. BARNES	BABY PLEASE COME HOME	CLOUDY DAYS	5.00
75	2064	DORIS DUKE	FULL TIME WOMAN	YOUR BEST FRIEND	5.00
75	2065	HOWEEFEEL	JUST CAN'T DO WITHOUT YOUR LOVE	THE DEVIL'S ON THE RUN	75.00
75	2066	unissued ?			
75	2067	SNOOKY	SUGAR LIPS	WAITING FOR YOU	4.00
75	2068	BANZAI	CHINESE KUNG FU	same: disco version	6.00
75	2069	ARMADA ORCHESTRA	FEEL THE NEED IN ME	THE DRIFTER	4.00
75	2070	BESSIE BANKS	BABY YOU SURE KNOW HOW TO GET TO ME	TRY TO LEAVE ME IF YOU CAN	40.00
75	2071	ULTRAFUNK	STING YOUR JAWS	STING YOUR JAWS Part2	10.00
75	2072	PATTI DREW	MIGHTY O.J.	same: instrumental	5.00

75	2073	SEEDS OF THE EARTH	ZION + I	PHIRE	30.00
75	2074	OTIS LEAVILL	TELL THE WORLD	I LOVE YOU	10.00
75	2075	OSCAR TONEY JR.	CHICKEN HEADS	EVERYBODY'S NEEDED	10.00
75	2076	THIRD TIME AROUND	SOON EVERYTHING IS GOING TO BE	same: instrumantal	10.00
75	2077	OLIVER SAIN	GET UP AND HUSTLE	SHE'S A DISCO DANCER	8.00
75	2078	ARMADA ORCHESTRA	TELL ME WHAT YOU WANT	CLASSIC BUMP	3.00
75	2079	TAMIKO JONES	I'M SPELLBOUND	T.J. MAGIC	5.00
76	2080	JUGGY JONES	INSIDE AMERICA	INSIDE AMERICA PART2	6.00
76	2081	OLIVER SAIN	PARTY HEARTY	APRICOT SPLASH	8.00
76	2082	BOOGIE MAN ORCHESTRA	LADY LADY LADY	same: instrumental	5.00
76	2083	ARMADA ORCHESTRA	BAND OF GOLD	THE HUSTLE	4.00
76	2084	A.J. GAYE DISCO BAND	MOONLIGHT SERENADE	HAPPY GATE	4.00
76	2085	MR. SUPERBAD & MIGHTY POWER	MR. SUPERBAD	same: instrumental	4.00
76	2086	SIR MACK RICE	IT TAKES ONE TO KNOW ONE	same: instrumental	4.00
76	2087	DOROTHY MOORE	MISTY BLUE	HERE IT IS	4.00
76	2088	TAMIKO JONES	LET IT FLOW	LET IT FLOW TAMIKO	4.00
76	2089	ARMADA ORCHESTRA	THE LOVE I LOST	THE LOVE I LOST part 2	4.00
76	2090	TED TAYLOR	STEALAWAY	YOU MAKE LOVING YOU EASY	4.00
76	2091	EDDIE FLOYD	PARADISE	SOMEBODY TOUCH ME	4.00
76	2092	DOROTHY MOORE	FUNNY HOW TIME SLIPS AWAY	IT'S SO GOOD	4.00
76	2093	DON HIGH & MIGHTY BLACK KOJAK	LOVE IT COMES IN ALL COLOURS	same: instrumental	4.00
76	2094	TAMIKO JONES	REACH OUT FOR YOUR LOVE	AFRAID OF LOSING YOU	4.00
76	2095	JIMMY JAMES	RIVER BOAT JENNY	IF I WASN'T BLACK	4.00
76	2096	BOBBY BYRD	HERE FOR THE PARTY	THANK YOU FOR YOUR LOVE	6.00
76	2097	REUBEN BELL	I STILL HAVE TO SAYGOODBYE	ASKING FOR THE TRUTH	5.00
76	2098	TED TAYLOR	I'M GONNA HATE MYSELF IN THE	STICK BY ME	4.00
76	2099	SKIP MAHONEY and the CASUALS	BLESS MY SOUL	LAND OF LOVE	5.00
76	2100	ULTRAFUNK	GOTHAM CITY BOOGIE	INDIGO COUNTRY	6.00
76	2101	EDDIE FLOYD	CHI-TOWN HUSTLER	NEVER TOO OLD	3.00
76	2102	SPARKY & INNER CITIZENS	GOLDEN GATE GET DOWN	disco version	3.00
76	2103	KING FLOYD	BODY ENGLISH	I REALLY LOVE YOU	4.00
76	2104	DUPARS feat. VENETTA FIELDS	LOVE COOKIN'	WE ROCKIN'	100.00
77	2105	J.J. BARNES	SHE'S MINE	ERROLL FLYNN	6.00
77	2106	ALICE STREET GANG	BAIA	BRAZILIAN STREET HUSTLE	4.00
77	2107	DOROTHY MOORE	FOR OLD TIMES SAKE	DADDY'D EYES	5.00
77	2108	ARMADA ORCHESTRA	PHILLY ARAMDA	YOU MAKE ME FEEL BRAND NEW	4.00
77	2109	SAM and DAVE	WHY DID YOU DO IT	DON'T MESS WITH MY MONEY	4.00
77	2110	ALVIN CASH	ALI SHUFFLE	DOING THE FEELING	3.00
77	2111	J.J. BARNES	SARA SMILE	LET ME FEEL THE FUNK	5.00
77	2112	JERRY RIX	DISCO TRAIN	same: instrumental	3.00
77	2113	TONY GREGORY	DANCE ON	HEY SUN	4.00
77	2114	unissued ?			
77	2115	BOBBY PATTERSON	IF HE HADN'T SLIPPED UP AND GOT	I GOT TO GET OVER	6.00
77	2116	RED BEANBS AND RICE	RED BEANBS AND RICE THEME	SYMPHONIC SALSA	5.00
77	2117	MAJOR LANCE	HOW CAN YOU SAY GOODBYE	GIMME A LITTLE SIGN	20.00
77	2118	OLIVER SAIN	B OOGIE	FEEL LIKE DANCIN	4.00
77	2119	CLOUD ONE	ATMOSPHERE STRUTT	ATMOSPHERE STRUTT PART2	5.00
77	2120	CHARLIE WHITEHEAD	I WAS DANCING WHEN I FELL IN LOVE	PEOPLE TELL ME I'M LOSING IT	5.00
77	2121	MIKE CONTEH BAND	JUMP THE GUN	JUMP THE GUN part 2	3.00
77	2122	EASTBOUND EXPRESSWAY	CLOUDBURST	CLOUDBURST part 2	4.00
77	2123	J.J. BARNES	I'M THE ONE WHO LOVES YOU	HOW LONG	15.00
77	2124	SAM & DAVE	YOU DON'T KNOW LIKE I KNOW	WE CAN WORK IT OUT + HOLD ON I'M COMING	5.00
77	2125	RED BEANS AND RICE	DISCO DANCING	BLUE DANUBE HUSTLE	3.00
77	2126	VIOLA REITTOWSKY	YOU CAN DANCE	YOU CAN DANCE part 2	3.00
77	2127	HOMO SAPIENS	TILL TOMORROW	DANCE	3.00
77	2128	ALI BABA BAND	ABDULLAH'S WEDDING	DESERT SONG	3.00
77	2129	DANIEL JACKSON EXPLOSION	CINDERELLA	HYMN FOR AFRICA	3.00
77	2130	TAMIKO JONES	CREEPIN'	BOY YOU'RE GROWING ON ME	5.00
77	2131	unissued ?			
78	2132	SLIM ALI	SWEET MOTHER	AKI SPECIAL	3.00
78	8001 unissued	JOE TEX	SHOW ME	HOLD ON TO WHAT YOU'VE GOT	UN
78	8002 unissued	WILLIE TEE	WALKING UP A ONE WAY STREET	THANK YOU JOHN	UN
78	8003 unissued	CLARENCE CARTER	LOOKING FOR A FOX	PATCHES	UN
78	8004 unissued	BARBARA LEWIS	HELLO STRANGER	BABY I'M YOURS	UN
78	8005 unissued	DARRELL BANKS	OPEN THE DOOR TO YOUR HEART	ANGEL BABY	UN

CONTEMPO RARIES

Contempo's reissue oldies label, missing numbers are not soul related and have been omitted.

74	9001	JIMMY CONWELL	CIGARETTE ASHES	SECOND HAND HAPPINESS	8.00
74	9002	AFRICAN MUSIC MACHINE	BLACK WATER GOLD	MAKING NASSAU FRUIT JUICE	15.00
74	9003	KETTY LESTER cw BURNETTE	LOVE LETTERS	HEY LITTLE ONE	4.00
74	9004	JEWELL AKENS c/w TEDDY BEARS	THE BIRDS AND THE BEES	TO KNOW HIM IS TO LOVE HIM	4.00
74	9005	WILLIE HENDERSON	THE DANCE MASTER	THE DANCE MASTER PART2	4.00
74	9006	OLYMPICS	WESTERN MOVIES	SHIMMY LIKE KATE	6.00
74	9007	DORIS DUKE	TO THE OTHER WOMAN (I'M THE OTHER	FEET START WALKING	5.00
74	9008	INCREDIBLES	THERE'S NOTHING ELSE TO SAY BABY	ANOTHER DIRTY DEAL	10.00
74	9009	AARON NEVILLE	TELL IT LIKE IT IS	WHY WORRY	8.00
74	9010	ROBERT PARKER	I CAUGHT YOU IN A LIE	BAREFOOTIN'	15.00
74	9014	JOHN FRED & THE PLAYBOYS	JUDY IN DISGUISE	WHEN THE LIGHTS GO OUT	4.00

74	9015	MAJOR LANCE	AIN'T NO SOUL (LEFT IN THESE OLD	THE RIGHT TRACK	5.00
74	9016	BOB AND EARL	HARLEM SHUFFLE	HARLEM SHUFFLE (INSTRU.)	5.00
74	9017	JACKIE LEE	THE DUCK	THE DUCK part 2	6.00
74	9018	MIDNIGHT MOVERS UNLTD.	FOLLOW THE WIND PART1	FOLLOW THE WIND PART2	6.00
74	9019	BETTYE SWANN	MAKE ME YOURS	I WILL NOT CRY	8.00
74	9020	FREDDIE NORTH	SHE'S ALL I GOT	AIN'T NOTHING IN THE NEWS	4.00
74	9023	OLYMPICS	BABY, DO THE PHILLY DOG	SECRET AGENTS	6.00
74	9024	CASINOS	THEN YOU CAN TELL ME GOODBYE	I STILL LOVE YOU	5.00
75	9025	SHIRLEY BROWN	I AIN'T GONNA TELL NOBODY	LOVE IS BUILT ON A STRONG FOUN	8.00
74	9026	TAMI LYNN	I'M GONNA RUN AWAY FROM YOU	THE BOY NEXT DOOR	6.00
75	9027	BELLES	DON'T PRETEND	WORDS CAN'T EXPLAIN	8.00
75	9028	BOBBY WILLIAMS	LET'S JAM	YOU'RE MY BABY	25.00
75	9029	AD LIBS	JOHNNY MY BOY	THE BOY FROM NEW YORK CITY	15.00
75	9030	CAPITOLS	COOL JERK	AIN'T THAT TERRIBLE	8.00
75	9031	DEON JACKSON	I CAN'T GO ON	LOVE MAKES THE WORLD GO ROUND	25.00
75	9032	SHANGRI-LAS	LEADER OF THE PACK	REMEMBER (WALKING IN THE SAND)	4.00
75	9035	JACKIE LEE	THE SHOTGUN AND THE DUCK	DO THE TEMPTATION WALK	5.00
75	9036	PLATTERS	THE GREAT PRETENDER	ONLY YOU (AND YOU ALONE)	4.00
76	9037	DIXIE CUPS	CHAPEL OF LOVE	PEOPLE SAY	6.00
76	9039	MIRETTES	HE'S ALRIGHT WITH ME	YOUR KIND AIN'T NO GOOD	8.00
76	9040	RICHARD TEMPLE	THAT BEATIN' RHYTHM	COULD IT BE	10.00
76	9041	JIMMY THOMAS	WHERE THERE'S A WILL	JUST TRYING TO PLEASE YOU	6.00

COOL TEMPO

Mid 80s UK label that concentrated more of 12" dance releases below are some of the 7" 45s that would interest soul collectors.

85	106	SYLVESTER	HEAVEN	SEX	4.00
85	109 PS	CHANGE	OH WHAT A FEELING	OH WHAT A FEELING part 2	4.00
86	110 PS	BB + Q	GENIE	GENIE diff. Mix	4.00
86	111 PS	CHANGE	MUTUAL ATTRACTION	LOVE THE WAY]YOU LOVE ME	4.00
86	112 PS	BB + Q	MINUTES AWAY	THE MAIN ATTRACTION	4.00
86	123 PS	THOMAS AND TAYLOR	YOU CAN'T BLAME LOVE	WE NEED COMPANY	4.00
86	126 PS	MAIN INGREDIENT	DO ME RIGHT	same: instrumental	4.00
86	132 PS	BB + Q	DREAMER	DREAMER dub version	5.00
86	154 PS	BB + Q	RICOCHET	GENIE	4.00
88	167 PS	BRAND NEW HEAVIES	GOT TO GIVE	GOT TO GIVE part 2	4.00
89	185 PS	ADEVA	WARNING	RESPECT	4.00
89	192 PS	ADEVA	I DON'T NEED YOU	I THANK YOU	4.00
89	196 PS	PAUL SIMPSON feat. ANTHONY	WALK AWAY FROM LOVE	GOD BLESS THE DAY	4.00
91	235 PS	KENNY THOMAS	THINKING ABOUT YOUR LOVE	THINKING ABOUT YOUR LOVE diff. Mix	4.00
91	243 PS	KENNY THOMAS	BEST OF YOU	DE GROOVESKI	4.00

CORAL

Coral is of great interest to soul fans as it was UK Decca's outlet for USA Brunswick releases from 1958 to 1967. Although very little of the USA catalogue was issued in the UK as 45's, the ones that were became corner stones of the 60's teenager soul movement that later evolved into what was christened the Northern Soul scene in the early seventies. Jackie Wilson covered the majority of releases and soon established himself with the soul fans after a period up until 1964, releasing rock and roll orientated R&B. It was a little later when the Artistics, Marvin Smith etc, became classic soul club plays and ultimately the demand and the value rose. Today one of the most prized 45's in UK soul collecting would be a blue and silver label promo of any Jackie Wilson classic or Artistics and the most sought after record on the label from Artistics lead vocalist Marvin Smith. Recently the emergence of the R&B influence on the Northern Soul scene has led to the Frances Burnett 45 becoming a little more valuable than just being sought by Tamla Motown fans, as an early Berry Gordy production.

58	72290	JACKIE WILSON	REET PETITE	BY THE LIGHT OF THE SILVERY MO	10.00
58	72306	JACKIE WILSON	TO BE LOVED	COME BACK TO ME	20.00
58	72332	JACKIE WILSON	I'M WANDERIN'	AS LONG AS I LIVE	20.00
58	72338	JACKIE WILSON	WE HAVE LOVE	SINGING A SONG	20.00
58	72347	JACKIE WILSON	LONELY TEARDROPS	IN THE BLUE OF THE EVENING	22.00
59	72366	JACKIE WILSON	THAT'S WHY (I LOVE YOU SO)	LOVE IS ALL	10.00
59	72372	JACKIE WILSON	I'LL BE SATISFIED	ASK	15.00
59	72374 tri	FRANCES BURNETT	I MISS YOU SO	PLEASE REMEMBER ME	100.00
59	72374 round	FRANCES BURNETT	I MISS YOU SO	PLEASE REMEMBER ME	85.00
59	72380	JACKIE WILSON	YOU BETTER KNOW IT	NEVER GO AWAY	15.00
59	72384	JACKIE WILSON	TALK THAT TALK	ONLY YOU, ONLY ME	10.00
60	72393	JACKIE WILSON	DOGGIN' AROUND	THE MAGIC OF LOVE	15.00
60	72393 DJ	JACKIE WILSON	DOGGIN' AROUND	THE MAGIC OF LOVE	22.00
60	72407	JACKIE WILSON	A WOMAN, A LOVER, A FRIEND	(YOU WERE MADE FOR) ALL MY LOVE	10.00
60	72407 DJ	JACKIE WILSON	A WOMAN, A LOVER, A FRIEND	(YOU WERE MADE FOR) ALL MY LOV	15.00
60	72412	JACKIE WILSON	ALONE AT LAST	AM I THE MAN	10.00
60	72412 DJ	JACKIE WILSON	ALONE AT LAST	AM I THE MAN	15.00
61	72421 DJ	JACKIE WILSON	THE TEAR FOR THE YEAR	MY EMPTY ARMS	75.00
61	72423	LINDA HOPKINS	I DIDDLE DUM DUM	ALL IN MY MIND	20.00
61	72423 DJ	LINDA HOPKINS	I DIDDLE DUM DUM	ALL IN MY MIND	25.00
61	72424	JACKIE WILSON	THE TEAR OF THE YEAR	YOUR ONE AND ONLY LOVE	10.00
61	72424 DJ	JACKIE WILSON	THE TEAR OF THE YEAR	YOUR ONE AND ONLY LOVE	18.00
61	72426	ROSIE	LONELY BLUE NIGHTS	WE'LL HAVE A CHANCE	15.00
61	72426 DJ	ROSIE	LONELY BLUE NIGHTS	WE'LL HAVE A CHANCE	20.00
61	72430	JACKIE WILSON	PLEASE TELL ME WHY	(SO MANY) CUTE LITTLE GIRLS	10.00
61	72430 DJ	JACKIE WILSON	PLEASE TELL ME WHY	(SO MANY) CUTE LITTLE GIRLS	15.00
61	72434	JACKIE WILSON	I'M COMIN' ON BACK TO YOU	LONELY LIFE	12.00
61	72434 DJ	JACKIE WILSON	I'M COMIN' ON BACK TO YOU	LONELY LIFE	18.00
61	72439	JACKIE WILSON	YOU DON'T KNOW WHAT IT MEANS	YEARS FROM NOW	10.00
61	72439 DJ	JACKIE WILSON	YOU DON'T KNOW WHAT IT MEANS	YEARS FROM NOW	15.00

61	72444	JACKIE WILSON	THE WAY I AM	MY HEART BELONGS TO YOU	10.00
61	72444 DJ	JACKIE WILSON	THE WAY I AM	MY HEART BELONGS TO YOU	15.00
62	72448	LINDA HOPKINS	MAMA'S DOING THE TWIST	MY MOTHER'S EYES	22.00
62	72448 DJ	LINDA HOPKINS	MAMA'S DOING THE TWIST	MY MOTHER'S EYES	20.00
62	72450	JACKIE WILSON	THE GREATEST HURT	THERE'LL BE NO NEXT TIME	10.00
62	72450 DJ	JACKIE WILSON	THE GREATEST HURT	THERE'LL BE NO NEXT TIME	15.00
62	72453	JACKIE WILSON and LINDA HOPKINS	SING (AND TELL THE BLUES SO LONG)	I FOUND LOVE	10.00
62	72453 DJ	JACKIE WILSON and LINDA HOPKINS	SING (AND TELL THE BLUES SO LONG)	I FOUND LOVE	15.00
62	72454	JACKIE WILSON	I JUST CAN'T HELP IT	MY TALE OF WOE	10.00
62	72454 DJ	JACKIE WILSON	I JUST CAN'T HELP IT	MY TALE OF WOE	15.00
63	72460	JACKIE WILSON	BABY WORKOUT	WHAT GOOD AM I WITHOUT YOU	10.00
63	72460 DJ	JACKIE WILSON	BABY WORKOUT	WHAT GOOD AM I WITHOUT YOU	15.00
63	72464	LINDA HOPKINS & JACKIE WILSON	SHAKE A HAND	SAY I DO	10.00
63	72464 DJ	LINDA HOPKINS & JACKIE WILSON	SHAKE A HAND	SAY I DO	15.00
63	72465	JACKIE WILSON	SHAKE! SHAKE! SHAKE!	HE'S A FOOL	15.00
63	72465 DJ	JACKIE WILSON	SHAKE! SHAKE! SHAKE!	HE'S A FOOL	20.00
63	72467	JACKIE WILSON	BABY GET IT	THE NEW BREED	10.00
63	72467 DJ	JACKIE WILSON	BABY GET IT	THE NEW BREED	15.00
64	72470	DEMETRISS TAPP	LIPSTICK PAINT A SMILE ON ME	YOU FIND LOVE	15.00
64	72470 DJ	DEMETRISS TAPP	LIPSTICK PAINT A SMILE ON ME	YOU FIND LOVE	25.00
64	72474	JACKIE WILSON	BE MY GIRL	BIG BOSS LINE	10.00
64	72474 DJ	JACKIE WILSON	BE MY GIRL	BIG BOSS LINE	20.00
64	72476	JACKIE WILSON	SQUEEZE HER - TEASE HER (BUT LOVE	GIVE ME BACK MY HEART	10.00
64	72476 DJ	JACKIE WILSON	SQUEEZE HER - TEASE HER (BUT LOVE	GIVE ME BACK MY HEART	18.00
65	72480	LINDA HOPKINS & JACKIE WILSON	YES INDEED	WHEN THE SAINTS GO MARCHING IN	10.00
65	72480 DJ	LINDA HOPKINS & JACKIE WILSON	YES INDEED	WHEN THE SAINTS GO MARCHING IN	15.00
65	72481	JACKIE WILSON	NO PITY (IN THE NAKED CITY)	I'M SO LONELY	20.00
65	72481 DJ	JACKIE WILSON	NO PITY (IN THE NAKED CITY)	I'M SO LONELY	30.00
65	72482	JACKIE WILSON	I BELIEVE I'LL LOVE ON	LONELY TEARDROPS	10.00
65	72482 DJ	JACKIE WILSON	I BELIEVE I'LL LOVE ON	LONELY TEARDROPS	20.00
66	72484	JACKIE WILSON	TO MAKE A BIG MAN CRY	BE MY LOVE	30.00
66	72484 DJ	JACKIE WILSON	TO MAKE A BIG MAN CRY	BE MY LOVE	40.00
66	72485	DICK ROMAN	IVY	GREEN YEARS	10.00
66	72485 DJ	DICK ROMAN	IVY	GREEN YEARS	20.00
66	72486	MARVIN SMITH	HAVE MORE TIME	TIME STOPPED	75.00
66	72486 DJ	MARVIN SMITH	HAVE MORE TIME	TIME STOPPED	125.00
66	72487	JACKIE WILSON	WHISPERS	THE FAIREST OF THEM ALL	20.00
66	72487 DJ	JACKIE WILSON	WHISPERS	THE FAIREST OF THEM ALL	85.00
66	72488	ARTISTICS	HOPE WE HAVE	I'M GONNA MISS YOU	40.00
66	72488 DJ	ARTISTICS	HOPE WE HAVE	I'M GONNA MISS YOU	100.00
67	72489	YOUNG HOLT TRIO	WACK WACK	THIS LITTLE LIGHT OF MINE	30.00
67	72489 DJ	YOUNG HOLT TRIO	WACK WACK	THIS LITTLE LIGHT OF MINE	50.00
67	72490	GENE CHANDLER	THE GIRL DON'T CARE	MY LOVE	20.00
67	72490 DJ	GENE CHANDLER	THE GIRL DON'T CARE	MY LOVE	30.00
67	72492	ARTISTICS	GIRL I NEED YOU	I'M GLAD I MET YOU	40.00
67	72492 DJ	ARTISTICS	GIRL I NEED YOU	I'M GLAD I MET YOU	85.00
67	72493	JACKIE WILSON	I'M THE ONE TO DO IT	HIGHER & HIGHER	25.00
67	72493 DJ	JACKIE WILSON	I'M THE ONE TO DO IT	HIGHER AND HIGHER	85.00
67	72496	JACKIE WILSON	THE WHO WHO SONG	SINCE YOU SHOWED ME HOW TO BE HAPPY	30.00
67	72496 DJ	JACKIE WILSON	THE WHO WHO SONG	SINCE YOU SHOWED ME HOW TO BE HAPPY	100.00

COTILLION

76	10781	LUTHER	IT'S GOOD FOR THE SOUL	IT'S GOOD FOR THE SOUL part 2	20.00
76	10817	JOHN EDWARDS	BABY, HOLD ON TO ME	THE KEY TO MY LIFE	4.00
76	10876	SISTER SLEDGE	CREAM OF THE CROP	LOVE AIN'T EASY	4.00
77	10898	MASS PRODUCTION	WELCOME TO OUR WORLD OF MERRY MUSIC MAGIC 4.00			
77	10966	MASS PRODUCTION	WINE FLOW DISCO	FUN IN THE SUN	4.00
77	11021	MASS PRODUCTION	I BELIEVE IN MUSIC	COSMIC LUST	

CRC

84	002	LINDA CLIFFORD	RUNAWAY LOVE	YOU ARE, YOU ARE	10.00

CREAM

Another small label that attempted to cash in on the booming Northern Soul era of that incredibly hot summer of 1976. This Manchester based label was part of the collectable vinyl shop and mail order company Global Records. It released some top quality material, and is now consequently a highly collectable label with values of the 45's, recently becoming stronger as any surplus copies have long been filed into collections. Global Records had the rights to Philadelphia based Swan releasing Eddie Carlton's – "It Will Be Done"as their first outing. In 1976 the UK all niter attendances were becoming huge, and at these events the "instrumental" was king! So Cream wisely pulled two previously unissued instrumentals from the Swan vaults. Cream's debut 45 carried the instrumental version on the flip and the obscurer Jaywalkers release had the instrumental version of Shelia Ferguson's – "Heartbroken Memories" on it's flipside. To this day, those two 45's are unique. Surprisingly Global only released six 45's on the eye-catching Cream label. They thought they had the rights to William Bell's Atlanta Peachtree label, but were met with pressure from Decca over the rights of the Johnny Jones – "Purple Haze" (withdrawn and later released by Decca on UK Brunswick) perhaps this soured the adventure, after the release of the Northern Soul classic The Four Perfections – "I'm Not Strong Enough" – there were no more 45's under the banner.
Cream was a label, which for soul collectors prematurely ceased releasing 45's. When you look at the six releases you can see they were picked with care. The James Fountain release was at the time the most valuable 45 in the country with its Peachtree original changing hands for £170 shortly 3 weeks before it's UK pressing. We can only surmise at what could have surfaced on the Cream label, with the rights to two such respected USA labels and an eye for picking a good title it could have been a much more influential and memorable label.

76	5001	EDDIE CARLTON	IT WILL BE DONE	same: instrumental	10.00
76	5002	JAMES FOUNTAIN	SEVEN DAY LOVER	MALNUTRITION	15.00
76	5003	JAYWALKERS	CAN'T LIVE WITHOUT YOU	HEARTBROKEN MEMORIES instrumental	10.00
76	5004 withdrawn	JOHNNY JONES	PURPLE HAZE	HORSING AROUND	20.00

76	5005	SHOWSTOPPERS	AIN'T NOTHING BUT A HOUSE PARTY	WHAT CAN A MAN DO	8.00
76	5006	FOUR PERFECTIONS	I'M NOT STRONG ENOUGH	same: Instrumental	15.00

CREAM
This label had no connection with Global Records.

80	104	WILLIE MITCHELL	THAT DRIVING BEAT	MERCY + EVERYTHING IS GONNA BE	6.00

CREOLE

74	101	CHEQUERS	UNDECIDED LOVE	UNDECIDED LOVE part 1	5.00
74	101 DJ	CHEQUERS	UNDECIDED LOVE	UNDECIDED LOVE part 1	6.00
74	107	GRAND ARMY	FAME	YOU GOT ROCK N' ROLL	4.00
74	107 DJ	GRAND ARMY	FAME	YOU GOT ROCK N' ROLL	5.00
75	111	CHEQUERS	ROCK ON BROTHER	THEME ONE	3.00
75	111 DJ	CHEQUERS	ROCK ON BROTHER	THEME ONE	4.00
75	113	BUTCH BARKER	THE JOKER	JUICIE BRUCIE	8.00
75	113 DJ	BUTCH BARKER	THE JOKER	JUICIE BRUCIE	10.00
75	115	WEST COAST DRIVE	PLEASE LOVE ME AGAIN	WEST COAST DRIVE	5.00
75	115 DJ	WEST COAST DRIVE	PLEASE LOVE ME AGAIN	WEST COAST DRIVE	6.00
76	135	ICE	TIME WILL TELL	BOBO STEP	6.00
76	135 DJ	ICE	TIME WILL TELL	BOBO STEP	8.00
77	138	RONI HILL	I WOULDN'T GIVE YOU UP	YOU KEEP ME HANGING ON	20.00
77	138 DJ	RONI HILL	I WOULDN'T GIVE YOU UP	YOU KEEP ME HANGING ON	25.00
77	141	RUBY WINTERS	I WILL	BLUER DAYS AHEAD	6.00
77	141 DJ	RUBY WINTERS	I WILL	BLUER DAYS AHEAD	8.00
78	149	EAST COAST CONNECTION	YOU'RE SO RIGHT FOR ME	OVER PLEASE	8.00
78	149 DJ	EAST COAST CONNECTION	YOU'RE SO RIGHT FOR ME	OVER PLEASE	10.00
78	152	ONA WATSON	TAKE THIS JOB AND SHOVE IT	FALLING IN LOVE AGAIN	6.00
78	152 DJ	ONA WATSON	TAKE THIS JOB AND SHOVE IT	FALLING IN LOVE AGAIN	8.00
78	153	RUBY WINTERS	TREAT ME RIGHT	COME TO ME !	8.00
78	153 DJ	RUBY WINTERS	TREAT ME RIGHT	COME TO ME !	10.00
79	171	RUBY WINTERS	BABY LAY DOWN	LOVIN' ME IS A FULL TIME JOB	8.00
79	171 DJ	RUBY WINTERS	BABY LAY DOWN	LOVIN' ME IS A FULL TIME JOB	10.00
79	174	RUBY WINTERS	BACK TO LOVE	I'VE BEEN WAITING DFOR YOU ALL	8.00
79	174 DJ	RUBY WINTERS	BACK TO LOVE	I'VE BEEN WAITING DFOR YOU ALL	10.00
79	183	CHIFFONS	HE'S SO FINE + ONE FINE DAY	SWEET TALKING GUY	4.00
80	218	GLADYS KNIGHT & THE PIPS	BEST THING THAT EVER HAPPENED TO ME	EVERY BEAT OF MY HEART + MIDNIGHT TRAIN	3.00
84	218	ROBERT PARKER	BAREFOOTIN'	HAPPY FEET	6.00
84	219	CAPITOLS c/w CURTIS LEE	COOL JERK	UNDER THE MOON OF LOVE + PRETTY LITTLE	6.00

CREWE

70	2	BEN E. KING	I CAN'T TAKE IT LIKE A MAN	GOODBYE MY OLD GIRL	15.00
70	2 DJ	BEN E. KING	I CAN'T TAKE IT LIKE A MAN	GOODBYE MY OLD GIRL	20.00
70	3	FAITH HOPE & CHARITY	SO MUCH LOVE	LET'S TRY IT OVER	10.00
70	3 DJ	FAITH HOPE & CHARITY	SO MUCH LOVE	LET'S TRY IT OVER	15.00
70	3	FAITH HOPE & CHARITY	SO MUCH LOVE	LIFE WON'T BE THE SAME WITHOUT	15.00
70	3 DJ	FAITH HOPE & CHARITY	SO MUCH LOVE	LIFE WON'T BE THE SAME WITHOUT	20.00

CRUSH MUSIC

	6103 PS	LENNY WILLIAMS	GIVIN' UP ON LOVE	same: instrumental	6.00

CRYSTAL

75	7020	SAX OF SOUL	SEA CRUISE	Same: instrumental	5.00
75	7020 DJ	SAX OF SOUL	SEA CRUISE	Same: instrumental	6.00
75	7021	SOUNDS OF SUNSET	CANADIAN SUNSET	Same: instrumental	5.00
75	7021 DJ	SOUNDS OF SUNSET	CANADIAN SUNSET	Same: instrumental	6.00
75	7022	COTTAGE	THIS THING CALLED LOVE	Same: instrumental	6.00
75	7022 DJ	COTTAGE	THING THING CALLED LOVE	Same: instrumental	8.00
75	7023	EDE ROBIN	THERE MUST BE A LOVE SOMEWHERE	SOUL OVER EASY	10.00
75	7023 DJ	EDE ROBIN	THERE MUST BE A LOVE SOMEWHERE	SOUL OVER EASY	15.00
75	7024	BERRY STREET STATION	CHOCOLATE SUGAR	ALL I WANT IS YOU	60.00
75	7024 DJ	BERRY STREET STATION	CHOCOLATE SUGAR	ALL I WANT IS YOU	75.00
75	7025	DIANE JENKINS	TOW-A-WAY ZONE	ANNIVERSARY	15.00
75	7025 DJ	DIANE JENKINS	TOW-A-WAY ZONE	ANNIVERSARY	25.00
76	7026	WISDOM	NEFERTITI	WHAT-CHA-GONNA-DO-ABOUT-YOU	10.00
76	7026 DJ	WISDOM	NEFERTITI	WHAT-CHA-GONNA-DO-ABOUT-YOU	15.00

CTI

75	001	HUBERT LAWS	THE CHICAGO THEME (LOVE LOOP)	I HAD A DREAM	5.00
75	002	GEORGE BENSON	SUPERSHIP	MY LATIN BROTHER	6.00
76	5005	LALO SCHIFRIN	JAWS	QUITE VILLAGE	5.00
73	4000	DEODATO	ALSO SPRACH ZARATHRUSTRA (2001)	SPIRIT OF SUMMER	4.00
73	4001	DEODATO	SUPER STRUT	RHAPSODY IN BLUE	8.00
73	4003	DEODATO-AIRTO	DO IT AGAIN	BRANCHES	4.00

CUBE

72	21	JIMMY HELMS	SO LONG LOVE	DREAM MERCHANT	4.00
73	27	JIMMY HELMS	GONNA MAKE YOU AN OFFER YOU CAN'T REFUSE	WORDS AND MUSIC	4.00
73	30	JIMMY HELMS	WHAT'LL DO WITH MY MIND	JACK HORNER'S HOLIDAY	4.00
73	33	JIMMY HELMS	I'LL TAKE GOOD CARE OF YOU	FLY AWAY	4.00

73	34	MAJESTICS	SHE TROUBLES MY MIND	LIVING IT ALL AGAIN		15.00
74	36	JIMMY HELMS	WHEN CAN BROWN BEGIN	THERE'LL BE ANOTHER NIGHT		4.00
75	60	JIMMY HELMS	GONNA MAKE YOU AN OFFER YOU CAN'T REFUSE	SO LONG LOVE THERE'LL BE ANOTHER		4.00
75	60 DJ	JIMMY HELMS	GONNA MAKE YOU AN OFFER YOU CAN'T REFUSE	SO LONG LOVE THERE'LL BE ANOTHER		5.00
77	75	JIMMY CHAMBERS	LOVE DON'T COME EASILY, GIRL	DOIN' NALRIGHT		8.00
77	75 DJ	JIMMY CHAMBERS	LOVE DON'T COME EASILY, GIRL	DOIN' ALRIGHT		10.00
84	98	JIMMY HELMS	GONNA MAKE YOU AN OFFER YOU CAN'T REFUSE	SO LONG LOVE		4.00

CURTOM

Distributed in the UK by Kinney, this Curtis Mayfield created label had all its pre-1975 45's released through the Buddah label.

75	16536	LEROY HUTSON	ALL BECAUSE OF YOU	LUCKY FELLOW		20.00
75	16536 DJ	LEROY HUTSON	ALL BECAUSE OF YOU	LUCKY FELLOW		25.00
75	16583	NATURAL FOUR	LOVE'S SO WONDERFUL	WHAT'S HAPPENING HERE		15.00
75	16583 DJ	NATURAL FOUR	LOVE'S SO WONDERFUL	WHAT'S HAPPENING HERE		20.00
75	16638	IMPRESSIONS	FIRST IMPRESSIONS	OLD BEFORE MY TIME		5.00
75	16638 DJ	IMPRESSIONS	FIRST IMPRESSIONS	OLD BEFORE MY TIME		6.00
76	16696	NOTATIONS	THINK BEFORE YOU STOP	I'M LOSING		8.00
76	16696 DJ	NOTATIONS	THINK BEFORE YOU STOP	I'M LOSING		10.00
76	16702	LEROY HUTSON	FEEL THE SPIRIT	same: part 2		5.00
76	16702 DJ	LEROY HUTSON	FEEL THE SPIRIT	same: part 2		6.00
77	16736	IMPRESSIONS	I WISH I'D STAYED IN BED	I'M SO GLAD		10.00
77	16736 DJ	IMPRESSIONS	I WISH I'D STAYED IN BED	I'M SO GLAD		15.00
78	17078	LINDA CLIFFORD	FROM NOW ON	YOU CAN DO IT		8.00
78	17078 DJ	LINDA CLIFFORD	FROM NOW ON	YOU CAN DO IT		10.00
78	17163	LINDA CLIFFORD	RUNAWAY LOVE	IF YOUR FRIENDS COULD SEE ME NOW		10.00
78	17163 DJ	LINDA CLIFFORD	RUNAWAY LOVE	IF YOUR FRIENDS COULD SEE ME NOW		15.00

DARK HORSE

76	5504	ATTITUDES	AIN'T LOVE ENOUGH	WHOLE WORLD'S CRAZY		5.00
76	5505	STAIRSTEPS	FROM US TO YOU	TIME		4.00
76	5507	STAIRSTEPS	PASADO	THROWING STONES		4.00
76	5508	ATTITUDES	SWEET SUMMER MUSIC	IF WE WANT TO		4.00

DART

73	2006	REPARATA & the DELRONS	OCTOPUS'S GARDEN	YOUR LIFE IS GONE		5.00
74	2049	OUTRIDERS	THE TELEGRAM SONG	LOVE YOU MORE THAN ANY OTHER		8.00
75	2055	SALLY SAGOE	STOP	A LITLE BIT OF LOVE		8.00
76	2057	REPARATA & the DELRONS	OCTOPUS'S GARDEN	YOUR LIFE IS GONE		4.00

DEBUT

87	3024	BARBARA ACKLIN	AM I THE SAME GIRL	LOVE MAKES A WOMAN		6.00
91	3109	FRANCES NERO	FOOTSTEPS FOLLOWING ME	FOOTSTEPS FOLLOWING ME solo		4.00
	3119	CHUCK JACKSON	ALL OVER THE WORLD	TIME STANDS STILL		6.00

DECCA

Founded 1929 by stockbroker Edward Lewis, apparently the term DECCA is surrounded by mystery as no-one seems to know for sure where the name came from. One theory is, the opening notes of one of Beethoven's symphonies is D E C C A and Beethoven's cameo was a logo on Decca records for many years. With artists like Bing Crosby and Al Jolson the early years of Decca were very successful which encouraged to buy out various rival companies. Until the year before the Second War War broke out Decca and EMI were the only two record companies in the British Isles. In 1942 Decca released the best selling single of all-time in Bing Crosby's – "White Christmas" – The Company just went from strength to strength, their London subsidiary label released all the Blues, Rock N'Roll, R&B and Doo-wop throughout the 50's, and London continued the trend with Soul Music thoughout the 60's. Then disaster struck in 1966 when Atlantic switch distribution from Decca to Polydor. But Decca itself was perhaps the most important UK label as far as Brit Soul is concerned. The whole catalogue is peppered with cover versions and soul influenced recordings mostly by British artists who failed to achieve significant success.

68	1006 export	LITTLE RICHARD	TRY SOME OF MINE	SHE'S TOGETHER		45.00
61	11418	EDEN KANE	A NEW KIND OF LOVIN'	FORGET ME NOT		10.00
61	11418 DJ	EDEN KANE	A NEW KIND OF LOVIN'	FORGET ME NOT		15.00
62	11464	DON CHARLES	THE HERMIT OF MISTY MOUNTAIN	MOONLIGHT RENDEZVOUS		20.00
62	11464 DJ	DON CHARLES	THE HERMIT OF MISTY MOUNTAIN	MOONLIGHT RENDEZVOUS		28.00
62	11506	KATHY KIRBY	BIG MAN	SLOWLY		10.00
62	11506 DJ	KATHY KIRBY	BIG MAN	SLOWLY		18.00
63	11572	BILLIE DAVIS	TELL HIM	I'M THANKFUL		6.00
63	11572 DJ	BILLIE DAVIS	TELL HIM	I'M THANKFUL		8.00
63	11707	BERYL MARSDEN	I KNOW	I ONLY CARE ABOUT YOU		15.00
63	11707 DJ	BERYL MARSDEN	I KNOW	I ONLY CARE ABOUT YOU		22.00
63	11739	BRIAN POOLE and the TREMELOS	DO YOU LOVE ME	WHY CAN'T YOU LOVE ME		4.00
63	11739 DJ	BRIAN POOLE and the TREMELOS	DO YOU LOVE ME	WHY CAN'T YOU LOVE ME		6.00
63	11751	JEAN MARTIN	AIN'T GONNA KISS YA	THREE TIMES THREE IS LOVE		10.00
63	11751 DJ	JEAN MARTIN	AIN'T GONNA KISS YA	THREE TIMES THREE IS LOVE		15.00
63	11757	PETER JAY and the JAYWALKERS	KANSAS CITY	THE PARADE OF TIN SOLDIERS		8.00
63	11757 DJ	PETER JAY and the JAYWALKERS	KANSAS CITY	THE PARADE OF TIN SOLDIERS		10.00
63	11770	BERN ELLIOTT and the FENMEN	MONEY	NOBODY BUT ME		6.00
63	11770 DJ	BERN ELLIOTT and the FENMEN	MONEY	NOBODY BUT ME		8.00
63	11788	SHIRLEY JACKSON	BROKEN HOME	NO GREATER LOVE THAN MINE		15.00
63	11788 DJ	SHIRLEY JACKSON	BROKEN HOME	NO GREATER LOVE THAN MINE		20.00
63	11790	DOUG SHELDON	MICKEY'S MONKEY	FALLING IN LOVE WITH LOVE		10.00
63	11790 DJ	DOUG SHELDON	MICKEY'S MONKEY	FALLING IN LOVE WITH LOVE		15.00
64	11819	BERYL MARSDEN	WHEN THE LOVELIGHT STARTS SHINING	LOVE IS GOING TO HAPPEN TO ME		15.00
64	11819 DJ	BERYL MARSDEN	WHEN THE LOVELIGHT STARTS SHINING	LOVE IS GOING TO HAPPEN TO ME		25.00
64	11827	BEAZERS	BLUE BEAT	I WANNA SHOUT		30.00

64	11827 DJ	BEAZERS	BLUE BEAT	I WANNA SHOUT	45.00
64	11854	JOHNNY CARR and the CADILLACS	RESPECTABLE	REMEMBER THAT NIGHT	20.00
64	11854 DJ	JOHNNY CARR and the CADILLACS	RESPECTABLE	REMEMBER THAT NIGHT	28.00
64	11874	KINGSIZE TAYLOR	STUPIDITY	BAD BOY	30.00
64	11874 DJ	KINGSIZE TAYLOR	STUPIDITY	BAD BOY	40.00
64	11875	LOUISE CORDETT	TWO LOVERS	DON'T MAKE ME OVER	15.00
64	11875 DJ	LOUISE CORDETT	TWO LOVERS	DON'T MAKE ME OVER	22.00
64	11884	LULU and the LUVERS	SHOUT	FORGET ME BABY	8.00
64	11884 DJ	LULU and the LUVERS	SHOUT	FORGET ME BABY	22.00
64	11897	JEAN MARTIN	SAVE THE LAST DANCE FOR ME	WILL YOU STILL LOVE ME TOMORRO	8.00
64	11897 DJ	JEAN MARTIN	SAVE THE LAST DANCE FOR ME	WILL YOU STILL LOVE ME TOMORRO	12.00
64	11909	GRAHAM BOND ORGANISATION	LONG TALL SHORTY	LONG LEGGED BABY	45.00
64	11909 DJ	GRAHAM BOND ORGANISATION	LONG TALL SHORTY	LONG LEGGED BABY	60.00
64	11925	JOHNNY HOWARD BAND	RINKY DINK	JAVA	15.00
64	11925 DJ	JOHNNY HOWARD BAND	RINKY DINK	JAVA	20.00
64	11928	ELKIE BROOKS	HELLO STRANGER	SOMETHING'S GOT A HOLD ON ME	15.00
64	11928 DJ	ELKIE BROOKS	HELLO STRANGER	SOMETHING'S GOT A HOLD ON ME	22.00
64	11935	KINGSIZE TAYLOR	SOMEBODY'S ALWAYS TRYING	LOOKING FOR MY BABY	40.00
64	11935 DJ	KINGSIZE TAYLOR	SOMEBODY'S ALWAYS TRYING	LOOKING FOR MY BABY	60.00
64	11954	ZOOT MONEY	THE UNCLE WILLIE	ZOOT'S SUIT	30.00
64	11954 DJ	ZOOT MONEY	THE UNCLE WILLIE	ZOOT'S SUIT	40.00
64	11961	LADY LEE	I'M INTO SOMETHING GOOD	WHEN LOVE COMES ALONG	10.00
64	11961 DJ	LADY LEE	I'M INTO SOMETHING GOOD	WHEN LOVE COMES ALONG	15.00
64	11965	LULU	CAN'T HEAR YOU NO MORE	I AM IN LOVE	10.00
64	11965 DJ	LULU	CAN'T HEAR YOU NO MORE	I AM IN LOVE	15.00
64	11966	TOM JONES	CHILLS AND FEVER	BREATHLESS	40.00
64	11966 DJ	TOM JONES	CHILLS AND FEVER	BREATHLESS	50.00
64	11972	OTIS SPANN	STIRS ME UP	I LOVE YOU	20.00
64	11972 DJ	OTIS SPANN	STIRS ME UP	I LOVE YOU	28.00
64	11978	LENA MARTELL	ALL CRIED OUT	I'M A FOOL TO WANT YOU	10.00
64	11978 DJ	LENA MARTELL	ALL CRIED OUT	I'M A FOOL TO WANT YOU	15.00
64	11983	ELKIE BROOKS	NOTHING LEFT TO DO BUT CRY	STRANGE THOUGH IT SEEMS	20.00
64	11983 DJ	ELKIE BROOKS	NOTHING LEFT TO DO BUT CRY	STRANGE THOUGH IT SEEMS	30.00
64	11986	BO STREET RUNNERS	BO STREET RUNNER	TELL ME	45.00
64	11986 DJ	BO STREET RUNNERS	BO STREET RUNNER	TELL ME	55.00
64	12001	GLORIA ROMA	IT HURTS ME SO	I DIDN'T KNOW WHAT TIME IT WAS	75.00
64	12001 DJ	GLORIA ROMA	IT HURTS ME SO	I DIDN'T KNOW WHAT TIME IT WAS	85.00
64	12012	RONNIE JONES and the NIGHT-TIMERS	I NEED YOUR LOVING	LET'S PIN A ROSE ON YOU	40.00
64	12012 DJ	RONNIE JONES and the NIGHT-TIMERS	I NEED YOUR LOVING	LET'S PIN A ROSE ON YOU	50.00
64	12030	BOBBY PATRICK BIG SIX	MONKEY TIME	SWEET TALK ME BABY	12.00
64	12030 DJ	BOBBY PATRICK BIG SIX	MONKEY TIME	SWEET TALK ME BABY	20.00
64	12041	STEVE ALDO & the CHALLENGERS	CAN I GET A WITNESS	BABY WHAT YOU WANT ME TO DO	40.00
64	12041 DJ	STEVE ALDO & the CHALLENGERS	CAN I GET A WITNESS	BABY WHAT YOU WANT ME TO DO	50.00
65	12046	DODIE WEST	GOIN' OUT OF MY HEAD	IS HE FEELING BLUE	10.00
65	12046 DJ	DODIE WEST	GOIN' OUT OF MY HEAD	IS HE FEELING BLUE	15.00
65	12056	MARIONETTES	WHIRLPOOL OF LOVE	NOBODY BUT YOU	8.00
65	12056 DJ	MARIONETTES	WHIRLPOOL OF LOVE	NOBODY BUT YOU	10.00
65	12061	ELKIE BROOKS	THE WAY YOU DO THE THINGS YOU DO	BLUE TONIGHT	15.00
65	12061 DJ	ELKIE BROOKS	THE WAY YOU DO THE THINGS YOU DO	BLUE TONIGHT	22.00
64	12065	JOHNNY HOWARD BAND	EL PUSSY CAT	A TUNE CALLED HARRY	20.00
64	12065 DJ	JOHNNY HOWARD BAND	EL PUSSY CAT	A TUNE CALLED HARRY	28.00
64	12066	RONNIE JONES	MY LOVE	IT'S ALL OVER	15.00
64	12066 DJ	RONNIE JONES	MY LOVE	IT'S ALL OVER	22.00
65	12067	ADRIENNE POSTER	THE WAY YOU DO THE THINGS YOU DO	HE DOESN'T LOVE ME	20.00
65	12067 DJ	ADRIENNE POSTER	THE WAY YOU DO THE THINGS YOU DO	HE DOESN'T LOVE ME	28.00
65	12069	PATRICK KERR	MAGIC POTION	IT'S NOT TROUBLE TO LOVE YOU	25.00
65	12069 DJ	PATRICK KERR	MAGIC POTION	IT'S NOT TROUBLE TO YOU LOVE	45.00
65	12070	GOLDIE and the GINGERBREADS	CAN'T YOU HEAR MY HEARTBEAT	LITTLE BOY	15.00
65	12070 DJ	GOLDIE and the GINGERBREADS	CAN'T YOU HEAR MY HEARTBEAT	LITTLE BOY	20.00
65	12111	BARRY ST. JOHN	MIND HOW YOU GO	DON'T YOU FEEL PROUD	4.00
65	12111 DJ	BARRY ST. JOHN	MIND HOW YOU GO	DON'T YOU FEEL PROUD	6.00
65	12116	SOUL BROS.	I KEEP RINGING MY BABY	I CAN'T TAKE IT	6.00
65	12116 DJ	SOUL BROS.	I KEEP RINGING MY BABY	I CAN'T TAKE IT	10.00
65	12119	ELEANOR TONER	ALL CRIED OUT	A HUNDRED GUITARS	8.00
65	12119 DJ	ELEANOR TONER	ALL CRIED OUT	A HUNDRED GUITARS	10.00
65	12126	GOLDIE and the GINGERBREADS	THE SKIP	THAT'S WHY I LOVE YOU	8.00
65	12126 DJ	GOLDIE and the GINGERBREADS	THE SKIP	THAT'S WHY I LOVE YOU	10.00
65	12137	HIPSTER IMAGE	CAN'T LET HER GO	MAKE HER MINE	100.00
65	12137 DJ	HIPSTER IMAGE	CAN'T LET HER GO	MAKE HER MINE	130.00
65	12140	BIRDS	LEAVING HERE	NEXT IN LINE	75.00
65	12140 DJ	BIRDS	LEAVING HERE	NEXT IN LINE	85.00
65	12145	BARRY ST. JOHN	HEY BOY	I'VE BEEN CRYING	10.00
65	12145 DJ	BARRY ST. JOHN	HEY BOY	I'VE BEEN CRYING	15.00
65	12150	STEVE STEPHENSON SHOWBAND	HE'S A STRANGER	PENCIL AND PAPER	15.00
65	12150 DJ	STEVE STEPHENSON SHOWBAND	HE'S A STRANGER	PENCIL AND PAPER	20.00
65	12151	LARRY WILLIAMS	SWEET LITTLE BABY	SLOW DOWN	15.00
65	12151 DJ	LARRY WILLIAMS	SWEET LITTLE BABY	SLOW DOWN	20.00
65	12152	PHILLIPPA LEWIS	JUST LIKE IN THE MOVIES	GET ALONG WITHOUT YOU	50.00
65	12152 DJ	PHILLIPPA LEWIS	JUST LIKE IN THE MOVIES	GET ALONG WITHOUT YOU	70.00

65	12155	JANIE MARDEN	THIS EMPTY PLACE	THEY LONG TO BE CLOSE TO YOU	30.00
65	12155 DJ	JANIE MARDEN	THIS EMPTY PLACE	THEY LONG TO BE CLOSE TO YOU	40.00
65	12169	LULU	LEAVE A LITTLE LOVE	HE DON'T WANT YOUR LOVE ANYMOR	25.00
65	12169 DJ	LULU	LEAVE A LITTLE LOVE	HE DON'T WANT YOUR LOVE ANYMOR	40.00
65	12171	BERN ELLIOTT	LIPSTICK TRACES	VOODOO WOMAN	8.00
65	12171 DJ	BERN ELLIOTT	LIPSTICK TRACES	VOODOO WOMAN	10.00
65	12183	POOR SOULS	WHEN MY BABY CRIES	MY BABY SHE'S NOT THERE	15.00
65	12183 DJ	POOR SOULS	WHEN MY BABY CRIES	MY BABY SHE'S NOT THERE	20.00
65	12189	JOY MARSHALL	HEARTACHES HURRY ON BY	HE'S FOR ME	50.00
65	12189 DJ	JOY MARSHALL	HEARTACHES HURRY ON BY	HE'S FOR ME	75.00
65	12192	ELEANOR TONER	WILL YOU STILL LOVE ME TOMORROW	BETWEEN THE WINDOW AND THE PHO	8.00
65	12192 DJ	ELEANOR TONER	WILL YOU STILL LOVE ME TOMORROW	BETWEEN THE WINDOW AND THE PHO	10.00
65	12194 test press	GOLDEN APPLES OF THE SUN	MONKEY TIME	CHOVCOLATE ROLLS, TEA AND MONOPOLY	75.00
65	12206	ART WOODS	GOODBYE SISTERS	SHE KNOWS WHAT TO DO	30.00
65	12206 DJ	ART WOODS	GOODBYE SISTERS	SHE KNOWS WHAT TO DO	45.00
65	12210	CATHERINE PARR	HE'S MY GUY	YOU BELONG TO ME	20.00
65	12210 DJ	CATHERINE PARR	HE'S MY GUY	YOU BELONG TO ME	28.00
65	12217	ALAN PRICE SET	ANY DAY NOW (MY WILD BEAUTIFUL	NEVER BE SICK ON SUNDAY	6.00
65	12217 DJ	ALAN PRICE SET	ANY DAY NOW (MY WILD BEAUTIFUL	NEVER BE SICK ON SUNDAY	8.00
65	12218	SONNY CHILDE	GIVING UP ON LOVE	MIGHTY NICE	200.00
65	12218 DJ	SONNY CHILDE	GIVING UP ON LOVE	MIGHTY NICE	250.00
65	12233	HI - NUMBERS	DANCING IN THE STREET	MY HEART BELONGS TO YOU	40.00
65	12233 DJ	HI - NUMBERS	DANCING IN THE STREET	MY HEART BELONGS TO YOU	50.00
65	12251	CAESARS	ON THE OUTSIDE LOOKING IN	CAN YOU BLAME ME	20.00
65	12251 DJ	CAESARS	ON THE OUTSIDE LOOKING IN	CAN YOU BLAME ME	28.00
65	12288	MARC BOLAN	THE WIZZARD	BEYOND THE RISING SUN	400.00
65	12288 DJ	MARC BOLAN	THE WIZZARD	BEYOND THE RISING SUN	350.00
65	12292	TOM JONES	KEY TO MY HEART	THUNDERBALL	15.00
65	12292 DJ	TOM JONES	KEY TO MY HEART	THUNDERBALL	25.00
65	12295	NEW BREED	FRIENDS AND LOVERS FOREVER	UNTO US	30.00
65	12295 DJ	NEW BREED	FRIENDS AND LOVERS FOREVER	UNTO US	45.00
65	12304	EMERALDS	KING LONELY THE BLUE	SOMEONE ELSE'S FOOL	30.00
65	12304 DJ	EMERALDS	KING LONELY THE BLUE	SOMEONE ELSE'S FOOL	40.00
66	12315 export	TOM JONES	TO MAKE A BIG MAN CRY	I'LL NEVER LET YOU GO	20.00
66	12318	ST. LOUIS UNION	RESPECT	GIRL	15.00
66	12318 DJ	ST. LOUIS UNION	RESPECT	GIRL	22.00
66	12326	LULU	CALL ME	AFTER YOU	6.00
66	12326 DJ	LULU	CALL ME	AFTER YOU	8.00
66	12329	ADRIENNE POSTER	SOMETHING BEAUTIFUL	SO GLAD YOU'RE MINE	30.00
66	12329 DJ	ADRIENNE POSTER	SOMETHING BEAUTIFUL	SO GLAD YOU'RE MINE	45.00
66	12349	TOM JONES	STOP BREAKING MY HEART	NEVER GIVE AWAY LOVE	10.00
66	12349 DJ	TOM JONES	STOP BREAKING MY HEART	NEVER GIVE AWAY LOVE	20.00
66	12356	NEWS	THE ENTERTAINERS	I COUNT THE TEARS	8.00
66	12356 DJ	NEWS	THE ENTERTAINERS	I COUNT THE TEARS	10.00
66	12364	GENE LATTER	JUST A MINUTE OR TWO	DREAM LOVER	8.00
66	12364 DJ	GENE LATTER	JUST A MINUTE OR TWO	DREAM LOVER	10.00
66	12367	ALAN PRICE SET	I PUT A SPELL ON YOU	IECHYD-DA	8.00
66	12367 DJ	ALAN PRICE SET	I PUT A SPELL ON YOU	IECHYD-DA	10.00
66	12371	CYAN THREE	SINCE I LOST MY BABY	FACE OF A LOSER	20.00
66	12371 DJ	CYAN THREE	SINCE I LOST MY BABY	FACE OF A LOSER	28.00
66	12373	TRULY SMITH	MY SMILE IS JUST A FROWN TURNED	LOVE IS ME, LOVE IS YOU	75.00
66	12373 DJ	TRULY SMITH	MY SMILE IS JUST A FROWN TURNED	LOVE IS ME, LOVE IS YOU	100.00
66	12378	STEVE KIMBLE	ALL THE TIME IN THE WORLD	SOME THING TAKE A LITTLE TIME	20.00
66	12378 DJ	STEVE KIMBLE	ALL THE TIME IN THE WORLD	SOME THING TAKE A LITTLE TIME	28.00
66	12392	SENSATIONS	LOOK AT MY BABY	WHAT A WONDERFUL BABY	10.00
66	12392 DJ	SENSATIONS	LOOK AT MY BABY	WHAT A WONDERFUL BABY	15.00
66	12397	GENE LATTER	MOTHER'S LITTLE HELPER	PLEASE COME BACK TO ME AGAIN	8.00
66	12397 DJ	GENE LATTER	MOTHER'S LITTLE HELPER	PLEASE COME BACK TO ME AGAIN	10.00
66	12422	JOY MARSHALL	THE MORE I SEE YOU	A TASTE OF HONEY	20.00
66	12422 DJ	JOY MARSHALL	THE MORE I SEE YOU	A TASTE OF HONEY	28.00
66	12435	DAVE BERRY	WALK, WALK, TALK, TALK	MAMA	8.00
66	12435 DJ	DAVE BERRY	WALK, WALK, TALK, TALK	MAMA	15.00
66	12438	WISHFUL THINKING	TURNING AROUND	V.I.P.	15.00
66	12438 DJ	WISHFUL THINKING	TURNING AROUND	V.I.P.	22.00
66	12439	STORYTELLERS	LET'S GET BCK TO THE LOVE SCENE	JUST A FRIEND	50.00
66	12439 DJ	STORYTELLERS	LET'S GET BCK TO THE LOVE SCENE	JUST A FRIEND	75.00
66	12451	NEIL LANDON	I'M YOUR PUPPET	I STILL LOVE YOU	10.00
66	12451 DJ	NEIL LANDON	I'M YOUR PUPPET	I STILL LOVE YOU	15.00
66	12463	MARTELLS	TIME TO SAY GOODNIGHT	THE CHERRY SONG	10.00
66	12463 DJ	MARTELLS	TIME TO SAY GOODNIGHT	THE CHERRY SONG	15.00
66	12469	GAME	GONNA GET ME SOMEONE	GOTTA WAIT	85.00
66	12469 DJ	GAME	GONNA GET ME SOMEONE	GOTTA WAIT	100.00
66	12501	RAY GATES	HAVE YOU EVER HAD THE BLUES	IT'S SUCH A SHAME	10.00
66	12501 DJ	RAY GATES	HAVE YOU EVER HAD THE BLUES	IT'S SUCH A SHAME	15.00
66	12513	DAVE BERRY	PICTURE M GONE	ANN	15.00
66	12513 DJ	DAVE BERRY	PICTURE M GONE	ANN	25.00
66	12522	SIGNS	YOU AIN'T GOT A HEART	STOP, DON'T DO IT	20.00
66	12522 DJ	SIGNS	YOU AIN'T GOT A HEART	STOP, DON'T DO IT	30.00
67	12599	TOM JONES	I'LL NEVER LET YOU GO	FUNNY FAMILIAR FORGOTTEN FEELINGS	6.00

67	12599 DJ	TOM JONES	I'LL NEVER LET YOU GO	FUNNY FAMILIAR FORGOTTEN FEELINGS	6.00
67	12613	ERROL DIXON	SIX QUESTIONS	NOT AGAIN	15.00
67	12613 DJ	ERROL DIXON	SIX QUESTIONS	NOT AGAIN	20.00
67	12645	TRULY SMITH	I WANNA GO BACK THERE AGAIN	WINDOW CLEANER	15.00
67	12645 DJ	TRULY SMITH	I WANNA GO BACK THERE AGAIN	WINDOW CLEANER	22.00
67	12650	CHANTS	A LOVER'S STORY	WEARING A SMILE	6.00
67	12650 DJ	CHANTS	A LOVER'S STORY	WEARING A SMILE	8.00
67	12662	BARNEY J. BARNES	CAN'T STAND THE PAIN	IT MUST BE LOVE	20.00
67	12662 DJ	BARNEY J. BARNES	CAN'T STAND THE PAIN	IT MUST BE LOVE	30.00
67	12685	JOHN E. PAUL	I WANNA KNOW	PRINCE OF PLAYERS	125.00

first original has inverted master number beneath the 12685 release number

67	12685 DJ	JOHN E. PAUL	I WANNA KNOW	PRINCE OF PLAYERS	200.00
75	12685	JOHN E. PAUL	I WANNA KNOW	PRINCE OF PLAYERS	15.00

Second press has the master number beneath the 12685 release number, the same way up.

67	12695	BOBBY HANNA	GOIN' WHERE THE LOVIN' IS	BLAME IT ON ME	10.00
67	12695 DJ	BOBBY HANNA	GOIN' WHERE THE LOVIN' IS	BLAME IT ON ME	15.00
67	12717	ERROL DIXON c/w JUDY KAY	TRUE LOVE NEVER RUNS SMOOTH	WHAT YOU GONNA DO	15.00
67	12717 DJ	ERROL DIXON c/w JUDY KAY	TRUE LOVE NEVER RUNS SMOOTH	WHAT YOU GONNA DO	20.00
68	12721	FEARNS BRASS FOUNDRY	DON'T CHANGE IT	JOHN WHITE	25.00
68	12721 DJ	FEARNS BRASS FOUNDRY	DON'T CHANGE IT	JOHN WHITE	40.00
68	12738	BOBBY HANNA	TOO MUCH LOVE	WHAT DO I WANT FOR TOMORROW	10.00
68	12738 DJ	BOBBY HANNA	TOO MUCH LOVE	WHAT DO I WANT FOR TOMORROW	15.00
68	12755	PETE KELLY SOLUTION	MIDNIGHT CONFESSION	IF YOUR LOVE DON'T SWING	20.00
68	12755 DJ	PETE KELLY SOLUTION	MIDNIGHT CONFESSION	IF YOUR LOVE DON'T SWING	28.00
68	12767	AL TORINO	INSIDE, OUTSIDE, UPSIDE DOWN	CAN'T NOBODY LOVE YOU	10.00
68	12767 DJ	AL TORINO	INSIDE, OUTSIDE, UPSIDE DOWN	CAN'T NOBODY LOVE YOU	15.00
68	12781	EDWIN BEE	CALLIN' FOR MY BABY	I'VE BEEN LOVIN' YOU	10.00
68	12781 DJ	EDWIN BEE	CALLIN' FOR MY BABY	I'VE BEEN LOVIN' YOU	15.00
68	12783	BOBBY HANNA	EVERYBODY NEEDS LOVE	WRITTEN ON THE WIND	20.00
68	12783 DJ	BOBBY HANNA	EVERYBODY NEEDS LOVE	WRITTEN ON THE WIND	30.00
68	12795	TONY NEWMAN	LET THE GOOD TIMES ROLL	SOUL THING	20.00
68	12795 DJ	TONY NEWMAN	LET THE GOOD TIMES ROLL	SOUL THING	30.00
68	12816	BUGALOO BRASS	GRAZING IN THE GRASS	ONCE UPON A TIME	8.00
68	12816 DJ	BUGALOO BRASS	GRAZING IN THE GRASS	ONCE UPON A TIME	10.00
68	12823	BILLIE DAVIS	I WANT YOU TO BE MY BABY	SUFFER	6.00
68	12823 DJ	BILLIE DAVIS	I WANT YOU TO BE MY BABY	SUFFER	8.00
68	12826	ERROL DIXON	BACK TO THE CHICKEN SHACK	I DONE FOUND OUT	15.00
68	12826 DJ	ERROL DIXON	BACK TO THE CHICKEN SHACK	I DONE FOUND OUT	22.00
68	12833	BOBBY HANNA	TO WAIT FOR LOVE (IS TO WASTE YOUR	IS IT WRONG	10.00
68	12833 DJ	BOBBY HANNA	TO WAIT FOR LOVE (IS TO WASTE YOUR	IS IT WRONG	15.00
68	12835	FEARNS BRASS FOUNDRY	LOVE, SINK AND DROWN	NOW I TASTE THE TEARS	10.00
68	12835 DJ	FEARNS BRASS FOUNDRY	LOVE, SINK AND DROWN	NOW I TASTE THE TEARS	15.00
68	12849	TAM WHITE	GIRL WATCHER	WAITING TILL THE NIGHT COMES	10.00
68	12849 DJ	TAM WHITE	GIRL WATCHER	WAITING TILL THE NIGHT COMES	15.00
69	12870	BILLIE DAVIS	MAKE THE FEELING GO AWAY	I'LL COME HOME	15.00
69	12870 DJ	BILLIE DAVIS	MAKE THE FEELING GO AWAY	I'LL COME HOME	15.00
69	12899	JIMMY JUSTICE	THERE GOES MY WORLD	RUNNING OUT OF TIME	10.00
69	12899 DJ	JIMMY JUSTICE	THERE GOES MY WORLD	RUNNING OUT OF TIME	15.00
69	12909	RONNIE ALDRICH	RIDE MY SEESAW	ROMANCE ON THE NORTH SEA	15.00
69	12909 DJ	RONNIE ALDRICH	RIDE MY SEESAW	ROMANCE ON THE NORTH SEA	20.00
69	12923	BILLIE DAVIS	NOBODY'S HOME TO GO HOME TO	I CAN REMEMBER	20.00
69	12923 DJ	BILLIE DAVIS	NOBODY'S HOME TO GO HOME TO	I CAN REMEMBER	28.00
69	12931	GOLDIE	CAN'T YOU HEAR MY HEARTBEAT	THAT'S WHY I LOVE YOU	8.00
69	12931 DJ	GOLDIE	CAN'T YOU HEAR MY HEARTBEAT	THAT'S WHY I LOVE YOU	10.00
69	12967	DAVID ESSEX	THE DAY THE EARTH STOOD STILL	IS IT SO STRANGE	30.00
69	12967 DJ	DAVID ESSEX	THE DAY THE EARTH STOOD STILL	IS IT SO STRANGE	40.00
70	13041	TONY NEWMAN	SOUL THING	LET THE GOOD TIMES ROLL	15.00
70	13041 DJ	TONY NEWMAN	SOUL THING	LET THE GOOD TIMES ROLL	25.00
.70	13047	ELI BONAPARTE	NEVER AN EVERYDAY THING	THE MAN FROM BIRMINGHAM	10.00
70	13047 DJ	ELI BONAPARTE	NEVER AN EVERYDAY THING	THE MAN FROM BIRMINGHAM	15.00
70	13061	TOM JONES	STOP BREAKING MY HEART	I (WHO HAVE NOTHING)	10.00
70	13061 DJ	TOM JONES	STOP BREAKING MY HEART	I (WHO HAVE NOTHING)	15.00
71	13145	SUSAN SHIFRIN	25 MILES	TO LOVE	20.00
71	13145 DJ	SUSAN SHIFRIN	25 MILES	TO LOVE	30.00
72	13303	BLOODSTONE	JUDY JUDY	GIRL YOU LOOK SO FINE	4.00
72	13303 DJ	BLOODSTONE	JUDY JUDY	GIRL YOU LOOK SO FINE	6.00
72	13324	COOL BREEZE	SUMMERTIME SUNSHINE	SING OUT YOUR LOVE	8.00
72	13324 DJ	COOL BREEZE	SUMMERTIME SUNSHINE	SING OUT YOUR LOVE	10.00
73	13382	BLOODSTONE	NATURAL HIGH	THIS THING IS HEAVY	6.00
73	13382 DJ	BLOODSTONE	NATURAL HIGH	THIS THING IS HEAVY	8.00
73	13432	TIMOTHY WILSON	SHINE	PHONEY PEOPLE	4.00
73	13432 DJ	TIMOTHY WILSON	SHINE	PHONEY PEOPLE	6.00
74	13445	KRISTINE SPARKLE	GONNA GET ALONG WITHOUT YOU NOW	I'LL BE YOUR BABY TONIGHT	6.00
74	13445 DJ	KRISTINE SPARKLE	GONNA GET ALONG WITHOUT YOU NOW	I'LL BE YOUR BABY TONIGHT	8.00
74	13454	BLOODSTONE	NEVER LET YOU GO	YOU KNOW WE'VE LEARNED	15.00
74	13454 DJ	BLOODSTONE	NEVER LET YOU GO	YOU KNOW WE'VE LEARNED	20.00
74	13491	CHERRY ROLAND	HERE IS WHERE THE LOVE IS	I CAN GIVE YOU BACK YOURSELF	10.00
74	13491 DJ	CHERRY ROLAND	HERE IS WHERE THE LOVE IS	I CAN GIVE YOU BACK YOURSELF	15.00
74	13493	BLOODSTONE	OUTSIDE WOMAN	DUMB DUDE	6.00
74	13493 DJ	BLOODSTONE	OUTSIDE WOMAN	DUMB DUDE	8.00

74	13521	BLOODSTONE	THAT'S NOT HOW IT GOES	EVERYBODY NEEDS LOVE	4.00
74	13521 DJ	BLOODSTONE	THAT'S NOT HOW IT GOES	EVERYBODY NEEDS LOVE	6.00
74	13529	BARRY ST. JOHN	BRIGIIT SHINES THE LIGHT	MY MAN	8.00
74	13529 DJ	BARRY ST. JOHN	BRIGHT SHINES THE LIGHT	MY MAN	10.00
74	13555	MICKEY MOONSHINE	NAME IT YOU GOT IT	BABY BLUE	30.00
74	13555 DJ	MICKEY MOONSHINE	NAME IT YOU GOT IT	BABY BLUE	60.00
74	13556	CHOCOLATE BOYS	VOLTAIRE PIER	EL BIMBO	50.00
74	13556 DJ	CHOCOLATE BOYS	VOLTAIRE PIER	EL BIMBO	60.00
75	13571	BLOODSTONE	MY LITTLE LADY	LOVING YOU IS JUST A PASTIME	8.00
75	13571 DJ	BLOODSTONE	MY LITTLE LADY	LOVING YOU IS JUST A PASTIME	10.00
75	13580	ATTRACTIONS	BABY I'M COMIN' HOME	OH IT'S A CRIME	5.00
75	13580 DJ	ATTRACTIONS	BABY I'M COMIN' HOME	OH IT'S A CRIME	6.00
75	13596	TABOU COMBO	NEW YORK CITY	NEW YORK CITY part 2	3.00
75	13596 DJ	TABOU COMBO	NEW YORK CITY	NEW YORK CITY part 2	4.00
75	13601	SOUL ON DELIVERY	HUSTLE (DANCE OF THE DAY)	CRESCENT BOOGIE	4.00
75	13601 DJ	SOUL ON DELIVERY	HUSTLE (DANCE OF THE DAY)	CRESCENT BOOGIE	5.00
75	13604	CHIPS	TWICE A WEEK	REEL IN THE YEARS	4.00
75	13604 DJ	CHIPS	TWICE A WEEK	REEL IN THE YEARS	5.00
75	13611	BLOODSTONE	SOMETHING'S MISSING	GIVE ME YOUR HEART	6.00
75	13611 DJ	BLOODSTONE	SOMETHING'S MISSING	GIVE ME YOUR HEART	8.00
75	13613	HAZEL DEAN	OUR DAY WILL COME	same: instrumental	6.00
75	13613 DJ	HAZEL DEAN	OUR DAY WILL COME	same: instrumental	8.00
75	13619	ANDRE GAGNON	WOW	SAMBA	4.00
75	13619 DJ	ANDRE GAGNON	WOW	SAMBA	5.00
76	13622	HAZEL DEAN	I COULDN'T LIVE A DAY WITHOUT YOUR LOVE	YOU PROMISED ME THE LOVE	6.00
76	13622 DJ	HAZEL DEAN	I COULDN'T LIVE A DAY WITHOUT YOUR LOVE	YOU PROMISED ME THE LOVE	8.00
76	13627	JOHN MILES	MUSIC	PUTTING MY NEW SONG TOGETHER	4.00
76	13627 DJ	JOHN MILES	MUSIC	PUTTING MY NEW SONG TOGETHER	6.00
76	13628	BLOODSTONE	LET'S DO IT	FUNKY PARK	4.00
76	13628 DJ	BLOODSTONE	LET'S DO IT	FUNKY PARK	5.00
76	13630	BLACK ABBOTTS	SHE'S ALRIGHT	TWICE A WEEK	4.00
76	13630 DJ	BLACK ABBOTTS	SHE'S ALRIGHT	TWICE A WEEK	5.00
76	13640	SU KRAMER	YOU'VE GOT THE POWER	YOU'VE GOT THE POWER PARTII	10.00
76	13640 DJ	SU KRAMER	YOU'VE GOT THE POWER	YOU'VE GOT THE POWER PARTII	15.00
76	13646	CISSY STONE	GONE BUT NOT FORGOTTEN	PART OF THE BAND	20.00
76	13646 DJ	CISSY STONE	GONE BUT NOT FORGOTTEN	PART OF THE BAND	30.00
76	13660	BLOODSTONE	JUST LIKE IN THE MOVIES	LITTLE LINDA	5.00
76	13660 DJ	BLOODSTONE	JUST LIKE IN THE MOVIES	LITTLE LINDA	6.00
76	13674	CAROL GRIMES	I BETCHA DIDN'T KNOW THAT	DYNAMITE	4.00
76	13674 DJ	CAROL GRIMES	I BETCHA DIDN'T KNOW THAT	DYNAMITE	5.00
77	13688	OTIS WAYGOOD BAND	GET IT STARTED	RED HOT PASSION	4.00
77	13688 DJ	OTIS WAYGOOD BAND	GET IT STARTED	RED HOT PASSION	5.00
77	13731	KENNY WILLIAMS	GIVE ME MY HEART BACK	(YOU'RE) FABULOUS BABE	10.00
77	13731 DJ	KENNY WILLIAMS	GIVE ME MY HEART BACK	(YOU'RE) FABULOUS BABE	15.00
78	13755	MANU DIBANGO	BIG BLOW	ALOKO PARTY	8.00
78	13755 DJ	MANU DIBANGO	BIG BLOW	ALOKO PARTY	6.00
78	13786	SPOOKEY	MAGIC	MAMA'S LITTLE BABY	15.00
78	13786 DJ	SPOOKEY	MAGIC	MAMA'S LITTLE BABY	20.00
78	13810	MANU DIBANGO	BIG BLOW	SUN EXPLOSION	8.00
78	13810 DJ	MANU DIBANGO	BIG BLOW	SUN EXPLOSION	10.00
79	13918	DOBIE GRAY	THE IN CROWD	+ 2 track by other artists	4.00
79	13918 DJ	DOBIE GRAY	THE IN CROWD	+ 2 track by other artists	6.00
79	13901	HARRY THUMANN	UNDERWATER	AMERICAN EXPRESS	6.00
79	13901 DJ	HARRY THUMANN	UNDERWATER	AMERICAN EXPRESS	8.00
82	13918	DOBIE GRAY	THE "IN" CROWD	BE A MAN	4.00
82	13918 DJ	DOBIE GRAY	THE "IN" CROWD	BE A MAN	5.00
66	22376	FRANKIE & JOHNNY	I'LL HOLD YOU	(I'M) NEVER GONNA LEAVE YOU	250.00
66	22376 DJ	FRANKIE & JOHNNY	I'LL HOLD YOU	(I'M) NEVER GONNA LEAVE YOU	**299.00**
66	22419	LOS BRAVOS	BLACK IS BLACK	I WANT A NAME	4.00
66	22419 DJ	LOS BRAVOS	BLACK IS BLACK	I WANT A NAME	20.00
66	22484	LOS BRAVOS	I DON'T CARE	DON'T LET LET OUT IN THE COLD	6.00
66	22484 DJ	LOS BRAVOS	I DON'T CARE	DON'T LET LET OUT IN THE COLD	20.00
66	22534	BATS	LISTEN TO MY HEART	STOP DON'T DO IT	20.00
66	22534 DJ	BATS	LISTEN TO MY HEART	STOP DON'T DO IT	30.00
69	22888	GLEN SOUTH	TOO LATE FOR TEARS	PASADENA	10.00
69	22888 DJ	GLEN SOUTH	TOO LATE FOR TEARS	PASADENA	20.00
70	22937	SATIN BELLS	I STAND ACCUSED (OF LOVING YOU)	SWEET DARLIN'	15.00
70	22937 DJ	SATIN BELLS	I STAND ACCUSED (OF LOVING YOU)	SWEET DARLIN'	20.00
70	23044	SATIN BELLS	THE POWER OF LOVE	BABY COME BACK	6.00
70	23044 DJ	SATIN BELLS	THE POWER OF LOVE	BABY COME BACK	8.00

DEEP SOUL

In 1969 Dave Godin continued to pursue his quest of introducing independent USA soul to the UK market. After just six releases and disappointing sales, Dave decided to use his energies in music journalism. Every record in the series is now very difficult to find, and the original company sleeves are even harder. To my knowledge there are no demonstration DJ copies of any of his releases on the Deep Soul label. As with his Soul City label, Deep Soul is an essential must complete, and much sought after series of six.

69	9101	JEAN STANBACK	I STILL LOVE YOU	IF I EVER NEEDED LOVE	50.00
69	9102	AD LIBS	GIVING UP	APPRECIATION	15.00
69	9103	NICKIE LEE	AND BLACK IS BEAUTIFUL	FAITH WITHIN	15.00

69	9104	EMOTIONS	SOMEBODY NEW	BUSHFIRE	22.00
69	9105	JIMMY & LOUISE TIG	A LOVE THAT NEVER GROWS COLD	WHO CAN I TURN TO	45.00
69	9106	ROY HAMILTON	DARK END OF THE STREET	100 YEARS AGO	40.00

DE-LITE
| 80 | 38 | COFFEE | CASANOVA | A PROMISE | 5.00 |

DEMAND

As I've stated on a number of UK pressed labels. I have no right to pass comment on the legitimacy of any labels releases. This label, like so many labels that dedicated themselves to supplying the Northern Soul collectors with classic releases, most probably never owned the rights to release them. Who knows for sure, all I can say is that over the years, these releases are now considered collectable. I have no idea who owned or was responsible for the distribution of the Demand label. All presses are from the early 1980's, and considered slightly inferior in sound and presentation to the more legitimate releases from companies who sourced and used the master tapes.

	101	TRIUMPHS	I'M COMING TO YOUR RESCUE	THE WORLD OWES ME A LOVIN'	8.00
	102	MARSHA GEE	BABY, I NEED YOU	I'LL NEVER BE FREE	10.00
	103	FULLER BROTHERS	TIMES A WASTING	MOANING, GROANING & CRYING	10.00
	202	DON VARNER & THE GENERAL ASSEMBLY	SENSITIVE MIND	LOVIN' TIME	8.00
	203	CHANDLERS	YOUR LOVE MAKES ME LONELY	I NEED YOUR LOVE	15.00
	204	STEMMONS EXPRESS	WOMAN LOVE THIEF	LOVE POWER	10.00
	205	WILBUR WALTON JR.	TWENTY FOUR HOURS OF LONELINES	FOR THE LOVE OF A WOMAN	8.00

DEMON

| | 1018 | LAMONT DOZIER | RIGHT WHERE I WANNA BE | SCARLETT O'HARA | 6.00 |

DERAM

A label set up by Decca for its alternative artists of the mid-sixties. Cat Stevens was perhaps their best selling artist, with Amen Corner, The Move, Procol Harum, helping to keep the label more than viable. Deram is noted amongst rock collectors for its progressive LP's and obscurer psyche 45's. The soul 45's released by this specialist arm of Decca were a small percentage of the label releases. But there are several surprises, the Welsh band - Eyes Of Blue did two recordings that are wonderful Northern Soul: their cover version of the Detroit recording of The Parliaments – "Heart Trouble" – I consider second only to Jimmy James's – "This Heart Of Mine" as the finest UK cover version of a USA soul of all-time. The Flirtations, Danny Williams and to some extent Timebox carried the soul torch for Deram, but out of all the soul releases this label put out they never had a hit!

66	101	BEVERLEY	WHERE THE GOOD TIMES ARE	HAPPY NEW YEAR	20.00
66	101 DJ	BEVERLEY	WHERE THE GOOD TIMES ARE	HAPPY NEW YEAR	30.00
66	106	EYES OF BLUE	HEART TROUBLE	UP AND DOWN	75.00
66	106 DJ	EYES OF BLUE	HEART TROUBLE	UP AND DOWN	100.00
67	114	EYES OF BLUE	SUPERMARKET FULL OF CANS	DON'T ASK ME TO MEND YOUR BROK	50.00
67	114 DJ	EYES OF BLUE	SUPERMARKET FULL OF CANS	DON'T ASK ME TO MEND YOUR BROK	75.00
67	121	QUIK	BERT'S APPLE CRUMBLE	LOVE IS A BEAUTIFUL	150.00
67	121 DJ	QUIK	BERT'S APPLE CRUMBLE	LOVE IS A BEAUTIFUL	175.00
67	125	OUTER LIMITS	JUST ONE MORE CHANCE	HELP ME PLEASE	40.00
67	125 DJ	OUTER LIMITS	JUST ONE MORE CHANCE	HELP ME PLEASE	60.00
67	133	JON GUNN	I JUST MADE UP MY MIND	NOW IT'S MY TURN	10.00
67	133 DJ	JON GUNN	I JUST MADE UP MY MIND	NOW IT'S MY TURN	15.00
67	139	QUIK	MY GIRL	KING OF THE WORLD	25.00
67	139 DJ	QUIK	MY GIRL	KING OF THE WORLD	30.00
67	149	DANNY WILLIAMS	WHOSE LITTLE GIRL ARE YOU	NEVER MY LOVE	50.00
67	149 DJ	DANNY WILLIAMS	WHOSE LITTLE GIRL ARE YOU	NEVER MY LOVE	75.00

This 45 was re-issued by Decca using the original label design and release number. The original first 1967 press has the master number 41266 upside down over the top of DM 149

| 67 | 149 2nd. press | DANNY WILLIAMS | WHOSE LITTLE GIRL ARE YOU | NEVER MY LOVE | 8.00 |
| 67 | 149 2nd. Press DJ | DANNY WILLIAMS | WHOSE LITTLE GIRL ARE YOU | NEVER MY LOVE | 15.00 |

The second 1977 repress has the master number 41266 the same way up as DM 149

67	153	TIMEBOX	WALKING THROUGH THE STREETS	DON'T MAKE PROMISES	20.00
67	153 DJ	TIMEBOX	WALKING THROUGH THE STREETS	DON'T MAKE PROMISES	28.00
67	155	QUIK	I CAN'T SLEEP	SOUL FULL OF SORROW	30.00
67	155 DJ	QUIK	I CAN'T SLEEP	SOUL FULL OF SORROW	40.00
67	165	DOUBLE FEATURE	HANDBAGS TO GLADRAGS	JUST ANOTHER LONELY NIGHT	15.00
67	165 DJ	DOUBLE FEATURE	HANDBAGS TO GLADRAGS	JUST ANOTHER LONELY NIGHT	22.00
68	194	TIMEBOX	BEGGIN'	A WOMAN THAT'S WAITING	25.00
68	194 DJ	TIMEBOX	BEGGIN'	A WOMAN THAT'S WAITING	40.00
68	195	FLIRTATIONS	HOW CAN YOU TELL ME	SOMEONE OUT THERE	10.00
68	195 DJ	FLIRTATIONS	SOMEONE OUT THERE	HOW CAN YOU TELL ME	15.00
68	199	DANNY WILLIAMS	EVERYBODY NEEDS SOMEBODY (I NEED YOU)	THEY WILL NEVER UNDERSTAND	10.00
68	199 DJ	DANNY WILLIAMS	EVERYBODY NEEDS SOMEBODY (I NEED YOU)	THEY WILL NEVER UNDERSTAND	15.00
68	202	CLYDE McPHATTER	ONLY A FOOL	THANK YOU LOVE	20.00
68	202 DJ	CLYDE McPHATTER	ONLY A FOOL	THANK YOU LOVE	30.00
68	209	CATS EYES	I THANK YOU MARIANNE	TURN AROUND (GIVE ME A LITTLE	8.00
68	209 DJ	CATS EYES	I THANK YOU MARIANNE	TURN AROUND (GIVE ME A LITTLE	10.00
68	216	FLIRTATIONS	NOTHING BUT A HEARTACHE	CHRISTMAS TIME IS HERE AGAIN	20.00
68	216 DJ	FLIRTATIONS	NOTHING BUT A HEARTACHE	CHRISTMAS TIME IS HERE AGAIN	30.00
68	219	TIMEBOX	GIRL DON'T MAKE ME WAIT	GONE IS THE SAD MAN	25.00
68	219 DJ	TIMEBOX	GIRL DON'T MAKE ME WAIT	GONE IS THE SAD MAN	35.00
69	223	CLYDE McPHATTER	BABY YOU'VE GOT IT	BABY I COULD BE SO GOOD AT LOV	30.00
69	223 DJ	CLYDE McPHATTER	BABY YOU'VE GOT IT	BABY I COULD BE SO GOOD AT LOV	40.00
69	246	TIMEBOX	POOR LITTLE HEARTBREAKER	BAKER JAM ROLL IN YOUR EYE	10.00
69	246 DJ	TIMEBOX	POOR LITTLE HEARTBREAKER	BAKER JAM ROLL IN YOUR EYE	15.00
69	252	FLIRTATIONS	WHAT'S GOOD ABOUT GOODBYE MY	ONCE I HAD A LOVE	10.00
69	252 DJ	FLIRTATIONS	WHAT'S GOOD ABOUT GOODBYE MY	ONCE I HAD A LOVE	15.00
69	264	FANTASTICS	FACE TO FACE WITH HEARTACHE	THIS MUST BE MY RAINY DAY	6.00
69	264 DJ	FANTASTICS	FACE TO FACE WITH HEARTACHE	THIS MUST BE MY RAINY DAY	8.00

69	271	TIMEBOX	YELLOW VAN	YOU'VE GOT THE CHANCE	10.00
69	271 DJ	TIMEBOX	YELLOW VAN	YOU'VE GOT THE CHANCE	15.00
70	281	FLIRTATIONS	KEEP ON SEARCHING	MOMMA I'M COMING HOME	8.00
70	281 DJ	FLIRTATIONS	KEEP ON SEARCHING	MOMMA I'M COMING HOME	10.00
70	283	FANTASTICS	ASK THE LONELY	WAITING ROUND FOR HEARTACHES	15.00
70	283 DJ	FANTASTICS	ASK THE LONELY	WAITING ROUND FOR HEARTACHES	25.00
70	295	FLIRTATIONS	EVERYBODY NEEDS SOMEBODY (TO LOVE)	CAN'T STOP LOVING YOU	10.00
70	295	FLIRTATIONS	EVERYBODY NEEDS SOMEBODY (TO LOVE)	CAN'T STOP LOVING YOU	15.00
70	318	SUE & SUNNY	AIN'T THAT TELLIN' YOU PEOPLE	DIDN'T I BLOW YOUR MIND	8.00
70	318 DJ	SUE & SUNNY	AIN'T THAT TELLIN' YOU PEOPLE	DIDN'T I BLOW YOUR MIND	10.00
70	319	JOHNNY GOODISON	A LITTLE UNDERSTANDING	ONE MISTAKE	30.00
70	319 DJ	JOHNNY GOODISON	A LITTLE UNDERSTANDING	ONE MISTAKE	45.00
70	327	BROTHERHOOD OF MAN	REACH OUT YOUR HAND	BETTER TOMORROW	10.00
70	327 DJ	BROTHERHOOD OF MAN	REACH OUT YOUR HAND	BETTER TOMORROW	15.00
71	328	SUE & SUNNY	FREEDOM	BREAK UP	5.00
71	328 DJ	SUE & SUNNY	FREEDOM	BREAK UP	6.00
71	329	FLIRTATIONS	THIS MUST BE THE END OF THE LINE	GIVE ME LOVE	8.00
71	329 DJ	FLIRTATIONS	GIVE ME LOVE	THIS MUST BE THE END OF THE LI	15.00
71	334	FANTASTICS	FOR OLD TIMES SAKE	EXODUS MAIN THEME	5.00
71	334 DJ	FANTASTICS	FOR OLD TIMES SAKE	EXODUS MAIN THEME	6.00
71	351	FLIRTATIONS	NEED YOUR LOVING	I WANNA BE THERE	15.00
71	351 DJ	FLIRTATIONS	NEED YOUR LOVING	I WANNA BE THERE	20.00
72	355	SUE & SUNNY	I'M GONNA MAKE YOU LOVE ME	HIGH ON THE THOUGHT OF YOU	6.00
72	355 DJ	SUE & SUNNY	I'M GONNA MAKE YOU LOVE ME	HIGH ON THE THOUGHT OF YOU	8.00
72	370	COLIN AREETY	HOLY COW	I CAN'T DO IT FOR YOU	4.00
72	370 DJ	COLIN AREETY	HOLY COW	I CAN'T DO IT FOR YOU	5.00
72	383	COLIN AREETY	ONE NIGHT AFFAIR	I DON'T WANT TO BE RIGHT	10.00
72	383 DJ	COLIN AREETY	ONE NIGHT AFFAIR	I DON'T WANT TO BE RIGHT	15.00
73	387	JUNIOR CAMPBELL	SWEET ILLUSION	ODE TO KAREN	5.00
73	387 DJ	JUNIOR CAMPBELL	SWEET ILLUSION	ODE TO KAREN	6.00

DESTINY

This Nottingham based label, owned by the now defunct Colony Records, had a somewhat erratic numbering system. Several release numbers were missed out in the series. The label quickly lost credibility with the soul fans when it started recording it's own versions of classics Northern Soul tunes, release numbers 1013, 1014, 1017 did little to help sales, and after nineteen release the label ceased trading. Having said that, it did have some notable releases like Rita & the Tiaras, John Leach etc. which are considered highly collectable today.

79	1001	DOBIE GRAY	OUT ON THE FLOOR	BE A MAN	8.00
79	1001 DJ	DOBIE GRAY	OUT ON THE FLOOR	BE A MAN	10.00
79	1001 DJ PS	DOBIE GRAY	OUT ON THE FLOOR	BE A MAN	15.00
79	1002	RITA & THE TIARAS	GONE WITH THE WIND IS MY LOVE	WILD TIMES	20.00
79	1002 DJ	RITA & THE TIARAS	GONE WITH THE WIND IS MY LOVE	WILD TIMES	25.00
79	1002 PS	RITA & THE TIARAS	GONE WITH THE WIND IS MY LOVE	WILD TIMES	15.00
79	1002 DJ PS	RITA & THE TIARAS	GONE WITH THE WIND IS MY LOVE	WILD TIMES	30.00
79	1003	unissued ?			
79	1004	JAMES COIT	BLACK POWER	PHILADRINE	5.00
79	1004 DJ	JAMES COIT	BLACK POWER	PHILADRINE	8.00
79	1004 PS	JAMES COIT	BLACK POWER	PHILADRINE	6.00
79	1005	CREATION c/w PROMISED LAND	I GET THE FEVER	CHEYANNE	8.00
79	1005 DJ	CREATION c/w PROMISED LAND	I GET THE FEVER	CHEYANNE	10.00
79	1006	MISS DEE DEE	ON A MAGIC CARPET RIDE	AT THE DISCO (STRINGS A GO-GO)	4.00
79	1006 DJ	MISS DEE DEE	ON A MAGIC CARPET RIDE	AT THE DISCO (STRINGS A GO-GO)	6.00
79	1007	SHARONETTES c/w DESTINY	SUGAR DUMPLING	SPRING RAIN	5.00
79	1007	SHARONETTES c/w DESTINY	SUGAR DUMPLING	SPRING RAIN	6.00
79	1008 DJ	CONNIE LAVERNE c/w CHANTELLES	A HOUSE FOR SALE	RUNAWAY	5.00
79	1008 DJ	CONNIE LAVERNE c/w CHANTELLES	A HOUSE FOR SALE	RUNAWAY	5.00
79	1009	GENERAL ASSEMBLY	SENSITIVE MIND	LOVIN' TIME	6.00
79	1009 DJ	GENERAL ASSEMBLY	SENSITIVE MIND	LOVIN' TIME	8.00
79	1010	TAMALA LEWIS	YOU WON'T SAY NOTHING	IF YOU CAN STAND ME	10.00
79	1010 DJ	TAMALA LEWIS	YOU WON'T SAY NOTHING	IF YOU CAN STAND ME	15.00
79	1011	JOHN LEACH	PUT THAT WOMAN DOWN	LOVE DON'T TURN YOUR BACK	10.00
79	1011 DJ	JOHN LEACH	PUT THAT WOMAN DOWN	LOVE DON'T TURN YOUR BACK ON M	15.00
79	1012	unissued ?			
79	1013	CAROL KAY	STOP YOU'LL BECOME AWARE	MESSIN' ME AROUND	5.00
79	1014	unissued ?			
79	1015	CHICO REVILL c/w LITTLE HELEN	THIS BEAUTIFUL DAY	YOU'RE READY NOW	4.00
79	1015 DJ	CHICO REVILL c/w LITTLE HELEN	THIS BEAUTIFUL DAY	YOU'RE READY NOW	6.00
79	1016 acetate only	APPRECIATIONS	I CAN'T HIDE IT	blank	150.00

Unissued: known as an acetate only

79	1017	JOHN DREVARS	THE CLOSER SHE GETS	THE SNAPPER	4.00

not the same recording as MGM 1367 most probably not the same artist.

80	1022	DE-LITES	LOVER	DO THE ZOMBIE	20.00
80	1022 DJ	DE-LITES	LOVER	DO THE ZOMBIE	25.00
80	1026	E.J. CHANDLER	I CAN'T STAND TO LOSE YOU	BELIEVE IN ME	5.00
80	1026 DJ	E.J. CHANDLER	I CAN'T STAND TO LOSE YOU	BELIVE IN ME	10.00

DICE

62	4	JIMMY JAMES	I DON'T WANT TO CRY	BEWILDERED AND BLUE	20.00

DIRECT

67	5002	ERROL DIXON	THE HOOP	I DON'T WANT	200.00

DIRECTION

After the CBS commitment to soul music on its own label, they started an attractively designed label in late 67, complete with an individual black and yellow sleeve. This distinctive label soon alerted soul-hounds that if it was on Direction, it was most likely to be soul. The label released a hotchpotch of music but 80% of it will certainly be of interest to the readers of these pages. Considering CBS had the UK rights of some wonderful USA labels that were strong on black music of the time, labels included Arctic, Date, Dynamo, Okeh, Phil La Soul, and Rojac and of course the whole of the Columbia & Epic labels. So I've decided to list every 45 I know was released on Direction even though it includes a few which are rock or reggae, as I know that no UK Soul 45 collector would ever pass up a Direction label 45 no matter what the genre. Inclusion of Elmer Gantry & Velvet Opera may be a surprise but remember John Ford was a member; his name will turn up a few times within these pages with a few very desirable 45s.

The numbering system for Direction, was in sequence with CBS's other UK labels that is why none of the numbers seem to run concurrently, but one quick comparison with the CBS label numbering, all becomes clear.

Direction also had a policy of supporting up and coming black artists living in the UK or regular visitors from the Caribbean. Groups like The Gladiators who did a few excellent and highly regarded cover versions, Locomotive and Jackie Edwards underlined that the executives at CBS considered Direction to be a "black music" vehicle for them. They also had a measure of success, the Bandwagon's hit and ultimately a classic – "Breakin' Down The Walls Of Heartache" – was a disco dance floor filler for almost two decades and sold in vast numbers being issued and reissued on various labels over the next 20 years. Exactly the same can be said about California's Sly & The Family Stone's all-time soul dance classic – "Dance To The Music" – which CBS quickly withdrew from it's week old 1968 UK Columbia DB8369 release to repromote on the newly formed Direction label. I consider the Direction label, a label a true UK collector should try and complete as just one read down its list of releases you would see it is full of wonderful soul vinyl.

CBS only kept this label on the market for a little over three years. Ten years later it was reactivated it, to promote Ska/Mod/Soul bands and artists. They included Noel McCalla's version of The Four Seasons & Timebox – "Beggin" – and two failed releases from an energetic white soul band – The Step – their young lead singer once told me, he loved this soul stuff, cause his Mum played it when he was young: 26 years later they're still playing it, collecting it and searching for it, worldwide.

67	2712	INEZ & CHARLIE FOXX	I AIN'T GOING FOR THAT	UNDECIDED	10.00
67	2712 DJ	INEZ & CHARLIE FOXX	I AIN'T GOING FOR THAT	UNDECIDED	10.00
67	3068	MICKEY FINN	GARDEN OF MY MIND	TIME TO STOP LOVING YOU	6.00
67	3068 DJ	MICKEY FINN	GARDEN OF MY MIND	TIME TO STOP LOVING YOU	8.00
67	3082	OTELLO SMITH & THE TOBAGO BAD BOYS	MY HOME TOWN	TROUBLE	6.00
67	3082 DJ	OTELLO SMITH & THE TOBAGO BAD BOYS	MY HOME TOWN	TROUBLE	8.00
67	3083	ELMER GANTRY'S VELVET OPERA	FLAMES	SALISBURY PLAIN	5.00
67	3083 DJ	ELMER GANTRY'S VELVET OPERA	FLAMES	SALISBURY PLAIN	6.00
67	3084	GLORIES	(I LOVE YOU BABE BUT) GIVE ME MY FREEDOM	SECURITY	20.00
67	3084 DJ	GLORIES	(I LOVE YOU BABE BUT) GIVE ME MY FREEDOM	SECURITY	28.00
67	3096	PEACHES & HERB	LOVE IS STRANGE	TWO LITTLE KIDS	4.00
67	3096 DJ	PEACHES & HERB	LOVE IS STRANGE	TWO LITTLE KIDS	6.00
67	3114	LOCOMOTIVE	RUDY A MESSAGE TO YOU	A BROKEN HEART	10.00
67	3114 DJ	LOCOMOTIVE	RUDY A MESSAGE TO YOU	A BROKEN HEART	15.00
67	3115	FIVE TOWNS	IT ISN'T WHAT YOU'VE GOT	ADVICE	5.00
67	3115 DJ	FIVE TOWNS	IT ISN'T WHAT YOU'VE GOT	ADVICE	6.00
67	3132	PREGNANT INSOMNIA	WALLPAPER	YOU INTRIGUE ME	5.00
67	3132 DJ	PREGNANT INSOMNIA	WALLPAPER	YOU INTRIGUE ME	6.00
67	3192	INEZ & CHARLIE FOXX	(1-2-3-4-5-6-7) COUNT THE DAYS	A STRANGER I DON'T KNOW	6.00
67	3192 DJ	INEZ & CHARLIE FOXX	(1-2-3-4-5-6-7) COUNT THE DAYS	A STRANGER I DON'T KNOW	10.00
67	3215	CHAMBERS BROTHERS	UPTOWN	LOVE ME LIKE THE RAIN	5.00
67	3215 DJ	CHAMBERS BROTHERS	UPTOWN	LOVE ME LIKE THE RAIN	6.00
68	3216	TOMMY HUNT	I NEED A WOMAN OF MY OWN	SEARCHING FOR MY BABY	15.00
68	3216 DJ	TOMMY HUNT	I NEED A WOMAN OF MY OWN	SEARCHING FOR MY BABY	22.00
68	3248	MOTIVATION	COM E ON DOWN	LITTLE MAN	5.00
68	3248 DJ	MOTIVATION	COM E ON DOWN	LITTLE MAN	6.00
68	3253	CAT'S PYJAMAS	BABY I LOVE YOU	VIRGINIA WATER	5.00
68	3253 DJ	CAT'S PYJAMAS	BABY I LOVE YOU	VIRGINIA WATER	6.00
68	3245	GENE LATTER	A TRIBUTE TO OTIS	BRING YOUR LOVE HOME	10.00
68	3245 DJ	GENE LATTER	A TRIBUTE TO OTIS	BRING YOUR LOVE HOME	12.00
68	3261	LAVELL HARDY	DON'T LOSE YOUR GROOVE	WOMEN OF THE WORLD	15.00
68	3261 DJ	LAVELL HARDY	DON'T LOSE YOUR GROOVE	WOMEN OF THE WORLD	22.00
68	3267	BROOKS & JERRY	I GOT WHAT IT TAKES	I GOT WHAT IT TAKES (Part2)	15.00
68	3267 DJ	BROOKS & JERRY	I GOT WHAT IT TAKES	I GOT WHAT IT TAKES (Part2)	30.00
68	3300	GLORIES	SING ME A LOVE SONG	OH BABY THAT'S LOVE	20.00
68	3300 DJ	GLORIES	SING ME A LOVE SONG	OH BABY THAT'S LOVE	28.00
68	3301	PRETTY PURDIE	FUNKY DONKEY	CARAVAN	10.00
68	3301 DJ	PRETTY PURDIE	FUNKY DONKEY	CARAVAN	12.00
68	3312	BIG MAYBELLE	QUITTIN' TIME	I CAN'T WAIT ANY LONGER	25.00
68	3312 DJ	BIG MAYBELLE	QUITTIN' TIME	I CAN'T WAIT ANY LONGER	32.00
68	3339	SAM, ERV & TOM	SOUL TEACHER	HARD TO GET	6.00
68	3339 DJ	SAM, ERV & TOM	SOUL TEACHER	HARD TO GET	8.00
68	3382	BARBARA MASON	AIN'T GOT NOBODY	OH, HOW IT HURTS	40.00
68	3382 DJ	BARBARA MASON	AIN'T GOT NOBODY	OH, HOW IT HURTS	50.00
68	3415	PEACHES & HERB	I NEED YOUR LOVE SO DESPERATELY	LET IT BE ME	15.00
68	3415 DJ	PEACHES & HERB	I NEED YOUR LOVE SO DESPERATELY	LET IT BE ME	22.00
68	3453	SQUIBBY & THE REFLECTIONS	RAGAMUFFIN	FOR A LITTLE WHILE	5.00
68	3453 DJ	SQUIBBY & THE REFLECTIONS	RAGAMUFFIN	FOR A LITTLE WHILE	6.00
68	3481	ELMER GANTRY'S VELVET OPERA	MARY JANE	CREAMY	5.00
68	3481 DJ	ELMER GANTRY'S VELVET OPERA	MARY JANE	CREAMY	6.00
68	3482	CAT'S PYJAMAS	CAMERA MAN	HOUSE FOR SALE	5.00
68	3482 DJ	CAT'S PYJAMAS	CAMERA MAN	HOUSE FOR SALE	6.00
68	3511	VIBRATIONS	LOVE IN THEM THERE HILLS	REMEMBER THE RAIN	15.00
68	3511 DJ	VIBRATIONS	LOVE IN THEM THERE HILLS	REMEMBER THE RAIN	20.00
68	3518	CLIFF NOBLES	THE HORSE	LOVE IS ALL RIGHT	10.00

68	3518 DJ	CLIFF NOBLES	THE HORSE	LOVE IS ALL RIGHT	22.00
68	3520	BANDWAGON	BABY MAKE YOUR OWN SWEET MUSIC	ON THE DAY WE FALL IN LOVE	8.00
68	3520 DJ	BANDWAGON	BABY MAKE YOUR OWN SWEET MUSIC	ON THE DAY WE FALL IN LOVE	10.00
68	3547	TAJ MAHAL	EVERYBODY'S GOT TO CHANGE SOMETIME	STATESBORO BLUES	6.00
68	3547 DJ	TAJ MAHAL	EVERYBODY'S GOT TO CHANGE SOMETIME	STATESBORO BLUES	8.00
68	3548	PEACHES & HERB	UNITED	THANK YOU	8.00
68	3548 DJ	PEACHES & HERB	UNITED	THANK YOU	10.00
68	3568	SLY & THE FAMILY STONE	DANCE TO THE MUSIC	LET ME HEAR IT FROM YOU	6.00
68	3568 DJ	SLY & THE FAMILY STONE	DANCE TO THE MUSIC	LET ME HEAR IT FROM YOU	10.00
68	3574	VIVIAN REED	I WANNA BE FREE	YOURS UNTIL TOMORROW	8.00
68	3574 DJ	VIVIAN REED	I WANNA BE FREE	YOURS UNTIL TOMORROW	10.00
68	3597	FLAVOR	SALLY HAD A PARTY	SHOP AROUND	6.00
68	3597 DJ	FLAVOR	SALLY HAD A PARTY	SHOP AROUND	8.00
68	3603	PALMER JONES	DANCING MASTER	THE GREAT MAGIC OF LOVE	20.00
68	3603 DJ	PALMER JONES	DANCING MASTER	THE GREAT MAGIC OF LOVE	28.00
68	3628	BERNARD PRETTY PURDIE	SOUL CLAPPIN	BLOW YOUR LID (BUT WATCH YOUR COOL)	8.00
68	3628 DJ	BERNARD PRETTY PURDIE	SOUL CLAPPIN	BLOW YOUR LID (BUT WATCH YOUR COOL)	10.00
68	3630	SQUIBBY & THE REFLECTIONS	LOVING HYOU HAS MADE MY LIFE	BETTER OFF WITHOUT YOU	5.00
68	3630 DJ	SQUIBBY & THE REFLECTIONS	LOVING HYOU HAS MADE MY LIFE	BETTER OFF WITHOUT YOU	6.00
68	3646	GLORIES	MY SWEET SWEET BABY	STAND BY (I'M COMIN' HOME)	12.00
68	3646 DJ	GLORIES	MY SWEET ,SWEET BABY	STAND BY! (I'M COMING HOME)	20.00
68	3670	BANDWAGON	BREAKIN' DOWN THE WALLS OF HEARTACHE	DANCIN' MASTER	8.00
68	3670 DJ	BANDWAGON	BREAKIN' DOWN THE WALLS OF HEARTACHE	DANCIN' MASTER	20.00
68	3671	CHAMBERS BROTHERS	TIME HAS COME TODAY	DINAH	6.00
68	3671 DJ	CHAMBERS BROTHERS	TIME HAS COME TODAY	DINAH	8.00
68	3678	BRENDA & THE TABULATIONS	BABY YOU'RE SO RIGHT FOR ME	TO THE ONE I LOVE	10.00
68	3678 DJ	BRENDA & THE TABULATIONS	BABY YOU'RE SO RIGHT FOR ME	TO THE ONE I LOVE	15.00
68	3701	COASTERS	SHE CAN	EVERYBODY'S WOMAN	6.00
68	3701 DJ	COASTERS	SHE CAN	EVERYBODY'S WOMAN	8.00
68	3707	SLY & THE FAMILY STONE	M'LADY	LIFE	8.00
68	3707 DJ	SLY & THE FAMILY STONE	M'LADY	LIFE	10.00
68	3721	JAMES BOYS	THE HORSE	THE MULE (instrumental)	15.00
68	3721 DJ	JAMES BOYS	THE HORSE	THE MULE (instrumental)	22.00
68	3738	CLIFF NOBLES	JUDGE BABY I'M BACK	HORSE FEVER (instrumental)	10.00
68	3738 DJ	CLIFF NOBLES	JUDGE BABY I'M BACK	HORSE FEVER (instrumental)	15.00
68	3760	CHAMBERS BROTHERS	TIME HAS COME TODAY	DINAH	5.00
68	3760 DJ	CHAMBERS BROTHERS	TIME HAS COME TODAY	DINAH	6.00
68	3799	BARBARA & BRENDA	NEVER LOVE A ROBIN	SALLY'S PARTY	25.00
68	3799 DJ	BARBARA & BRENDA	NEVER LOVE A ROBIN	SALLY'S PARTY	30.00
68	3814	LOCOMOTIVE	RUDY A MESSAGE TO YOU	BROKEN HEART	10.00
68	3814 DJ	LOCOMOTIVE	RUDY A MESSAGE TO YOU	BROKEN HEART	15.00
68	3816	INEZ & CHARLIE FOXX	BABY DROP A DIME	COME ON IN	10.00
68	3816 DJ	INEZ & CHARLIE FOXX	BABY DROP A DIME	COME ON IN	15.00
68	3829	PEACHES & HERB	LET'S MAKE A PROMISE	ME AND YOU	6.00
68	3829 DJ	PEACHES & HERB	LET'S MAKE A PROMISE	ME AND YOU	8.00
68	3854	GLADIATORS	GIRL DON'T MAKE ME WAIT	CAN'T GET AWAY FROM HEARTBREAK	20.00
68	3854 DJ	GLADIATORS	GIRL DON'T MAKE ME WAIT	CAN'T GET AWAY FROM HEARTBREAK	30.00
68	3865	CHAMBERS BROTHERS	I CAN'T TURN YOU LOOSE	DO YOUR THING	8.00
68	3865 DJ	CHAMBERS BROTHERS	I CAN'T TURN YOU LOOSE	DO YOUR THING	10.00
68	3899	DIPLOMATS	I CAN GIVE YOU LOVE	I'M SO GLAD I FOUND YOU	10.00
68	3899 DJ	DIPLOMATS	I CAN GIVE YOU LOVE	I'M SO GLAD I FOUND YOU	15.00
68	3903	TYMES	PEOPLE	FOR LOVE OF IVY	5.00
68	3903 DJ	TYMES	PEOPLE	FOR LOVE OF IVY	6.00
68	3909	LORD NELSON	MICHEAL	NO HOT SUMMER	8.00
68	3909 DJ	LORD NELSON	MICHEAL	NO HOT SUMMER	10.00
68	3923	JOHNNY JOHNSON & the BANDWAGON	YOU	YOU BLEW YOUR COOL AND LOST YOUR FOOL	8.00
68	3923 DJ	JOHNNY JOHNSON & the BANDWAGON	YOU	YOU BLEW YOUR COOL AND LOST YOUR FOOL	10.00
68	3924	ELMER GANTRY'S VELVET OPERA	VOLCANO	QUICK B	5.00
68	3924 DJ	ELMER GANTRY'S VELVET OPERA	VOLCANO	QUICK B	6.00
69	3938	SLY & THE FAMILY STONE	EVERYDAY PEOPLE	SING A SIMPLE SONG	8.00
69	3938 DJ	SLY & THE FAMILY STONE	EVERYDAY PEOPLE	SING A SIMPLE SONG	10.00
69	3970	SPELLBINDERS	HELP ME (GET MYSELF BACK TOGETHER AGAIN)	CHAIN REACTION	25.00
69	3970 DJ	SPELLBINDERS	HELP ME (GET MYSELF BACK TOGETHER AGAIN)	CHAIN REACTION	35.00
69	4033	SQUIBBY & THE REFLECTIONS	YOU GOT IT	COME BACK TO ME	6.00
69	4033 DJ	SQUIBBY & THE REFLECTIONS	YOU GOT IT	COME BACK TO ME	8.00
69	4042	INEZ & CHARLIE FOXX	BABY GIVE IT TO ME	YOU FIXED MY HEARTACHE	6.00
69	4042 DJ	INEZ & CHARLIE FOXX	BABY GIVE IT TO ME	YOU FIXED MY HEARTACHE	8.00
69	4044	TAJ MAHAL	EE ZEE RIDER	YOU DON'T MISS YOUR WATER	6.00
69	4044 DJ	TAJ MAHAL	EE ZEE RIDER	YOU DON'T MISS YOUR WATER	8.00
69	4059	MASKMAN & THE AGENTS	ONE EYE OPEN	Y'AWLL	10.00
69	4059 DJ	MASKMAN & THE AGENTS	ONE EYE OPEN	Y'AWLL	15.00
69	4085	PEACHES & HERB	WHEN HE TOUCHES ME	THANK YOU	5.00
69	4085 DJ	PEACHES & HERB	WHEN HE TOUCHES ME	THANK YOU	6.00
69	4086	MONGO SANTAMARIA	CLOUD NINE	SON OF A PREACHER MAN	15.00
69	4086 DJ	MONGO SANTAMARIA	CLOUD NINE	SON OF A PREACHER MAN	20.00
69	4096	JACKIE EDWARDS	WHY MUST I BE ALONE	I'M GONNA MAKE YOU CRY	6.00
69	4096 DJ	JACKIE EDWARDS	WHY MUST I BE ALONE	I'M GONNA MAKE YOU CRY	8.00
69	4097	SCREAMING JAY HAWKINS	I PUT A SPELL ON YOU	LITTLE DEMON	15.00
69	4097 DJ	SCREAMING JAY HAWKINS	I PUT A SPELL ON YOU	LITTLE DEMON	22.00

69	4098	CHAMBERS BROTHERS	ARE YOU READY	YOU GOT THE POWER - TO TURN ME	6.00
69	4098 DJ	CHAMBERS BROTHERS	ARE YOU READY	YOU GOT THE POWER - TO TURN ME	6.00
69	4180	JOHNNY JOHNSON & the BANDWAGON	LET'S HANG ON	DON'T LET IT IN	8.00
69	4180 DJ	JOHNNY JOHNSON & the BANDWAGON	LET'S HANG ON	I AIN'T LYIN'	15.00
69	4205	CLIFF NOBLES & CO	SWITCH IT ON	BURNING DESIRE	15.00
69	4205 DJ	CLIFF NOBLES & CO	SWITCH IT ON	BURNING DESIRE	20.00
69	4212	UDELL T. ANDERSON	LOVE AIN'T LOVE	FUNKY WALK	15.00
69	4212 DJ	UDELL T. ANDERSON	LOVE AIN'T LOVE	FUNKY WALK	22.00
69	4279	SLY & THE FAMILY STONE	STAND !	I WANT TO TAKE YOU HIGHER	6.00
69	4279 DJ	SLY & THE FAMILY STONE	STAND !	I WANT TO TAKE YOU HIGHER	8.00
69	4308	GLADIATORS	I'LL ALWAYS LOVE YOU	WAITING ON THE SHORES OF NOWHE	20.00
69	4308 DJ	GLADIATORS	I'LL ALWAYS LOVE YOU	WAITING ON THE SHORES OF NOWHE	28.00
69	4318	CHAMBERS BROTHERS	PEOPLE GET READY	NO, NO, NO, DON'T SAY GOODBYE	6.00
69	4318 DJ	CHAMBERS BROTHERS	PEOPLE GET READY	NO, NO, NO, DON'T SAY GOODBYE	8.00
69	4367	CHAMBERS BROTHERS	WAKE UP	EVERYBODY NEEDS SOMEONE	6.00
69	4367 DJ	CHAMBERS BROTHERS	WAKE UP	EVERYBODY NEEDS SOMEONE	8.00
69	4402	JACKIE EDWARDS	TOO EXPERIENCED	SOMEONE TO LOVE	10.00
69	4402 DJ	JACKIE EDWARDS	TOO EXPERIENCED	SOMEONE TO LOVE	15.00
69	4430	MONGO SANTAMARIA	TWENTY FIVE MILES	EL TRES	15.00
69	4430 DJ	MONGO SANTAMARIA	TWENTY FIVE MILES	EL TRES	20.00
69	4450	TYMES	FIND MY WAY	IF YOU LOVE ME BABY	10.00
69	4450 DJ	TYMES	FIND MY WAY	IF YOU LOVE ME BABY	15.00
69	4455	TAJ MAHAL	EE ZEE RIDER	YOU DON'T MISS YOUR WATER	8.00
69	4455 DJ	TAJ MAHAL	EE ZEE RIDER	YOU DON'T MISS YOUR WATER	10.00
69	4459	UDELL T. ANDERSON	KEEP ON LOVING ME	THANK YOU DARLING	10.00
69	4459 DJ	UDELL T. ANDERSON	KEEP ON LOVING ME	THANK YOU DARLING	15.00
69	4471	SLY & THE FAMILY STONE	HOT FUN IN THE SUMMERTIME	FUN	6.00
69	4471 DJ	SLY & THE FAMILY STONE	HOT FUN IN THE SUMMERTIME	FUN	8.00
69	4507	GLADIATORS	AS LONG AS I LIVE	EVERYTHING	6.00
69	4507 DJ	GLADIATORS	AS LONG AS I LIVE	EVERYTHING	8.00
69	4521	JACKIE THOMPSON	BAD WOMEN A DIME A DOZEN	GAMES PEOPLE PLAY	8.00
69	4521 DJ	JACKIE THOMPSON	BAD WOMEN A DIME A DOZEN	GAMES PEOPLE PLAY	10.00
70	4586	TAJ MAHAL	GIVE YOUR WOMAN WHAT SHE WANTS	FARTHER ON DOWN THE ROAD	6.00
70	4586 DJ	TAJ MAHAL	GIVE YOUR WOMAN WHAT SHE WANTS	FARTHER ON DOWN THE ROAD	8.00
70	4630	JACKIE EDWARDS	HERE WE GO AGAIN	OH MANIO	15.00
70	4630 DJ	JACKIE EDWARDS	HERE WE GO AGAIN	OH MANIO	22.00
70	4645	UDELL T. ANDERSON	DON'T GO AWAY	THANK YOU DARLING	8.00
70	4645 DJ	UDELL T. ANDERSON	DON'T GO AWAY	THANK YOU DARLING	10.00
70	4660	GLADIATORS	THE TWELVE OF NEVER	LOVIN' MY BABY BACK HOME	6.00
70	4660 DJ	GLADIATORS	THE TWELVE OF NEVER	LOVIN' MY BABY BACK HOME	8.00
70	4675	STEELERS	GET IT FROM THE BOTTOM	I'M SORRY	10.00
70	4675 DJ	STEELERS	GET IT FROM THE BOTTOM	I'M SORRY	15.00
70	4751	METERS	LOOK-KA PY PY	THIS IS MY LAST AFFAIR	8.00
70	4751 DJ	METERS	LOOK-KA PY PY	THIS IS MY LAST AFFAIR	10.00
70	4782	SLY & THE FAMILY STONE	THANK YOU (falettinme be mice elf again)	EVERYBODY IS A STAR	8.00
70	4782 DJ	SLY & THE FAMILY STONE	THANK YOU (falettinme be mice elf again)	EVERYBODY IS A STAR	10.00
70	4816	MARY WELLS	DIG THE WAY I FEEL	LOVE SHOOTING BANDIT	10.00
70	4816 DJ	MARY WELLS	DIG THE WAY I FEEL	LOVE SHOOTING BANDIT	12.00
70	4846	CHAMBERS BROTHERS	LOVE PEACE AND HAPPINESS	IF YOU WANT ME TO	5.00
70	4846 DJ	CHAMBERS BROTHERS	LOVE PEACE AND HAPPINESS	IF YOU WANT ME TO	6.00
70	4909	PEACHES & HERB	SATISFY MY HUNGER	IT'S JUST A GAME, LOVE	5.00
70	4909 DJ	PEACHES & HERB	SATISFY MY HUNGER	IT'S JUST A GAME, LOVE	6.00
70	4969	VILLAGE SOUL CHOIR	THE CAT WALK	THE COUNTRY WALK	10.00
70	4969 DJ	VILLAGE SOUL CHOIR	THE CAT WALK	THE COUNTRY WALK	15.00
70	5033	CHAMBERS BROTHERS	LET'S DO IT	TO LOVE SOMEBODY	5.00
70	5033 DJ	CHAMBERS BROTHERS	LET'S DO IT	TO LOVE SOMEBODY	6.00
70	5249	PEACHES & HERB	SOOTHE ME WITH YOUR LOVE	WE'RE SO MUCH IN LOVE	6.00
70	5249 DJ	PEACHES & HERB	SOOTHE ME WITH YOUR LOVE	WE'RE SO MUCH IN LOVE	8.00
80	8731	NOEL McCALLA	BEGGIN'	ONE MORE HEARTACHE	5.00
80	8731 DJ	NOEL McCALLA	BEGGIN'	ONE MORE HEARTACHE	6.00
80	8733 PS	STEP	THE LAND OF A THOUSAND DANCES	KNOCK ON WOOD + LOVE LETTER	6.00
80	8733 PS DJ	STEP	THE LAND OF A THOUSAND DANCES	KNOCK ON WOOD + LOVE LETTER	8.00
80	9311 PS	STEP	TEARS THAT I CRY	SHAKE + BACK WITH YOU	6.00
80	9311 PS DJ	STEP	TEARS THAT I CRY	SHAKE + BACK WITH YOU	8.00

DJM

D.J.M. stood for Dick James Music and was responsible for issuing many highly collectable soul related 45's in amongst some ordinary soul releases that would interest the completist, for instance Geno Washington's DJM releases were bordering on rock music but he played such a big part in formulating the UK soul scene in the 60's, I felt his 45's needed to be included.

DJM promos 45's, up until 1980 were accompanied by interesting promo black and white special picture plus artist info sleeves, these were unique to this label. DJM were champions of small artists and felt the information sleeves would help reviews and encourage radio airplay.

This label can hardly be considered an oasis for soul collectors, it's largest sales came from it's major artist Elton John, and even released records by John "Are You Being Served" Inman, Jasper Carrott, Kenny Everett, Max Wall and all manner novelty, soft rock, punk etc. in fact covered all areas of music. But some of DJM's UK artists did record good soul influenced music, none more so than Moon Williams who at the time remained an unknown performer struggling to get exposure, but is now his 45's are considered to be highly collectable as almost all his releases on DJM fit into that Northern Soul seventies dance mould.

70	10216	MR. BLOE	GROOVIN' WITH MR. BLOE	SINFUL	6.00
70	10216 DJ	MR. BLOE	GROOVIN' WITH MR. BLOE	SINFUL	8.00
70	10216 DJ PS	MR. BLOE	GROOVIN' WITH MR. BLOE	SINFUL	10.00
70	10229	MR. BLOE	CURRIED SOUL	MIGHTY MOUSE	5.00

70	10229 DJ	MR. BLOE	CURRIED SOUL	MIGHTY MOUSE	6.00
70	10229 DJ PS	MR. BLOE	CURRIED SOUL	MIGHTY MOUSE	8.00
71	10259	BIRDS OF A FEATHER	FOR BETTER OR WORSE	TIME OF LIFE	10.00
71	10259 DJ	BIRDS OF A FEATHER	FOR BETTER OR WORSE	TIME OF LIFE	15.00
71	10259 DJ PS	BIRDS OF A FEATHER	FOR BETTER OR WORSE	TIME OF LIFE	20.00
73	10283	MOON WILLIAMS	ALL FOR YOU	FOREVER KIND OF LOVE	300.00
73	10283 DJ	MOON WILLIAMS	ALL FOR YOU	FOREVER KIND OF LOVE	350.00
73	10283 DJ PS	MOON WILLIAMS	ALL FOR YOU	FOREVER KIND OF LOVE	400.00
74	10299	MOON WILLIAMS	I CAN'T LIVE WITHOUT YOU	EXCUSE ME	30.00
74	10299 DJ	MOON WILLIAMS	I CAN'T LIVE WITHOUT YOU	EXCUSE ME	35.00
74	10299 DJ PS	MOON WILLIAMS	I CAN'T LIVE WITHOUT YOU	EXCUSE ME	40.00
74	10311	MOON WILLIAMS	STICKS AND STONES	SEAWEED	30.00
74	10311 DJ	MOON WILLIAMS	STICKS AND STONES	SEAWEED	35.00
74	10311 DJ PS	MOON WILLIAMS	STICKS AND STONES	SEAWEED	40.00
74	10332	MOON WILLIAMS	SHE'S GONE	SENTIMENTAL FOOL	25.00
74	10332 DJ	MOON WILLIAMS	SHE'S GONE	SENTIMENTAL FOOL	30.00
74	10332 DJ PS	MOON WILLIAMS	SHE'S GONE	SENTIMENTAL FOOL	35.00
74	10346	MR. BLOE	LAND OF A THOUSAND DANCES	DANCING MACHINE	8.00
74	10346 DJ	MR. BLOE	LAND OF A THOUSAND DANCES	DANCING MACHINE	10.00
74	10346 DJ PS	MR. BLOE	LAND OF A THOUSAND DANCES	DANCING MACHINE	15.00
75	10363	HELEN SHAPIRO	THAT'S THE REASON I LOVE YOU	YOU'RE A LOVE CHILD	6.00
75	10363 DJ	HELEN SHAPIRO	THAT'S THE REASON I LOVE YOU	YOU'RE A LOVE CHILD	8.00
75	10363 DJ PS	HELEN SHAPIRO	THAT'S THE REASON I LOVE YOU	YOU'RE A LOVE CHILD	10.00
75	10365	GENO WASHINGTON	THE END OF OUR ROAD	TELL ME TELL ME PLEASE	4.00
75	10365 DJ	GENO WASHINGTON	THE END OF OUR ROAD	TELL ME TELL ME PLEASE	5.00
75	10365 DJ PS	GENO WASHINGTON	THE END OF OUR ROAD	TELL ME TELL ME PLEASE	8.00
75	10371	NEW CENSATION	FIRST ROUND KNOCKOUT	EVERYBODY'S GOT A STORY	6.00
75	10371 DJ	NEW CENSATION	FIRST ROUND KNOCKOUT	EVERYBODY'S GOT A STORY	8.00
75	10371 DJ PS	NEW CENSATION	FIRST ROUND KNOCKOUT	EVERYBODY'S GOT A STORY	10.00
75	10375	MOON WILLIAMS	SUSPICIOUS LOVE	END OF ANOTHER DAY	10.00
75	10375 DJ	MOON WILLIAMS	SUSPICIOUS LOVE	END OF ANOTHER DAY	15.00
75	10375 DJ PS	MOON WILLIAMS	SUSPICIOUS LOVE	END OF ANOTHER DAY	20.00
75	10381	SELENA JONES	IN LOVE LIKE YOU AND ME	TELL IT L;IKE IT IS	4.00
75	10381 DJ	SELENA JONES	IN LOVE LIKE YOU AND ME	TELL IT L;IKE IT IS	5.00
75	10381 DJ PS	SELENA JONES	IN LOVE LIKE YOU AND ME	TELL IT L;IKE IT IS	6.00
75	10392	GENO WASHINGTON	HOLD ON MAMA	HELP ME I'M IN LOVE AGAIN	3.00
75	10392 DJ	GENO WASHINGTON	HOLD ON MAMA	HELP ME I'M IN LOVE AGAIN	4.00
75	10392 DJ PS	GENO WASHINGTON	HOLD ON MAMA	HELP ME I'M IN LOVE AGAIN	5.00
75	10398	DONNIE ELBERT	I CAN'T HELP MYSELF	NEVER CAN SAY GOODBYE	4.00
75	10398 DJ	DONNIE ELBERT	I CAN'T HELP MYSELF	NEVER CAN SAY GOODBYE	5.00
75	10398 DJ PS	DONNIE ELBERT	I CAN'T HELP MYSELF	NEVER CAN SAY GOODBYE	6.00
75	10403	ROY HAMILTON	PRETTY FLAMINGO	TAXI IN THE RAIN	4.00
75	10403 DJ	ROY HAMILTON	PRETTY FLAMINGO	TAXI IN THE RAIN	5.00
75	10403 DJ PS	ROY HAMILTON	PRETTY FLAMINGO	TAXI IN THE RAIN	6.00
76	10620	JOHNNY GUITAR WATSON	AIN'T THAT A BITCH	WON'T YOU FORGIVE M,E BABY	5.00
76	10620 DJ	JOHNNY GUITAR WATSON	AIN'T THAT A BITCH	WON'T YOU FORGIVE M,E BABY	6.00
76	10620 DJ PS	JOHNNY GUITAR WATSON	AIN'T THAT A BITCH	WON'T YOU FORGIVE M,E BABY	8.00
76	10622	SELENA JONES	AIN'T WE GOT LOVE	WHERE PEACEFUL WATERS FLOW	10.00
76	10622 DJ	SELENA JONES	AIN'T WE GOT LOVE	WHERE PEACEFUL WATERS FLOW	15.00
76	10622 DJ PS	SELENA JONES	AIN'T WE GOT LOVE	WHERE PEACEFUL WATERS FLOW	20.00
76	10635	SELENA JONES	IMAGINE ME WITHOUT YOU	TAKE MY HAND	4.00
76	10635 DJ	SELENA JONES	IMAGINE ME WITHOUT YOU	TAKE MY HAND	5.00
76	10635 DJ PS	SELENA JONES	IMAGINE ME WITHOUT YOU	TAKE MY HAND	6.00
76	10640	ISLEY BROTHERS	TWIST AND SHOUT	TIME AFTER TIME	3.00
76	10640 DJ	ISLEY BROTHERS	TWIST AND SHOUT	TIME AFTER TIME	4.00
76	10640 DJ PS	ISLEY BROTHERS	TWIST AND SHOUT	TIME AFTER TIME	5.00
76	10642	GENO WASHINGTON	LOVE ME, LOVE ME	HOLD ON	3.00
76	10642 DJ	GENO WASHINGTON	LOVE ME, LOVE ME	HOLD ON	4.00
76	10642 DJ PS	GENO WASHINGTON	LOVE ME, LOVE ME	HOLD ON	5.00
76	10659	MOON WILLIAMS	EVERYTIME I TAKE THE TIME	WHEN TE RIVER STOPS FLOWING	25.00
76	10659 DJ	MOON WILLIAMS	EVERYTIME I TAKE THE TIME	WHEN TE RIVER STOPS FLOWING	35.00
76	10659 DJ PS	MOON WILLIAMS	EVERYTIME I TAKE THE TIME	WHEN TE RIVER STOPS FLOWING	45.00
76	10669	GENO WASHINGTON	OH PRETTY WOMAN	B S E LOVE	3.00
76	10669 DJ	GENO WASHINGTON	OH PRETTY WOMAN	B S E LOVE	4.00
76	10669 DJ PS	GENO WASHINGTON	OH PRETTY WOMAN	B S E LOVE	5.00
76	10670	DON THOMAS	COME ON TRAIN	same: instrumental	25.00
76	10670 DJ	DON THOMAS	COME ON TRAIN	same: instrumental	30.00
76	10670 DJ PS	DON THOMAS	COME ON TRAIN	same: instrumental	35.00
76	10681	GLADYS KNIGHT & the PIPS	EVERY BEAT OF MY HEART	QUEEN OF TEARS	5.00
76	10681 DJ	GLADYS KNIGHT & the PIPS	EVERY BEAT OF MY HEART	QUEEN OF TEARS	8.00
76	10681 DJ PS	GLADYS KNIGHT & the PIPS	EVERY BEAT OF MY HEART	QUEEN OF TEARS	10.00
76	10684	SWAMP DOGG	THE OTHER MAN	BELIEVE IN ME, BABY	3.00
76	10684 DJ	SWAMP DOGG	THE OTHER MAN	BELIEVE IN ME, BABY	4.00
76	10684 DJ PS	SWAMP DOGG	THE OTHER MAN	BELIEVE IN ME, BABY	5.00
76	10687	HORACE FAITH	I CAN'T UNERSTAND IT	GIMME GOOD LOVIN'	30.00
76	10687 DJ	HORACE FAITH	I CAN'T UNERSTAND IT	GIMME GOOD LOVIN'	35.00
76	10687 DJ PS	HORACE FAITH	I CAN'T UNERSTAND IT	GIMME GOOD LOVIN'	40.00
76	10689	FIDELS	TRY A LITTLE HARDER	same: instrumental	15.00
76	10689 DJ	FIDELS	TRY A LITTLE HARDER	same: instrumental	20.00

76	10689 DJ PS	FIDELS	TRY A LITTLE HARDER	same: instrumental	30.00
76	10693	MOON WILLIAMS	I WANNA MAKE AN HONEST WOMAN	A MAN LIKE ME, WITH A WOMAN LI	30.00
76	10693 DJ	MOON WILLIAMS	I WANNA MAKE AN HONEST WOMAN	A MAN LIKE ME, WITH A WOMAN LI	35.00
76	10693 DJ PS	MOON WILLIAMS	I WANNA MAKE AN HONEST WOMAN	A MAN LIKE ME, WITH A WOMAN LI	40.00
76	10694	JOHNNY GUITAR WATSON	I NEED IT	SINCE I MET YOU BABY	5.00
76	10694 DJ	JOHNNY GUITAR WATSON	I NEED IT	SINCE I MET YOU BABY	6.00
76	10694 DJ PS	JOHNNY GUITAR WATSON	I NEED IT	SINCE I MET YOU BABY	8.00
76	10700 EP PS	VAROIUS ARTISTS	INC: Dixie Cups – Chapel Of Love + 1	Shangri-las – Remember, Walking in the Sand + 1	5.00
76	10704	ROY HAMILTON	DAYS AREN'T LONG ENOUGH	SWEET SWEET MUSIC	3.00
76	10704 DJ	ROY HAMILTON	DAYS AREN'T LONG ENOUGH	SWEET SWEET MUSIC	4.00
76	10704 DJ PS	ROY HAMILTON	DAYS AREN'T LONG ENOUGH	SWEET SWEET MUSIC	5.00
76	10710	NEWBEATS	BREAD AND BUTTER	EVVERYTHING'S ALRIGHT	4.00
76	10710 DJ	NEWBEATS	BREAD AND BUTTER	EVVERYTHING'S ALRIGHT	5.00
76	10710 DJ PS	NEWBEATS	BREAD AND BUTTER	EVVERYTHING'S ALRIGHT	6.00
76	10712	GENO WASHINGTON	YOU'RE LOVE KEEPS ON HAUNTING ME	LA LA LA	4.00
76	10712 DJ	GENO WASHINGTON	YOU'RE LOVE KEEPS ON HAUNTING ME	LA LA LA	5.00
76	10712 DJ PS	GENO WASHINGTON	YOU'RE LOVE KEEPS ON HAUNTING ME	LA LA LA	6.00
76	10717	FRED HUGHES	OO WEE BABY, I LOVE YOU	MY HEART CRIES OH	6.00
76	10717 DJ	FRED HUGHES	OO WEE BABY, I LOVE YOU	MY HEART CRIES OH	8.00
76	10717 DJ PS	FRED HUGHES	OO WEE BABY, I LOVE	MY HEART CRIES OH	10.00
76	10722	JOHNNY GUITAR WATSON	SUPERMAN LOVER	WE'RE NO EXCEPTION	4.00
76	10722 DJ	JOHNNY GUITAR WATSON	SUPERMAN LOVER	WE'RE NO EXCEPTION	5.00
76	10722 DJ PS	JOHNNY GUITAR WATSON	SUPERMAN LOVER	WE'RE NO EXCEPTION	6.00
76	10727 EP	VARIOUS ARTISTS	BLACK ECHOES EXTENDED PLAY	1976 4 classic Vee Jay 60s 45s	5.00
76	10727 EP PS	VARIOUS ARTISTS	BLACK ECHOES EXTENDED PLAY	1976 4 classic Vee Jay 60s 45s	10.00

4 track EP with 4 Artist picture cover: tracks are 1. Betty Everett – It's In His Kiss 2. Gene Chandler – Duke Of Earl 3. Jerry Butler – Make It Easy On Yourself 4. Dee Clark – Raindrops.

77	10738	RARE PLEASURE	LET ME DOWN EASY	same: long version	30.00
77	10738 DJ	RARE PLEASURE	LET ME DOWN EASY	same: long version	40.00
77	10738 DJ PS	RARE PLEASURE	LET ME DOWN EASY	same: long version	50.00
77	10761	GENO WASHINGTON	SOOTHE ME BABY	MY KIND OF LOVE	4.00
77	10761 DJ	GENO WASHINGTON	SOOTHE ME BABY	MY KIND OF LOVE	5.00
77	10761 DJ PS	GENO WASHINGTON	SOOTHE ME BABY	MY KIND OF LOVE	6.00
77	10762	JOHNNY GUITAR WATSON	A REAL MOTHER FOR YA	NOTHING LEFT TO BE DESIRED	5.00
77	10762 DJ	JOHNNY GUITAR WATSON	A REAL MOTHER FOR YA	NOTHING LEFT TO BE DESIRED	6.00
77	10762 DJ PS	JOHNNY GUITAR WATSON	A REAL MOTHER FOR YA	NOTHING LEFT TO BE DESIRED	8.00
77	10772	JIMMY RADCLIFFE	LONG AFTER TONIGHT IS ALL OVER	WHAT I WANT I CAN NEVER HAVE	8.00
77	10772 DJ	JIMMY RADCLIFFE	LONG AFTER TONIGHT IS ALL OVER	WHAT I WANT I CAN NEVER HAVE	15.00
77	10772 DJ PS	JIMMY RADCLIFFE	LONG AFTER TONIGHT IS ALL OVER	WHAT I WANT I CAN NEVER HAVE	20.00
77	10790	JOHNNY GUITAR WATSON	REAL DEAL	TARZAN	4.00
77	10790 DJ	JOHNNY GUITAR WATSON	REAL DEAL	TARZAN	5.00
77	10790 DJ PS	JOHNNY GUITAR WATSON	REAL DEAL	TARZAN	6.00
77	10803	GENO WASHINGTON	WHY DID YOU GO AWAY	BOOGIE QUEEN	3.00
77	10803 DJ	GENO WASHINGTON	WHY DID YOU GO AWAY	BOOGIE QUEEN	4.00
77	10803 DJ PS	GENO WASHINGTON	WHY DID YOU GO AWAY	BOOGIE QUEEN	5.00
77	10825	GENO WASHINGTON	PROUD MARY	STIR IT UP	3.00
77	10825 DJ	GENO WASHINGTON	PROUD MARY	STIR IT UP	4.00
77	10825 DJ PS	GENO WASHINGTON	PROUD MARY	STIR IT UP	5.00
77	10838	JOHNNY GUITAR WATSON	IT'S A DAMN SHAME	LOVE THAT WILL NOT DIE	4.00
77	10838 DJ	JOHNNY GUITAR WATSON	IT'S A DAMN SHAME	LOVE THAT WILL NOT DIE	5.00
77	10838 DJ PS	JOHNNY GUITAR WATSON	IT'S A DAMN SHAME	LOVE THAT WILL NOT DIE	6.00
77	10863	JAMES & BOBBY PURIFY	EASY AS PIE	KEEPING IN TOUCH	4.00
77	10863 DJ	JAMES & BOBBY PURIFY	EASY AS PIE	KEEPING IN TOUCH	5.00
77	10863 DJ PS	JAMES & BOBBY PURIFY	EASY AS PIE	KEEPING IN TOUCH	6.00
78	10881	JOHNNY GUITAR WATSON	MISS FRISCO THE QUEEN OF THE DISCO	TU JOURS	3.00
78	10881 DJ	JOHNNY GUITAR WATSON	MISS FRISCO THE QUEEN OF THE DISCO	TU JOURS	4.00
78	10881 DJ PS	JOHNNY GUITAR WATSON	MISS FRISCO THE QUEEN OF THE DISCO	TU JOURS	5.00
79	10882	BEN MOORE	LOVE MUSIC	SLIPPIN' AWAY	5.00
79	10882 DJ	BEN MOORE	LOVE MUSIC	SLIPPIN' AWAY	6.00
79	10882 DJ PS	BEN MOORE	LOVE MUSIC	SLIPPIN' AWAY	8.00
79	10890	JOHNNY GUITAR WATSON	GANGSTER OF LOVE	YOU CAN STAY, BUT THE NOISE MUST GO	5.00
79	10890 DJ	JOHNNY GUITAR WATSON	GANGSTER OF LOVE	YOU CAN STAY, BUT THE NOISE MUST GO	6.00
79	10890 DJ PS	JOHNNY GUITAR WATSON	GANGSTER OF LOVE	YOU CAN STAY, BUT THE NOISE MUST GO	8.00
79	18005	GENO WASHINGTON	MY MONEY, YOUR MONEY	GET SOME BAD TONIGHT	3.00
79	18005 DJ	GENO WASHINGTON	MY MONEY, YOUR MONEY	GET SOME BAD TONIGHT	4.00
79	18005 DJ PS	GENO WASHINGTON	MY MONEY, YOUR MONEY	GET SOME BAD TONIGHT	5.00
79	10904	JOHNNY GUITAR WATSON	IT'S A DAMN SHAME	LOVE WILL NOT DIE	4.00
79	10904 DJ	JOHNNY GUITAR WATSON	IT'S A DAMN SHAME	LOVE WILL NOT DIE	5.00
79	10904 DJ PS	JOHNNY GUITAR WATSON	IT'S A DAMN SHAME	LOVE WILL NOT DIE	6.00
79	10919	GENO WASHINGTON	MY MONEY, YOUR MONEY	GET SOME BAD TONIGHT	3.00
79	10919 DJ	GENO WASHINGTON	MY MONEY, YOUR MONEY	GET SOME BAD TONIGHT	4.00
±79	10919 DJ PS	GENO WASHINGTON	MY MONEY, YOUR MONEY	GET SOME BAD TONIGHT	5.00
80	10943	JOHNNY GUITAR WATSON	BOOTY OOTY	JET PLANE	3.00
80	10943 PS	JOHNNY GUITAR WATSON	BOOTY OOTY	JET PLANE	4.00
80	10947	FRANK HOOKER & POSITIVE	THIS FEELIN'	I WANNA KNOW YOUR NAME	5.00
80	10947 DJ	FRANK HOOKER & POSITIVE	THIS FEELIN'	I WANNA KNOW YOUR NAME	6.00
80	10956	JEROME	IF YOU WALK OUT THAT DOOR	TOKEN	6.00
80	10956 DJ	JEROME	IF YOU WALK OUT THAT DOOR	TOKEN	8.00

DOCTOR BIRD

Highly respected, very sought after and collectable Jamaican ska / reggae label # 1089 bucks the trend with a soul recording. The Glen Miller release is pure soul and a **most desirable** Northern Soul style dance recording. Value quoted was for a vg+ copy auctioned in 2005. A mint copy would possibly sell for £450 +

67	1089	GLEN MILLER	WHERE IS THE LOVE	FUNKY BROADWAY	357.00

DOMAIN

Colourful independent London based label, who had six or seven releases were distributed by ??? . For me this label is important as it highlights the embryonic All Night Club scene, with releases # 3 and 4 doing excellent cover versions of Leon Haywood song's. Note the backing groups name, possibly hinting at the closing time of several All Nighters of the era the Nite Owl in Leicester, Mojo of Sheffield all had music through until 6 o'clock in the morning. Those two release just show how small UK bands in 1968 where looking to cover USA recordings. Irocially or by design they covered Leon Haywood, who's Fat Fish recording –Baby Reconsider – had famously changed hands for the previously unheard of sum of £10. Release numbers 6 and 7 are not soul related.

68	1	NEW JUMP BAND	THE ONLY KIND OF GIRL	SEVEN KINDS OF LOVING	8.00
68	2	GARY STREET and the FAIRWAYS	HOLD ME CLOSER	FLIPPERTY FLOP	10.00
68	3	ROY DOCKER & MUSIC THROUGH SIX	MELLOW MOONLIGHT	RIFF RAFF	15.00
68	4	unissed?			
68	5	JASON SIMMS & MUSIC THROUGH SIX	IT'S GOT TO BE MELLOW	FLOPPY EARS	30.00

DORE

05	2005	RITA & THE TIARAS c/w SWANS	GONE WITH THE WIND IS MY LOVE	NITTY GRITTY CITY	10.00

DOT

65	16756	BARRY YOUNG	SHOW ME THE WAY	ONE HAS MY NAME	15.00
65	16756 DJ	BARRY YOUNG	SHOW ME THE WAY	ONE HAS MY NAME	25.00
68	101	AMERICAN BREED	GREEN LIGHT	DON'T IT MAKE YOU CRY	10.00
68	101 DJ	AMERICAN BREED	GREEN LIGHT	DON'T IT MAKE YOU CRY	15.00
68	103	LALO SCHIFRIN	MISSION: IMPOSSIBLE	JIM ON THE MOVE	15.00
68	103 DJ	LALO SCHIFRIN	MISSION: IMPOSSIBLE	JIM ON THE MOVE	20.00
68	106	AMERICAN BREED	READY, WILLING AND ABLE	TAKE ME IF YOU WANT ME	8.00
68	106 DJ	AMERICAN BREED	READY, WILLING AND ABLE	TAKE ME IF YOU WANT ME	10.00
69	129	MITCH RYDER & DETROIT WHEELS	SUGAR BEE	I BELIEVE (THERE MUST BE SOMEO	5.00
69	129 DJ	MITCH RYDER & DETROIT WHEELS	SUGAR BEE	I BELIEVE (THERE MUST BE SOMEO	6.00
73	145	JOE STAMPLEY	NOT TOO LONG AGO	SOUL SONG	10.00
73	145 DJ	JOE STAMPLEY	NOT TOO LONG AGO	SOUL SONG	15.00

DURIUM

Italian based label, which only had one release of interest to soul fans in the UK. Contrary to belief Northern Soul classic from Rocky Roberts and the Airedales – "Just Because Of You" – has never been confirmed as a UK release, although Pop Singles Quaterly showed it got released on # 9237. It was certainly issued in France, Greece, Italy & the USA, and copies of the European release occasionally turned up on these shores throughout the late 60's and early seventies but a genuine UK 45 is still unconfirmed. Little Tony, probably another Italian artist did release an upbeat Northern Soul style dancer that is difficult to fine, and remains largely unknown.

67	9237	ROCKY ROBERTS and the AIREDALES	JUST BECAUSE OF YOU	STASERA MI BUTTO	UN
67	54012	LITTLE TONY	PEOPLE TALK TO ME ABOUT YOU	LONG IS THE LONELY NIGHT	20.00
67	54012 DJ	LITTLE TONY	PEOPLE TALK TO ME ABOUT YOU	LONG IS THE LONELY NIGHT	25.00

EBONY

78	5	INNER CITY EXPRESS	FAT ON FUNK	SHO' DIG DANCIN'	8.00

ECHO

79	7001	DONNIE ELBERT	ARE YOU READY (WILLING AND ABLE)	YOU KEEP ME CRYING (WITH YOUR	6.00

EG

	183 PS	SCREAMING JAY HAWKINS	I PUT A SPELL ON YOU	ARMPIT no. 6	4.00

ELECTRIC RECORD CO.

76	1	MARSHA HUNT	DO YOU BELIEVE IN VOODOO	C'EST LA VIE	4.00
76	6	MARSHA HUNT	BEST KIND OF FEELING	CALL ME PARADISE	4.00
78	23	AL MATTHEWS	PEOPLE ARE PEOPLE	RUN TO YOU	4.00
79	34	AL MATTHEWS	I CAN'T FACE THE MUSIC	YOU WITHOUT ME	4.00
79	41	COGNAC feat: SALSOUL	HOW HIGH	NOTHING CAN CHANGE THIS LOVE	5.00

ELEKTRA

85	22 PS	STARPOINT	EMOTIONS	SEND ME A LETTER	5.00
84	9702	PATRICE RUSHEN	GET OFF	same: instrumental	5.00
84	9742	PATRICE RUSHEN	FEELS SO REAL	same: instrumental	5.00
79	12372	TERRY CALLIER	SIGN OF THE TIMES	OCCASIONAL RAIN	10.00
79	12336	PATRICE RUSHEN	HANG IT UP	JUST A NATURAL THING	5.00
79	12368	FIVE SPECIAL	WHY LEAVE US ALONE	same: instrumental	8.00
79	12388	FIVE SPECIAL	YOU'RE SOMETHING SPECIAL	IT'S SUCH A GROOVE pt 2	6.00
79	12414	PATRICE RUSHEN	HAVEN'T YOU HEARD	KEEPING FAITH IN LOVE	8.00
79	12414 DJ	PATRICE RUSHEN	HAVEN'T YOU HEARD	KEEPING FAITH IN LOVE	10.00
79	12494	PATRICE RUSHEN	NEVER GONNA GIVE YOU UP	DON'T BLAME ME	5.00
81	12542	PATRICE RUSHEN	DON'T BLAME ME	TIME WILL TELL	5.00
82	12588	FIVE SPECIAL	WHY LEAVE US ALONE	JUST A FEELING	6.00
82	13184 PS	PATRICE RUSHEN	I WAS TIRED OF BEING ALONE	NUMBER ONE instrumental	4.00
69	45051	RHINOCEROS	YOU'RE MY GIRL (I DON'T WANT TO	APRICOT BRANDY	10.00
69	45070	DOROTHY MORRISON	ALL GOD'S CHILDREN GOT SOUL	PUT A LITTLE LOVE IN YOUR HEAR	4.00
70	2101013	VOICES OF EAST HARLEM	RIGHT ON BE FREE	GOTTA BE A CHANGE + OH YEAH	5.00
70	2101018	VOICES OF EAST HARLEM	NO NO NO	MUSIC IN THE AIR	5.00

EMBER

62	168	LITA ROZA	MAMA (HE TREATS YOUR DAUGHTER	(HE'S MY) DREAMBOAT	40.00
62	168 DJ	LITA ROZA	MAMA (HE TREATS YOUR DAUGHTER	(HE'S MY) DREAMBOAT	50.00
63	174	LITTLE ESTHER PHILIPS	AM I THAT EASY TO FORGET	I REALLY DON'T WANT TO KNOW	10.00
63	174 DJ	LITTLE ESTHER PHILIPS	AM I THAT EASY TO FORGET	I REALLY DON'T WANT TO KNOW	18.00
64	192	JOHNNY OTIS SHOW	HAND JIVE ONE MORE TIME	BABY I GOT NEWS FOR YOU	10.00
64	192 DJ	JOHNNY OTIS SHOW	HAND JIVE ONE MORE TIME	BABY I GOT NEWS FOR YOU	15.00
64	196	B.B. KING	ROCK ME BABY	I CAN'T LOSE	18.00
64	196 DJ	B.B. KING	ROCK ME BABY	I CAN'T LOSE	25.00
64	198	LYNN HOLLAND	AND THE ANGELS SING	I CAN'T READ YOUR WRITING	10.00
64	198 DJ	LYNN HOLLAND	AND THE ANGELS SING	I CAN'T READ YOUR WRITING	15.00
66	211	VALUES	RETURN TO ME	THAT'S THE WAY	45.00
66	211 DJ	VALUES	RETURN TO ME	THAT'S THE WAY	60.00
66	216	JAMES BROWN	TELL ME WHAT YOU'RE GONNA DO	LOST SOMEONE	20.00
66	216 PS	JAMES BROWN	TELL ME WHAT YOU'RE GONNA DO	LOST SOMEONE	30.00
66	216 DJ	JAMES BROWN	TELL ME WHAT YOU'RE GONNA DO	LOST SOMEONE	40.00
66	219	JEWELL AKENS	DANCING JENNY	WE BIT MORE OF YOUR LOVING	15.00
66	219 DJ	JEWELL AKENS	DANCING JENNY	WE BIT MORE OF YOUR LOVING	20.00
66	221	LITTLE ESTHER PHILIPS	RELEASE ME	BE HONEST WITH ME	15.00
66	221 DJ	LITTLE ESTHER PHILIPS	RELEASE ME	BE HJONEST WITH ME	22.00
66	222	BROTHERS GRIMM	LOOKY LOOKY	A MAN NEEDS LOVE	85.00
66	222 DJ	BROTHERS GRIMM	LOOKY LOOKY	A MAN NEEDS LOVE	125.00
66	229	FADING COLOURS	(JUST LIKE) ROMEO AND JULIET	BILLY CHRISTIAN	15.00
66	229 DJ	FADING COLOURS	(JUST LIKE) ROMEO AND JULIET	BILLY CHRISTIAN	22.00
67	230	ROY C	TWISTIN' PNEUMONIA	TEAR AVENUE	8.00
67	230 DJ	ROY C	TWISTIN' PNEUMONIA	TEAR AVENUE	10.00
67	231	RAY SINGER	WHAT'S DONE HAS BEEN DONE	WON'T IT BE FINE	25.00
67	231 DJ	RAY SINGER	WHAT'S DONE HAS BEEN DONE	WON'T IT BE FINE	30.00
67	232	LOU LAWTON	I AM SEARCHING (FOR MY BABY)	DOIN' THE PHILLY DOG	20.00
67	232 DJ	LOU LAWTON	I AM SEARCHING (FOR MY BABY)	DOIN' THE PHILLY DOG	30.00
67	235	CHECKMATES LTD.	DO THE WALK (THE TEMPTATION	GLAD FOR YOU	20.00
67	235 DJ	CHECKMATES LTD.	DO THE WALK (THE TEMPTATION	GLAD FOR YOU	30.00
67	239	TWIGGY	BEAUTIFUL DREAMS	I NEED YOUR HAND IN MINE	20.00
67	239 PS	TWIGGY	BEAUTIFUL DREAMS	I NEED YOUR HAND IN MINE	30.00
67	239 DJ	TWIGGY	BEAUTIFUL DREAMS	I NEED YOUR HAND IN MINE	40.00
67	240	SONNY CHARLES and the CHECKMATES	MASTEREDTHE ART OF LOVE	PLEASE DON'T TAKE MY WORLD AWA	75.00
67	240 DJ	SONNY CHARLES and the CHECKMATES	MASTEREDTHE ART OF LOVE	PLEASE DON'T TAKE MY WORLD AWA	85.00
67	241	CASINO'S	THAT'S THE WAY	TOO GOOD TO BE TRUE	25.00
67	241 DJ	CASINO'S	THAT'S THE WAY	TOO GOOD TO BE TRUE	40.00
67	245	BOBBY JOHNSON and the ATOMS	TRAMP	DO IT AGAIN A LITTLE BIT SLOWE	15.00
67	245 PS	BOBBY JOHNSON and the ATOMS	TRAMP	DO IT AGAIN A LITTLE BIT SLOWE	20.00
67	245 DJ	BOBBY JOHNSON and the ATOMS	TRAMP	DO IT AGAIN A LITTLE BIT SLOWE	28.00
69	254	INTRUDERS	COWBOYS TO GIRLS	TURN BACK THE HANDS OF TIME	15.00
69	254 DJ	INTRUDERS	COWBOYS TO GIRLS	TURN BACK THE HANDS OF TIME	25.00
70	290	TONY & TYRONE	EVERYDAY FUN	WHIP YOUR LOVING ON ME	15.00
70	290 PS	TONY & TYRONE	EVERYDAY FUN	WHIP YOUR LOVING ON ME	20.00
70	290 DJ	TONY & TYRONE	EVERYDAY FUN	WHIP YOUR LOVING ON ME	20.00
70	301	EDDIE ROBINSON	HEY BLACKMAN	HEY BLACKMAN part 2	5.00
70	301 DJ	EDDIE ROBINSON	HEY BLACKMAN	HEY BLACKMAN part 2	8.00
70	301 PS	EDDIE ROBINSON	HEY BLACKMAN	HEY BLACKMAN part 2	8.00
70	311	FORK IN THE ROAD	I CAN'T TURN AROUND	SKELETON IN MY CLOSET	250.00
70	311 DJ	FORK IN THE ROAD	I CAN'T TURN AROUND	SKELETON IN MY CLOSET	350.00
71	312	MR. FLOOD PARTY	COMPARED TO WHAT	UNBREAKABLE TOY	12.00
71	312 DJ	MR. FLOODS PARTY	COMPARED TO WHAT	UNBREAKABLE TOY	25.00
72	315	MILT MATTHEWS INC.	CAN'T SEE MYSELF DOING YOU WRONG	DISASTER AREA	4.00
72	315 DJ	MILT MATTHEWS INC.	CAN'T SEE MYSELF DOING YOU WRONG	DISASTER AREA	5.00
72	320	MICKY STEVENSON	HERE I AM	JOE POOR LOVES DAPHNE ELIZABE	8.00
72	320 DJ	MICKY STEVENSON	HERE I AM	JOE POOR LOVES DAPHNE ELIZABE	10.00
72	321	ALBINO GORILLA	SHAKE ME, WAKE ME	GOING TO A GO GO	5.00
72	321 DJ	ALBINO GORILLA	SHAKE ME, WAKE ME	GOING TO A GO GO	6.00
72	325	INTRUDERS	COWBOYS TO GIRLS	SHAKE A HAND	8.00
72	325 DJ	INTRUDERS	COWBOYS TO GIRLS	SHAKE A HAND	10.00
73	326	GLADYS KNIGHT & The PIPS	EVERY BEAT OF MY HEART	ROOM IN YOUR HEART	5.00
73	326 DJ	GLADYS KNIGHT & The PIPS	EVERY BEAT OF MY HEART	ROOM IN YOUR HEART	8.00
75	342	PAULA KNIGHT	IT'S THE SAME OLD SONG	LA LA SONG	5.00
75	342 DJ	PAULA KNIGHT	IT'S THE SAME OLD SONG	LA LA SONG	8.00
75	345	JOHNNY OTIS	JAWS	GOOD TO THE LAST DROP	10.00
75	345 DJ	JOHNNY OTIS	JAWS	GOOD TO THE LAST DROP	15.00
62	705	CLYDE McPHATTER & JACKIE WILSON	TENDERLY	HARBOUR LIGHTS	250.00
64	4527 EP PS	RICHARD BERRY & the PHAROAHS	RHYTHM AND BLUES vol. 3	louie louie + 3	200.00
64	4535 EP PS	LULA REED& SYL JOHNSON	RHYTHM AND BLUES BLUE BEAT STYLE	11963 4 track EP with cover	60.00
64	4536 EP PS	LULA REED& FREDDIE KING	LULA REED AND FREDDIE KING	1963 4 track EP with cover	40.00
64	4549 EP PS	JAMES BROWN & THE FAMOUS FLAMES	I DO JUST WHAT I WANT	4 track EP	30.00
64	4561 EP PS	JOHN LEE HOOKER	THINKING BLUES	4 track EP with cover	30.00

EMI

EMI stands for Electric and Musical Industries. Whilst being responsible for the UK greatest 60's labels, Stateside, Tamla Motown, Capitol etc, it wasn't until 1973 that it actually released 45's under its own Logo EMI.

79	104	WILSON PICKETT	LOVE OF MY LIFE	GROOVE CITY	6.00
79	104 DJ	WILSON PICKETT	LOVE OF MY LIFE	GROOVE CITY	8.00
81	120	WILSON PICKETT	AIN'T GONNA GIVE YOU NO MORE	DON'T UNDERESTIMATE THE POWER	3.00
81	120 DJ	WILSON PICKETT	AIN'T GONNA GIVE YOU NO MORE	DON'T UNDERESTIMATE THE POWER	4.00
82	146 PS	MELBA MOORE	LOVE'S COMIN' AT YA	LET'S GO BACK TO LOVIN'	5.00
74	501	100% PURE POISON	YOU KEEP COMING BACK	(AND WHEN I SAID) I LOVE YOU	60.00
74	501 DJ	100% PURE POISON	YOU KEEP COMING BACK	(AND WHEN I SAID) I LOVE YOU	75.00
74	502	CHARLIE THOMAS & the DRIFTERS	A MIDSUMMER NIGHT IN HARLEM	LONELY DRIFTER DON'T CRY	5.00
74	502 DJ	CHARLIE THOMAS & the DRIFTERS	A MIDSUMMER NIGHT IN HARLEM	LONELY DRIFTER DON'T CRY	8.00
75	506	CHARLIE THOMAS & the DRIFTERS	RUN, RUN ROADRUNNER	I'M GONNA TAKE YOU HOME	15.00
75	506 DJ	CHARLIE THOMAS & the DRIFTERS	RUN, RUN ROADRUNNER	I'M GONNA TAKE YOU HOME	20.00
75	507	JOHNNY JOHNSON & the BANDWAGON	I DON'T KNOW WHY	HONEY BEE	6.00
75	507 DJ	JOHNNY JOHNSON & the BANDWAGON	I DON'T KNOW WHY	HONEY BEE	8.00
75	510	JIMMY JAMES	A MAN LIKE ME	SURVIVAL	8.00
75	510 DJ	JIMMY JAMES	A MAN LIKE ME	SURVIVAL	10.00
75	513	EBONY RHYTHM FUNK	HOW'S YOUR WIFE (AND MY CHILD)	OH BABY	6.00
75	513 DJ	EBONY RHYTHM FUNK	HOW'S YOUR WIFE (AND MY CHILD)	OH BABY	8.00
75	514	BARBARA HALL	YOU BROUGHT IT ON YOURSELF	DROP MY HEART OFF AT THE DOOR	30.00
75	514 DJ	BARBARA HALL	YOU BROUGHT IT ON YOURSELF	DROP MY HEART OFF AT THE DOOR	40.00
75	515	B.T. EXPRESS	GIVE IT WHAT YOU GOT	HAPPINESS	5.00
75	515 DJ	B.T. EXPRESS	GIVE IT WHAT YOU GOT	HAPPINESS	6.00
76	518	B.T. EXPRESS	PEACEPIPE	WHATCHA THINK ABOUT THAT	5.00
76	518 DJ	B.T. EXPRESS	PEACEPIPE	WHATCHA THINK ABOUT THAT	6.00
76	521	TLC ORCHESTRA feat: LEON THOMAS	I JUST WANNA SAY I LOVE YOU	same: instrumental	15.00
76	521 DJ	TLC ORCHESTRA feat: LEON THOMAS	I JUST WANNA SAY I LOVE YOU	same: instrumental	20.00
76	522	B.T. EXPRESS	I CAN'T STOP GROOVIN' - NOW I WANT TO DO IT - SOME MORE HERBS		5.00
76	522 DJ	B.T. EXPRESS	I CAN'T STOP GROOVIN' - NOW I WANT TO DO IT - SOME MORE HERBS		6.00
76	526	B.T. EXPRESS	ENERGY TO BURN	TIME TUNNEL	5.00
76	526 DJ	B.T. EXPRESS	ENERGY TO BURN	TIME TUNNEL	6.00
77	536	BO KIRKLAND & RUTH DAVIS	EASY LOVING	CAN YOU FEEL IT	3.00
77	536 DJ	BO KIRKLAND & RUTH DAVIS	EASY LOVING	CAN YOU FEEL IT	4.00
77	536 PS	BO KIRKLAND & RUTH DAVIS	EASY LOVING	CAN YOU FEEL IT	4.00
77	537	B.T. EXPRESS	FUNKY MUSIC	WE GOT IT TOGETHER	5.00
77	537 DJ	B.T. EXPRESS	FUNKY MUSIC	WE GOT IT TOGETHER	6.00
78	548	B.T. EXPRESS	SHOUT IT OUT	RIDE ON B.T.	5.00
78	548 DJ	B.T. EXPRESS	SHOUT IT OUT	RIDE ON B.T.	6.00
78	556	RUFUS LUMLEY	I'M STANDING	LET'S HIDE AWAY (ME AND YOU)	10.00
78	556 DJ	RUFUS LUMLEY	I'M STANDING	LET'S HIDE AWAY (ME AND YOU)	20.00
73	2001	REAL THING	PLASTIC MAN	CHECK IT OUT	3.00
73	2001 DJ	REAL THING	PLASTIC MAN	CHECK IT OUT	4.00
73	2011	JOHNNY JOHNSON	GIVE ME YOR LOVE AGAIN	ALL THE WAY	3.00
73	2011 DJ	JOHNNY JOHNSON	GIVE ME YOR LOVE AGAIN	ALL THE WAY	4.00
73	2014	MANDINGO	MEDICINE MAN	BLACK RITE	8.00
73	2014 DJ	MANDINGO	MEDICINE MAN	BLACK RITE	10.00
73	2114	JOHNNY JOHNSON & the BANDWAGON	STRONG LOVE PROUD LOVE	FAST RUNNING OUT OF WORLD	15.00
73	2114 DJ	JOHNNY JOHNSON & the BANDWAGON	STRONG LOVE PROUD LOVE	FAST RUNNING OUT OF WORLD	20.00
73	2025	REAL THING	LISTEN JOE McGINTOO	I DON'T MIND	3.00
73	2025 DJ	REAL THING	LISTEN JOE McGINTOO	I DON'T MIND	4.00
73	2084	REAL THING	CHUCK IT OUT	HUMPTY DUMPTY	3.00
73	2084 DJ	REAL THING	CHUCK IT OUT	HUMPTY DUMPTY	4.00
74	2116	REAL THING	VICIOUS CIRCLES	VICIOUS CIRCLES part 2	3.00
74	2116 DJ	REAL THING	VICIOUS CIRCLES	VICIOUS CIRCLES part 2	4.00
74	2127	JIMMY JAMES & THE VAGABONDS	MARBLE & IRON	I AIN'T LYING	10.00
74	2127 DJ	JIMMY JAMES & THE VAGABONDS	MARBLE & IRON	I AIN'T LYING	15.00
75	2250	GRAHAM BONNEY	SUPER GIRL	HILL OF LOVIN'	6.00
75	2250 DJ	GRAHAM BONNEY	SUPER GIRL	HILL OF LOVIN'	8.00
75	2275	GERALDINE HUNT	YOU	IT'S ALL FOR YOU	5.00
75	2275 DJ	GERALDINE HUNT	YOU	IT'S ALL FOR YOU	6.00
76	2386	JESSE GREEN	NICE AND SLOW	EASY	6.00
76	2386 DJ	JESSE GREEN	NICE AND SLOW	EASY	8.00
76	2424	MARBOO	WHAT ABOUT LOVE	I REMEMBER SUNDAY MORNING	20.00
76	2424 DJ	MARBOO	WHAT ABOUT LOVE	I REMEMBER SUNDAY MORNING	28.00
76	2432	PHILADELPHIA FLYERS	HUMMING OUT A DIFFERENT TUNE	same: instrumental	8.00
76	2432 DJ	PHILADELPHIA FLYERS	HUMMING OUT A DIFFERENT TUNE	same: instrumental	10.00
76	2437	GLORIA JONES	GET IT ON	GET IT ON version	5.00
76	2437 DJ	GLORIA JONES	GET IT ON	GET IT ON version	6.00
76	2492	JESSE GREEN	NICE AND SLOW	same: instrumental	5.00
76	2492 DJ	JESSE GREEN	NICE AND SLOW	same: instrumental	6.00
76	2522	GLORIA JONES	I AIN'T GOING NOWHERE	SIMPLICITY BLUES	15.00
76	2522 DJ	GLORIA JONES	I AIN'T GOING NOWHERE	SIMPLICITY BLUES	20.00
77	2570	GLORIA JONES	GO NOW	DRIVE ME CRAZY	5.00
77	2570 DJ	GLORIA JONES	GO NOW	DRIVE ME CRAZY	6.00
77	2572	MARC BOLAN & GLORIA JONES	TO KNOW YOU IS TO LOVE YOU	CITY PORT	15.00
77	2572 DJ	MARC BOLAN & GLORIA JONES	TO KNOW YOU IS TO LOVE YOU	CITY PORT	20.00
77	2580	GONZALEZ	BLESS YOU	THE RIDE	8.00
77	2580 DJ	GONZALEZ	BLESS YOU	THE RIDE	10.00

77	2615	JESSE GREEN	COME WITH ME	same: instrumental	4.00
77	2615 DJ	JESSE GREEN	COME WITH ME	same: instrumental	5.00
77	2706	GONZALEZ	I HAVEN'T STOP DANCING YET	CARNIVAL	4.00
77	2706 DJ	GONZALEZ	I HAVEN'T STOP DANCING YET	CARNIVAL	5.00
77	2720	GLORIA JONES	BRING ON THE LOVE (WHY CAN'T WE BE	CRY BABY	10.00
77	2720 DJ	GLORIA JONES	BRING ON THE LOVE (WHY CAN'T WE BE	CRY BABY	15.00
78	2769	EXPRESSIONS	ROUND AND ROUND IN CIRCLES	SAX & STRINGS IN CIRCLES	8.00
78	2769 DJ	EXPRESSIONS	ROUND AND ROUND IN CIRCLES	SAX & STRINGS IN CIRCLES	10.00
78	2846	DOMINO	HEAVEN MUST HAVE SENT YOU	THAT LOOK OF LOVE	5.00
78	2846 DJ	DOMINO	HEAVEN MUST HAVE SENT YOU	THAT LOOK OF LOVE	6.00
78	2846 DJ PS	DOMINO	HEAVEN MUST HAVE SENT YOU	THAT LOOK OF LOVE	8.00
80	5086	CECIL PARKER	REALLY REALLY LOVE YOU	REALLY REALLY LOVE YOU part 2	5.00
80	5086 DJ	CECIL PARKER	REALLY REALLY LOVE YOU	REALLY REALLY LOVE YOU part 2	6.00
80	5101	WILLIAM DEVAUGHN	BE THANKFUL FOR WHAT YOU'VE GOT	I'VE NEVER FOUND A GIRL	6.00
80	5101 DJ	WILLIAM DEVAUGHN	BE THANKFUL FOR WHAT YOU'VE GOT	I'VE NEVER FOUND A GIRL	8.00
81	5139	CECIL PARKER	WHAT IT IS	YOU WERE THERE	4.00
81	5139 DJ	CECIL PARKER	WHAT IT IS	YOU WERE THERE	5.00
82	5319	LIGHT OF THE WORLD	NO. 1 GIRL	DON'T RUN	4.00
82	5319 DJ	LIGHT OF THE WORLD	NO. 1 GIRL	DON'T RUN	5.00
82	5337	REAL THING	SEEN TO SMILE	LOOK UP	3.00
82	5337 DJ	REAL THING	SEEN TO SMILE	LOOK UP	4.00
85	5514	JIMMY RUFFIN	THE BACKSTABBERS	THEE WILL NEVER BE ANOTHER YOU	4.00
85	5514 PS	JIMMY RUFFIN	THE BACKSTABBERS	THEE WILL NEVER BE ANOTHER YOU	5.00

EMIDISC

EMI acetates were made for all EMI releases before the master plates were made. Please note in the late 60's and early 70's. Northern Soul "pirates" had many Northern Soul in-demand titles cut onto "EMI DISCS" at various acetate cutting operators. These were sold at Northern Soul clubs and were usually cut on BOTH sides with two currently popular titles. These discs are regarded as very low value in today's market. As EMI dealt and sold acetates with labels to independent mastering companies you often see a "rare" soul 45, however beware of EMIDISCS being mistaken for original EMI cut acetate masters.

I've only listed one EMIDISC as this title failed to get UK release, but was issued in the USA. Other genuine EMI acetates should be valued as separate items, maybe at a value between the original stock release and promo could be a benchmark but beware of the sound quality as acetates fidelity deteriorates with age.

66	3	CHANTELLES	OUT OF MY MIND	blank:	100.00

Not issued on 45 in the UK but was released in the USA on GNP Crescendo

ENERGY

	1 PS	VALENTINE BROTHERS	MONEY'S TOO TIGHT (TO MENTION)	same: instrumental	4.00

ENSIGN

77	3	DANNY WILLIAMS	DANCIN' EASY	NO MORE CANE	3.00
77	7	DANNY WILLIAMS	I HATE HATE	I HATE HATE (Disco)	15.00
79	22	LIGHT OF THE WORLD	SWINGIN'	WORLD IS OUT	4.00
79	29	LIGHT OF THE WORLD	MIDNIGHT GROOVIN'	EMERGENCY	4.00
80	36	LIGHT OF THE WORLD	THE BOYS IN BLUE	THIS IS THIS	4.00
80	37	SHO NUFF	IT'S ALRIGHT	same: instrumental	5.00
80	43	LIGHT OF THE WORLD	LONDON TOWN	PETE'S CRUSADE	4.00
80	44	INCOGNITO	PARISIENNE GIRL	SUMMER'S END	4.00
80	46	LIGHT OF THE WORLD	I SHOT THE SHERRIF	NEW SOFT SONG	4.00
81	210	DAVID BENETH	FEEL THE REAL	MAKE IT POP	6.00
81	211	INCOGNITO	INCOGNITO	TRACY	6.00
81	221	INCOGNITO	NORTH LONDON BOY	A SECOND CHANCE	4.00
81	229	PHIL FEARON & GALAXY	HEAD OVER HEELS	same: instrumental	4.00
84	501	PHIL FEARON & GALAXY	DANCING TIGHT	same: instrumental	4.00
84	503	PHIL FEARON & GALAXY	WAIT UNTIL TONIGHT	WAIT UNTIL TONIGHT part 2	4.00
84	510	PHIL FEARON & GALAXY	WHAT TO DO	WHAT TO DO part 2	4.00
84	515	PHIL FEARON & GALAXY	EVERYBODY'S LAUGHIN'	same: instrumental	4.00
85	517	PHIL FEARON & GALAXY	YOU DON'T NEED A REASON	YOU DON'T NEED A REASON part 2	4.00
85	521	PHIL FEARON & GALAXY	THIS KIND OF LOVE	SHARING LOVE	4.00
83	ENS2 EP	INEZ & CHARLIE FOXX	MOCKINGBIRD	HURT BY LOVE + HERE WE GO ROUND THE MULB	5.00
87	PF2 PS	PHIL FEARON & GALAXY	AIN'T NOTHING BUT A HOUSE PARTY	BURNING ALL MY BRIDGES	4.00
87	PF3 PS	PHIL FEARON & GALAXY	NOTHING'S TOO GOOD FOR YOU	YOU'VE STILL GOT MY LOVE	4.00

EPIC

Subsiduary of CBS Records, as with other CBS related labels the numbering system is very confusing with the years not running in line with the release number. We have omitted releases by the Jacksons, Michael Jackson etc, as they are of little interest to soul collectors. Whilst we list all we could on the Isley Brothers, Sly & the Family stone etc. This label reissued their best selling soul 45s sometimes using the same release number but pressing them on the current label design, these releases have been noted.

97	1 DJ promo only	JIMMY FRASER c/w PATTI AUSTIN OF HOPES & DREAMS & TOMBSTONES		ARE WE READY FOR LOVE	15.00
73	1007	JOHNNY WILLIAMS	SLOW MOTION	SHALL WE GATHER BY THE WATER	6.00
73	1007 DJ	JOHNNY WILLIAMS	SLOW MOTION	SHALL WE GATHER BY THE WATER	8.00
81	1025	MTUME	YOU CAN'T WAIT FOR LOVE	EVERYTHING GOOD TO ME	3.00
81	1025 DJ	MTUME	YOU CAN'T WAIT FOR LOVE	EVERYTHING GOOD TO ME	4.00
72	1042	BRENTON WOOD	STICKY BOOM BOOM TO COLD	STICKY BOOM BOOM TO COLD part 2	5.00
72	1042 DJ	BRENTON WOOD	STICKY BOOM BOOM TO COLD	STICKY BOOM BOOM TO COLD part 2	6.00
73	1055	BILLY PAUL	ME & MRS JONES	YOUR SONG	5.00
73	1055 DJ	BILLY PAUL	ME & MRS JONES	YOUR SONG	6.00
81	1122	ISLEY BROTHERS	TONIGHT'S THE NIGHT	WHO SAID?	3.00
81	1122 DJ	ISLEY BROTHERS	TONIGHT'S THE NIGHT	WHO SAID?	4.00
73	1148	SLY & THE FAMILY STONE	DANCE TO THE MUSIC	FAMILY AFFAIR	4.00
73	1148 DJ	SLY & THE FAMILY STONE	DANCE TO THE MUSIC	FAMILY AFFAIR	5.00

73	1177	BUNNY SIGLER	TOSSIN' AND TURNIN'	PICTURE US	5.00
73	1177 DJ	BUNNY SIGLER	TOSSIN' AND TURNIN'	PICTURE US	6.00
81	1301	BOBBY THURSTON	VERY LAST DROP	LIFE IS WHAT YOU MAKE IT	5.00
81	1301 DJ	BOBBY THURSTON	VERY LAST DROP	LIFE IS WHAT YOU MAKE IT	6.00
73	1309	TIMMY WILLIS	GIVE ME A LITTLE SIGN	DON'T WANT TO SET ME FREE	10.00
73	1309 DJ	TIMMY WILLIS	GIVE ME A LITTLE SIGN	DON'T WANT TO SET ME FREE	15.00
73	1313	BILLY PAUL	BROWN BABY	IT'S TOO LATE	5.00
73	1313 DJ	BILLY PAUL	BROWN BABY	IT'S TOO LATE	6.00
73	1361	BRENDA & THE TABULATIONS	ONE GIRL TOO LATE	MAGIC OF YOUR LOVE	10.00
73	1361 DJ	BRENDA & THE TABULATIONS	ONE GIRL TOO LATE	MAGIC OF YOUR LOVE	12.00
73	1383	BRENTON WOOD	ANOTHER SATURDAY NIGHT	ATTEMPTED LOVE	5.00
73	1383 DJ	BRENTON WOOD	ANOTHER SATURDAY NIGHT	ATTEMPTED LOVE	6.00
73	1521	DICK JENSEN	I DON'T WANT TO CRY	TAMIKA (COME BACK LATER)	8.00
73	1521 DJ	DICK JENSEN	I DON'T WANT TO CRY	TAMIKA (COME BACK LATER)	10.00
73	1547	JOHNNY WILLIAMS	IT'S SO WONDERFUL	PUT IT IN MOTION	10.00
73	1547 DJ	JOHNNY WILLIAMS	IT'S SO WONDERFUL	PUT IT IN MOTION	15.00
73	1554	RICHARD DIMPLES FIELDS	I LIKE YOUR LOVING	LOVELY LADY	4.00
73	1554 DJ	RICHARD DIMPLES FIELDS	I LIKE YOUR LOVING	LOVELY LADY	5.00
73	1655	SLY & THE FAMILY STONE	IF YOU WANT ME TO STAY	THANKFUL & THOUGHTFUL	4.00
73	1655 DJ	SLY & THE FAMILY STONE	IF YOU WANT ME TO STAY	THANKFUL & THOUGHTFUL	5.00
81	1662	LUTHER VANDROSS	SUGAR AND SPICE (I FOUND ME A GIRL)	DON'T YOU KNOW THAT	5.00
81	1662 DJ	LUTHER VANDROSS	SUGAR AND SPICE (I FOUND ME A GIRL)	DON'T YOU KNOW THAT	6.00
73	1704	ISLEY BROTHERS	THAT LADY	THAT LADY part 2	4.00
73	1704 DJ	ISLEY BROTHERS	THAT LADY	THAT LADY part 2	5.00
73	1720	BOBBY TAYLOR	I CAN'T QUIT YOUR LOVE	QUEEN OF THE GHETTO	5.00
73	1720 DJ	BOBBY TAYLOR	I CAN'T QUIT YOUR LOVE	QUEEN OF THE GHETTO	6.00
81	1741	ISLEY BROTHERS	INSIDE OF YOU	INSIDE OF YOU part 2	3.00
81	1741 DJ	ISLEY BROTHERS	INSIDE OF YOU	INSIDE OF YOU part 2	4.00
81	1881	GAYLE ADAMS	I DON'T WANNA HEART IT	LOVE FEVER	5.00
81	1881 DJ	GAYLE ADAMS	I DON'T WANNA HEART IT	LOVE FEVER	8.00
81	1918	RICHARD DIMPLES FIELDS	I'VE GOT TO LEARN TO SAY NO	SHE'S GOT PAPERS ON ME	3.00
81	1918 DJ	RICHARD DIMPLES FIELDS	I'VE GOT TO LEARN TO SAY NO	SHE'S GOT PAPERS ON ME	4.00
81	1918 PS DJ	RICHARD DIMPLES FIELDS	I'VE GOT TO LEARN TO SAY NO	SHE'S GOT PAPERS ON ME	6.00
73	1980	ISLEY BROTHERS	THE HIGHWAYS OF MY LIFE	DON'T LET ME BE LONELY TONIGHT	4.00
73	1980 DJ	ISLEY BROTHERS	THE HIGHWAYS OF MY LIFE	DON'T LET ME BE LONELY TONIGHT	5.00
74	1981	SLY & THE FAMILY STONE	QUE SREA, SERA (WHATEVER WILL BE,)	IF IT WERE LEFT UP TO ME	4.00
74	1981 DJ	SLY & THE FAMILY STONE	QUE SREA, SERA (WHATEVER WILL BE)	IF IT WERE LEFT UP TO ME	5.00
74	1997	BRENDA & THE TABULATIONS	I'M IN LOVE	WALK ON IN	5.00
74	1997 DJ	BRENDA & THE TABULATIONS	I'M IN LOVE	WALK ON IN	6.00
82	2167	GAYLE ADAMS	BABY I NEED YOUR LOVING	DON'T JUMP TO CONCLUSIONS	30.00
82	2167 DJ	GAYLE ADAMS	BABY I NEED YOUR LOVING	DON'T JUMP TO CONCLUSIONS	50.00
74	2244	ISLEY BROTHERS	SUMMER BREEZE	SUMMER BREEZE part 2	4.00
74	2244 DJ	ISLEY BROTHERS	SUMMER BREEZE	SUMMER BREEZE part 2	5.00
74	2508 yellow label	BILLY BUTLER	RIGHT TRACK	CAN'T LIVE WITHOUT YOU	10.00
74	2508 yellow label DJ	BILLY BUTLER	RIGHT TRACK	CAN'T LIVE WITHOUT YOU	15.00
78	2508 orange label	BILLY BUTLER	CAN'T LIVE WITHOUT HER	RIGHT TRACK	6.00
78	2508 orange label DJ	BILLY BUTLER	CAN'T LIVE WITHOUT HER	RIGHT TRACK	8.00
74	2530	SLY & the FAMILY STONE	TIME FOR LIVIN'	SMALL TALK	3.00
74	2530 DJ	SLY & the FAMILY STONE	TIME FOR LIVIN'	SMALL TALK	4.00
74	2578	ISLEY BROTHERS	LIVE IT UP	LIVE IT UP part 2	3.00
74	2578 DJ	ISLEY BROTHERS	LIVE IT UP	LIVE IT UP part 2	4.00
74	2597	JOHNNY JOHNSON & the BANDWAGON	BREAKING DOWN THE WALLS OF HEARTACHE	DANCIN' MASTER	6.00
74	2597 DJ	JOHNNY JOHNSON & the BANDWAGON	BREAKING DOWN THE WALLS OF HEARTACHE	DANCIN' MASTER	8.00
82	2697	STANLEY CLARKE	STRAIGHT TO THE TOP	THE FORCE OF LOVE	15.00
82	2697 DJ	STANLEY CLARKE	STRAIGHT TO THE TOP	THE FORCE OF LOVE	20.00
74	2803	ISLEY BROTHERS	NEED A LITTLE TASTE	IF YOU WERE THERE	3.00
74	2803 DJ	ISLEY BROTHERS	NEED A LITTLE TASTE	IF YOU WERE THERE	4.00
74	2852	LABELLE.	LADY MARMALADE	SPACE CHILDREN	5.00
74	2852 DJ	LABELLE.	LADY MARMALADE	SPACE CHILDREN	6.00
75	2882	SLY & the FAMILY STONE	LOOSE BOOTY	CAN'T STRAIN MY BRAIN	5.00
75	2882 DJ	SLY & the FAMILY STONE	LOOSE BOOTY	CAN'T STRAIN MY BRAIN	6.00
75	3034	ISLEY BROTHERS	MIDNIGHT SKY	MIDNIGHT SKY part 2	4.00
75	3034 DJ	ISLEY BROTHERS	MIDNIGHT SKY	same:	4.00
75	3048	SLY & the FAMILY STONE	DANCE TO THE MUSIC + COLOUR ME	RIDE THE RHYTHM	3.00
75	3048 DJ	SLY & the FAMILY STONE	DANCE TO THE MUSIC + COLOUR ME	RIDE THE RHYTHM	4.00
74	3121	MINNIE RIPPERTON	LOVIN' YOU	THE EDGE OF A DREAM	5.00
74	3121 DJ	MINNIE RIPPERTON	LOVIN' YOU	THE EDGE OF A DREAM	6.00
75	3255	DOMINO	I'M GONNA LOVE YOU	IF YOUR FAVOURITE GUY GOES AWA	4.00
75	3255 DJ	DOMINO	I'M GONNA LOVE YOU	IF YOUR FAVOURITE GUY GOES AWA	5.00
75	3299	T.D. VALENTINE	LOVE TRAP	ALLISON TOOK ME AWAY	8.00
75	3299 DJ	T.D. VALENTINE	LOVE TRAP	ALLISON TOOK ME AWAY	15.00
82	3313 PS	LUTHER VANDROSS	YOU'RE THE SWEETEST ONE	SHE'S A SUPER LADY	4.00
82	3313 PS	LUTHER VANDROSS	YOU'RE THE SWEETEST ONE	SHE'S A SUPER LADY	5.00
75	3318	BIDDU ORCHESTRA	NORTHERN DANCER	SUMMER OF '42	4.00
75	3318 DJ PS	BIDDU ORCHESTRA	NORTHERN DANCER	SUMMER OF '42	5.00
99	3363	MARVIN & TAMARA	NORTH, SOUTH, EAST WEST	same: northern soul mix	3.00
99	3363 DJ	MARVIN & TAMARA	NORTH, SOUTH, EAST WEST	same: northern soul mix	4.00
75	3424	MTUME	JUICY FRUIT	JUICY FRUIT part 2	4.00
75	3424 DJ	MTUME	JUICY FRUIT	JUICY FRUIT part 2	5.00

75	3434	ISLEY BROTHERS	FIGHT THE POWER	FIGHT THE POWER part 2	3.00
75	3434 DJ	ISLEY BROTHERS	FIGHT THE POWER	FIGHT THE POWER part 2	4.00
75	3458	JOHNNY JOHNSON & the BANDWAGON	MUSIC TO MY HEART	LOOKIN' LEAN FEELIN' MEAN	6.00
75	3458 DJ	JOHNNY JOHNSON & the BANDWAGON	MUSIC TO MY HEART	LOOKIN' LEAN FEELIN' MEAN	8.00
83	3513	ISLEY BROTHERS	BETWEEN THE SHEETS	BETWEEN THE SHEETS part 2	4.00
83	3513 DJ	ISLEY BROTHERS	BETWEEN THE SHEETS	BETWEEN THE SHEETS part 2	5.00
75	3589	ESSENCE	SWEET FOOLS	SWEET FOOLS	5.00
75	3589 DJ	ESSENCE	SWEET FOOLS	SWEET FOOLS	6.00
83	3690	ISLEY BROTHERS	CHOOSEY LOVER	CHOOSEY LOVER part 2	3.00
83	3690 DJ	ISLEY BROTHERS	CHOOSEY LOVER	CHOOSEY LOVER part 2	4.00
83	3805	LEW KIRTON	TALK TO ME	same: instrumental	6.00
83	3805 DJ	LEW KIRTON	TALK TO ME	same: instrumental	8.00
76	3818	BATAAN	THE BOTTLE (LA BOTELLA)	WHEN YOU'RE DOWN (FUNKY MAMBO	8.00
76	3818 DJ	BATAAN	THE BOTTLE (LA BOTELLA)	WHEN YOU'RE DOWN (FUNKY MAMBO	10.00
76	3865	ISLEY BROTHERS	FOR THE LOVE OF YOU	YOU WALK YOUR WAY	5.00
76	3865 DJ	ISLEY BROTHERS	FOR THE LOVE OF YOU	YOU WALK YOUR WAY	6.00
76	4084	BIDDU ORCHESTRA	EXODUS	RAIN FOREST	6.00
76	4084 DJ	BIDDU ORCHESTRA	EXODUS	RAIN FOREST	10.00
76	4097	TEMPREES	I FOUND LOVE ON A DISCO FLOOR	THERE AIN'T A DREAM BEEN DREAM	3.00
76	4097 DJ	TEMPREES	I FOUND LOVE ON A DISCO FLOOR	THERE AIN'T A DREAM BEEN DREAM	4.00
76	4186	SANDI SHELDON	YOU'RE GONNA MAKE ME LOVE YOU	BABY YOU'RE MINE	15.00
76	4186 DJ	SANDI SHELDON	YOU'RE GONNA MAKE ME LOVE YOU	BABY YOU'RE MINE	25.00
76	4369	ISLEY BROTHERS	HARVEST FOR THE WORLD	LET ME DOWN EASY	5.00
76	4369 DJ	ISLEY BROTHERS	HARVEST FOR THE WORLD	LET ME DOWN EASY	6.00
76	4373	ISLEY BROTHERS	WHO LOVES YOU BETTER	WHO LOVES YOU BETTER part 2	3.00
76	4373 DJ	ISLEY BROTHERS	WHO LOVES YOU BETTER	WHO LOVES YOU BETTER part 2	4.00
76	4421	WEBSTER LEWIS	DO IT WITH STYLE	THEME	4.00
76	4421 DJ	WEBSTER LEWIS	DO IT WITH STYLE	THEME	5.00
76	4593	WILD CHERRY	PLAY THAT FUNKY MUSIC	THE LADY WANTS YOUR MONEY	5.00
76	4593 DJ	WILD CHERRY	PLAY THAT FUNKY MUSIC	THE LADY WANTS YOUR MONEY	6.00
77	4897	JOHNNY JOHNSON & the BANDWAGON	MUSIC TO MY HEART	BREAKIN' DOWN THE WALLS OF HEARTACE	4.00
77	4897 blue vinyl	JOHNNY JOHNSON & the BANDWAGON	MUSIC TO MY HEART	BREAKIN' DOWN THE WALLS OF HEARTACE	5.00
77	4897 DJ blue vinyl	JOHNNY JOHNSON & the BANDWAGON	MUSIC TO MY HEART	BREAKIN' DOWN THE WALLS OF HEARTACE	6.00
77	4899 blue vinyl	BRENDA & THE TABULATIONS	ONE GIRL TOO LATE	MAGIC OF YOUR LOVE	10.00
77	4899 DJ blue vinyl	BRENDA & THE TABULATIONS	ONE GIRL TOO LATE	MAGIC OF YOUR LOVE	15.00
77	4903	PEACHES & HERB	SOOTHE ME WITH YOUR LOVE	SATISFY MY HUNGER	4.00
77	4903 DJ	PEACHES & HERB	SOOTHE ME WITH YOUR LOVE	SATISFY MY HUNGER	5.00
77	4904	TEMPREES	I DARE YOU blue vinyl	I FOUND LOVE ON A DISCO FLOOR	4.00
77	5052 DJ	JIMMY RUFFIN	FALLIN' IN LOVE WITH YOU	same: instrumental	5.00
77	5105	ISLEY BROTHERS	PRIDE	PRIDE part 2	3.00
77	5105 DJ	ISLEY BROTHERS	PRIDE	PRIDE part 2	4.00
77	5156	REALISTICS	SOMEONE OUGHT TO WRITE A SONG	UNCHAIN ME	25.00
77	5156 DJ	REALISTICS	SOMEONE OUGHT TO WRITE A SONG	UNCHAIN ME	30.00
77	5374	JOE TEX	HUNGRY FOR YOUR LOVE	WE HELD ON	3.00
77	5374 DJ	JOE TEX	HUNGRY FOR YOUR LOVE	WE HELD ON	4.00
77	5416	BIDDU ORCHESTRA	SOUL COAXING	NIRVANA	3.00
77	5416 DJ	BIDDU ORCHESTRA	SOUL COAXING	NIRVANA	4.00
71	5422	VIVIAN REED	MISSING YOU	LEAN ON ME	10.00
71	5422 DJ	VIVIAN REED	MISSING YOU	LEAN ON ME	15.00
77	5439	REALISTICS	THE MAGIC THAT YOU DO	LOVE VIBRATIONS	40.00
77	5439 DJ	REALISTICS	THE MAGIC THAT YOU DO	LOVE VIBRATIONS	50.00
77	5443	ISLEY BROTHERS	VOYAGE TO ATLANTIS	TELL ME WHEN YOU NEED IT AGAIN	3.00
77	5443 DJ	ISLEY BROTHERS	VOYAGE TO ATLANTIS	TELL ME WHEN YOU NEED IT AGAIN	4.00
77	5573	DOROTHY MOORE	I BELIEVE YOU	LOVE ME	3.00
77	5573 DJ	DOROTHY MOORE	I BELIEVE YOU	LOVE ME	4.00
77	5723	REALISTICS	SO SAD	THE MAGIC THAT YOU DO	75.00
77	5723 DJ	REALISTICS	SO SAD	THE MAGIC THAT YOU DO	85.00
78	6292	ISLEY BROTHERS	TAKE ME TO THE NEXT PHASE	LIVIN' THE LIFE	3.00
78	6292 DJ	ISLEY BROTHERS	TAKE ME TO THE NEXT PHASE	LIVIN' THE LIFE	4.00
78	6353	STANLEY CLARKE	MORE HOT FUN	SLOW DANCE	3.00
78	6353 DJ	STANLEY CLARKE	MORE HOT FUN	SLOW DANCE	4.00
85	6439 PS	CARL ANDERSON	LET'S TALK	LIGHT ME	3.00
85	6439 PS DJ	CARL ANDERSON	LET'S TALK	LIGHT ME	4.00
78	6481	ISLEY BROTHERS	GROOVE WITH YOU	FOOTSTEPS IN THE DARK	3.00
78	6481 DJ	ISLEY BROTHERS	GROOVE WITH YOU	FOOTSTEPS IN THE DARK	4.00
79	7070	SLY & the FAMILY STONE	DANCE TO THE MUSIC	STAND	4.00
79	7070 DJ	SLY & the FAMILY STONE	DANCE TO THE MUSIC	STAND	5.00
79	7078	ISLEY BROTHERS	IT'S YOUR THING	LOVE THE ONE YOU'RE WITH	4.00
79	7078 DJ	ISLEY BROTHERS	IT'S YOUR THING	LOVE THE ONE YOU'RE WITH	5.00
86	7263	LOU RAWLS	STOP ME FROM STARTING THIS FEELING	LOVE ALLYOUR BLUES AWAY	3.00
86	7263 DJ	LOU RAWLS	STOP ME FROM STARTING THIS FEELING	LOVE ALLYOUR BLUES AWAY	4.00
71	7387	VIVIAN REED	I FEEL THE EARTH MOVE	DON'T CLOSE THE DOOR ON ME	8.00
71	7387 DJ	VIVIAN REED	I FEEL THE EARTH MOVE	DON'T CLOSE THE DOOR ON ME	10.00
71	7632	SLY & the FAMILY STONE	FAMILY AFFAIR	LUV N' HAIGHT	4.00
71	7632 DJ	SLY & the FAMILY STONE	FAMILY AFFAIR	LUV N' HAIGHT	5.00
79	7757	ISLEY BROTHERS	LIFE IN THE CITY	LIFE IN THE CITY	3.00
79	7757 DJ	ISLEY BROTHERS	LIFE IN THE CITY	LIFE IN THE CITY	4.00
79	7795	ISLEY BROTHERS	WINNER TAKES ALL	FUN AND GAMES	3.00
79	7795 DJ	ISLEY BROTHERS	WINNER TAKES ALL	FUN AND GAMES	4.00

72	7810	SLY & the FAMILY STONE	RUNNING AWAY	BRAVE AND STRONG	5.00
72	7810 DJ	SLY & the FAMILY STONE	RUNNING AWAY	BRAVE AND STRONG	6.00
72	7896	JOHNNY OTIS SHOW	THE WATTS BREAKAWAY	YOU CAN DEPEWND ON ME	15.00
72	7896 DJ	JOHNNY OTIS SHOW	THE WATTS BREAKAWAY	YOU CAN DEPEWND ON ME	20.00
80	7911	ISLEY BROTHERS	IT'S A DISCO NIGHT	IT'S A DISCO NIGHT part 2	3.00
80	7911 DJ	ISLEY BROTHERS	IT'S A DISCO NIGHT	IT'S A DISCO NIGHT part 2	4.00
72	7943	DONNIE ELBERT	ALONG CAME PRIDE	GET READY	6.00
72	7943 DJ	DONNIE ELBERT	ALONG CAME PRIDE	GET READY	8.00
79	8017	SLY STONE	DANCE TO THE MUSIC	SING A SIMPLE SONG	4.00
79	8017 DJ	SLY STONE	DANCE TO THE MUSIC	SING A SIMPLE SONG	5.00
72	8071	JOHNNY OTIS SHOW	THE WATTS BREAKAWAY	WILLIE AND THE HAND JIVE	10.00
72	8071 DJ	JOHNNY OTIS SHOW	THE WATTS BREAKAWAY	WILLIE AND THE HAND JIVE	15.00
79	8137	GEORGE DUKE	I WANT YOU FOR MYSELF	DOG-MAN	3.00
79	8137 DJ	GEORGE DUKE	I WANT YOU FOR MYSELF	DOG-MAN	4.00
74	8315	JOHNNY JOHNSON & the BANDWAGON	BREAKING DOWN THE WALLS OF HEARACHE	DANCIN' MASTER	5.00
74	8315 DJ	JOHNNY JOHNSON & the BANDWAGON	BREAKING DOWN THE WALLS OF HEARACHE	DANCIN' MASTER	6.00
72	8320	BRENDA & the TABULATIONS	A LITTLE BIT OF LOVE	LET ME BE HAPPY	8.00
72	8320 DJ	BRENDA & the TABULATIONS	A LITTLE BIT OF LOVE	LET ME BE HAPPY	8.00
80	8348	BOBBY THURSTON	CHECK OUT THE GROOVE	SITTIN' IN THE PARK	5.00
80	8348 DJ	BOBBY THURSTON	CHECK OUT THE GROOVE	SITTIN' IN THE PARK	6.00
80	8371	NDUGU and the CHOCOLATE	LOVE ANEW (WHAT YOU FEEL INSIDE)	SHADOW DANCING	3.00
80	8371 DJ	NDUGU and the CHOCOLATE	LOVE ANEW (WHAT YOU FEEL INSIDE)	SHADOW DANCING	4.00
73	8404	MAJOR LANCE	SWEET MUSIC	UM, UM, UM, UM, UM, UM.	5.00
73	8404 DJ	MAJOR LANCE	SWEET MUSIC	UM, UM, UM, UM, UM, UM.	6.00
72	8476	INTRUDERS	(WIN, PLACE OR SHOW) SHE'S A WINNER	MEMORIES ARE HERE TO STAY	5.00
72	8476 DJ	INTRUDERS	(WIN, PLACE OR SHOW) SHE'S A WINNER	MEMORIES ARE HERE TO STAY	6.00
80	8664	ISLEY BROTHERS	DON'T SAY GOODNIGHT	DON'T SAY GOODNIGHT part 2	3.00
80	8664 DJ	ISLEY BROTHERS	DON'T SAY GOODNIGHT	DON'T SAY GOODNIGHT part 2	4.00
80	8836	DOROTHY MOORE	CRAZY IN LOVE	THERE'LL NEVER BE ANOTHER NIGH	3.00
80	8836 DJ	DOROTHY MOORE	CRAZY IN LOVE	THERE'LL NEVER BE ANOTHER NIGH	4.00
80	8853	SLY & the FAMILY STONE	DANCE TO THE MUSIC	EVERYDAY PEOPLE	3.00
80	8853 DJ	SLY & the FAMILY STONE	DANCE TO THE MUSIC	EVERYDAY PEOPLE	4.00
80	8861	ISLEY BROTHERS	SUMMER BREEZE	THAT LADY	3.00
80	8861 DJ	ISLEY BROTHERS	SUMMER BREEZE	THAT LADY	4.00
80	8987	GAYLE ADAMS	YOUR LOVE IS A LIFESAVER	FOR THE LOVE OF MY MAN	4.00
80	8987 DJ	GAYLE ADAMS	YOUR LOVE IS A LIFESAVER	FOR THE LOVE OF MY MAN	5.00
80	9457	L.A.X.	ALL MY LOVE	THANKS BUT NO THANKS	5.00
80	9457 DJ	L.A.X.	ALL MY LOVE	THANKS BUT NO THANKS	6.00
80	9572	SHARON REDD	CAN YOU HANDLE IT	LEAVING YOU EASIER SAID THAN D	4.00
80	9572 DJ	SHARON REDD	CAN YOU HANDLE IT	LEAVING YOU EASIER SAID THAN D	5.00
75	152241	MAJOR LANCE	THE MONKEY TIME	UM, UM, UM, UM, UM, UM	6.00
75	152241 DJ	MAJOR LANCE	THE MONKEY TIME	UM, UM, UM, UM, UM, UM	8.00
75	152242	MAJOR LANCE	HEY LITTLE GIRL	THE MATADOR	5.00
75	152242 DJ	MAJOR LANCE	HEY LITTLE GIRL	THE MATADOR	6.00
75	152282	SLY & the FAMILY STONE	DANCE TO THE MUSIC	LIFE	3.00
75	152282 DJ	SLY & the FAMILY STONE	DANCE TO THE MUSIC	LIFE	4.00
75	152331	SLY & the FAMILY STONE	IF YOU WANT TO STAY	FRISKY	3.00
75	152331 DJ	SLY & the FAMILY STONE	IF YOU WANT TO STAY	FRISKY	4.00
75	152233	SLY & the FAMILY STONE	ITCHYCOO PARK	I'M ONLY DREAMING	4.00
75	152233 DJ	SLY & the FAMILY STONE	ITCHYCOO PARK	I'M ONLY DREAMING	5.00
75	152302	SLY & the FAMILY STONE	M'LADY	HOT FUN IN THE SUMMERTIME	4.00
75	152302 DJ	SLY & the FAMILY STONE	M'LADY	HOT FUN IN THE SUMMERTIME	5.00
75	152303	SLY & the FAMILY STONE	THANK YOU	EVERYBODY'S A STAR	3.00
75	152303 DJ	SLY & the FAMILY STONE	THANK YOU	EVERYBODY'S A STAR	4.00
75	152304	SLY & the FAMILY STONE	STAND	I WANT TO TAKE YOU HIGHER	3.00
75	152304 DJ	SLY & the FAMILY STONE	STAND	I WANT TO TAKE YOU HIGHER	4.00
75	152305	SLY & the FAMILY STONE	EVERYDAY PEOPLE	SING A SIMPLE SONG	4.00
75	152305 DJ	SLY & the FAMILY STONE	EVERYDAY PEOPLE	SING A SIMPLE SONG	5.00
75	152317	SLY & the FAMILY STONE	FAMILY AFFAIR	RUNNING AWAY	3.00
75	152317 DJ	SLY & the FAMILY STONE	FAMILY AFFAIR	RUNNING AWAY	4.00
91	657676 PS	TEMPTATIONS	MY GIRL	THEME FROM "MY GIRL"	4.00

ERC

84	117	JIMMY RUFFIN	YOUNG HEART (HANG ON)	HOLD ON TO MY LOVE + instrumental	6.00

EVOLUTION

Evolution is a label of ZEL records, 63 Old Compton Street, London W1 distributed by RCA reads the blue and white company sleeve. Evolution had only three releases to interest soul fans on this rather attractive and intriguing label The last release was a Northern Soul play and got covered-up as Eddie Foster!

69	2442	OTIS REDDING	SHE'S ALRIGHT	TUFF ENUFF	15.00
69	2444	FASHIONS	I.O.U. (A LIFETIME OF LOVE)	HE GIVES ME LOVE	15.00
71	3004	BLACK ABBOTS	THE PAINTER	LOVE IS ALIVE	30.00
71	3004 DJ	BLACK ABBOTS	THE PAINTER	LOVE IS ALIVE	40.00

EXPANSION

01	EXSR7-4	BOBBY THURSTON	JUST ASK ME	TREAT ME THE SAME WAY	8.00
86	EXPAN3	LEO'S SUNSHINE	GIVE ME THE SUNSHINE		8.00
03	720021	BOBBY REED	THE TIME IS RIGHT FOR LOVE	IF I DON'T LOVE YOU	10.00
00	76	JIMMY COBB	SO NOBODY ELSE CAN HEAR	PISTACHIO	5.00
01	EXSR7-4	BOBBY THURSTON	JUST ASK ME	TREAT ME THE SAME WAY	8.00

02	EXSR7-8	JEFFREE	LOVE LOAN	CALL IT LOVE	8.00
	EXSR7-9	SIDNEY JOE QUALLS	I DON'T DO THIS	RUN TO ME	10.00
01	scex7-1	SAM MOORE	PLENTY GOOD LOVIN	same: mono	15.00
03	SCEX7-2	FRANK POPP ESSEMBLE	BREAKAWAY	YOU'VE BEEN GONE TOO LONG	10.00

EXPLOSION

73	2056	TOMORROW'S CHILDREN	SISTER, BIG STUFF	GIRL	30.00

FAB

66	1	ERROL DIXON	NEED SOMEONE TO LOVE ME	I WANT	30.00
66	1 DJ	ERROL DIXON	NEED SOMEONE TO LOVE ME	I WANT	40.00

FABULOUS

02	7007	JOEY DELORENZO	WAKE UP TO THE SUNSHINE GIRL	LOST MY SENSE OF DIRECTION	15.00
02	7014	MELBA MOORE c/w HONEY & the BEES	THE MAGIC TOUCH	NEVER IN A MILLION YEARS	10.00
02	7014 DJ	MELBA MOORE c/w HONEY & the BEES	THE MAGIC TOUCH	NEVER IN A MILLION YEARS	20.00
02	7015 DJ	GLEN MILLER c/w VIRGIL HENRY	WHERE IS THE LOVE	YOU AIN'T A SAYING NOTHNIN NEW	30.00
	test press	MELBA MOORE c/w HONEY & the BEES	THE MAGIC TOUCH	NEVER IN A MILLION YEARS	20.00

FANTASY

74	113	BLACKBYRDS	DO IT FLUID	SUMMER LOVE	6.00
74	113 DJ	BLACKBYRDS	DO IT FLUID	SUMMER LOVE	8.00
75	114	BLACKBYRDS	WALKING IN RHYTHM	THE BABY	6.00
75	114 DJ	BLACKBYRDS	WALKING IN RHYTHM	THE BABY	8.00
75	115	PLEASURE	MIDNIGHT AT THE OASIS	DUST YOURSELF OFF	5.00
75	115 DJ	PLEASURE	MIDNIGHT AT THE OASIS	DUST YOURSELF OFF	5.00
75	116	THREE PIECES	I NEED YOU GIRL	SHORT'NIN' BREAD	15.00
75	116 DJ	THREE PIECES	I NEED YOU GIRL	SHORT'NIN' BREAD	20.00
75	117	BLACKBYRDS	I NEED YOU	ALL I ASK	5.00
75	117 DJ	BLACKBYRDS	I NEED YOU	ALL I ASK	6.00
75	118	BETTY EVERETT	KEEP IT UP	GOD ONLY KNOWS	6.00
75	118 DJ	BETTY EVERETT	KEEP IT UP	GOD ONLY KNOWS	8.00
76	122	BLACKBYRDS	ROCK CREEK PARK	FLYING HIGH	5.00
76	122 DJ	BLACKBYRDS	ROCK CREEK PARK	FLYING HIGH	6.00
76	124	JOHNNY GUITAR WATSON	I DON'T WANT TO BE A LONE RANGER	YOU CAN STAY BUT THE NOISE MUSIC	5.00
76	124 DJ	JOHNNY GUITAR WATSON	I DON'T WANT TO BE A LONE RANGER	YOU CAN STAY BUT THE NOISE MUSIC	6.00
76	129	BLACKBYRDS	HAPPY MUSIC	A LOVE SO FINE	5.00
76	129 DJ	BLACKBYRDS	HAPPY MUSIC	A LOVE SO FINE	6.00
76	132	RODGER COLLINS	YOU SEXY SUGAR PLUM (BUT I LIKE IT)	I'LL BE HERE (WHEN THE MORNING	5.00
76	132 DJ	RODGER COLLINS	YOU SEXY SUGAR PLUM (BUT I LIKE IT)	I'LL BE HERE (WHEN THE MORNING	10.00
76	134	RODGER COLLINS	SHE'S LOOKING GOOD	I'M SERVING TIME	8.00
76	134 DJ	RODGER COLLINS	SHE'S LOOKING GOOD	I'M SERVING TIME	10.00
77	137	ARTHUR ADAMS	LOVE AND PEACE	REGGAE DISCO	4.00
77	137 DJ	ARTHUR ADAMS	LOVE AND PEACE	REGGAE DISCO	5.00
77	138	PLEASURE	GHETTO OF MY MIND	I'M MAD	4.00
77	138 DJ	PLEASURE	GHETTO OF MY MIND	I'M MAD	5.00
77	139	SPIDERS WEB	I DON'T KNOW WHAT'S ON YOUR MIND	REGGAE BUMP	6.00
77	139 DJ	SPIDERS WEB	I DON'T KNOW WHAT'S ON YOUR MIND	REGGAE BUMP	8.00
77	140	PAULETTE McWILLIAMS	DANCIN'	WHAT'S LEFT TO SAY	4.00
77	140 DJ	PAULETTE McWILLIAMS	DANCIN'	WHAT'S LEFT TO SAY	5.00
77	141	BLACKBYRDS	TIME IS MOVIN'	LADY	5.00
77	141 DJ	BLACKBYRDS	TIME IS MOVIN'	LADY	6.00
77	144	SYLVESTER	OVER AND OVER	TIPSONG	6.00
77	144 DJ	SYLVESTER	OVER AND OVER	TIPSONG	8.00
77	145	SIDE EFFECT	GOIN' BANANAS	same: instrumental	5.00
77	145 DJ	SIDE EFFECT	GOIN' BANANAS	same: instrumental	6.00
77	146	PLEASURE	LET ME BE THE ONE	LET'S DANCE	5.00
77	146 DJ	PLEASURE	LET ME BE THE ONE	LET'S DANCE	6.00
78	147	HOODOO RHYTHM DEVILS	GOT A LOT OF LOVE IN MY SOUL	DOCTOR OF LOVE	10.00
78	147 DJ	HOODOO RHYTHM DEVILS	GOT A LOT OF LOVE IN MY SOUL	DOCTOR OF LOVE	15.00
78	150	BLACKBYRDS	STREET GAMES	SOFT AND EASY	5.00
78	150 DJ	BLACKBYRDS	STREET GAMES	SOFT AND EASY	6.00
77	151	LEON HAYWOOD	BABY RECONSIDER	WOULD I	15.00
77	151 DJ	LEON HAYWOOD	BABY RECONSIDER	WOULD I	25.00
78	152	SYLVESTER	DOWN, DOWN, DOWN	CHANGES	4.00
78	152 DJ	SYLVESTER	DOWN, DOWN, DOWN	CHANGES	5.00
78	156	HOODOO RHYTHM DEVILS	WORKING IN A COAL MINE	SWEET CITY STREET	5.00
78	156 DJ	HOODOO RHYTHM DEVILS	WORKING IN A COAL MINE	SWEET CITY STREET	6.00
78	157	SIDE EFFECT	KEEP THAT SAME OLD FEELING	IT'S ALL IN YOUR MIND	5.00
78	157 DJ	SIDE EFFECT	KEEP THAT SAME OLD FEELING	IT'S ALL IN YOUR MIND	6.00
78	160	SYLVESTER	YOU MAKE ME FEEL (MIGHTY REAL)	WAS IT SOMETHING I SAID	4.00
78	160 DJ	SYLVESTER	YOU MAKE ME FEEL (MIGHTY REAL)	WAS IT SOMETHING I SAID	5.00
78	161	PHIL HURTT	GIVING IT BACK	WHERE THE LOVE IS	5.00
78	161 DJ	PHIL HURTT	GIVING IT BACK	WHERE THE LOVE IS	6.00
78	163	SYLVESTER	DANCE	GRATEFUL	3.00
78	163 DJ	SYLVESTER	DANCE	GRATEFUL	4.00
78	165	DAMON HARRIS	IT'S MUSIC	RIDE ON	4.00
78	165 DJ	DAMON HARRIS	IT'S MUSIC	RIDE ON	5.00

78	166	DAVID SIMMONS	WILL THEY MISS ME		IT'S A SHAME	5.00
78	166 DJ	DAVID SIMMONS	WILL THEY MISS ME		IT'S A SHAME	6.00
79	170	SIDE EFFECT	DISCO JUNCTION		I'M A WINNER	3.00
79	170 DJ	SIDE EFFECT	DISCO JUNCTION		I'M A WINNER	4.00
79	171	SYLVESTER	I WHO HAVE NOTHING		YOU MAKE ME FEEL MIGHTY REAL + I NEED SOME	3.00
79	171 DJ	SYLVESTER	I WHO HAVE NOTHING		YOU MAKE ME FEEL MIGHTY REAL + I NEED SOME	4.00
79	172	DAMON HARRIS	SILK		FUN DAY	4.00
79	172 DJ	DAMON HARRIS	SILK		FUN DAY	5.00
86	173	PHILLY CREAM	SOUL MAN		JAMMIN' AT THE DISCO	3.00
86	173 DJ	PHILLY CREAM	SOUL MAN		JAMMIN' AT THE DISCO	4.00

FEELGOOD

78	110	WILLIE CHEETHAM	GETAWAY		THE SUN IT DON'T SHINE NO MORE	6.00

FFRR

	148	ARTHUR MILES	TRIPPIN' ON YOUR LOVE		HELPING HAND	8.00

FLAME RECORDS

88	7	GWEN McCRAE	90% OF ME IS YOU		ALL THIS LOVE I'M GIVING	6.00

FLAMINGO

79	1	BOMBERS	(EVERYBODY) GET DANCIN'		MUSIC FEVER	4.00
81	11	G.C. CAMERON	LIVE FOR LOVE		IF I LOVE YOU	100.00
81	11 DJ	G.C. CAMERON	LIVE FOR LOVE		IF I LOVE YOU	200.00
81	14	PAULA DESMOND	HAVE FAITH IN YOUR LOVE		IF IT FEELS GOOD	15.00
81	14	PAULA DESMOND	IF IT FEELS GOOD		HAVE FAITH IN YOUR LOVE	6.00

FLEETVILLE

84	303	IKE TURNER	NEW BREED		NEW BREED part 2	8.00

FLOORFILLERS

98	7 DJ PS	LAVERN BAKER c/w BERNIE WILLIAMS	I'M THE ONE TO DO IT		EVER AGAIN	10.00

FONTANA

UK Fontana label was responsible for releasing both USA recording and UK homegrown soulful talent. Notable releases include 4 early Motown recordings by Eddie Holland, Miracles & The Marvelettes before distribution for the UK moved to Oriole. Another highly desirable release by Sandy Wynns should be included into any UK Tamla Motown collection as it was recorded by the Los Angeles branch of Motown and is credited to the Motown Jobette music listing. Another important soul label that Fontana had the UK releasing right to was Vee Jay: Jerry Butler, Betty Everett, Fred Hughes were amongst many interesting releases to come from the Chicago based company.

Homegrown artists also made a considerable contribution to forming the soul / mod scene in 60's England. Kiki Dee's vocal talents won her a contract in 1969 with USA Motown, for who she released several 45's and had a now highly acclaimed LP release after releasing a string of soul influence 45's, EP's and LP's for Fontana. Spencer Davis Group is probably the most famous of all UK mod bands who released numerous 45's that were welcome by all soul DJ's of the time, it wasn't from the pen of the talent youngster Stevie Winwood, but Jamaican icon Jackie Edward who provided the material. Fontana played a big part in introducing the soul sound to the UK record buying public, but it's not one of the most desirable labels. One of the reasons could be that the early promo releases were presented the same way that UK Mercury was, with a Yellow Painted rubber stamp – promotional copy not for sale – I have not listed every early release with separate prices for DJ or stock as many collectors do not consider "Rubber stamped" promo copy as the real deal. You could add 20% / 25% to the price of the promo copy again for the stock copy valuation, as long as the yellow rubber stamp promo does not deface the title or artist credits. Later from 1967 UK Fontana did release their promo copies with a white label, black lettering and a two line red A, which collectors do find very collectable, I have priced those separately.

59	173	COBY DIJON	LOCKED IN THE ARMS OF LOVE		I GO	20.00
59	193	ROY HAMILTON	I NEED YOUR LOVIN'		SOMEWHERE ALONG THE WAY	30.00
61	271	ARETHA FRANKLIN	LOVE IS THE ONLY THING		TODAY I SING THE BLUES	20.00
61	273	JAMES BROWN & FAMOUS FLAMES	THIS OLD HEART		WONDER WHEN YOU'RE COMING HOME	30.00
61	298	ROY HAMILTON	YOU CAN HAVE HER		ABIDE WITH ME	20.00
61	299	H.B. BARNUM	LOST LOVE		HALLEUJAH	10.00
61	320	ROY HAMILTON	YOU'RE GONNA NEED MAGIC		TO THE ONE I LOVE	10.00
62	339	DAVE BRUBECK QUARTET	TAKE FIVE		BLUE RONDO A LA TURK	5.00
61	343	ARETHA FRANKLIN	OPERATION HEARTBREAK		ROCK-A-BYE YOUR BABY WITH A DI	15.00
61	354	MARIE KNIGHT	COME TOMORROW		NOTHING	40.00
61	355	MARVELETTES	PLEASE MR.POSTMAN		SO LONG BABY	40.00
62	379	CARMEN McRAE & DAVE BRUBECK	TAKE FIVE		IT'S A RAGGY WALTZ	30.00
62	384	MIRACLES	WHAT'S SO GOOD ABOUT GOODBYE		I'VE BEEN GOOD TO YOU	150.00
62	386	MARVELETES	TWISTIN' POSTMAN		I WANT A GUY	75.00
62	387	EDDIE HOLLAND	JAMIE		TAKE A CHANCE ON ME	250.00
63	394	KIKI DEE	EARLY NIGHT		LUCKY HIGH HEELS	15.00
63	414	KIKI DEE	I WAS ONLY KIDDING		DON'T PUT YOUR HEART IN HIS HANDS	8.00
64	443	KIKI DEE	MIRACLES		THAT'S RIGHT, WALK ON BY	8.00
64	449	MILLIE	MY BOY LOLLIPOP		SOMETHING'S GOTTA BE DONE	2.00
64	453	ESCORTS	DIZZY MISS LIZZY		ALL I WANT IS YOU	15.00
64	455	LES REED COMBO	SPANISH ARMADA		MADRID	10.00
64	465	JACKIE EDWARDS	SEA CRUISE		LITTLE PRINCESS	15.00
64	471	SPENCER DAVIS GROUP	DIMPLES		SITTIN' AND THINKIN'	25.00
64	490	KIKI DEE	(YOU DON'T KNOW) HOW GLAD I AM		BABY I DON'T CARE	8.00
64	497	WAYNE FONTANA	UM, UM, UM, UM, UM, UM		FIRST TASTE OF LOVE	4.00
64	499	SPENCER DAVIS GROUP	I CAN'T STAND IT		MIDNIGHT TRAIN	15.00
64	507	BOOMERANGS	DON'T LET HER BE YOUR BABY		ROCKIN' ROBIN	30.00
65	517	KAROL KEYES	YOU BEAT ME TO THE PUNCH		NO-ONE CAN TAKE YOUR PLACE	15.00
65	517 PS	KAROL KEYES	YOU BEAT ME TO THE PUNCH		NO-ONE CAN TAKE YOUR PLACE	30.00
65	519	LITTLE RICHARD	BLUEBERRY HILL		CHERRY RED	10.00
65	520	BETTY EVERETT	GETTING MIGHTY CROWDED		CHAINED TO A MEMORY	20.00

65	522	DON COLE & ALLEYNE	GOTTA FIND MY BABY	SOMETHING'S GOT A HOLD OF ME	10.00
65	528	BETTY EVERETT & JERRY BUTLER	SMILE	LOVE IS STRANGE	6.00
65	530	SPENCER DAVIS GROUP	EVERY LITTLE BIT HURTS	IT HURTS ME SO	15.00
65	542	ALAN HAVEN	IMAGE	ROMANCE ON THE NORTH SEA	15.00
65	550	SANDY WYNNS	THE TOUCH OF VENUS	A LOVER'S QUARREL	250.00
65	553	JERRY BUTLER	GOOD TIMES	I'VE GROWN ACCUSTOMED TO HER F	15.00
65	561 unissued	ANGLOS	INCENSE	YOU'RE FOOLING ME	UN
65	566	DONTELLS	IN YOUR HEART (YOU KNOW I'M RIGHT)	NOTHING BUT NOTHING	75.00
65	571	SPENCER DAVIS GROUP	THIS HAMMER	STRONG LOVE	20.00
65	583	FRED HUGHES	OO WEE BABY I LOVE YOU	LOVE ME BABY	20.00
65	584	ADLIBS	LOVELY LADIES	NEIGHBOUR NEIGHBOUR	18.00
65	584 DJ	ADLIBS	LOVELY LADIES	NEIGHBOUR NEIGHBOUR	25.00
65	588	JERRY BUTLER	I CAN'T STAND TO SEE YOU CRY	NOBODY NEEDS YOUR LOVE	15.00
65	588 DJ	JERRY BUTLER	I CAN'T STAND TO SEE YOU CRY	NOBODY NEEDS YOUR LOVE	25.00
65	589	ANGLOS	INCENSE	YU'RE FOOLING ME	30.00
65	596	KIKI DEE	RUNNIN' OUT OF FOOLS	THERE HE GOES	8.00
65	600 DJ	JOHNNY CARR	DO YOU LOVE THAT GIRL	GIVE ME A LITTLE TIME	10.00
65	602	LEADERS	NIGHT PEOPLE	LOVE WILL FIND A WAY	10.00
65	610	ALEX HARVEY	AGENT OO SOUL	GO AWAY BABY	25.00
65	610 2nd press	ALEX HARVEY	AGENT OO SOUL	GO AWAY BABY	8.00
65	618	RATTLES	CANDY TO ME	COME ON AND SING	10.00
65	618 DJ	RATTLES	CANDY TO ME	COME ON AND SING	15.00
65	632	SPENCER DAVIS GROUP	KEEP ON RUNNING	HIGH TIME BABY	8.00
65	641	JIMMY CLIFF	CALL ON ME	PRIDE AND PASSION	40.00
65	642	WAYNE FONTANA	IT WAS EASIER TO HURT HER	YOU MADE ME WHAT I AM TODAY	10.00
65	646	JACKIE LEE	THE DUCK	LET YOUR CONSCIENCE BE YOUR GU	15.00
66	652	LITTLE RICHARD	I DON'T KNOW WHAT YOU GOT, BUT IT'S	same: part 2	15.00
66	666	ANDEE SILVER	ONLY YOUR LOVE CAN SAVE ME	WINDOW SHOPPING	30.00
66	667	BOBBIE GRAHAM	GROTTY DRUMS	TEENSVILLE	20.00
66	668	BLUESOLOGY	MR. FRANTIC	TIME'S GETTING' TOUGHER THAN T	400.00
66	669	KIKI DEE	WHY DON'T I RUN AWAY FROM YOU	SMALL TOWN	20.00
66	672	JENNY WREN	CHASING MY DREAM ALL OVER TOWN	THE THOUGHT OF YOU	100.00
66	678	OLYMPICS	WE GO TOGETHER (PRETTY BABY)	SECRET AGENTS	25.00
66	679	SPENCER DAVIS GROUP	SOMEBODY HELP ME	STEVIE'S BLUES	8.00
66	681	MILLIE	MY STREET	IT'S TOO LATE	10.00
66	684	WAYNE FONTANA	COME ON HOME	MY EYES BREAK OUT IN TEARS	5.00
66	693	GOLDIE	THINK ABOUT THE GOOD TIMES	I DO	25.00
66	706	ALEXIS KORNER	EVERYDAY I HAVE THE BLUES	RIVER'S INVITATION	20.00
66	716	CHANTS	COME BACK AND GET THIS LOVING	LOVE LIGHT	8.00
66	735	HAPPENINGS	HE THINKS HE'S A HERO	SEE YOU IN SEPTEMBER	6.00
66	736	FRIDAY BROWN	32nd LOVE AFFAIR	BORN A WOMAN	100.00
66	739	SPENCER DAVIS GROUP	TRAMPOLINE	WHEN I COME HOME	10.00
66	745	MANCHESTER PLAYBOYS	I FEEL SO GOOD	I CLOSE MY EYES	150.00
66	762	SPENCER DAVIS GROUP	GIMME SOME LOVING	BLUES IN F	10.00
66	764	ALEX HARVEY	WORK SONG	I CAN DO WITHOUT YOUR LOVE	20.00
66	769	ED E. LYNCH	HURT BY LOVE	LITTLE CHILD	10.00
66	770	WAYNE FONTANA	SOMETHING KEEPS CALLING ME BACK	PAMELA, PAMELA	10.00
66	772	JENNY WREN	THE MERRY GO ROUND (IS SLOWING DOWN)	TAKE A WALK BOBBY	10.00
66	778	OLYMPICS	BABY, DO THE PHILLY DOG	WESTERN MOVIES	20.00
66	779	CALIFORNIA IN CROWD	HAPPINESS IN MY HEART	QUESTIONS AND ANSWERS	40.00
67	785	SPENCER DAVIS GROUP	I'M A MAN	I CAN'T GET ENOUGH OF IT	15.00
67	792	KIKI DEE	I'M GOING OUT (THE SAME WAY I CAME IN)	WE'VE GOT EVERYTHING GOING FOR	10.00
67	792 DJ	KIKI DEE	I'M GOING OUT (THE SAME WAY I CAME IN)	WE'VE GOT EVERYTHING GOING FOR	15.00
67	795	LOWELL FULSOM	TRAMP	PICO	40.00
67	795 DJ	LOWELL FULSOM	TRAMP	PICO	50.00
67	817	ALEXIS KORNER	ROSIE	ROCK ME	20.00
67	817 DJ	ALEXIS KORNER	ROSIE	ROCK ME	25.00
67	823	JOHNNY CARR	YOU GOT ME BABY	THINGS GET BETTER	45.00
67	823 DJ	JOHNNY CARR	YOU GOT ME BABY	THINGS GET BETTER	70.00
67	833	KIKI DEE	I	STOCK AND THINK	6.00
67	833 DJ	KIKI DEE	I	STOCK AND THINK	8.00
67	835	ALAN HAVEN	IMAGE	ROMANCE ON THE NORTH SEA	15.00
67	835 DJ	ALAN HAVEN	IMAGE	ROMANCE ON THE NORTH SEA	22.00
67	846	KAROL KEYES	CAN YOU HEAR THE MUSIC	THE SWEEEST TOUCH	10.00
67	846 DJ	KAROL KEYES	CAN YOU HEAR THE MUSIC	THE SWEEEST TOUCH	15.00
67	854	SPENCER DAVIS GROUP	DON'T WANT YOU NO MORE	TIME SELLER	5.00
67	854 DJ	SPENCER DAVIS GROUP	DON'T WANT YOU NO MORE	TIME SELLER	10.00
67	870	KIKI DEE	EXCUSE ME	PATTERNS	6.00
67	870 DJ	KIKI DEE	EXCUSE ME	PATTERNS	10.00
68	879	LOVELACE WATKINS	YOU CAN'T STOP LOVE	I APOLOGISE BABY	10.00
68	879 DJ	LOVELACE WATKINS	YOU CAN'T STOP LOVE	I APOLOGISE BABY	15.00
68	885	NITE PEOPLE	SUMMERTIME BLUES	IN THE MEANTIME	10.00
68	885 DJ	NITE PEOPLE	SUMMERTIME BLUES	IN THE MEANTIME	15.00
68	915	VINCE EVERETT	EVERY NOW AND THEN	BARBARELLA	15.00
68	915 DJ	VINCE EVERETT	EVERY NOW AND THEN	BARBARELLA	20.00
68	926	KIKI DEE	CAN'T TAKE ME EYES OFF YOU	HUNGRY HEART	6.00
68	926 DJ	KIKI DEE	CAN'T TAKE ME EYES OFF YOU	HUNGRY HEART	10.00
68	927	SIGHT & SOUND	OUR LOVE (IS IN THE POCKET)	EBENEZER	30.00
68	927 DJ	SIGHT & SOUND	OUR LOVE (IS IN THE POCKET)	EBENEZER	50.00

68	951	BUDDY GUY	MARY HAD A LITTLE LAMB		SWEET LITTLE ANGEL	22.00
68	951 DJ	BUDDY GUY	MARY HAD A LITTLE LAMB		SWEET LITTLE ANGEL	30.00
68	965	PERISHERS	HOW DOES IT FEEL		BYE BYE BABY	30.00
68	965 DJ	PERISHERS	HOW DOES IT FEEL		BYE BYE BABY	45.00
68	967	ROBERTA REX	I CAN FEEL IT		JOEY	10.00
68	967 DJ	ROBERTA REX	I CAN FEEL IT		JOEY	15.00
68	970	HARLEM JOHNS RESHUFFLE	YOU ARE THE ONE I LOVE		GOOD LOVIN'	20.00
68	970 DJ	HARLEM JOHNS RESHUFFLE	YOU ARE THE ONE I LOVE		GOOD LOVIN'	30.00
68	974	JOHN O'HARA & THE PLAYBOYS	SHOW ME		I STARTED A JOKE	12.00
68	974 DJ	JOHN O'HARA & THE PLAYBOYS	SHOW ME		I STARTED A JOKE	20.00
68	983	KIKI DEE	ON A MAGIC CARPET RIDE		NOW THE FLOWERS CRY	**219.00**
68	983 DJ	KIKI DEE	ON A MAGIC CARPET RIDE		NOW THE FLOWERS CRY	UN
69	1004	HARLEM JOHNS RESHUFFLE	LET LOVE COME BETWEEN US		EVERYTHING UNDER THE SUN	15.00
69	1004 DJ	HARLEM JOHNS RESHUFFLE	LET LOVE COME BETWEEN US		EVERYTHING UNDER THE SUN	20.00
69	1031	MORRIS VAUGHN	MY LOVE KEEPS GROWING		MAKE IT LOOK GOOD	45.00
69	1031 DJ	MORRIS VAUGHN	MY LOVE KEEPS GROWING		MAKE IT LOOK GOOD	60.00
69	1051	RUBY JAMES	GETTIN' MIGHTY CROWDED		DON'T PLAY THAT SONG	25.00
69	1051 DJ	RUBY JAMES	GETTIN' MIGHTY CROWDED		DON'T PLAY THAT SONG	40.00
	17226 EP PS	COUNT BASIE & his ORCHESTRA	SOUNDS OF JAZZ		4 track EP with cover	8.00
65	17443 EP PS	KIKI DEE	KIKI DEE		4 track EP with cover	75.00
66	17443 EP PS	KIKI DEE	IN CLOVER		4 track EP with cover	75.00
62	267263	LONNIE RUSS	SOMETHING OLD SOMETHING NEW		MY WIFE CAN'T COOK	10.00
65	270146 export release	FRED HUGHES	OO WEE BABY I LOVE YOU		LOVE ME BABY	22.00
62	270109	VOLUMES	I LOVE YOU		DREAMS	75.00
62	467217 EP PS	ARETHA FRANKLIN	TODAY I SING THE BLUES		4 track EP with cover	40.00
74	6007040	BRIAN BENNETT	CHASE SIDE SHOOT - UP		PEGASUS	8.00

FOX RECORDS

84	007 DJ	WILLIE KENDRICKS c/w DEAN COURTNEY CHANGE YOUR WAYS			I'LL ALWAYS NEED YOU	10.00

Bonus third track: Carstairs – "It really hurts me girl" - three track promo EP legitimately dubious.

GAIEE

75	101	VALENTINO	I WAS BORN THIS WAY		LIBERATION	10.00

GAS

69	115	PAT KELLEY	HOW LONG WILL IT TAKE		TRY TO REMEMBER	10.00

GB RECORDS

001	EDDIE CORNELIUS	THAT'S LOVE MAKING IN YOUR EYES	HURRY UP	30.00	

GLITTER

85	86	CISSY HOUSTON	WITH YOU I COULD HAVE IT ALL		WHATCHA GONNA DO ABOUT OUR LOV	4.00

GM

74	020	PHILADELPHIA FLYERS	HOT LINE		OH GIRL (WHY YOU WANNA GET MAR	10.00
74	026	PHILADELPHIA FLYERS	RUN AND HIDE		RUN AND HIDE part 2	15.00
75	034	PHILADELPHIA FLYERS	L.O.V.E.		MOUNTAIN OF LOVE	8.00

GO

CBS distributed label, very difficult to find any 45's on this label as all release were non-hits. Carl Douglas's – "Something For Nothing" – is perhaps the best Northern Soul track on the label which also saw release in 1967 in the USA on the Okeh label release # 7287. His previous release is also highly regarded. All releases had promo copies made which were white with a big orange A, attractive and very hard to find

66	11401	CARL DOUGLAS & the BIG STAMPEDE	CRAZY FEELING		KEEP IT TO MYSELF	40.00
66	11401 DJ	CARL DOUGLAS & the BIG STAMPEDE	CRAZY FEELING		KEEP IT TO MYSELF	60.00
66	11402	SAMANTHA JUSTE	IF TREES COULD TALK		NO ONE NEEDS MY LOVE TODAY	50.00
66	11402 DJ	SAMANTHA JUSTE	IF TREES COULD TALK		NO ONE NEEDS MY LOVE TODAY	75.00
67	11408	CARL DOUGLAS & the BIG STAMPEDE	SOMETHING FOR NOTHING		LET THE BIRDS SING	75.00
67	11408 DJ	CARL DOUGLAS & the BIG STAMPEDE	SOMETHING FOR NOTHING		LET THE BIRDS SING	100.00
67	11409	SUGAR SIMONE	IT'S ALRIGHT		TAKE IT EASY	15.00
67	11409 DJ	SUGAR SIMONE	IT'S ALRIGHT		TAKE IT EASY	22.00

GOLD N BLACK

95	001 EP PS	VARIOUS ARTISTS	21st. ANNIVERSARY WOLVERAMPTON		4 track EP limited edition	25.00

Never commercially released: issued in a numbered art sleeve and a limited press of 200. Given away on the door at Wolverhampton Civic Hall 21st. Anniversary 1995. The 4 tracks are 1. Martha Star – "Love is the only solution" 2. Prophets – "I got the fever" 3. Richard Temple – "That beatin' rhythm" 4. Walter Jackson – "Where have all the flowers gone". This is the only way of owning Martha Star's highly sought after Thelma recording on a UK press.

GOLDEN EYE

	1001	SOUL BROS. INC	PYRAMID		THE MICHIGAN MOVE	30.00

GOLDMINE

	1 EP PS	JOHNSON, LOU	MAGIC POTION EP		repro of the London 4 track EP	6.00

GOLDMINE TEST PRESS

The below are white labels with handwritten credits.

03		TIMMIE & THE PERSIONETTES	GOT NO TIME		I WANT MY LOVIN' FROM YOU	20.00
04		BYERS, ANN c/w INSPIRATIONS	YOUR LOVE IS A WONDERFUL THING		TREAT MYSELF TO A NEW LOVE	20.00

GOLDSOUL

03	001 DJ	ELGINS	DON'T WAIT AROUND	same:	5.00
03	002 DJ	AMBELIQUE	TALK LIKE THAT	TALK LIKE THAT version	5.00
04	003 DJ	LOU LAWTON c/w DON FARDON	NIK NAK PADDY WACK	I'M ALIVE	6.00
04	004 DJ	SVEN ZETTERBERG c/w EXCUSES	HEARTACHES WAS ALL YOU GOT	TRICKBAG	6.00
04	005 DJ	BOB COLLINS c/w EMBERS	INVENTORY ON HEARTACHES	WATCH OUT GIRL	6.00

GOODEAR

74	103	VIOLA WILLS	RUN TO THE NEAREST EXIT	DAY IN THE LIFE OF A WOMAN	8.00
74	103 DJ	VIOLA WILLS	RUN TO THE NEAREST EXIT	DAY IN THE LIFE OF A WOMAN	10.00
74	106	MIKE PATTO	SITTING IN THE PARK	GET UP AND DIG IT	6.00
74	106 DJ	MIKE PATTO	SITTING IN THE PARK	GET UP AND DIG IT	8.00
74	1602	VIOLA WILLS	I BELIEVE IN MIRACLES	SET ME FREE	4.00
74	1602 DJ	VIOLA WILLS	I BELIEVE IN MIRACLES	SET ME FREE	5.00
75	605	CAROL GRIMES	I BETCHA DIDN'T KNOW THAT	DYNAMITE	5.00
75	605 DJ	CAROL GRIMES	I BETCHA DIDN'T KNOW THAT	DYNAMITE	6.00
75	609	VIOLA WILLS	DAY IN THE LIFE OF A WOMAN	SOME OTHER DAY	4.00
75	609 DJ	VIOLA WILLS	DAY IN THE LIFE OF A WOMAN	SOME OTHER DAY	5.00

GORDY

Numbers for this label fit exactly into the TMG numbering for MOTOWN series of UK release

83	1288	BOBBY M feat: JEAN CARN	LETS STAY TOGTHER	CHARLIE'S BACK BEAT	15.00
83	1288 DJ	BOBBY M feat: JEAN CARN	LETS STAY TOGTHER	CHARLIE'S BACK BEAT	20.00
83	1294	HIGH INERGY	HE'S A PRETENDER	DON'T LET UP ON THE GROOVE	4.00
83	1294 DJ	HIGH INERGY	HE'S A PRETENDER	DON'T LET UP ON THE GROOVE	4.00
83	1296	DeBARGE	I LIKE IT	HESITATED	4.00
83	1296 DJ	DeBARGE	I LIKE IT	HESITATED	5.00
83	1301	MARY JANE GIRLS	CANDY MAN	same: instrumental	5.00
83	1301 DJ	MARY JANE GIRLS	CANDY MAN	same: instrumental	6.00
83	1308	DeBARGE	ALL THIS LOVE	I'M IN LOVE WITH LOVE	4.00
83	1308 DJ	DeBARGE	ALL THIS LOVE	I'M IN LOVE WITH LOVE	5.00
83	1309	MARY JANE GIRLS	ALL NIGHT LONG	MUSICAL LOVE	4.00
83	1309 DJ	MARY JANE GIRLS	ALL NIGHT LONG	MUSICAL LOVE	4.00
83	1314	RICK JAMES	COLD BLOODED	same: instrumental	4.00
83	1314 DJ	RICK JAMES	COLD BLOODED	same: instrumental	5.00
83	1315	MARY JANE GIRLS	BOYS	YOU ARE MY HEAVEN	4.00
83	1315 DJ	MARY JANE GIRLS	BOYS	YOU ARE MY HEAVEN	4.00
83	1316	STONE CITY BAND	LADIES CHOICE	same: instrumental	4.00
83	1316 DJ	STONE CITY BAND	LADIES CHOICE	same: instrumental	4.00
83	1327	RICK JAMES & FRIEND	EBONY EYES	1, 2, 3 (YOU, HER AND ME)	4.00
83	1327 DJ	RICK JAMES & FRIEND	EBONY EYES	1, 2, 3 (YOU, HER AND ME)	5.00
83	1329	DeBARGE	TIME WILL REVEAL	I'LL NEVER FALL IN LOVE AGAIN	4.00
83	1329 DJ	DeBARGE	TIME WILL REVEAL	I'LL NEVER FALL IN LOVE AGAIN	5.00
84	1334	DENNIS EDWARDS	I THOUGHT I COULD HANDLE IT	DON'T LOOK ANY FURTHER	6.00
84	1334 DJ	DENNIS EDWARDS	I THOUGHT I COULD HANDLE IT	DON'T LOOK ANY FURTHER	8.00
84	1340	DENNIS EDWARDS	(YOU'RE MY) APHRODISIAC	SHAKE HANDS (COME OUT DANCING	4.00
84	1340 DJ	DENNIS EDWARDS	(YOU'RE MY) APHRODISIAC	SHAKE HANDS (COME OUT DANCING	4.00
84	1359	RICK JAMES	YOU TURN ME ON	FIRE AND DESIRE	4.00
84	1359 DJ	RICK JAMES	YOU TURN ME ON	FIRE AND DESIRE	5.00
85	1376	DeBARGE	RHYTHM OF THE NIGHT	QUEEN OF THE NIGHT	4.00
85	1376 DJ	DeBARGE	RHYTHM OF THE NIGHT	QUEEN OF THE NIGHT	5.00
85	1377	MARY JANE GIRLS	IN MY HOUSE	same: instrumental	5.00
85	1377 DJ	MARY JANE GIRLS	IN MY HOUSE	same: instrumental	6.00
85	1378	RICK JAMES	CAN'T STOP	OH WHAT A NIGHT (4 LUV)	4.00
85	1378 DJ	RICK JAMES	CAN'T STOP	OH WHAT A NIGHT (4 LUV)	5.00
85	40213 PS	DeBARGE	WHO'S HOLDING DONNA NOW	BE MY LADY	3.00
85	40223 PS	RICK JAMES	GLOW	same: instrumental	3.00
85	40271 PS	MARY JANE GIRLS	WILD AND CRAZY LOVE	same: instrumental	4.00
85	40345 PS Gordy label	EL DeBARGE with DeBARGE	YOU WEAR IT WELL	BABY WON'TCHA COME QUICK	3.00
85	40419 PS	VAL YOUNG	SEDUCTION	same: instrumental	3.00

GPL

82	317	LINDA TAYLOR	YOU AND ME JUST STARTED	same: club mix	15.00

GRAPEVINE

Launched by soul dealer John Anderson of Soul Bowl Records, Kings Lynn and distributed by RCA the series was of superb quality. The high quality mastering, design and packaging have made this the most collectable of all the seventies UK soul labels that catered for the Northern Soul scene. Every 45 in this series is desirable as collectors try and finish the label.

76	100	RICHARD POPCORN WYLIE	ROSEMARY WHAT HAPPENED	same: instrumental	8.00
76	100 DJ	RICHARD POPCORN WYLIE	ROSEMARY WHAT HAPPENED	same: instrumental	15.00
76	101	SOUL TWINS	GIVE THE MAN A CHANCE	QUICK CHANGE ARTIST	10.00
76	101 DJ	SOUL TWINS	GIVE THE MAN A CHANCE	QUICK CHANGE ARTIST	25.00
76	102	STANLEY WOODRUFF	WHAT TOOK YOU SO LONG	NOW IS FOREVER	8.00
76	102 DJ	STANLEY WOODRUFF	WHAT TOOK YOU SO LONG	NOW IS FOREVER	10.00
76	103	MILTON WRIGHT	I BELONG TO YOU	THE GALLOP	10.00
76	103 DJ	MILTON WRIGHT	I BELONG TO YOU	THE GALLOP	20.00
77	104	FLAMING EMERALDS	HAVE SOME EVERYBODY	same: Instrumental	15.00
77	104 DJ	FLAMING EMERALDS	HAVE SOME EVERYBODY	same: Instrumental	20.00
77	105	KEANYA COLLINS	LOVE BANDIT	I CALL YOU DADDY	10.00

77	105 DJ	KEANYA COLLINS	LOVE BANDIT	I CALL YOU DADDY	15.00
77	106	JUDY STREET	WHAT	YOU TURN ME ON	10.00
77	106 DJ	JUDY STREET	WHAT	YOU TURN ME ON	15.00
77	107	LOVELITES	GET HIM OFF MY CONSCIENCE	OH WHAT A DAY	8.00
77	107 DJ	LOVELITES	GET IT OFF MY CONSCIENCE	OH, WHAT A DAY	15.00
78	108	RONNIE LOVE	LET'S MAKE LOVE	NOTHING TO IT	10.00
78	108 DJ	RONNIE LOVE	LET'S MAKE LOVE	NOTHING TO IT	20.00
78	108 DJ sticker promo	RONNIE LOVE	LET'S MAKE LOVE	NOTHING TO IT	15.00
78	109	SMITH BROTHERS	THERE CAN BE A BETTER WAY	PAYBACKS A DRAG	10.00
78	109 DJ	SMITH BROTHERS	THERE CAN BE A BETTER WAY	PAYBACK'S A DRAG	20.00
78	110	HAPPY CATS	DESTROY THAT BOY	THESE BOOTS ARE MADE FOR WALKING	10.00
78	110 DJ	HAPPY CATS	DESTROY THAT BOY	THESE BOOTS ARE MADE FOR WALKING	15.00
78	111	RAY GODFREY	COME AND GET THESE MEMORIES	I'M THE OTHER HALF OF YOU	10.00
78	111 DJ	RAY GODFREY	COME AND GET THESE MEMORIES	I'M THE OTHER HALF OF YOU	15.00
78	112	DEL CAPRIS c/w EULA COOPER	HEY LITTLE WAY OUT GIRL	BEGGARS CANT BE CHOOSY	10.00
78	112 PS	DEL CAPRIS c/w EULA COOPER	HEY LITTLE WAY OUT GIRL	BEGGARS CAN'T BE CHOOSEY	12.00
78	112 DJ	DEL CAPRIS c/w EULA COOPER	HEY LITTLE WAY OUT GIRL	BEGGARS CAN'T BE CHOOSEY	20.00
79	113	CAPREEZ	HOW TO MAKE A SAD MAN GLAD	IT'S GOOD TO BE HOME AGAIN	10.00
79	113 DJ	CAPREEZ	HOW TO MAKE A SAD MAN GLAD	IT'S GOOD TO BE HOME AGAIN	15.00
79	114	ELLINGTONS c/w MILLIONAIRES	DESTINED TO BECOME A LOSER	YOU'VE GOT TO LOVE YOUR BABY	10.00
79	114 DJ	ELLINGTONS c/w MILLIONAIRES	DESTINED TO BECOME A LOSER	YOU'VE GOT TO LOVE YOUR BABY	15.00
78	115	TONY MIDDLETON	PARIS BLUES	OUT OF THIS WORLD	25.00
78	115 DJ	TONY MIDDLETON	PARIS BLUES	OUT OF THIS WORLD	40.00
78	116	WILLIAMS, SAM c/w TOWANDA BARNES	LOVE SLIPPED THROUGH MY FINGERS	YOU DON'T MEAN IT	30.00
78	116 DJ	WILLIAMS, SAM c/w TOWANDA BARNES	LOVE SLIPPED THROUGH MY FINGERS	YOU DON'T MEAN IT	40.00
79	117	JAMES BYNUM	TIME PASSES BY	LOVE YOU	8.00
79	117 DJ	JAMES BYNUM	TIME PASSES BY	LOVE YOU	10.00
79	118	JIMMY BURNS	I REALLY LOVE YOU	I LOVE YOU GIRL	20.00
79	118 DJ	JIMMY BURNS	I REALLY LOVE YOU	I LOVE YOU GIRL	30.00
79	119	EDDIE PARKER	LOVE YOU BABY	Same: instrumental	15.00
79	119 DJ	EDDIE PARKER	LOVE YOU BABY	Same: instrumental	25.00
79	119 DJ PS	EDDIE PARKER	LOVE YOU BABY	same: instrumental	30.00
79	119 PS	EDDIE PARKER	LOVE YOU BABY	Same: instrumental	20.00
79	120	LARRY CLINTON	SHE'S WANTED IN THREE STATES	IF I KNEW	40.00
79	120 DJ	LARRY CLINTON	SHE'S WANTED IN THREE STATES	IF I KNEW	50.00
79	121	CODY MICHAELS	7 DAYS - 52 WEEKS	DON'T LOOK BACK	10.00
79	121 DJ	CODY MICHAELS	7 DAYS - 52 WEEKS	DON'T LOOK BACK	15.00
79	122	TAMANGOES	I REALLY LOVE YOU	YOU'VE BEEN GONE SO LONG	20.00
79	122 DJ	TAMANGOES	I REALLY LOVE YOU	YOU'VE BEEN GONE SO LONG	15.00
79	123	FLAME N KING & the BOLD ONES	HO HAPPY DAY	AIN'T NOBODY JIVE IN	50.00
79	123 DJ	FLAME N KING & the BOLD ONES	HO HAPPY DAY	AIN'T NOBODY JIVE IN	75.00
79	124	BOBBY WELLS	BE'S THAT WAY SOMETIMES	RECIPE FOR LOVE	20.00
79	124 DJ	BOBBY WELLS	BE'S THAT WAY SOMETIMES	RECIPE FOR LOVE	30.00
79	125	BETTY BOO	SAY IT ISN'T SO	same: instrumental	20.00
79	125 DJ	BETTY BOO	SAY IT ISN'T SO	same: instrumental	30.00
79	126	THRILLS	WHAT CAN GO WRONG	SHOW THE WORLD WHERE IT'S AT	10.00
79	126 DJ	THRILLS	SHOW THE WORLD WHERE IT'S AT	WHAT CAN GO WRONG	15.00
79	127	DE-LITES	LOVER	TELL ME WHY	20.00
79	127 DJ	DE-LITES	LOVER	TELL ME WHY	30.00
79	128	MORRIS CHESTNUT	TOO DARN SOULFUL	YOU DON'T LOVE ME ANYMORE	30.00
79	128 DJ	MORRIS CHESTNUT	TOO DARN SOULFUL	YOU DON'T LOVE ME ANYMORE	25.00
79	129	PRECISIONS	SUCH MISERY	A LOVER'S PLEA	15.00
79	129 DJ	PRECISIONS	SUCH MISERY	A LOVERS PLEA	20.00
80	130	SEVENTH WONDER	CAPTAIN OF MY SHIP	PHARAOH	10.00
80	130 DJ	SEVENTH WONDER	CAPTAIN OF MY SHIP	PHARAOH	20.00
80	131	SOUL GENERATION	HOLD ON	THE LONELY SEA	10.00
80	131 DJ	SOUL GENERATION	HOLD ON	THE LONELY SEA	20.00
80	132	SAM & KITTY	I'VE GOT SOMETHING GOOD	LOVE IS THE GREATEST	30.00
80	132 DJ	SAM & KITTY	I'VE GOT SOMETHING GOOD	LOVE IS THE GREATEST	45.00
80	133	CAROL ANDERSON	SAD GIRL	I'LL GET OFF AT THE NEXT STOP	25.00
80	133 DJ	CAROL ANDERSON	SAD GIRL	I'LL GET OFF AT THE NEXT STOP	20.00
80	134	EDWARD HAMILTON & the ARABIANS	BABY DON'T YOU WEEP	I'M GONNA LOVE YOU	25.00
80	134 DJ	EDWARD HAMILTON & the ARABIANS	BABY DON'T YOU WEEP	I'M GONNA LOVE YOU	45.00
80	135	LAURA GREENE	CAN'T HELP LOVING THAT MAN	IT'S A GOOD DAY FOR A PARADE	6.00
80	135 DJ	LAURA GREENE	CAN'T HELP LOVING THAT MAN	IT'S A GOOD DAY FOR A PARADE	10.00
80	136	AL WILLIAMS	I AM NOTHING	BRAND NEW LOVE	50.00
80	136 DJ	AL WILLIAMS	I AM NOTHING	BRAND NEW LOVE	75.00
80	137 unissued	RONNIE & ROBYN	AS LONG AS YOU LOVE ME (I'LL STAY)	SIDRA'S THEME	250.00

the only unissued number in the series, test presses may exist.

80	138	LESTER TIPTON c/w MASQUERADERS	THIS WON'T CHANGE	HOW	50.00
80	138 DJ sticker promo	LESTER TIPTON c/w MASQUERADERS	THIS WON'T CHANGE	HOW	50.00
80	139	BILLY HAMBRIC	SHE SAID GOODBYE	I FOUND TRUE LOVE	75.00
80	139 DJ	BILLY HAMBRIC	SHE SAID GOODBYE	I FOUND TRUE LOVE	20.00
80	140	BLACK NASTY	CUT YOUR MOTOR OFF	KEEP ON STEPPING	10.00
80	140 DJ sticker promo	BLACK NASTY	CUT YOUR MOTOR OFF	KEEP ON STEPPING	8.00
80	141	DENA BARNES	IF YOU EVER WALK OUT OF MY LIFE	WHO AM I	40.00
80	141 DJ sticker promo	DENA BARNES	IF YOU EVER WALK OUT OF MY LIFE	WHO AM I	30.00
80	142	AGENTS	TROUBLE	THE LOVE I HOLD	10.00
80	142 DJ	AGENTS	THE LOVE I HOLD	TROUBLE	15.00

80	143	NABAY	BELIEVE IT OR NOT	same: instrumental	60.00
80	143 DJ sticker promo	NABAY	BELIEVE IT OR NOT	same: instrumental	75.00
80	144	NEW WANDERERS	THIS MAN IN LOVE	ADAM & EVE	15.00
80	144 DJ	NEW WANDERERS	THIS MAN IN LOVE	ADAM & EVE	25.00
80	145	DUKE BROWNER	CRYING OVER YOU	same: instrumental	45.00
80	145 DJ sticker promo	DUKE BROWNER	CRYING OVER YOU	same: instrumental	50.00
80	146	KADDO STRINGS	NOTHING BUT LOVE	CRYING OVER YOU	15.00
80	146 DJ sticker promo	KADDO STRINGS	NOTHING BUT LOVE	CRYING OVER YOU	20.00
80	147	ANTHONY RAYE	GIVE ME ONE MORE CHANCE	HOLD ON TO WHAT YOU GOT	10.00
80	147 DJ sticker promo	ANTHONY RAYE	GIVE ME ONE MORE CHANCE	HOLD ON TO WHAT YOU GO	20.00
78	red 1	BRIMSTONE INGRAM	WHAT HAPPENED TO THE SONGS	SONGS WE USED TO SING	10.00
78	red 1 DJ	BRIMSTONE INGRAM	WHAT HAPPENED TO THE SONGS	SONGS WE USED TO SING	15.00
79	red 3	LEO'S SUNSHIPP	GIVE ME THE SUNSHINE	I'M BACK FOR MORE	20.00

GRAPEVINE 2000

Part of Grapevine Music Group, 17 Blenheim Road, Wakefield, WF1 3JZ
Twenty years after the demise of the Grapevine label John Anderson along with partner Gary Cape again show the other Northern Soul companies how it should be done. Already a collectable label with many titles deleted and all new releases eagerly awaited.

00	100	VICKI LABATT c/w GUITAR RAY	GOT TO KEEP HANGING ON	YOU'RE GONNA WRECK MY LIFE	10.00
00	100 DJ	VICKI LABATT c/w GUITAR RAY	GOT TO KEEP HANGING ON	YOUR GONNA WRECK MY LIFE	20.00
00	101	ELECTRIC EXPRESS	HEARSAY	same: instrumental	10.00
00	101 DJ	ELECTRIC EXPRESS	HEARSAY	same: instrumental	20.00
00	102	CHOICE OF COLOUR	YOUR LOVE	LOVE IS GONE	10.00
00	102 DJ	CHOICE OF COLOUR	YOUR LOVE	LOVE IS GONE	20.00
00	103	BOBBY WAYNE	LONG HARD ROAD	DO I LOVE YOU (INDEED I DO)	5.00
00	103 DJ	BOBBY WAYNE	LONG HARD ROAD	DO I LOVE YOU (INDEED I DO)	10.00
00	104	MAGNETICS feat: JOHNNY McKINNEY	THE LOOK ON YOUR FACE	YOU WERE MADE FOR LOVE	10.00
00	104 DJ	MAGNETICS feat: JOHNNY McKINNEY	THE LOOK ON YOUR FACE	YOU WERE MADE FOR LOVE	15.00

Label changes design from pale green to yellow and red.

01	105	TRUE IMAGE	I'M NOT OVER YOU	I'M NOT OVER YOU (EXTENDED)	10.00
01	105 DJ	TRUE IMAGE	I'M NOT OVER YOU YET	I'M NOT OVER YOU (EXTENDED)	20.00
01	106	TAVASCO	LOVE IS TRYING TO GET A HOLD OF ME	same: radio edit	10.00
01	106 DJ	TAVASCO	LOVE IS TRYING TO GET A HOLD OF ME	same: radio edit	20.00
01	106 DJ	LITTLE HANK	TRY TO UNDERSTAND	MR. BANG BANG MAN	20.00
01	107	MATT BROWN	THANK YOU BABY	SWEET THING	10.00
01	107 DJ	MATT BROWN	SWEET THING	THANK YOU BABY	20.00
01	108	LITTLE HANK	TRY TO UNDERSTAND	MR. BANG BANG MAN	10.00
01	108 DJ	LITTLE HANK	TRY TO UNDERSTAND	MR. BANG BANG MAN	20.00
01	109	GEORGE HOBSON	LET IT BE REAL	A PLACE IN YOUR HEART	10.00
01	109 DJ	GEORGE HOBSON	LET IT BE REAL	A PLACE IN YOUR HEART	20.00
01	110	ERNEST BAKER	ALONE AGAIN	DO IT WITH FEELING	10.00
01	110 DJ	ERNEST BAKER	ALONE AGAIN	DO IT WITH FEELING	20.00
01	111	FORTSON & SCOTT c/w ROBBY FORTSON	SWEET LOVER	ARE YOU FOR REAL	10.00
01	111 DJ	FORTSON & SCOTT c/w ROBBY FORTSON	SWEET LOVER	ARE YOU FOR REAL	20.00
01	112	NATHAN WILLIAMS	WHAT PRICE	REACHING HIGHER	10.00
01	112 DJ	NATHAN WILLIAMS	WHAT PRICE	REACHING HIGHER	20.00
01	113	SEX	IT'S YOU (BABY IT'S YOU)	same: extended version	10.00
01	113 DJ	SEX	ITS YOU (BABY IT'S YOU)	same: extended version	20.00
01	114	MONTCLAIRS	HEY YOU! DON'T FIGHT IT!	NEVER ENDING LOVE	10.00
01	114 DJ	MONTCLAIRS	HEY YOU! DON'T FIGHT IT!	NEVER ENDING LOVE	20.00
01	115	ARCHIE HODGE	I REALLY WANT TO SE YOU GIRL	IF I DIDN'T NEED YOU WOMAN	10.00
01	115 DJ	ARCHIE HODGE	I REALLY WANT TO SE YOU GIRL	IF I DIDN'T NEED YOU WOMAN	20.00
01	116	SERVICEMEN	ARE YOU ANGRY	I NEED A HELPING HAND	10.00
01	116 DJ	SERVICEMEN	ARE YOU ANGRY	I NEED A HELPING HAND	20.00
01	117	BILL CODAY c/w SANDRA WRIGHT	A MAN CAN'T BE A MAN (WITHOUT A	A MAN CAN'T BE A MAN (WITHOUT	10.00
01	117 DJ	BILL CODAY c/w SANDRA WRIGHT	A MAN CAN'T BE A MAN (WITHOUT A	A MAN CAN'T BE A MAN (WITHOUT	20.00
01	118	SWISS MOVEMENT	I WISH OUR LOVE WOULD LAST	ONE IN A MILLION	10.00
01	118 DJ	SWISS MOVEMENT	I WISH OUR LOVE WOULD LAST	ONE IN A MILLION	20.00
01	119	MAGNETICS	I'LL KEEP HOLDING ON	(JACKIE BABY) CAN YOU DO IT	10.00
01	119 DJ	MAGNETICS	I'LL KEEP HOLDING ON	JACKIE BABY (YOU CAN DO IT)	20.00
02	120	DON GARDNER	CHEATIN' KIND	IS THIS REALLY LOVE	10.00
02	120 DJ	DON GARDNER	CHEATIN' KIND	IS THIS REALLY LOVE	20.00
02	121	SPRINGERS	NOTHING'S TOO GOOD FOR MY BABY	I CAN'T BELIEVE	10.00
02	121 DJ	SPRINGERS	NOTHING'S TOO GOOD FOR MY BABY	I CAN'T BELIEVE	20.00
02	122	FOUR DYNAMICS	THINGS THAT A LADY AIN'T SUPPOSED	THAT'S WHAT GIRLS ARE MADE FOR	10.00
02	122 DJ	FOUR DYNAMICS	THINGS THAT A LADY AIN'T SUPPOSED	THAT'S WHAT GIRLS ARE MADE FOR	20.00
02	123	JONES BROTHERS	GOOD OLD DAYS	LUCKY LADY	10.00
02	123 DJ	JONES BROTHERS	GOOD OLD DAYS	LUCKY LADY	20.00
02	124	MELVIN BROWN & JAMES MATTHEWS	LOVE STORMY WEATHER	SOUL MAN	10.00
02	124 DJ	MELVIN BROWN & JAMES MATTHEWS	LOVE STORMY WEATHER	SOUL MAN	20.00
02	125	CARBON COPIES	JUST DON'T LOVE YOU	BABY I'M COMING HOME	10.00
02	125 DJ	CARBON COPIES	JUST DON'T LOVE YOU	BABY I'M COMING HOME	20.00
02	126	EDDIE BILLUPS	ASK MY HEART	A SOLDIER'S PRAYER	10.00
02	126 DJ	EDDIE BILLUPS	ASK MY HEART	A SOLDIER'S PRAYER	20.00
02	127	C.P. LOVE	TRICK BAG	PLENTY OF ROOM FOR MORE	10.00
02	127 DJ	C.P. LOVE	TRICK BAG	PLENTY OF ROOM FOR MORE	20.00
02	128	WILLIE TEE	I'M HAVING SO MUCH FUN	FIRST TASTE OF HURT	10.00
02	128 DJ	WILLIE TEE	I'M HAVING SO MUCH FUN	FIRST TASTE OF HURT	20.00

02	129	L.V. JOHNSON	TRYING TO HOLD ON	I LOVE YOU, I WANT YOU, I NEED	10.00
02	129 DJ	L.V. JOHNSON	TRYING TO HOLD ON	I LOVE YOU, I WANT YOU, I NEED	20.00
02	130	MAGNETICS	WHEN I'M WITH MY BABY	COUNT THE DAYS	10.00
02	130 DJ	MAGNETICS	WHEN I'M WITH MY BABY	COUNT THE DAYS	20.00
03	131	RON HENDERSON & CHOICE OF COLOUR	GEMINI LADY	GOODBYE MY LOVE	10.00
03	131 DJ	RON HENDERSON & CHOICE OF COLOUR	GEMINI LADY	GOODBYE MY LOVE	20.00
03	133	MATT BROWN	EVERYDAY (I LOVE YOU JUST A LITTLE	BABY I'M A WANT YOU	10.00
03	133 DJ	MATT BROWN	EVERYDAY (I LOVE YOU JUST A LITTLE	BABY I'M A WANT YOU	20.00
03	134	CHESTERFIELDS	THINK IT OVER	WHY DID YOU LEAVE ME BABY	10.00
03	134 DJ	CHESTERFIELDS	THINK IT OVER	WHY DID YOU LEAVE ME BABY	20.00
03	135	CYNTHIA SHEELER c/w NORMA JEAN	I'LL CRY OVER YOU	I'VE TAKEN OVER	10.00
03	135 DJ	CYNTHIA SHEELER c/w NORMA JEAN	I'LL CRY OVER YOU	I'VE TAKEN OVER	20.00
03	136	SERVICEMEN	I'LL STOP LOVING YOU	SWEET MAGIC	10.00
03	136 DJ	SERVICEMEN	I'LL STOP LOVING YOU	SWEET MAGIC	20.00
03	137	TOMMY TATE	DO YOU THINK THERE'S A CHANCE	IF YOU GOT TO LOVE SOMEBODY	10.00
03	137 DJ	TOMMY TATE	IF YOU GOTTA LOVE SOMEBODY	DO YOU THINK THERE'S A CHANCE	20.00
03	138	EDDIE HOLMAN	HOLD ME IN YOUR ARMS	DIGGIN' IT	10.00
03	138 DJ	EDDIE HOLMAN	HOLD ME IN YOUR ARMS	DIGGIN' IT	20.00
03	139	BOBBY RICH	THERE'S A GIRL SOMEWHERE FOR ME	I CAN'T HELP MYSELF	10.00
03	139 DJ	BOBBY RICH	THERE'S A GIRL SOMEWHERE (FOR ME)	I CAN'T HELP MYSELF	20.00
03	140	SYL JOHNSON	DO YOU KNOW WHAT LOVE IS	ALL I NEED IS SOMEONE LIKE YOU	10.00
03	140 DJ	SYL JOHNSON	DO YOU KNOW WHAT LOVE IS	ALL I NEED IS SOMEONE LIKE YOU	20.00
03	141	CAROL ANDERSON	SAD GIRL	TAKING MY MIND OFF LOVE	10.00
03	141 DJ	CAROL ANDERSON	SAD GIRL	TAKING MY MIND OFF LOVE	20.00
03	142	WILLIE TEE	TEASING YOU AGAIN	TEASING YOU	10.00
03	142 DJ	WILLIE TEE	TEASING YOU AGAIN	TEASING YOU	20.00
03	143	GERRI HALL c/w JADES	WHAT CAN I RUN TO	LUCKY FELLOW	10.00
03	143 DJ	GERRI HALL c/w JADES	WHAT CAN I RUN TO	LUCKY FELLOW	20.00
03	144	COREY BLAKE	HOW CAN I GO ON WITHOUT YOU	YOUR LOVE LIKE A BOOMERANG	10.00
03	144 DJ	COREY BLAKE	HOW CAN I GO ON WITHOUT YOU	YOUR LOVE IS LIKE A BOOMERANG	20.00
04	145	BOBBY JAMES c/w LOVELITES	I REALLY LOVE YOU	I'M NOT LIKE THE OTHERS	10.00
04	145 DJ	BOBBY JAMES c/w LOVELITES	I REALLY LOVE YOU	I'M NOT LIKE THE OTHERS	20.00
04	146	VINES	AFTER THE RAIN	SO IT BE	10.00
04	146 DJ	VINES	AFTER THE RAIN	SO BE IT	20.00
04	147	JOHNNY MOORE	YESTERDAY, TODAY AND TOMORROW	COME FLY WITH ME	10.00
04	147 DJ	JOHNNY MOORE	YESTERDAY TODAY AND TOMORROW	COME FLY WITH ME	20.00
04	148	THE SAINTS c/w CAL BRANDON	I'LL LET YOU SLIDE	I KEPT ON SMILIN'	10.00
04	148 DJ	THE SAINTS c/w CAL BRANDON	I'LL LET YOU SLIDE	I KEEP ON SMILIN	20.00
04	149	HERMAN HITSON	YOU CAN'T KEEP A GOOD MAN DOWN	AIN'T NO OTHER WAY	10.00
04	149 DJ	HERMAN HITSON	YOU CAN'T KEEP A GOOD MAN DOWN	AIN'T NO OTHER WAY	20.00
04	150	EDDIE HOLMAN	SHE'S WANTED (IN THE THREE STATES)	SUNSET ON RIDGE	10.00
04	150 DJ	EDDIE HOLMAN	SHE'S WANTED (IN THE THREE STATES)	SUNSET ON RIDGE	20.00
	151	JERRY WILLIAMS	WHEN YOU MOVE YOU LOSE	THAT'S THE GROOVE	10.00
05	151 DJ	JERRY WILLIAMS	WHEN YOU MOVE YOU LOSE	THAT'S THE GROOVE	20.00
05	152	DOTTIE PEARSON	A HOUSE MADE OF LOVE	BRING IT OVER BABY	10.00
05	152 DJ	DOTTIE PEARSON	A HOUSE MADE OF LOVE	BRING IT OVER BABY	20.00
05	153	CHUCK BROOKS c/w ANNETTE ROBBINS	LAST MINUTE PLANS	I CAN STAND LITTLE BIT MORE	10.00
05	153 DJ	CHUCK BROOKS c/w ANNETTE ROBBINS	LAST MINUTE PLANS	I CAN STAND LITTLE BIT MORE	20.00
05	154	PRECIOUS THREE c/w WENDELL WATTS	I NEED A MAN	YOU GIRL	10.00
05	154 DJ	PRECIOUS THREE c/w WENDELL WATTS	I NEED A MAN	YOU GIRL	20.00
02	acetate	SERVICEMEN	I'LL STOP LOVING YOU	same:	30.00
02	acetate 2	LOUIS KING	IT'S YOUR TIME TO CRY	blank:	40.00

GREENLIGHT

Another late 60s "bootleg" label catering for the R&B / Soul explosion amongst the UK teenagers. All six titles were late 60's all nighter plays that had been deleted by their original UK releasing company. Only small quantities pressed and all the discs are now very hard to find. Maybe from the same source as the Soul Sounds releases.

68	2000	BAND OF ANGELS c/w SOUL SISTERS INVITATION		GOOD TIME TONIGHT	15.00
68	2001	LITTLE ANTHONY c/w HOMER BANKS GONNA FIX YOU GOOD		HOOKED BY LOVE	4.00
68	2002	ROSCO ROBINSON c/w PLATTERS THAT'S ENOUGH		SWEET SWEET LOVIN	15.00

GROOVESVILLE

99	1	J.J. BARNES	SWEET SHERRY	OUR LOVE (IS IN THE POCKET)	10.00
99	1 DJ	HERMAN LEWIS	WHO'S KISSING YOU TONIGHT	blank:	15.00
99	2	STEVE MANCHA	HE STOLE A LOVE THAT WAS MINE	COME ON BABY	10.00

GROOVEY GROOVES

84	001	YVONNE VERNEE	JUST LIKE YOU DID ME	same:	10.00

GSF

73	1	EDDIE HOLMAN	MY MIND KEEPS TELLING ME	STRANDED IN A DREAM	8.00
73	1 DJ	EDDIE HOLMAN	MY MIND KEEPS TELLING ME	STRANDED IN A DREAM	10.00
73	2	HANS STAYMER BAND	DIG A HOLE	STAYMERS SHUFFLE	6.00
73	2 DJ	HANS STAYMER BAND	DIG A HOLE	STAYMERS SHUFFLE	8.00
73	3	JOE QUARTERMAN	(I GOT) SO MUCH TROUBLE IN MY MIND	(I GOT) SO MUCH TROUBLE IN MY	15.00
73	3 DJ	JOE QUARTERMAN	(I GOT) SO MUCH TROUBLE IN MY MIND	(I GOT) SO MUCH TROUBLE IN MY	20.00
73	5	LLOYD PRICE	JUST FOR BABY	LOVE MUSIC	10.00
73	5 DJ	LLOYD PRICE	JUST FOR BABY	LOVE MUSIC	15.00
73	7	SKULL SNAPS	MY HANG UP IS YOU	IT'S A NEW DAY	50.00

73	7 DJ	SKULL SNAPS	MY HANG UP IS YOU	IT'S A NEW DAY	75.00
73	9	WHATNAUTS	INSTIGATING (TROUBLE MAKING FOOL)	I CAN'T STAND TO SEE YOU CRY	20.00
73	9 DJ	WHATNAUTS	INSTIGATING (TROUBLE MAKING FOOL)	I CAN'T STAND TO SEE YOU CRY	25.00
73	11	LLOYD PRICE	THEY GET DOWN	TRYING TO SLIP AWAY	8.00
73	11 DJ	LLOYD PRICE	THEY GET DOWN	TRYING TO SLIP AWAY	10.00
74	12	JOE QUARTERMAN	THANKS DAD	THANKS DAD PART 2	10.00
74	12 DJ	JOE QUARTERMAN	THANKS DAD	THANKS DAD PART 2	15.00

GTO

75	17	DONNA SUMMER	LOVE TO LOVE YOU BABY	NEED A MAN BLUES	4.00
75	36	BILLY OCEAN	WHOSE LITTLE GIRL ARE YOU	CREAM ON THE TOP	4.00
76	52	BILLY OCEAN	LOVE REALLY HURTS WITHOUT YOU	YOU'RE RUNNING OUTA FOOLS	6.00
76	59	HEATWAVE	AIN'T NO HALF STEPPING	SPECIAL OFFER	3.00
76	60	DONNA SUMMER	COULD THIS BE MAGIC	WHISPERING WAVES	3.00
76	62	BILLY OCEAN	L.O.D. (LOVE ON DELIVERY)	MR BUSINESS MAN	4.00
76	65	EDWIN STARR	ACCIDENT	EAVESDROPPER	4.00
76	68	HEATWAVE	SUPER SOUL SISTER	TURN OUT THE LAMP LIGHT	3.00
76	72	BILLY OCEAN	LET'S PUT YOUR EMOTIONS IN MOTION	STOP ME IF YOU'VE HEARD IT BEFORE	3.00
76	76	DONNA SUMMER	WINTER MELODY	WASTED	3.00
77	77	HEATWAVE	BOOGIE NIGHTS	ALL YOU DO IS DAIL	4.00
77	85	BILLY OCEAN	RED LIGHT (SPELLS DANGER)	SWEET MEMORIES	3.00
77	91	HEATWAVE	TOO HOT TO HANDLE	SLIP YOUR DISC TO THIS	3.00
77	100	DONNA SUMMER	I FEEL LOVE	CAN'T WE JUST SIT DOWN	4.00
77	107	DONNA SUMMER	I REMEMBER YESTERDAY	SPRING AFFAIR	3.00
77	117	DONNA SUMMER	LOVE'S UNKNIND	AUTUMN CHANGES	3.00
78	115	HEATWAVE	GROOVE LINE	HAPPINESS TOGETHERNESS	4.00
78	236	HEATWAVE	MIND BLOWING DECISIONS	ALWAYS AND FOREVER	4.00
79	224	BILLY OCEAN	AMERICAN ARTS	MY LOVE	3.00
79	226	HEATWAVE	MIND BLOWING DECISIONS	BEAT YOUR BODY	3.00
79	258	HEATWAVE	THERM WARFARE	DISCO	3.00
79	259	BILLY OCEAN	ARE YOU READY	MAYBE TONIGHT	4.00
79	259 PS	BILLY OCEAN	ARE YOU READY	MAYBE TONIGHT	5.00
80	266	ANNIS	DON'T PLAY YOUR GAMES	AFTER ME	20.00
80	274 PS	MARI WILSON	LOVE MAN	IF THAT'S WHAT YOU WANT	8.00
81	285	HEATWAVE	GANGSTERS IN THE GROOVE	SOMEONE LIKE YOU	4.00
81	290	HEATWAVE	GOIN' CRAZY	JITTERBUGGIN'	3.00
81	294	HEATWAVE	WHERE DID I GO WRONG	POSIN' TIL CLOSIN'	3.00

GULL

75	21	PHILADELPHIA SOCIETY	100 SOUTH OF BROADWAY	100 SOUTH OF BROADWAY part 2	6.00
75	21 DJ	PHILADELPHIA SOCIETY	100 SOUTH OF BROADWAY	100 SOUTH OF BROADWAY part 2	8.00
75	32	S.S.O.	TONIGHT'S THE NIGHT	FUNKY PEOPLE	4.00
75	32 DJ	S.S.O.	TONIGHT'S THE NIGHT	FUNKY PEOPLE	5.00
75	40	RON WALTON	SOUL DISCO	ALWAYS BE THE ONE	6.00
75	40 DJ	RON WALTON	SOUL DISCO	ALWAYS BE THE ONE	8.00
76	43	CHAIN REACTION	NEVER LOSE, NEVER WIN	THIS ETERNAL FLAME	20.00
76	43 DJ	CHAIN REACTION	NEVER LOSE, NEVER WIN	THIS ETERNAL FLAME	25.00
76	47	S.S.O.	CAN'T SAY NO	TONIGHT'S THE NIGHT	6.00
76	47 DJ	S.S.O.	CAN'T SAY NO	TONIGHT'S THE NIGHT	8.00
76	53	CHAIN REACTION	WHY CAN'T WE BE LOVERS	HOGTIED	40.00
76	53 DJ	CHAIN REACTION	WHY CAN'T WE BE LOVERS	HOGTIED	50.00
76	60	CHAIN REACTION	NEVER LOSE, NEVER WIN	CHASE A MIRACLE	15.00
76	60 DJ	CHAIN REACTION	NEVER LOSE, NEVER WIN	CHASE A MIRACLE	20.00
78	63	CLEVELAND EATON	BAMA BOOGIE WOOGIE	FUNKY CELLO	4.00
78	63 DJ	CLEVELAND EATON	BAMA BOOGIE WOOGIE	FUNKY CELLO	5.00

HALAGALA

67	26	RAM-RAM-GO-GO-SOUND	PEP-77	U.S.A. OUT-CRY	100.00

H&L

H&L stands for Hugo Peretti and Luigi Creatore, a prolific duo who teamed up in the 50's to produce music. They had a measure of success on the Mercury label in the mid-fifties, their main association with "black music" was to produce Georgia Gibbs mostly covering Lavern Baker's hits. It was at RCA that the H&L team really got noticed by "soul" collectors as their logo Hugo & Luigi prominently stood out on the label. One of the first producers to insist that all their work carried their unique logo on the label of any vinyl release. At RCA they produced such soul giants as Sam Cooke, Isley Brothers, Della Reese etc. They went some way to being responsible for turning Sam Cooke away from Gospel to a more 'middle of the road' style that so neatly fitted in with Cooke's vocal style. You will also notice the "Hugo and Luigi" logo on their considerable work on Roulette, where they underlined their diversity by turning folk-pop singer Jimmie Rodgers into a chart topper. In the early seventies they emerged again to the fore of the soul market when they produced a string of hits for sweet soul harmony band The Stylistics, for Avco/Embassy. Such was the duo's standing within the music industry Avco gave them their very own label H&L in 1975. Throughout their highly successful career they were recognised for their slick orchestral driven production. If there is a "Hugo & Luigi" logo on a label you can be sure, it will be a production with a full-on orchestral accompaniment.

76	STL 1 EP	STYLISTICS	YOU'LL NEVER GET TO HEAVEN + A MIRACLE	YOU ARE BEAUTIFUL + COUNTRY LIVING	4.00
77	6105050	STYLISTICS	CAN'T HELP FALLING IN LOVE	MAYBE IT'S BECAUSE YOUR LONELY	4.00
77	6105065	VAN McCOY	SOUL CHA CHA	AFRICAN SYMPHONY	4.00
77	6105076	VAN McCOY	THE SHUFFLE	THAT'S THE JOINT	4.00
77	6105078	SOFTONES	(WHERE DO I BEGIN) LOVE STORY	LAUNDROMAT	4.00
77	6105083	VAN McCOY	SPANISH BOOGIE	LOVE CHILD	4.00
78	6105088	STYLISTICS	WONDER WOMAN	LUCKY ME	4.00
79	6105089	BRENDA & HERB	SWEET DREAMER	TONIGHT I'M GONNA MAKE YOU A STAR	8.00
79	6105091	SANDY MERCER	NOW THAT YOU'RE IN	WORK YOUR BODY	15.00

HANDSHAKE

80	1	REVELATION	FEEL IT	WHEN I FALL IN LOVE	10.00
80	1 DJ	REVELATION	FEEL IT	WHEN I FALL IN LOVE	15.00

HARTHON

00	1 DJ	CINDY SCOTT	WORLD OF HAPPINESS	BIRD WALKIN'	30.00

HARVEST

70	5018	IKE & TINA TURNER	BOLD SOUL SISTER	THE HUNTER	15.00
70	5018 DJ	IKE & TINA TURNER	BOLD SOUL SISTER	THE HUNTER	20.00

HAYLEY

Coventry based independent, totally dedicated to releasing previously unissued soul recordings from the vaults, all directed at the Northern Soul market and pressed in very small quantities of 150 copies or less making this label a sure bet for collectability in the future. Owner Rob Moss also plans more release in the future.

99	001 white label promo	CHARLES BRIMMER	SHOW AND TELL	blank:	30.00
99	002 white label promo	LYNN VARNADO	AIN'T THAT SOMETHING	blank:	30.00
00	003	JUST BROTHERS	HONEY	CARLENA	10.00
00	004	LORRETTA KENDRICK	MY FEELINGS KEEP GETTING IN THE	NEITHER ONE OF US	10.00
01	005	THUNDERBIRD SOUND	IN HEAVEN AND EARTH	OUR FINEST HOUR	10.00
01	006	J.J BARNES.	LOVE AT FIRST SIGHT	I THINK I GOT A GOOD CHANCE	10.00
04	007	MANCHA, STEVE c/w JIMMY RUFFIN	ONE IN A MILLION	THE ENTERTAINER	10.00
05	008	DATHAN JONES	CONTRACT ON LOVE	MYSTERIOUS DESIRE	10.00
05	008 DJ	DATHAN JONES	CONTRACT ON LOVE	MYSTERIOUS DESIRE	15.00

HDH

HDH stands for Holland – Dozier – Holland. This UK reissue label released a total of 13 45's from 1983 to 1985

83	451	FREDA PAYNE	BAND OF GOLD	YOU BROUGHT THE JOY	4.00
84	452	CHAIRMEN OF THE BOARD	YOU'VE GOT ME DANGLING ON A STRING	TRICKED AND TRAPPED	5.00
84	453	LAURA LEE	RIP OFF	TWO LONELY PILLOWS	4.00
84	454	HONEY CONE	WANT ADS	GIRL'S IT AIN'T EASY	4.00
84	456	8TH. DAY	I CAN'T FOOL MYSELF	TOO MANY COOKS	6.00
84	457	PARLIAMENT	I CALL MY BABY PUSSYCAT	LITTLE OLE COUNTRY BOY	4.00
84	458	GLASS HOUSE	CRUMBS OFF THE TABLE	BAD BILL OF GOODS	4.00
84	459	BRIAN HOLLAND	I'M SO GLAD	DON'T LEAVE ME	5.00
84	4510	GENERAL JOHNSON	ONLY TIME WILL TELL	same: instrumental	4.00
84	4511	CHAIRMEN OF THE BOARD	GIVE ME JUST A LITTLE MORE TIME	WORKING ON A BUILDING OF LOVE	4.00
85	4512	FLAMING EMBER	WESTBOUND NO. 9	MIND BODY AND SOUL	4.00
85	4513	HOLLAND - DOZIER	WHY CAN'T WE BE LOVERS	DON'T LEAVE ME	5.00

HI

85	7001	AL GREEN	LET'S STAY TOGETHER	I'M STILL IN LOVE WITH YOU	4.00
85	7002	ANN PEEBLES	I CAN'T STAND THE RAIN	A LOVE VIBRATION	4.00
85	7003	AL GREEN	NEVER MET A GIRL LIKE YOU	HIGHER PLANE	4.00

HICKORY

In 1964 PYE gave this Nashville Tennessee label it's own named label in the UK. They did confuse for record collectors in later years because they used exactly the same catalogue numbers as the USA releases.

64	1240	SUE THOMPSON	I'D LIKE TO KNOW YOU BETTER	BIG DADDY	8.00
64	1240 DJ	SUE THOMPSON	I'D LIKE TO KNOW YOU BETTER	BIG DADDY	10.00
64	1255	SUE THOMPSON	BAD BOY	TOYS	10.00
64	1255 DJ	SUE THOMPSON	BAD BOY	TOYS	15.00
64	1269 blue & black	NEWBEATS	BREAD AND BUTTER	TOUGH LITTLE BUGGY	10.00
64	1269 pink	NEWBEATS	BREAD AND BUTTER	TOUGH LITTLE BUGGY	8.00
64	1269 DJ	NEWBEATS	BREAD AND BUTTER	TOUGH LITTLE BUGGY	25.00
64	1272	LARRY HENLEY	STICKIN' UP FOR MY BABY	MY REASON FOR LIVING	40.00
64	1272 DJ	LARRY HENLEY	STICKIN' UP FOR MY BABY	MY REASON FOR LIVING	50.00
64	1282	NEWBEATS	EVERYTHING'S ALRIGHT	PINK DALLY RUE	8.00
64	1282 DJ	NEWBEATS	EVERYTHING'S ALRIGHT	PINK DALLY RUE	15.00
65	1284	SUE THOMPSON	PAPER TIGER	MAMA DON'T CRY AT MY WEDDING	15.00
65	1284 DJ	SUE THOMPSON	PAPER TIGER	MAMA DON'T CRY AT MY WEDDING	25.00
65	1290	NEWBEATS	BREAK AWAY (FROM THAT BOY)	HEY-O-DADDY-O	10.00
65	1290 DJ	NEWBEATS	BREAK AWAY (FROM THAT BOY)	HEY-O-DADDY-O	15.00
65	1305	NEWBEATS	THE BIRDS ARE FOR THE BEES	BETTER WATCH YOR STEP	8.00
65	1305 DJ	NEWBEATS	THE BIRDS ARE FOR THE BEES	BETTER WATCH YOR STEP	15.00
65	1320	NEWBEATS	I CAN'T HEAR YOU NO MORE	LITTLE CHILD	15.00
65	1320 DJ	NEWBEATS	I CAN'T HEAR YOU NO MORE	LITTLE CHILD	22.00
65	1323	BARBARA MILLS	QUEEN OF FOOLS	MAKE IT LAST (TAKE YOUR TIME)	450.00
65	1323 DJ	BARBARA MILLS	QUEEN OF FOOLS	MAKE IT LAST (TAKE YOUR TIME)	600.00
65	1328	SUE THOMPSON	IT'S BREAK-UP TIME	AFRAID	15.00
65	1328 DJ	SUE THOMPSON	IT'S BREAK-UP TIME	AFRAID	22.00
65	1332	NEWBEATS	RUN, BABY RUN (BACK INTO MY ARMS)	MEAN WOOLLY WILLIE	30.00
65	1332 DJ	NEWBEATS	RUN, BABY RUN (BACK INTO MY ARMS)	MEAN WOOLLY WILLIE	50.00
65	1340	SUE THOMPSON	SWEET HUNK OF MISERY	JUST KISS ME	22.00
65	1340 DJ	SUE THOMPSON	SWEET HUNK OF MISERY	JUST KISS ME	30.00
65	1359	SUE THOMPSON	WALKIN' MY BABY	I'M LOOKING FOR A WORLD	8.00
65	1359 DJ	SUE THOMPSON	WALKIN' MY BABY	I'M LOOKING FOR A WORLD	10.00
66	1366	NEWBEATS	TOO SWEET TO BE FORGOTTEN	SHAKE HANDS (AND COME OUT CRYI	20.00
66	1366 DJ	NEWBEATS	TOO SWEET TO BE FORGOTTEN	SHAKE HANDS (AND COME OUT CRYI	30.00

65	1381	SUE THOMPSON	WHAT SHOULD I DO	AFTER THE HEARTACHE	6.00
65	1381 DJ	SUE THOMPSON	WHAT SHOULD I DO	AFTER THE HEARTACHE	10.00
65	1387	NEWBEATS	CRYING MY HEART OUT	SHORTON LOVE	40.00
65	1387 DJ	NEWBEATS	CRYING MY HEART OUT	SHORT ON LOVE	60.00
65	1392	BARBARA MILLS	TRY	LET'S MAKE A MEMORY	30.00
65	1392	BARBARA MILLS	TRY	LET'S MAKE A MEMORY	40.00
66	1395	B.J. THOMAS and the TRIUMPHS	NEVER TELL	BILLY & SUE	20.00
66	1395 DJ	B.J. THOMAS and the TRIUMPHS	NEVER TELL	BILLY & SUE	30.00
69	1422	NEWBEATS	PATENT ON LOVE	MY YESTERDAY LOVE	8.00
69	1422 DJ	NEWBEATS	PATENT ON LOVE	MY YESTERDAY LOVE	15.00
65	1503 EP PS	NEWBEATS	NEWBEATS	1965 4 track EP with cover	30.00
65	1506 EP PS	NEWBEATS	AIN'T THAT LOVIN' YOU BABY	1965 4 track EP with cover	30.00
64	1507 EP PS	SUE THOMPSON c/w KRIS JENSEN	INTRODUCING	1964 4 track EP with cover	20.00
66	1510 EP PS	NEWBEATS	OH! GIRLS GIRLS	1966 4 track EP with cover	30.00
65	8428	NEWBEATS	BREAD AND BUTTER	1965 UK press	40.00

HIGHBALLS

81	3	BUBBA LOU & THE HIGHBALLS	OVER YOU	LOVE ALL OVER THE PLACE	30.00

HIPPODROME

85	101 PS	EDWIN STARR	IT AIN'T FAIR	RED HOT	5.00
85	103 PS	DUSTY SPRINGFIELD	I WANNA CONTROL YOU	SOMETIMES LIKE BUTTERFLIES	5.00
85	105 PS	EDWIN STARR	MISSILES	MISSILES part 2	5.00
86	107	EDWIN STARR	GRAPEVINE	I NEED YOUR LOVE	5.00
86	108	EDWIN STARR	SOUL SINGER	EYE TO EYE CONTACT	5.00

HIS MASTERS VOICE

HMV is one of the world's most famous record labels. What record collector is not familiar with the little mixed breed bull and fox terrier listening at the phonograph. Nipper was born in Bristol in 1884, in 1887 Nipper's owner Mark Barraud died, leaving his brother Francis Barraud to look after the three year old inquisitive dog. Francis was an artist working in Liverpool, in Francis's home Nipper spent much of his time beside the cylindrical phonograph recording and playing machine with his ear to the speaker horn, as if waiting to hear "His Masters Voice".

Nipper died aged 11 years old, 3 years after his death Francis Barraud started painting Nipper sitting next to the phonograph. Barraud tried in vain to sell his painting to the Edison Bell Company who considered his painting ridiculous. Soon after Barraud was successful when he sold his painting to the English Gramophone Company who requested that the phonograph in the original painting was changed into a record playing machine. The changes were made Barraud, was paid £100 and one of the world's most cherished and best-loved trademark logo makes its debut in January 1900. Barraud was smart enough to copyright his painting "Dog looking and listening to a Phonograph" and in 1901 Victor Talking Machine Company bought the logo, distributing it worldwide, covering needle tins, record labels, jugs, letterheads and all manner of merchandise. A healthy worldwide collectors market for all things HMV has now developed. The HMV logo with it's changed phonograph to incorporate a more attractive brass horn was then bought by the inventor of the "flat" record Emil Berliner who promptly registered it as a trademark in the USA.

In the UK His Master Voice 45's were distributed by EMI up until 1967 during the period of interest to soul 45 collectors -1959 to 1967. EMI had access to the catalogues of ABC Paramount, Scepter plus a host of independent USA subsidiaries like Sam Cooke's Keen label. Also UK talent was released through the His Masters Voice label, with young talents like Kenny Lynch, Judi Johnson, Elkie Brooks all releasing highly desirable Brit Soul vinyl. But the bulk of the collectable and sought after 45's came from the USA ABC Paramount releases which included some of Americas finest soul artists of the period. The Impressions, Sapphires and the Tams to name just a few.

59	528	OLYMPICS	WESTERN MOVIES	WELL!	18.00
59	528 DJ	OLYMPICS	WESTERN MOVIES	WELL!	28.00
59	564	OLYMPICS	(I WANNA) DANCE WITH THE TEACHER	EVERYBODY NEEDS LOVE	20.00
59	564 DJ	OLYMPICS	(I WANNA) DANCE WITH THE TEACHER	EVERYBODY NEEDS LOVE	28.00
58	568	SAM COOKE	LOVE YOU MOST OF ALL	WIN YOUR LOVE FOR ME	40.00
58	568 DJ	SAM COOKE	LOVE YOU MOST OF ALL	WIN YOUR LOVE FOR ME	50.00
59	580	LLOYD PRICE	STAGGER LEE	YOU NEED LOVE	8.00
59	580 DJ	LLOYD PRICE	STAGGER LEE	YOU NEED LOVE	15.00
59	598	LLOYD PRICE	WHERE WERE YOU (ON OUR WEDDING	IS IT REALLY LOVE	8.00
59	598 DJ	LLOYD PRICE	WHERE WERE YOU (ON OUR WEDDING	IS IT REALLY LOVE	10.00
59	610	SAM COOKE	EVERYBODY LIKES TO CHA CHA CHA	THE LITTLE THINGS YOU DO	30.00
59	610 DJ	SAM COOKE	EVERYBODY LIKES TO CHA CHA CHA	THE LITTLE THINGS YOU DO	45.00
59	626	LLOYD PRICE	PERSONALITY	HAVE YOU EVER HAD THE BLUES	8.00
59	626 DJ	LLOYD PRICE	PERSONALITY	HAVE YOU EVER HAD THE BLUES	10.00
59	642	SAM COOKE	ONLY SIXTEEN	LET'S GO STEADY AGAIN	15.00
59	642 DJ	SAM COOKE	ONLY SIXTEEN	LET'S GO STEADY AGAIN	30.00
59	650	LLOYD PRICE	I'M GONNA GET MARRIED	THREE LITTLE PIGS	8.00
59	650 DJ	LLOYD PRICE	I'M GONNA GET MARRIED	THREE LITTLE PIGS	10.00
59	672	LLOYD PRICE	WON'TCHA COME HOME	COME INTO MY HEART	8.00
59	672 DJ	LLOYD PRICE	WON'TCHA COME HOME	COME INTO MY HEART	10.00
59	675	SAM COOKE	THERE, I'VE SAID IT AGAIN	ONE HOUR AHEAD OF THE POSSE	30.00
59	675 DJ	SAM COOKE	THERE, I'VE SAID IT AGAIN	ONE HOUR AHEAD OF THE POSSE	45.00
60	712	LLOYD PRICE	LADY LUCK	NEVER LET ME GO	8.00
60	712 DJ	LLOYD PRICE	LADY LUCK	NEVER LET ME GO	10.00
60	754	SAM COOKE	WONDERFUL WORLD	ALONG THE NAVAJO TRAIL	20.00
60	754 DJ	SAM COOKE	WONDERFUL WORLD	ALONG THE NAVAJO TRAIL	40.00
60	772	LLOYD PRICE	QUESTION	IF I LOOK A LITTLE BLUE	8.00
60	772 DJ	LLOYD PRICE	QUESTION	IF I LOOK A LITTLE BLUE	10.00
60	774	RAY CHARLES	STICKS AND STONES	WORRIED LIFE BLUES	8.00
60	774 DJ	RAY CHARLES	STICKS AND STONES	WORRIED LIFE BLUES	10.00
60	792	RAY CHARLES	GEORGIA ON MY MIND	CARRY ME BACK TO OLD VIRGINNY	8.00
60	792 DJ	RAY CHARLES	GEORGIA ON MY MIND	CARRY ME BACK TO OLD VIRGINNY	10.00
60	799	LLOYD PRICE	JUST CALL ME (AND I'LL UNDERSTAND)	WHO COULDA' TOLD YOU (THEY LIE	8.00
60	799 DJ	LLOYD PRICE	JUST CALL ME (AND I'LL UNDERSTAND)	WHO COULDA' TOLD YOU (THEY LIE	10.00
60	825	RAY CHARLES	RUBY	HARDHEARTED HANNAH	6.00
60	825 DJ	RAY CHARLES	RUBY	HARDHEARTED HANNAH	8.00
61	826	LLOYD PRICE ORCHESTRA	KNOW WHAT YOU'RE DOIN'	THAT'S WHY TEARS COME AND GO	8.00

61	826 DJ	LLOYD PRICE ORCHESTRA	KNOW WHAT YOU'RE DOIN'	THAT'S WHY TEARS COME AND GO	10.00
61	838	RAY CHARLES	THEM THAT GOT	I WONDER	5.00
61	838 DJ	RAY CHARLES	THEM THAT GOT	I WONDER	8.00
61	862	RAY CHARLES	ONE MINT JULEP	LET'S GO	6.00
61	862 DJ	RAY CHARLES	ONE MINT JULEP	LET'S GO	8.00
61	899	PHILIP UPCHURCH COMBO	YOU CAN'T SIT DOWN	YOU CAN'T SIT DOWN part 2	35.00
61	899 DJ	PHILIP UPCHURCH COMBO	YOU CAN'T SIT DOWN	YOU CAN'T SIT DOWN part 2	50.00
61	926	LLOYD PRICE	BOO HOO	I MADE YOU CRY	8.00
61	926 DJ	LLOYD PRICE	BOO HOO	I MADE YOU CRY	10.00
61	935	RAY CHARLES	HIT THE ROAD JACK	THE DANGER ZONE	8.00
61	935 DJ	RAY CHARLES	HIT THE ROAD JACK	THE DANGER ZONE	30.00
61	947	HANK LEVINE	IMAGE PART 1	IMAGE PART 2	20.00
61	947 DJ	HANK LEVINE	IMAGE PART 1	IMAGE PART 2	30.00
61	961	IMPRESSIONS	GYPSY WOMAN	AS LONG AS YOU LOVE ME	30.00
61	961 DJ	IMPRESSIONS	GYPSY WOMAN	AS LONG AS YOU LOVE ME	50.00
62	969	RAY CHARLES	UNCHAIN MY HEART	BUT ON THE OTHER HAND BABY	6.00
62	969 DJ	RAY CHARLES	UNCHAIN MY HEART	BUT ON THE OTHER HAND BABY	8.00
62	983	LLOYD PRICE	BE A LEADER	'NOTHER FAIRY TALE	6.00
62	983 DJ	LLOYD PRICE	BE A LEADER	'NOTHER FAIRY TALE	8.00
62	1017	RAY CHARLES	HIDE NOR HAIR	AT THE CLUB	10.00
62	1017 DJ	RAY CHARLES	HIDE NOR HAIR	AT THE CLUB	18.00
62	1019	SHIRELLES	SOLDIER BOY	LOVE IS A SWINGIN' THING	10.00
62	1019 DJ	SHIRELLES	SOLDIER BOY	LOVE IS A SWINGIN' THING	20.00
62	1025 blue	JIMMY SMITH& the BIG BAND	WALK ON THE WILD SIDE	same: part 2	8.00
62	1025 DJ	JIMMY SMITH& the BIG BAND	WALK ON THE WILD SIDE	same: part 2	12.00
62	1025 black	JIMMY SMITH& the BIG BAND	WALK ON THE WILD SIDE	same: part 2	6.00
62	1034	RAY CHARLES	I CAN'T STOP LOVING YOU	BORN TO LOSE	5.00
62	1034 DJ	RAY CHARLES	I CAN'T STOP LOVING YOU	BORN TO LOSE	10.00
62	1041	NATHANIEL MAYER	VILLAGE OF LOVE	I WANT A WOMAN	40.00
62	1041 DJ	NATHANIEL MAYER	VILLAGE OF LOVE	I WANT A WOMAN	50.00
62	1064	RAY CHARLES	YOU DON'T OWN ME	CARELESS LOVE	5.00
62	1064 DJ	RAY CHARLES	YOU DON'T OWN ME	CARELESS LOVE	10.00
62	1067	TEDDY RANDAZZO & the DAZZLERS	DANCE THE LOCOMOTION	COTTONFIELDS	10.00
62	1067 DJ	TEDDY RANDAZZO & the DAZZLERS	DANCE THE LOCOMOTION	COTTONFIELDS	15.00
62	1090	KENNY LYNCH	UP ON THE ROOF	JUMP ON YOUR BROOMSTICK	5.00
62	1090 DJ	KENNY LYNCH	UP ON THE ROOF	JUMP ON YOUR BROOMSTICK	8.00
62	1091	FREDA PAYNE	HE WHO LAUGHS LAST	SLIGHTLY OUT OF TUNE	30.00
62	1091 DJ	FREDA PAYNE	HE WHO LAUGHS LAST	SLIGHTLY OUT OF TUNE	50.00
62	1099	RAY CHARLES	YOUR CHEATING HEART	YOU ARE MY SUNSHINE	5.00
62	1099 DJ	RAY CHARLES	YOUR CHEATING HEART	YOU ARE MY SUNSHINE	8.00
62	1100	LLOYD PRICE	UNDER YOUR SPELL AGAIN	HAPPY BIRTHDAY MAMA	6.00
62	1100 DJ	LLOYD PRICE	UNDER YOUR SPELL AGAIN	HAPPY BIRTHDAY MAMA	8.00
62	1101	B.B. KING	TOMORROW NIGHT	MOTHER'S LOVE	8.00
62	1101 DJ	B.B. KING	TOMORROW NIGHT	MOTHER'S LOVE	10.00
62	1102	MAXINE BROWN	AM I FALLING IN LOVE	PROMISE ME ANYTHING	150.00
62	1102 DJ	MAXINE BROWN	AM I FALLING IN LOVE	PROMISE ME ANYTHING	225.00
63	1129	IMPRESSIONS	I'M THE ONE WHO LOVES YOU	I NEED YOUR LOVE	30.00
63	1129 DJ	IMPRESSIONS	I'M THE ONE WHO LOVES YOU	I NEED YOUR LOVE	50.00
63	1133	RAY CHARLES	THE BRIGHTEST SMILE IN TOWN	DON'T SET ME FREE	5.00
63	1133 DJ	RAY CHARLES	THE BRIGHTEST SMILE IN TOWN	DON'T SET ME FREE	8.00
63	1136	KENNY LYNCH	SHUT THE DOOR	MISERY	4.00
63	1136 DJ	KENNY LYNCH	SHUT THE DOOR	MISERY	6.00
63	1155	OLYMPICS	SIDEWALK SERENADE	NOTHING	10.00
63	1155 DJ	OLYMPICS	SIDEWALK SERENADE	NOTHING	15.00
63	1161	RAY CHARLES	TAKE THESE CHAINS FROM MY HEART	NO LETTER TODAY	5.00
63	1161 DJ	RAY CHARLES	TAKE THESE CHAINS FROM MY HEART	NO LETTER TODAY	8.00
63	1164	FATS DOMINO	THERE GOES (MY HEART AGAIN)	CAN'T GO ON WITHOUT YOU	10.00
63	1164 DJ	FATS DOMINO	THERE GOES (MY HEART AGAIN)	CAN'T GO ON WITHOUT YOU	15.00
63	1165	KENNY LYNCH	CRAZY CRAZES	YOU CAN NEVER STOP LOVING ME	5.00
63	1165 DJ	KENNY LYNCH	CRAZY CRAZES	YOU CAN NEVER STOP LOVING ME	8.00
63	1185	PERCY MAYFIELD	THE RIVER'S INVITATION	BABY PLEASE	8.00
63	1185 DJ	PERCY MAYFIELD	THE RIVER'S INVITATION	BABY PLEASE	10.00
63	1197	FATS DOMINO	WHEN I'M WALKIN'	I'VE GOT A RIGHT TO CRY	8.00
63	1197 DJ	FATS DOMINO	WHEN I'M WALKIN'	I'VE GOT A RIGHT TO CRY	10.00
63	1202	RAY CHARLES	NO ONE	WITHOUT LOVE (THERE IS NOTHING	5.00
63	1202 DJ	RAY CHARLES	NO ONE	WITHOUT LOVE (THERE IS NOTHING	8.00
63	1215	MADELINE BELL	I LONG FOR YOUR LOVE	BECAUSE YOU DIDN'T CARE	12.00
63	1215 DJ	MADELINE BELL	I LONG FOR YOUR LOVE	BECAUSE YOU DIDN'T CARE	20.00
63	1221	RAY CHARLES	BUSTED	MAKING BELIEVE	6.00
63	1221 DJ	RAY CHARLES	BUSTED	MAKING BELIEVE	10.00
63	1226	IMPRESSIONS	IT'S ALL RIGHT	YOU'LL WANT ME BACK	20.00
63	1226 DJ	IMPRESSIONS	IT'S ALL RIGHT	YOU'LL WANT ME BACK	40.00
63	1251	RAY CHARLES	THAT LUCKY OLD SUN	MISSISSIPPI MUD	5.00
63	1251 DJ	RAY CHARLES	THAT LUCKY OLD SUN	MISSISSIPPI MUD	8.00
63	1254	TAMS	WHAT KIND OF FOOL (DO YOU THINK I AM)	LAUGH IT OFF	20.00
63	1254 DJ	TAMS	WHAT KIND OF FOOL (DO YOU THINK I AM)	LAUGH IT OFF	30.00
64	1262	IMPRESSIONS	TALKING ABOUT MY BABY	NEVER TOO MUCH LOVE	20.00
64	1262 DJ	IMPRESSIONS	TALKING ABOUT MY BABY	NEVER TOO MUCH LOVE	40.00
64	1265	FATS DOMINO	JUST A LONELY MAN	WHO CARES	8.00

64	1265 DJ	FATS DOMINO	JUST A LONELY MAN	WHO CARES	10.00
64	1272	RAY CHARLES	MY HEART CRIES FOR YOU	BABY DON'T YOU CRY	5.00
64	1272 DJ	RAY CHARLES	MY HEART CRIES FOR YOU	BABY DON'T YOU CRY	8.00
64	1280	KENNY LYNCH	STAND BY ME	BABY IT'S TRUE	8.00
64	1280 DJ	KENNY LYNCH	STAND BY ME	BABY IT'S TRUE	10.00
64	1281	FATS DOMINO	LAZY LADY	I DON'T WANT TO SET THE WORLD	8.00
64	1281 DJ	FATS DOMINO	LAZY LADY	I DON'T WANT TO SET THE WORLD	10.00
64	1283	GLENDA COLLINS	BABY IT HURTS	NICE WASN'T IT	60.00
64	1283 DJ	GLENDA COLLINS	BABY IT HURTS	NICE WASN'T IT	75.00
64	1295	IMPRESSIONS	I'M SO PROUD	I MADE A MISTAKE	20.00
64	1295 DJ	IMPRESSIONS	I'M SO PROUD	I MADE A MISTAKE	30.00
64	1298	TAMS	IT'S ALL RIGHT (YOU'RE JUST IN LOVE)	YOU LIED TO YOUR DADDY	18.00
64	1298 DJ	TAMS	IT'S ALL RIGHT (YOU'RE JUST IN LOVE)	YOU LIED TO YOUR DADDY	28.00
64	1303	FATS DOMINO	IF YOU DON'T KNOW WHAT LOVE IS	SOMETHING YOU GOT BABY	50.00
64	1303 DJ	FATS DOMINO	IF YOU DON'T KNOW WHAT LOVE IS	SOMETHING YOU GOT BABY	**201.00**
64	1315	RAY CHARLES	MY BABY DON'T DIG ME	SOMETHING'S WRONG	5.00
64	1315 DJ	RAY CHARLES	MY BABY DON'T DIG ME	SOMETHING'S WRONG	8.00
64	1317	IMPRESSIONS	AMEN	I LOVE YOU (YEAH)	15.00
64	1317 DJ	IMPRESSIONS	AMEN	I LOVE YOU (YEAH)	30.00
64	1324	FATS DOMINO	MARY OH MARY	PACKIN' UP	6.00
64	1324 DJ	FATS DOMINO	MARY OH MARY	PACKIN' UP	8.00
64	1325	DANNY WILLIAMS	THE WORLD AROUND ME	THE SEVENTH DAWN	15.00
64	1325 DJ	DANNY WILLIAMS	THE WORLD AROUND ME	THE SEVENTH DAWN	22.00
64	1331	TAMS	HEY GIRL DON'T BOTHER ME	TAKE AWAY	150.00
64	1331 DJ	TAMS	HEY GIRL, DON'T BOTHER ME	TAKE AWAY	225.00
64	1333	RAY CHARLES	NO ONE TO CRY TO	A TEAR FELL	5.00
64	1333 DJ	RAY CHARLES	NO ONE TO CRY TO	A TEAR FELL	8.00
64	1338	JOHN LEYTON & the LE ROYS	I WANT A LOVE I CAN SEE	DON'T LET HER GO AWAY	40.00
64	1338 DJ	JOHN LEYTON & the LE ROYS	I WANT A LOVE I CAN SEE	DON'T LET HER GO AWAY	60.00
64	1343	IMPRESSIONS	YOU MUST BELIEVE ME	SEE THE REALME	20.00
64	1343 DJ	IMPRESSIONS	YOU MUST BELIEVE ME	SEE THE REALME	30.00
64	1350	RAY CHARLES	SMACK DAB IN THE MIDDLE	I WAKE UP CRYING	5.00
64	1350 DJ	RAY CHARLES	SMACK DAB IN THE MIDDLE	I WAKE UP CRYING	8.00
64	1367	KENNY LYNCH	MY OWN TWO FEET	SO MUCH TO LOVE YOU FOR	45.00
64	1367 DJ	KENNY LYNCH	MY OWN TWO FEET	SO MUCH LOVE FOR YOU	60.00
64	1370	FATS DOMINO	KANSAS CITY	HEARTBREAK HILL	6.00
64	1370 DJ	FATS DOMINO	KANSAS CITY	HEARTBREAK HILL	8.00
64	1371	JUDI JOHNSON	MY BABY'S FACE	MAKE THE MOST OF IT	20.00
64	1371 DJ	JUDI JOHNSON	MY BABY'S FACE	MAKE THE MOST OF IT	28.00
64	1372	DANNY WILLIAMS	FORGET HER, FORGET HER	LOLLIPOPS AND ROSES	40.00
64	1372 DJ	DANNY WILLIAMS	FORGET HER, FORGET HER	LOLLIPOPS AND ROSES	60.00
65	1383	RAY CHARLES	MAKIN' WHOOPEE	MOVE IT ON OVER	5.00
65	1383 DJ	RAY CHARLES	MAKIN' WHOOPEE	MOVE IT ON OVER	8.00
65	1390	HANK LEVINE	IMAGE PART 1	IMAGE PART 2	18.00
65	1390 DJ	HANK LEVINE	IMAGE PART 1	IMAGE PART 2	25.00
65	1392	RAY CHARLES	CRY	TEARDROPS IN MY EYES	5.00
65	1392 DJ	RAY CHARLES	CRY	TEARDROPS IN MY EYES	8.00
65	1399	JUDI JOHNSON and the PERFECTIONS	A WAY OUT	HOW MANY TIMES	15.00
65	1399 DJ	JUDI JOHNSON and the PERFECTIONS	A WAY OUT	HOW MANY TIMES	25.00
65	1408	IMPRESSIONS	PEOPLE GET READY	I'VE BEEN TRYING	15.00
65	1408 DJ	IMPRESSIONS	PEOPLE GET READY	I'VE BEEN TRYING	25.00
65	1410	DANNY WILLIAMS	MASQUERADE	GO AWAY	25.00
65	1410 DJ	DANNY WILLIAMS	MASQUERADE	GO AWAY	40.00
65	1414	RAY CHARLES	LIGHT OUT OF DARKNESS	PLEASE FORGIVE AND FORGET	5.00
65	1414 DJ	RAY CHARLES	LIGHT OUT OF DARKNESS	PLEASE FORGIVE AND FORGET	6.00
65	1421	FATS DOMINO	WHY DON'T YOU DO RIGHT	WIGS	8.00
65	1421 DJ	FATS DOMINO	WHY DON'T YOU DO RIGHT	WIGS	10.00
65	1428	WEST FIVE	JUST LIKE ROMEO AND JULIET	SOMEONE AIN'T RIGHT	25.00
65	1428 DJ	WEST FIVE	JUST LIKE ROMEO AND JULIET	SOMEONE AIN'T RIGHT	40.00
65	1429	IMPRESSIONS	WOMAN'S GOT SOUL	GET UP AND MOVE	30.00
65	1429 DJ	IMPRESSIONS	WOMAN'S GOT SOUL	GET UP AND MOVE	50.00
65	1430	KENNY LYNCH	I'LL STAY BY YOU	FOR LOVIN' YOU BABY	8.00
65	1430 DJ	KENNY LYNCH	I'LL STAY BY YOU	FOR LOVIN' YOU BABY	10.00
65	1431	ELKIE BROOKS	HE'S GOTTA LOVE ME	WHEN YOU APPEAR	20.00
65	1431 DJ	ELKIE BROOKS	HE'S GOTTA LOVE ME	WHEN YOU APPEAR	30.00
65	1432	SOUPY SALES	THE MOUSE	PACHALFAKA	15.00
65	1432 DJ	SOUPY SALES	THE MOUSE	PACHALFAKA	22.00
65	1433	MARVELOWS	I DO	MY HEART	30.00
65	1433 DJ	MARVELOWS	I DO	MY HEART	50.00
65	1435	TOM & JERRIO	BOO-GA-LOO	BOOMERANG	40.00
65	1435 DJ	TOM & JERRIO	BOO-GA-LOO	BOOMERANG	60.00
65	1437	RAY CHARLES	I GOTTA WOMAN	WITHOUT A SONG	10.00
65	1437 DJ	RAY CHARLES	I GOTTA WOMAN	WITHOUT A SONG	15.00
65	1441	SAPPHIRES	GOTTA HAVE YOUR LOVE	GEE BABY I'M SORRY	250.00
65	1441 DJ	SAPPHIRES	GOTTA HAVE YOUR LOVE	GEE BABY I'M SORRY	400.00
65	1446	IMPRESSIONS	MEETING OVER YONDER	I'VE FOUND THAT I'VE LOST	20.00
65	1446 DJ	IMPRESSIONS	MEETING OVER YONDER	I'VE FOUND THAT I'VE LOST	35.00
65	1450	DELLA REESE	HOW DO YOU KEEP FROM CRYING	AFTER LOVING YOU	8.00
65	1450 DJ	DELLA REESE	HOW DO YOU KEEP FROM CRYING	AFTER LOVING YOU	10.00

65	1452	MARVELS FIVE	DON'T PLAY THAT SONG	FORGIVE	15.00
65	1452 DJ	MARVELS FIVE	DON'T PLAY THAT SONG	FORGIVE	22.00
65	1453	DIXIE CUPS	THAT'S WHERE IT'S AT	TWO-WAY-POC-A-WAY	20.00
65	1453 DJ	DIXIE CUPS	THAT'S WHERE IT'S AT	TWO-WAY-POC-A-WAY	30.00
65	1457	RAY CHARLES	LOVE'S GONNA LIVE HERE	I'M A FOOL TO CARE	5.00
65	1457 DJ	RAY CHARLES	LOVE'S GONNA LIVE HERE	I'M A FOOL TO CARE	7.00
65	1461	SAPPHIRES	EVIL ONE	HOW COULD I SAY GOODBYE	**210.00**
65	1461 DJ	SAPPHIRES	EVIL ONE	HOW COULD I SAY GOODBYE	350.00
65	1464	TAMS	CONCRETE JUNGLE	TILL THE END OF TIME	15.00
65	1464 DJ	TAMS	CONCRETE JUNGLE	TILL THE END OF TIME	25.00
65	1472	IMPRESSIONS	NEVER COULD YOU BE	I NEED YOU	20.00
65	1472 DJ	IMPRESSIONS	NEVER COULD YOU BE	I NEED YOU	30.00
65	1473	RAY WHITLEY	I'VE BEEN HURT	THERE IS ONE BOY	200.00
65	1473 DJ	RAY WHITLEY	I'VE BEEN HURT	THERE IS ONE BOY	300.00
65	1484	RAY CHARLES	THE CINCINNATI KID	THAT'S ALL I AM TO YOU	5.00
65	1484 DJ	RAY CHARLES	THE CINCINNATI KID	THAT'S ALL I AM TO YOU	8.00
65	1486	DELLA REESE	AND THAT REMINDS ME	I ONLY WANT A BUDDY NOT A LOVER	5.00
65	1486 DJ	DELLA REESE	AND THAT REMINDS ME	I ONLY WANT A BUDDY NOT A LOVER	6.00
65	1489	BERYL REID	LOVE MAKES THE WORLD GO ROUND	WHEN THE CIRCUS COMES TO TOWN	15.00
65	1489 DJ	BERYL REID	LOVE MAKES THE WORLD GO ROUND	WHEN THE CIRCUS COMES TO TOWN	20.00
65	1492	IMPRESSIONS	AMEN	LONG LONG WINTER	20.00
65	1492 DJ	IMPRESSIONS	AMEN	LONG LONG WINTER	30.00
66	1498	IMPRESSIONS	YOU'VE BEEN CHEATING	JUST ONE KISS FROM YOU	.45.00
66	1498 DJ	IMPRESSIONS	YOU'VE BEEN CHEATING	JUST ONE KISS FROM YOU	85.00
66	1502	RAY CHARLES	CRYIN' TIME	WHEN MY DREAM BOAT COMES HOME	5.00
66	1502 DJ	RAY CHARLES	CRYIN' TIME	WHEN MY DREAM BOAT COMES HOME	8.00
66	1504	DELLA REESE	HER LITTLE HEART WENT TO	HOME	10.00
66	1504 DJ	DELLA REESE	HER LITTLE HEART WENT TO	HOME	15.00
66	1506	DANNY WILLIAMS	I'VE GOT TO FIND THAT GIRL AGAIN	THROW A LITTLE LOVE MY WAY	30.00
66	1506 DJ	DANNY WILLIAMS	I'VE GOT TO FIND THAT GIRL AGAIN	THROW A LITTLE LOVIN' MY WAY	40.00
66	1516	IMPRESSIONS	SINCE I LOST THE ONE I LOVE	FALLING IN LOVE WITH YOU	20.00
66	1516 DJ	IMPRESSIONS	SINCE I LOST THE ONE I LOVE	FALLING IN LOVE WITH YOU	40.00
66	1519	RAY CHARLES	TOGETHER AGAIN	YOU'RE JUST ABOUT TO LOSE YOUR	5.00
66	1519 DJ	RAY CHARLES	TOGETHER AGAIN	YOU'RE JUST ABOUT TO LOSE YOUR	8.00
66	1524	DIXIE CUPS	WHAT KIND OF FOOL	DANNY BOY	25.00
66	1524 DJ	DIXIE CUPS	WHAT KIND OF FOOL.	DANNY BOY	35.00
66	1526	IMPRESSIONS	NO ONE ELSE	TOO SLOW	20.00
66	1526 DJ	IMPRESSIONS	NO ONE ELSE	TOO SLOW	40.00
66	1531	STEVE ALAIMO	SO MUCH LOVE	TRUER THAN TRUE	20.00
66	1531 DJ	STEVE ALAIMO	SO MUCH LOVE	TRUER THAN TRUE	30.00
66	1537	RAY CHARLES	THE TRAIN	LET'S GET STONED	15.00
66	1537 DJ	RAY CHARLES	THE TRAIN	LET'S GO GET STONED	25.00
66	1544	IKE & TINA TURNER	ANYTHING YOU WASN'T BORN WITH	BEAUTY IS JUST SKIN DEEP	25.00
66	1544 DJ	IKE & TINA TURNER	ANYTHING YOU WASN'T BORN WITH	BEAUTY IS JUST SKIN DEEP	40.00
66	1545	IMPRESSIONS	CAN'T SATISFY	THIS MUST END	40.00
66	1545 DJ	IMPRESSIONS	CAN'T SATISFY	THIS MUST END	85.00
66	1548	HIGH & MIGHTY	ESCAPE FROM CUBA	TRYIN' TO STOP CRYIN'	30.00
66	1548 DJ	HIGH & MIGHTY	ESCAPE FROM CUBA	TRYIN' TO STOP CRYIN'	45.00
66	1551	RAY CHARLES	I CHOSE TO SING THE BLUES	HOPELESSLY	20.00
66	1551 DJ	RAY CHARLES	I CHOSE TO SING THE BLUES	HOPELESSLY	30.00
66	1553	DELLA REESE	IT WAS A VERY GOOD YEAR	SOLITARY WOMAN	6.00
66	1553 DJ	DELLA REESE	IT WAS A VERY GOOD YEAR	SOLITARY WOMAN	8.00
66	1557	DIXIE CUPS	LOVE AIN'T SO BAD (AFTER ALL)	DADDY SAID NO	10.00
66	1557 DJ	DIXIE CUPS	LOVE AIN'T SO BAD (AFTER ALL)	DADDY SAID NO	18.00
66	1560	DANNY WILLIAMS	RAIN (FALLING FROM THE SKIES)	I'M SO LOST	30.00
66	1560 DJ	DANNY WILLIAMS	RAIN (FALLING FROM THE SKIES)	I'M SO LOST	50.00
66	1566	RAY CHARLES	I DON'T NEED NO DOCTOR	PLEASE SAY YOU'RE FOOLING	50.00
66	1566 DJ	RAY CHARLES	I DON'T NEED NO DOCTOR	PLEASE SAY YOU'RE FOOLING	100.00
66	1568	B.B. KING	DON'T ANSWER THE DOOR part 1	DON'T ANSWER THE DOOR part 2	8.00
66	1568 DJ	B.B. KING	DON'T ANSWER THE DOOR	DON'T ANSWER THE DOOR Part 2	10.00
67	1577	KENNY LYNCH	IT'S TOO LATE	I JUST WANNA LOVE YOU	25.00
67	1577 DJ	KENNY LYNCH	IT'S TOO LATE	I JUST WANNA LOVE YOU	30.00
67	1579	JIMMY REED	TWO WAYS TO SKIN A CAT	GOT NOWHERE TO GO	15.00
67	1579 DJ	JIMMY REED	TWO WAYS TO SKIN A CAT	GOT NOWHERE TO GO	22.00
67	1580	B.B. KING	NIGHT LIFE	WAITIN' ON YOU	6.00
67.	1580 DJ	B.B. KING	NIGHT LIFE	WAITIN' ON YOU	8.00
67	1581	IMPRESSIONS	YOU ALWAYS HURT ME	LITTLE GIRL	20.00
67	1581 DJ	IMPRESSIONS	YOU ALWAYS HURT ME	LITTLE GIRL	30.00
67	1582	FATS DOMINO	I'M LIVING RIGHT	I DON'T WANT TO SET THE WORLD	6.00
67	1582 DJ	FATS DOMINO	I'M LIVING RIGHT	I DON'T WANT TO SET THE WORLD	8.00
66	1583	IKE & TINA TURNER	DUST MY BROOM	I'M HOOKED	60.00
66	1583 DJ	IKE & TINA TURNER	DUST MY BROOM	I'M HOOKED	**137.00**
67	1589	RAY CHARLES	YOU WIN AGAIN	BYE BYE LOVE	6.00
67	1589 DJ	RAY CHARLES	YOU WIN AGAIN	BYE BYE LOVE	6.00
67	1591	RAELETS	ONE ROOM PARADISE	ONE HURT DESERVES ANOTHER	30.00
67	1591 DJ	RAELETS	ONE ROOM PARADISE	ONE HURT DESERVES ANOTHER	45.00
67	1594	B.B. KING	THINK IT OVER	I DON'T EWANT YOU CUTTIN' OFF	10.00
67	1594 DJ	B.B. KING	THINK IT OVER	I DON'T EWANT YOU CUTTIN' OFF	15.00
67	1595	RAY CHARLES	SOMEBODY OUGHTA WRITE A BOOK	HERE WE GO AGAIN	5.00

67	1595 DJ	RAY CHARLES	SOMEBODY OUGHTA WRITE A BOOK	HERE WE GO AGAIN	6.00
67	1604	KENNY LYNCH	MOVIN' AWAY	COULD I COUNT ON YOU	150.00
67	1604 DJ	KENNY LYNCH	MOVIN' AWAY	COULD I COUNT ON YOU	200.00
67	1607	RAY CHARLES	SOMETHING'S GOT TO CHANGE	IN THE HEAT OF THE NIGHT	15.00
62	8729 EP PS	RAY CHARLES	HIT THE ROAD JACK	1962 4 track EP with cover	20.00
63	8781 EP PS	RAY CHARLES	I CAN'T STOP LOVING YOU	1962 4 track EP with cover	10.00
65	8801 EP PS	RAY CHARLES	SWINGING STYLE	1965 4 track EP with cover	10.00
65	8812 EP PS	RAY CHARLES	TA\KE THESE CHAINS FROM MY HEART	1965 4 track EP with cover	10.00
65	8861 EP PS	RAY CHARLES	RAY CHARLES SINGS	1965 4 track EP with cover	10.00
65	8862 EP PS	FATS DOMINO	RED SAILS IN THE SUNSET	1965 4 track EP with cover	15.00
65	8896 EP PS	IMPRESSIONS	IT'S ALL RIGHT	1965 4 track EP with cover	40.00
65	8932 EP PS	RAY CHARLES	LIVE IN CONCERT	1965 4 track EP with cover	10.00
65	8954 EP PS	IMPRESSIONS	SOULFULLY	4 track EP with cover	30.00

HIT & RUN

	5001	EDDIE GILES	MARRIED LADY	ARE YOU LIVKING WITH THE ONE	5.00
	5002	MIGHTY SAM	NEVER TOO BUSY	MR. & MRS UNTRUE	15.00
	5003	GEORGE PERKINS	KEEP ON TRYING	WHAT THE DEAL IS	6.00

HORACES

A label launched by Adey Croasdale, and distributed by Ace records. The label name comes from his affectionate nickname "Harborough Horace", being brought up in the small town of Market Harborough in Leicestershire. A small town it may have been but in 1970 it was the location of a small but highly respected "Lantern" club, which played rare soul through the night to a large travelling fan base. As with every vinyl adventure Adey has been involved in, the product was a genuine limited press and consequently all titles have become highly collectable. Also see Kent's 100 club annual anniversary release 45s listing.

88	001	MELBA MOORE c/w TOMMY HUNT	THE MAGIC TOUCH	THE PRETTY PART OF YOU	25.00
88	002	ROOSVELT GRIER c/w LAVERN BAKER	IN MY TENEMENT	WRAPPED TIED AND TANGLED	10.00
89	003	HECTOR RIVERA	PLAYING IT COOL	I WANT A CHANCE FOR ROMANCE	10.00
90	004	EDDIE DAYE & 4 BARS c/w JIMMY ARMSTRONG	GUESS WHO LOVES YOU	MYSTERY	10.00
90	005	RAY POLLARD c/w CIAROS	THIS TIME (I'M GONNA BE TRUE)	STOP OVER LOOKING ME	20.00
90	006	LITTLE JOHNNY HAMILTON c/w ENTERTAINERS FOUR	OH HOW I LOVE YOU	GETTIN' BACK INTO CIRCULATION	10.00
91	007	BARBARA LEWIS c/w CARLA THOMAS	THE STARS	I'LL NEVER STOP LOVING YOU	20.00

HORSE

1		JACKIE EDWARDS	I MUST GO BACK	BABY I WANT TO BE NEAR YOU	10.00
1 PS		JACKIE EDWARDS	I MUST GO BACK	BABY I WANT TO BE NEAR YOU	20.00

HOT WAX

71	101	FLAMING EMBER	WESTBOUND No.9	WHY DON'T YOU SAY	5.00
71	101 DJ	FLAMING EMBER	WESTBOUND No.9	WHY DON'T YOU SAY	10.00
71	102	100 PROOF AGED IN SOUL	SOMEBODY'S BEEN SLEEPING	I'SE COME TO SAVE YOU	5.00
71	102 DJ	100 PROOF AGED IN SOUL	SOMEBODY'S BEEN SLEEPING	I'SE COME TO SAVE YOU	8.00
71	103	HONEY CONE	WHILE YOU'RE OUT LOOKING FOR	THE FEELING'S GONE	8.00
71	103 DJ	HONEY CONE	WHILE YOU'RE OUT LOOKING FOR	THE FEELING'S GONE	15.00
71	104	FLAMING EMBER	I'M NOT MY BROTHER'S KEEPER	MIND, BODY AND SOUL	4.00
71	104 DJ	FLAMING EMBER	I'M NOT MY BROTHER'S KEEPER	MIND, BODY AND SOUL	6.00
71	105	HONEY CONE	GIRLS IT AIN'T EASY	TAKE ME WITH YOU	6.00
71	105 DJ	HONEY CONE	GIRLS IT AIN'T EASY	TAKE ME WITH YOU	8.00
71	106	FLAMING EMBER	SHADES OF GREEN	STOP THE WORLD AND LET ME OFF	6.00
71	106 DJ	FLAMING EMBER	SHADES OF GREEN	STOP THE WORLD AND LET ME OFF	8.00
71	107	HONEY CONE	WANT ADS	WE BELONG TOGETHER	5.00
71	107 DJ	HONEY CONE	WANT ADS	WE BELONG TOGETHER	6.00
71	108	100 PROOF	I'VE COME TO SAVE YOU	SOMEBODY'S BEEN SLEEPING	6.00
71	108 DJ	100 PROOF	I'VE COME TO SAVE YOU	SOMEBODY'S BEEN SLEEPING	10.00
71	109	HONEY CONE	TAKE ME WITH YOU	DEAF, BLIND, PARALYSED	5.00
71	109 DJ	HONEY CONE	TAKE ME WITH YOU	DEAF, BLIND, PARALYSED	8.00
71	110	SILENT MAJORITY	FRIGHTENED GIRL	COLOURS OF MY LOVE	8.00
71	110 DJ	SILENT MAJORITY	FRIGHTENED GIRL	COLOURS OF MY LOVE	10.00
71	111	HONEY CONE	ONE MONKEY DON'T STOP NO SHOW	STICK UP	6.00
71	111 DJ	HONEY CONE	ONE MONKEY DON'T STOP NO SHOW	STICK UP	10.00
71	112	HONEY CONE	THE DAY I FOUND MYSELF	WHEN WILL IT END	5.00
71	112 DJ	HONEY CONE	THE DAY I FOUND MYSELF	WHEN WILL IT END	8.00
72	113	100 PROOF	EVERYTHING GOOD IS BAD	I'D RATHER FIGHT THAN SWITCH	5.00
72	113 DJ	100 PROOF	EVERYTHING GOOD IS BAD	I'D RATHER FIGHT THAN SWITCH	8.00
72	114	POLITICIANS	FREE YOUR MIND	LOVE MACHINE	15.00
72	114 DJ	POLITICIANS	FREE YOUR MIND	LOVE MACHINE	20.00
72	115	LAURA LEE	RIP OFF	TWO LOVELY PILLOWS	6.00
72	115 DJ	LAURA LEE	RIP OFF	TWO LOVELY PILLOWS	15.00
72	116	HONEY CONE	SITTIN' ON A TIME BOMB	IT'S BETTER TIO HAVE LOVED AND	5.00
72	116 DJ	HONEY CONE	SITTIN' ON A TIME BOMB	IT'S BETTER TIO HAVE LOVED AND	8.00
	117	FLAMING EMBER	EMPTY CROWDED ROOM	IF IT'S GOOD TO YOU	6.00
	117 DJ	FLAMING EMBER	EMPTY CROWDED ROOM	IF IT'S GOOD TO YOU	6.00
	118	LAURA LEE	WEDLOCK IS A PADLOCK	SINCE I FELL FOR YOU	6.00
	118 DJ	LAURA LEE	WEDLOCK IS A PADLOCK	SINCE I FELL FOR YOU	8.00
73	119	LAURA LEE	CRUMBS OFF THE TABLE	YOU'VE GOT THE LOVE TO SAVE ME	10.00
73	119 DJ	LAURA LEE	CRUMBS OFF THE TABLE	YOU'VE GOT THE LOVE TO SAVE ME	15.00
73	120	100 PROOF	NEVER MY LOVE	SINCE YOU BEEN GONE	5.00
73	120 DJ	100 PROOF	NEVER MY LOVE	SINCE YOU BEEN GONE	8.00

HOUSE OF SOUNDS

80s	100	FANTASTIC JOHNNY C c/w GEORGE CLINTON	DON'T DEPEND ON ME	PLEASE DON'T RUN	10.00
80s	102	VARIOUS ARTISTS	HUNG UP ON YOUR LOVE	TIME MARCHES ON + JUST SAY YOUR WANTED	10.00

Three track maxi-single three artists are: Montclairs, Lainie Hill and Gwen Owens.

ICE

78	14	PIONEERS	MY GOOD FRIEND JAMES	SECRET OF YOU	**241.00**

ILLUSION

	781001	BRENDA HOLLOWAY	YOU DIDN'T SAY A WORD	LEND A HAND	5.00

IMMEDIATE

Manufactured and distributed by Philips Records Ltd. The Immediate label is most revered for its collectable rock and pop 45's many collectors worldwide are trying to complete the label. Looking down the list of releases that soul & northern soul collectors would be interested in, I'm sure the purists would point a finger at Chris Farlowe, The McCoys and ask what are they to do with soul. But as any long standing UK collector will quickly mention Chris Farlowe's 1966 LP – "14 Things To Think About" – Immediate imsp 005 instantly gained him the respect of the mid-sixties soul searching collectors with excellent cover versions of Garnet Mimms – Looking For You, O'Jays – Lipstick Traces, and his own recording - Don't Just Look At Me - which later saw it played as a single at The Blackpool Mecca, Wigan Casino, Cleethorpes Pier, and the Catacoombs etc. So Chris Farlowe, with his all powerful vocal was very much a part of the Brit-Soul movement and very much an acceptable part of UK "Soul" collecting, although I have omitted his singles which are basically rock or pop.

One soul artist to dominate the label was P.P.Arnold, she was one of the few female black artists recording in the UK at the time, born in 1945 in Los Angeles as Patrica Ann Cole, she unexpectedly entered the music business after a successful but unexpected audition with Gloria Scott and Maxine Smith which won her a place with Ike and Tina Turner's girl backing group in the Ikettes. On tour in the USA for two years and playing legendary theatre's like The Apollo, New York and The Uptown, Philadelphia she quickly became a seasoned performer. One night in 1966 at The Galaxy Club, Sunset Strip, Los Angeles, a chance meeting would change her life. Two English guys walked in the club, to check out the Ike & Tina Turner Revue, who had just released – River Deep Mountain High – they were so impressed so Bill Wyman and Charlie Watts invited the Revue to England the perform with them. "River Deep" was consequently a massive hit in the UK. P.P.Arnold's love of the UK had begun and in February 1967 she released her first solo single, which is regarded today as one of the finest Northern Soul 45's ever made on these shores, and surprisingly – "Everything's Gonna Be Alright" – never saw release in her homeland. P.P. had five UK releases for Immediate and one for Polydor, before in 1970 joining the cast of the hit musical "Catch My Soul" in which she graced the stage alongside P.J. Proby.

65	001	McCOYS	HANG ON SLOOPY	I CAN'T EXPLAIN IT	8.00
65	001 DJ	McCOYS	HANG ON SLOOPY	I CAN'T EXPLAIN IT	15.00
65	007	STRANGELOVES	CARA-LIN	ROLL ON MISSISSIPPI	15.00
65	007 DJ	STRANGELOVES	CARA-LIN	ROLL ON MISSISSIPPI	20.00
65	008	VAN LENTON	YOU DON'T CARE	GOTTA GET AWAY	40.00
65	008 DJ	VAN LENTON	YOU DON'T CARE	GOTTA GET AWAY	50.00
65	009	FACTOTUMS	IN MY LONELY ROOM	A RUN IN THE GREEN AND TANGERI	25.00
65	009 DJ	FACTOTUMS	IN MY LONELY ROOM	A RUN IN THE GREEN AND TANGERI	35.00
65	011	BARBARA LYNN	YOU CAN'T BUY MY LOVE	THAT'S WHAT A FRIEND WILL DO	50.00
65	011 DJ	BARBARA LYNN	YOU CAN'T BUY MY LOVE	THAT'S WHAT A FRIEND WILL DO	75.00
65	021	McCOYS	FEVER	SORROW	10.00
65	021 DJ	McCOYS	FEVER	SORROW	15.00
65	023	CHRIS FARLOWE	DON'T JUST LOOK AT ME	THINK	15.00
65	023 DJ	CHRIS FARLOWE	DON'T JUST LOOK AT ME	THINK	30.00
66	024	POETS	BABY DON'T YOU DO IT	IT'LL COME HOME	75.00
66	024 DJ	POETS	BABY DON'T YOU DO IT	IT'LL COME HOME	100.00
66	026	GOLDIE	HEADLINES	GOIN' BACK	20.00
66	026 DJ	GOLDIE	HEADLINES	GOIN' BACK	30.00
66	029	McCOYS	UP AND DOWN	IF YOU TELL A LIE	10.00
66	029 DJ	McCOYS	UP AND DOWN	IF YOU TELL A LIE	15.00
66	035	CHRIS FARLOWE	OUT OF TIME	BABY MAKE IT SOON	8.00
66	035 DJ	CHRIS FARLOWE	OUT OF TIME	BABY MAKE IT SOON	15.00
66	038	CHRIS FARLOWE	HEADLINES	RIDE ON BABY	10.00
66	038 DJ	CHRIS FARLOWE	HEADLINES	RIDE ON BABY	15.00
66	040	P.P. ARNOLD	EVERYTHING'S GONNA BE ALRIGHT	LIFE IS BUT NOTHIN'	150.00
66	040 DJ	P.P. ARNOLD	EVERYTHING'S GONNA BE ALRIGHT	LIFE IS BUT NOTHIN'	250.00
67	041	CHRIS FARLOWE	YOU'RE SO GOOD TO ME	MY WAY OF GIVING	15.00
67	041 DJ	CHRIS FARLOWE	YOU'RE SO GOOD TO ME	MY WAY OF GIVING	20.00
67	047	P.P. ARNOLD	THE FIRST CUT IS THE DEEPEST	SPEAK TO ME	10.00
67	047 DJ	P.P. ARNOLD	THE FIRST CUT IS THE DEEPEST	SPEAK TO ME	20.00
67	049	CHRIS FARLOWE	YESTERDAYS PAPERS	LIFE IS B UT NOTHING	8.00
67	049 DJ	CHRIS FARLOWE	YESTERDAYS PAPERS	LIFE IS B UT NOTHING	10.00
67	055	P.P. ARNOLD	IF YOU SEE WHAT I MEAN	THE TIME HAS COME	10.00
67	055 DJ	P.P. ARNOLD	IF YOU SEE WHAT I MEAN	THE TIME HAS COME	15.00
67	056	CHRIS FARLOWE	MOANIN'	WHAT HAVE I BEEN DOING	6.00
67	056 DJ	CHRIS FARLOWE	MOANIN'	WHAT HAVE I BEEN DOING	10.00
67	061	P.P. ARNOLD	(IF YOU THINK YOU'RE) GROOVY	THOUGH IT HURTS ME BADLY	15.00
67	061 DJ	P.P. ARNOLD	(IF YOU THINK YOU'RE) GROOVY	THOUGH IT HURTS ME BADLY	20.00
67	065	CHRIS FARLOWE	HANDBAGS TO GLADRAGS	EVERYONE MAKES A MISTAKE	10.00
67	065 DJ	CHRIS FARLOWE	HANDBAGS TO GLADRAGS	EVERYONE MAKES A MISTAKE	15.00
68	067	P.P. ARNOLD	ANGEL OF THE MORNING	LIFE IS BUT NOTHIN'	10.00
68	067 DJ	P.P. ARNOLD	ANGEL OF THE MORNING	LIFE IS BUT NOTHIN'	15.00
69	078	CHRIS FARLOWE	OUT OF TIME	RIDE ON BABY	6.00
69	078 DJ	CHRIS FARLOWE	OUT OF TIME	RIDE ON BABY	8.00
69	079	P.P. ARNOLD	FIRST CUT IS THE DEEPEST	THE TIME HAS COME	8.00
69	079 DJ	P.P. ARNOLD	FIRST CUT IS THE DEEPEST	THE TIME HAS COME	12.00
75	101	CHRIS FARLOWE	OUT OF TIME	MY WAY OF GIVING	4.00
77	109	P.P. ARNOLD	FIRST CUT IS THE DEEPEST	KING OF KINGS	6.00

IMPULSE

76	7001	JOHN HANDY	HARD WORK	YOUNG ENOUGH TO DREAM	5.00

INFERNO

Walsall based label started by Northern Soul DJ and record wholesaler Neil Rushton with his first release in July 1979. Although test presses were made of every title only three titles were ever pressed as labeled promo copies. The whole label is now highly sought after and collectable. As some of the titles sold as little as 500 copies, as the Northern Soul market started to collapse in 1980. The label includes some totally exclusive titles like The Showstoppers previously unissued incredible Northern dancer – Gotta get closer to my love – and the instrumental of the Four Perfections classic –"I'm not strong enough" - plus a sensational Tom Moulton remix of The Carstairs – "It really hurts me girl." Neil always presented his product professionally, some in picture sleeves some in coloured vinyl. The confusing numbering system was mainly due to Neil.

79	1 PS black vinyl	AD LIBS	NEW YORK IN THE DARK	THE BOY FROM NEW YORK CITY	6.00
79	1 PS green vinyl	AD LIBS	NEW YORK IN THE DARK	THE BOY FROM NEW YORK CITY	10.00
79	1 PS red vinyl	AD LIBS	NEW YORK IN THE DARK	THE BOY FROM NEW YORK CITY	10.00
79	2 orange vinyl	JOHNNY BRAGG	THEY'RE TALKING ABOUT ME	IS IT TRUE	8.00
79	2 PS orange vinyl	JOHNNY BRAGG	THEY'RE TALKING ABOUT ME	IS IT TRUE	15.00
79	3 green	RAL DONNER	DON'T LET IT SLIP AWAY	WAIT A MINUTE NOW	5.00
79	3 PS green	RAL DONNER	DON'T LET IT SLIP AWAY	WAIT A MINUTE NOW	6.00
79	4 clear vinyl	FRANK BEVERLY & the BUTLERS	IF THAT'S WHAT YOU WANTED	LOVE (YOUR PAIN GOES DEEP)	8.00
79	4 PS clear vinyl	FRANK BEVERLY & the BUTLERS	IF THAT'S WHAT YOU WANTED	LOVE (YOUR PAIN GOES DEEP)	15.00
79	4 PS black vinyl	FRANK BEVERLY & the BUTLERS	IF THAT'S WHAT YOU WANTED	LOVE (YOUR PAIN GOES DEEP)	10.00
79	5 blue vinyl	PHIL COULTER	A GOOD THING GOING	RUNAWAY BUNION	8.00
79	5 PS	PHIL COULTER	A GOOD THING GOING	RUNAWAY BUNION	5.00
79	6	GLORIA JONES c/w SANDY WYNNS	TAINTED LOVE	A TOUCH OF VENUS	10.00
79	6 blue vinyl	GLORIA JONES c/w SANDY WYNNS	TAINTED LOVE	A TOUCH OF VENUS	15.00
79	7	CARSTAIRS	IT REALLY HURTS ME GIRL	same: Tom moulton mix 2	15.00
79	8	FRANKIE & JOHNNY	I'LL HOLD YOU	NEVER GONNA LEAVE YOU	15.00
79	8 test press	FRANKIE & JOHNNY	I'LL HOLD YOU	NEVER GONNA LEAVE YOU	20.00
80	9	BARBARA MILLS	QUEEN OF FOOLS	(MAKE IT LAST) TAKE YOUR TIME	10.00
80	10	NEWBEATS	CRYING MY HEART OUT	RUN BABY RUN	15.00
80	11	FOUR PERFECTIONS	I'M NOT STRONG ENOUGH	same: instrumental	15.00
80	12	SHOWSTOPPERS	GOTTA GET CLOSER TO MY LOVE	AIN'T NOTHING BUT A HOUSE PARTY	15.00
80	12 DJ	SHOWSTOPPERS	GOTTA GET CLOSER TO MY LOVE	I'M NOT STRONG ENOUGH intrumental	30.00
80	14	FANTASTIC PUZZLES c/w JELLY BEANS	COME BACK	YOU DON'T MEAN ME NO GOOD	30.00
80	14	CROW	YOUR AUTUMN OF TOMORROW	UNCLE FUNK	20.00
80	14 DJ	CROW	YOUR AUTUMN OF TOMORROW	UNCLE FUNK	30.00
80	14 test press	CROW	YOUR AUTUMN OF TOMORROW	UNCLE FUNK	25.00
80	15	ELOISE LAWS c/w JUST BROTHERS	LOVE FACTORY	SLICED TOMATOES	15.00
80	16	CHAIRMEN OF THE BOARD	GIVE ME JUST A LITTLE MORE TIME	YOU'VE GOT ME DANGLING ON	5.00
80	17	FREDA PAYNE	BAND OF GOLD	BAND OF GOLD extended version	4.00
80	17 gold vinyl	FREDA PAYNE	BAND OF GOLD	BAND OF GOLD extended version	6.00
80	17 DJ	FREDA PAYNE	BAND OF GOLD	BAND OF GOLD extended version	8.00
80	20	ANN SEXTON c/w LITTLE RITCHIE	YOU'VE BEE GONE TOO LONG	JUST ANOTHER HEARTACHE	15.00
80	22	GIL SCOTT-HERON	THE BOTTLE	THE BOTTLE (Drunk mix)	6.00
80	22 dup #	SHORT PEOPLE	WHY'D YOU PUT IT TO ME BABY	TALL PEOPLE	5.00
80	24	SHELLEY WINTERS	NINE TIMES OUT OF TEN	same: instrumental	4.00
81	25 test press only	GLORIA JONES	COME GO WITH ME	RUN ONE FLIGHT OF STAIRS + FINDERS KEEPERS 200.00
81	26	MR. FLOODS PARTY	COMPARED TO WHAT	UNBREAKABLE TOY	8.00
83	burn 2	DOBIE GRAY	OUT ON THE FLOOR 83 tour ltd. Ed.	OUT ON THE FLOOR (niter mix)	6.00
83	burn 2 PS	DOBIE GRAY	OUT ON THE FLOOR	OUT ON THE FLOOR (niter mix)	8.00
83	burn 2 PS lyric	DOBIE GRAY	OUT ON THE FLOOR lyric cover	FUNKY FUNKY FEELIN'	10.00
83	burn 2P pic disc	DOBIE GRAY c/w FURYS + MURIEL DAY	OUT ON THE FLOOR + NINE TIMES OUT OF TEN	I'M SATISFIED WITH YOU instru.	15.00
83	burn 3	J.J. BARNES	SWEET SHERRY	SWEET SHERRY (LONG VERSION)	6.00
83	burn 4	LOU RAGLAND	DIDN'T I TELL YOU + SINCE YOU SAID	I TRAVEL ALONE (live)	20.00
83	burn 5	TINA LEWIS	BACK STREET	THE WAY YOU'VE BEEN ACTING LATELY	5.00
83	burn 6	GLORIA JONES c/w SANDY WYNNS	TAINTED LOVE	A TOUCH OF VENUS	10.00
83	burn 6 blue vinyl	GLORIA JONES c/w SANDY WYNNS	TAINTED LOVE	A TOUCH OF VENUS	10.00
83	burn 7	J.J. BARNES	COMPETITION AIN'T NOTHING	same: instrumental	6.00
83	burn 7 PD EP	J.J. BARNES c/w CHECKERBOARD SQUARES	COMPETITION AIN'T NOTHING	DOUBLE COOKIN'	10.00
83	burn 8	JOHNNY BRAGG c/w SUSPICIONS	THEY'RE TALKING ABOUT ME	OUR LOVE IS IN THE POCKET	6.00
83	burn 8 PS	JOHNNY BRAGG c/w SUSPICIONS	THEY'RE TALKING ABOUT ME	OUR LOVE IS IN THE POCKET	8.00
83	burn 9	CHECKERBOARD SQUARES c/w FATHERS	ANGELS DOUBLE COOKIN'	BOK TO BACH	8.00
83	burn 9 DJ	CHECKERBOARD SQUARES c/w FATHERS	ANGELS DOUBLE COOKIN'	BOK TO BACH	8.00
83	burn 10 DJ	JIMMEY SOUL CLARK	SWEET DARLING handwritten credits	DO I LOVE YOU instrumental	20.00
83	demo 1 DJ	SHOWSTOPPERS	GOTTA GET CLOSER TO MY LOVE	I'M NOT STRONG ENOUGH instrumental	30.00
83	demo 2 DJ	JELLY BEANS c/w CROW	YOU DON'T MEAN ME NO GOOD	YOUR AUTUMN OF TOMORROW	10.00

INFINITY

78	101 DJ	DOBIE GRAY	YOU CAN DO IT	SHARING THE NIGHT TOGETHER	4.00
79	102	MARVA HICKS	LOOKING OVER MY SHOULDER	HERE I GO AGAIN	20.00
79	102 DJ	MARVA HICKS	LOOKING OVER MY SHOULDER	HERE I GO AGAIN	30.00
79	104	ORSA LIA	I NEVER SAID I LOVE YOU	NO WALLS, NO CIELINGS, NO FLOORS	5.00
79	104 DJ	ORSA LIA	I NEVER SAID I LOVE YOU	NO WALLS, NO CIELINGS, NO FLOORS	6.00
79	111 PS	SPYRO GYRA	MORNING DANCE	JUBILEE + HELIOPOLIS	4.00
79	115 PS	DOBIE GRAY	THE IN CROWD	SPENDING TIME MAKING LOVE AND	5.00
79	118	NATURE'S DEVINE	I JUST CAN'T CONTROL MYSELF	NATURE DIVINE	8.00
79	118 DJ	NATURE'S DEVINE	I JUST CAN'T CONTROL MYSELF	NATURE DIVINE	10.00
79	120	RUPERT HOLMES	ESCAPE	DROP IT	6.00
79	120 DJ	RUPERT HOLMES	ESCAPE	DROP IT	8.00

INVICTUS

After contractual problems and seeking more control and greater rewards, Motown's most prolific composers Eddie Holland, Lamont Dozier & Brian Holland left Berry Gordy's Motown family to form their very own record company; so in late 1968 Invictus Records was born along with sister company Hot Wax. For contractual reasons it was not until 1970 the names Holland – Dozier – Holland would appear on either label, before then all the Holland – Dozier – Holland works were credited to Dunbar & Wayne.

In the UK the label got off to a flying start with three huge hits in quick succession, all are today still considered not only soul club classics but night club classics also. The trio always seem to be able to produce records that could cross any boundaries to create universal admiration and ultimately good sales. After the success of the early releases, hits became harder to come by. In 1973 Lamont Dozier left to pursue a solo career with Warner Brothers. 1974 saw less releases that 1973, as did 1975, until in 1977 the label ceased releasing 45's in the UK. Many of their classic Invictus recordings were made available in the UK on the H – D – H label.

70	501	CHAIRMEN OF THE BOARD	GIVE ME JUST A LITTLE MORE TIME	SINCE THE DAYS OF PIGTAILS	6.00
70	501 DJ	CHAIRMEN OF THE BOARD	GIVE ME JUST A LITTLE MORE TIME	SINCE THE DAYS OF PIGTAILS	30.00
70	502	FREDA PAYNE	BAND OF GOLD	THE EASIEST WAY TO FALL	6.00
70	502 DJ	FREDA PAYNE	BAND OF GOLD	THE EASIEST WAY TO FALL	30.00
70	503	unissued			
70	504	CHAIRMEN OF THE BOARD	YOU'VE GOT ME DANGLING ON A STRING	PATCHES	6.00
70	504 DJ	CHAIRMEN OF THE BOARD	YOU'VE GOT ME DANGLING ON A STRING	PATCHES	15.00
70	505	FREDA PAYNE	DEEPER AND DEEPER	UNHOOKED GENERATION	6.00
70	505 DJ	FREDA PAYNE	DEEPER AND DEEPER	UNHOOKED GENERATION	10.00
71	506	GLASS HOUSE	STEALING MOMENTS FROM ANOTHER	IF IT AIN'T LOVE, IT DON'T MATTER	6.00
71	506 DJ	GLASS HOUSE	STEALING MOMENTS FROM ANOTHER	IF IT AIN'T LOVE, IT DON'T MATTER	8.00
71	507	CHAIRMEN OF THE BOARD	EVERYTHING'S TUESDAY	BLESS YOU	8.00
71	507 DJ	CHAIRMEN OF THE BOARD	EVERYTHING'S TUESDAY	BLESS YOU	15.00
71	508	unissued			
71	509	FREDA PAYNE	CHERISH WHAT IS DEAR TO YOU	THE WORLD DON'T OWE YOU A THIN	6.00
71	509 DJ	FREDA PAYNE	CHERISH WHAT IS DEAR TO YOU	THE WORLD DON'T OWE YOU A THIN	10.00
71	510	GLASS HOUSE	I CAN'T BE YOU (YOU CAN'T BE ME)	HE'S IN MY LIFE	8.00
71	510 DJ	GLASS HOUSE	I CAN'T BE YOU (YOU CAN'T BE ME)	HE'S IN MY LIFE	10.00
71	511	CHAIRMEN OF THE BOARD	PAY TO THE PIPER	WHEN WILL SHE TELL ME SHE NEED	6.00
71	511 DJ	CHAIRMEN OF THE BOARD	PAY TO THE PIPER	WHEN WILL SHE TELL ME SHE NEED	15.00
71	512	FREDA PAYNE	ROCK ME IN THE CRADLE (OF YOUR LOVING ARMS)	NOW IS THE TIME TO SAY GOODBYE	6.00
71	512 DJ	FREDA PAYNE	ROCK ME IN THE CRADLE (OF YOUR LOVING ARMS)	NOW IS THE TIME TO SAY GOODBYE	10.00
71	513	PARLIAMENT	THE SILENT BOATMAN	LIVIN THE LIFE	15.00
71	513 DJ	PARLIAMENT	THE SILENT BOATMAN	LIVIN THE LIFE	20.00
71	514	8TH. DAY	SHE'S NOT JUST ANOTHER WOMAN	I CAN'T FOOL MYSELF	6.00
71	514 DJ	8TH. DAY	SHE'S NOT JUST ANOTHER WOMAN	I CAN'T FOOL MYSELF	8.00
71	515	FREDA PAYNE	BRING THE BOYS HOME	ODDS AND ENDS	6.00
71	515 DJ	FREDA PAYNE	BRING THE BOYS HOME	ODDS AND ENDS	10.00
71	516	CHAIRMEN OF THE BOARD	CHAIRMEN OF THE BOARD	HANGING ON TO A MEMORY	6.00
71	516 DJ	CHAIRMEN OF THE BOARD	CHAIRMEN OF THE BOARD	HANGING ON TO A MEMORY	10.00
71	516 alternative flip	CHAIRMEN OF THE BOARD	CHAIRMEN OF THE BOARD	WHEN WILL SHE TELL ME SHE NEED	6.00
71	517	unissued			
71	518	FREDA PAYNE	YOU'VE GOT TO LOVE SOMEBODY	MAMA'S GONE	10.00
71	518 DJ	FREDA PAYNE	YOU'VE GOT TO LOVE SOMEBODY	MAMA'S GONE	15.00
72	519	CHAIRMEN OF THE BOARD	WORKING ON A BUILDING OF LOVE	TRY ON MY LOVE FOR SIZE	6.00
72	519 DJ	CHAIRMEN OF THE BOARD	WORKING ON A BUILDING OF LOVE	TRY ON MY LOVE FOR SIZE	15.00
72	520	FREDA PAYNE	YOU BROUGHT THE JOY	SUDDENLY IT WAS YESTERDAY	6.00
72	520 DJ	FREDA PAYNE	YOU BROUGHT THE JOY	SUDDENLY IT WAS YESTERDAY	10.00
72	521	8TH. DAY	EENY-MEENY-MINY-MO	ROCKS IN MY HEAD	5.00
72	521 DJ	8TH. DAY	EENY-MEENY-MINY-MO	ROCKS IN MY HEAD	8.00
72	522	PARLIAMENT	COME IN OUT OF THE RAIN	LITTLE OLD COUNTRY BOY	8.00
72	522 DJ	PARLIAMENT	COME IN OUT OF THE RAIN	LITTLE OLD COUNTRY BOY	12.00
72	523	BARRINO BROTHERS	I SHALL NOT BE MOVED	WHEN LOVE WAS A CHILD	20.00
72	523 DJ	BARRINO BROTHERS	I SHALL NOT BE MOVED	WHEN LOVE WAS A CHILD	30.00
72	524	CHAIRMEN OF THE BOARD	ELMO JAMES	BITTERSWEET	6.00
72	524 DJ	CHAIRMEN OF THE BOARD	ELMO JAMES	BITTERSWEET	15.00
72	525	HOLLAND-DOZIER	WHY CAN'T WE BE LOVERS	DON'T LEAVE ME instrumental	8.00
72	525 DJ	HOLLAND-DOZIER	WHY CAN'T WE BE LOVERS	DON'T LEAVE ME instrumental	15.00
72	526	FREDA PAYNE	UNHOOKED GENERATION	COME BACK	6.00
72	526 DJ	FREDA PAYNE	UNHOOKED GENERATION	COME BACK	10.00
73	527	CHAIRMEN OF THE BOARD	I'M ON MY WAY TO A BETTER PLACE	SO GLAD YOU'RE MINE	6.00
73	527 DJ	CHAIRMEN OF THE BOARD	I'M ON MY WAY TO A BETTER PLACE	SO GLAD YOU'RE MINE	15.00
73	528	HOLLAND-DOZIER	DON'T LEAVE ME STARVIN' FOR YOUR LOVE same: part 2		6.00
73	528 DJ	HOLLAND-DOZIER	DON'T LEAVE ME STARVIN' FOR YOUR LOVE same: part 2		10.00
73	529	FREDA PAYNE	I SHALL NOT BE MOVED	THRU' THE MEMORY OF MY MIND	10.00
73	529 DJ	FREDA PAYNE	I SHALL NOT BE MOVED	THRU' THE MEMORY OF MY MIND	15.00
73	530	CHAIRMEN OF THE BOARD	FINDER'S KEEPERS	same: instrumental	6.00
73	530 DJ	CHAIRMEN OF THE BOARD	FINDER'S KEEPERS	same: instrumental	8.00
73	531	GENERAL JOHNSON	ONLY TIME WILL TELL	Same: instrumental	6.00
73	531 DJ	GENERAL JOHNSON	ONLY TIME WILL TELL	Same: instrumental	8.00
73	532	DANNY WOODS	EVERYBODY'S TIPPIN'	ROLLER COASTER	10.00
73	532 DJ	DANNY WOODS	EVERYBODY'S TIPPIN'	ROLLER COASTER	15.00
73	533	FREDA PAYNE	BAND OF GOLD	THE EASIEST WAY TO FALL	15.00
73	533 DJ	FREDA PAYNE	BAND OF GOLD	THE EASIEST WAY TO FALL	30.00
74	2523	CHAIRMEN OF THE BOARD	EVERYBODY PARTY ALL NIGHT	MORNING GLORY (instrumental)	5.00
74	2523 DJ	CHAIRMEN OF THE BOARD	EVERYBODY PARTY ALL NIGHT	MORNING GLORY (instrumental)	6.00
74	2542	TYRONE EDWARDS	CAN'T GET ENOUGH OF YOU	YOU TOOK ME FROM A WORLD OUTSIDE	15.00
74	2542 DJ	TYRONE EDWARDS	CAN'T GET ENOUGH OF YOU	YOU TOOK ME FROM A WORLD OUTSI	22.00
74	2553	BRIAN HOLLAND	I'M SO GLAD	I'M SO GLAD PART2	15.00

74	2553 DJ	BRIAN HOLLAND	I'M SO GLAD	I'M SO GLAD PART2	22.00
74	2654	LAURA LEE	I NEED IT JUST AS BAD AS YOU	IF I'M GOOD ENOUGH TO LOVE	6.00
74	2654 DJ	LAURA LEE	I NEED IT JUST AS BAD AS YOU	IF I'M GOOD ENOUGH TO LOVE	10.00
76	4507	CHAIRMEN OF THE BOARD	YOU'VE GOT EXTRA ADDED POWER IN	EVERYBODY PARTY ALL NIGHT	5.00
76	4507 blue vinyl	CHAIRMEN OF THE BOARD	YOU'VE GOT EXTRA ADDED POWER IN	EVERYBODY PARTY ALL NIGHT	6.00
76	4507 DJ	CHAIRMEN OF THE BOARD	YOU'VE GOT EXTRA ADDED POWER IN	LET'S HAVE SOME FUN	8.00
77	4905	CHAIRMEN OF THE BOARD	YOU'VE GOT THAT EXTRA ADDED POWER	EVERYBODY PARTY ALL NIGHT	4.00
77	4905 blue vinyl	CHAIRMEN OF THE BOARD	YOU'VE GOT THAT EXTRA ADDED POWER	EVERYBODY PARTY ALL NIGHT	5.00
77	4905 DJ	CHAIRMEN OF THE BOARD	YOU'VE GOT THAT EXTRA ADDED POWER	EVERYBODY PARTY ALL NIGHT	6.00
77	5247	ELOISE LAWS	LOVE GOES DEEPER THAN THAT	CAMOUFLAGE	12.00
77	5247 DJ	ELOISE LAWS	LOVE GOES DEEPER THAN THAT	CAMOUFLAGE	15.00
77	5312	NEW YORK PORT AUTHORITY	I GOT IT	I GOT IT part 2	8.00
77	5312 DJ	NEW YORK PORT AUTHORITY	I GOT IT	I GOT IT part 2	10.00

ISLAND

Island Records is one of the most collectable labels within these pages. Island was formed by Chris Blackwell in 1959 in Jamaica, hence the name Island. In the beginning it focused itself on Calypso and Ska, the local popular style music. But by the mid-sixties it was firmly supporting Soul music in the UK, they released records by then obscure artists Joe Haywood, Roy C, Robert Parker etc. but the main attraction for soul collectors are the Jamaican artists who recorded soul, these are the artists who are the most sought after on Island. Within its release listing are Jackie Edwards, Jackie Opel, Philip James all doing fine soul recordings. As Chris Blackwell's label started to establish itself, he pressed other off-shoot labels like Sue, Jump, Aladdin, Black Swan etc. More ska was released on that most eye-catching red and white Island label with the Blues, Soul and R&B being released through its highly regarded Sue label.

Island Records always had a commitment to rock music, releasing some of the finest and most collectable rock LP's over the last 40 years. In 1971 they signed Bob Marley, in 1980 they added U2 to the labels rosta. Island Records became, possibly the most successful UK independent label of the era. It was no surprise when in 1989 Chris Blackwell sold out to Polygram. Today Island records is just as influential in the industry as it's ever been. In 2004 they signed Keane, McFly, and Busted. But for the 45rpm collector those red & white labeled heavy vinyl 45s, the pink labeled releases (Pink was a colour no other label had ever used in the UK) and later the palm tree design are all much prized to Soul, Ska, Reggae and rock 45 collectors alike.

62	031	WILBERT HARRISON	I'M BROKE	OFF TO SCHOOL	15.00
83	101 PS palm tree	DAVID JOSEPH	YOU CAN'T HIDE (YOUR LOVE FROM ME)	same: part 2	4.00
65	189 white & red	RUDY SEEDORF	ONE MILLION STARS	MR. BLUE	15.00
65	203	JACKIE OPAL	DON'T TAKE YOUR LOVE	WIPE THOSE TEARS	30.00
65	214	BLUES BUSTERS	HOW SWEET IT IS	I HAD A DREAM	25.00
65	218	JOE HAYWOOD	WARM AND TENDER LOVE	I WOULD IF I COULD	20.00
65	219	PHILIP JAMES	WIDE AWAKE IN A DREAM	TELL ME THE REASON	150.00
65	251	LEE ROY	OH EE BABY	MY LOVING - COME BACK	45.00
65	252	OWEN GRAY	SHOOK SHIMMY AND SHAKE	I'M GOING BACK	15.00
65	255	JACKIE EDWARDS	WHITE CHRISTMAS	MY LOVE AND I	10.00
65	256	ROSCOE GORDON	SURELY I LOVE YOU	WHAT YOU DO TO ME	20.00
65	257	SHIRLEY & LEE	LET THE GOOD TIMES ROLL	I'M GONE	15.00
65	258	SOUND SYSTEM	TAKE ME SERIOUS	YOU DON'T KNOW LIKE I KNOW	25.00
66	270	JACKIE EDWARDS	COME ON HOME	SOMETIMES	20.00
66	272	ROSCOE GORDON	NO MORE DOGGIN'	GOIN' HOME	25.00
66	273	ROY C	SHOTGUN WEDDING	HIGH SCHOOL DROPOUT	15.00
66	273 alternate flipside	ROY C	SHOTGUN WEDDING	I'M GONNA MAKE IT	25.00
66	274	JACKIE EDWARDS	L-O-V-E	WHAT'S YOUR NAME	15.00
66	275	LEAPERS CREEPERS SLEEPERS	PRECIOUS WORDS	BA BOO	10.00
66	280	WYNDER K. FROG	TURN ON YOUR LOVELIGHT	ZOOMING	30.00
66	286	ROBERT PARKER	BAREFOOTIN'	LET'S GO BABY (where the actio	12.00
66	287	JACKIE EDWARDS	THINK TWICE	OH MARY	4.00
66	3006	JACKIE EDWARDS	I FEEL SO BAD	I DON'T WANT TO BE MADE A FOOL	**407.00**
66	3008	ROBERT PARKER	HAPPY FEET	THE SCRATCH	15.00
66	3011	WYNDER K. FROG	SUNSHINE SUPERMAN	BLUES FOR A FROG	15.00
66	3018	JACKIE EDWARDS	ROYAL TELEPHONE	IT'S NO SECRET	10.00
66	3019	JOYCE BOND	TELL ME WHAT IT'S ALL ABOUT	TELL ME RIGHT NOW	30.00
67	3030	JACKIE EDWARDS	ONLY A FOOL BREAKS HIS OWN HEART	THE END	10.00
67	3031	BUSTER BROWN	MY BLUE HEAVEN	TWO WOMEN	45.00
67	3157	JACKIE EDWARDS	YOU'RE MY GIRL	HEAVEN ONLY KNOWS	15.00

pink label design begins.

67	6000	OWEN GRAY	INCENSE	HELP ME	18.00
67	6004	JIMMY CLIFF	GIVE AND TAKE	AIM AND AMBITION	10.00
67	6005	V.I.P.'S	STRAIGHT TO THE BOTTOM	IN A DREAM	30.00
67	6006	WYNDER K. FROG	GREEN DOOR	DANCING FROG	25.00
67	6007	TIM TAM & the TURNONS	WAIT A MINUTE	OPELIA	30.00
67	6008	JACKIE EDWARDS	COME BACK GIRL	TELL HIM YOU LIED	20.00
67	6009	JULIEN COVEY and the MACHINE	A LITTLE BIT HURT	SWEET BACON	40.00
67	6010	JOYCE BOND	DO THE TEASY	SUGAR	15.00
67	6011	JIMMY CLIFF	I GOT A FEELING (AND I CAN'T STOP)	HARD ROAD TO TRAVEL	20.00
68	6014	WYNDER K. FROG	I AM A MAN	SHOOK SHIMMY SHAKE	25.00
68	6024	JIMMY CLIFF	THANK YOU	THAT'S THE WAY LIFE GOES	10.00
68	6026	JACKIE EDWARDS	JULIE ON MY MIND	IF THIS IS HEAVEN	8.00
68	6039	JIMMY CLIFF	WATERFALL	THE REWARD	45.00
68	6040	SOUL PURPOSE	HUMMIN'	SOUL DRINK	25.00
68	6042	JACKIE EDWARDS and JIMMY CLIFF	YOU'RE MY GIRL	HEAVEN ONLY KNOWS	6.00
68	6044	WYNDER K. FROG	JUMPING JACK FLASH	BALDY	15.00
68	6051	JOYCE BOND	OB-LA-DI, OB-I A-DA	ROBIN HOOD RIDES AGAIN	6.00
68	6053	BOB & EARL	HARLEM SHUFFLE	I'LL KEEP RUNNING BACK	8.00
69	6061	ANGLOS	INCENSE	YOU'RE FOOLING ME	25.00
70	6087	JIMMY CLIFF	WILD WORLD	BE AWARE	6.00

palm tree label design begins

74	001	ROBERT PARKER	GET TA STEPPIN'	GET RIGHT ON DOWN	5.00
74	002	SWAMP DOGG	DID I COME BACK TOO SOON	I WOULDN'T LEAVE HERE	5.00
74	003	RALFI	WONDERFUL THING	GAMBLER	5.00
74	005	METERS	CHICKEN STRUT	TIPPI TOES	5.00
75	006	BOBBY McCLURE c/w DAYBREAK	YOU BRING OUT THE LOVE IN ME	SURVIVAL KIT	40.00
75	006 DJ	BOBBY McCLURE c/w DAYBREAK	YOU BRING OUT THE LOVE IN ME	SURVIVAL KIT	40.00
75	008	FANTASTIC JOHNNY C	DON'T DEPEND ON ME	WAITIN' FOR THE RAIN	8.00
75	008 DJ	FANTASTIC JOHNNY C	DON'T DEPEND ON ME	WAITIN' FOR THE RAIN	10.00
78	010 EP PS	SPENCER DAVIS GROUP	KEEP ON RUNNING + SOMEBODY HELP ME	I AM A MAN +EVERY LITTLE BIT HURTS + GIMME	6.00
76	6267	WAR	LOW RIDER	SO	6.00
76	6273	JAY DEE BRYANT	I WANT TO THANK YOU	STANDING OVATION FOR LOVE	15.00
76	6273 DJ	JAY DEE BRYANT	I WANT TO THANK YOU	STANDING OVATION FOR LOVE	22.00
76	6280	BARBARA PENNINGTON	RUNNING IN ANOTHER DIRECTION	RUNNING AWAY	4.00
76	6280 DJ	BARBARA PENNINGTON	RUNNING IN ANOTHER DIRECTION	RUNNING AWAY	6.00
76	6285	JACKIE EDWARDS	I FEEL SO BAD	COME ON HOME	20.00
76	6285 DJ	JACKIE EDWARDS	I FEEL SO BAD	COME ON HOME	20.00
76	6303	WAR	ME AND BABY BROTHER	IN YOUR EYES	4.00
76	6303 DJ	WAR	ME AND BABY BROTHER	IN YOUR EYES	5.00
77	6384	GEORGIE FAME	DAYLIGHT	THREE LEGGED MULE	15.00
77	6384 DJ	GEORGIE FAME	DAYLIGHT	THREE LEGGED MULE	20.00
78	6422	HI TENSION	HI-TENSION	GIRL I BETCHA	4.00
78	6442	JULIEN COVEY and the MACHINE	A LITTLE BIT HURT	SWEET BACON	20.00
78	6442 DJ	JULIEN COVEY and the MACHINE	A LITTLE BIT HURT	SWEET BACON	28.00
78	6446	HI TENSION	BRITISH HUSTLE	PEACE ON EARTH	3.00
79	6493	HI TENSION	THERE'S A REASON	IT MOVES ME	8.00

I-SPY
81	9	EDDIE FLOYD	BEAT SONG	LONDON	5.00

JAM
72	7	TYRONE & CARR	I WANT TO GIVE YOU MY EVERYTHING	I'M STILL IN LOVE WITH YOU	50.00
73	34	NEWBEATS	THE WAY YOU DO THE THINGS YOU	DOES YOUR BODY NEED LOVING	6.00
73	35	JESTERS	CAN'T LIVE WITHOUT YOU	FOOL FOR A DAY	20.00
73	37	MOON WILLIAMS	LOOKING FOR BLOVE	SEAWEED AVENUE	10.00

JAMA
77	35	WILLIE FISHER	PUT YOUR LOVIN ON ME	TAKE TIME TO KNOW HER	40.00

JANUS

A Phonogram label mostly dedicated to early 70's USA release soul. Notably, Eastbound, Westbound, USA Janus releases included some soul icons like Denise LaSalle, Little Anthony, Whispers, and the highly successful 70s disco recorders The Detroit Emeralds. There were a few "rock and pop" releases which I've added as I know many collectors would like to run the label, missing numbers between 001 & As with all Philips distributed labels of the period, the 45's usually left the factory with large holes dinked out and a small three pronged spider center in the middle. However some copies escaped the dinking process leaving a solid center with a small hole, these are far rarer and more desirable, we have priced these releases, accordingly. There are some missing numbers in this series, at the moment we don't know if these were issued or not. After release number 6141032 there were no soul related releases to our knowledge.

71	6146001 lh	FUNKADELIC	CAN YOU GET TO THAT	BACK IN YOUR MINDS	6.00
71	6146001 sh	FUNKADELIC	CAN YOU GET TO THAT	BACK IN YOUR MINDS	8.00
71	6146002 lh	DENISE LASALLE	TRAPPED BY A THING CALLED LOVE	KEEP IT COMING	6.00
71	6146002 sh	DENISE LASALLE	TRAPPED BY A THING CALLED LOVE	KEEP IT COMING	8.00
71	6146003 lh	CISSY HOUSTON	DARLING TAKE ME BACK	HANG ON TO A DREAM	6.00
71	6146003 sh	CISSY HOUSTON	DARLING TAKE ME BACK	HANG ON TO A DREAM	8.00
71	6146004 lh	DETROIT EMERALDS	WEAR THIS RING (WITH LOVE)	I BET YOU GET THE ONE (WHO LOV	6.00
71	6146004 sl	DETROIT EMERALDS	WEAR THIS RING (WITH LOVE)	I BET YOU GET THE ONE (WHO LOV	8.00
71	6146005 lh	LITTLE ANTHONY & the IMPERIALS	FATHER, FATHER	EACH ONE ONE TEACH ONE	6.00
71	6146005 sh	LITTLE ANTHONY & the IMPERIALS	FATHER, FATHER	EACH ONE ONE TEACH ONE	8.00
71	6146006	JONATHAN ROUND	DIDN'T IT MAKE YOU WANT TO GO HOME	TRAIN A COMIN'	4.00
71	6146007 lh	DETROIT EMERALDS	YOU WANT IT, YOU GOT IT	TILL YOU DECIDE TO COME HOME	6.00
71	6147007 sh	DETROIT EMERALDS	YOU WANT IT, YOU GOT IT	TILL YOU DECIDE TO COME HOME	10.00
72	6146008 lh	INTRIGUES	TO MAKE A WORLD	MOJO HANA	10.00
72	6146008 sh	INTRIGUES	TO MAKE A WORLD	MOJO HANA	12.00
72	6146009 lh	OHIO PLAYERS	PAIN	PAIN part 2	5.00
72	6146009 sh	OHIO PLAYERS	PAIN	PAIN part 2	6.00
72	6146010 lh	DENISE LASALLE	NOW RUN AND TELL THAT	THE DEEPER I GO (THE BETTER IT	5.00
72	6146010 sh	DENISE LASALLE	NOW RUN AND TELL THAT	THE DEEPER I GO (THE BETTER IT	6.00
72	6146012 lh	LITTLE ANTHONY & the IMPERIALS	WHERE DO I BEGIN	THERE'S AN ISLAND	6.00
72	6146012 sh	LITTLE ANTHONY & the IMPERIALS	WHERE DO I BEGIN	THERE'S AN ISLAND	8.00
72	6146013 lh	COUNTS	(WHY NOT) START ALL OVER AGAIN	THINKING SINGLE	8.00
72	6146013 sh	COUNTS	(WHY NOT) START ALL OVER AGAIN	THINKING SINGLE	8.00
72	6146014	MICHAEL GATELY	COLOUR ALL THE WORLD	HOOK ANOTHER HORSE	4.00
72	6146015 lh	DETROIT EMERALDS	DO ME RIGHT	BABY LET ME TAKE YOU (IN MY AR	6.00
72	6146015 sh	DETROIT EMERALDS	DO ME RIGHT	BABY LET ME TAKE YOU (IN MY AR	8.00
72	6146016 lh	DAMON SHAWN	FEEL THE NEED IN ME	I'M WISHING	10.00
72	6146016 sh	DAMON SHAWN	FEEL THE NEED IN ME	I'M WISHING	15.00
72	6146017 sh	OHIO PLAYERS	I GOT PLEASURE	I WANNA HEAR FROM YOU	8.00
72	6146017 lh	OHIO PLAYERS	I GOT PLEASURE	I WANNA HEAR FROM YOU	8.00
72	6146019 lh	DIANNE DAVIDSON	SYMPATHY	ALL I WANTED (ALL THE TIME)	10.00
72	6146019 sh	DIANNE DAVIDSON	SYMPATHY	ALL I WANTED (ALL THE TIME)	15.00
72	6146020 lh	DETROIT EMERALDS	FEEL THE NEED IN ME	AND I LOVE HER	6.00
72	6146020 sh	DETROIT EMERALDS	FEEL THE NEED IN ME	AND I LOVE HER	8.00

73	6146022 lh	AL DOWNING	BRING YOUR GOOD LOVIN' HOME	THANK YOU BABY	5.00
73	6146022 sh	AL DOWNING	BRING YOUR GOOD LOVIN' HOME	THANK YOU BABY	6.00
73	6146023 lh	WHISPERS	A MOTHER FOR MY CHILDREN	WHAT MORE CAN A GIRL ASK FOR	5.00
73	6146023 sh	WHISPERS	A MOTHER FOR MY CHILDREN	WHAT MORE CAN A GIRL ASK FOR	6.00
74	6146024	HARVEY MANDEL	UNO INO	SHANGRENADE	4.00
74	6146026 lh	WHISPERS	BINGO	SOMEONE'S WAITING	10.00
74	6146026 sh	WHISPERS	BINGO	SOMEONE'S WAITING	12.00
74	6146027 lh	CISSY HOUSTON	MIDNIGHT TRAIN TO GEORGIA	I'M SO GLAD I CAN LOVE AGAIN	5.00
74	6146027 sh	CISSY HOUSTON	MIDNIGHT TRAIN TO GEORGIA	I'M SO GLAD I CAN LOVE AGAIN	6.00
74	6146028	CLAUDINE LONGET	WHO BROKE YOUR HEART	GODBYE JIMMY GOODBYE	4.00
74	6146029	GOLDIE ZELKOWITZ	EASY LADY	GET IT BACK	4.00
74	6146031 lh	WHISPERS	BINGO	ONCE MORE WITH FEELING	8.00
74	6146031sh	WHISPERS	BINGO	ONCE MORE WITH FEELING	10.00
74	6146032 lh	AL DOWNING	I'LL BE HOLDING ON	HANDS	5.00
74	6146032 sh	AL DOWNING	I'LL BE HOLDING ON	HANDS	6.00

JAY BOY

69	01	DORIS WILLINGHAM	YOU CAN'T DO THAT	LOST AGAIN	20.00
69	01 DJ	DORIS WILLINGHAM	YOU CAN'T DO THAT	LOST AGAIN	28.00
69	02	SHADROCKS	THERE IS	JIGSAW	10.00
69	02 DJ	SHADROCKS	THERE IS	JIGSAW	15.00
69	03	COUNTRYMEN	AFTER ALL	WHITE ROSE OF ATHENS	6.00
69	03 DJ	COUNTRYMEN	AFTER ALL	WHITE ROSE OF ATHENS	10.00
69	04	MIGIL FIVE	IF I HAD MY WAY	SOMEBODY'S STOLEN THE MOONS	8.00
69	04 DJ	MIGIL FIVE	IF I HAD MY WAY	SOMEBODY'S STOLEN THE MOONS	10.00
69	05	HOGS	IT'S ALL COMING TO ME NOW	MOTOR CYCLE RIDER	5.00
69	05 DJ	HOGS	IT'S ALL COMING TO ME NOW	MOTOR CYCLE RIDER	10.00
69	06	CHORDS FIVE	SOME PEOPLE	BATTERSEA FAIR	6.00
69	06 DJ	CHORDS FIVE	SOME PEOPLE	BATTERSEA FAIR	10.00
69	07	MIKE QUINN	TOOTHBRUSH NELL	FAIRYCAKES FOR TEA	8.00
69	07 DJ	MIKE QUINN	TOOTHBRUSH NELL	FAIRYCAKES FOR TEA	10.00
69	08	DEE & QUOTUM	SEND SOME FLOWERS TO JUNE	SOMEDAY YOU'LL NEED SOMEONE	8.00
69	08 DJ	DEE & QUOTUM	SEND SOME FLOWERS TO JUNE	SOMEDAY YOU'LL NEED SOMEONE	10.00
69	09	LYONS & MALONE	DOCTOR GENTLE	SHE'S ALRIGHT	8.00
69	09 DJ	LYONS & MALONE	DOCTOR GENTLE	SHE'S ALRIGHT	10.00
69	10	SHELLEY PAUL	CLOWNS ARE COMING IN	TAKE ME TO YOUR HEART	6.00
69	10 DJ	SHELLEY PAUL	CLOWNS ARE COMING IN	TAKE ME TO YOUR HEART	10.00
11	unissued?				
69	12	E.K. BUNCH	BANANA	FREE	10.00
69	12 DJ	E.K. BUNCH	BANANA	FREE	15.00
69	13	ROUGH RIDERS	BOSS	PRESIDENT HOUSE	10.00
69	13 DJ	ROUGH RIDERS	BOSS	PRESIDENT HOUSE	15.00
69	14	BEDBUGS	FREEDUM SOUNDS	MESSAGE TO YOU	8.00
69	14 DJ	BEDBUGS	FREEDUM SOUNDS	MESSAGE TO YOU	10.00
69	15	ALTERATIONS	WORK IT UP	WORK REST AND PLAY	8.00
69	15 DJ	ALTERATIONS	WORK IT UP	WORK REST AND PLAY	10.00
69	16	SUGARLUMPS	SUGAR SUGAR	CAN'T WE BE FRIENDS	6.00
69	16 DJ	SUGARLUMPS	SUGAR SUGAR	CAN'T WE BE FRIENDS	8.00
70	17	GASLIGHT	MOVE	AND SO TO SLEEP	8.00
70	17 DJ	GASLIGHT	MOVE	AND SO TO SLEEP	10.00
70	18	ROUND TABLE	SATURDAY GIGUE	SCARBOROUGH FAIR	8.00
70	18 DJ	ROUND TABLE	SATURDAY GIGUE	SCARBOROUGH FAIR	10.00
70	19	SWAMP	THAT'S THE WAY I LIKE IT	REGGAE 70	8.00
70	19 DJ	SWAMP	THAT'S THE WAY I LIKE IT	REGGAE 70	10.00
70	20	SUGARLUMPS	SATAN'S PEOPLE	SHAME SHAME	8.00
70	20 DJ	SUGARLUMPS	SATAN'S PEOPLE	SHAME SHAME	10.00
70	21	NIYAH & the SUNFLAKES	TWO LITTLE BOYS	HOLDING ON	10.00
70	21 DJ	NIYAH & the SUNFLAKES	TWO LITTLE BOYS	HOLDING ON	15.00
70	22	RAY MERRELL	TEARS OF JOY	SEARCHING	**259.00**
70	22 DJ	RAY MERRELL	TEARS OF JOY	SEARCHING	300.00
70	22 second press	RAY MERRELL	TEARS OF JOY	SEARCHIN'	20.00
70	23	COMPLETE CYCLE	I'M ON THE ROAD AGAIN	BACK ON THE ROAD AGAIN	10.00
70	23 DJ	COMPLETE CYCLE	I'M ON THE ROAD AGAIN	BACK ON THE ROAD AGAIN	12.00
70	24	INVITATIONS	HOW'D YOU EVER GET THIS WAY	PICKING UP	10.00
70	24 DJ	INVITATIONS	HOW'D YOU EVER GET THIS WAY	PICKING UP	15.00
70	25	BOB AND EARL	HARLEM SHUFFLE	SEND FOR ME, I'LL BE THERE	6.00
70	25 DJ	BOB AND EARL	HARLEM SHUFFLE	SEND FOR ME, I'LL BE THERE	10.00
70	26	JACKIE LEE	DO THE TEMPTATION WALK	THE SHOTGUN AND THE DUCK	8.00
70	26 DJ	JACKIE LEE	DO THE TEMPTATION WALK	THE SHOTGUN AND THE DUCK	10.00
70	27	OLYMPICS	HULLY GULLY	BIG BOY PETE	8.00
70	27 DJ	OLYMPICS	HULLY GULLY	BIG BOY PETE	10.00
70	28	JACKIE LEE	YOU'RE EVERYTHING	WOULD YOU BELIEVE	8.00
70	28 DJ	JACKIE LEE	YOU'RE EVERYTHING	WOULD YOU BELIEVE	10.00
70	29	HIDEAWAYS	HIDE OUT	JOLLY JOE	8.00
70	29 DJ	HIDEAWAYS	HIDE OUT	JOLLY JOE	10.00
70	30	SHEPPARDS	HOW DO YOU LIKE IT	STUBBORN HEART	45.00
70	30 DJ	SHEPPARDS	STUBBORN HEART	HOW DO YOU LIKE IT	100.00
70	31	RICHARD TEMPLE	THAT BEATIN' RHYTHM	COULD IT BE	20.00
70	31 DJ	RICHARD TEMPLE	THAT BEATIN' RHYTHM	COULD IT BE	30.00

70	32	DONALD HEIGHT	TALK OF THE GRAPEVINE	THERE'LL BE NO TOMORROW	15.00
70	32 DJ	DONALD HEIGHT	TALK OF THE GRAPEVINE	THERE'LL BE NO TOMORROW	20.00
71	33	JERRY O	KARATE BOO-GA-LOO	THE PEARL	6.00
71	33 DJ	JERRY O	KARATE BOO-GA-LOO	THE PEARL	10.00
71	34	FREDDIE SCOTT	JUST LIKE A FLOWER	SPANISH HARLEM	8.00
71	34 DJ	FREDDIE SCOTT	JUST LIKE A FLOWER	SPANISH HARLEM	10.00
71	35	JACKIE MOORE	DEAR JOHN	HERE I AM	8.00
71	35 DJ	JACKIE MOORE	DEAR JOHN	HERE I AM	15.00
71	36	ERMA FRANKLIN	I JUST AIN'T READY FOR LOVE	THE RIGHT TO CRY	10.00
71	36 DJ	ERMA FRANKLIN	I JUST AIN'T READY FOR LOVE	THE RIGHT TO CRY	15.00
71	37	PHILLIP MITCHELL	THE WORLD NEEDS MORE PEOPLE LIKE YOU	I'M GONNA BUILD CALIFORNIA ALL OVER THE	40.00
71	37 DJ	PHILLIP MITCHELL	THE WORLD NEEDS MORE PEOPLE LIKE YOU	I'M GONNA BUILD CALIFORNIA ALL OVER THE	60.00
71	38	EXCITERS	SOUL MOTION	YOU KNOW IT AIN'T RIGHT	8.00
71	38 DJ	EXCITERS	SOUL MOTION	YOU KNOW IT AIN'T RIGHT	10.00
71	39	CHARLES LEONARD	FUNKY DRIVER ON A FUNKY BUS	FUNKY DRIVER ON A FUNKY BUS part 2	8.00
71	39 DJ	CHARLES LEONARD	FUNKY DRIVER ON A FUNKY BUS	FUNKY DRIVER ON A FUNKY BUS part 2	10.00
71	40	LIBERTY BELLES	SHING-A-LING TIME	JUST TRY ME	6.00
71	40 DJ	LIBERTY BELLES	SHING-A-LING TIME	JUST TRY ME	10.00
71	41	ERMA FRANKLIN	PIECE OF MY HEART	BIG BOSS MAN	8.00
71	41 DJ	ERMA FRANKLIN	PIECE OF MY HEART	BIG BOSS MAN	10.00
71	42	DREAMS	(THEY CALL ME) JESSE JAMES	CHARGE	10.00
71	42 DJ	DREAMS	(THEY CALL ME) JESSE JAMES	CHARGE	15.00
71	43	VIRGIL GRIFFIN	LA DA DA DA DA	CLIMBING	10.00
71	43 DJ	VIRGIL GRIFFIN	LA DA DA DA DA	CLIMBING	15.00
71	44	BLUES BUSTERS	I CAN'T STOP	INSPIRED TO LOVE YOU	8.00
71	44 DJ	BLUES BUSTERS	I CAN'T STOP	INSPIRED TO LOVE YOU	10.00
71	45	BARONS	NO MORE BABY LOVE	SOCIETY DON'T LET US DOWN	10.00
71	45 DJ	BARONS	NO MORE BABY LOVE	SOCIETY DON'T LET US DOWN	15.00
71	46	RANDOLF WALKER	I LOVE HER MORE	GOOD OLE SOUL	8.00
71	46 DJ	RANDOLF WALKER	I LOVE HER MORE	GOOD OLE SOUL	10.00
71	47	HOWARD JOHNSON	SLIDE	THAT MAGIC TOUCH CAN SEND YOU	10.00
71	47 DJ	HOWARD JOHNSON	SLIDE	THAT MAGIC TOUCH CAN SEND YOU	15.00
71	48	GEORGE TORRENCE & the NATURALS	SO LONG, GOOD BYE	LICKIN' STICK	10.00
71	48 DJ	GEORGE TORRENCE & the NATURALS	SO LONG, GOOD BYE	LICKIN' STICK	15.00
71	49	CHARLES LATTIMORE	DO THE THING	WE TRY HARDER	8.00
71	49 DJ	CHARLES LATTIMORE	DO THE THING	WE TRY HARDER	10.00
72	50	SHAN MILES	SOUL PEOPLE	SOUL PEOPLE part 2	8.00
72	50 DJ	SHAN MILES	SOUL PEOPLE	SOUL PEOPLE part 2	10.00
72	51	DONALD HEIGHT	THREE HUNDRED AND SIXTY FIVE DAYS	I'M WILLING TO WAIT	8.00
72	51 DJ	DONALD HEIGHT	THREE HUNDRED AND SIXTY FIVE DAYS	I' M WILLING TO WAIT	10.00
72	52	JACKIE LEE & DOLORES HALL	WHETHER IT'S RIGHT OR WRONG	BABY I'M SATISFIED	8.00
72	52 DJ	JACKIE LEE & DOLORES HALL	WHETHER IT'S RIGHT OR WRONG	BABY I'M SATISFIED	10.00
72	53	JERRY O	FUNKY BOOGALOO	PUSH PUSH	8.00
72	53 DJ	JERRY O	FUNKY BOOGALOO	PUSH PUSH	10.00
72	54	GEORGE FREEMAN	WHY ARE YOU DOING THIS TO ME	I'M LIKE A FISH	30.00
72	54 DJ	GEORGE FREEMAN	WHY ARE YOU DOING THIS TO ME	I'M LIKE A FISH	40.00
72	55	BILLY YOUNG	I'M AVAILABLE	SWEET WOMAN	10.00
72	55 DJ	BILLY YOUNG	I'M AVAILABLE	SWEET WOMAN	15.00
72	56	OLYMPICS	BABY, DO THE PHILLY DOG	SECRET AGENTS	6.00
72	56 DJ	OLYMPICS	BABY, DO THE PHILLY DOG	SECRET AGENTS	10.00
72	57	PHILLIP MITCHELL	FREE FOR ALL (WINNER TAKES ALL)	FLOWER CHILD	15.00
72	57 DJ	PHILLIP MITCHELL	FREE FOR ALL (WINNER TAKES ALL)	FLOWER CHILD	30.00
72	58	ERNIE & ED	INDICATION	BEAUTIFUL WORLD	60.00
72	58 DJ	ERNIE & ED	INDICATION	BEAUTIFUL WORLD	75.00
72	59	FREDDIE SCOTT	ARE YOU LONELY FOR ME BABY	THE WOMAN OF MY LOVE	8.00
72	59 DJ	FREDDIE SCOTT	ARE YOU LONELY FOR ME BABY	THE WOMAN OF MY LOVE	12.00
72	60	DONALD HEIGHT	I CAN'T GET ENOUGH	WE GOTTA MAKE UP	10.00
72	60 DJ	DONALD HEIGHT	I CAN'T GET ENOUGH	WE GOTTA MAKE UP	15.00
72	61	FURYS	WHAT IS SOUL	I LOST MY BABY	10.00
72	61 DJ	FURYS	WHAT IS SOUL	I LOST MY BABY	15.00
72	62	JERRY O	DANCE WHAT CHA WANNA	AFRO TWIST TIME (UM-GOW-WOW)	8.00
72	62 DJ	JERRY O	DANCE WHAT CHA WANNA	AFRO TWIST TIME (UM-GOW-WOW)	12.00
72	63	LOU & LAURA POOLE	ONLY YOU KNOW AND I KNOW	LOOK AT ME	10.00
72	63 DJ	LOU & LAURA POOLE	ONLY YOU KNOW AND I KNOW	LOOK AT ME	15.00
72	64	JIMMY CONWELL	CIGARETTE ASHES	SECOND HAND HAPPINESS	10.00
72	64 DJ	JIMMY CONWELL	CIGARETTE ASHES	SECOND HAND HAPPINESS	25.00
72	65	MIRETTES	NOW THAT I FOUND YOU, BABY	HE'S ALL RIGHT WITH ME	10.00
72	65 DJ	MIRETTES	NOW THAT I FOUND YOU, BABY	HE'S ALL RIGHT WITH ME	15.00
72	66	JACKIE LEE	OH, MY DARLIN'	DON'T BE ASHAMED	15.00
72	66 DJ	JACKIE LEE	OH MY DARLIN'	DON'T BE ASHAMED	30.00
72	67	JIMMY THOMAS	WHERE THERE'S A WILL	JUST RYIN' TO PLEASE YOU	8.00
72	67 DJ	JIMMY THOMAS	WHERE THERE'S A WILL	JUST TRYIN' TO PLEASE YOU	15.00
73	68	FURYS	I'M SATISFIED WITH YOU	JUST A LITTLE MIXED UP	20.00
72	68 DJ	FURYS	I'NM SATISFIED WITH YOU	JUST A LITTLE MIXED UP	30.00
72	69	FI-DELS	TRY A LITTLE HARDER	YOU NEVER DO RIGHT (MY BABY)	20.00
72	69 DJ	FI-DELS	TRY A LITTLE HARDER	YOU NEVER DO RIGHT (MY BABY)	30.00
72	70	DONNIE ELBERT	HALF AS OLD	BABY LET ME LOVE YOU TONITE	8.00
72	70 DJ	DONNIE ELBERT	HALF AS OLD	BABY LET ME LOVE YOU TONIGHT	10.00
72	71	WATTS 103rd. ST. RHYTHM	SPREADIN' HONEY	CHARLEY	10.00

72	71 DJ	WATTS 103rd. ST. RHYTHM	SPREADIN' HONEY	CHARLEY	15.00
72	72	BOB AND EARL	I CAN'T GET AWAY	I'LL KEEP RUNNING BACK	25.00
72	72 DJ	BOB AND EARL	I CAN'T GET AWAY	I'LL KEEP RUNNING BACK	40.00
73	73	BOB AND EARL BAND	MY LITTLE GIRL	HIS AND HER'S SHUFFLE	15.00
73	73 DJ	BOB AND EARL BAND	MY LITTLE GIRL	HIS AND HERS SHUFFLE	25.00
73	74	OLYMPICS	THE SAME OLD THING	I'LL DO A LITTLE BIT MORE	15.00
73	74 DJ	OLYMPICS	THE SAME OLD THING	I'LL DO A LITTLE BIT MORE	25.00
73	75	BOBBY WOMACK	WHAT IS THIS	I WONDER	15.00
73	75 DJ	BOBBY WOMACK	WHAT IS THIS	I WONDER	25.00
73	76	JACKIE LEE	BRING IT HOME	AFRICAN BOOGALOO	10.00
73	76 DJ	JACKIE LEE	BRING IT HOME	AFRICAN BOOGALOO	15.00
72	77	DELORES HALL	GOOD LOVIN' MAN	W-O-M-A-N	10.00
72	77 DJ	DELORES HALL	GOOD LOVIN' MAN	W-O-M-A-N	15.00
72	78	CLAY HAMMOND	DANCE LITTLE GIRL	TWIN BROTHER	10.00
72	78 DJ	CLAY HAMMOND	DANCE LITTLE GIRL	TWIN BROTHER	15.00
72	79	LITTLE WAYNE ANTHONY	HEY NAW	FREEDOM TO LOVE	8.00
72	79 DJ	LITTLE WAYNE ANTHONY	HEY NAW	FREEDOM TO LOVE	12.00
74	80	K.C. & the SUNSHINE BAND	BLOW YOUR WHISTLE	BLOW YOUR WHISTLE part 2	4.00
74	80 DJ	K.C. & the SUNSHINE BAND	BLOW YOUR WHISTLE	BLOW YOUR WHISTLE part 2	5.00
74	81	MIAMI	PARTY FREAKS	PART FREAKS PART2	5.00
74	81 DJ	MIAMI	PARTY FREAKS	PART FREAKS PART2	6.00
74	82	ALLEY	SINGING IN POVERTY	TIP TOE	5.00
74	82 DJ	ALLEY	SINGING IN POVERTY	TIP TOE	6.00
74	83	K.C. & the SUNSHINE BAND	SOUND YOUR FUNKY HORN	WHY DON'T WE GET TOGETHER	4.00
74	83 DJ	K.C. & the SUNSHINE BAND	SOUND YOUR FUNKY HORN	WHY DON'T WE GET TOGETHER	5.00
74	84	AFRO DIMENSIONS	JUST BECAUSE	IF YOU DON'T WANT MY LOVE	20.00
74	84 DJ	AFRO DIMENSIONS	JUST BECAUSE	IF YOU DON'T WANT MY LOVE	30.00
74	85	GEORGE McCRAE	ROCK YOUR BABY	ROCK YOUR BABY part 2	4.00
74	85 DJ	GEORGE McCRAE	ROCK YOUR BABY	ROCK YOUR BABY part 2	8.00
78	85 ink	GEORGE McCRAE	ROCK YOUR BABY	ROCK YOUR BABY part 2	3.00
75	86 DJ	MIAMI	HEY Y'ALL WE'RE MIAMI	CHICKEN YELLOW	5.00
75	86 DJ	MIAMI	HEY Y'ALL WE'RE MIAMI	CHICKEN YELLOW	8.00
75	87	RUBY WILSON & the BLUE NOTES	NUMBER ONE IN MY HEART	I'LL BE RIGHT HERE (WHEN YOU R	8.00
75	87 DJ	RUBY WILSON & the BLUE NOTES	NUMBER ONE IN MY HEART	I'LL BE RIGHT HERE (WHEN YOU R	10.00
75	88	K.C. & the SUNSHINE BAND	QUEEN OF CLUBS	DO IT GOOD	4.00
75	88 DJ	K.C. & the SUNSHINE BAND	QUEEN OF CLUBS	DO IT GOOD	5.00
75	88 ink	K.C. & the SUNSHINE BAND	QUEEN OF CLUBS	DO IT GOOD	3.00
75	89	SUNSHINE BAND	SHOOTGUN SHUFFLE	HEY J	4.00
75	89 DJ	SUNSHINE BAND	SHOOTGUN SHUFFLE	HEY J	5.00
75	90	GEORGE McCRAE	I CAN'T LEAVE YOU ALONE	YOU GOT MY HEART	4.00
75	90 DJ	GEORGE McCRAE	I CAN'T LEAVE YOU ALONE	YOU GOT MY HEART	5.00
75	91	unissued?			
75	92	GEORGE McCRAE	YOU CAN HAVE IT ALL	MAKE IT RIGHT	4.00
75	92 DJ	GEORGE McCRAE	YOU CAN HAVE IT ALL	MAKE IT RIGHT	5.00
75	93	K.C. & the SUNSHINE BAND	GET DOWN TONIGHT	YOU DON'T KNOW	4.00
75	93 DJ	K.C. & the SUNSHINE BAND	GET DOWN TONIGHT	YOU DON'T KNOW	5.00
75	94	WILLIE & ANTHONY	SUGAR, SUGAR, SUGAR	IT'S NEVER TOO LATE	6.00
75	94 DJ	WILLIE & ANTHONY	SUGAR, SUGAR, SUGAR	IT'S NEVER TOO LATE	8.00
75	95	GEORGE McCRAE	I GET LIFTED	SING A HAPPY SONG	4.00
75	95 DJ	GEORGE McCRAE	I GET LIFTED	SING A HAPPY SONG	5.00
75	96	MIAMI	FUNK IT UP	FREAK ON DOWN MY WAY	5.00
75	96 DJ	MIAMI	FUNK IT UP	FREAK ON DOWN MY WAY	6.00
75	97	FIRE	OH THAT'S MY MAN	YOU DON'T KNOW	4.00
75	97 DJ	FIRE	OH THAT'S MY MAN	YOU DON'T KNOW	5.00
75	98	SEVEN SEAS	SUPER JAWS	PAT'S JAM	5.00
75	98 DJ	SEVEN SEAS	SUPER JAWS	PAT'S JAM	6.00
75	99	K.C. & the SUNSHINE BAND	THAT'S THE WAY (I LIKE IT)	AIN'T NOTHIN' WRONG	4.00
75	99 DJ	K.C. & the SUNSHINE BAND	THAT'S THE WAY (I LIKE IT)	AIN'T NOTHIN' WRONG	5.00
75	100	GEORGE McCRAE	IT'S BEEN SO NLONG	YOU GOT TO KNOW	4.00
75	100 DJ	GEORGE McCRAE	IT'S BEEN SO NLONG	YOU GOT TO KNOW	5.00
75	101	K.C. & the SUNSHINE BAND	I'M SO CRAZY (BOUT YOU)	BOOGIE SHOES	4.00
75	101 DJ	K.C. & the SUNSHINE BAND	I'M SO CRAZY (BOUT YOU)	BOOGIE SHOES	5.00
76	102	JACKEY BEAVERS	TRYING TO GET BACK TO YOU, GIRL	same: Part2	15.00
76	102 DJ	JACKEY BEAVERS	TRYING TO GET BACK TO YOU, GIRL	same: Part2	25.00
76	103	ALLEY	TRUCKLOAD	TIP TOE	4.00
76	103 DJ	ALLEY	TRUCKLOAD	TIP TOE	5.00
76	104	SUNSHINE BAND	ROCK YOUR BABY	SUNSHINE CITY	4.00
76	104 DJ	SUNSHINE BAND	ROCK YOUR BABY	SUNSHINE CITY	6.00
76	105	GEORGE McCRAE	I AIN'T LYING	TREAT ME BAD	4.00
76	105 DJ	GEORGE McCRAE	I AIN'T LYING	TREAT ME BAD	5.00
76	106	RUBY WILSON	MAN AND A BABY	SKY HIGH	4.00
76	106 DJ	RUBY WILSON	MAN AND A BABY	SKY HIGH	5.00
76	107	GEORGE McCRAE	HONEY I	TAKE THIS LOVE OF MINE BACK	4.00
76	107 DJ	GEORGE McCRAE	HONEY I	TAKE THIS LOVE OF MINE BACK	5.00
76	108	PAUL REVERE and the RAIDERS	AIN'T NOTHING WRONG	YOU'RE REALLY SAYING SOMETHING	4.00
76	108 DJ	PAUL REVERE and the RAIDERS	AIN'T NOTHING WRONG	YOU'RE REALLY SAYING SOMETHING	5.00
76	109	FOXY	GET OFF YOUR AAHH AND DANCE	same: part 2	4.00
76	109 DJ	FOXY	GET OFF YOUR AAHH AND DANCE	same: part 2	6.00
76	110	KC & THE SUNSHINE BAND	(SHAKE SHAKE SHAKE) SHAKE YOUR	I'M A PUSHOVER	4.00

76	110 DJ	KC & THE SUNSHINE BAND	(SHAKE SHAKE SHAKE) SHAKE YOUR		I'M A PUSHOVER	5.00
76	111	MIAMI	KILL THAT ROACH		MR. NOTORIOUS	6.00
76	111 DJ	MIAMI	KILL THAT ROACH		MR. NOTORIOUS	8.00
76	112	K.C. the SUNSHINE BAND	KEEP IT COMING		WRAP YOUR ARMS AROUND ME	4.00
76	112 DJ	K.C. the SUNSHINE BAND	KEEP IT COMING		WRAP YOUR ARMS AROUND ME	5.00
77	113	ATLANTIS	IT'S EASY		WHO LOVES YOU MORE	4.00
77	113 DJ	ATLANTIS	IT'S EASY		WHO LOVES YOU MORE	5.00
77	114	BEVERLY ROBINSON	DISCO DANCING		MENAGE A TROIS	4.00
77	114 DJ	BEVERLY ROBINSON	DISCO DANCING		MENAGE A TROIS	5.00
77	115	FLINT	THIS SIDE OF MIDNIGHT		LOVE BE A SHINING STAR	4.00
77	115 DJ	FLINT	THIS SIDE OF MIDNIGHT		LOVE BE A SHINING STAR	5.00
77	116	FLINT	ROCKET LOVE		TEACHER TEACHER	4.00
77	116 DJ	FLINT	ROCKET LOVE		TEACHER TEACHER	5.00

JET

78	134	KIM MORRISON	ONE IN A MILLION		HOLLYWOOD AND VINE	6.00
78	36382	RITA WRIGHT	TOUCH ME, TAKE ME		LOVE IS ALL YOU NEED	**131.00**

JIVE

	146 test press	PRECIOUS WILSON	ONLY THE STRONG SURVIVE		AIN'T NO LOVE	8.00

JOE BOY

00	002	PAT LEWIS	IT'LL NEVER BE OVER FOR ME		blank:	6.00
00	002V2	JOSEPH MOORE c/w MOUSIE & TRAPS	I STILL CAN'T GET YOU		IT'S ALL IN THE WAY	10.00
01	003 PS	GIRLS FROM U.N.C.L.E.	AGENT FOR LOVE		THE SPY	15.00
01	003 DJ	GIRLS FROM U.N.C.L.E.	AGENT FOR LOVE		THE SPY	10.00
98	1 PS	DONNIE ELBERT	SO SOON		CAN'T GET OVER LOSING YOU	20.00
99	1 PS export	DONNIE ELBERT	SO SOON		CAN'T GET OVER LOSING YOU	20.00
98	2 EP PS	BIG MAYBELLE	YESTERDAY'S KISSES		4 track 1998 UK EP	10.00
98	3 DJ	RAY MARCHAND c/w PUFFS	YOUR SHIP OF FOOLS		I ONLY CRY ONCE A DAY NOW	15.00
98	3 PS	RAY MARCHAND c/w PUFFS	YOUR SHIP OF FOOLS		I ONLY CRY ONCE A DAY NOW	10.00
98	3 PS + postcard	RAY MARCHAND c/w PUFFS	YOUR SHIP OF FOOLS		I ONLY CRY ONCE A DAY NOW	15.00
00	007 DJ	TIMMY WILLIS	SUCH MISERY		blank:	30.00

Lea Hall Club Rugely 1st. anniversary commemorative single. Pre-release promo for Soul HQ 007 release.

01	4 DJ	FALCONS	YOU'VE GOT THE POWER		I JUST WANT TOP LOVE YOU (INNE	15.00
01	6 DJ	CONTOURS	I'M SO GLAD YOUR HERE		THE GROOVE	25.00
01	9 PS	RITA & THE TIARAS	GONE WITH THE WIND (IS MY LOVE)		ON A DAY WHEN IT'S RAINING + 1	10.00
01	10 DJ	LITTLE JOHNNY HAMILTON	KEEPON MOVING		OH HOW I LOVE YOU	15.00
01	12	DRIZA BONE	PRESSURE		blank:	8.00
01	007	VARIOUS ARTISTS	NIGHT OWL 3: box set		5 x 45s box set with special slip over cover	50.00

JOKER

Same as labels like Demand, S.O.S., etc. the Joker label was an early eighties label dedicated to releasing Northern Soul. The origin of the label is vague. Recordings were most probably not taken from master tapes.

1		ENCHANTMENTS c/w MARSHA GEE	I'M IN LOVE WITH YOUR DAUGHTER		THE PEANUT DUCK	10.00
2		TONY MIDDLETON c/w METROS	SPANISH MAIDEN		SINCE I FOUND MY BABY	8.00
3 EP		VARIOUS ARTISTS	GIRL ACROSS THE STREET + 3		4 track EP no cover	10.00

A four track EP with no special cover: Tracks include Mose Smith – Girl Across The Sreet 2. Orlons – Envy 3. Julian Covay – A Little Bit Hurt 4. Showmen – Our Love Will Grow

4		POOKIE HUDSON c/w PADDED CELL	THIS GET TO ME		MISTER MISERY	8.00

JOKER

01	716	FRANK WILSON	MY SUGAR BABY		same: instrumental	6.00

JOX

69	005 test press	AMBASSADORS	ALL YOU GOT GIRL (IS ALL YOU NEED)		same: instrumental	1000.00

White label UK test press with handwritten credits. Pulled from the Ambassadors USA Arctic LP "Soul Summit" with a previously unissued instrumental version on the flip. Label name is stamped into the deadwax.

K&B

77	5540	PATRICK ALLEN	GROOVY FEELING		same: instrumental	150.00

KAMA SUTRA

The 200 series was distributed by Pye International and as was Pye's policy on import releases from the USA to give the 45's the same release number as it's USA counterpart. There was very little soul released on Kama Sutra compared to itS Rock catalogue with such high profile bands as Lovin' Spoonful, Sopwith Camel, Sha Na Na etc.

One white artist with a lot of soul, was Billy Harner, his 1968 USA Kama Sutra #242 – "What About The Music" – was creating big demand with the underground soul clubs of the late sixties Twisted Wheel, Up The Junction, Catacoombs all had this title at the top of their play lists. In 1970, a UK collecting legend was born. The nearest to the true story, is still clouded by a little mystery but this is how I remember the birth of the UK mispress 45 – "What About The Music"- *instrumental* version. I believe it was Alan Day and friends who approached Kama Sutra to press 300 copies of this currently top tune –"What About The Music" – to sell to the collectors and punters of the soul club circuit. Imagine their disappointment when they eagerly opened the boxes only to find a mis-press of – "What About The Music" – instead of the vocal version, Kama Sutra had pressed a short instrumental version. Alledgedly a handful escaped before they were returned to Kama Sutra to be replaced by the correct vocal version. A short while later the vocal version was on general release. The instrumental then started to receive exposure in the clubs. When Alan Day asked if they could send the instrumental version 45's back to him, he was told they had all been destroyed. I can remember for two or three years from 1971 the BBC occasionally used the instrumental on Radio One as the low volume backing to various talk-overs. The instrumental version was NOT a promo copy with no mention of demo or promo on the label. The easiest way to identify the instrumental version without playing the disc, is to check the deadwax width. On the instrumental the deadwax is three times wider than on the vocal. Perhaps only five copies are know to exist today, one certainly has damaged vinyl with a cigarette burn on the a-side. Today at auction we would expect at least a four figure sum for it. Other than that 45 Kama Sutra is an unexciting label for the soul collector.

66	202	TRADE WINDS	MIND EXCURSION	LITTLE SUSAN'S DREAMING	10.00
66	202 DJ	TRADE WINDS	MIND EXCURSION	LITTLE SUSAN'S DREAMING	15.00
66	208	LOVIN' SPOONFUL	SIX O'CLOCK	THE FINALE	15.00
66	208 DJ	LOVIN' SPOONFUL	SIX O'CLOCK	THE FINALE	20.00
69	2013012	MOE KOFFMAN	CURRIED SOUL	COUNTRY SOUL	5.00
70	2013024	SHANGRI-LAS	LEADER OF THE PACK	REMEMBER (WALKIN' IN THE SAND)	5.00
70	2013029 instru	BILLY HARNER	WHAT ABOUT THE MUSIC	PLEASE SPARE ME THIS TIME	1000.00
71	2013029 solid	BILLY HARNER	WHAT ABOUT THE MUSIC	PLEASE SPARE ME THIS TIME	25.00
71	2013029 lh	BILLY HARNER	WHAT ABOUT THE MUSIC	PLEASE SPARE ME THIS TIME	15.00

KENT

A label dedicated to releasing obscure USA soul recordings on CD, they have so far release 26 vinyl 45's. Distributed by Ace Records quantities pressed are relatively low, with deletion on any of these titles this has always made the price rise. A label to buy as soon as they release new product. Guaranteed collectable label, as every release is a hand picked winner, with many being previously uinissued tracks from the vaults.

85	TOWN 101	ADAMS APPLES c/w JACKIE WILSON	DON'T TAKE IT OUT ON THIS WORLD	I DON'T WANT TO LOSE YOU	8.00
85	TOWN 102	JACK MONTGOMEREY c/w MARIE KNIGHT	DEARLY BELOVED	THAT'S NO WAY TO TREAT A GIRL	15.00
85	TOWN 103	IVORYS c/w TOMMY HUNT	PLEASE STAY	THE WORK SONG	30.00
85	TOWN 104 withdrawn	CANDY & the KISSES c/w CHUCK JACKSON	MR. CREATOR	HAND IT OVER	75.00
85	TOWN 105	LITTLE CARL CARLTON c/w HESITATIONS	COMPETITION AIN'T NOTHING	I'M NOT BUILT THAT WAY	20.00
85	TOWN 106	JOHNNY CASWELL c/w STEINWAYS	YOU DON'T LOVE ME ANYMORE	YOU'VE BEEN LEADING ME ON	20.00
85	TOWN 107	JACKIE LEE c/w EDDIE BISHOP	DARKEST DAYS	CALL ME	25.00
85	TOWN 108 EP PS	BOBBYBLAND	SHOES + GETTING USED TO THE BLUES	CALL ON ME + GOOD TIME CHARLIE	15.00
85	TOWN 109	EDDIE HOLMAN c/w PATRICK BRADLEY	I SURRENDER	JUST ONE MORE CHANCE	15.00
86	TOWN 110	MAXINE BROWN	IT'S TORTURE	I GOT LOVE	20.00
98	TOWN 111	LITTLE ANN c/w O.C. TOLBERT	WHAT SHOULD I DO	I'M SHOOTING HIGH	15.00
99	TOWN 112	LITTLE ANN	WHO ARE YOU TRYING TO FOOL	I GOT TO HAVE YOU	15.00
02	TOWN 113	MILLIE JACKSON c/w MAYBERRY MOVEMENT	DON'T SEND NOBODY ELSE	TWO WRONGS DON'T MAKE A RIGHT	6.00
03	TOWN 114	DAVIS, LARRY c/w DANNY MONDAY	I'VE BEEN HURT SO MANY TIMES	BABY WITHOUT YOU	6.00
02	TOWN 115	JOHN EDWARDS c/w BILL BRANDON	TIN MAN	THE STREETS GOT MY LADY	6.00
02	TOWN 116	TOBI LARK c/w O.C. TOLBERT	CHALLENGE MY LOVE	YOU GOT ME TURNED AROUND	6.00
02	TOWN 117	CARLA THOMAS	I'LL NEVER STOP LOVING YOU	I PLAY FOR KEEPS	6.00
02	TOWN 118	DOROTHY WILLIAMS c/w ALBERT WASHINGTON	THE WELL'S GONE DRY	I'M THE MAN	6.00
02	TOWN 119	MELBA MOORE c/w DEAN PARRISH	THE MAGIC TOUCH	BRICKS BROKEN BOTTLES AND STICKS	6.00
03	TOWN 120	DOTTIE and MILLIE c/w TOBI LARK	TALKIN' ABOUT MY BABY	HAPPINESS IS HERE	6.00
02	TOWN 121	LITTLE ANN	WHAT SHOULD I DO	WHO ARE YOU TRYING TO FOOL	6.00
03	TOWN 122	THEMES c/w PENTAGONS	DO YOURSELF A FAVOR	GONNA WAIT FOR YOU	6.00
03	TOWN 123	BOBBY GARRETT c/w CURTIS LEE	I CAN'T GET AWAY	IS SHE IN YOUR TOWN	6.00
82	TOWN 501	MARY LOVE c/w WILLIE HUTCH	YOU TURNED MY BITTER INTO SWEET	I CAN'T GET ENOUGH + THIS COUL	10.00
82	TOWN 501 DJ	MARY LOVE c/w WILLIE HUTCH	YOU TURNED MY BITTER INTO SWEET	I CAN'T GET ENOUGH + THIS COUL	15.00
82	TOWN 502 EP	DANNY MONDAY c/w MARY LOVE	BABY WITHOUT YOU	LAY THIS BURDEN DOWN	15.00
86	studio acetate 10"	MELBA MOORE	THE MAGIC TOUCH	blank:	**305.00**

KENT 6Ts

100 CLUB ANNIVERSARY SERIES

85	6T 1	MARY LOVE, IKETTES, ETTA JAMES	HEY, STONEY FACE	IT'S BEEN SO LONG + WALLFLOWER	15.00
86	6T 2	MELBA MOORE c/w CHUCK JACKSON	THE MAGIC TOUCH	LITTLE BY LITTLE	45.00
87	6T 3	PLATTERS c/w SAMMY AMBROSE	NOT MY GIRL	WELCOME TO DREAMSVILLE	40.00
88	6T 4	PEGGY WOODS	LOVE IS GONNA GET YOU	YOU JUST CHEAT AND LIE	30.00
89	6T 5	WALLY COX c/w SIX TEASERS	THIS MAN WANTS YOU	DOING THE HUNDRED	20.00
90	6T 6	FABULOUS IMPACTS c/w PLATTERS	BABY BABY, I WANT YOU	NO NO NO NO NO NO NOT MY GIRL	40.00

the above 45 at the time in 1990 was credited to the Fabulous Impacts later identified as The Moments release on Hog

91	6T 7 DJ	CARLA THOMAS	I'LL NEVER STOP LOVING YOU	PEACHES BABY	50.00
92	6T 8 DJ	CHUCK JACKSON	WHAT'S WITH THIS LONELINESS	SURF AND SOUL	40.00
93	6T 9	CHUBBY CHECKER c/w TEARDROPS	YOU CAN'T LOSE SOMETHING YOU	HERE COMES LONELINESS	20.00
94	6T 10	PHIL TERRELL	LOVE HAS PASSED ME BY	WHY DID SHE LIE	30.00
95	6T 11	JOHN EDWARDS c/w LOLETTA HOLLOWAY	AIN'T THAT GOOD ENOUGH	THIS MANS ARMS	30.00
96	6T 12	SHARON SCOTT c/w DEAN COURTNEY	(PUTTING MY HEART UNDER) LOCK & KEY	TODAY IS MY DAY	40.00
97	6T 13	LORRAINE CHANDLER c/w METROS	YOU ONLY LIVE TWICE	MY IMAGINATION	50.00
98	6T 14	PEGGY GAINES	WHEN THE BOY THAT YOU LOVE	MAKE UP YOUR MIND	30.00
99	6T 15	JOHNNIE TAYLOR c/w JUDY CLAY	PLEASE LET ME IN	SINCE YOU CAME ALONG	30.00
00	6T 16	JUNIOR McCANTS c/w GARLAND GREEN	TRY ME FOR YOUR NEW LOVE	COME THROUGH ME	75.00
01	6T 17	MILL EVANS c/w MILLIONAIRES	AIN'T YOU GLAD	I'M THE ONE WHO LOVES YOU	30.00
02	6T 18	M&M and the PEANUTS c/w CHARMAINES	CAN'T SAY NO	I IDOLIZE YOU	30.00
03	6T 19	DEBRA JOHNSON c/w DIPLOMATS	TO GET LOVE YOU'VE GOT TO BRING	I REALLY LOVE YOU	30.00
04	6T 20	MAGICIANS c/w WEE WILLIE WALKER	(JUST A LITTLE) FAITH AND UNDERSTANDING	I DON'T WANT TO TAKE A CHANCE	75.00

KGH

KGH stands for King George's Hall, this commemorative 45 was given away free on Saturday 23rd. January 1999 at the 4th. Anniversary All Nighter at King George's Hall, Blackburn.

99	1 DJ	BELITA WOODS c/w DARRELL BANKS	THAT'S WHEN I'LL STOP LOVING YOU	OPEN THE DOOR TO YOUR HEART	10.00

KING

The UK King label has no connection with the USA Cincinnati iconic black music record company. UK King was owned by Rita and Benny King and was part of R & B Discs Ltd., 282B Stamford Hill London N16. Hence the R&B stood for Rita and Benny, and the King stood for their surname. An ironic coincidence that R&B and KING had two totally difference references than the soul collector would at first presume. The King label had perhaps as many as 84 releases. Its catalogue covered a wide range of music from Irish Folk to Ska & Reggae. In amongst it were some very important soul 45 releases most notably Mary Love's double sided Northern soul classic released in 1965 on KG1024 and Jackie Opel's soul version of Marie Knight's classic soul ballad. Plus a mysterious and unconfirmed rumour that unissued test presses of Mary Love's – "Lay This Burden Down" – may exist. But without knowing it's alleged release number I've missed it off the listing. This attractive label which had its own company sleeve, the two matched together are one of the most attractive collectable 45s you could possibly wish to see. The label tried every form of music to gain a major hit, but in maybe 84 attempts, they failed to do so.

64	1002	BETTY EVERETT	YOUR LOVING ARMS	HAPPY I LONG TO BE	15.00
64	1007	DYNAMICS	SO IN LOVE WITH ME	SAY YOU WILL	25.00
64	1008	DOBBY DOBSON & the DELTAS	CRY A LITTLE CRY	DIAMONDS AND PEARLS	10.00
64	1009	SONNY HINES	ANYTIME, ANY DAY, ANYWHERE	NOTHING LIKE YOR LOVE	30.00
64	1011	JACKIE OPEL	CRY ME A RIVER	ETERNAL LOVE	25.00
65	1017	ALEXIS KORNER'S ALL STARS	SEE SEE RIDER	BLUES A LA KING	30.00
65	1021	RUMBLERS	SOULFUL JERK	HEY DID A DA DA	100.00
65	1024	MARY LOVE	YOU TURNED MY BITTER INTO SWEET	I'M IN YOUR HANDS	**254.00**
65	1031	ROCOMARS	ALL IN BLACK WOMAN	GIVE ME TIME	8.00
66	1035	VOGUES	HUMPTY DUMPTY	MAGIC TOWN	10.00
66	1038	JUNE ADAMS	RIVER KEEP MOVIN'	HEAVENLY FATHER	40.00
66	1041	SAM and DAVE	NO MORE PAIN	YOU AIN'T NO BIG THING BABY	20.00
66	1044	GUESS WHO	HEY GIRL	IT'S MY PRIDE	25.00
66	1050	SOVEREIGNS	BRING ME HOME LOVE	THAT'S THE WAY LOVE IS	15.00

KINGDOM

81	8012	WAYNE GIBSON	UNDER MY THUMB	YESTERDAY'S PAPERS	8.00

KLIK

76	617	DONNIE ELBERT	A LITTLE PIECE OF LEATHER	DOWN HOME BLUES	8.00

KOOL KAT

Label owned by the Inferno label entrepreneur Neil Rushton. This UK only, previously unissued from the vaults of Palmer Records Detroit Northern Soul dance record was released at a time when Northern Soul was at its lowest point in popularity. Consequently this 45 saw low sales and ultimately has become a rarity. A 45 that can only rise in value in the years to come.

87	5	ERIC & the VIKINGS c/w WILLIE JONES	HURTING	MY BABY AIN'T NO PLAY THING	20.00
87	5 red vinyl	ERIC & the VIKINGS c/w WILLIE JONES	HURTING	MY BABY AIN'T NO PLAY THING	30.00

KRP

83	102	SIMONE	I CAN FEEL THE ICE MELTING	IT'S TO LATE	6.00

KTDA

93	2 PS	MUSIC & MYSTERY feat: GWEN McCRAE	ALL THIS LOVE I'M GIVING	ALL THIS LOVE I'M GIVING edit	6.00

KUDU

73	4000	ESTHER PHILLIPS	HOME IS WHERE THE HATRED IS	TIL MY BACK AIN'T GOT NO BONE	30.00
73	4000 DJ	ESTHER PHILLIPS	HOME IS WHERE THE HATRED IS	TIL MY BACK AIN'T GOT NO BONE	40.00
73	4001	GROVER WASHINGTON JR.	INNER CITY BLUES	AIN'T NO SUNSHINE	5.00
73	4001 DJ	GROVER WASHINGTON JR.	INNER CITY BLUES	AIN'T NO SUNSHINE	6.00
73	4002	ESTHER PHILLIPS	I'VE NEVER FOUND A MAN	CHERRY RED	15.00
73	4002 DJ	ESTHER PHILLIPS	I'VE NEVER FOUND A MAN	CHERRY RED	20.00
75	924	GROVER WASHINGTON JR.	MR. MAGIC	BLACK FROST	4.00
75	924 DJ	GROVER WASHINGTON JR.	MR. MAGIC	BLACK FROST	5.00
75	925 paper	ESTHER PHILLIPS	WHAT A DIFFERENCE A DAY MAKES	TURN AROUND LOOK AT ME	6.00
75	925 DJ	ESTHER PHILLIPS	WHAT A DIFFERENCE A DAY MAKES	TURN AROUND LOOK AT ME	10.00
75	925 ink	ESTHER PHILLIPS	WHAT A DIFFERENCE A DAY MAKES	TURN AROUND LOOK AT ME	5.00
75	927	RON CARTER	ANYTHING GOES	B IG FRO	4.00
75	927 DJ	RON CARTER	ANYTHING GOES	B IG FRO	5.00
76	929	ESTHER PHILLIPS	FEVER	FOR ALL WE KNOW	6.00
76	929 DJ	ESTHER PHILLIPS	FEVER	FOR ALL WE KNOW	8.00
76	930	GROVER WASHINGTON JR.	KNUCKLEHEAD	KNUCKLEHEAD part 2	5.00
76	930 DJ	GROVER WASHINGTON JR.	KNUCKLEHEAD	KNUCKLEHEAD part 2	6.00
76	931	HANK CRAWFORD	I HEAR A SYMPHONY	ADISON	4.00
76	931 DJ	HANK CRAWFORD	I HEAR A SYMPHONY	ADISON	5.00
77	934	DAVID MATTHEWS	SHOOGIE WANNA BOOGIE	GOTTA BE WHERE YOU ARE	5.00
77	934 DJ	DAVID MATTHEWS	SHOOGIE WANNA BOOGIE	GOTTA BE WHERE YOU ARE	6.00
77	935	IDRIS MUHAMMAD	COULD HEAVEN EVER BE LIKE THIS	TURN THIS MUTHA OUT	5.00
77	935 DJ	IDRIS MUHAMMAD	COULD HEAVEN EVER BE LIKE THIS	TURN THIS MUTHA OUT	6.00
78	943	IDRIS MUHAMMAD	BOOGIE TO THE TOP	BOOGIE TO THE TOP part 2	5.00
78	943 DJ	IDRIS MUHAMMAD	BOOGIE TO THE TOP	BOOGIE TO THE TOP part 2	6.00

KWANZA

Kwanza had just three releases in the UK, all in 1974. A short lived but significant label, that did some high quality pre-disco soul. Kwanza was distributed within the UK by Kinney, all release numbers are preceded by the letter K. Terry Collins had another important USA Kwanza recording this was issued in 1973 on UK Warner Bros K16426.

74	19500	BLACK IVORY	NO ONE ELSE WILL DO	WHAT GOES AROUND (COMES AROUND	6.00
74	19500 DJ	BLACK IVORY	NO ONE ELSE WILL DO	WHAT GOES AROUND (COMES AROUND	8.00
74	19501	CLASSIC SULLIVANS	PAINT YOURSELF IN THE CORNER	I DON'T WANT TO LOSE YOU	20.00
74	19501 DJ	CLASSIC SULLIVANS	PAINT YOURSELF IN THE CORNER	I DON'T WANT TO LOSE YOU	28.00
74	19502 DJ	SPYDER TURNER	HAPPY DAYS	SINCE I DON'T HAVE YOU	10.00
74	19502 DJ	SPYDER TURNER	HAPPY DAYS	SINCE I DON'T HAVE YOU	15.00

LIBERTY

Hollywood based Liberty Records was founded in 1955 by Simon Waronker. Waronker was a violin playing prodigy, after he left school he got a scholarship to study violin in Philadelphia and then France, and ended up in Germany during the rise of Adolf Hitler. Escaping from the pursuing Nazi youth, Jewish Waronker was pleased to get back to the United States and return home to Los Angeles where in 1939 he landed a job working for 20th Century Fox playing his violin on musical scores for movies. In his last year with Fox, in 1955, his cousin Herb Newman suggested they go into the record business. After much consideration Simon Waronker gave up his highly paid job, and decided to start a record company called Liberty Records. Ironically Herb Newman had changed direction on the proposed partnership and started his own label, which would become another West Coast giant ERA Records. The first release on the label was 55000 which corresponded with the year of the release.

Liberty was distributed in the UK by EMI records and as you can see all Liberty USA 45 release carried the same release number on UK presses. The first record to interest "Soul" was 410, released after its first 45 was pressed; underlining how prolific Liberty Records were.

Other Liberty labels released in the UK were Imperial, Minit, and Johnny River's Soul City. On the Imperial USA releases, if they gain a UK release again the USA serial release number was retained. The Minit label being formed in New Orleans was primarily releasing R&B and Soul releases along with Soul City this strengthened the interest in the label, from a soul collecting perspective. The last 45 to be issued on the Liberty label in the USA was in 1971, after that year all Liberty release came out on United Artists, although EMI have occasionally used the Liberty name and logo on various reissues.

63	10115	WILSON PICKETT	IT'S TOO LATE	I'M GONNA LOVE YOU	20.00
63	10115 DJ	WILSON PICKETT	IT'S TOO LATE	I'M GONNA LOVE YOU	28.00
63	10130	GENE McDANIELS	ANYONE ELSE	NEW LOVE IN OLD MEXICO	8.00
63	10130 DJ	GENE McDANIELS	ANYONE ELSE	NEW LOVE IN OLD MEXICO	10.00
64	10175	JACKIE DESHANNON	BE GOOD BABY	DON'T TURN YOUR BACK ON ME	5.00
64	10175 DJ	JACKIE DESHANNON	BE GOOD BABY	DON'T TURN YOUR BACK ON ME	8.00
64	10177	TIMI YURO	HURT	BE ANYTHING (BUT BE MINE)	8.00
64	10177 DJ	TIMI YURO	HURT	BE ANYTHING (BUT BE MINE)	100
65	10187	GARY LEWIS & THE PLAYBOYS	THIS DIAMOND RING	TIJUANA WEDDING	15.00
65	10187 DJ	GARY LEWIS & THE PLAYBOYS	THIS DIAMOND RING	TIJUANA WEDDING	20.00
65	10191	FLEETWOODS	BEFORE AND AFTER (LOSING YOU)	ALMOST THERE	20.00
65	10191 DJ	FLEETWOODS	BEFORE AND AFTER (LOSING YOU)	ALMOST THERE	28.00
65	10202	JACKIE DESHANNON	WHAT THE WORLD NEEDS NOW IS LOVE	IT'S LOVE BABY (24 HOURS A DAY	6.00
65	10202 DJ	JACKIE DESHANNON	WHAT THE WORLD NEEDS NOW IS LOVE	IT'S LOVE BABY (24 HOURS A DAY	10.00
65	10206	P.J. PROBY	I DON'T WANT TO HEAR IT ANYMORE	LET THE WATER RUN DOWN	6.00
65	10206 DJ	P.J. PROBY	I DON'T WANT TO HEAR IT ANYMORE	LET THE WATER RUN DOWN	10.00
66	10236	P.J. PROBY	TO MAKE A BIG MAN CRY	WICKED WOMAN	8.00
66	10236 DJ	P.J. PROBY	TO MAKE A BIG MAN CRY	WICKED WOMAN	10.00
66	12018	T-BONE WALKER	PARTY GIRL	HERE IN THE DARK	15.00
66	12018 DJ	T-BONE WALKER	PARTY GIRL	HERE IN THE DARK	18.00
66	12023	JOHNNY RIVERS	SECRET AGENT MAN	TOM DOOLEY	25.00
66	12023 DJ	JOHNNY RIVERS	SECRET AGENT MAN	TOM DOOLEY	35.00
66	12028	HOMER BANKS	A LOT OF LOVE	FIGHTING TO WIN	40.00
66	12028 DJ	HOMER BANKS	A LOT OF LOVE	FIGHTING TO WIN	75.00
66	12040	JIMMY HOLIDAY	BABY I LOVE YOU	YOU WON'T GET AWAY	15.00
66	12040 DJ	JIMMY HOLIDAY	BABY I LOVE YOU	YOU WON'T GET AWAY	25.00
66	12042	JOHNNY SAYLES	ANYTHING FOR YOU	DEEP DOWN IN MY HEART	40.00
66	12042 DJ	JOHNNY SAYLES	ANYTHING FOR YOU	DEEP DOWN IN MY HEART	60.00
66	12047	HOMER BANKS	60 MINUTES OF YOUR LOVE	DO YOU KNOW WHAT	25.00
66	12047 DJ	HOMER BANKS	60 MINUTES OF YOUR LOVE	DO YOU KNOW WHAT	45.00
66	12048	JIMMY HOLIDAY	GIVE ME YOUR LOVE	THE TURNING POINT	20.00
66	12048 DJ	JIMMY HOLIDAY	GIVE ME YOUR LOVE	THE TURNING POINT	28.00
67	12051	5TH. DIMENSION	TOO POOR TO DIE	GO WHERE YOU WANNA GO	22.00
67	12051 DJ	5TH. DIMENSION	TOO POOR TO DIE	GO WHERE YOU WANNA GO	30.00
67	12053	JIMMY HOLIDAY	I'M GONNA MOVE TO THE CITY	EVERYBODY NEEDS HELP	15.00
67	12053 DJ	JIMMY HOLIDAY	I'M GONNA MOVE TO THE CITY	EVERYBODY NEEDS HELP	28.00
67	12055	FATS DOMINO	IT KEEPS RAINING	BLUE MONDAY	18.00
67	12055 DJ	FATS DOMINO	IT KEEPS RAINING	BLUE MONDAY	28.00
67	12056	5TH. DIMENSION	ANOTHER DAY, ANOTHER HEARTACHE	ROSECRANS BLVD	5.00
67	12056 DJ	5TH. DIMENSION	ANOTHER DAY, ANOTHER HEARTACHE	ROSECRANS BLVD	6.00
67	12058	JIMMY HOLIDAY & CLYDIE KING	READY, WILLING AND ABLE	WE GOT A GOOD THING GOING	40.00
67	12058 DJ	JIMMY HOLIDAY & CLYDIE KING	READY, WILLING AND ABLE	WE GOT A GOOD THING GOING	75.00
67	12060	HOMER BANKS	HOOKED BY LOVE	LADY OF STONE	40.00
67	12060 DJ	HOMER BANKS	HOOKED BY LOVE	LADY OF STONE	60.00

LIBERTY changes it's label design from the EMI distributed black label with silver credits, to the Philips distributed ? dark blue left hand side ? light blue design label with a white "Statue of Liberty" logo.

67	15021	BRENTON WOOD	GIMME LITTLE SIGN	I THINK YOU'VE GOT YOUR FOOLS	10.00
67	15037	5TH. DIMENSION	POOR SIDE OF TOWN	PAPER CUP	6.00
68	15044	AL WILSON	NOW I KNOW WHAT LOVE IS	DO WHAT YOU GOTTA DO	40.00
68	15052	5TH. DIMENSION	CARPET MAN	MAGIC GARDEN	5.00
68	15065	BRENTON WOOD	BABY YOU GOT IT	CATCH YOU ON THE REBOUND	10.00
68	15081	5TH. DIMENSION	TICKET TO RIDE	ORANGE AIR	4.00
68	15092	TIMI YURO	SOMETHING BAD ON MY MIND	WRONG	8.00
68	15098	FATS DOMINO	WALKING TO NEW ORLEANS	BLUEBERRY HILL	5.00
68	15103	BRENTON WOOD	SOME GOT IT, SOME DON'T	ME AND YOU	8.00
68	15120	SHIRLEY & ALFRED	TOO MUCH, TOO SOON	KID GAMES AND NURSERY RHYMES	6.00
68	15121	AL WILSON	THE SNAKE	WHO COULD BE LOVIN' YOU	50.00
68	15142	TIMI YURO	I MUST HAVE BEEN OUT OF MY MIND	INTERLUDE	20.00
69	15177	CLASSIC IV	TWENTY FOUR HOURS OF LONELINESS	STORMY	15.00
68	15182	TIMI YURO	IT'LL NEVER BE OVER FOR ME	AS LONG AS THERE IS YOU	**455.00**
69	15190	DORSEY BURNETTE	THE GREATEST LOVE	THIN LITTLE PLAIN LITTLE SIMPL	10.00
69	15193	5TH. DIMENSION	AQUARIUS - LET THE SUNSHINE IN	DON'TCHAHEAR ME CALLING YOU	4.00
69	15221	VENTURES	HAWAII FIVE - 0	HIGHER THAN THOU	10.00
69	15233	IKE & TINA TURNER	CRAZY 'BOUT YOU BABY	I'VE BEEN LOVING YOU TOO LONG	4.00
69	15236	AL WILSON	SHAKE ME WAKE ME	I STAND ACCUSED	8.00
69	15243	5TH. DIMENSION	WORKING ON A GROOVY THING	SUNSHINE OF YOUR LOVE	8.00
69	15257	AL WILSON	LODI	BY THE TIME I GET TO PHEONIX	5.00
69	15274	FATS DOMINO	I'M READY	THE FAT MAN	10.00
69	15288	5TH. DIMENSION	WEDDING BELL BLUES	LET IT BE ME	4.00
70	15303	IKE & TINA TURNER	COME TOGETHER	HONKY TONK WOMAN	6.00
70	15334	DEE CLARK	24 HOURS OF LONELINESS	WHERE DID ALL THE GOOD TIMES G	12.00
70	15356	5TH. DIMENSION	TRAIN, KEEP ON MOVIN'	I'LL BE LOVIN' YOU FOREVER	22.00
70	15356	5TH. DIMENSION	I'LL BE LOVIN' YOU FOREVER	TRAIN, KEEP ON MOVIN'	20.00

70	15367	IKE & TINA TURNER	I WANT TO TAKE YOU HIGHER	CONTACT HIGH	5.00

LIBERTY changes label design to black label with silver lettering, black Statue Of Liberty on a white oblong background. Left hand side sky blue to green then yellow rainbow effect finish the label redesign, that never released more than a handful of soul releases. Promo's had a solid large silver A to one side. Demonstration copies are rare.

15367

70	15392	HOMER BANKS	60 MINUTES OF YOUR LOVE	I KNOW YOU KNOW IKNOW I KNOW	10.00
70	15392 DJ	HOMER BANKS	60 MINUTES OF YOUR LOVE	I KNOW YOU KNOW IKNOW I KNOW	25.00
70	15428	BETTY EVERETT	I GOT TO TELL SOMEBODY	WHY ARE YOU LEAVING ME	15.00
70	15428	BETTY EVERETT	I GOT TO TELL SOMEBODY	WHY ARE YOU LEAVING ME	25.00
71	15432	IKE & TINA TURNER	FUNKIER THAN A MOSQUITO'S TWEETER	PROUD MARY	8.00
71	15432 DJ	IKE & TINA TURNER	FUNKIER THAN A MOSQUITO'S TWEETER	PROUD MARY	10.00
71	15443	WAR	SUN OF SUN	LONELY FEELIN'	6.00
71	15443 DJ	WAR	SUN OF SUN	LONELY FEELIN'	8.00

EPs

62	2054 EP PS	GENE McDANIELS	A TEAR + CHIP CHIP	SHE'S COME BACK + ANOTHER TEAR	20.00
62	2192 EP PS	P.J. PROBY	P.J.PROBY: inc: stagger lee **+3**	1965 4 track EP with cover	8.00
65	2214 EP PS	TIMI YURO	SOUL!	1965 4 track EP with cover	25.00
66	2253 EP PS	TIMI YURO	MAKE THE WORLD GO AWAY	1966 4 track EP with cover	20.00
65	4035 EP PS	IRMA THOMAS	TIME IS ON MY SIDE	1965 4 track EP with cover	60.00
65	4036 EP PS	VARIOUS ARTISTS	WE SING THE BLUES	1965 4 track EP with cover	45.00

55000 series these series used the same release numbers as the USA LIBERTY label.

62	55410	TIMI YURO	SATAN NEVER SLEEPS	LET ME CALL YOU SWEETHEART	10.00
62	55410 DJ	TIMI YURO	SATAN NEVER SLEEPS	LET ME CALL YOU SWEETHEART	15.00
62	55405	GENE McDANIELS	ANOTHER TEARS FALLS	CHIP CHIP	6.00
62	55405 DJ	GENE McDANIELS	ANOTHER TEARS FALLS	CHIP CHIP	10.00
62	55410	TIMI YURO	SATAN NEVER SLEEPS	LET ME CALL YOU SWEETHEART	10.00
62	55410 DJ	TIMI YURO	SATAN NEVER SLEEPS	LET ME CALL YOU SWEETHEART	15.00
62	55469	TIMI YURO	WHAT'S THE MATTER BABY (IS IT HURTIN)	THIRTEENTH HOUR	15.00
62	55469 DJ	TIMI YURO	WHAT'S THE MATTER BABY (IS IT HURTIN)	THIRTEENTH HOUR	22.00
62	55480	GENE McDANIELS	POINT OF NO RETURN	WARMER THAN A WHISPER	10.00
62	55480 DJ	GENE McDANIELS	POINT OF NO RETURN	WARMER THAN A WHISPER	15.00
62	55510	GENE McDANIELS	SOMEBODY'S WAITING	SPANISH LACE	20.00
62	55510 DJ	GENE McDANIELS	SOMEBODY'S WAITING	SPANISH LACE	28.00
63	55519	TIMI YURO	I AIN'T GONNA CRY NO MORE	THE LOVE OF A BOY	30.00
63	55519 DJ	TIMI YURO	I AIN'T GONNA CRY NO MORE	THE LOVE OF A BOY	45.00
63	55541	GENE McDANIELS	CRY BABY CRY	THE PUZZLE	10.00
63	55541 DJ	GENE McDANIELS	CRY BABY CRY	THE PUZZLE	15.00
63	55553	RIVINGTONS	I'M LOSING MY GRIP	THE BIRDS THE WORD	10.00
63	55553 DJ	RIVINGTONS	I'M LOSING MY GRIP	THE BIRDS THE WORD	15.00
63	55587	TIMI YURO	MAKE THE WORLD GO AWAY	LOOK DOWN	8.00
63	55587 DJ	TIMI YURO	MAKE THE WORLD GO AWAY	LOOK DOWN	10.00
63	55597	GENE McDANIELS	IT'S A LONELY TOWN (WITHOUT YOU)	FALSE FRIENDS	30.00
63	55597 DJ	GENE McDANIELS	IT'S A LONELY TOWN (WITHOUT YOU)	FALSE FRIENDS	45.00
63	55634	TIMI YURO	GOTTA TRAVEL ON	DOWN IN THE VALLEY	8.00
63	55634 DJ	TIMI YURO	GOTTA TRAVEL ON	DOWN IN THE VALLEY	10.00
64	55723	GENE McDANIELS	IN TIMES LIKE THESE	MAKE ME A PRESENT OF YOU	10.00
64	55723 DJ	GENE McDANIELS	IN TIMES LIKE THESE	MAKE ME A PRESENT OF YOU	15.00
65	55752	GENE McDANIELS	(THERE GOES) THE FORGOTTEN MAN	EMILY	75.00
65	55752 DJ	GENE McDANIELS	(THERE GOES) THE FORGOTTEN MAN	EMILY	100.00
65	55805	GENE McDANIELS	WALK WITH A WINNER	A MIRACLE	150.00
65	55805 DJ	GENE McDANIELS	WALK WITH A WINNER	A MIRACLE	200.00
66	55842	TOMMY SANDS	THE STATUE	LITTLE ROSITA	50.00
66	55842 DJ	TOMMY SANDS	THE STATUE	LITTLE ROSITA	**103.00**
66	55866	DEL SHANNON	THE BIG HURT	I GOT IT BAD	10.00
66	55866 DJ	DEL SHANNON	THE BIG HURT	I GOT IT BAD	15.00
66	55867	U.S. T-BONES	MOMENT OF SOFTNESS	SIPPIN' AND CHIPPIN'	10.00
66	55867 DJ	U.S. T-BONES	MOMENT OF SOFTNESS	SIPPIN' AND CHIPPIN'	15.00
66	55898	GARY LEWIS & THE PLAYBOYS	MY HEART'S SYMPHONY	TINA (I HELD YOU IN MY ARMS)	22.00
66	55898 DJ	GARY LEWIS & THE PLAYBOYS	MY HEART'S SYMPHONY	TINA (I HELD YOU IN MY ARMS)	40.00
66	55936	P.J. PROBY	NIKI HOEKY	GOOD THINGS ARE COMING MY WAY	10.00
66	55936 DJ	P.J. PROBY	NIKI HOEKY	GOOD THINGS ARE COMING MY WAY	45.00
67	55953	MARK JAMES	I CAN'T LET YOU GO	BIMBO KNOWS	10.00
67	55953 DJ	MARK JAMES	I CAN'T LET YOU GO	BIMBO KNOWS	15.00
67	55974	P.J. PROBY	YOU CAN'T COME HOME AGAIN	WORK WITH ME ANNIE	12.00
67	55974 DJ	P.J. PROBY	YOU CAN'T COME HOME AGAIN	WORK WITH ME ANNIE	20.00
67	55983	MICHAEL CLARK	NONE OF THESE GIRLS	WORK OUT	10.00
67	55983 DJ	MICHAEL CLARK	NONE OF THESE GIRLS	WORK OUT	15.00

66000 serires used the same release numbers as the USA IMPERIAL label releases

64	66009	MAJORS	OOH WEE BABY	I'LL BE THERE	25.00
64	66009 DJ	MAJORS	OOH WEE BABY	I'LL BE THERE	30.00
64	66041	IRMA THOMAS	TIME IS ON MY SIDE	ANYONE WHO KNOWS WHAT LOVE IS	25.00
64	66041 DJ	IRMA THOMAS	TIME IS ON MY SIDE	ANYONE WHO KNOWS WHAT LOVE IS	50.00
65	66080	IRMA THOMAS	HE'S MY GUY	(I WANT A) TRUE, TRUE LOVE	20.00
65	66080 DJ	IRMA THOMAS	HE'S MY GUY	(I WANT A) TRUE, TRUE LOVE	28.00
65	66082	FENWAYS	WALK	WHIP AND JERK	15.00
65	66082 DJ	FENWAYS	WALK	WHIP AND JERK	20.00
65	66094	JIMMY McCRACKLIN	EVERY NIGHT EVERY DAY	CAN'T RAISE ME	10.00
65	66094 DJ	JIMMY McCRACKLIN	EVERY NIGHT EVERY DAY	CAN'T RAISE ME	15.00
65	66095	IRMA THOMAS	SOME THINGS YOU NEVER GET USED TO	YOU DON'T MISS A GOOD THING	20.00

65	66095 DJ	IRMA THOMAS	SOME THINGS YOU NEVER GET USED TO	YOU DON'T MISS A GOOD THING	40.00
65	66102	O'JAYS	LIPSTICK TRACES	THINK IT OVER, BABY	50.00
65	66102 DJ	O'JAYS	LIPSTICK TRACES	THINK IT OVER, BABY	75.00
65	66106	IRMA THOMAS	I'M GONNA CRY TILL MY TEARS RUN	NOBODY WANTS TO HEAR NOBODY'S	22.00
65	66106 DJ	IRMA THOMAS	I'M GONNA CRY TILL MY TEARS RUN	NOBODY WANTS TO HEAR NOBODY'S	30.00
66	66113	MEL CARTER	HOLD ME, THRILL ME, KISS ME	SWEET LITTLE GIRL	20.00
66	66113 DJ	MEL CARTER	HOLD ME, THRILL ME, KISS ME	SWEET LITTLE GIRL	28.00
66	66129	JIMMY McCRACKLIN	THINK	STEPIN' UP IN CLASS	10.00
66	66129 DJ	JIMMY McCRACKLIN	THINK	STEPIN' UP IN CLASS	15.00
66	66137	IRMA THOMAS	WHAT ARE YOU TRYING TO DO	TAKE A LOOK	100.00
66	66137 DJ	IRMA THOMAS	WHAT ARE YOU TRYING TO DO	TAKE A LOOK	**224.00**
66	66175	JOHNNY RIVERS	ROOGALATOR	I WASHED MY HANDS IN MUDDY WATER	15.00
66	66175 DJ	JOHNNY RIVERS	ROOGALATOR	I WASHED MY HANDS IN MUDDY WATER	25.00
66	66178	IRMA THOMAS	IT'S A MAN'S-WOMAN'S WORLD PART1	SAME: PART2	15.00
66	66178 DJ	IRMA THOMAS	IT'S A MAN'S-WOMAN'S WORLD PART1	SAME: PART2	22.00
66	66197	O'JAYS	STAND IN FOR LOVE	FRIDAY NIGHT	20.00
66	66197 DJ	O'JAYS	STAND IN FOR LOVE	FRIDAY NIGHT	30.00
66	66205	JOHNNY RIVERS	POOR SIDE OF TOWN	A MAN CAN CRY	25.00
66	66205 DJ	JOHNNY RIVERS	POOR SIDE OF TOWN	A MAN CAN CRY	35.00
67	66224	JACKIE DESHANNON	FIND ME LOVE	COME ON DOWN	20.00
67	66224 DJ	JACKIE DESHANNON	FIND ME LOVE	COME ON DOWN	22.00
67	66227	JOHNNY RIVERS	BABY I NEED YOUR LOVIN'	GETTING READY FOR TOMORROW	6.00
67	66227 DJ	JOHNNY RIVERS	BABY I NEED YOUR LOVIN'	GETTING READY FOR TOMORROW	10.00
67	66244	JOHNNY RIVERS	THE TRACKS OF MY TEARS	ROSECRANS BLVD.	5.00
67	66244 DJ	JOHNNY RIVERS	THE TRACKS OF MY TEARS	ROSECRANS BLVD.	8.00

LIGHTNING

78	9016	ODDJOB	EXPRESS YOURSELF	RASSHOPPER	15.00

LONDON

UK Decca's flagship label, that pressed all manner of material from releases from around the world. London, is considered by many as the most important label ever made in the UK, it was over the years certainly the most prolific. London was responsible for bringing more 50's Rock & Roll, Blues, R&B, Doo-Wop to the UK record shops than any other label. In the 60's only EMI's Stateside could rival London for Soul, and during the 70's when the Stateside label ceased to be pressed, it again became the frontrunner for soul releases from the USA.

Early releases of London promo 45's where orange and came as TWO different discs of A-side and B-side with blank flips. To hold their original value you require BOTH discs. Single discs without its partner are considered half-a-disc and valued accordingly. Some London collectors do not consider early orange promo copies as collectable as the black and silver stock releases. It is not until the white then later yellow double sided promo copies came into being that the price difference became significant.

Although London released 100's of 45's by black artists during the 1950's I've only listed those that will appeal to the soul collector.

84	37	MAJOR HARRIS	ALL MY LIFE	same: dub mix	4.00
84	48	TERI WELLS	I'LL BE AROUND	same: instrumental	8.00
84	48 PS	TERI WELLS	I'LL BE AROUND	same: instrumental	10.00
58	7035 export	JIMMY McCRACKLIN	THE WALK	I'M TO BLAME	30.00
60	7095 export	MARV JOHNSON	I LOVE THE WAY YOU LOVE ME	LET ME LOVE YOU	30.00
61	7114 export	DRIFTERS	SAVE THE LAST DANCE FOR ME	THIS MAGIC MOMENT	15.00
61	7115 export	DRIFTERS	I COUNT THE TEARS	DANCE WITH ME	20.00
57	8447 tri	BIG MAYBELLE	I DON'T WANT TO CRY	ALL OF ME	50.00
57	8506 tri	SAM COOKE	YOU SEND ME	SUMMERTIME	25.00
57	8561 tri	CHANTELS	MAYBE	COME MY LITTLE BABY	450.00
58	8581 tri	RENE HALL'S ORCHESTRA	TWICHY	FLIPPIN	40.00
58	8580 tri	CHAMPS	TEQUILA	TRAIN TO NOWHERE	15.00
58	8598 tri	JIMMY McCRACKLIN	THE WALK	I'M TO BLAME	40.00
58	8615 tri	SAM COOKE	THAT'S ALL I NEED TO KNOW	I DON'T WANT TO CRY	50.00
58	8644 tri	BOBBY FREEMAN	DO YOU WANT TO DANCE	BIG FAT WOMAN	20.00
58	8684 tri	DUBS	GONNA MAKE A CHANGE	BESIDE MY LOVE	350.00
76	8685 EP PS DJ	AL GREEN	I TRIED TO TELL MYSELF	4 track promo EP with cover	20.00
58	8697 tri	JERRY BUTLER	FOR YOUR PRECIOUS LOVE	SWEET WAS THE WINE	125.00
58	8704 tri	LITTLE ANTHONY & the IMPERIALS	TEARS ON MY PILLOW	TWO PEOPLE IN THE WORLD	50.00
58	8768 tri	RAY CHARLES	ROCKHOUSE	ROCKHOUSE part 2	25.00
59	8784 tri	ANDY WILLIAMS	HOUSE OF BAMBOO	HAWAIIAN WEDDING SONG	15.00
59	8784 tri	ANDY WILLIAMS	HOUSE OF BAMBOO	HAWAIIAN WEDDING SONG	22.00
59	8848 tri	LITTLE ANTHONY & the IMPERIALS	SO MUCH	OH YEAH	35.00
59	8852 tri	DAVE BABY CORTEZ	THE HAPPY ORGAN	LOVE ME AS I LOVE YOU	15.00
59	8854 tri	BIG MAYBELLE	BABY, WON'T YOU PLEASE COME HOME	SAY IT ISN'T SO	30.00
59	8856 tri	MARV JOHNSON	COME TO ME	WHISPER	100.00
58	8870 tri	FIESTAS	SO FINE	LAST NIGHT I DREAMED	100.00
59	8876 tri	FALCONS	YOU'RE SO FINE	GODDESS OF ANGELS	100.00
59	8892 tri	DRIFTERS	THERE GOES MY BABY	OH, MY LOVE	20.00
59	8892 tri DJ	DRIFTERS	THERE GOES MY BABY	blank:	30.00
59	8913 tri	BO DIDDLEY	THE GREAT GRANDFATHER	CRACKIN' UP	40.00
59	8915 tri	DEE CLARK	JUST KEEP IT UP	WHISPERING GRASS	20.00
59	8917 tri	RAY CHARLES	WHAT'D I SAY	WHAT'D I SAY part 2	20.00
59	8919 tri	DAVE BABY CORTEZ	THE WHISTLING ORGAN	I'M HAPPY	15.00
59	8940 tri	EUGENE CHURCH	I AIN'T GOING FOR THAT	MIAMI	50.00
59	8940 round	EUGENE CHURCH	I AIN'T GOING FOR THAT	MIAMI	30.00
59	8942	FATS DOMINO	I'M GONNA BE A BIG WHEEL SOMEDAY	I WANT TO WALK YOU HOME	10.00
59	8950	EARL NELSON	COME ON	NO TIME TO CRY	25.00
59	8954	CRESTS	THE ANGELS LISTENED IN	I THANK THE MOON	40.00
59	8975	BO DIDDLEY	SAY MAN	THE CLOCK STRIKES TWELVE	40.00

59	8988	DRIFTERS	DANCE WITH ME	TRUE LOVE, TRUE LOVE	15.00
59	8998	PAUL GAYTEN	THE HUNCH	HOT CROSS BUNS	200.00
59	8998 DJ	PAUL GAYTEN	THE HUNCH	blank:	100.00
59	8998 DJ	PAUL GAYTEN	HOT CROSS BUNS	blank:	40.00
		the two above discs sold as a pair value 250.00			
59	9009	RAY CHARLES	I'M MOVING ON	I BELIEVE TO MY SOUL	10.00
59	9013	MARV JOHNSON	YOU GOT WHAT IT TAKES	DON'T LEAVE ME	15.00
59	9013 DJ	MARV JOHNSON	YOU GOT WHAT IT TAKES	blank:	30.00
59	9013 DJ	MARV JOHNSON	DON'T LEAVE ME	blank:	10.00
		the two above discs sold as a pair value 100.00			
60	9020	COASTERS	WHAT ABOUT US	RUN RED RUN	10.00
60	9023	LAVERN BAKER	TINY TIM	FOR LOVE OF YOU	60.00
60	9024	TITUS TURNER	TAKING CARE OF BUSINESS	WE TOLD YOU NOT TO MARRY	20.00
60	9031	BOBBY FREEMAN	EBB TIDE (THE SEA)	SINBAD	10.00
60	9055	BIG JOE TURNER	HONEY HUSH	TOMORROW NIGHT	75.00
60	9056	GOOGIE RENE COMBO	FOREVER	EZ-ZEE	15.00
60	9058	RAY CHARLES	LET THE GOOD TIMES ROLL	DON'T LET THE SUN CATCH YOU CR	10.00
60	9062	SAMMY TURNER	PARADISE	I'D BE A FOOL AGAIN	10.00
60	9065	LITTLE RICHARD	BABY	I GOT IT	15.00
60	9079	CLYDE McPHATTER	JUST GIVE ME A RING	DON'T DOG ME	40.00
60	9081	DRIFTERS	THIS MAGIC MOMENT	BALTIMORE	10.00
60	9088	BARRETT STRONG	MONEY (THAT'S WHAT I WANT)	OH I APOLOGIZE	150.00
60	9088 DJ	BARRETT STRONG	MONEY (THAT'S WHAT I WANT)	blank:	100.00
60	9088 DJ	BARRETT STRONG	OH I APOLOGIZE	blank:	50.00
		the two above discs sold as a pair value 250.00			
60	9093	RUTH BROWN	I BURNED YOU LETTER	DON'T DECIEVE ME	50.00
60	9093 DJ	RUTH BROWN	I BURNED YOU LETTER	blank:	45.00
60	9093 DJ	RUTH BROWN	DON'T DECIEVE ME	blank:	10.00
		the two above discs sold as a pair value 85.00			
60	9094	LENNY WELCH	YOU DON'T KNOW ME	NEED SOMEONE	8.00
60	9096	BILLY BLAND	LET THE LITTLE GIRL DANCE	SWEET THING	15.00
60	9109	MARV JOHNSON	I LOVE THE WAY YOU LOVE	LET ME LOVE YOU	20.00
60	9109 DJ	MARV JOHNSON	I LOVE THE WAY YOU LOVE	blank:	25.00
60	9109 DJ	MARV JOHNSON	LET ME LOVE YOU	blank:	10.00
		the two above discs sold as a pair value 45.00			
60	9111	COASTERS	BESAME MUCHO	BESAME MUCHO part 2	10.00
60	9112	BO DIDDLEY	ROAD RUNNER	MY STORY	50.00
60	9117	JESSIE HILL	OOH POO PAH DOO	OOH POO PAH DOO part 2	15.00
60	9119	BIG JOE TURNER	MY LITTLE HONEY DRIPPER	BABY I STILL WANT YOU	50.00
60	9139	ETTA JAMES	ALL I COULD DO WAS CRY	TOUGH MARY	30.00
60	9145	DRIFTERS	LONELY WINDS	HEY SENORITA	15.00
60	9151	COASTERS	WAKE ME, SHAKE ME	STEWBALL	10.00
60	9163	FATS DOMINO	WALKING TO NEW ORLEANS	DON'T COME KNOCKIN'	10.00
60	9165	MARV JOHNSON	AIN'T GONNA BE THAT WAY	ALL THE LOVE I'VE GOT	20.00
60	9165	MARV JOHNSON	AIN'T GONNA BE THAT WAY	blank:	25.00
60	9165	MARV JOHNSON	ALL THE LOVE I'VE GOT	blank:	10.00
		the two above discs sold as a pair value 50.00			
60	9175	LITTLE WALTER	MY BABE	BLUE MIDNIGHT	30.00
60	9180	ETTA & HARVEY	IF I CAN'T HAVE YOU	MY HEART CRIES	50.00
60	9181	RAY CHARLES	TELL THE TRUTH	YOU BE MY BABY	10.00
60	9187	MARV JOHNSON	(I'VE GOT TO) MOVE TWO MOUNTAINS	I NEED YOU	20.00
60	9187	MARV JOHNSON	(I'VE GOT TO) MOVE TWO MOUNTAINS	blank:	25.00
60	9187	MARV JOHNSON	I NEED YOU	blank:	10.00
		the two above discs sold as a pair value 50.00			
60	9198	FATS DOMINO	THREE NIGHTS A WEEK	PUT YOUR ARMS AROUND ME HONEY	10.00
60	9201	DRIFTERS	SAVE THE LAST DANCE FOR ME	NOBODY BUT ME	6.00
60	9208	COASTERS	SHOPPIN' FOR CLOTHES	THE SNAKE AND THE BOOKWORM	10.00
60	9226	IKE & TINA TURNER	A FOOL IN LOVE	THE WAY YOU LOVE ME	20.00
60	9233	SHIRELLES	TONIGHT'S THE NIGHT	THE DANCE IS OVER	20.00
60	9234	ETTA JAMES	MY DEAREST DARLING	GIRL OF MY DREAMS	30.00
60	9237	AZIE MORTIMER	LIPS	WRAPPED UP IN A DREAM	100.00
60	9237 DJ	AZIE MORTIMER	LIPS	blank:	120.00
60	9237 DJ	AZIE MORTIMER	WRAPPED UP IN A DREAM	blank:	10.00
		the two above discs sold as a pair value 150.00			
60	9244	FATS DOMINO	MY GIRL JOSEPHINE	NATURAL BORN LOVER	8.00
60	9245	DEE DEE FORD	GOOD-MORNING BLUES	I JUST CAN'T BELIEVE	50.00
60	9251	RAY CHARLES	COME RAIN OR COME SHINE	TELL ME YOU'LL WAIT FOR ME	8.00
60	9252	LAVERN BAKER	BUMBLE BEE	MY TURN WILL COME	20.00
60	9258	BEN E.KING	SPANISH HARLEM	FIRST TASTE OF LOVE	10.00
60	9258 DJ	BEN E.KING	SPANISH HARLEM	FIRST TASTE OF LOVE	20.00
60	9265	MARV JOHNSON	HAPPY DAYS	BABY, BABY	20.00
60	9265 DJ	MARV JOHNSON	HAPPY DAYS	BABY, BABY	50.00
60	9266	ROSIE & THE ORIGINALS	ANGEL BABY	GIVE ME LOVE	40.00
60	9266 DJ	ROSIE & THE ORIGINALS	ANGEL BABY	GIVE ME LOVE	50.00
61	9272	RONNIE LOVE	CHILLS AND FEVER	PLEDGING MY LOVE	75.00
61	9272 DJ	RONNIE LOVE	CHILLS AND FEVER	PLEDGING MY LOVE	100.00
61	9276	MIRACLES	SHOP AROUND	WHO'S LOVIN' YOU	50.00
61	9276 DJ	MIRACLES	SHOP AROUND	WHO'S LOVIN' YOU	100.00
61	9283	CHIMES	ONCE IN A WHILE	SUMMER NIGHT	20.00

61	9283 DJ	CHIMES	ONCE IN A WHILE	SUMMER NIGHT	30.00
61	9286	MAXINE BROWN	ALL IN MY MIND	HARRY, LET'S MARRY	25.00
61	9286 DJ	MAXINE BROWN	ALL IN MY MIND	HARRY, LET'S MARRY	35.00
61	9287	DRIFTERS	I COUNT THE TEARS	SADIE MY LADY	25.00
61	9287 DJ	DRIFTERS	I COUNT THE TEARS	SADIE MY LADY	35.00
61	9293	COASTERS	WAIT A MINUTE	THUMBIN' A RIDE	8.00
61	9293 DJ	COASTERS	WAIT A MINUTE	THUMBIN' A RIDE	10.00
61	9300	LAVERN BAKER & JIMMY RICKS	YOU'RE THE BOSS	I'LL NEVER BE FREE	50.00
61	9300 DJ	LAVERN BAKER & JIMMY RICKS	YOU'RE THE BOSS	I'LL NEVER BE FREE	75.00
61	9301	FATS DOMINO	WHAT A PRICE	AIN'T THAT JUST LIKE A WOMAN	10.00
61	9301 DJ	FATS DOMINO	WHAT A PRICE	AIN'T THAT JUST LIKE A WOMAN	15.00
61	9310	CARLA THOMAS	GEE WHIZ	FOR YOU	25.00
61	9310 DJ	CARLA THOMAS	GEE WHIZ	FOR YOU	40.00
61	9311	MARV JOHNSON	MERRY-GO-ROUND	TELL ME THAT YOU LOVE ME	50.00
61	9311 DJ	MARV JOHNSON	MERRY-GO-ROUND	TELL ME THAT YOU LOVE ME	60.00
61	9317 mis-press	DEL SHANNON	RUNAWAY	JUDY	30.00

mispressed! Some b-sides play Maximillian – The Snake

61	9319	GENE McDANIELS	A HUNDRED POUNDS OF CLAY	TAKE A CHANCE ON LOVE	15.00
61	9319 DJ	GENE McDANIELS	A HUNDRED POUNDS OF CLAY	TAKE A CHANCE ON LOVE	22.00
61	9326	DRIFTERS	SOME KIND OF WONDEFUL	HONEY BEE	10.00
61	9326 DJ	DRIFTERS	SOME KIND OF WONDEFUL	HONEY BEE	18.00
61	9327	FATS DOMINO	FELL IN LOVE ON MONDAY	SHU-RAH	10.00
61	9327 DJ	FATS DOMINO	FELL IN LOVE ON MONDAY	SHU-RAH	12.00
61	9330	ERNIE K-DOE	MOTHER-IN-LAW	WANTED $10,000.00 REWARD	15.00
61	9330 DJ	ERNIE K-DOE	MOTHER-IN-LAW	WANTED $10,000.00 REWARD	25.00
61	9349	COASTERS	LITTLE EGYPT	KEEP ON ROLLING	8.00
61	9349 DJ	COASTERS	LITTLE EGYPT	KEEP ON ROLLING	10.00
61	9356	MAXIMILIAN	THE SNAKE	THE WANDERER	50.00
61	9356 DJ	MAXIMILIAN	THE SNAKE	THE WANDERER	75.00
61	9358	BEN E. KING	STAND BY ME	ON THE HORIZON	12.00
61	9358 DJ	BEN E. KING	STAND BY ME	ON THE HORIZON	30.00
61	9359	CARLA THOMAS	PROMISES	A LOVE OF MY OWN	15.00
61	9359 DJ	CARLA THOMAS	PROMISES	A LOVE OF MY OWN	25.00
61	9364	RAY CHARLES	EARLY IN THE MORNING	A BIT OF SOUL	5.00
61	9364 DJ	RAY CHARLES	EARLY IN THE MORNING	A BIT OF SOUL	6.00
61	9366	MIRACLES	AIN'T IT BABY	THE ONLY ONE I LOVE	**209.00**
61	9366 DJ	MIRACLES	AIN'T IT BABY	THE ONLY ONE I LOVE	250.00
61	9374	FATS DOMINO	IT KEEPS RAINING	I JUST CRY	25.00
61	9374 DJ	FATS DOMINO	IT KEEPS RAINING	I JUST CRY	45.00
61	9382	DRIFTERS	PLEASE STAY	NO SWEET LOVIN'	10.00
61	9382 DJ	DRIFTERS	PLEASE STAY	NO SWEET LOVIN'	18.00
61	9383	BILL BLACK'S COMBO	YOGI	OLD BUTTERMILK SKY	8.00
61	9383 DJ	BILL BLACK'S COMBO	YOGI	OLD BUTTERMILK SKY	10.00
61	9390	ERNIE K-DOE	TE-TA-TE-TA-TA	REAL MAN	20.00
61	9390 DJ	ERNIE K-DOE	TE-TA-TE-TA-TA	REAL MAN	28.00
61	9393	BOBBY PARKER	WATCH YOUR STEP	STEAL YOUR HEART AWAY	40.00
61	9393 DJ	BOBBY PARKER	WATCH YOUR STEP	STEAL YOUR HEART AWAY	50.00
61	9396	GENE McDANIELS	A TEAR	SHE'S COME BACK	10.00
61	9396 DJ	GENE McDANIELS	A TEAR	SHE'S COME BACK	15.00
61	9399	MAR-KEYS	LAST NIGHT	NIGHT BEFORE	18.00
61	9399 DJ	MAR-KEYS	LAST NIGHT	NIGHT BEFORE	30.00
61	9403	TIMI YURO	HURT	I APOLOGISE	15.00
61	9403 DJ	TIMI YURO	HURT	I APOLOGISE	22.00
61	9410	CHRIS KENNER	I LIKE IT LIKE THAT	I LIKE IT LIKE THAT part 2	20.00
61	9410 DJ	CHRIS KENNER	I LIKE IT LIKE THAT	I LIKE IT LIKE THAT part 2	28.00
61	9413	COASTERS	GIRLS! GIRLS! GIRLS!	GIRLS! GIRLS! GIRLS! Part 2	8.00
61	9413 DJ	COASTERS	GIRLS! GIRLS! GIRLS!	GIRLS! GIRLS! GIRLS! Part 2	12.00
61	9415	FATS DOMINO	LET THE FOUR WINDS BLOW	COLD HEARTED WOMAN	10.00
61	9415 DJ	FATS DOMINO	LET THE FOUR WINDS BLOW	COLD HEARTED WOMAN	15.00
61	9416	BEN E.KING	AMOR, AMOR	SOUVENIR OF MEXICO	15.00
61	9416 DJ	BEN E.KING	AMOR, AMOR	SOUVENIR OF MEXICO	25.00
61	9427	DRIFTERS	SWEETS FOR MY SWEET	LONELINESS OR HAPPINESS	15.00
61	9427 DJ	DRIFTERS	SWEETS FOR MY SWEET	LONELINESS OR HAPPINESS	22.00
61	9428	CHANTELS	LOOK IN MY EYES	GLAD TO BE BACK	25.00
61	9428 DJ	CHANTELS	LOOK IN MY EYES	GLAD TO BE BACK	30.00
61	9435	RAY CHARLES	I WONDER WHO	HARD TIMES	8.00
61	9435 DJ	RAY CHARLES	I WONDER WHO	HARD TIMES	10.00
61	9448	GENE McDANIELS	TOWER OF STRENGTH	THE SECRET	12.00
61	9448 DJ	GENE McDANIELS	TOWER OF STRENGTH	THE SECRET	22.00
61	9449	MAR-KEYS	MORNING AFTER	DIANA	15.00
61	9449 DJ	MAR-KEYS	MORNING AFTER	DIANA	25.00
61	9451	IKE & TINA TURNER	IT'S GONNA WORK OUT FINE	WON'T YOU FORGIVE ME	15.00
61	9451 DJ	IKE & TINA TURNER	IT'S GONNA WORK OUT FINE	WON'T YOU FORGIVE ME	25.00
61	9454	SOLOMON BURKE	JUST OUT OF REACH (OF MY TWO OPEN	BE BOP GRANDMA	25.00
61	9454 DJ	SOLOMON BURKE	JUST OUT OF REACH (OF MY TWO OPEN	BE BOP GRANDMA	30.00
61	9456	FATS DOMINO	WHAT A PARTY	ROCKIN' BICYCLE	10.00
61	9456 DJ	FATS DOMINO	WHAT A PARTY	ROCKIN' BICYCLE	12.00
61	9457	BEN E.KING	YOUNG BOY BLUES	HERE COMES THE NIGHT	15.00
61	9457 DJ	BEN E.KING	YOUNG BOY BLUES	HERE COMES THE NIGHT	22.00

61	9463		JUSTIN JONES	DANCE BY YOURSELF	LOVE	150.00
61	9463 DJ		JUSTIN JONES	DANCE BY YOURSELF	LOVE	225.00
61	9479		BILL BLACKS COMBO	MY GIRL JOSEPHINE	TWIST-HER	20.00
61	9479 DJ		BILL BLACKS COMBO	MY GIRL JOSEPHINE	TWIST-HER	30.00
62	9480		CHANTELS	WELL I TOLD YOU SO	STILL	25.00
62	9480 DJ		CHANTELS	WELL I TOLD YOU SO	STILL	30.00
62	9481		SHOWMEN	IT WILL STAND	COUNTRY FOOL	40.00
62	9481 DJ		SHOWMEN	IT WILL STAND	COUNTRY FOOL	**72.00**
62	9484		TIMI YURO c/w JOHNNIE RAY	SMILE	I BELIEVE	15.00
62	9484 DJ		TIMI YURO c/w JOHNNIE RAY	SMILE	I BELIEVE	18.00
62	9487		ERNIE K-DOE	A CERTAIN GIRL	I CRIED MY LAST TEAR	25.00
62	9487 DJ		ERNIE K-DOE	A CERTAIN GIRL	I CRIED MY LAST TEAR	40.00
62	9488		SAMMY TURNER	RAINCOAT IN THE RIVER	FALLING	45.00
62	9488 DJ		SAMMY TURNER	RAINCOAT IN THE RIVER	FALLING	60.00
62	9493		COASTERS	(AIN'T THAT) JUST LIKE ME	BAD BLOOD	8.00
62	9493 DJ		COASTERS	(AIN'T THAT) JUST LIKE ME	BAD BLOOD	10.00
62	9496		ROBERT KNIGHT	FREE ME	THE OTHER HALF OF MAN	30.00
62	9496 DJ		ROBERT KNIGHT	FREE ME	THE OTHER HALF OF MAN	45.00
62	9500		DRIFTERS	ROOM FULL OF TEARS	SOMEBODY NEW DANCIN' WITH YOU	10.00
62	9500 DJ		DRIFTERS	ROOM FULL OF TEARS	SOMEBODY NEW DANCIN' WITH YOU	18.00
62	9508		IKETTES	I'M BLUE	FIND MY BABY	15.00
62	9508 DJ		IKETTES	I'M BLUE	FIND MY BABY	25.00
62	9510		MAR-KEYS	FOXY	ONE DEGREE NORTH	15.00
62	9510 DJ		MAR-KEYS	FOXY	ONE DEGREE NORTH	25.00
62	9512		SOLOMON BURKE	CRY TO ME	I ALMOST LOST MY MIND	**251.00**
62	9512 DJ		SOLOMON BURKE	CRY TO ME	I ALMOST LOST MY MIND	275.00
62	9513		BARBARA GEORGE	I KNOW (YOU DON'T LOVE ME	LOVE (IS JUST A CHANCE YOU TAK	30.00
62	9513 DJ		BARBARA GEORGE	I KNOW (YOU DON'T LOVE ME	LOVE (IS JUST A CHANCE YOU TAK	45.00
62	9517		BEN E. KING	ECSTASY	YES	15.00
62	9517 DJ		BEN E. KING	ECSTASY	YES	25.00
62	9522		DRIFTERS	WHEN MY LITTLE GORL IS SMILING	MEXICAN DIVORCE	15.00
62	9522 DJ		DRIFTERS	WHEN MY LITTLE GORL IS SMILING	MEXICAN DIVORCE	25.00
62	9523		ARTHUR ALEXANDER	YOU BETTER MOVE ON	A SHOT OF RHYTHM AND BLUES	40.00
62	9523 DJ		ARTHUR ALEXANDER	YOU BETTER MOVE ON	A SHOT OF RHYTHM AND BLUES	60.00
62	9527		KETTY LESTER	LOVE LETTERS	I'M A FOOL TO WANT YOU	8.00
62	9527 DJ		KETTY LESTER	LOVE LETTERS	I'M A FOOL TO WANT YOU	20.00
62	9529		DON & JUAN	WHAT'S YOUR NAME	CHICKEN NECKS	30.00
62	9529 DJ		DON & JUAN	WHAT'S YOUR NAME	CHICKEN NECKS	45.00
62	9532		CHANTELS	HERE IT COMES AGAIN	SUMMERTIME	20.00
62	9532 DJ		CHANTELS	HERE IT COMES AGAIN	SUMMERTIME	28.00
62	9544		BEN E.KING	THE HERMIT OF MISTY MOUNTAIN	DON'T PLAY THAT SONG (YOU LIED)	20.00
62	9544 DJ		BEN E.KING	THE HERMIT OF MISTY MOUNTAIN	DON'T PLAY THAT SONG (YOU LIED)	40.00
62	9547		KING CURTIS & the NOBLE KNIGHTS	SOUL TWIST	TWISTIN' TIME	15.00
62	9547 DJ		KING CURTIS & the NOBLE KNIGHTS	SOUL TWIST	TWISTIN' TIME	22.00
62	9552		RITCHIE BARRETT	SOME OTHER GUY	TRICKY DICKY	50.00
62	9552 DJ		RITCHIE BARRETT	SOME OTHER GUY	TRICKY DICKY	75.00
62	9557		FATS DOMINO	MY REAL NAME	MY HEART IS BLEEDING	10.00
62	9557 DJ		FATS DOMINO	MY REAL NAME	MY HEART IS BLEEDING	15.00
62	9560		SOLOMON BURKE	DOWN IN THE VALLEY	I'M HANGING UP MY HEART FOR YO	20.00
62	9560 DJ		SOLOMON BURKE	DOWN IN THE VALLEY	I'M HANGING UP MY HEART FOR YO	30.00
62	9565		FALCONS	I FOUND LOVE	SWIM	40.00
62	9565 DJ		FALCONS	I FOUND LOVE	SWIM	50.00
62	9566		ARTHUR ALEXANDER	SOLDIER OF LOVE	WHERE HAVE YOU BEEN	30.00
62	9566 DJ		ARTHUR ALEXANDER	SOLDIER OF LOVE	WHERE HAVE YOU BEEN	45.00
62	9570		BENNY SPELLMAN	FORTUNE TELLER	LIPSTICK TRACES	**95.00**
62	9570 DJ		BENNY SPELLMAN	FORTUNE TELLER	LIPSTICK TRACES	150.00
62	9571		SHOWMEN	THE WRONG GIRL	I LOVE YOU CAN'T YOU SEE	150.00
62	9571 DJ		SHOWMEN	THE WRONG GIRL	I LOVE YOU CAN'T YOU SEE	250.00
62	9574		KETTY LESTER	BUT NOT FOR ME	MOSCOW NIGHTS	8.00
62	9574 DJ		KETTY LESTER	BUT NOT FOR ME	MOSCOW NIGHTS	15.00
62	9581		LITTLE EVA	THE LOCO-MOTION	HE IS THE BOY	8.00
62	9581 DJ		LITTLE EVA	THE LOCO-MOTION	HE IS THE BOY	45.00
67	9581 boxed logo		LITTLE EVA	THE LOCO-MOTION	HE IS THE BOY	5.00
62	9586		BEN E.KING	TOO BAD	MY HEART CRIES FOR YOU	15.00
62	9586 DJ		BEN E.KING	TOO BAD	MY HEART CRIES FOR YOU	25.00
62	9590		FATS DOMINO	DANCE WITH MR. DOMINO	NOTHING NEW (SAME OLD THING)	10.00
62	9590 DJ		FATS DOMINO	DANCE WITH MR. DOMINO	NOTHING NEW (SAME OLD THING)	12.00
62	9595		BOOKER T. & THE MG'S	GREEN ONIONS	BEHAVE YOURSELF	15.00
62	9595 DJ		BOOKER T. & THE MG'S	GREEN ONIONS	BEHAVE YOURSELF	40.00
62	9596		CHRIS MONTEZ	LET'S DANCE	YOU'RE THE ONE	5.00
62	9596 DJ		CHRIS MONTEZ	LET'S DANCE	YOU'RE THE ONE	15.00
62	9601		LENNY WELCH	TASTE OF HONEY	OLD CATHEDRAL	8.00
62	9601 DJ		LENNY WELCH	TASTE OF HONEY	OLD CATHEDRAL	10.00
62	9608		KETTY LESTER	RIVER OF SALT	YOU CAN'T LIE TO A LIAR	30.00
62	9608 DJ		KETTY LESTER	RIVER OF SALT	YOU CAN'T LIE TO A LIAR	45.00
62	9611		CRYSTALS	HE'S A REBEL	I LOVE YOU EDDIE	15.00
62	9611 DJ		CRYSTALS	HE'S A REBEL	I LOVE YOU EDDIE	25.00
62	9616		FATS DOMINO	DID YOU EVER SEE A DREAM WALKING	STOP THE CLOCK	10.00
62	9616 DJ		FATS DOMINO	DID YOU EVER SEE A DREAM WALKING	STOP THE CLOCK	12.00

62	9618	CARLA THOMAS	I'LL BRING IT ON HOME TO YOU	I CAN'T TAKE IT	15.00
62	9618 DJ	CARLA THOMAS	I'LL BRING IT ON HOME TO YOU	I CAN'T TAKE IT	25.00
62	9625	SHERRYS	POP POP POP-PIE	YOUR HAND IN MINE	15.00
62	9625 DJ	SHERRYS	POP POP POP-PIE	YOUR HAND IN MINE	22.00
62	9626	DRIFTERS	UP ON THE ROOF	ANOTHER SATURDAY WITH THE BOYS	10.00
62	9626 DJ	DRIFTERS	UP ON THE ROOF	ANOTHER SATURDAY WITH THE BOYS	30.00
62	9627	MAJORS	SHE'S A TROUBLEMAKER	A LITTLE BIT NOW	22.00
62	9627 DJ	MAJORS	SHE'S A TROUBLEMAKER	A LITTLE BIT NOW	30.00
62	9631	BEN E.KING	WALKING IN THE FOOTTEPS OF A FOOL	I'M STANDING BY	15.00
62	9631 DJ	BEN E.KING	WALKING IN THE FOOTTEPS OF A FOOL	I'M STANDING BY	28.00
62	9633	LITTLE EVA	KEEP YOUR HANDS OFF MY BABY	WHERE DO I GO	8.00
62	9633 DJ	LITTLE EVA	KEEP YOUR HANDS OFF MY BABY	WHERE DO I GO	15.00
62	9634	COOKIES	STRANGER IN MY ARMS	CHAINS	15.00
62	9634 DJ	COOKIES	STRANGER IN MY ARMS	CHAINS	28.00
62	9641	ARTHUR ALEXANDER	ANNA	HANG MY HEAD AND CRY	40.00
62	9641 DJ	ARTHUR ALEXANDER	ANNA	HANG MY HEAD AND CRY	75.00
62	9643	MEL TORME	COMING HOME BABY	RIGHT NOW	30.00
62	9643 DJ	MEL TORME	COMIN' HOME BABY	RIGHT NOW	60.00
63	9646	BOB B SOXX & THE BLUE JEANS	ZIP-A-DEE-DOO-DAH	FLIP AND NITTY	10.00
63	9646 DJ	BOB B SOXX & THE BLUE JEANS	ZIP-A-DEE-DOO-DAH	FLIP AND NITTY	18.00
63	9661	CRYSTALS	HE'S SURE THE BOY I LOVE	WALKING ALONG (LA-LA-LA)	18.00
63	9661 DJ	CRYSTALS	HE'S SURE THE BOY I LOVE	WALKING ALONG (LA-LA-LA)	28.00
63	9667	ARTHUR ALEXANDER	GO HOME GIRL	YOU'RE THE REASON	30.00
63	9667 DJ	ARTHUR ALEXANDER	GO HOME GIRL	YOU'RE THE REASON	45.00
63	9670	BOOKER T. & THE MG'S	JELLY BREAD	AW' MERCY	15.00
63	9670 DJ	BOOKER T. & THE MG'S	JELLY BREAD	AW' MERCY	22.00
63	9679	RUBY & THE ROMANTICS	OUR DAY WILL COME	MOONLIGHT AND MUSIC	15.00
63	9679 DJ	RUBY & THE ROMANTICS	OUR DAY WILL COME	MOONLIGHT AND MUSIC	22.00
63	9680	JIMMY HUGHES	MY LOVING TIME	I'M QUALIFIED	50.00
63	9680 DJ	JIMMY HUGHES	MY LOVING TIME	I'M QUALIFIED	75.00
63	9681	SHEPHERD SISTERS	DON'T MENTION MY NAME	WHAT MAKES LITTLE GIRLS CRY	50.00
63	9681 DJ	SHEPHERD SISTERS	DON'T MENTION MY NAME	WHAT MAKES LITTLE GIRLS CRY	85.00
63	9684	RUMBLERS	BOSS	I DON'T NEED YOU NO MORE	20.00
63	9684 DJ	RUMBLERS	BOSS	I DON'T NEED YOU NO MORE	25.00
63	9686	SHERRYS	LET'S STOMP AGAIN	SLOOP TIME	15.00
63	9686 DJ	SHERRYS	LET'S STOMP AGAIN	SLOOP TIME	22.00
63	9687	LITTLE EVA	LET'S TURKEY TROT	OLD SMOKEY LOCOMOTION	10.00
63	9687 DJ	LITTLE EVA	LET'S TURKEY TROT	OLD SMOKEY LOCOMOTION	22.00
63	9689	JERRY JACKSON	GYPSY EYES	TURN BACK	50.00
63	9689 DJ	JERRY JACKSON	GYPSY EYES	TURN BACK	75.00
63	9691	BEN E.KING	HOW CAN I FORGET	GLORIA GLORIA	15.00
63	9691 DJ	BEN E.KING	HOW CAN I FORGET	GLORIA GLORIA	25.00
63	9694	BOB B SOXX & THE BLUE JEANS	WHY DO LOVER'S BREAK EACH OTHERS	DR. KAPLAN'S OFFICE	15.00
63	9694 DJ	BOB B SOXX & THE BLUE JEANS	WHY DO LOVER'S BREAK EACH OTHERS	DR. KAPLAN'S OFFICE	25.00
62	9698	KETTY LESTER	THIS LAND IS YOUR LAND	LOVE BELONGS TO EVERYONE	8.00
62	9698 DJ	KETTY LESTER	THIS LAND IS YOUR LAND	LOVE BELONGS TO EVERYONE	10.00
63	9698	KETTY LESTER	A WARM SUMMER DAY	I'LL NEVER STOP LOVING YOU	8.00
63	9698 DJ	KETTY LESTER	A WARM SUMMER DAY	I'LL NEVER STOP LOVING YOU	10.00
63	9699	DRIFTERS	ON BROADWAY	LET THE MUSIC PLAY	10.00
63	9699 DJ	DRIFTERS	ON BROADWAY	LET THE MUSIC PLAY	20.00
63	9702	EARLS	NEVER	KEEP-A TELLIN' YOU	40.00
63	9702 DJ	EARLS	NEVER	KEEP-A TELLIN' YOU	50.00
63	9704	COOKIES	DON'T SAY NOTHING BAD ABOUT MY	SOFTLY IN THE NIGHT	25.00
63	9704 DJ	COOKIES	DON'T SAY NOTHING BAD ABOUT MY	SOFTLY IN THE NIGHT	35.00
63	9708	LITTLE RICHARD	CRYING IN THE CHAPEL	HOLE IN THE WALL	10.00
63	9708 DJ	LITTLE RICHARD	CRYING IN THE CHAPEL	HOLE IN THE WALL	12.00
63	9709	DUPREES	GONE WITH THE WIND	LET'S MAKE LOVE AGAIN	10.00
63	9709 DJ	DUPREES	GONE WITH THE WIND	LET'S MAKE LOVE AGAIN	12.00
63	9715	SOLOMON BURKE	IF YOU NEED ME	YOU CAN MAKE IT IF YOU TRY	15.00
63	9715 DJ	SOLOMON BURKE	IF YOU NEED ME	YOU CAN MAKE IT IF YOU TRY	25.00
63	9724	BARBARA LEWIS	HELLO STRANGER	THINK A LITTLE SUGAR	22.00
63	9724 DJ	BARBARA LEWIS	HELLO STRANGER	THINK A LITTLE SUGAR	45.00
63	9725	DARLENE LOVE	(TODAY I MET) THE BOY I'M GONNA MARRY	PLAYING FOR KEEPS	20.00
63	9725 DJ	DARLENE LOVE	(TODAY I MET) THE BOY I'M GONNA MARRY	PLAYING FOR KEEPS	30.00
63	9730	JAMES BROWN & THE FAMOUS	PRISONER OF LOVE	CHOO-CHOO (LOCOMOTION)	20.00
63	9730 DJ	JAMES BROWN & THE FAMOUS	PRISONER OF LOVE	CHOO-CHOO (LOCOMOTION)	28.00
63	9732	CRYSTALS	DA DOO RON RON	GIT' IT	8.00
63	9732 DJ	CRYSTALS	DA DOO RON RON	GIT' IT	30.00
63	9733	VOLUMES	TEENAGE PARADISE	SANDRA	60.00
63	9733 DJ	VOLUMES	TEENAGE PARADISE	SANDRA	70.00
63	9734	RUBY & THE ROMANTICS	MY SUMMER LOVE	SWEET LOVE AND SWEET FORGIVEN	15.00
63	9734 DJ	RUBY & THE ROMANTICS	MY SUMMER LOVE	SWEET LOVE AND SWEET FORGIVEN	22.00
63	9738	FATS DOMINO	YOU ALWAYS HURT THE ONE YOU LOVE	TROUBLE BLUES	10.00
63	9738 DJ	FATS DOMINO	YOU ALWAYS HURT THE ONE YOU LOVE	TROUBLE BLUES	12.00
63	9743	RIGHTEOUS BROTHERS	LITTLE LATIN LUPE LU	I'M SO LONELY	20.00
63	9743 DJ	RIGHTEOUS BROTHERS	LITTLE LATIN LUPE LU	I'M SO LONELY	28.00
63	9747	MIRIAM MAKEBA	CLICK SONG	MBUBE	6.00
63	9747 DJ	MIRIAM MAKEBA	CLICK SONG	MBUBE	8.00
63	9749	DORIS TROY	JUST ONE LOOK	BOSSA NOVA BLUES	20.00

Picture Sleeves

Together For The First Time!
THE SOUL CLAN
SOLOMON BURKE • ARTHUR CONLEY • DON COVAY • BEN E. KING • JOE TEX
"SOUL MEETING"
c/w "THAT'S HOW IT FEELS"
ATLANTIC
Atlantic 584 202

RYTHM & BLUES

BETTYE SWANN
CBS 2942

'MAKE ME YOURS'

FIDELS
DJS 10689

TRY A LITTLE HARDER (Vocal)
B/W
TRY A LITTLE HARDER (Instrumental)

PROMOTION COPY
NOT FOR SALE

DJM RECORDS
OLDIE

FIDELS
Written by "Harlem Shuffle" performers, Bob Relf and
Earl Nelson, and produced by Bob Relf and
Fred Smith for the latter's Keymen label. "Try A Little
Harder" has become something of a disco/soul
classic since first released in 1967.
The Fidels, who had initially approached Fred Smith
for the chance to record, have since lapsed into
obscurity due to the record's lack of success when
first released, but now DJM Records have acquired
the rights to the single, plus the "B" side—the
instrumental version by the Keymen Strings—
through the current licensing agreement with Vee
Jay International.
So another classic is re-released. Another DJM
oldie hits the streets.

For further information contact Press Administration
DJM (Distributors) Ltd., James House, 71-75 New Oxford Street,
London WC1A 1DP   Telephone: 01-836 4864   Telex 27135

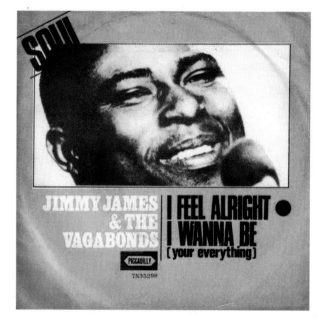

SOUL

JIMMY JAMES & THE VAGABONDS
I FEEL ALRIGHT ●
I WANNA BE
(your everything)
PICCADILLY
7N35298

PHILADELPHIA INTERNATIONAL ALL STARS:

LET'S CLEAN UP THE GHETTO

LOU RAWLS
BILLY PAUL
ARCHIE BELL
TEDDY PENDERGRASS
O'JAYS
DEE DEE SHARP GAMBLE

VOCAL

5451

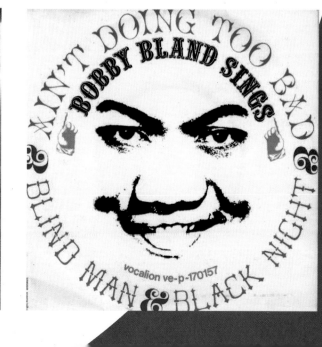

AIN'T DOING TOO BAD
BOBBY BLAND SINGS
BLIND MAN & BLACK NIGHT

vocalion ve-p-170157

ANOTHER KIND OF FELLOW
(R. Parker)
Island Music
Sue RECORDS
WI-4025
(A)
LYDIA MARCELLE
Arranged by W. Querengue

THAT'S HOW
HEARTACHES ARE MADE
M.C.P.S.
Sue RECORDS
WI-302
BABY WASHINGTON

DADDY ROLLIN' STONE
Copyright Control
Sue RECORDS
WI-308
DERAK MARTIN

SO FINE
(J. Otis)
Leeds Music
Sue RECORDS
WI-4020
A
THE SANTELLS
Produced by K. Brown

I DON'T WANNA
(Bateman—Watts)
C.P.S.
Clarmke Records
U.S.A.
Sue RECORDS
WI-347A
Time: 2.30
JUNE BATEMAN
Produced by
Clarence Lachson

KEEP MY WOMAN HOME
(Hayes—Porter)
Atlas Records
U.S.A.
M.C.P.S.
Sue RECORDS
WI-4031
(A)
Time: 2.45
DANNY WHITE

Sue

Records sleeve listing (repeated background text): louisiana red □ the olympics □ willie mabon □ ike and tina turner □ betty everett □ john lee hooker □ etta james □ jimmy mcgriff □ big al downing □ chris kenner □ inez and charlie foxx □ elmore james □ anita wood □ freddy king □ frankie ford □ roscoe shelton □ mercy baby □ wilbert harrison □ harold burrage □ otis re... redding □ the wallace broth... brothers □ joe tex □ huey 'pi... 'piano' smith and the clov... clowns □ willie mae... thornton □ june batem... bateman □ bobby pete... peterson □ the pleas... pleasures □ derek ma... martin □ paul reve... revere and the raiders □ barbara george □ tim... whitsett baby washin... washington □ sonny boy w... williamson □ james brown and the... famous flames □ patti labelle and the bluebelles □ the daylighters □ earl king □ bobby lee trammell □ hank jacobs □ lightnin hopkins □ j b l... lenoir □ homesick james □ lightnin slim □ the soul sisters □ louisiana red □ etta james □ the olympics □ roscoe shelton □ joe tex □

Record 1:
YOU'LL LOSE A GOOD THING
(Barbara L. Ozen)
Jamie Records U.S.A.
Time: 2.35
WI-4038 (A)
BARBARA LYNN
Produced by: Huey P. Meaux

Record 2:
I'VE GOT A NEW LOVE
(G. Redd—P. Martin)
United Artists Music
Time: 2.02
WI-4041 (B)
PAUL MARTIN
Produced by: Gene Redd Inc.
Arranged and Conducted by: Gene Redd
℗ 1967

Record 3:
SHIMMY SHIMMY WALK PT. I
M.C.P.S.
WI-325 (A)
THE MEGATONS

Record 4:
I'VE GOT A CLAIM ON YOU
(Betty Everett)
One-Der-Ful Records U.S.A.
Time: 2.27
WI-352 (A)
BETTY EVERETT

Record 5:
SOMEBODY HELP ME
(Jackie Edwards)
Island Music
WI-4013 (A)
THE JAYBIRDS
Arranged & Conducted by: Lenny Fallen
Produced by: Chris Blackwell

Record 6:
PRECIOUS WORDS
(Claudy Robinson)
Sims Records U.S.A.
M.C.P.S.
WI-334 A
WALLACE BROTHERS

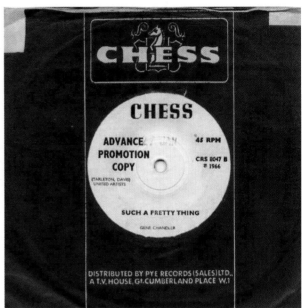

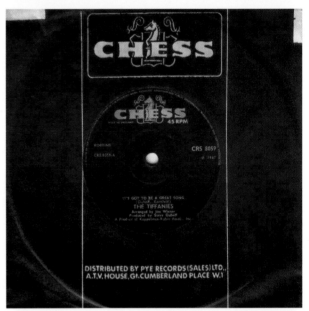

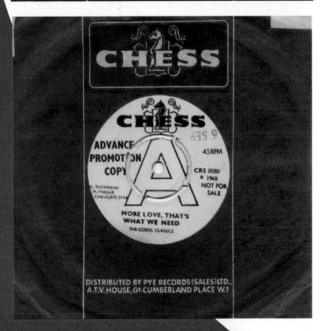

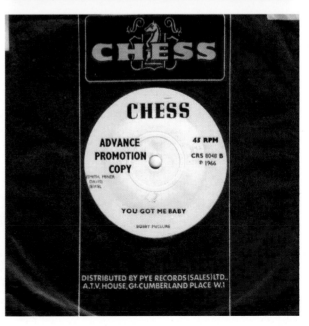

ORIOLE

ATLANTIC

CBS RECORDS

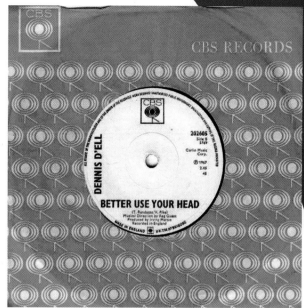

COLUMBIA

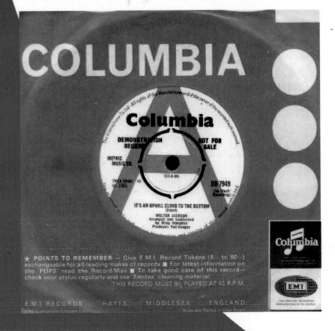

63	9749 DJ	DORIS TROY	JUST ONE LOOK	BOSSA NOVA BLUES	40.00
63	9750	DRIFTERS	RAT RACE	IF YOU DON'T COME BACK	15.00
63	9750 DJ	DRIFTERS	RAT RACE	IF YOU DON'T COME BACK	28.00
63	9754	BOB B SOXX & THE BLUE JEANS	NOT TOO YOUNG TO GET MARRIED	ANNETTE	15.00
63	9754 DJ	BOB B SOXX & THE BLUE JEANS	NOT TOO YOUNG TO GET MARRIED	ANNETTE	22.00
63	9756	LITTLE RICHARD	TRAVLIN' SHOES	IT IS NO SECRET	10.00
63	9756 DJ	LITTLE RICHARD	TRAVELIN' SHOES	IT IS NO SECRET	15.00
63	9757	GARNELL COOPER	GREEN MONKEY	LONG DISTANCE	25.00
63	9757 DJ	GARNELL COOPER	GREEN MONKEY	LONG DISTANCE	30.00
63	9759	GERRI GRANGER	WHAT'S WRONG WITH ME	JUST TELL HIM JANE SAID HELLO	15.00
63	9759 DJ	GERRI GRANGER	WHAT'S WRONG WITH ME	JUST TELL HIM JANE SAID HELLO	22.00
63	9763	SOLOMON BURKE	STUPIDITY	CAN'T NOBODY LOVE YOU	22.00
63	9763 DJ	SOLOMON BURKE	STUPIDITY	CAN'T NOBODY LOVE YOU	40.00
63	9765	DARLENE LOVE	WAIT 'TIL MY BOBBY GETS HOME	TAKE IT FROM ME	25.00
63	9765 DJ	DARLENE LOVE	WAIT 'TIL MY BOBBY GETS HOME	TAKE IT FROM ME	35.00
63	9768	HIGH KEYES	QUE SERA, SERA	DADDY OOH LONG LEGS	25.00
63	9768 DJ	HIGH KEYES	QUE SERA, SERA	DADDY OOH LONG LEGS	50.00
63	9771	RUBY & THE ROMANTICS	HEY THERE LONELY BOY	NOT A MOMENT TOO SOON	15.00
63	9771 DJ	RUBY & THE ROMANTICS	HEY THERE LONELY BOY	NOT A MOMENT TOO SOON	25.00
63	9773	CRYSTALS	THEN HE KISSED ME	BROTHER JULIUS	8.00
63	9773 DJ	CRYSTALS	THEN HE KISSED ME	BROTHER JULIUS	30.00
63	9775	JAMES BROWN & THE FAMOUS FLAMES	(CAN YOU) FEEL IT	THESE FOOLISH THINGS	20.00
63	9775 DJ	JAMES BROWN & THE FAMOUS FLAMES	(CAN YOU) FEEL IT	THESE FOOLISH THINGS	28.00
63	9778	BEN E.KING	THE BEGINNING OF TIME	I (WHO HAVE NOTHING)	15.00
63	9778 DJ	BEN E.KING	THE BEGINNING OF TIME	I (WHO HAVE NOTHING)	22.00
63	9779	BARBARA LEWIS	IF YOU LOVE HER	STRAIGHTEN UP YOUR HEART	25.00
63	9779 DJ	BARBARA LEWIS	IF YOU LOVE HER	STRAIGHTEN UP YOUR HEART	45.00
63	9784	BOOKER T. & THE MG'S	CHINESE CHECKERS	PLUM NELLIE	15.00
63	9784 DJ	BOOKER T. & THE MG'S	CHINESE CHECKERS	PLUM NELLIE	28.00
63	9785	DRIFTERS	I'LL TAKE YOU HOME	I FEEL GOOD ALL OVER	10.00
63	9785 DJ	DRIFTERS	I'LL TAKE YOU HOME	I FEEL GOOD ALL OVER	25.00
63	9792	SUNNY & the SUNGLOWS	TALK TO ME	EVERY WEEK, EVERY MONTH, EVERY	20.00
63	9792 DJ	SUNNY & the SUNGLOWS	TALK TO ME	EVERY WEEK, EVERY MONTH, EVERY	30.00
63	9793	RONETTES	BE MY BABY	TEDESCO AND PITMAN	10.00
63	9793 DJ	RONETTES	BE MY BABY	TEDESCO AND PITMAN	30.00
63	9795	AMOS MILBURN JR.	GLORIA	LOOK AT ME FOOL	15.00
63	9795 DJ	AMOS MILBURN JR.	GLORIA	LOOK AT ME FOOL	20.00
63	9796	BETTY HARRIS	CRY TO ME	I'LL BE A LIAR	25.00
63	9796 DJ	BETTY HARRIS	CRY TO ME	I'LL BE A LIAR	35.00
63	9799	RUFUS THOMAS	WALKING THE DOG	FINE AND MELLOW	22.00
63	9799 DJ	RUFUS THOMAS	WALKING THE DOG	FINE AND MELLOW	45.00
63	9801	RUBY & THE ROMANTICS	YOUNG WINGS CAN FLY	DAY DREAMING	15.00
63	9801 DJ	RUBY & THE ROMANTICS	YOUNG WINGS CAN FLY	DAY DREAMING	25.00
63	9805	LOU JOHNSON	MAGIC POTION	REACH OUT FOR ME	85.00
63	9805 DJ	LOU JOHNSON	MAGIC POTION	REACH OUT FOR ME	130.00
63	9809	DYNAMICS	MISERY	I'M THE MAN	40.00
63	9809 DJ	DYNAMICS	MISERY	I'M THE MAN	60.00
63	9810	LENNY WELCH	SINCE I FELL FOR YOU	ARE YOU SINCERE	8.00
63	9810 DJ	LENNY WELCH	SINCE I FELL FOR YOU	ARE YOU SINCERE	12.00
63	9814	RIGHTEOUS BROTHERS	MY BABE	FEE-FI-FIDLY-I-OH	10.00
63	9814 DJ	RIGHTEOUS BROTHERS	MY BABE	FEE-FI-FIDLY-I-OH	50.00
63	9815	DARLENE LOVE	A FINE FINE BOY	MARSHMALLOW WORLD	25.00
63	9815 DJ	DARLENE LOVE	A FINE FINE BOY	MARSHMALLOW WORLD	30.00
63	9819	BEN E. KING	GYPSY	I COULD HAVE DANCED ALL NIGHT	15.00
63	9819 DJ	BEN E. KING	GYPSY	I COULD HAVE DANCED ALL NIGHT	22.00
63	9824	SHIRLEY ELLIS	THE NITTY GRITTY	GIVE ME A LIST	10.00
63	9824 DJ	SHIRLEY ELLIS	THE NITTY GRITTY	GIVE ME A LIST	20.00
63	9826	RONETTES	BABY, I LOVE YOU	MISS JOAN AND MR. SAM	8.00
63	9826 DJ	RONETTES	BABY, I LOVE YOU	MISS JOAN AND MR. SAM	30.00
64	9832	BARBARA LEWIS	SNAP YOUR FINGERS	PUPPY LOVE	25.00
64	9832 DJ	BARBARA LEWIS	SNAP YOUR FINGERS	PUPPY LOVE	35.00
64	9833	OTIS REDDING	PAIN IN MY HEART	SOMETHING IS WORRYING ME	20.00
64	9833 DJ	OTIS REDDING	PAIN IN MY HEART	SOMETHING IS WORRYING ME	30.00
64	9837 DJ	CRYSTALS	LITTLE BOY	UPTOWN	75.00
64	9840	BEN E.KING	AROUND THE CORNER	GROOVIN'	15.00
64	9840 DJ	BEN E.KING	AROUND THE CORNER	GROOVIN'	25.00
64	9846	GLORIA LYNNE	I WISH YOU LOVE	THROUGH A LONG AND SLEEPLESS N	8.00
64	9846 DJ	GLORIA LYNNE	I WISH YOU LOVE	THROUGH A LONG AND SLEEPLESS N	10.00
64	9848	DRIFTERS	VAYA CON DIOS	THE LAND OF MAKE BELIVE	10.00
64	9848 DJ	DRIFTERS	VAYA CON DIOS	THE LAND OF MAKE BELIVE	20.00
64	9849	SOLOMON BURKE	HE'LL HAVE TO GO	ROCKIN' SOUL	15.00
64	9849 DJ	SOLOMON BURKE	HE'LL HAVE TO GO	ROCKIN' SOUL	25.00
64	9850	RUFUS THOMAS	CAN YOUR MONKEY DO THE DOG	I WANT TO GET MARRIED	10.00
64	9850 DJ	RUFUS THOMAS	CAN YOUR MONKEY DO THE DOG	I WANT TO GET MARRIED	20.00
64	9852	CRYSTALS	I WONDER	LITTLE BOY	20.00
64	9852 DJ	CRYSTALS	I WONDER	LITTLE BOY	30.00
64	9863	COASTERS	T'AIN'T NOTHIN' TO ME	SPEEDO'S BACK IN TOWN	8.00
64	9863 DJ	COASTERS	T'AIN'T NOTHIN' TO ME	SPEEDO'S BACK IN TOWN	10.00
64	9868	JIMMY HOLIDAY	I LIED	ALLISON	15.00

64	9868 DJ	JIMMY HOLIDAY	I LIED	ALLISON	22.00
64	9875	VIBRATIONS	MY GIRL SLOOPY	DADDY WOO WOO	15.00
64	9875 DJ	VIBRATIONS	MY GIRL SLOOPY	DADDY WOO-WOO	40.00
64	9876	OTIS REDDING	COME TO ME	DON'T LEAVE ME THIS WAY	25.00
64	9876 DJ	OTIS REDDING	COME TO ME	DON'T LEAVE ME THIS WAY	40.00
64	9880	LENNY WELCH	EBB TIDE	CONGRATULATIONS BABY	8.00
64	9880 DJ	LENNY WELCH	EBB TIDE	CONGRATULATIONS BABY	10.00
64	9881	RUBY & THE ROMANTICS	MUCH BETTER OFF THAN I'VE EVER	OUR EVERLASTING LOVE	40.00
64	9881 DJ	RUBY & THE ROMANTICS	MUCH BETTER OFF THAN I'VE EVER	OUR EVERLASTING LOVE	60.00
64	9884	RUFUS THOMAS	SOMEBODY STOLE MY DOG	I WANT TO BE LOVED	15.00
64	9884 DJ	RUFUS THOMAS	SOMEBODY STOLE MY DOG	I WANT TO BE LOVED	22.00
64	9886	DRIFTERS	ONE WAY LOVE	DIDN'T IT	15.00
64	9886 DJ	DRIFTERS	ONE WAY LOVE	DIDN'T IT	22.00
64	9887	SOLOMON BURKE	GOODBYE BABY (BABY GOODBYE)	SOMEONE TO LOVE ME	15.00
64	9887 DJ	SOLOMON BURKE	GOODBYE BABY (BABY GOODBYE)	SOMEONE TO LOVE ME	25.00
64	9896	LITTLE RICHARD	BAMA LAMA BAMA LOO	ANNIE IS BACK	8.00
64	9896 DJ	LITTLE RICHARD	BAMA LAMA BAMA LOO	ANNIE IS BACK	10.00
64	9897	DON & DEWEY	GET YOUR HAT	ANNIE LEE	20.00
64	9897 DJ	DON & DEWEY	GET YOUR HAT	ANNIE LEE	25.00
64	9899	ARTHUR ALEXANDER	BLACK NIGHT	OLE JOHN AMOS	30.00
64	9899 DJ	ARTHUR ALEXANDER	BLACK NIGHT	OLE JOHN AMOS	45.00
64	9905	RONETTES	(THE BEST PART OF) BREAKING UP	BIG RED	8.00
64	9905 DJ	RONETTES	(THE BEST PART OF) BREAKING UP	BIG RED	30.00
64	9908	ROUND ROBIN	KICK THAT LITTLE FOOT SALLY ANN	SLAUSON PARTY	60.00
64	9908 DJ	ROUND ROBIN	KICK THAT LITTLE FOOT SALLY ANN	SLAUSON PARTY	100.00
64	9909	CRYSTALS	ALL GROWN UP	IRVING (JAGGERED SIXTEENTHS)	15.00
64	9909 DJ	CRYSTALS	ALL GROWN UP	IRVING (JAGGERED SIXTEENTHS)	30.00
64	9910	LENNY WELCH	IF YOU SEE MY LOVE	FATHER SEBASTIAN	8.00
64	9910 DJ	LENNY WELCH	IF YOU SEE MY LOVE	FATHER SEBASTIAN	10.00
64	9916	RUBY & THE ROMANTICS	BABY COME HOME	EVERY DAY'S A HOLIDAY	40.00
64	9916 DJ	RUBY & THE ROMANTICS	BABY COME HOME	EVERY DAY'S A HOLIDAY	75.00
64	9917	LOU JOHNSON	WOULDN'T THAT BE SOMETHING	(THERE'S) ALWAYS SOMETHING THERE TO REM	45.00
64	9917 DJ	LOU JOHNSON	WOULDN'T THAT BE SOMETHING	(THERE'S) ALWAYS SOMETHING THERE TO REM	100.00
64	9918	BARBARA LYNN	OH! BABY (WE GOT A GOOD THING	UNFAIR	50.00
64	9918 DJ	BARBARA LYNN	OH! BABY (WE GOT A GOOD THING	UNFAIR	85.00
64	9921	BOBBY JAMESON	I'M SO LONELY	I WANNA LOVE YOU	25.00
64	9921 DJ	BOBBY JAMESON	I'M SO LONELY	I WANNA LOVE YOU	40.00
64	9922	RONETTES	DO I LOVE YOU	WHEN I SAW YOU	8.00
64	9922 DJ	RONETTES	DO I LOVE YOU	WHEN I SAW YOU	30.00
64	9925	BILL BLACK'S COMBO	LITTLE QUEENIE	BOO-RAY	50.00
64	9925 DJ	BILL BLACK'S COMBO	LITTLE QUEENIE	BOO-RAY	120.00
64	9926	WILLIE MITCHELL	SECRET HOME	20 - 75	20.00
64	9926 DJ	WILLIE MITCHELL	SECRET HOME	20 - 75	45.00
68	9926 boxed logo	WILLIE MITCHELL	SECRET HOME	20 - 75	10.00
64	9929	LOU JOHNSON	THE LAST ONE TO BE LOVED	A MESSAGE TO MARTHA (KENTUCKY BLUEBIRD)	20.00
64	9929 DJ	LOU JOHNSON	THE LAST ONE TO BE LOVED	A MESSAGE TO MARTHA (KENTUCKY BLUEBIRD)	30.00
64	9931	RONETTES	(WALKING) IN THE RAIN	HOW DOES IT FEEL	15.00
64	9931 DJ	RONETTES	(WALKING) IN THE RAIN	HOW DOES IT FEEL	30.00
64	9932	TOMMY TUCKER	OH! WHAT A FEELING	WINE BOTTLES	75.00
64	9932 DJ	TOMMY TUCKER	OH! WHAT A FEELING	WINE BOTTLES	100.00
64	9935	RUBY & THE ROMANTICS	WHEN YOUY'RE YOUNG AND IN LOVE	I CRY ALONE	15.00
64	9935 DJ	RUBY & THE ROMANTICS	WHEN YOUY'RE YOUNG AND IN LOVE	I CRY ALONE	22.00
65	9941	BIG MAYBELLE	CARELESS LOVE	MY MOTHER'S EYES	15.00
65	9941 DJ	BIG MAYBELLE	CARELESS LOVE	MY MOTHER'S EYES	25.00
64	9942	BOBBY SKEL	KISS AND RUN	SAY IT NOW	15.00
64	9942 DJ	BOBBY SKEL	KISS AND RUN	SAY IT NOW	25.00
65	9945	JAMES BROWN	HAVE MERCY BABY	JUST WON'T DO RIGHT	15.00
65	9945 DJ	JAMES BROWN	HAVE MERCY BABY	JUST WON'T DO RIGHT	25.00
65	9946	SHIRLEY ELLIS	THE NAME GAME	WHISPER TO ME WIND	15.00
65	9946 DJ	SHIRLEY ELLIS	THE NAME GAME	WHISPER TO ME WIND	22.00
65	9952	RONETTES	BORN TO BE TOGETHER	BLUES FOR BABY	20.00
65	9952 DJ	RONETTES	BORN TO BE TOGETHER	BLUES FOR BABY	30.00
65	9953	DOBIE GRAY	THE IN CROWD	BE A MAN	20.00
65	9953 DJ	DOBIE GRAY	THE IN CROWD	BE A MAN	100.00
65	9954	JEWEL AKENS	THE BIRDS AND THE BEES	TIC TAC TOE	8.00
65	9954 DJ	JEWEL AKENS	THE BIRDS AND THE BEES	TIC TAC TOE	15.00
65	9959	CAROLYN CARTER	IT HURTS	I'M THRU	45.00
65	9959 DJ	CAROLYN CARTER	IT HURTS	I'M THRU	75.00
65	9961	SHIRLEY ELLIS	THE CLAPPING SONG	THIS IS BEAUTIFUL	5.00
65	9961 DJ	SHIRLEY ELLIS	THE CLAPPING SONG	THIS IS BEAUTIFUL	25.00
65	9962	RIGHTEOUS BROTHERS	JUST ONCE IN MY LIFE	THE BLUES	50.00
65	9962 DJ	RIGHTEOUS BROTHERS	JUST ONCE IN MY LIFE	THE BLUES	40.00
65	9964	SIR DOUGLAS QUINTET	SHE'S ABOUT A MOVER	WE'LL TAKE OUR LAST WALK TONIGHT	10.00
65	9964 DJ	SIR DOUGLAS QUINTET	SHE'S ABOUT A MOVER	WE'LL TAKE OUR LAST WALK TONIGHT	22.00
65	9965	LOU JOHNSON	PLEASE, STOP THE WEDDING	PARK AVENUE	15.00
65	9965 DJ	LOU JOHNSON	PLEASE, STOP THE WEDDING	PARK AVENUE	28.00
65	9969	JEWEL AKENS	GEORGIE PORGIE	AROUND THE CORNER	8.00
65	9969 DJ	JEWEL AKENS	GEORGIE PORGIE	AROUND THE CORNER	15.00
65	9970	SOUL SISTERS	GOOD TIME TONIGHT	FOOLISH DREAMER	75.00

65	9970 DJ	SOUL SISTERS	GOOD TIME TONIGHT	FOOLISH DREAMER	100.00
65	9971	INEZ & CHARLIE FOXX	MY MOMMA TOLD ME	I FEEL ALRIGHT	15.00
65	9971 DJ	INEZ & CHARLIE FOXX	MY MOMMA TOLD ME	I FEEL ALRIGHT	25.00
65	9972	RUBY & THE ROMANTICS	YOUR BABY DOESN'T LOVE ME	WE'LL MEET AGAIN	15.00
65	9972 DJ	RUBY & THE ROMANTICS	YOUR BABY DOESN'T LOVE ME	WE'LL MEET AGAIN	22.00
65	9973	SHIRLEY ELLIS	THE PUZZLE SONG	I SEE IT, I LIKE IT, I WANT IT	10.00
65	9973 DJ	SHIRLEY ELLIS	THE PUZZLE SONG	I SEE IT, I LIKE IT, I WANT IT	15.00
65	9974	TINA BRITT	THE REAL THING	TEARDROPS FELL	60.00
65	9974 DJ	TINA BRITT	THE REAL THING	TEARDROPS FELL	100.00
65	9975	RIGHTEOUS BROTHERS	UNCHAINED MELODY	HUNG ON YOU	10.00
65	9975 DJ	RIGHTEOUS BROTHERS	UNCHAINED MELODY	HUNG ON YOU	28.00
65	9976	RONETTES	YOU BABY	IS THIS WSORTH WHAT I GET FOR	15.00
65	9976 DJ	RONETTES	YOU BABY	IS THIS WSORTH WHAT I GET FOR	30.00
65	9977	BARBARA MASON	YES, I'M READY	KEEP HIM	50.00
65	9977 DJ	BARBARA MASON	YES, I'M READY	KEEP HIM	75.00
65	9981	LENNY WELCH	DARLING TAKE ME BACK (I'M SORRY)	TIME AFTER TIME	20.00
65	9981 DJ	LENNY WELCH	DARLING TAKE ME BACK (I'M SORRY)	TIME AFTER TIME	30.00
65	9983	BURT BACHARACH & his ORCH.	MY LITTLE RED BOOK	WHAT'S NEW PUSSYCAT	25.00
65	9983 DJ	BURT BACHARACH & his ORCH.	MY LITTLE RED BOOK	WHAT'S NEW PUSSYCAT	40.00
65	9987	BABY WASHINGTON	ONLY THOSE IN LOVE	BALLAD OF BOBBY DAWN	25.00
65	9987 DJ	BABY WASHINGTON	ONLY THOSE IN LOVE	BALLAD OF BOBBY DAWN	35.00
65	9990	JAMES BROWN & FAMOUS FLAMES	PAPA'S GOT A BRAND NEW BAG	PAPA'S GOT A BRAND NEW BAG 2	20.00
65	9990 DJ	JAMES BROWN & FAMOUS FLAMES	PAPA'S GOT A BRAND NEW BAG	PAPA'S GOT A BRAND NEW BAG 2	45.00
65	9991	LENNY WELCH	TWO DIFFERENT WORLDS	I WAS THERE	8.00
65	9991 DJ	LENNY WELCH	TWO DIFFERENT WORLDS	I WAS THERE	15.00
65	9994	LOU JOHNSON	UNSATISFIED	A TIME TO LOVE, A TIME 2 CRY	75.00
65	9994 DJ	LOU JOHNSON	UNSATISFIED	A TIME TO LOVE, A TIME TO CRY	150.00
65	9996	VOGUES	YOU'RE THE ONE	SOME WORDS	15.00
65	9996 DJ	VOGUES	YOU'RE THE ONE	SOME WORDS	22.00
65	9998	BONNIE & the TREASURES	HOME OF THE BRAVE	OUR SONG	30.00
65	9998 DJ	BONNIE & the TREASURES	HOME OF THE BRAVE	OUR SONG	45.00
65	9999 DJ	AL DE LORY	TRAFFIC JAM	YESTERDAY	15.00
65	9999 DJ	AL DE LORY	TRAFFIC JAM	YESTERDAY	25.00
65	10003	CASTAWAYS	LIAR, LIAR	SAM	30.00
65	10003 DJ	CASTAWAYS	LIAR, LIAR	SAM	50.00
65	10004	WILLIE MITCHELL	THAT DRIVING BEAT	EVERYTHING'S GONNA BE ALRIGHT	25.00
65	10004 DJ	WILLIE MITCHELL	THAT DRIVING BEAT	EVERYTHING'S GONNA BE ALRIGHT	60.00
65	10004 boxed logo	WILLIE MITCHELL	THAT DRIVING BEAT	EVERYTHING'S GONNA BE ALRIGHT	10.00
65	10009	INEZ & CHARLIE FOXX	HUMMINGBIRD	IF I NEED ANYONE (LET IT BE U)	15.00
65	10009 DJ	INEZ & CHARLIE FOXX	HUMMINGBIRD	IF I NEED ANYONE (LET IT BE YO	22.00
65	10010	LENNY WELCH	RUN TO MY LOVIN' ARMS	CORONET BLUE	30.00
65	10010 DJ	LENNY WELCH	RUN TO MY LOVIN' ARMS	CORONET BLUE	45.00
65	10011	RIGHTEOUS BROTHERS	EBB TIDE	(I LOVE YOU) FOR SENTIMENTAL R	8.00
65	10011 DJ	RIGHTEOUS BROTHERS	EBB TIDE	(I LOVE YOU) FOR SENTIMENTAL R	10.00
66	10014	VOGUES	FIVE O'CLOCK WORLD	NOTHING TO OFFER YOU	10.00
66	10014 DJ	VOGUES	FIVE O'CLOCK WORLD	NOTHING TO OFFER YOU	15.00
66	10016	RAY STEVENS	ABC	PARTY PEOPLE	40.00
66	10016 DJ	RAY STEVENS	ABC	PARTY PEOPLE	50.00
66	10018	EXCITERS	A LITTLE BIT OF SOAP	I'M GONNA GET HIM SOMEDAY	15.00
66	10018 DJ	EXCITERS	A LITTLE BIT OF SOAP	I'M GONNA GET HIM SOMEDAY	22.00
66	10020	STRANGELOVES	NIGHT TIME	RHYTHM OF LOVE	22.00
66	10020 DJ	STRANGELOVES	NIGHT TIME	RHYTHM OF LOVE	30.00
66	10021	SHIRLEY ELLIS	EVER SEE A DIVER KISS HIS WIFE WHILE	STARDUST	6.00
66	10021 DJ	SHIRLEY ELLIS	EVER SEE A DIVER KISS HIS WIFE WHILE	STARDUST	8.00
65	10023	ARTHUR ALEXANDER	(BABY) FOR YOU	THE OTHER WOMAN	30.00
65	10023 DJ	ARTHUR ALEXANDER	(BABY) FOR YOU	THE OTHER WOMAN	45.00
66	10024	DARROW FLETCHER	THE PAIN GETS A LITTLE DEEPER	MY JUDGEMENT DAY	75.00
66	10024 DJ	DARROW FLETCHER	THE PAIN GETS A LITTLE DEEPER	MY JUDGEMENT DAY	125.00
66	10031	LENNY WELCH	RAGS TO RICHES	I WANT YOU TO WORRY	10.00
66	10031 DJ	LENNY WELCH	RAGS TO RICHES	I WANT YOU TO WORRY	20.00
66	10037	AMERICAN POETS	SHE BLEW A GOOD THING	OUT TO LUNCH	100.00
66	10037 DJ	AMERICAN POETS	SHE BLEW A GOOD THING	OUT TO LUNCH	**176.00**
66	10038	EXCITERS	WEDDINGS MAKE ME CRY	YOU BETTER COME HOME	60.00
66	10038 DJ	EXCITERS	WEDDINGS MAKE ME CRY	YOU BETTER COME HOME	100.00
66	10039	WILLIE MITCHELL	BAD EYE	SUGAR T	10.00
66	10039 DJ	WILLIE MITCHELL	BAD EYE	SUGAR T	15.00
66	10046	IKE & TINA TURNER	RIVER DEEP - MOUNTAIN HIGH	I'LL KEEP YOU HAPPY	6.00
66	10046 DJ	IKE & TINA TURNER	RIVER DEEP - MOUNTAIN HIGH	I'LL KEEP YOU HAPPY	35.00
66	10057	JOE SIMON	LONG HOT SUMMER	TEENAGER'S PRAYER	45.00
66	10057 DJ	JOE SIMON	LONG HOT SUMMER	TEENAGER'S PRAYER	75.00
66	10059	JIMMY BEAUMONT	YOU GOT TOO MUCH GOING FOR YOU	I NEVER LOVED HER ANYWAY	100.00
66	10059 DJ	JIMMY BEAUMONT	YOU GOT TOO MUCH GOING FOR YOU	I NEVER LOVED HER ANYWAY	150.00
66	10062	DONALD HEIGHT	TALK OF THE GRAPEVINE	THERE'LL BE NO TOMORROW	**190.00**
66	10062 DJ	DONALD HEIGHT	TALK OF THE GRAPEVINE	THERE'LL BE NO TOMORROW	**280.00**
66	10066	RIGHTEOUS BROTHERS	JUST ONCE IN MY LIFE	THE BLUES	6.00
66	10066 DJ	RIGHTEOUS BROTHERS	JUST ONCE IN MY LIFE	THE BLUES	10.00
66	10069	INTRUDERS	UP AND DOWN THE LADDER	UNITED	75.00
66	10069 DJ	INTRUDERS	UP AND DOWN THE LADDER	UNITED	100.00
66	10070 DJ	DARRELL BANKS	OPEN THE DOOR TO YOUR HEART	OUR LOVE VG condition	**614.00**

66	10070 DJ	DARRELL BANKS	OPEN THE DOOR TO YOUR HEART	OUR LOVE	VG+ condition	**764.00**
66	10070 DJ	DARRELL BANKS	OPEN THE DOOR TO YOUR HEART	OUR LOVE	excellent condition	900.00
66	10070 unconfirmed	DARRELL BANKS	OPEN THE DOOR TO YOUR HEART	OUR LOVE		UN
66	10078	MARGARET WHITING	NOTHING LASTS FOREVER	THE WHEEL OF HURT		20.00
66	10078 DJ	MARGARET WHITING	NOTHING LASTS FOREVER	THE WHEEL OF HURT		30.00
66	10081	IKETTES	WHAT'CHA GONNA DO	DOWN, DOWN		50.00
66	10081 DJ	IKETTES	WHAT'CHA GONNA DO	DOWN, DOWN		85.00
66	10083	IKE & TINA TURNER	HOLD ON BABY	A LOVE LIKE YOURS (DON'T COME KNOCKING)		10.00
66	10083 DJ	IKE & TINA TURNER	HOLD ON BABY	A LOVE LIKE YOURS (DON'T COME KNOCKING)		22.00
66	10084	NINO & APRIL TEMPO	ALL STRUNG OUT	I CAN'T GO ON LIVING BABY WITH		6.00
66	10084 DJ	NINO & APRIL TEMPO	ALL STRUNG OUT	I CAN'T GO ON LIVING BABY WITH		10.00
66	10085	WILLIE MITCHELL	MERCY	STICKS AND STONES		20.00
66	10085 DJ	WILLIE MITCHELL	MERCY	STICKS AND STONES		30.00
66	10086	RIGHTEOUS BROTHERS	THE WHITE CLIFFS OF DOVER	BABY SHE'S MINE		6.00
66	10086 DJ	RIGHTEOUS BROTHERS	THE WHITE CLIFFS OF DOVER	BABY SHE'S MINE		10.00
66	10087 DJ	RONETTES	I CAN HEAR MUSIC	WHEN I SAW YOU		45.00
66	10090 withdrawn	LITTLE HANK	MR. BANG BANG MAN	DON'T YOU KNOW		250.00
66	10090 DJ	LITTLE HANK	MR. BANG BANG MAN	DON'T YOU KNOW		150.00
66	10094	BARBARA LYNN	YOU LEFT THE WATER RUNNING	UNTIL I'M FREE		50.00
66	10094 DJ	BARBARA LYNN	YOU LEFT THE WATER RUNNING	UNTIL I'M FREE		75.00
66	10097	ROY HEAD	TO MAKE A BIG MAN CRY	DON'T CRY NO MORE		15.00
66	10097 DJ	ROY HEAD	TO MAKE A BIG MAN CRY	DON'T CRY NO MORE		25.00
66	10102	KNICKERBOCKERS	PLEASE DON'T LOVE HIM	CAN YOU HELP ME		10.00
66	10102 DJ	KNICKERBOCKERS	PLEASE DON'T LOVE HIM	CAN YOU HELP ME		15.00
66	10103	FREDDIE SCOTT	ARE YOU LONELY FOR ME BABY	WHERE WERE YOU		12.00
66	10103 DJ	FREDDIE SCOTT	ARE YOU LONELY FOR ME BABY	WHERE WERE YOU		20.00
66	10104 silvertop	CHARLIE RICH	LOVE IS AFTER ME	PASS ON BY		30.00
66	10104 DJ	CHARLIE RICH	LOVE IS AFTER ME	PASS ON BY		**105.00**
69	10104 boxed logo	CHARLIE RICH	LOVE IS AFTER ME	PASS ON BY		10.00
66	10107	TOMMY G. and the CHARMS	I KNOW WHAT I WANT	I WANT YOU SO BAD		20.00
66	10107 DJ	TOMMY G. and the CHARMS	I KNOW WHAT I WANT	I WANT YOU SO BAD		30.00
67	10114	MARGARET WHITING	JUST LIKE A MAN	THE WORLD INSIDE YOUR ARMS		6.00
67	10114 DJ	MARGARET WHITING	JUST LIKE A MAN	THE WORLD INSIDE YOUR ARMS		8.00
67	10116	DONALD HEIGHT	THREE HUNDRED AND SIXTY FIVE DAYS	I'M WILLING TO WAIT		50.00
67	10116 DJ	DONALD HEIGHT	THREE HUNDRED AND SIXTY FIVE DAYS	I'M WILLING TO WAIT		70.00
67	10120	FORUM	THE RIVER IS WIDE	I FALL IN LOVE		15.00
67	10120 DJ	FORUM	THE RIVER IS WIDE	I FALL IN LOVE		22.00
67	10121	EARL HARRISON	HUMPHREY STOMP	CAN YOU FORGIVE ME		45.00
67	10121 DJ	EARL HARRISON	HUMPHREY STOMP	CAN YOU FORGIVE ME		85.00
67	10123	FREDDIE SCOTT	CRY TO ME	NO ONE COULD EVER LOVE YOU		15.00
67	10123 DJ	FREDDIE SCOTT	CRY TO ME	NO ONE COULD EVER LOVE YOU		25.00
67	10127	BRENDA & THE TABULATIONS	DRY YOUR EYES	THE WASH		15.00
67	10127 DJ	BRENDA & THE TABULATIONS	DRY YOUR EYES	THE WASH		20.00
67	10128	JERRY JAYE	MY GIRL JOSEPHINE	FIVE MILES FROM HOME		30.00
67	10128 DJ	JERRY JAYE	MY GIRL JOSEPHINE	FIVE MILES FROM HOME		40.00
67	10129	EDDIE FLOYD	SET MY SOUL ON FIRE	WILL I BE THE ONE		15.00
67	10129 DJ	EDDIE FLOYD	SET MY SOUL ON FIRE	WILL I BE THE ONE		25.00
67	10137	O.V. WRIGHT	EIGHT MEN, FOUR WOMEN	FED UP WITH THE BLUES		15.00
67	10137 DJ	O.V. WRIGHT	EIGHT MEN, FOUR WOMEN	FED UP WITH THE BLUES		25.00
67	10139	FREDDIE SCOTT	AM I GROOVING YOU?	NEVER YOU MIND		10.00
67	10139 DJ	FREDDIE SCOTT	AM I GROOVING YOU?	NEVER YOU MIND		15.00
67	10144	GAYLE WINTERS	SNAP YOUR FINGERS	FIND MYSELF A NEW LOVE		25.00
67	10144 DJ	GAYLE WINTERS	SNAP YOUR FINGERS	FIND MYSELF A NEW LOVE		35.00
67	10146	WILSON PICKETT	BILLY THE KID	I DON'T WANT NO PART-TIME LOVE		10.00
67	10146 DJ	WILSON PICKETT	BILLY THE KID	I DON'T WANT NO PART-TIME LOVE		15.00
67	10155	IKE & TINA TURNER	SAVE THE LAST DANCE FOR ME	I'LL NEVER NEED MORE THAN THIS		8.00
67	10155 DJ	IKE & TINA TURNER	SAVE THE LAST DANCE FOR ME	I'LL NEVER NEED MORE THAN THIS		15.00
67	10162	JERRY O	KARATE-BOO-GA-LOO	THE PEARL		10.00
67	10162 DJ	JERRY O	KARATE-BOO-GA-LOO	THE PEARL		25.00
67	10164	HELENA FERGUSON	MY TERMS	WHERE IS THE PARTY?		25.00
67	10164 DJ	HELENA FERGUSON	MY TERMS	WHERE IS THE PARTY?		35.00
67	10169	FANTASTIC JOHNNY C.	BOOGALOO DOWN BROADWAY	LOOK WHAT LOVE CAN MAKE YOU DO		10.00
67	10169 DJ	FANTASTIC JOHNNY C.	BOOGALOO DOWN BROADWAY	LOOK WHAT LOVE CAN MAKE YOU DO		28.00
67	10170	ERMA FRANKLIN	PIECE OF MY HEART	BIG BOSS MAN		10.00
67	10170 DJ	ERMA FRANKLIN	PIECE OF MY HEART	BIG BOSS MAN		20.00
67	10172	FREDDIE SCOTT	RUN JOE	HE AIN'T GIVE YOU NONE		15.00
67	10172 DJ	FREDDIE SCOTT	RUN JOE	HE AIN'T GIVE YOU NONE		25.00
67	10174	BRENDA & THE TABULATIONS	WHEN YOU'RE GONE	HEY BOY		15.00
67	10174 DJ	BRENDA & THE TABULATIONS	WHEN YOU'RE GONE	HEY BOY		25.00
68	10180	HESITATIONS	PUSH A LITTLE HARDER	BORN FREE		40.00
68	10180 DJ	HESITATIONS	PUSH A LITTLE HARDER	BORN FREE		50.00
68	10181	GEORGE TORRENCE	LICKIN' STICK	SO LONG GOODBYE		15.00
68	10181 DJ	GEORGE TORRENCE	LICKIN' STICK	SO LONG GOODBYE		22.00
68	10186	WILLIE MITCHELL	SOUL SERENADE	BUSTER BROWNE		8.00
68	10186 DJ	WILLIE MITCHELL	SOUL SERENADE	BUSTER BROWNE		15.00
68	10188	WEBS	TOMORROW	THIS THING CALLED LOVE		15.00
68	10188 DJ	WEBS	TOMORROW	THIS THING CALLED LOVE		25.00
68	10189	IKE & TINA TURNER	SO FINE	SO BLUE OVER YOU		10.00
68	10189 DJ	IKE & TINA TURNER	SO FINE	SO BLUE OVER YOU		20.00

68	10198	HESITATIONS	THE IMPOSSIBLE DREAM (the quest)	NOBODY WANTS TO KNOW YOU WHEN	10.00
68	10198 DJ	HESITATIONS	THE IMPOSSIBLE DREAM (the quest)	NOBODY WANTS TO KNOW YOU WHEN	15.00
68	10201	ERMA FRANKLIN	OPEN UP YOUR SOUL	I JUST AIN'T READY	10.00
68	10201 DJ	ERMA FRANKLIN	OPEN UP YOUR SOUL	I JUST AIN'T READY	15.00
68	10212	FANTASTIC JOHNNY C.	HITCH IT TO THE HORSE	COOL BROADWAY	10.00
68	10212 DJ	FANTASTIC JOHNNY C.	HITCH IT TO THE HORSE	COOL BROADWAY	25.00
68	10215	WILLIE MITCHELL	PRAYER MEETIN'	RUM DADDY	8.00
68	10215 DJ	WILLIE MITCHELL	PRAYER MEETIN'	RUM DADDY	12.00
68	10216	BILL BLACK'S COMBO	TURN ON YOUR LOVELIGHT	RIBBON OF DARKNESS	6.00
68	10216 DJ	BILL BLACK'S COMBO	TURN ON YOUR LOVELIGHT	RIBBON OF DARKNESS	8.00
68	10217	IKE & TINA TURNER	WE NEED AN UNDERSTANDING	IT SHO' AIN'T ME	10.00
68	10217 DJ	IKE & TINA TURNER	WE NEED AN UNDERSTANDING	IT SHO' AIN'T ME	15.00
68	10220	ERMA FRANKLIN	THE RIGHT TO CRY	DON'T CATCH THE DOG'S BONE	15.00
68	10220 DJ	ERMA FRANKLIN	THE RIGHT TO CRY	DON'T CATCH THE DOG'S BONE	22.00
68	10221	GROVER MITCHELL	TURNED ON	BLUE OVER YOU	8.00
68	10221 DJ	GROVER MITCHELL	TURNED ON	BLUE OVER YOU	10.00
68	10224	WILLIE MITCHELL	UP HARD	BEALE STREET MOOD	10.00
68	10224 DJ	WILLIE MITCHELL	UP HARD	BEALE STREET MOOD	15.00
68	10227	MARGARET WHITING	CAN'T GET YOU OUT OF MY MIND	MAYBE JUST ONE MORE	15.00
68	10227 DJ	MARGARET WHITING	CAN'T GET YOU OUT OF MY MIND	MAYBE JUST ONE MORE	20.00
68	10231	UNIFICS	WHICH ONE SHOULD I CHOOSE	COURT OF LOVE	15.00
68	10231 DJ	UNIFICS	WHICH ONE SHOULD I CHOOSE	COURT OF LOVE	25.00
67	10233	JACKIE LEE	THE DUCK	DANCING IN THE STREET	10.00
68	10233 DJ	JACKIE LEE	THE DUCK	DANCING IN THE STREET	20.00
68	10235	ROYAL GUARDSMEN	SO RIGHT (TO BE IN LOVE)	BABY LET'S WAIT	6.00
68	10235 DJ	ROYAL GUARDSMEN	SO RIGHT (TO BE IN LOVE)	BABY LET'S WAIT	8.00
69	10239	CRYSTALS	DA DOO RON RON	HE'S A REBEL	6.00
69	10239 DJ	CRYSTALS	DA DOO RON RON	HE'S A REBEL	10.00
69	10240	RONETTES	BE MY BABY	BABY I LOVE YOU	6.00
69	10240 DJ	RONETTES	BE MY BABY	BABY I LOVE YOU	10.00
69	10241	RIGHTEOUS BROTHERS	YOU'VE LOST THAT LOVING FEELING	UNCHAINED MELODY	6.00
69	10241 DJ	RIGHTEOUS BROTHERS	YOU'VE LOST THAT LOVING FEELING	UNCHAINED MELODY	10.00
69	10242	IKE & TINA TURNER	RIVER - DEEP MOUNTAIN - HIGH	SAVE THE LAST DANCE FOR ME	6.00
69	10242 DJ	IKE & TINA TURNER	RIVER - DEEP MOUNTAIN - HIGH	SAVE THE LAST DANCE FOR ME	10.00
69	10243	BOB SOXX & THE BLUE JEANS	ZIP-A-DEE-DOO-DAH	WHY DO LOVERS BREAK EACH OTHER	6.00
69	10243 DJ	BOB SOXX & THE BLUE JEANS	ZIP-A-DEE-DOO-DAH	WHY DO LOVERS BREAK EACH OTHER	10.00
68	10244	DARLENE LOVE	WAIT 'TIL MY BOBBY GETS HOME	(TODAY I MET) THE BOY I'M GONNA MARRY	8.00
68	10244 DJ	DARLENE LOVE	WAIT 'TIL MY BOBBY GETS HOME	(TODAY I MET) THE BOY I'M GONNA MARRY	12.00
69	10245	NINO & APRIL TEMPO	ALL STRUNG OUT	MY OLD FLAME	5.00
69	10245 DJ	NINO & APRIL TEMPO	ALL STRUNG OUT	MY OLD FLAME	6.00
68	10246	WILLIE MITCHELL	EVERYTHING IS GONNA BE ALRIGHT	MERCY	10.00
68	10246 DJ	WILLIE MITCHELL	EVERYTHING IS GONNA BE ALRIGHT	MERCY	15.00
69	10247	VOGUES	FIVE O'CLOCK WORLD	YOU'RE THE ONE	6.00
69	10247 DJ	VOGUES	FIVE O'CLOCK WORLD	YOU'RE THE ONE	8.00
69	10248	SIR DOUGLAS QUINTET	SHE'S ABOUT A MOVER	THE RAINS CAME	5.00
69	10248 DJ	SIR DOUGLAS QUINTET	SHE'S ABOUT A MOVER	THE RAINS CAME	6.00
69	10250 unissued	INEZ & CHARLIE FOXX	MOCKINGBIRD	HUMMINGBIRD	UN
69	10255	JIMMY HELMS	IF YOU LET ME	I DON'T CARE WHO KNOWS IT	8.00
69	10255 DJ	JIMMY HELMS	IF YOU LET ME	I DON'T CARE WHO KNOWS IT	10.00
69	10258	BILLY ADAMS	I NEED YOUR LOVE	WHY DON'T YOU BELIEVE ME	20.00
69	10258 DJ	BILLY ADAMS	I NEED YOUR LOVE	WHY DON'T YOU BELIEVE ME	30.00
68	10262	RAY BARRETTO	ACID	MERCY MERCY BABY	15.00
68	10262 DJ	RAY BARRETTO	ACID	MERCY MERCY BABY	20.00
68	10264	HUEYS	COO-COO OVER YOU	YOU AIN'T NO HIPPIE	10.00
68	10264 DJ	HUEYS	COO-COO OVER YOU	YOU AIN'T NO HIPPIE	15.00
69	10266	MARTHA VELEZ	COME HERE SWEET MAN	IT TAKES A LOT TO LAUGH, IT TAKES A TRAIN	6.00
69	10266 DJ	MARTHA VELEZ	COME HERE SWEET MAN	IT TAKES A LOT TO LAUGH, IT TAKES A TRAIN	8.00
69	10267	IKE & TINA TURNER	I'LL NEVER NEED MORE THAN THIS	A LOVE LIKE YOURS	8.00
69	10267 DJ	IKE & TINA TURNER	I'LL NEVER NEED MORE THAN THIS	A LOVE LIKE YOURS	10.00
69	10268	DOBIE GRAY	THE "IN" CROWD	BE A MAN	8.00
69	10268 DJ	DOBIE GRAY	THE "IN" CROWD	BE A MAN	12.00
76	10268 ink	DOBIE GRAY	THE "IN" CROWD	BE A MAN	5.00
69	10269	LOU JOHNSON	THERE'S ALWAYS SOMETHING THERE TO	MESSAGE TO MARTHA	8.00
69	10269 DJ	LOU JOHNSON	THERE'S ALWAYS SOMETHING THERE TO	MESSAGE TO MARTHA	12.00
69	10270	NEWBEATS	BREAD AND BUTTER	PINK DALLY RUE	5.00
69	10270 DJ	NEWBEATS	BREAD AND BUTTER	PINK DALLY RUE	6.00
69	10271	CHIFFONS	SWEET TALKING GUY	ONE FINE DAY	5.00
69	10271 DJ	CHIFFONS	SWEET TALKING GUY	ONE FINE DAY	6.00
69	10272	MUSIC EXPLOSION	A LITTLE BIT 'O SOUL	EVERYBODY	5.00
69	10272 DJ	MUSIC EXPLOSION	A LITTLE BIT 'O SOUL	EVERYBODY	6.00
69	10274	BOBBY BENNETT	BIG NEW YORK	BABY, TRY ME	15.00
69	10274 DJ	BOBBY BENNETT	BIG NEW YORK	BABY, TRY ME	22.00
69	10280	MARTHA VELEZ	TELL MAMA	SWAMPMAN	15.00
69	10280 DJ	MARTHA VELEZ	TELL MAMA	SWAMPMAN	22.00
69	10282	WILLIE MITCHELL	YOUNG PEOPLE	KITTEN KORNER	6.00
69	10282 DJ	WILLIE MITCHELL	YOUNG PEOPLE	KITTEN KORNER	8.00
69	10293	INTRIGUES	IN A MOMENT	SCOTCHMAN	25.00
69	10293 DJ	INTRIGUES	IN A MOMENT	SCOTCHMAN	40.00
70	10299	NEWBEATS	GROOVIN' (OUT ON LIFE)	ERVERYTHING'S ALRIGHT	8.00

70	10299 DJ	NEWBEATS	GROOVIN' (OUT ON LIFE)	ERVERYTHING'S ALRIGHT	10.00
70	10300	AL GREEN	YOU SAY	GOTTA FIND NEW WORLD	6.00
70	10300 DJ	AL GREEN	YOU SAY	GOTTA FIND NEW WORLD	8.00
70	10307	WILBERT HARRISON	LET'S WORK TOGETHER	STAGGER LEE	8.00
70	10307 DJ	WILBERT HARRISON	LET'S WORK TOGETHER	STAGGER LEE	10.00
70	10308	KOOL & THE GANG	KOOL AND THE GANG	RAW HAMBURGERS	20.00
70	10308 DJ	KOOL & THE GANG	KOOL AND THE GANG	RAW HAMBURGERS	25.00
70	10313	WILLIE MITCHELL	ROBIN'S NEST	SIX TO GO	8.00
70	10313 DJ	WILLIE MITCHELL	ROBIN'S NEST	SIX TO GO	10.00
70	10322	ANN PEEBLES	I STILL LOVE YOU	PART TIME LOVE	5.00
70	10322 DJ	ANN PEEBLES	I STILL LOVE YOU	PART TIME LOVE	6.00
70	10324	AL GREEN	I CAN'T GET NEXT TO YOU	RIDE SALLY RIDE	5.00
70	10324 DJ	AL GREEN	I CAN'T GET NEXT TO YOU	RIDE SALLY RIDE	8.00
70	10328	ANN PEEBLES	HEARTACHES, HEARTACHES	I PITY THE FOOL	6.00
70	10328 DJ	ANN PEEBLES	HEARTACHES, HEARTACHES	I PITY THE FOOL	8.00
70	10325	BRENDA & THE TABULATIONS	'SCUSE UZ Y'ALL	A CHILD NMO ONE WANTED	8.00
70	10325 DJ	BRENDA & THE TABULATIONS	'SCUSE UZ Y'ALL	A CHILD NMO ONE WANTED	10.00
71	10331	CHUBBY CHECKER	LET'S GO DOWN	GOODBYE VICTORIA	5.00
71	10331 DJ	CHUBBY CHECKER	LET'S GO DOWN	GOODBYE VICTORIA	6.00
71	10337	AL GREEN	TIRED OF BEING ALONE	RIGHT NOW RIGHT NOW	4.00
71	10337 DJ	AL GREEN	TIRED OF BEING ALONE	RIGHT NOW RIGHT NOW	10.00
71	10341	NEWBEATS	RUN, BABY RUN	AM, I NOT MY BROTHERS KEEPER	6.00
71	10341 DJ	NEWBEATS	RUN, BABY RUN	AM, I NOT MY BROTHERS KEEPER	8.00
71	10346	ANN PEEBLES	SLIPPED TRIPPED AND FELL IN LOVE	99 LBS	5.00
71	10346 DJ	ANN PEEBLES	SLIPPED TRIPPED AND FELL IN LOVE	99 LBS	6.00
71	10348	AL GREEN	LET'S STAY TOGETHER	TOMORROW'S DREAM	5.00
71	10348 DJ	AL GREEN	LET'S STAY TOGETHER	TOMORROW'S DREAM	6.00
71	10352	DONNIE ELBERT	WHERE DID OUR LOVE GO	THAT'S IT YOU LOVE ME	4.00
71	10352 DJ	DONNIE ELBERT	WHERE DID OUR LOVE GO	THAT'S IT YOU LOVE ME	10.00
72	10354	PONDEROSA TWINS + ONE	HEY GIRL	YOU SEND ME	10.00
72	10354 DJ	PONDEROSA TWINS + ONE	HEY GIRL	YOU SEND ME	15.00
72	10356	NEWBEATS	THOU SHALT NOT STEAL	BAD DREAMS	5.00
72	10356 DJ	NEWBEATS	THOU SHALT NOT STEAL	BAD DREAMS	6.00
72	10361	ANN PEEBLES	BREAKING UP SOMEBODY'S HOME	TROUBLES, HEARTACHES AND SADNE	5.00
72	10361 DJ	ANN PEEBLES	BREAKING UP SOMEBODY'S HOME	TROUBLES, HEARTACHES AND SADNE	6.00
72	10368	LINDA JONES	FOR YOUR PRECIOUS LOVE	DON'T GO	15.00
72	10368 DJ	LINDA JONES	FOR YOUR PRECIOUS LOVE	DON'T GO	22.00
72	10369	AL GREEN	I'VE NEVER FOUND A GIRL	LOOK WHAT YOU DONE FOR ME	6.00
72	10369 DJ	AL GREEN	I'VE NEVER FOUND A GIRL	LOOK WHAT YOU DONE FOR ME	8.00
72	10370	ANN PEEBLES	IF I CAN'T HAVE YOU	A LITTLE PIECE OF LEATHER '72	5.00
72	10370 DJ	ANN PEEBLES	IF I CAN'T HAVE YOU	A LITTLE PIECE OF LEATHER '72	6.00
72	10373	GEORGE JACKSON	I'M GONNA WAIT	ARETHA, SING ONE FOR ME	10.00
72	10373 DJ	GEORGE JACKSON	I'M GONNA WAIT	ARETHA, SING ONE FOR ME	15.00
72	10378	MOMENTS	LOVE ON A TWO WAY STREET	I WON'T DO ANYTHING	6.00
72	10378 DJ	MOMENTS	LOVE ON A TWO WAY STREET	I WON'T DO ANYTHING	8.00
72	10380	BILL BLACK'S COMBO	MY GIRL JOSEPHINE	YOGI	5.00
72	10380 DJ	BILL BLACK'S COMBO	MY GIRL JOSEPHINE	YOGI	6.00
72	10382	AL GREEN	I'M STILL IN LOVE WITH YOU	OLD TIME LOVIN'	5.00
72	10382 DJ	AL GREEN	I'M STILL IN LOVE WITH YOU	OLD TIME LOVIN'	8.00
72	10385	ANN PEEBLES	SOMEBODY'S ON YOUR CASE	I'VE BEEN THERE BEFORE	5.00
72	10385 DJ	ANN PEEBLES	SOMEBODY'S ON YOUR CASE	I'VE BEEN THERE BEFORE	6.00
72	10389	MOMENTS	JUST BECAUSE HE WANTS TO MAKE	SO THIS IS GOODBYE	5.00
72	10389 DJ	MOMENTS	JUST BECAUSE HE WANTS TO MAKE	SO THIS IS GOODBYE	6.00
72	10394	QUIET ELEGANCE	I'M AFRAID OF LOSING YOU	DO YOU LOVE ME	6.00
72	10394 DJ	QUIET ELEGANCE	I'M AFRAID OF LOSING YOU	DO YOU LOVE ME	8.00
72	10396	JIMMY HICKS	TELL HER THAT I LOVE HER	I'M MR. BIG STUFF	20.00
72	10396 DJ	JIMMY HICKS	TELL HER THAT I LOVE HER	I'M MR. BIG STUFF	30.00
72	10397	OTIS CLAY	TRYING TO LIVE MY LIFE WITHOUT YOU	LET ME BE THE ONE	10.00
72	10397 DJ	OTIS CLAY	TRYING TO LIVE MY LIFE WITHOUT YOU	LET ME BE THE ONE	15.00
72	10403	SYL JOHNSON	WE DID IT	ANY WAY THE WIND BLOWS	10.00
72	10403 DJ	SYL JOHNSON	WE DID IT	ANY WAY THE WIND BLOWS	15.00
73	10404	PEOPLES CHOICE	LET ME DO MY THING	ON A CLOUDY DAY	8.00
73	10404 DJ	PEOPLES CHOICE	LET ME DO MY THING	ON A CLOUDY DAY	10.00
73	10405	ANN PEEBLES	I'M GONNA TEAR YOUR PLAYHOUSE	ONE WAY STREET	5.00
73	10405 DJ	ANN PEEBLES	I'M GONNA TEAR YOUR PLAYHOUSE	ONE WAY STREET	6.00
73	10407	WILLIE MITCHELL	SIX TO GO	LAST TANGO IN PARIS	5.00
73	10407 DJ	WILLIE MITCHELL	SIX TO GO	LAST TANGO IN PARIS	6.00
73	10409	QUIET ELEGANCE	I NEED LOVE	MAMA SAID	6.00
73	10409 DJ	QUIET ELEGANCE	I NEED LOVE	MAMA SAID	8.00
73	10413	GEORGE JACKSON	LET 'EM KNOW YOU CARE	PATRICIA	25.00
73	10413 DJ	GEORGE JACKSON	LET 'EM KNOW YOU CARE	PATRICIA	30.00
73	10415	SYLVIA	MY THING	PILLOW TALK	10.00
73	10415 DJ	SYLVIA	MY THING	PILLOW TALK	15.00
72	10418	BOBO MR. SOUL	HITCH HIKING TO HEARTBREAK	SHE'S MY WOMAN, SHE'S MY GIRL	15.00
72	10418 DJ	BOBO MR. SOUL	HITCH HIKING TO HEARTBREAK	SHE'S MY WOMAN, SHE'S MY GIRL	22.00
73	10419	AL GREEN	LOVE AND HAPPINESS	SO YOU'RE LEAVING	5.00
73	10419 DJ	AL GREEN	LOVE AND HAPPINESS	SO YOU'RE LEAVING	6.00
73	10421	GENE ANDERSON	FORGIVE THIS FOOLISH MAN	I'M YOUR LOVER - NOT YOUR BROT	10.00
73	10421 DJ	GENE ANDERSON	FORGIVE THIS FOOLISH MAN	I'M YOUR LOVER - NOT YOUR BROT	12.00

73	10423	MANU DIBANGO	SOUL MAKOSSA	LILY	6.00
73	10423 DJ	MANU DIBANGO	SOUL MAKOSSA	LILY	8.00
73	10426	AL GREEN	HERE I AM (COME AND TAKE ME)	I'M GLAD YOU'RE MINE	5.00
73	10426 DJ	AL GREEN	HERE I AM (COME AND TAKE ME)	I'M GLAD YOU'RE MINE	6.00
73	10428	ANN PEEBLES	I CAN'T STAND THE RAIN	I'VE BEEN THERE BEFORE	6.00
73	10428 DJ	ANN PEEBLES	I CAN'T STAND THE RAIN	I'VE BEEN THERE BEFORE	8.00
73	10429	SYLVIA	HAVE YOU HAD ANY LATELY	DIDN'T I	4.00
73	10429 DJ	SYLVIA	HAVE YOU HAD ANY LATELY	DIDN'T I	5.00
73	10432	RAY CHARLES	COME LIVE WITH ME	EVERYBODY SING	4.00
73	10432 DJ	RAY CHARLES	COME LIVE WITH ME	EVERYBODY SING	5.00
73	10435	BOBBY HARRIS	MR. SUCCESS	STICKY, STICKY	15.00
73	10435 DJ	BOBBY HARRIS	MR. SUCCESS	STICKY, STICKY	20.00
73	10437	COASTERS	LOVE POTION NO. 9	D.W. WASHBURN	4.00
73	10437 DJ	COASTERS	LOVE POTION NO. 9	D.W. WASHBURN	5.00
73	10438	SYL JOHNSON	BACK FOR A TASTE OF YOUR LOVE	WIND, BLOW HER BACK MY WAY	6.00
73	10438 DJ	SYL JOHNSON	BACK FOR A TASTE OF YOUR LOVE	WIND, BLOW HER BACK MY WAY	8.00
73	10443	AL GREEN	LIVIN' FOR YOU	IT AIN'T NO FUN TO ME	5.00
73	10443 DJ	AL GREEN	LIVIN' FOR YOU	IT AIN'T NO FUN TO ME	6.00
73	10444	PHILLIP MITCHELL	AIN'T NO LOVE IN MY LIFE	TURNING OVER THE GROUND	40.00
73	10444 DJ	PHILLIP MITCHELL	AIN'T NO LOVE IN MY LIFE	TURNING OVER THE GROUND	50.00
74	10449	MOMENTS	SEXY MAM	WHERE CAN I FIND HER	6.00
74	10449 DJ	MOMENTS	SEXY MAM	WHERE CAN I FIND HER	8.00
74	10452	AL GREEN	LET'S GET MARRIED	SO GOOD TO BE HERE	3.00
74	10452 DJ	AL GREEN	LET'S GET MARRIED	SO GOOD TO BE HERE	5.00
74	10455	OLYMPIC RUNNERS	DO IT OVER	PUT THE MUSIC WHERE YOU MOUTH	5.00
74	10455 DJ	OLYMPIC RUNNERS	DO IT OVER	PUT THE MUSIC WHERE YOU MOUTH	6.00
74	10460	ANN PEEBLES	DO I NEED YOU	A LOVE VIBRATION	4.00
74	10460 DJ	ANN PEEBLES	DO I NEED YOU	A LOVE VIBRATION	5.00
74	10464	HAMMOND BROS.	SOUL OVER EASY	THE GARBAGE MAN	8.00
74	10464 DJ	HAMMOND BROS.	SOUL OVER EASY	THE GARBAGE MAN	10.00
74	10467	OTIS CLAY	YOU DID SOMETHING TO ME	IT WAS JEALOUSY	10.00
74	10467 DJ	OTIS CLAY	YOU DID SOMETHING TO ME	IT WAS JEALOUSY	12.00
74	10468	ANN PEEBLES	(YOU KEEP ME) HANGING ON	RUN, RUN, RUN	4.00
74	10468 DJ	ANN PEEBLES	(YOU KEEP ME) HANGIN' ON	RUN, RUN, RUN	5.00
74	10469	LARRY SAUNDERS	ON THE REAL SIDE	LET ME BE THE SPECIAL ONE	40.00
74	10469 DJ	LARRY SAUNDERS	ON THE REAL SIDE	LET ME BE THE SPECIAL ONE	60.00
74	10470	AL GREEN	SHA-LA-LA (MAKE ME HAPPY)	SCHOOL DAYS	4.00
74	10470 DJ	AL GREEN	SHA-LA-LA (MAKE ME HAPPY)	SCHOOL DAYS	6.00
74	10471	SYL JOHNSON	I HEAR THE LOVE CHIMES	I WANT TO TAKE YOU HOME	5.00
74	10471 DJ	SYL JOHNSON	I HEAR THE LOVE CHIMES	I WANT TO TAKE YOU HOME	6.00
74	10476	SYL JOHNSON	LET YOURSELF GO	PLEASE DON'T GIVE UP ON ME	5.00
74	10476 DJ	SYL JOHNSON	LET YOURSELF GO	PLEASE DON'T GIVE UP ON ME	6.00
74	10477	SHIRLEY	I HEAR THOSE CHURCH BELLS	I DO LOVE YOU	4.00
74	10477 DJ	SHIRLEY	I HEAR THOSE CHURCH BELLS	I DO LOVE YOU	5.00
74	10479	MILT MATTHEWS	ALL THESE CHANGES	WHEN KIDS RULE THE WORLD	8.00
74	10479 DJ	MILT MATTHEWS	ALL THESE CHANGES	WHEN KIDS RULE THE WORLD	10.00
74	10480	McCOYS	FEVER	HANG ON SLOOPY	5.00
74	10480 DJ	McCOYS	FEVER	HANG ON SLOOPY	6.00
74	10482	AL GREEN	L-O-V-E (LOVE)	I WISH YOU WERE HERE WITH ME	5.00
74	10482 DJ	AL GREEN	L-O-V-E (LOVE)	I WISH YOU WERE HERE WITH ME	6.00
74	10483	BILL BLACKS COMBO	LITTLE QUEENIE	BOO-RAY	8.00
74	10483 DJ	BILL BLACKS COMBO	LITTLE QUEENIE	BOO-RAY	15.00
74	10484	ANN PEEBLES	BEWARE	YOU GOT TO FEED THE FIRE	4.00
74	10484 DJ	ANN PEEBLES	BEWARE	YOU GOT TO FEED THE FIRE	5.00
75	10486	SYL JOHNSON	COULD I BE FALLING IN LOVE	TAKE ME TO THE RIVER	5.00
75	10486 DJ	SYL JOHNSON	COULD I BE FALLING IN LOVE	TAKE ME TO THE RIVER	6.00
75	10487	ROY HEAD	THE MOST WANTED WOMAN IN TOWN	GINGERS BREADMAN	8.00
75	10487 DJ	ROY HEAD	THE MOST WANTED WOMAN IN TOWN	GINGERS BREADMAN	10.00
75	10489	ACE CANNON	SEA CRUISE	PEACE IN THE VALLEY	8.00
75	10489 DJ	ACE CANNON	SEA CRUISE	PEACE IN THE VALLEY	15.00
75	10490	LOUISE FREEMAN	HOW COULD YOU RUN AWAY	I CAN DO IT (IF I SEE IT)	8.00
75	10490 DJ	LOUISE FREEMAN	HOW COULD YOU RUN AWAY	I CAN DO IT (IF I SEE IT)	10.00
75	10491	BARBARA MILLS	QUEEN OF FOOLS	(MAKE IT LAST) TAKE YOUR TIME	10.00
75	10491 DJ	BARBARA MILLS	QUEEN OF FOOLS	(MAKE IT LAST) TAKE YOUR TIME	22.00
75	10492	CLARENCE PAUL	I'M IN LOVE AGAIN	BLUE TUESDAY	5.00
75	10492 DJ	CLARENCE PAUL	I'M IN LOVE AGAIN	BLUE TUESDAY	6.00
75	10493	AL GREEN	OH ME, OH MY (DREAMS IN MY ARMS)	STRONG AS DEATH (SWEET AS LOVE	4.00
75	10493 DJ	AL GREEN	OH ME, OH MY (DREAMS IN MY ARMS)	STRONG AS DEATH (SWEET AS LOVE	5.00
75	10494	RONNIE McNEIR	WENDY IS GONE	GIVE ME A SIGN	10.00
75	10494 DJ	RONNIE McNEIR	WENDY IS GONE	GIVE ME A SIGN	15.00
75	10496	BOBBI MARTIN	MAN WAS MADE TO LOVE WOMAN	DON'T BE DOWN ON ME	10.00
75	10496 DJ	BOBBI MARTIN	MAN WAS MADE TO LOVE WOMAN	DON'T BE DOWN ON ME	15.00
75	10501	ERMA FRANKLIN	PIECE OF MY HEART	BIG BOSS MAN	8.00
75	10501 DJ	ERMA FRANKLIN	PIECE OF MY HEART	BIG BOSS MAN	10.00
75	10503	J.J. JACKSON	LET ME TRY AGAIN	WHEN LOVE MEETS LOVE	8.00
75	10503 DJ	J.J. JACKSON	LET ME TRY AGAIN	WHEN LOVE MEETS LOVE	10.00
75	10505	RAY CHARLES	LIVING FOR THE CITY	FOR MAMA	4.00
75	10505 DJ	RAY CHARLES	LIVING FOR THE CITY	FOR MAMA	5.00
75	10507	JACK ASHFORD & SOUND OF NEW DETROIT	DO THE CHOO - CHOO	DO THE CHOO - CHOO part 2	10.00

75	10507 DJ	JACK ASHFORD & SOUND OF NEW DETROIT	DO THE CHOO - CHOO	DO THE CHOO - CHOO part 2	15.00
75	10508	ANN PEEBLES	COME TO MAMA	I'M LEAVING YOU	4.00
75	10508 DJ	ANN PEEBLES	COME TO MAMA	I'M LEAVING YOU	5.00
75	10511	AL GREEN	FULL OF FIRE	CULD I BE THE ONE	4.00
75	10511 DJ	AL GREEN	FULL OF FIRE	CULD I BE THE ONE	5.00
76	10514	JEAN PLUM	BACK TO YOU	LOOK AT THE BOY	40.00
76	10514 DJ	JEAN PLUM	BACK TO YOU	LOOK AT THE BOY	50.00
76	10515	CHUBBY CHECKER	(AT THE) DISCOTHEQUE	SLOW TWISTIN'	10.00
76	10515 DJ	CHUBBY CHECKER	(AT THE) DISCOTHEQUE	SLOW TWISTIN	15.00
76	10517	ANN PEEBLES	DR. LOVE POWER	I STILL LOVE YOU	4.00
76	10517 DJ	ANN PEEBLES	DR. LOVE POWER	I STILL LOVE YOU	5.00
76	10518	BUNNY SIGLER	GIRL DON'T MAKE ME WAIT	LET THE GOOD TIMES ROLL	10.00
76	10518 DJ	BUNNY SIGLER	GIRL DON'T MAKE ME WAIT	LET THE GOOD TIMES ROLL	20.00
76	10521	MICHAEL ZAGER BAND	DO IT WITH FEELING	THIS IS YOUR LIFE	4.00
76	10521 DJ	MICHAEL ZAGER BAND	DO IT WITH FEELING	THIS IS YOUR LIFE	5.00
76	10523	SYL JOHNSON	STAR BRIGHT, STAR LITE	THAT'S JUST MY LUCK	4.00
76	10523 DJ	SYL JOHNSON	STAR BRIGHT, STAR LITE	THAT'S JUST MY LUCK	5.00
76	10526	MUSCLE SHOALS HORNS	BORN TO GET DOWN (BORN TO MESS AROUND)	HUSTLE TO THE MUSIC	5.00
76	10526 DJ	MUSCLE SHOALS HORNS	BORN TO GET DOWN (BORN TO MESS AROUND)	HUSTLE TO THE MUSIC	6.00
76	10529	ANN PEEBLES	I DON'T LEND MY MAN	I NEED SOMEBODY	5.00
76	10529 DJ	ANN PEEBLES	I DON'T LEND MY MAN	I NEED SOMEBODY	6.00
76	10534	? and the MYSTERIANS	96 TEARS	8 TEEN	8.00
76	10534 DJ	? and the MYSTERIANS	96 TEARS	8 TEEN	10.00
76	10535	PAUL DELICATO	IT'S THE SAME OLD SONG	I'LL BE THERE	5.00
76	10535 DJ	PAUL DELICATO	IT'S THE SAME OLD SONG	I'LL BE THERE	6.00
76	10542	AL GREEN	KEEP ME CRYING	THERE IS LOVE	4.00
76	10542 DJ	AL GREEN	KEEP ME CRYING	THERE IS LOVE	5.00
76	10543	CATCH	MR.NICE GUY	MEPHISTO'S NIGHTMARE	8.00
76	10543 DJ	CATCH	MR.NICE GUY	MEPHISTO'S NIGHTMARE	10.00
76	10545 large A	WILLIE MITCHELL	THE CHAMPION	THE CHAMPION part 2	15.00
76	10545 small A	WILLIE MITCHELL	THE CHAMPION	THE CHAMPION Part2	10.00
76	10545 DJ	WILLIE MITCHELL	THE CHAMPION	THE CHAMPION Part2	25.00
76	10553	YVONNE BAKER c/w BOBBY PARIS	YOU DIDN'T SAY A WORD	NIGHT OWL	20.00
76	10553 DJ	YVONNE BAKER c/w BOBBY PARIS	YOU DIDN'T SAY A WORD	NIGHT OWL	25.00
76	10557	CHUBBY CHECKER	YOU JUST DON'T KNOW	TWO HEARTSD MAKE ONE LOVE	20.00
76	10557 DJ	CHUBBY CHECKER	YOU JUST DON'T KNOW	TWO HEARTS MAKE ONE LOVE	30.00
76	10557 DJ Press Sheet	CHUBBY CHECKER	YOU JUST DON'T KNOW	TWO HEARTS MAKE ONE LOVE	50.00
promo 45 plus press sheet referring to the Northern soul secene					
76	10559	HODGES, JAMES, & SMITH	WHAT HAVE YOU DONE FOR LOVE	FALLING IN LOVE	4.00
76	10559 DJ	HODGES, JAMES, & SMITH	WHAT HAVE YOU DONE FOR LOVE	FALLING IN LOVE	5.00
76	10565	EDDIE HORAN	WHEN I FLY WITH YOU	TURN MY WORLD BACK AROUND	5.00
76	10565 DJ	EDDIE HORAN	WHEN I FLY WITH YOU	TURN MY WORLD BACK AROUND	6.00
76	10573	HODGES, JAMES, & SMITH	AIN'T THAT PECULIAR	DANCING IN THE STREET	4.00
76	10573 DJ	HODGES, JAMES, & SMITH	AIN'T THAT PECULIAR	DANCING IN THE STREET	5.00
80	10579	RAY CHARLES	COMPARED TO WHAT	NOW THAT WE'VE FOUND EACH OTHER	6.00
80	10579 DJ	RAY CHARLES	COMPARED TO WHAT	NOW THAT WE'VE FOUND EACH OTHER	10.00
82	10642	ANN PEEBLES	I CAN'T STAND THE RAIN	I'VE BEEN THERE BEFORE	4.00
82	10642 DJ	ANN PEEBLES	I CAN'T STAND THE RAIN	I'VE BEEN THERE BEFORE	5.00
60	1233 EP PS	DAVE BABY CORTEZ	DAVE BABY CORTEZ	1960 4 track EP with cover	40.00
61	1282 EP PS	DRIFTERS	GREATEST HITS:	1961 4 track EP with cover	20.00
61	1298 EP PS	GENE McDANIELS	GENE McDANIELS	1961 4 track EP with cover	50.00
61	1306 EP PS	RAY CHARLES	WHAT'D I SAY	1961 4 track EP with cover	15.00
62	1348 EP PS	KETTY LESTER	KETTY LESTER	1962 4 track EP with cover	40.00
63	1355 EP PS	DRIFTERS	THE DRIFTERS	1963 4 track EP with cover	40.00
63	1361 EP PS	BEN E. KING	BEN E. KING	1963 4 track EP with cover	45.00
63	1363 EP PS	SHERRYS	DO THE POPEYE	1963 4 track EP with cover	75.00
63	1364 EP PS	ARTHUR ALEXANDER	ALEXANDER THE GREAT	1963 4 track EP with cover	125.00
63	1367 PS EP	BOOKER T. & THE MG'S	R&B WITH BOOKER T.	1963 4 track EP with cover	18.00
63	1372 EP PS	MEL TORME	COMIN' HOME BABY + THE GIFT	1963 4 track EP with cover	25.00
63	1379 EP PS	SOLOMON BURKE	TONIGHT MY HEART SHE IS CRYING	1963 4 track EP with cover	75.00
63	1381 EP PS	CRYSTALS	DA DOO RON RON	1963 4 track EP with cover	45.00
63	1385 EP PS	DRIFTERS	DRIFTIN'	1963 4 track EP with cover	30.00
63	1386 EP PS	BEN E. KING	I'M STANDING BY	1963 4 track EP with cover	75.00
63	1389 EP PS	RUBY & THE ROMANTICS	OUR DAY WILL COME	1963 4 track EP with cover	75.00
63	1390 EP PS	VARIOUS ARTISTS	THE ORIGINAL HITS	1963 4 track EP with cover Ritchie Barrett, Drifters, etc	45.00
63	1401 EP PS	ARTHUR ALEXANDER	ARTHUR ALEXANDER	1963 4 track EP with cover	125.00
63	1403 EP PS	VARIOUS ARTISTS	SINGING THE BLUES EP	1963 4 track EP with cover	70.00
63	1408 EP PS	RAY CHARLES	YOU ALWAYS MISS THE WATER + 1	1963 4 track EP with cover	10.00
63	1410 EP PS	JAMES BROWN& FAMOUS FLAMES	JAMES BROWN AND THE FAMOUS	1963 4 track EP with cover	40.00
64	1411 EP PS	DARLENE LOVE	WAIT TILL MY BOBBY COMES HOME	1964 4 track EP with cover	200.00
64	1427 EP PS	RUBY & THE ROMANTICS	HEY THERE LONELY BOY	1964 4 track EP with cover	75.00
64	1438 EP PS	LOU JOHNSON	MAGIC POTION OF:	1964 4 track EP with cover	100.00
	2457 EP PS	ARTHUR ALEXANDER	YOU BETTER MOVE ON	4 Dot recordings	175.00
	3432 DJ	MARV JOHNSON	COME TO ME	HAVE I TOLD YOU LATELY THAT I LOVE YOU	45.00
60	4349 DJ	JESSIE HILL	OOH POO PAH DOO part 1	OOH POO PAH DOO part 2	22.00

LONDON TRAFFIC

98	1 DJ	FLIRTATIONS	NOTHING BUT A HEARTACHE	blank:	15.00

LOWTON

| 99 | 101 DJ | CELESTE HARDIE c/w DONI BURDICK | YOU'RE GONE | | CANDLE | 25.00 |
| 00 | 6 DJ | TY KARIM c/w J.D. BRYANT | AIN'T THAT LOVE ENOUGH | | I WON'T BE COMING BACK | 10.00 |

LYNTONE

| 74 | 2639 flexi | JACKSON 5 | TALK AND SING PERSONALLY TO VALENTINE READERS | free flexi with VALENTINE MAG | | 8.00 |
| 74 | 2639 flexi + MAG | JACKSON 5 | TALK AND SING PERSONALLY TO VALENTINE READERS | free flexi with VALENTINE MAG | | 15.00 |

MAGNET

75	31	ZENDA JACKS	EARTHQUAKE	same: instrumental	10.00
75	31 DJ	ZENDA JACKS	EARTHQUAKE	same: instrumental	15.00
76	73	J.A.L.N. BAND	DISCO MUSIC / I LIKE IT	UNIVERSAL LOVE	4.00
76	73 DJ	J.A.L.N. BAND	DISCO MUSIC / I LIKE IT	UNIVERSAL LOVE	5.00
76	78	J.A.L.N. BAND	LET'S DO IT NOW	LIFE IS A FIGHT	10.00
76	78 DJ	J.A.L.N. BAND	LET'S DO IT NOW	LIFE IS A FIGHT	15.00
77	97	J.A.L.N. BAND	SAY SAY SAY	I GOT TO SING	10.00
77	97 DJ	J.A.L.N. BAND	SAY SAY SAY	I GOT TO SING	15.00
77	103	RAY CRUMLEY	ALL THE WAY IN LOVE WITH YOU	IT'S UNCANNY	20.00
77	103 DJ	RAY CRUMLEY	ALL THE WAY IN LOVE WITH YOU	IT'S UNCANNY	30.00
77	105	J.A.L.N. BAND	SO GOOD	STILL LOVE YOU GIRL	4.00
77	105 DJ	J.A.L.N. BAND	SO GOOD	STILL LOVE YOU GIRL	5.00
78	113	RICHIE PITTS	(LOVE IS) ONE STEP AWAY	LOOKS LIKE T'S GONNA RAIN AGAIN	10.00
78	113 DJ	RICHIE PITTS	(LOVE IS) ONE STEP AWAY	LOOKS LIKE T'S GONNA RAIN AGAIN	15.00
78	118	J.A.L.N. BAND	GOT THINGS TO DO	GET UP (AND LET YOURSELF GO)	6.00
78	118 DJ	J.A.L.N. BAND	GOT THINGS TO DO	GET UP (AND LET YOURSELF GO)	8.00
78	130	MARSHA HUNT	OTHERSIDE OF MIDNIGHT	HEARTACHE	4.00
78	130 DJ	MARSHA HUNT	OTHERSIDE OF MIDNIGHT	HEARTACHE	5.00
78	131	J.A.L.N. BAND	UNIVERSAL LOVE	EVERYBODY'S GOTTA DO SOMETHING	4.00
78	131 DJ	J.A.L.N. BAND	UNIVERSAL LOVE	EVERYBODY'S GOTTA DO SOMETHING	5.00
78	148	MIDNITE	LOVE GONNA HIT YOU LIKE A BULLET	MINUTE TO MIDNIGHT	30.00
78	148 DJ	MIDNITE	LOVE GONNA HIT YOU LIKE A BULLET	MINUTE TO MIDNIGHT	40.00
80	162	JOHNNY DARROW MOORE	STILL CAN'T SHAKE YOUR LOVE	LADY LOVES TO DANCE	15.00
80	162 DJ	JOHNNY DARROW MOORE	STILL CAN'T SHAKE YOUR LOVE	LADY LOVES TO DANCE	20.00

MAINSTREAM

73	302	DORIS DUKE	BUSINESS DEAL	NOBODY BUT YOU	10.00
73	302 DJ	DORIS DUKE	BUSINESS DEAL	NOBODY BUT YOU	15.00
73	303	CHUBUKOS	HOUSE OF THE RISING FUNK	WITCH DOCTOR BUMP	10.00
73	303 DJ	CHUBUKOS	HOUSE OF THE RISING FUNK	WITCH DOCTOR BUMP	15.00
74	305	SARAH VAUGHN	I NEED YOU (MORE THAN EVER NOW)	DO AWAY WITH APRIL	35.00
74	305 DJ	SARAH VAUGHN	I NEED YOU (MORE THAN EVER NOW)	DO AWAY WITH APRIL	50.00
74	307	LENNY WELCH	WHEN THERE'S NO SUCH THING AS LOVE	THE MINX	5.00
74	307 DJ	LENNY WELCH	WHEN THERE'S NO SUCH THING AS LOVE	THE MINX	6.00

MAJOR MINOR

Short lived but colourful UK only label that covered all genres of music. Its best selling "soul" artist was Johnny Nash but within Major Minor's catalogue sits some highly prized collectors 45s. Especially Los Canarios's classic soul club dancer on #532 that is now very difficult to find but Major Minor's main attraction was it UK only release by homegrown artists like Karen Young, Sandra Bryant & Derek Christien. Why Major Minor only relesased 45's for lees than 5 years is a mystery because it had had significant pop hits with Malcom Roberts, Tommy James & the Shondells, and David McWilliams. No promos as far as I know exist in this series, if they do they are very rare indeed.

67	502	LOS CANARIOS	TWO THREE ONE AH	WHAT CAN I DO FOR YOU	10.00
67	511	TOMMY JAMES & the SHONDELLS	I THINK WE'RE ALONE NOW	GONE GONE GONE	6.00
67	532	LOS CANARIOS	GET ON YOUR KNEES	KEEP ON THE RIGHT SIDE	40.00
67	540	RAISINS	AIN'T THAT LOVIN' YOU BABY	STRANGER THINGS HAVE HAPPENED	15.00
68	553	SANDRA BRYANT	THERE'S NO LOCK ON MY DOOR	OUT TO GET YOU	25.00
68	558	TOMMY JAMES & the SHONDELLS	GET OUT NOW	WISH IT WERE TRUE	10.00
68	559	RAYMOND LEFERVE & HIS ORCH.	SOUL COAXING (AME CALINE)	WHEN A MAN LOVES A WOMAN	10.00
68	564	JOHNNY CURTIS	PICKIN' UP PEBBLES	GENTLE ON MY MIND	5.00
68	566	ISABEL BOND	WHEN A WOMAN LOVES A MAN	CRY	10.00
68	566 PS	ISABEL BOND	WHEN A WOMAN LOVES A MAN	CRY	15.00
68	567	TOMMY JAMES & the SHONDELLS	MONY MONY	ONE TWO THREE AND I FELL	6.00
68	584	KAREN YOUNG	TOO MUCH OF A GOOD THING	YOU BETTER SIT DOWN KIDS	40.00
68	586	JOHNNY NASH	YOU GOT SOUL	DON'T CRY	6.00
69	600	SECOND CITY SOUND	A TOUCH OF VELVET A STING OF BRASS	THE DREAM OF OLWYN	10.00
69	602	RAISINS	I THANK YOU	DON'T LEAVE ME LIKE THIS	6.00
69	603	JOHNNY NASH	CUPID	PEOPLE IN LOVE	6.00
69	609	CRAZY ELEPHANT	GIMME GIMME GOOD LOVIN'	DARK PART OF MY MIND	6.00
69	611	JENNIE DARREN	RIVER DEEP, MOUNTAIN HIGH	JULIE	4.00
69	619	KIM WESTON	WE TRY HARDER	FROM BOTH SIDES NOW	5.00
69	621	ISLEY BROTHERS	IT'S YOUR THING	DON'T GIVE IT AWAY	10.00
69	627	ISABEL BOND	DON'T FORGET ABOUT ME	YOU'LL NEVER GET THE CHANCE AGAIN	8.00
69	630	JOHNNY NASH	YOU GOT TO CHANGE YOUR WAYS	LOVE AND PEACE	6.00
69	631	ISLEY BROTHERS	I TURNED YOU ON	I KNOW WHO YOU BEEN SOCKING IT	8.00
69	632	JOE RICHARDSON	TAKE IT OFF	BLUES TO TAKE IT OFF	10.00
69	646	JOHN NASH	LOVE ME TENDER	LOVE	5.00
69	655	SAM DEES	IF IT'S ALL WRONG (IT'S ALL RIGHT)	DON'T KEEP ME HANGING ON	40.00
70	676	DEREK CHRISTIEN	WHEN A WOMAN HAS A BABY	PLEASE DON'T GO AWAY	30.00
70	683	KIM WESTON	DANGER, HEARTBREAK DEAD AHEAD	I'LL BE THINKIN'	10.00
70	696	HOWARD TATE	IT'S TOO LATE	MY SOUL'S GOT A HOLE IN IT	10.00

70	700	CISSY HOUSTON	HE + I BELIEVE	I'LL BE THERE	5.00
70	701	JOHNNY NASH	YOU GOT SOUL	GROOVY FEELING	8.00
70	707	LENNY WELCH	BREAKING UP IS HARD TO DO	GOT TO SEE IF I CAN GET MY MOM	6.00
70	709	MAXINE BROWN	I CAN'T GET ALONG WITHOUT YOU	REASON TO BELIEVE	20.00
70	713	DEREK CHRISTIEN	SUDDENLY THERE'S A VALLEY	I'LL BE COMING HOME	150.00
70	716	CISSY HOUSTON	BE MY BABY	THE LONG AND WINDING ROAD	5.00

MALACO

82	3	DOROTHY MOORE	LAUGH IT OFF	1 2 3 YOU AND ME	4.00
83	22 PS	DENISE LASALLE	COME TO BED	RIGHT PLACE, RIGHT TIME	8.00

MAM

UK based, almost totally pop-motivated label with their biggest artists being Gilbert O'Sullivan, Stephanie DeSykes, they even recorded Kevin Keegan. Although J.R. Bailey recorded for USA M.A.M. there are no significant soul related 45's on this label. Out of the 100's of releases only 4 are remotely of interest to the UK soul collector.

70	9	JOHNNY NASH	FALLING IN AND OUT OF LOVE	PEOPLE IN LOVE	4.00
70	9 DJ	JOHNNY NASH	FALLING IN AND OUT OF LOVE	PEOPLE IN LOVE	5.00
71	16	WATSON T. BROWNE	FEELING BAD	I'M ON THE ROAD AGAIN	4.00
71	16 DJ	WATSON T. BROWNE	FEELING BAD	I'M ON THE ROAD AGAIN	5.00
72	87	WILD HONEY	THERE'S NO STOPPING US NOW	SOW THE SEEDS OF LOVE	6.00
72	87 DJ	WILD HONEY	THERE'S NO STOPPING US NOW	SOW THE SEEDS OF LOVE	8.00
75	134	DIANE JONES	UNDER THE BOARDWALK	GIMME TIME	4.00
75	134 DJ	DIANE JONES	UNDER THE BOARDWALK	GIMME TIME	5.00

MANGO MEDIA

	23	RAY ANTHONY	THE ARABIAN FUNK	TIME	50.00

MARMALADE

68	598003	BRIAN AUGER TRINITY	RED BEANS & RICE	RED BEANS & RICE part 2	20.00
68	598005	JULIE DRISCOLL	SAVE ME	SAVE ME part 2	25.00
68	598006	JULIE DRISCOLL & BRIAN AUGER	A KIND OF LOVE IN	THIS WHEEL'S ON FIRE	10.00
68	598011	JULIE DRISCOLL & BRIAN AUGER	ROAD TO CIARO	SHADOWS OF YOU	10.00
68	598015	BRIAN AUGER TRINITY	BUMPIN' ON SUNSET	WHAT YUOU GONNA DO?	20.00
69	598018	JULIE DRISCOLL & BRIAN AUGER	INDIAN ROPE MAN	TAKE ME TO THE WATER	30.00

MAYFIELD

03	7777	MAYFIELD SINGERS	DON'T START NONE	same: instrumental	25.00

MCA

78	3 EP	LEN BARRY	IT STRUCK IT RICH + IT'S THAT TIME OF	1 - 2 - 3 + LIKE A BABY	4.00
74	105	LEN BARRY	1 - 2 - 3	BULLSEYE	4.00
74	105 DJ	LEN BARRY	1 - 2 - 3	BULLSEYE	6.00
74	125	MARTHA REEVES	STAND BY ME	POWER OF LOVE	4.00
74	125 DJ	MARTHA REEVES	STAND BY ME	POWER OF LOVE	5.00
74	145	LOVE UNLIMITED	WALKIN' IN THE RAIN WITH THE ONE I LOVE	IS IT REALLY TRUE BOY	4.00
74	145 DJ	LOVE UNLIMITED	WALKIN' IN THE RAIN WITH THE ONE I LOVE	IS IT REALLY TRUE BOY	5.00
74	146	DOBIE GRAY	DRIFT AWAY	CITY STARS	4.00
74	146 DJ	DOBIE GRAY	DRIFT AWAY	CITY STARS	5.00
74	148	MARTHA REEVES	MY MAN (CHANGED MY TUNE)	WILD NIGHT	4.00
74	148 DJ	MARTHA REEVES	MY MAN (CHANGED MY TUNE)	WILD NIGHT	5.00
74	155	DANNY WHITE	CRACKED UP OVER YOU	TAKING INVENTORY	8.00
74	155 DJ	DANNY WHITE	CRACKED UP OVER YOU	TAKING INVENTORY	15.00
74	163	DOBIE GRAY	ROLL ON MISSISSIPPI	THE MUSIC'S REAL	3.00
74	163 DJ	DOBIE GRAY	ROLL ON MISSISSIPPI	THE MUSIC'S REAL	4.00
75	169	SONS OF MOSES	SOUL SYMPHONY	FATBACK	8.00
75	169 DJ	SONS OF MOSES	SOUL SYMPHONY	FATBACK	15.00
75	172	LADA EDMUND JR.	THE LARUE	SOUL AU GO GO	10.00
75	172 DJ	LADA EDMUND JR.	THE LARUE	SOUL AU GO GO	15.00
75	182	LOVE UNLIMITED	ANOTHER CHANCE	ARE YOU SURE	3.00
75	182 DJ	LOVE UNLIMITED	ANOTHER CHANCE	ARE YOU SURE	4.00
75	188	CHER	RESCUE ME	DIXIE GIRL	8.00
75	188 DJ	CHER	RESCUE ME	DIXIE GIRL	10.00
75	196	RUBIN	YOU'VE BEEN AWAY	BABY YOU'RE MY EVERYTHING	10.00
75	196 DJ	RUBIN	YOU'VE BEEN AWAY	BABY YOU'RE MY EVERYTHING	20.00
76	259	ROSE ROYCE	PUT YOUR MONEY WHERE YOUR MOUTH IS	ZIG ZAG	3.00
76	259 DJ	ROSE ROYCE	PUT YOUR MONEY WHERE YOUR MOUTH IS	ZIG ZAG	4.00
76	267	ROSE ROYCE	CAR WASH	WATER	5.00
76	267 DJ	ROSE ROYCE	CAR WASH	WATER	6.00
76	278	ROSE ROYCE	I WANNA GET NEXT TO YOU	SUNRISE	4.00
76	278 DJ	ROSE ROYCE	I WANNA GET NEXT TO YOU	SUNRISE	5.00
77	301	ROSE ROYCE	I'M GOING DOWN	YO YO	3.00
77	301 DJ	ROSE ROYCE	I'M GOING DOWN	YO YO	4.00
77	306	DETOURS	HIDEAWAY	OUR LOVE WILL KEEP ON GROWING	8.00
77	306 DJ	DETOURS	HIDEAWAY	OUR LOVE WILL KEEP ON GROWING	10.00
77	308	LIFESTYLE	KATRINA	LOVE CAN MAKE YOU CRY	15.00
77	308 DJ	LIFESTYLE	KATRINA	LOVE CAN MAKE YOU CRY	20.00
77	320	ROSE ROYCE	AMBUSH	VICTIM OF CIRCUMSTANCE	3.00
77	320 DJ	ROSE ROYCE	AMBUSH	VICTIM OF CIRCUMSTANCE	4.00
78	378	LEE ROYE	TEARS (NOTHING BUT TEARS)	WHO AM I	10.00

78	378 DJ	LEE ROYE	TEARS (NOTHING BUT TEARS)	WHO AM I		15.00
79	536	STIX HOOPER	CORDON BLEU	BRAZOS RIVER BREAKDOWN		4.00
79	536 DJ	STIX HOOPER	CORDON BLEU	BRAZOS RIVER BREAKDOWN		5.00
79	543	ATMOSFEAR	DANCING IN OUTER SPACE	OUTER SPACE		5.00
79	543 DJ	ATMOSFEAR	DANCING IN OUTER SPACE	OUTER SPACE		6.00
80	574	PRESSURE	CAN YOU FEEL IT	THAT'S THE THING TO DO		5.00
80	574 DJ	PRESSURE	CAN YOU FEEL IT	THAT'S THE THING TO DO		6.00
80	625	JOHN HIATT	I SPY (FOR THE FBI)	GOOD GIRL BAD WORLD		4.00
80	625 DJ	JOHN HIATT	I SPY (FOR THE FBI)	GOOD GIRL BAD WORLD		5.00
80	646	WILTON FELDER	INHERIT THE WIND	UNTIL THE MORNING COMES		6.00
80	646 DJ	WILTON FELDER	INHERIT THE WIND	UNTIL THE MORNING COMES		8.00
81	738	ONE WAY	PUSH	ALL OVER AGAIN		3.00
81	738 DJ	ONE WAY	PUSH	ALL OVER AGAIN		4.00
84	914	ALICIA MYERS	YOU GET THE BEST FROM ME	I WANT TO THANK YOU		8.00
84	914 DJ	ALICIA MYERS	YOU GET THE BEST FROM ME	I WANT TO THANK YOU		10.00
84	919 PS	WILTON FELDER feat. BOBBY WOMACK	I'LL STILL BE LOOKIN' UP TO YOU	LA LUZ		4.00
84	919 PS DJ	WILTON FELDER feat. BOBBY WOMACK	I'LL STILL BE LOOKIN' UP TO YOU	LA LUZ		5.00
85	933	ALICIA MYERS	APPRECIATION	SAY THAT		4.00
85	933 DJ	ALICIA MYERS	APPRECIATION	SAY THAT		5.00
68	1006	LITTLE RICHARD	TRY SOME OF MINE	SHE'S TOGETHER		10.00
68	1006 DJ	LITTLE RICHARD	TRY SOME OF MINE	SHE'S TOGETHER		15.00
68	1014	JACKIE WILSON & COUNT BASIE	UPTIGHT (EVERYTHING'S ALRIGHT)	FOR YOUR PRECIOUS LOVE		15.00
68	1014 DJ	JACKIE WILSON & COUNT BASIE	UPTIGHT (EVERYTHING'S ALRIGHT)	FOR YOUR PRECIOUS LOVE		22.00
68	1031	JOHNNY JONES & the KING CASUALS	SOUL POPPIN'	BLUES FOR THE BROTHERS		20.00
68	1031 DJ	JOHNNY JONES & the KING CASUALS	SOUL POPPIN'	BLUES FOR THE BROTHERS		28.00
68	1032	RICHARD KENT STYLE	LOVE WILL SHAKE THE WORLD AWAKE	CROCODILE TEARS		25.00
68	1032 DJ	RICHARD KENT STYLE	LOVE WILL SHAKE THE WORLD AWAKE	CROCODILE TEARS		35.00
68	1038	BARBARA ACKLIN	LOVE MAKES A WOMAN	COME AND SEE ME BABY		12.00
68	1038 DJ	BARBARA ACKLIN	LOVE MAKES A WOMAN	COME AND SEE ME BABY		20.00
69	1053	YOUNG HOLT UNLIMITED	SOULFUL STRUT	COUNTRY SLICKER JOE		10.00
69	1053 DJ	YOUNG HOLT UNLIMITED	SOULFUL STRUT	COUNTRY SLICKER JOE		15.00
69	1055	BETTY EVERETT	THERE'LL COME A TIME	TAKE ME		10.00
69	1055 DJ	BETTY EVERETT	THERE'LL COME A TIME	TAKE ME		15.00
69	1067	LEN BARRY	LIKE A BABY	1 – 2 – 3		6.00
69	1067 DJ	LEN BARRY	LIKE A BABY	1 – 2 – 3		8.00
69	1071	BARBARA ACKLIN	AM I THE SAME GIRL	BE BY MY SIDE		15.00
69	1071 DJ	BARBARA ACKLIN	AM I THE SAME GIRL	BE BY MY SIDE		22.00
69	1072	SAMMY DAVIS	THE POMPEII CLUB	RHYTHM OF LIFE		8.00
69	1072 DJ	SAMMY DAVIS	THE POMPEII CLUB	RHYTHM OF LIFE		10.00
69	1073	ERMA FRANKLIN	GOTTA FIND ME A LOVER (24 HOURS A DAY)	CHANGE MY THOUGHTS FROM YOU		15.00
69	1073 DJ	ERMA FRANKLIN	GOTTA FIND ME A LOVER (24 HOURS A DAY)	CHANGE MY THOUGHTS FROM YOU		20.00
69	1102	BARBARA ACKLIN	LOVE MAKES A WOMAN	COME AND SEE ME BABY		10.00
69	1102 DJ	BARBARA ACKLIN	LOVE MAKES A WOMAN	COME AND SEE ME BABY		15.00
69	1103	BARBARA ACKLIN	AM I THE SAME GIRL	BE BY MY SIDE		10.00
69	1103 DJ	BARBARA ACKLIN	AM I THE SAME GIRL	BE BY MY SIDE		15.00
69	1104	JACKIE WILSON	THE WHO WHO SONG	SINCE YOU SHOWED ME HOW TO BE HAPPY		10.00
69	1104 DJ	JACKIE WILSON	THE WHO WHO SONG	SINCE YOU SHOWED ME HOW TO BE HAPPY		18.00
69	1105	JACKIE WILSON	HELPLESS	DO IT THE RIGHT WAY		6.00
69	1105 DJ	JACKIE WILSON	HELPLESS	DO IT THE RIGHT WAY		10.00
70	1117	ARTISTICS	HOPE WE HAVE	I'M GONNA MISS YOU		15.00
70	1117 DJ	ARTISTICS	HOPE WE HAVE	I'M GONNA MISS YOU		22.00
70	1127	WILLIE HENDERSON	OO WEE BABY I LOVE YOU	FUNKY CHICKEN		8.00
70	1127 DJ	WILLIE HENDERSON	OO WEE BABY I LOVE YOU	FUNKY CHICKEN		10.00
70	1120	JIVE FYVE	IF YOU LET ME MAKE LOVE TO YOU THEN WHY CAN'T I TOUCH YOU	YOU SHOW ME THE		10.00
70	1120 DJ	JIVE FYVE	IF YOU LET ME MAKE LOVE TO YOU THEN WHY CAN'T I TOUCH YOU	YOU SHOW ME THE		15.00
70	1131	JACKIE WILSON	WHISPERS (GETTING' LOUDER)	HIGHER AND HIGHER		8.00
70	1131 DJ	JACKIE WILSON	WHISPERS (GETTING' LOUDER)	HIGHER AND HIGHER		10.00
71	1138	CHI-LITES	(FOR GOD'S SAKE) GIVE MORE POWER	TROUBLES A' COMIN		5.00
71	1138 DJ	CHI-LITES	(FOR GOD'S SAKE) GIVE MORE POWER	TROUBLES A' COMIN		6.00
71	1140	FREE MOVEMENT	I'VE FOUND SOMEONE OF MY OWN	I CAN'T CONVINCE MY HEART		6.00
71	1140 DJ	FREE MOVEMENT	I'VE FOUND SOMEONE OF MY OWN	I CAN'T CONVINCE MY HEART		8.00
72	1143	CHI-LITES	WHAT DO WE WISH FOR	WE ARE NEIGHBOURS		20.00
72	1143 DJ	CHI-LITES	WHAT DO WE WISH FOR	WE ARE NEIGHBOURS		30.00
72	1146	CHI-LITES	HAVE YOU SEEN HER	YES I'M READY (IF I DON'T GET THERE)		6.00
72	1146 DJ	CHI-LITES	HAVE YOU SEEN HER	YES I'M READY (IF I DON'T GET THERE)		8.00
72	1154 paper	DOBIE GRAY	THE IN CROWD	DRIFT AWAY		6.00
72	1154 DJ	DOBIE GRAY	THE IN CROWD	DRIFT AWAY		8.00
72	1154 ink	DOBIE GRAY	THE IN CROWD	DRIFT AWAY		4.00
72	1156	CHI-LITES	OH GIRL	BEING IN LOVE		6.00
72	1156 DJ	CHI-LITES	OH GIRL	BEING IN LOVE		8.00
72	1159	YOUNG-HOLT UNLTD.	JUST AIN'T NO LOVE	LOVE MAKES A WOMAN		10.00
72	1159 DJ	YOUNG-HOLT UNLTD.	JUST AIN'T NO LOVE	LOVE MAKES A WOMAN		15.00
72	1160	JACKIE WILSON	I GET THE SWEETEST FEELING	SOUL GALORE		6.00
72	1160 DJ	JACKIE WILSON	I GET THE SWEETEST FEELING	SOUL GALORE		10.00
72	1162	CHI-LITES	THE COLDEST DAYS OF MY LIFE	THE COLDEST DAYS OF MY LIFE 2		4.00
72	1162 DJ	CHI-LITES	THE COLDEST DAYS OF MY LIFE	THE COLDEST DAYS OF MY LIFE 2		5.00
72	1172	LEN BARRY	YOU BABY	1 - 2 - 3		8.00
72	1172 DJ	LEN BARRY	YOU BABY	1 - 2 - 3		15.00
73	1184	DOBIE GRAY	DRIFTAWAY	CITY STARS		4.00

73	1184 DJ	DOBIE GRAY	DRIFTAWAY	CITY STARS	5.00
73	1213	SHIRLEY ELLIS	THE NITTY GRITTY	THE CLAPPING SONG	6.00
73	1213 DJ	SHIRLEY ELLIS	THE NITTY GRITTY	THE CLAPPING SONG	8.00
88	1253	ROSE ROYCE	CAR WASH	IS IT LOVE YOU'RE AFTER	4.00
88	1253 DJ	ROSE ROYCE	CAR WASH	IS IT LOVE YOU'RE AFTER	6.00
75	2506	EL CHICANO	ONE MORE NIGHT	BARETTA'S THEME	25.00
75	2506 DJ	EL CHICANO	ONE MORE NIGHT	BARETTA'S THEME	30.00
75	2506 PS	EL CHICANO	ONE MORE NIGHT	BARETTA'S THEME	30.00
79	4181	REFLECTIONS c/w AUGUST & DENEEN	LIKE ADAM AND EVE	WE GO TOGETHER	6.00
79	4181 DJ	REFLECTIONS c/w AUGUST & DENEEN	LIKE ADAM AND EVE	WE GO TOGETHER	8.00
69	5005	JOHN RYDER CONGREGATION	HOLD ON	LOVE IS	5.00
69	5005 DJ	JOHN RYDER CONGREGATION	HOLD ON	LOVE IS	6.00
71	5064	TONY CHRISTIE	GIVE ME YOUR LOVE AGAIN	I DID WHAT I DID FOR MARIA	6.00
71	5064 DJ	TONY CHRISTIE	GIVE ME YOUR LOVE AGAIN	I DID WHAT I DID FOR MARIA	10.00
71	5075	FOUNDATIONS	STONEY GROUND	I'LL GIVE YOU LOVE	12.00
71	5075 DJ	FOUNDATIONS	STONEY GROUND	I'LL GIVE YOU LOVE	20.00

MCA SOUL BAG series

A nine release experiment by MCA that lasted a year before being abandoned. MCA pulled soul material from its Decca parent company and Brunswick & Uni subsidiaries. Low sales turned MCA off the idea of a soul only label after making a strong promotional push and even designing a special 45 sleeve, it all failed to lift the idea off the ground.

69	BAG 1	GENE CHANDLER & BARBARA ACKLIN	WILL I FIND LOVE	LITTLE GREEN APPLES	15.00
69	BAG 1 DJ	GENE CHANDLER & BARBARA ACKLIN	WILL I FIND LOVE	LITTLE GREEN APPLES	20.00
69	BAG 2	JACKIE WILSON	WHISPERS (GETTING' LOUDER)	HIGHER AND HIGHER	8.00
69	BAG 2 DJ	JACKIE WILSON	WHISPERS (GETTING' LOUDER)	HIGHER AND HIGHER	12.00
69	BAG 3	BETTY EVERETT	BETTER TOMORROW THAN TODAY	I CAN'T SAY NO TO YOU	10.00
69	BAG 3 DJ	BETTY EVERETT	BETTER TOMORROW THAN TODAY	I CAN'T SAY NO TO YOU	15.00
69	BAG 4	GREATEST LITTLE SOUL BAND	TENEMENT HALLS	FLAT, BLACK AND TOGETHER	6.00
69	BAG 4 DJ	GREATEST LITTLE SOUL BAND	TENEMENT HALLS	FLAT, BLACK AND TOGETHER	8.00
69	BAG 5	LEON HAYWOOD	MELLOW MOONLIGHT	TENNESSEE WALTZ	10.00
69	BAG 5 DJ	LEON HAYWOOD	MELLOW MOONLIGHT	TENNESSEE WALTZ	15.00
69	BAG 6	GREATEST LITTLE SOUL BAND	SOMETHING FOR MY PEOPLE	WIN LOSE OR DRAW	8.00
69	BAG 6 DJ	GREATEST LITTLE SOUL BAND	SOMETHING FOR MY PEOPLE	WIN LOSE OR DRAW	10.00
69	BAG 7	JACKIE WILSON & COUNT BASIE	CHAIN GANG	SINCE YOU SHOWED ME HOW TO BE	8.00
69	BAG 7 DJ	JACKIE WILSON & COUNT BASIE	CHAIN GANG	SINCE YOU SHOWED ME HOW TO BE	10.00
69	BAG 8	MIRETTES	AIN'T YOU TRYING TO CROSS OVER	WHIRLPOOL	15.00
69	BAG 8 DJ	MIRETTES	AIN'T YOU TRYING TO CROSS OVER	WHIRLPOOL	20.00
69	BAG 9	GARLAND GREEN	JEALOUS KINDA FELLOW	I CAN'T BELIEVE YOU QUIT ME	15.00
69	BAG 9 DJ	GARLAND GREEN	JEALOUS KINDA FELLOW	I CAN'T BELIEVE YOU QUIT ME	20.00

MERCURY

Chicago based label that was founded in 1945 by Irving Green, Arthur Talmadge & Berle Adams. Early recordings were Jazz, R&B, Blues, Rock and Roll, Classical and Country & Western. From two pressing plants, one in Chicago and one in St. Louis, Mercury was able to get a 24 hour from master to the streets pressing of 45's. This enabled the label to compete at the very top end of the record industry. It's not until the early 1961 when Dutch company Philips that's why Smash and Blue Rock 45s were issued on both Mercury & the UK Philips label. Being based in a Chicago, Mercury had a huge black talent pool to call on, and soul soon became a large percentage of its releases. Subsidaries included Blue Rock, Fontana, Limelight, Philips and Smash, all know for there soul releases. In addition, they leased and purchased material by independent labels and redistributed them under their own label, Mercury released all kinds of recordings from classical music to psychedelic rock. However, its subsidiaries focused on their own specialized categories of music. Blue Rock & Smash were directed heavily towards soul music, both labels have a release catalogue full of highly collectable soul & northern soul releases. Later in the 80's the pop/soul 45's were issued on the Def Jam label which was later absorbed by Island records.

64	802	VELVETTES	HE'S THE ONE I WANT	THAT LITTLE GIRL OF MINE	15.00
64	802 PS	VELVETTES	HE'S THE ONE I WANT	THAT LITTLE BOY OF MINE	22.00
64	802 DJ	VELVETTES	HE'S THE ONE I WANT	THAT LITTLE GIRL OF MINE	20.00
64	804	ETHNA CAMPBELL	WHAT'S EASY FOR TWO IS HARD FOR	AGAIN	10.00
64	804 DJ	ETHNA CAMPBELL	WHAT'S EASY FOR TWO IS HARD FOR	AGAIN	15.00
64	805	DAVE VENTURA	THE HURT STAYS IN THE HEART	IS A RED BIRD RED	10.00
64	805 DJ	DAVE VENTURA	THE HURT STAYS IN THE HEART	IS A RED BIRD RED	15.00
64	822	BROOK BENTON	ANOTHER CUP OF COFFEE	TOO LATE TO TURN BACK NOW	4.00
64	822 DJ	BROOK BENTON	ANOTHER CUP OF COFFEE	TOO LATE TO TURN BACK NOW	5.00
64	826	TIMI YURO	I'M AFRAID THE MASQUERADE IS OVER	IF	30.00
64	826 DJ	TIMI YURO	I'M AFRAID THE MASQUERADE IS OVER	IF	40.00
64	829	LESLEY GORE	WONDER BOY	MAYBE I KNOW	10.00
64	829 DJ	LESLEY GORE	WONDER BOY	MAYBE I KNOW	15.00
64	841	LITTLE RICHARD	JOY, JOY, JOY (DOWN IN MY HEART)	PEACE IN THE VALLEY	8.00
64	841 DJ	LITTLE RICHARD	JOY, JOY, JOY (DOWN IN MY HEART)	PEACE IN THE VALLEY	10.00
64	847	LESLEY DUNCAN	SEE THAT GUY	JUST FOR THE BOY	20.00
64	847 DJ	LESLEY DUNCAN	SEE THAT GUY	JUST FOR THE BOY	25.00
64	848	TIMI YURO	YOU CAN HAVE HIM	COULD THIS BE MAGIC	8.00
64	848 DJ	TIMI YURO	YOU CAN HAVE HIM	COULD THIS BE MAGIC	10.00
65	857	BRUCE SCOTT	I MADE AN ANGEL CRY	DON'T SAY GOODBYE TO ME	40.00
65	857 DJ	BRUCE SCOTT	I MADE AN ANGEL CRY	DON'T SAY GOODBYE TO ME	50.00
65	859	TIMI YURO	CAN'T STOP RUNNING AWAY	GET OUT OF MY LIFE	45.00
65	859 DJ	TIMI YURO	CAN'T STOP RUNNING AWAY	GET OUT OF MY LIFE	60.00
65	860	DEE DEE WARWICK	DO IT WITH ALL YOUR HEART	HAPPINESS	22.00
65	860 DJ	DEE DEE WARWICK	DO IT WITH ALL YOUR HEART	HAPPINESS	30.00
65	863	BROOK BENTON	LOVE ME NOW	A SLEEPIN' AT THE FOOT OF THE	4.00
65	863 DJ	BROOK BENTON	LOVE ME NOW	A SLEEPIN' AT THE FOOT OF THE	5.00
65	867	DEE DEE WARWICK	YOU DON'T KNOW (WHAT YOU DO TO	WE'RE DOING FINE	30.00
65	867 DJ	DEE DEE WARWICK	YOU DON'T KNOW (WHAT YOU DO TO	WE'RE DOING FINE	40.00
65	869	FATS DOMINO	I LEFT MY HEART IN SAN FRANCISCO	I DONE GOT OVER IT	6.00

65	869 DJ	FATS DOMINO	I LEFT MY HEART IN SAN FRANCISCO	I DONE GOT OVER IT	10.00
65	871	STEVIE LEWIS	TAKE ME FOR A LITTLE WHILE	MY WHOLE WORLD SEEMS TO BE TUM	25.00
65	871 DJ	STEVIE LEWIS	TAKE ME FOR A LITTLE WHILE	MY WHOLE WORLD SEEMS TO BE TUM	30.00
65	872	LESLEY GORE	MY TOWN, MY GUY AND ME	A GIRL IN LOVE	20.00
65	872 DJ	LESLEY GORE	MY TOWN, MY GUY AND ME	A GIRL IN LOVE	25.00
65	873	FATS DOMINO	WHAT'S THAT YOU GOT?	IT'S NEVER TOO LATE	8.00
65	873 DJ	FATS DOMINO	WHAT'S THAT YOU GOT?	IT'S NEVER TOO LATE	10.00
65	874	LEMME B. GOOD	I CAN'T STOP MYSELF	MOTHER MAY I	30.00
65	874 DJ	LEMME B. GOOD	I CAN'T STOP MYSELF	MOTHER MAY I	40.00
65	876	LESLEY DUNCAN	RUN TO LOVE	ONLY THE LONELY AND ME	8.00
65	876 DJ	LESLEY DUNCAN	RUN TO LOVE	ONLY THE LONELY AND ME	10.00
65	885	AL KOOPERAN	PARCHMAN FARM	YOU'RE THE LOVIN' END	15.00
65	885 DJ	AL KOOPERAN	PARCHMAN FARM	YOU'RE THE LOVIN' END	20.00
65	887	CHRISTINE HOLMES	GOIN' WHERE THE OVIN' IS	WHERE THERE'S SMOKE	10.00
65	887 DJ	CHRISTINE HOLMES	GOIN' WHERE THE OVIN' IS	WHERE THERE'S SMOKE	15.00
65	889	LESLEY GORE	I WON'T LOVE YOU ANYMORE (SORRY)	NO MATTER WHAT YOU DO	15.00
65	889 DJ	LESLEY GORE	I WON'T LOVE YOU ANYMORE (SORRY)	NO MATTER WHAT YOU DO	20.00
65	890	DEE DEE WARWICK	GOTTA GET A HOLD OF MYSELF	ANOTHER LONELY SATURDAY	20.00
65	890 DJ	DEE DEE WARWICK	GOTTA GET A HOLD OF MYSELF	ANOTHER SATURDAY NIGHT	30.00
65	898	SHARON TANDY	LOVE MAKES THE WORLD GO ROUND	BY MY SIDE	20.00
65	898 DJ	SHARON TANDY	LOVE MAKES THE WORLD GO ROUND	BY MY SIDE	25.00
65	902	LESLEY GORE	I JUST DON'T KNOW IF I CAN	YOUNG LOVE	15.00
65	902 DJ	LESLEY GORE	I JUST DON'T KNOW IF I CAN	YOUNG LOVE	20.00
65	903	TIMI YURO	ONCE A DAY	PRETEND	6.00
65	903 DJ	TIMI YURO	ONCE A DAY	PRETEND	8.00
65	909	DEE DEE WARWICK	WORTH EVERY TEAR THAT I CRY	LOVER'S CHANT	**231.00**
65	909 DJ	DEE DEE WARWICK	WORTH EVERY TEAR THAT I CRY	LOVER'S CHANT	250.00
65	911	FAVOURITE SONS	THAT DRIVING BEAT	WALKIN' WALKIN' WALKIN'	30.00
65	911 DJ	FAVOURITE SONS	THAT DRIVING BEAT	WALKIN' WALKIN' WALKIN'	40.00
65	912	ERNESTINE ANDERSON	YOU CAN'T BUY LOVE	JERK AND TWINE	20.00
65	912 DJ	ERNESTINE ANDERSON	YOU CAN'T BUY LOVE	JERK AND TWINE	30.00
65	916	SOUL BROTHERS	GOTTA GET A GOOD THING GOING	GOOD LOVIN' NEVER HURT	25.00
65	916 DJ	SOUL BROTHERS	GOTTA GET A GOOD THING GOING	GOOD LOVIN' NEVER HURT	30.00
65	923	ROBBIE ROYAL	ONLY ME	I DON'T NEED YOU	30.00
65	923 DJ	ROBBIE ROYAL	ONLY ME	I DON'T NEED YOU	40.00
65	932	JERRY BUTLER	LOVE (OH HOW SWEET IT IS)	LONELINESS	10.00
65	932 DJ	JERRY BUTLER	LOVE (OH HOW SWEET IT IS)	LONELINESS	15.00
65	937	DEE DEE WARWICK	I WANT TO BE WITH YOU	ALFIE	10.00
65	937 DJ	DEE DEE WARWICK	I WANT TO BE WITH YOU	ALFIE	15.00
65	940	KEITH	AIN'T GONNA LIE	IT STARTED ALL OVER AGAIN	15.00
65	940 DJ	KEITH	AIN'T GONNA LIE	IT STARTED ALL OVER AGAIN	18.00
65	943	KAREN YOUNG	ARE YOU KIDDING	I'M YOURS, YOU'RE MINE	30.00
65	943 DJ	KAREN YOUNG	ARE YOU KIDDING	I'M YOURS, YOU'RE MINE	40.00
65	946	LESLEY DAWSON	JUST SAY GOODBYE	JUST A PASSING PHASE	10.00
65	946 DJ	LESLEY DAWSON	JUST SAY GOODBYE	JUST A PASSING PHASE	15.00
65	949	TIMI YURO	TURN THE WORLD AROUND THE OTHER	JUST A RIBBON	6.00
65	949 DJ	TIMI YURO	TURN THE WORLD AROUND THE OTHER	JUST A RIBBON	8.00
65	952	PRINCE HAROLD	FORGET ABOUT ME	BABY, YOU'VE GOT ME	20.00
65	952 DJ	PRINCE HAROLD	FORGET ABOUT ME	BABY, YOU'VE GOT ME	30.00
65	953	DEE DEE WARWICK	YOURS TILL TOMORROW	I'M GONNA MAKE YOU LOVE ME	15.00
65	953 DJ	DEE DEE WARWICK	YOURS TILL TOMORROW	I'M GONNA MAKE YOU LOVE ME	20.00
66	955	KEITH	98.6	THE TEENY BOPPER SONG	8.00
66	955 DJ	KEITH	98.6	THE TEENY BOPPER SONG	10.00
66	958	CHUCK BERRY	CLUB NITTY GRITTY	LAUGH AND CRY	10.00
66	958 DJ	CHUCK BERRY	CLUB NITTY GRITTY	LAUGH AND CRY	15.00
66	960	JOE HENDERSON	INSTRA	CAT'S WHISKER'S	5.00
66	960 DJ	JOE HENDERSON	INSTRA	CAT'S WHISKER'S	6.00
66	962	SHANGRI-LAS	THE SWEET SOUND OF SUMMER	I'LL NEVER LEARN	8.00
66	962 DJ	SHANGRI-LAS	THE SWEET SOUND OF SUMMER	I'LL NEVER LEARN	10.00
66	963	LESLEY GORE	I'M GOING OUT (THE SAME WAY I CAME	CALIFORNIA NIGHTS	10.00
66	963 DJ	LESLEY GORE	I'M GOING OUT (THE SAME WAY I CAME	CALIFORNIA NIGHTS	15.00
66	964	JERRY BUTLER	I DIG YOU BABY	SOME KINDA MAGIC	10.00
66	964 DJ	JERRY BUTLER	I DIG YOU BABY	SOME KINDA MAGIC	15.00
66	965	LESLEY DAWSON	RUN FOR SHELTER	I'LL CLIMB ON A RAINBOW	50.00
66	965 DJ	LESLEY DAWSON	RUN FOR SHELTER	I'LL CLIMB ON A RAINBOW	60.00
66	968	KEITH	TELL IT TO MY FACE	I CAN'T GO WRONG	8.00
66	968 DJ	KEITH	TELL IT TO MY FACE	I CAN'T GO WRONG	10.00
66	969	PAUL NEWMAN and the X'CALIBURS	AIN'T YOU GOT A HEART	TEARS ON MY PILLOW	100.00
66	969 DJ	PAUL NEWMAN and the X'CALIBURS	AIN'T YOU GOT A HEART	TEARS ON MY PILLOW	120.00
66	973	LES McCANN	BUCKET O' GREASE	ALL	10.00
66	973 DJ	LES McCANN	BUCKET O' GREASE	ALL	15.00
66	974	DEE DEE WARWICK	WHEN LOVE SLIPS AWAY	HOUSE OF GOLD	50.00
66	974 DJ	DEE DEE WARWICK	WHEN LOVE SLIPS AWAY	HOUSE OF GOLD	60.00
66	976	MARGIE HENDRIX	I CALL YOU LOVER BUT AIN'T NOTHING	THE QUESTION	10.00
66	976 DJ	MARGIE HENDRIX	I CALL YOU LOVER BUT AIN'T NOTHING	THE QUESTION	15.00
66	978	TIMI YURO	CUTTIN' IN	WHY NOT NOW	6.00
66	978 DJ	TIMI YURO	CUTTIN' IN	WHY NOT NOW	8.00
66	979	SHANGRI-LAS	TAKE THE TIME	FOOTSTEPS ON THE ROOF	8.00
66	979 DJ	SHANGRI-LAS	TAKE THE TIME	FOOTSTEPS ON THE ROOF	10.00

66	984	LESLEY GORE	I'M FALLIN' DOWN	SUMMER AND SANDY	15.00
66	984 DJ	LESLEY GORE	I'M FALLIN' DOWN	SUMMER AND SANDY	20.00
66	989	KEITH	DAYLIGHT SAVING TIME	HAP[PY WALKING AROUND	20.00
66	989 DJ	KEITH	DAYLIGHT SAVING TIME	HAP[PY WALKING AROUND	28.00
66	994	CHUCK BERRY	BACK TO MEMPHIS	I DO REALLY LOVE YOU	5.00
66	994 DJ	CHUCK BERRY	BACK TO MEMPHIS	I DO REALLY LOVE YOU	6.00
66	997	PETE KLINT QUINTET	WALKIN' PROUD	SHAKE	15.00
66	997 DJ	PETE KLINT QUINTET	WALKIN' PROUD	SHAKE	20.00
67	1000	MAUDS	HOLD ON	C'MON AND MOVE	8.00
67	1000 DJ	MAUDS	HOLD ON	C'MON AND MOVE	10.00
67	1001	MARGIE HENDRIX	RESTLESS	ON THE RIGHT TRACK	40.00
67	1001 DJ	MARGIE HENDRIX	RESTLESS	ON THE RIGHT TRACK	50.00
67	1002	KEITH	SUGAR PIE	EASY AS PIE	4.00
67	1002 DJ	KEITH	SUGAR PIE	EASY AS PIE	5.00
67	1005	JERRY BUTLER	MR. DREAM MERCHANT	CAUSE I LOVE YOU SO	6.00
67	1005 DJ	JERRY BUTLER	MR. DREAM MERCHANT	CAUSE I LOVE YOU SO	8.00
67	1012	EVERGREEN BLUES	MIDNIGHT CONFESSIONS	(YES) THAT'S MY BABY	8.00
67	1012 DJ	EVERGREEN BLUES	MIDNIGHT CONFESSIONS	(YES) THAT'S MY BABY	10.00
68	1017	LESLEY GORE	IT'S A HAPPENING WORLD	MAGIC COLOURS	10.00
68	1017 DJ	LESLEY GORE	IT'S A HAPPENING WORLD	MAGIC COLOURS	15.00
68	1026	MOB	DISAPPEAR	I WISH YOU'D LEAVE ME ALONE	15.00
68	1026 DJ	MOB	DISAPPEAR	I WISH YOU'D LEAVE ME ALONE	22.00
68	1031	DAVE ANTHONY	HIDE AND SEEK	RACE WITH THE WIND	30.00
68	1031 DJ	DAVE ANTHONY	HIDE AND SEEK	RACE WITH THE WIND	40.00
68	1034 sh	JAY & THE TECHIQUES	BABY MAKE YOUR OWN SWEET MUSIC	HELP YOURSELF TO ALL MY LOVIN	25.00

small hole solid center first press, with different LONG intro.

68	1034 lh	JAY & THE TECHIQUES	BABY MAKE YOUR OWN SWEET MUSIC	HELP YOURSELF TO ALL MY LOVIN	10.00
68	1034 DJ	JAY & THE TECHIQUES	BABY MAKE YOUR OWN SWEET MUSIC	HELP YOURSELF TO ALL MY LOVIN	15.00
68	1035	JERRY BUTLER	NEVER GIVE YOU UP	BESIDE YOU	8.00
68	1035 DJ	JERRY BUTLER	NEVER GIVE YOU UP	BESIDE YOU	10.00
68	1056	JUNIOR WELLS	GIRL YOU LIT MY FIRE	IT'S A MAN DOWN THERE	15.00
68	1056 DJ	JUNIOR WELLS	GIRL YOU LIT MY FIRE	IT'S A MAN DOWN THERE	22.00
68	1057	SARAH VAUGHAN	BROKEN-HEARTED MELODY	MISTY	5.00
68	1057 DJ	SARAH VAUGHAN	BROKEN-HEARTED MELODY	MISTY	6.00
68	1058	JERRY BUTLER	SEND A TELEGRAM	JUST CAN'T FORGET ABOUT YOU	8.00
68	1058 DJ	JERRY BUTLER	SEND A TELEGRAM	JUST CAN'T FORGET ABOUT YOU	10.00
68	1061	DEE DEE WARWICK	MONDAY MONDAY	I'LL BE BETTER OFF (WITHOUT YO	30.00
68	1061 DJ	DEE DEE WARWICK	MONDAY MONDAY	I'LL BE BETTER OFF (WITHOUT YO	40.00
68	1062	MAUDS	SOUL DRIPPIN	FOREVER GONE	8.00
68	1062 DJ	MAUDS	SOUL DRIPPIN	FOREVER GONE	10.00
68	1065	BUDDY MILES EXPRESS	TRAIN	TRAIN part 2	6.00
68	1065 DJ	BUDDY MILES EXPRESS	TRAIN	TRAIN part 2	8.00
59	1071	SARAH VAUGHN	SMOOTH OPERATOR	PASSING STRANGER	25.00
59	1071 DJ	SARAH VAUGHN	SMOOTH OPERATOR	PASSING STRANGER	35.00
69	1077	MOVING FINGER	HIGHER AND HIGHER	SHAKE AND FINGER POP	20.00
69	1077 DJ	MOVING FINGER	HIGHER AND HIGHER	SHAKE AND FINGER POP	28.00
69	1078	JERRY BUTLER	ARE YOU HAPPY	(STRANGE) I STILL LOVE YOU	5.00
69	1078 DJ	JERRY BUTLER	ARE YOU HAPPY	(STRANGE) I STILL LOVE YOU	8.00
69	1081	PLATTERS	HARBOUR LIGHTS	(BY THE) SLEEPY LAGOON	5.00
69	1081 DJ	PLATTERS	HARBOUR LIGHTS	(BY THE) SLEEPY LAGOON	6.00
69	1084	DEE DEE WARWICK	FOOLISH HEART	THANK GOD	15.00
69	1084 DJ	DEE DEE WARWICK	FOOLISH HEART	THANK GOD	20.00
69	1090	RICHARD KENT STYLE	A LITTLE BIT O' SOUL	DON'T TELL ME LIES	30.00
69	1090 DJ	RICHARD KENT STYLE	A LITTLE BIT O' SOUL	DON'T TELL ME LIES	40.00
69	1093	SHIRELLES	THERE'S A STORM GOING ON IN MY	CALL ME (IF YOU WANT ME)	15.00
69	1093 DJ	SHIRELLES	THERE'S A STORM GOING ON IN MY	CALL ME (IF YOU WANT ME)	25.00
69	1094	JERRY BUTLER	ONLY THE STRONG SURVIVE	JUST BECAUSE I REALLY LOVE YOU	10.00
69	1094 DJ	JERRY BUTLER	ONLY THE STRONG SURVIVE	JUST BECAUSE I REALLY LOVE YOU	15.00
69	1097	PROPHETS	I GOT THE FEVER	SOUL CONTROL	30.00
69	1097 DJ	PROPHETS	I GOT THE FEVER	SOUL CONTROL	60.00
69	1098	BUDDY MILES EXPRESS	MISS LADY	'69 FREEDOM SPECIAL	5.00
69	1098 DJ	BUDDY MILES EXPRESS	MISS LADY	'69 FREEDOM SPECIAL	6.00
69	1101	PLATTERS	SMOKE GETS IN YOUR EYES	HARBOUR LIGHTS	4.00
69	1101 DJ	PLATTERS	SMOKE GETS IN YOUR EYES	HARBOUR LIGHTS	6.00
69	1104	FATS DOMINO	WHAT'S THAT YOU GOT ?	JAMBALAYA	8.00
69	1104 DJ	FATS DOMINO	WHAT'S THAT YOU GOT ?	JAMBALAYA	10.00
69	1107	SARAH VAUGHN	FEVER	BOY FROM IPANEMA	5.00
69	1107 DJ	SARAH VAUGHN	FEVER	BOY FROM IPANEMA	8.00
60	1108	CLYDE McPHATTER	I AIN'T GIVING UP NOTHIN' (IF I CAN'T	TA TA	10.00
60	1108 DJ	CLYDE McPHATTER	I AIN'T GIVING UP NOTHIN' (IF I CAN'T	TA TA	15.00
69	1109	CHARLIE RICH	MOHAIR SAM	I WASHED MY HANDS IN THE MUDDY	15.00
69	1109 DJ	CHARLIE RICH	MOHAIR SAM	I WASHED MY HANDS IN THE MUDDY	20.00
60	1116	DAMITA JO	I'LL SAVE THE LAST DANCE FOR YOU	FORGIVE	6.00
60	1116 DJ	DAMITA JO	I'LL SAVE THE LAST DANCE FOR YOU	FORGIVE	10.00
60	1120	CLYDE McPHATTER	YOU'RE FOR ME	I JUST WANT TO LOVE YOU	10.00
60	1120 DJ	CLYDE McPHATTER	YOU'RE FOR ME	I JUST WANT TO LOVE YOU	15.00
69	1122 lh	JERRY BUTLER	MOODY WOMAN	GO AWAY - FIND YOURSELF	20.00
69	1122 sh	JERRY BUTLER	MOODY WOMAN	GO AWAY - FIND YOURSELF	30.00
69	1122 DJ lh	JERRY BUTLER	MOODY WOMAN	GO AWAY - FIND YOURSELF	**279.00**

69	1122 DJ sh unconfirmed	JERRY BUTLER	MOODY WOMAN	GO AWAY - FIND YOURSELF	UN
75	1122 ink	JERRY BUTLER	MOODY WOMAN	GO AWAY-FIND YOURSELF	6.00
69	1125	DEE DEE WARWICK	THAT'S NOT LOVE	IT'S NOT FAIR	10.00
69	1125 DJ	DEE DEE WARWICK	THAT'S NOT LOVE	IT'S NOT FAIR	20.00
69	1127	MOMS MABLEY	SUNNY	ABRAHAM, MARTIN AND JOHN	5.00
69	1127 DJ	MOMS MABLEY	SUNNY	ABRAHAM, MARTIN AND JOHN	6.00
69	1132	JERRY BUTLER	WHAT'S THE USE OF BREAKING UP	A BRAND NEW ME	10.00
69	1132 DJ	JERRY BUTLER	WHAT'S THE USE OF BREAKING UP	A BRAND NEW ME	20.00
69	1133	BENNY & TINA	OVER MY DEAD BODY	THIS LOVE IS REAL	10.00
69	1133 DJ	BENNY & TINA	OVER MY DEAD BODY	THIS LOVE IS REAL	15.00
61	1136	CLYDE McPHATTER	I'LL LOVE YOU TILL THE COWS COME HOME	TOMORROW IS A-COMIN'	50.00
61	1136 DJ	CLYDE McPHATTER	I'LL LOVE YOU TILL THE COWS COME HOME	TOMORROW IS A-COMIN'	80.00
61	1148	BROOK BENTON	THE BOLL WEEVIL SONG	YOUR EYES	5.00
61	1148 DJ	BROOK BENTON	THE BOLL WEEVIL SONG	YOUR EYES	6.00
61	1165	LITTLE RICHARD	JOY JOY JOY (DOWN IN MY HEART)	HE'S NOT JUST AOLDIER	8.00
61	1165 DJ	LITTLE RICHARD	JOY JOY JOY (DOWN IN MY HEART)	HE'S NOT JUST AOLDIER	10.00
62	1171	BRUCE CHANNEL	HEY! BABY	DREAM GIRL	8.00
62	1171 DJ	BRUCE CHANNEL	HEY! BABY	DREAM GIRL	15.00
62	1174	CLYDE McPHATTER	LOVER PLEASE	LET'S FORGET ABOUT THE PAST	15.00
62	1174 DJ	CLYDE McPHATTER	LOVER PLEASE	LET'S FORGET ABOUT THE PAST	20.00
62	1181	CLYDE McPHATTER	LITTLE BITTY PRETTY ONE	NEXT TO ME	15.00
62	1181 DJ	CLYDE McPHATTER	LITTLE BITTY PRETTY ONE	NEXT TO ME	18.00
62	1189	LITTLE RICHARD	HE GOT WHAT HE WANTED (BUT HE	WHY DON'T YOU CHANGE YOUR WAYS	10.00
62	1189 DJ	LITTLE RICHARD	HE GOT WHAT HE WANTED (BUT HE	WHY DON'T YOU CHANGE YOUR WAYS	20.00
63	1202	XAVIER CUGAT	WATERMELON MAN	SWINGING SHEPHERD'S BLUES	15.00
63	1202 DJ	XAVIER CUGAT	WATERMELON MAN	SWINGING SHEPHERD'S BLUES	20.00
63	1211	ANGELS	MY BOYFRIEND'S BACK	(LOVE ME) NOW	15.00
63	1211 DJ	ANGELS	MY BOYFRIEND'S BACK	(LOVE ME) NOW	28.00
63	1215	ANGELS	I ADORE HIM	THANK YOU AND GOODNIGHT	10.00
63	1215 DJ	ANGELS	I ADORE HIM	THANK YOU AND GOODNIGHT	15.00
	9504 EP PS	PLATTERS	THE FABULOUS: 4 track ep	only you + magic touch + my pr	12.00
66	10036 EP PS	DEE DEE WARWICK	WE'RE DOING FINE	1966 4 track EP with cover	40.00
68	127360	JAY & THE TECHNIQUES	BABY MAKE YOUR OWN SWEET MUSIC	HELP YOURSELF TO ALL MY LOVIN'	8.00
68	127360	JAY & THE TECHNIQUES	BABY MAKE YOUR OWN SWEET MUSIC	HELP YOURSELF TO ALL MY LOVIN'	15.00
76	6007101	L.J. JOHNSON	DANCING ON THE EDGE OF A DREAM	DANCING ROUND THE WORLD	5.00
76	6007106	EQUALS	FUNKY LIKE A TRAIN	IF YOU DIDN'T MISS ME	25.00
76	6007110	L.J. JOHNSON	AIN'T NO VALUES ON YOUR LOVE	I'M STARING IN SPCE	5.00
77	6007147	PIONEERS	MY GOOD FRIEND JAMES	SECRETS OF YOU	**251.00**
78	6007198	RAHNI HARRIS & F.L.O.	SIX MILLION STEPS (WEST RUNS SOUTH)	same: part 2	5.00
78	6008003	GODFREY, RAY	CANDY CLOWN	I WANT TO BE YOUR ONLY LOVE	8.00
78	6008005	ACT ONE	GOODBYE LOVE (WE'RE THROUGH)	TOM THE PEEPER	6.00
71	6052027 paper	NEWBY & JOHNSON	I WANT TO GIVE YOU MY EVERYTHING	SWEET HAPPINESS	15.00
76	6052027 ink	NEWBY & JOHNSON	I WANT TO GIVE YOU MY EVERYTHING	SWEET HAPPINESS	8.00
71	6052033	GENE CHANDLER	GROOVY SITUATION	NOT THE MARRYING KIND	10.00
71	6052036	BUDDY MILES	THEM CHANGES	YOUR FEELING IS MINE	8.00
71	6052036 duplicate #	JERRY BUTLER	ONE NIGHT AFFAIR	WHAT'S SO GOOD ABOUT IT	6.00
71	6052067	JOE TEX	BAD FEET	I KNEW HIM	5.00
71	6052073	LORRAINE ELLISON	CALL ME ANYTIME YOU NEED SOME	PLEASE DON'T TEACH ME TO LOVE	20.00
71	6052077	BUDDY MILES	WHOLESALE LOVE	THAT'S THE WAY LIFE IS	5.00
71	6052087	GENE & JERRY	EVERYBODY IS WAITING	TEN AND TWO	5.00
71	6052098	GENE CHANDLER	YOU'RE A LADY	STONE COLD FEELING	15.00
71	6052109	MABLEY, MOMS	THAT'S POPS	I SURRENDER DEAR	5.00
71	6052110	JIMMY CASTOR	HAM HOCKS ESPANOL	HEY LEROY, YOUR MAMA'S CALLING	15.00
71	6052110	JIMMY CASTOR	BANG, BANG	HEY WILLIE	5.00
72	6052111	JOE TEX	GIVE THE BABY ANYTHING	TAKIN' A CHANCE	5.00
72	6052119	JERRY BUTLER	MOODY WOMAN	A BRAND NEW ME	8.00
72	6052120	KRYSTAL GENERATION	WANTED DEAD OR ALIVE	EVERY MAN SEEMS TO BE FOR HIMS	15.00
72	6052127	BUDDY MILES	GIVE AWAY NONE OF MY LOVE	TAKE IT OFF HIM AND PUT IT ON	5.00
72	6052129	JOE TEX	I GOTCHA	A MOTHER'S PRAYER	5.00
72	6052155	JERRY BUTLER & BRENDA LEE EAGER	AIN'T UNDERSTANDING MELLOW	I ONBLY HAVE EYES FOR YOU	6.00
72	6052156	JOE TEX	YOU SAID A BAD WORD	IT AIN'T GONNA WORK BABY	4.00
72	6052168	JERRY BUTLER	ONE NIGHT AFFAIR	WHAT'S SO GOOD ABOUT IT	8.00
72	6052185	JIMMY CASTOR	BANG BANG	HEY WILLIE	5.00
72	6052186	BILL BRANDON	(TAKE ANOTHER LITTLE) PIECE OF	I AM FREE OF YOUR LOVE	10.00
73	6052258	DON COVAY	LEAVE HIM	MEMPHIS	5.00
73	6052301 paper	MILLIONAIRES	NEVER FOR ME	IF I HAD YOU BABE	30.00
76	6052301 ink	MILLIONAIRES	NEVER FOR ME	IF I HAD YOU BABE	10.00
73	6052302	JAY & THE TECHNIQUES	APPLES, PEACHES, PUMPKIN PIE	CONTACT	6.00
73	6052367	ROY C	GOT TO GET ENOUGH	DON'T BLAME THE MAN	6.00
74	6052388	DON COVAY	BAD MOUTHING	I WAS CHECKING OUT	4.00
74	6052531	JONESES	HEY BABE (IS THE GETTIN' STILL	HEY BABE PART2	4.00
74	6052634	DON COVAY	IT'S BETTER TO HAVE (AND DON'T NEED)	LEAVE HIM Part 2	8.00
74	605367	ROY C	GOT TO GET ENOUGH (OF YOUR SWEET	DON'T BLAME THE MAN	4.00
75	6167007	GENE DOZIER & the UNITED FRONT	THE BEST GIRL I EVER HAD	GIVE THE WOMEN WHAT THEY WANT	20.00
75	6167012	OHIO PLAYERS	SKIN TIGHT	HEAVEN MUST BE LIKE THIS	4.00
75	6167064	KEITH	DAYLIGHT SAVIN' TIME	HAPPY WALKING AROUND	6.00
75	6167196	RALPH CARTER	WHEN YOU'RE YOUNG AND IN LOVE	WHEN YOU'RE YOUNG AND IN LOVE part 2	4.00
75	6167225	OHIO PLAYERS	LOVE ROLLER COASTER	ONE WORD ALONE	4.00
75	6167239	ROY C	DON'T BLAME THE MAN	I'M BUSTING MY ROCKS	5.00

76	6167286	RALPH CARTER	EXTRA EXTRA (READ ALL ABOUT IT)	EXTRA EXTRA (READ ALL ABOUT IT) part 2	4.00
76	6167324	JAMES & BOBBY PURIFY	I'M YOUR PUPPET	LAY ME DOWN EASY	5.00
76	6167331	LEE ELDRED	HOW'S YOUR LOVE LIFE	HOW'S YOUR LOVE LIFE part 1	4.00
76	6167379	RALPH CARTER	LOVE IS LIKE AN ITCHING IN MY HEART	BABY IT'S TRUE (CAUSE I LOVE Y	4.00
76	6167380	JAMES & BOBBY PURIFY	MORNING GLORY	TURNING BACK THE PAGES	4.00
76	6167385	OHIO PLAYERS	WHO'D SHE COO?	FOPP	4.00
76	6167420	OHIO PLAYERS	FIRE	SKIN TIGHT	4.00
77	6167424	WILLIAM BELL	TRYIN' TO LOVE TWO	IF SEX WAS ALL WE HAD	10.00
77	616743	CHI-LITES	HAPPY BEING LONELY	LOVE CAN BE HAZARDOUS TO YOUR	4.00
77	6167485	CHI-LITES	VANISHING LOVE	I TURN AWAY	4.00
77	6167526	DELLS	OUR LOVE	OUR LOVE (Edited Version)	5.00
77	6167548	JOE TEX	I GOTCHA	YOU SAIUD A BAD WORD	4.00
77	6167549	OHIO PLAYERS	OHIO	CAN YOU STILL LOVE ME	4.00
78	6167649	BAR-KAYS	LET'S HAVE SOME FUN	ATTITUDES	4.00
78	6167654	KENNIE DELT and PRANA	CONQUER ALL	same: instrumental	5.00
78	6167670	SAMONA COOKE	ONE NIGHT AFFAIR	YOU TO ME ARE EVERYTHING	5.00

MGM

Considering the size of this company's artist rosta, the percentage of "soul" releases was small, but with high quality production

Hollywood based movie industry MGM (Metro-Goldwyn-Mayer) made movies for decades before venturing into the record industry a year after the Second World War. At first, their catalogue mostly comprised of movie soundtracks. Slowly widening it's musical field as the years went by, early 50's legendary country & western icon Hank Williams recorded eleven songs which sold more than a million copies each between the years of 1949 and 1953 this elevated MGM Records to be considered a "major" along side the likes of Capitol, Columbia, Decca, Mercury, and RCA, like the big five MGM had its own pressing plants. It's 50's single 45 rpm chart success was mostly down to Connie Francis, Hank Williams and Conway Twitty. The interest to soul collectors possibly started when MGM signed artists like Clyde McPhatter, and added in 1961, Norman Granz's highly succesful Verve label. Although initially a Jazz label Verve took a turn towards soul and rock during the mid-sixties (see Verve notes further on this book).

Interesting point in the late 60's MGM ended up with masses of surplus stock, as they tried to compete in the rock and soul market, example when "acid rock" began hit the music scene in 1968, UK group The Animals were MGM's only band in this genre. A huge campaign followed with MGM chasing the market with the "Bosstown Rock" groups to try and emulate the Detroit success with rock, but they failed miserably during 1967 to 1969 it left MGM with losses of as much as $18 million in 1970 and in 1971 they just broke even. Heads of the record division gave over ambitious sales targets to the movie arm bosses. Sales campaigns loaded the retail shops with product, but MGM returns policy in that period caused MGM Records big problems with returns of unsold records from the stores, which led to masses of returns which were turned into cut-outs. Hence the massive load of MGM related 45's that turned up in many parts of Europe during the early 70's including the famous Leeds "find". In 1972, the label was sold to the newly-founded Dutch-German conglomerate PolyGram (Polydor and Phonogram), which tried to get a share of the American market by buying US record companies.

60	705 EP PS	CLYDE McPHATTER	TWICE AS NICE	1960 4 track EP with cover	150.00
60	739 EP PS	CLYDE McPHATTER	THIS IS NOT GOODBYE: 4 track EP	1960 4 track EP with cover	150.00
66	794 EP PS	SAM THE SHAM & the PHAROAHS	RED HOT	1966 4 track EP with cover	40.00
60	9079	CLYDE McPHATTER	THINK ME A KISS	WHEN THE RIGHT TIME COMES ALON	15.00
60	9079 DJ	CLYDE McPHATTER	THINK ME A KISS	WHEN THE RIGHT TIME COMES ALON	20.00
59	1015	IMPALAS	SORRY (I RAN ALL THE WAY HOME)	FOOL, FOOL, FOOL	15.00
59	1015 DJ	IMPALAS	SORRY (I RAN ALL THE WAY HOME)	FOOL, FOOL, FOOL	20.00
60	1102	WANDERERS	I COULD MAKE YOU MINE	I NEED YOU MORE	40.00
60	1102 DJ	WANDERERS	I COULD MAKE YOU MINE	I NEED YOU MORE	50.00
61	1123	RONNIE SAVOY	BIG CHAIN	AND THE HEAVEN'S CRIED	20.00
61	1123 DJ	RONNIE SAVOY	BIG CHAIN	AND THE HEAVEN'S CRIED	28.00
61	1131	RONNIE SAVOY	BEWITCHED	IT'S GOTTA BE LOVE	5.00
61	1131 DJ	RONNIE SAVOY	BEWITCHED	IT'S GOTTA BE LOVE	8.00
61	1143	STEREOS	PLEASE COME BACK TO ME	I REALLY LOVE YOU	25.00
61	1143 DJ	STEREOS	PLEASE COME BACK TO ME	I REALLY LOVE YOU	35.00
61	1149	STEREOS	SWEET WATER	THE BIG KNOCK	25.00
61	1149 DJ	STEREOS	SWEET WATER	THE BIG KNOCK	30.00
62	1165	CONNIE FRANCIS	IT'S GONNA TAKE ME SOME TIME	VACATION	25.00
62	1165 DJ	CONNIE FRANCIS	IT'S GONNA TAKE ME SOME TIME	VACATION	50.00
61	1169	WANDERERS	AS TIMEGOES BY	THERE IS NO GREATER LOVE	20.00
61	1169 DJ	WANDERERS	AS TIMEGOES BY	THERE IS NO GREATER LOVE	28.00
63	1210	ROY HAMILTON	THE SINNER (El Pecador)	THEME from THE V.I.P.'S	30.00
63	1210 DJ	ROY HAMILTON	THE SINNER (El Pecador)	THEME from THE V.I.P.'S	45.00
63	1226	JACKIE BURNS and the BO BELLS	DO THE BEST I CAN	HE'S MY GUY	85.00
63	1226 DJ	JACKIE BURNS and the BO BELLS	DO THE BEST I CAN	HE'S MY GUY	120.00
63	1238	ELMER BERNSTEIN	THE RAT RACE	SAINTS AND SINNERS	20.00
63	1238 DJ	ELMER BERNSTEIN	THE RAT RACE	SAINTS AND SINNERS THEME	28.00
64	1251	ROY HAMILTON	THE PANIS IS ON	THERE SHE IS	250.00
64	1251 DJ	ROY HAMILTON	THE PANIS IS ON	THERE SHE IS	**358.00**
65	1265	CONNIE FRANCIS	NO BETTER OFF	FORGET DOMANI	10.00
65	1265 DJ	CONNIE FRANCIS	NO BETTER OFF	FORGET DOMANI	15.00
65	1267	JOE SOUTH	CONCRETE JUNGLE	LAST ONE TO KNOW	6.00
65	1267 DJ	JOE SOUTH	CONCRETE JUNGLE	LAST ONE TO KNOW	10.00
65	1268	ROY HAMILTON	A THOUSAND TEARS AGO	SWEET VIOLET	10.00
65	1268 DJ	ROY HAMILTON	A THOUSAND TEARS AGO	SWEET VIOLET	15.00
65	1269	SAM THE SHAM & the PHAROAHS	WOOLY BULLY	AIN'T GONNA MOVE	12.00
65	1269 DJ	SAM THE SHAM & the PHAROAHS	WOOLY BULLY	AIN'T GONNA MOVE	45.00
65	1270	GINNY ARNELL	JUST LIKE A BOY	PORTRAIT OF A FOOL	15.00
65	1270 DJ	GINNY ARNELL	JUST LIKE A BOY	PORTRAIT OF A FOOL	22.00
65	1272	ROYALETTES	POOR BOY	WATCH WHAT HAPPENS	15.00
65	1272 DJ	ROYALETTES	POOR BOY	WATCH WHAT HAPPENS	22.00
65	1278	SAM THE SHAM & the PHAROAHS	JU JU HAND	BIG CITY LIGHTS	8.00
65	1278 DJ	SAM THE SHAM & the PHAROAHS	JU JU HAND	BIG CITY LIGHTS	15.00
65	1279	ROYALETTES	OUT OF SIGHT OUT OF MIND	IT'S GONNA TAKE A MIRACLE	40.00
65	1279 DJ	ROYALETTES	OUT OF SIGHT OUT OF MIND	IT'S GONNA TAKE A MIRACLE	75.00

65	1285	SAM THE SHAM & the PHAROAHS	RING DANG DOO	DON'T TRY IT	8.00
65	1285 DJ	SAM THE SHAM & the PHAROAHS	RING DANG DOO	DON'T TRY IT	12.00
65	1286	WILSON PICKETT	LET ME BE YOUR BOY	MY HEART BELONG TO YOU	85.00
65	1286 DJ	WILSON PICKETT	LET ME BE YOUR BOY	MY HEARTS BELONG TO YOU	150.00
65	1291	BRUCE SCOTT	SO MUCH TO LIVE FOR	ONCE A THIEF TWICE A THIEF	20.00
65	1291 DJ	BRUCE SCOTT	SO MUCH TO LIVE FOR	ONCE A THIEF TWICE A THIEF	28.00
65	1292	ROYALETTES	NEVER AGAIN	I WA\NT TO MEET HIM	30.00
65	1292 DJ	ROYALETTES	NEVER AGAIN	I WA\NT TO MEET HIM	45.00
66	1297	LOU CHRISTIE	LIGHTNIN' STRIKES	CRYING IN THE STREETS	20.00
66	1297 DJ	LOU CHRISTIE	LIGHTNIN' STRIKES	CRYING IN THE STREETS	45.00
66	1298	SAM THE SHAM & the PHAROAHS	RED HOT	LONG LONG WAY	8.00
66	1298 DJ	SAM THE SHAM & the PHAROAHS	RED HOT	LONG LONG WAY	12.00
66	1302	ROYALETTES	ONLY WHEN YOU'RE LONELY	YOU BRING ME DOWN	30.00
66	1302 DJ	ROYALETTES	ONLY WHEN YOU'RE LONELY	YOU BRING ME DOWN	50.00
66	1313	ROBIE PORTER	EITHER WAY I LOSE	LET IT BE ME	15.00
66	1313 DJ	ROBIE PORTER	EITHER WAY I LOSE	LET IT BE ME	22.00
66	1315	SAM THE SHAM & the PHAROAHS	LIL' RED RIDING HOOD	LOVE ME LIKE BEFORE	10.00
66	1315 DJ	SAM THE SHAM & the PHAROAHS	LIL' RED RIDING HOOD	LOVE ME LIKE BEFORE	15.00
66	1321	SANDY POSEY	CAUTION TO THE WIND	BORN A WOMAN	15.00
66	1321 DJ	SANDY POSEY	CAUTION TO THE WIND	BORN A WOMAN	25.00
66	1324	ROYALETTES	IT'S A BIG MISTAGE	I WANT TO MEET HIM	18.00
66	1324 DJ	ROYALETTES	IT'S A BIG MISTAGE	I WANT TO MEET HIM	28.00
66	1325	LOU CHRISTIE	IF ONLY MY CAR COULD TALK	SONG OF LITA	10.00
66	1325 DJ	LOU CHRISTIE	IF ONLY MY CAR COULD TALK	SONG OF LITA	15.00
66	1326	SAM THE SHAM & the PHAROAHS	THE HAIR ON MY CHINNY CHIN CHIN	THE OUT CROWD	8.00
66	1326 DJ	SAM THE SHAM & the PHAROAHS	THE HAIR ON MY CHINNY CHIN CHIN	THE OUT CROWD	12.00
66	1328	STEREOS	SWEET WATER	THE BIG KNOCK	15.00
66	1328 DJ	STEREOS	SWEET WATER	THE BIG KNOCK	20.00
66	1331	SAM THE SHAM & the PHAROAHS	HOW DO YOU CATCH A GIRL	THE LOVE YOU LEFT BEHIND	8.00
66	1331 DJ	SAM THE SHAM & the PHAROAHS	HOW DO YOU CATCH A GIRL	THE LOVE YOU LEFT BEHIND	12.00
66	1332	SPYDER TURNER	YOU'RE GOOD ENOUGH FOR ME	STAND BY ME	45.00
66	1332 DJ	SPYDER TURNER	YOU'RE GOOD ENOUGH FOR ME	STAND BY ME	70.00
67	1337	SAM THE SHAM & the PHAROAHS	OH THAT'S BAD NO THAT'S GOOD	TAKE WHAT YOU CAN GET	8.00
67	1337 DJ	SAM THE SHAM & the PHAROAHS	OH THAT'S BAD NO THAT'S GOOD	TAKE WHAT YOU CAN GET	12.00
67	1338	KIM WESTON	I GOT WHAT YOU NEED	SOMEONE LIKE YOU	28.00
67	1338 DJ	KIM WESTON	I GOT WHAT YOU NEED	SOMEONE LIKE YOU	50.00
67	1343	SAM THE SHAM & the PHAROAHS	BLACK SHEEP	MY DAY'S GONNA COME	8.00
67	1343 DJ	SAM THE SHAM & the PHAROAHS	BLACK SHEEP	MY DAY'S GONNA COME	12.00
67	1357	KIM WESTON	THAT'S GROOVY	LAND OF TOMORROW	15.00
67	1357 DJ	KIM WESTON	THAT'S GROOVY	LAND OF TOMORROW	25.00
67	1366	APRIL STEVENS	WANTING YOU	FALLING IN LOVE AGAIN	120.00
67	1366 DJ	APRIL STEVENS	WANTING YOU	FALLING IN LOVE AGAIN	220.00
67	1367	JOHN DREVAR'S EXPRESSION	THE CLOSER SHE GETS	WHEN I COME HOME	**200.00**
67	1367 DJ	JOHN DREVAR'S EXPRESSION	THE CLOSER SHE GETS	WHEN I COME HOME	275.00
67	1369	KRIS IFE	HUSH	THE SPECTATOR	10.00
67	1369 DJ	KRIS IFE	HUSH	THE SPECTATOR	20.00
68	1378	CALVIN ARNOLD	FUNKY WAY	SNATCHIN' BACK	10.00
68	1378 DJ	CALVIN ARNOLD	FUNKY WAY	SNATCHIN' BACK	15.00
68	1379	SAM THE SHAM & the PHAROAHS	YAKETY YAK	LET OUR LOVELIGHT SHINE	6.00
68	1379 DJ	SAM THE SHAM & the PHAROAHS	YAKETY YAK	LET OUR LOVELIGHT SHINE	10.00
68	1382	KIM WESTON	YOU'RE JUST THE KIND OF GUY	NOBODY	45.00
68	1382 DJ	KIM WESTON	YOU'RE JUST THE KIND OF GUY	NOBODY	85.00
68	1389	JESS & JAMES & the J.J. BAND	MOVE	WHAT WAS I BORN FOR	15.00
68	1389 DJ	JESS & JAMES & the J.J. BAND	MOVE	WHAT WAS I BORN FOR	40.00
68	1398	LUCAS & THE MIKE COTTON	SOUL SERENADE	WE GOT A THING GOING BABY	30.00
68	1398 DJ	LUCAS & THE MIKE COTTON	SOUL SERENADE	WE GOT A THING GOING BABY	45.00
68	1399	FORMATIONS	AT THE TOP OF THE STAIRS	MAGIC MELODY	175.00
68	1399 DJ	FORMATIONS	AT THE TOP OF THE STAIRS	MAGIC MELODY	**288.00**
68	1420	JESS & JAMES	SOMETHING FOR NOTHING	I LET THE DAY GO BY	15.00
68	1420 DJ	JESS & JAMES	SOMETHING FOR NOTHING	I LET THE DAY GO BY	22.00
68	1425	MAGISTRATES	GIRL	HERE COMES THE JUDGE	15.00
68	1425 DJ	MAGISTRATES	GIRL	HERE COMES THE JUDGE	22.00
68	1427	LUCAS & THE MIKE COTTON	MOTHER-IN-LAW	JACK AND THE BEANSTALK	10.00
68	1427 DJ	LUCAS & THE MIKE COTTON	MOTHER-IN-LAW	JACK AND THE BEANSTALK	15.00
68	1431	TRULY SMITH	THIS IS THE FIRST TIME	TAKING TIME	25.00
68	1431 DJ	TRULY SMITH	THIS IS THE FIRST TIME	TAKING TIME	40.00
68	1434	FANTASTICS	WHO COULD BE LOVING YOU	BABY MAKE YOUR OWN SWEET MUSIC	15.00
68	1434 DJ	FANTASTICS	WHO COULD BE LOVING YOU	BABY MAKE YOUR OWN SWEET MUSIC	30.00
68	1435	BLOSSOMS	TWEEDLE DEE	YOU GOT ME HUMMIN'	6.00
68	1435 DJ	BLOSSOMS	TWEEDLE DEE	YOU GOT ME HUMMIN'	10.00
68	1436	SHOWSTOPPERS	HOW EASY YOUR HEART FORGETS ME	EENY MEENY	15.00
68	1436 DJ	SHOWSTOPPERS	HOW EASY YOUR HEART FORGETS ME	EENY MEENY	30.00
68	1437	MAGISTRATES	AFTER THE FOX	TEAR DOWN THE WALLS	15.00
68	1437 DJ	MAGISTRATES	AFTER THE FOX	TEAR DOWN THE WALLS	15.00
68	1438	CHERRY PEOPLE	AND SUDDENLY	IMAGINATION	45.00
68	1438 DJ	CHERRY PEOPLE	AND SUDDENLY	IMAGINATION	75.00
68	1446	CONNIE FRANCIS	SOMEBODY ELSE IS TAKING MY PLACE	BROTHER, CAN YOU SPARE A DIME	6.00
68	1446 DJ	CONNIE FRANCIS	SOMEBODY ELSE IS TAKING MY PLACE	BROTHER, CAN YOU SPARE A DIME	8.00
68	1447	LARRY WILLIAMS	SHAKE YOUR BODY GIRL	LOVE, I CAN'T SEEM TO FIND	15.00

68	1447 DJ	LARRY WILLIAMS	SHAKE YOUR BODY GIRL	LOVE, I CAN'T SEEM TO FIND	25.00
68	1449	CALVIN ARNOLD	MAMA IN LAW	MINI SKIRT	10.00
68	1449 DJ	CALVIN ARNOLD	MAMA IN LAW	MINI SKIRT	15.00
68	1454	JESS & JAMES & the J.J. BAND	MOTHERLESS CHILD	THANK YOU SHOW BIZ	6.00
68	1454 DJ	JESS & JAMES & the J.J. BAND	MOTHERLESS CHILD	THANK YOU SHOW BIZ	8.00
68	1455	MARIE FRANKLIN	YOU AIN'T CHANGED	DON'TCHA BET NO MONEY	15.00
68	1455 DJ	MARIE FRANKLIN	YOU AIN'T CHANGED	DON'TCHA BET NO MONEY	22.00
68	1459	FATHERS ANGELS	BOK TO BACH	DON'T KNOCK IT	200.00
68	1459 DJ	FATHERS ANGELS	BOK TO BACH	DON'T KNOCK IT	**310.00**
69	1466	BILL DEAL & the RHONDELS	MAY I	DAY BY DAY MY LOVE GROWS STRON	10.00
69	1466 DJ	BILL DEAL & the RHONDELS	MAY I	DAY BY DAY MY LOVE GROWS STRON	15.00
69	1472	CHERRY PEOPLE	GOTTA GET BACK (TO THE GOOD LIFE)	I'M THE ONE WHO LOVES YOU	20.00
69	1472 DJ	CHERRY PEOPLE	GOTTA GET BACK (TO THE GOOD LIFE)	I'M THE ONE WHO LOVES YOU	28.00
69	1473	SAM THE SHAM & the PHAROAHS	WOOLLY BULLY	RING DANG DOO	6.00
69	1473 DJ	SAM THE SHAM & the PHAROAHS	WOOLLY BULLY	RING DANG DOO	15.00
69	1479	BILL DEAL & the RHONDELS	I'VE BEEN HURT	I'VE GOT MY NEEDS	15.00
69	1479 DJ	BILL DEAL & the RHONDELS	I'VE BEEN HURT	I'VE GOT MY NEEDS	20.00
69	1480	JOHNNY NASH	(I'M SO) GLAD YOU'RE MY BABY	STORMY	22.00
69	1480 DJ	JOHNNY NASH	(I'M SO) GLAD YOU'RE MY BABY	STORMY	30.00
69	1482	BETTY MADIGAN	I'M GONNA MAKE YOU LOVE ME	GOODNIGHT	8.00
69	1482 DJ	BETTY MADIGAN	I'M GONNA MAKE YOU LOVE ME	GOODNIGHT	12.00
69	1485	CLARA WARD	AMERICA THE BEAUTIFUL	I PRAY FOR PEOPLE	4.00
69	1485 DJ	CLARA WARD	AMERICA THE BEAUTIFUL	I PRAY FOR PEOPLE	6.00
69	1488	BILL DEAL & the RHONDELS	WHAT KIND OF FOOL DO YOU THINK I	ARE YOU READY FOR THIS	10.00
69	1488 DJ	BILL DEAL & the RHONDELS	WHAT KIND OF FOOL DO YOU THINK I	ARE YOU READY FOR THIS	18.00
69	1489	CHERRY PEOPLE	LIGHT OF LOVE	ON THE SOMETHING NEW	5.00
69	1489 DJ	CHERRY PEOPLE	LIGHT OF LOVE	ON THE SOMETHING NEW	8.00
71	2006048 paper	SAM THE SHAM & the PHAROAHS	WOOLY BULLY	LIL' RED RIDING HOOD	6.00
75	2006048 ink	SAM THE SHAM & the PHAROAHS	WOOLY BULLY	LIL' RED RIDING HOOD	5.00
71	2006065	LOU RAWLS	A NATURAL MAN	YOU CAN'T HOLD ON	4.00
73	2006278	MOB	TEAR THE HOUSE DOWN	ONE WAY TICKET TO NOWHERE	5.00
72	2006419	GLORIA GAYNOR	COME TONIGHT	HON EY BEE	15.00
72	2006422	BILL DEAL & the RHONDELS	I'VE BEEN HURT	I'VE GOT MY NEEDS	6.00
74	2006437	RAZZY	I HATE, HATE	SINGING OTHER PEOPLES SONGS	15.00
74	2006443	JOHNNY BRISTOL	HANG ON IN THERE BABY	TAKE CARE OF YOU FOR ME	5.00
74	2006463	GLORIA GAYNOR	NEVER CAN SAY GOODBYE	WE JUST CAN'T MAKE IT	4.00
75	2006471	JOHNNY BRISTOL	MEMORIES DON'T LEAVE LIKE PEOPLE DO	IT DON'T HURT NO MORE	4.00
75	2006499	GLORIA GAYNOR	REACH OUT, I'LL BE THERE	SEARCHIN'	4.00
75	2006505	JOHNNY BRISTOL	LEAVE MY WORLD	ALL GOODBYES AREN'T GONE	4.00
75	2006531	GLORIA GAYNOR	ALL I NEED IS YOUR SWEET LOVIN'	REAL GOOD PEOPLE	3.00
76	2006586 paper	APRIL STEVENS	WANTING YOU	FALLING IN LOVE AGAIN	15.00
78	2006586 ink	APRIL STEVENS	WANTING YOU	FALLING IN LOVE AGAIN	8.00
77	2006603 paper	VELOURS	I'M GONNA CHANGE	DON'T PITY ME	10.00
78	2006603 ink	VELOURS	I'M GONNA CHANGE	DON'T PITY ME	6.00

MIAMI
76	404	JIMMY JAMES & THE VAGABONDS	HELP YOURSELF	WHY	6.00

MIDNIGHT HOUR distributed by United Artists
75	35352	TIMMY WILLIS	MR. SOUL SATISFACTION	I'M WONDERING	6.00
75	35352 DJ	TIMMY WILLIS	MR. SOUL SATISFACTION	I'M WONDERING	8.00
75	35804	HOMER BANKS	HOOKED BY LOVE	60 MINUTES OF YOUR LOVE	6.00
75	35804 DJ	HOMER BANKS	HOOKED BY LOVE	60 MINUTES OF YOUR LOVE	8.00
75	35824	BRENTON WOOD	GIMME LITTLE SIGN	THE OOGUM BOOGUM SONG	6.00
75	35824 DJ	BRENTON WOOD	GIMME LITTLE SIGN	THE OOGUM BOOGUM SONG	6.00

MILESTONE
79	101	AZYMUTH	JAZZ CARNIVAL	FLY OVER THE HORIZON	6.00

MINIT
The Minit Label was formed in 1959 in New Orleans, Louisiana, by Joe Banashak and Larry McKinley. Joe Banashak was running A-1 Record Distributors in New Orleans when he decided to form the label. Local up and coming talent Allen Toussaint was mostly responsible for the labels early success, as he wrote and played on the local sessions even arranging and producing the music himself. This gave rise to a most distinctive New Orleans early soul sound. Ernest Kador - aka Ernie K. Doe, a young Aaron Neville, Irma Thomas, Benny Spellman and Allen Orange who went on to have a considerable career as a writer for the Sound Stage 7 label. You could see an early pool of talent of this calibre could hardly fail to be successful.

Minit got their first hit with a Toussaint production of Jessie Hill's "Ooh Poo Pah Doo" which reached # 28 in the R&B charts in summer of 1960. On the strength of that summer hit early in 1961 Minit landed a distribution deal with Imperial Records. Imperial records were almost instantly rewarded when Ernie K. Doe's "Mother In Law" was a nationwide # 1. Then Norman Johnson's Showmen had a minor hit with "It Will Stand" both records are considered soul classics to this day. When Allen Toussaint untimely Army call up came in 1963 the hits stopped coming and the New Orleans based Minit records was sold to the highly successful Imperial Records of Los Angeles. Later as Imperial Records was swallowed up by Si Waronker Liberty label, Los Angeles artists like Jimmy Holiday, former Ikette Clydie King, Bobby Womack, Jimmy McCracklin, Ike & Tina Turner all recorded for this highly collectable soul based label.

In the UK Minit New Orleans recordings of the early 60's were issued on London. As it became part of Imperial in 1963 all Minit recording were issued on EMI's Liberty. 1968 Minit gained its own UK status having 17 releases, all of which failed to sell in any significant quantities.

The Minit label was not pressed in any promotional form, although you sometimes find them with a white sticker with "Promotional Copy not for Sale" in red lettering. Please note from release # 11010 with both small hole centers and the large hole dinked out centers were pressed. The small hole 45s are much more desirable.

68	11001	BOBBY WOMACK	SOMEBODY SPECIAL	BROADWAY WALK	20.00
68	11002	JIMMY LEWIS	LET ME KNOW	THE GIRLS FROM TEXAS	30.00
68	11003	JIMMY McCRACKLIN	HOW YOU LIKE YOUR LOVE	GET TOGETHER	10.00
68	11004	HOMER BANKS	ROUND THE CLOCK LOVER MAN	FOOLISH HEARTS BREAK FAST	10.00

68	11005	BOBBY WOMACK	WHAT IS THIS	WHAT YOU GONNA DO	20.00
68	11006	JOHNNY LYTTLE	GONNA GET THAT BOAT	GONNA GET THAT BOAT part 2	25.00
68	11007	HOMER BANKS	A LOT OF LOVE	60 MINUTES OF YOUR LOVE	20.00
68	11008	JIMMY HOLIDAY	GIVE ME YOUR LOVE	THE BEAUTY OF A GIRL IN LOVE	15.00
68	11009	JIMMY McCRACKLIN	PRETTY LITTLE THING	A AND I	10.00
68	11010 sh	BOBBY WOMACK	TAKE ME	FLY ME TO THE MOON	15.00
68	11010 lh	BOBBY WOMACK	TAKE ME	FLY ME TO THE MOON	10.00
68	11011 sh	POPULAR FIVE	I'M A LOVE MAKER	LITTLE BITTY PRETTY ONE	15.00
68	11011 lh	POPULAR FIVE	I'M A LOVE MAKER	LITTLE BITTY PRETTY ONE	15.00
69	11012 sh	BOBBY WOMACK	CALIFORNIA DREAMIN'	BABY YOU OUGHTA THINK IT OVER	20.00
69	11012 lh	BOBBY WOMACK	CALIFORNIA DREAMIN'	BABY YOU OUGHTA THINK IT OVER	20.00
68	11013 sh	DEE IRWIN	I CAN'T STAND THE PAIN	MY HOPE TO DIE GIRL	25.00
68	11013 lh	DEE IRWIN	I CAN'T STAND THE PAIN	MY HOPE TO DIE GIRL	15.00
69	11014 sh	CLYDIE KING	ONE PART, TWO PART	LOVE NOW, PAY LATER	20.00
69	11014 lh	CLYDIE KING	ONE PART, TWO PART	LOVE NOW, PAY LATER	15.00
69	11015 sh	HOMER BANKS	(WHO YOU GONNA RUN TO) ME OR YOUR MAMA	I KNOW YOU KNOW I KNOW I KNOW	15.00
69	11015 lh	HOMER BANKS	(WHO YOU GONNA RUN TO) ME OR YOUR MAMA	I KNOW YOU KNOW I KNOW I KNOW	10.00
69	11016 sh	IKE & TINA TURNER	I'M GONNA DO ALL I CAN	YOU'VE GOT TOO MANY TIES THAT	15.00
69	11016 lh	IKE & TINA TURNER	I'M GONNA DO ALL I CAN	YOU'VE GOT TOO MANY TIES THAT	10.00
69	11017 sh	PERSUASIONS	PARTY IN THE WOODS	IT'S BETTER TO HAVE LOVED & LO	15.00
69	11017 lh	PERSUASIONS	PARTY IN THE WOODS	IT'S BETTER TO HAVE LOVED & LO	10.00

MINT

75	2	FREDDIE WATERS	GROOVIN' ON MY BABY'S LOVE	KUNG FU AND YOU TOO	10.00
75	2 DJ	FREDDIE WATERS	GROOVIN' ON MY BABY'S LOVE	KUNG FU AND YOU TOO	15.00
76	3	MYSTIC MOODS	HONEY TRIPPIN'	MIDNIGHT SHACK	10.00
76	3 DJ	MYSTIC MOODS	HONEY TRIPPIN'	MIDNIGHT SHACK	15.00
76	5	ROGER HATCHER	WE GONNA MAKE IT	HIGH BLOOD PRESSURE	8.00
76	5 DJ	ROGER HATCHER	WE GONNA MAKE IT	HIGH BLOOD PRESSURE	10.00
76	10	KELLEE PATTERSON	I'M GONNA LOVE YOU JUST A LITTLE BIT MORE	YOU ARE SO BEAUTIFUL	40.00
76	10 DJ	KELLEE PATTERSON	I'M GONNA LOVE YOU JUST A LITTLE BIT MORE	YOU ARE SO BEAUTIFUL	50.00
76	15	ZEBERA	WIND UP TOY	MY BIONICS MAN	5.00
76	15 DJ	ZEBERA	WIND UP TOY	MY BIONICS MAN	6.00

MOJO

Polydor distributed label that dedicated itself almost totally to USA soul music. Mojo did not press promotional copies but did put white stickers "Sample record not for sale – Release Date" in red lettering for Radio Station, DJs and reviewers copies.

Many UK collectors have only recently started to appreciate the quality of the soul releases put out in its short 4 year life. Mojo is a difficult label to complete as many of its non Northern Soul orientated releases only sold in very small quantities and are now extremely scarce.

71	2001118	BOBBY BYRD	I NEED HELP (I CAN'T DO IT ALONE)	same: part 2	15.00
71	2027001	FORMATIONS	AT THE TOP OF THE STAIRS	MAGIC MELODY	8.00
71	2027001 sticker DJ	FORMATIONS	AT THE TOP OF THE STAIRS	MAGIC MELODY	15.00
71	2027002	J.B.'S	THE GRUNT	THE GRUNT part 2	20.00
71	2027003	BOBBY BYRD	I KNOW YOU GOT SOUL	IF YOU DON'T WORK YOU CAN'T EA	15.00
71	2027004	FANTASTICS	WHO COULD BE LOVING YOU	BABY MAKE YOUR OWN SWEET MUSIC	5.00
71	2027005	KOOL & THE GANG	FUNKY MAN	KOOL & THE GANG/LET THE MUSIC	8.00
71	2027006	KOOL & THE GANG	THE PENGUIN	LOVE THE LIFE YOU LIVE	15.00
71	2027009	KOOL & THE GANG	MUSIC IS THE MESSAGE	MUSIC IS THE MESSAGE part 2	10.00
71	2027010	JEAN BATTLE	LOVE MAKING	WHEN A WOMAN LOVES A MAN	10.00
71	2027011	JIMMY DAWKINS	THE THINGS I USED TO DO	PUT IT ON THE HAWG	8.00
71	2027012	TIMMY THOMAS	WHY CAN'T WE LIVE TOGETHER	FUNKY ME	6.00
75	2027012 ink	TIMMY THOMAS	WHY CAN'T WE LIVE TOGETHER	FUNKY ME	4.00
71	2027013	BLOSSOMS	TOUCHDOWN	IT'S ALL UP TO YOU	5.00
71	2061155	J.B.'S	THESE ARE THE J.B.'S	THESE ARE THE J.B.'S part 2	10.00
75	209013 ink	JAMO THOMAS & the PARTY BROS	I SPY (FOR THE FBI)	SNAKE HIP MAMA	6.00
71	2092001 lh	TAMI LYNN	I'M GONNA RUN AWAY FROM YOU	THE BOY NEXT DOOR	10.00
71	2092001 sh	TAMI LYNN	I'M GONNA RUN AWAY FROM YOU	THE BOY NEXT DOOR	15.00
71	2092001 alt	THREE DEGREES	MAYBE	THERE'S SO MUCH LOVE AROUND ME	10.00
71	2092002	THREE DEGREES	YOU'RE THE ONE	ROSE GARDEN	6.00
71	2092003	FUZZ	I LOVE YOU FOR ALL SEASONS	I LOVE YOU FOR ALL SEASONS 2	6.00
71	2092004 lh	FASCINATIONS	GIRLS ARE OUT TO GET YOU	YOU'LL BE SORRY	10.00
71	2092004 sh	FASCINATIONS	GIRLS ARE OUT TO GET YOU	YOU'LL BE SORRY	15.00
71	2092005	DORIS DUKE	TO THE OTHER WOMAN	I DON'T CARE ANYMORE	8.00
71	2092006	OSCAR WEATHERS	THE SPOILER	YOU WANT TO PLAY	10.00
71	2092007	DELFONICS	HE DON'T REALLY LOVE YOU	WITHOUT YOU	8.00
71	2092008	FUZZ	LIKE AN OPEN DOOR	LEAVE IT ALL BEHIND ME	5.00
71	2092009	THREE DEGREES	THERE'S SO MUCH LOVE ALL AROUND	MAYBE	6.00
71	2092009 alt	THREE DEGREES	THERE'S SO MUCH LOVE ALL AROUND	YOURS	10.00
71	2092010	CHUCK WOOD	SEVEN DAYS IS TOO LONG	SOUL SHING-A-LING	10.00
71	2092011	DORIS TROY	I'LL DO ANYTHING (HE WANTS ME TO	BUT I LOVE HIM	10.00
71	2092012	TAMI LYNN	THAT'S UNDERSTANDING	NEVER NO MORE	6.00
71	2092012 sticker DJ	TAMI LYNN	THAT'S UNDERSTANDING	NEVER NO MORE	10.00
75	2092013 ink	JAMO THOMAS & the PARTY BROS	I SPY (FOR THE FBI)	SNAKE HIP MAMA	6.00
71	2092013 paper	JAMO THOMAS & the PARTY BROS	I SPY (FOR THE FBI)	SNAKE HIP MAMA	8.00
71	2092014	J.J. JACKSON	BUT IT'S ALRIGHT	DO THE BOOGALOO	8.00
71	2092015	AL KENT	YOU GOT TO PAY THE PRICE	WHERE DO I GO FROM HERE	300.00
71	2092016	JESSE JAMES	DON'T NOBODY WANT TO GET MARR	SAME: PART 2	8.00
71	2092017	DORIS DUKE	IF SHE'S YOUR WIFE WHO AM I?	IT SURE WAS FUN	8.00
71	2092018	FASCINATIONS	I'M SO LUCKY (HE LOVES ME)	SAY IT ISN'T SO	8.00

71	2092019	Z.Z. HILL	FAITHFUL AND TRUE	I THINK I'D DO IT	5.00
71	2092020	FREDDIE NORTH	SHE'S ALL I GOT	AIN'T NOTHING IN THE NEWS	5.00
71	2092021	FABULOUS COUNTS	GET DOWN PEOPLE	LUNAR FUNK	10.00
71	2092023	JEAN WELLS	AFTER LOVING YOU	PUTTING THE BEST ON THE OUTSID	8.00
71	2092024	PEOPLES CHOICE	I LIKES TO DO IT	BIG LADIE'S MAN	8.00
71	2092025 paper	WILLIE TEE	WALKIN' UP A ONE WAY STREET	TEASIN YOU + THANK YOU JOHN	10.00
75	2092025 ink	WILLIE TEE	WALKIN' UP A ONE WAY STREET	THANK YOU JOHN + TEASING YOU	6.00
72	2092028	B.J. ARNAU	I WANT TO GO BACK THERE AGAIN	I LOVE YOU	8.00
72	2092029	ORLONS	SPINNIN' TOP	ANYONE WHO HAD A HEART	8.00
72	2092030	BETTY LAVETTE	I FEEL GOOD (ALL OVER) + WHAT I	LET ME DOWN EASY	10.00
72	2092031	OLIVER SAIN	ST. LOUIS BREAKDOWN	AIN'T GONNA TELL NOBODY (S.BRO	15.00
72	2092032	FONTELLA BASS	WHO YOU GONNA BLAME	HOLD ON THIS TIME	8.00
72	2092033	LITTLE JOHNNY TAYLOR	EVERYBODY KNOWS ABOUT MY GOOD	same: part 2	5.00
72	2092034	POWELL, BOBBY	PEACE BEGINS WITHIN	QUESTION	8.00
72	2092035	TOUSAINT McCALL	NOTHING TAKES THE PLACE OF YOU	SHIMMY	8.00
72	2092036	ELEPHANT BAND	STONE PENGUIN	GROOVIN' AT THE APOLLO	85.00
72	2092037	BOBBY PATTERSON	HOW DO YOU SPELL LOVE	SHE DON'T HAVE TO SEE YOU	6.00
72	2092038	MIDNIGHT MOVERS	WHY CAN'T WE DO IT IN THE ROAD	same: part 2	8.00
72	2092039	unissued?			
72	2092040	DONNIE ELBERT	THIS OLD HEART OF MINE (IS WEAK FOR	GOOD TO ME	8.00
72	2092040 sticker DJ	DONNIE ELBERT	THIS OLD HEART OF MINE (IS WEAK FOR	GOOD TO ME	10.00
72	2092041	MARVA WHITNEY	DADDY DON'T KNOW ABOUT SUGAR	WE NEED MORE (BUT SOMEBODY GOT	25.00
72	2092042	unissued?			
72	2092043	FREDDIE NORTH	SWEETER THAN SWEETNESS	I DID THE WOMAN WRONG	5.00
72	2092044	LITTLE JOHNNY TAYLOR	IT'S MY FAULT DARLING	THERE'S SOMETHING ON YOUR MIND	5.00
72	2092045	FONTELLA BASS	I NEED TO BE LOVED	I WANT EVERYONE TO KNOW	5.00
72	2092046	AFRICAN MUSIC MACHINE	BLACK WATER GOLD (PEARL)	MAKING NASSAU FRUIT DRINK	10.00
72	2092047	JOE PERKINS	WRAPPED UP IN YOUR LOVE	LOOKING FOR A WOMAN	6.00
72	2092048	ART GENTRY	WONDERFUL DREAM	BREAKTHROUGH	20.00
72	2092049	BIRD ROLLINS	LOVE MAN FROM CAROLINA	SHE NEEDS LOVIN' ALL THE TIME	10.00
72	2092050	EL DORADOS	LOOSE BOOTY	LOOSE BOOTY PART2	8.00
72	2092051	unissued?			
72	2092052 paper	O'JAYS	I DIG YOUR ACT	I'LL SWEETER TOMORROW	10.00
75	2092052 ink	O'JAYS	I DIG YOUR ACT	I'LL BE SWEETER TOMORROW	8.00
72	2092053	JAMES CARR	THAT'S WHAT I WANT TO KNOW	FREEDOM TRAIN	10.00
72	2092054	MOSES & JOSHUA DILLARD	GET OUT OF MY HEART	MY ELUSIVE DREAMS	6.00
72	2092055	INVITATIONS	WHAT'S WRONG WITH MY BABY	WHY DID MY BABY TURN BAD	10.00
title mispelt, correctly spelt titles may exist but are at present unconfirmed					
72	2092055	INVITATIONS	WHAT'S WRONG WITH ME BABY	WHY DID MY BABY TURN BAD	UN
72	2092056	JAMES & BOBBY PURIFY	WISH YOU DIDN'T DIDN'T HAVE TO GO	I'M YOUR PUPPET	6.00
72	2092057	unissued?			
72	2092058	FLIRTATIONS	WHY DIDN'T I THINK OF IT	OH MIA BAMBA	5.00
72	2092059 paper	BETTYE SWANN	MAKE ME YOURS	I WILL NOT CRY	10.00
75	2092059 ink	BETTYE SWANN	MAKE ME YOURS	I WILL NOT CRY	6.00
72	2092060	JIMMY RUFFIN	MOTHER'S LOVE	WAITING ON YOU	5.00
72	2092061	unissued?			
72	2092062	DORIS TROY	BABY I LOVE YOU	TO MY FATHER'S HOUSE	5.00
72	2092063	IKETTES	PEACHES 'N' CREAM	SALLY GO ROUND THE ROSES	8.00
72	2093001	SONNY ROSS	IPER MUST BE PAID	ALAKAZAM	25.00
72	2093002	VERNON BROWN	I'M A LOVER	OF YOUR LIFE	6.00
72	2093003	JOE SIMON	YOU'RE THE ONE FOR ME	I AIN'T GIVING UP	5.00
72	2093006 paper	JAMES BROWN	HEY AMERICA	BROTHER RAPP PART1	6.00
75	2093006 ink	JAMES BROWN	HEY AMERICA!	BROTHER RAPP	4.00
72	2093007	J.B.'S	GIMME SOME MORE	THE RABBIT GOT THE GUN	10.00
72	2093008	JOE SIMON	DROWNING IN A SEA OF LOVE	LET ME BE THE ONE	6.00
72	2093009	LEE DORSEY	FREEDOM FOR THE STALLION	IF SHE WON'T (FIND SOMEONE WHO	5.00
72	2093010	HANK BALLAD	ANNIE HAD A BABY	TEARDROPS ON YOUR LETTER	8.00
72	2093011	MILLIE JACKSON	YOU'RE THE JOY OF MY LIFE	A CHILD OF GOD (IT'S HARD TO B	5.00
72	2093013	BOBBY BYRD	KEEP ON DOIN' WHAT YOU'RE DOIN'	LET ME KNOW	10.00
72	2093014	JOE SIMON	POOL OF BAD LUCK	YOU ARE EVERYTHING	5.00
72	2093015	MILLIE JACKSON	ASK ME WHAT YOU WANT	I JUST CAN'T STAND IT	8.00
72	2093016	J.B.'S	HOT PANTS ROAD	PASS THE PEAS	10.00
72	2093017	BOBBY BYRD	IF YOU GOT A LOVE YOU'D BETTER	YOU'VE GOT TO CHANGE YOUR MIND	10.00
72	2093017 sticker DJ	BOBBY BYRD	IF YOU GOT A LOVE YOU BETTER	YOU'VE GOT TO CHANGE YOUR MIND	10.00
72	2093018	BOBBY NEWSOME	JODY, COME BACK AND GET YOUR	POST OFFICE	8.00
72	2093019	WINFIELD PARKER	I'M ON MY WAY	STOP HER ON SIGHT	8.00
72	2093020	BOBBY BYRD	NEVER GET ENOUGH	MY CONCERTO	10.00
72	2093021	J.B.'S	GIVIN' UP FOOD FOR FUNK	GIVIN' UP FOOD FOR FUNK part 2	10.00
72	2093022 paper	MILLIE JACKSON	MY MAN, A SWEET MAN	I GOTTA GET AWAY	8.00
72	2093022 sticker DJ	MILLIE JACKSON	MY MAN, A SWEET MAN	I GOTTA GET AWAY (FROM MY OWN	15.00
75	2093022 ink	MILLIE JACKSON	MY MAN, A SWEET MAN	I GOTTA GET AWAY	6.00
73	2093023	JOE SIMON	POWER OF LOVE	THE MIRROR DON'T LIE	4.00
73	2093024	JOE SIMON	TROUBLE IN MY HOME	I FOUND MY DAD	6.00
73	2093025	WESLEY, FRED & the J.B'S	J.B. SHOUT	BACK STABBERS	10.00
73	2093026	ERNIE SHELBY	BEND OVER BACKWARDS	PUNISH ME	8.00
73	2093028	BOBBY BYRD c/w VICKI ANDERSON	SAYING IT AND DOING IT ARE TWO	DON'T THROW YOUR LOVE IN THE G	15.00
73	2093029	LYN COLLINS	THINK (ABOUT IT)	ME AND MY BABY GOT OUR OWN THI	15.00
73	2093030	JOE SIMON	STEP BY STEP	TALK DON'T BOTHER ME	5.00

MONUMENT

67	1004	JOE SIMON	MY SPECIAL PRAYER	TRAVELIN' MAN	10.00
67	1004 DJ	JOE SIMON	MY SPECIAL PRAYER	TRAVELIN' MAN	12.00
67	1008	ROBERT KNIGHT	EVERLASTING LOVE	SOMEBODY'S BABY	10.00
67	1008 DJ	ROBERT KNIGHT	EVERLASTING LOVE	SOMEBODY'S BABY	20.00
67	1009	SAM BAKER	I'M NUMBER ONE	I BELIEVE IN YOU	15.00
67	1009 DJ	SAM BAKER	I'M NUMBER ONE	I BELIEVE IN YOU	25.00
67	1010	JOE SIMON	THE GIRL'S ALRIGHT WITH ME	NINE POUND STEEL	15.00
67	1010 DJ	JOE SIMON	THE GIRL'S ALRIGHT WITH ME	NINE POUND STEEL	22.00
68	1014	JOE SIMON	NO SAD SONGS	COME ON AND GET IT	10.00
68	1014 DJ	JOE SIMON	NO SAD SONGS	COME ON AND GET IT	15.00
68	1016	ROBERT KNIGHT	BLESSED ARE THE LONELY	IT'S BEEN WORTH IT ALL	8.00
68	1016 DJ	ROBERT KNIGHT	BLESSED ARE THE LONELY	IT'S BEEN WORTH IT ALL	10.00
68	1017	ROBERT KNIGHT	LOVE ON A MOUNTAIN TOP	THE POWER OF LOVE	30.00
68	1017 DJ	ROBERT KNIGHT	LOVE ON A MOUNTAIN TOP	THE POWER OF LOVE	45.00
68	1018	CONTRASTS	WHAT A DAY	LONELY CHILD	15.00
68	1018 DJ	CONTRASTS	WHAT A DAY	LONELY CHILD	20.00
68	1019	JOE SIMON	(YOU KEEP ME) HANGIN' ON	WHAT MAKES A MAN FEEL GOOD	6.00
68	1019 DJ	JOE SIMON	(YOU KEEP ME) HANGIN' ON	WHAT MAKES A MAN FEEL GOOD	8.00
68	1025	JOE SIMON	I WORRY ABOUT YOU	MESSAGE FROM MARIA	8.00
68	1025 DJ	JOE SIMON	I WORRY ABOUT YOU	MESSAGE FROM MARIA	10.00
69	1029	JOE SIMON	LOOKING BACK	STANDING IN THE SAFETY ZONE	6.00
69	1029 DJ	JOE SIMON	LOOKING BACK	STANDING IN THE SAFETY ZONE	8.00
69	1030	ELLA WASHINGTON	HE CALLED ME BABY	YOU'RE GONNA CRY, CRY, CRY	15.00
69	1030 DJ	ELLA WASHINGTON	HE CALLED ME BABY	YOU'RE GONNA CRY, CRY, CRY	20.00
69	1031	TONY JOE WHITE	PORK SALAD ANNIE	ASPEN COLORADO	12.00
69	1031 DJ	TONY JOE WHITE	PORK SALAD ANNIE	ASPEN COLORADO	20.00
69	1032	JOE SIMON	THE CHOKIN' KIND	COME ON AND GET IT	10.00
69	1032 DJ	JOE SIMON	THE CHOKIN' KIND	COME ON AND GET IT	12.00
68	1036	TONY JOE WHITE	BABY SCRATCH MY BACK	WILLIE AND LAURA MAE JONES	15.00
68	1036 DJ	TONY JOE WHITE	BABY SCRATCH MY BACK	WILLIE AND LAURA MAE JONES	20.00
69	1038	JOE SIMON	SAN FRANCISCO IS A LONELY TOWN	IT'S HARD TO GET ALONG	6.00
69	1038 DJ	JOE SIMON	SAN FRANCISCO IS A LONELY TOWN	IT'S HARD TO GET ALONG	8.00
69	1040	TONY JOE WHITE	ROOSEVELT AND IRA LEE	THE MIGRANT	6.00
69	1040 DJ	TONY JOE WHITE	ROOSEVELT AND IRA LEE	THE MIGRANT	8.00
70	1042	JOE SIMON	MOON WALK	MOON WALK part 2	6.00
70	1042 DJ	JOE SIMON	MOON WALK	MOON WALK part 2	8.00
70	1043	TONY JOE WHITE	GROUPY GIRL	HIGH SHERIFF OF CALHOUN PARRIS	5.00
70	1043 DJ	TONY JOE WHITE	GROUPY GIRL	HIGH SHERIFF OF CALHOUN PARRIS	6.00
70	1044	JOE SIMON	FATHER ON DOWN THE ROAD	WOUNDED MAN	6.00
70	1044 DJ	JOE SIMON	FATHER ON DOWN THE ROAD	WOUNDED MAN	8.00
70	1045	LITTLE HANK	MISTER BANG BANG MAN	DON'T YOU KNOW	20.00
70	1045 DJ	LITTLE HANK	MISTER BANG BANG MAN	DON'T YOU KNOW	30.00
70	1048	TONY JOE WHITE	SAVE YOUR SUGAR FOR ME	MY FRIEND	5.00
70	1048 DJ	TONY JOE WHITE	SAVE YOUR SUGAR FOR ME	MY FRIEND	6.00
70	1049	JOE SIMON	I GOT A WHOLE LOT OF LOVIN'	YOURS LOVE	40.00
70	1049 DJ	JOE SIMON	I GOT A WHOLE LOT OF LOVIN'	YOURS LOVE	60.00
70	1051	JOE SIMON	WHEN	THAT'S THE WAY I WANT OUT LOVE	15.00
70	1051 DJ	JOE SIMON	WHEN	THAT'S THE WAY I WANT OUT LOVE	25.00
71	1099	ROBERT KNIGHT	EVERLASTING LOVE + NEVER MY LOVE	MY RAINBOW VALLEY	4.00
71	1099 DJ	ROBERT KNIGHT	EVERLASTING LOVE + NEVER MY LOVE	MY RAINBOW VALLEY	5.00
73	1875	ROBERT KNIGHT	LOVE ON A MOUNTAIN TOP	POWER OF LOVE	5.00
73	1875 DJ	ROBERT KNIGHT	LOVE ON A MOUNTAIN TOP	POWER OF LOVE	8.00
74	2106	ROBERT KNIGHT	EVERLASTING LOVE	SOMEBODY'S BABY	4.00
74	2106 DJ	ROBERT KNIGHT	EVERLASTING LOVE	SOMEBODY'S BABY	6.00
74	2274	ROBERT KNIGHT	BETTER GET READY FOR LOVE	SOMEBODY'S BABY	4.00
74	2274 DJ	ROBERT KNIGHT	BETTER GET READY FOR LOVE	SOMEBODY'S BABY	4.00
74	2344	ROBERT KNIGHT	BRANDED	MY RAINBOW VALLEY	6.00
74	2344 DJ	ROBERT KNIGHT	BRANDED	MY RAINBOW VALLEY	10.00
77	4900	ROBERT KNIGHT	LOVE ON A MOUNTAIN TOP	EVERLASTING LOVE	6.00
77	4900 DJ	ROBERT KNIGHT	LOVE ON A MOUNTAIN TOP	EVERLASTING LOVE	8.00

MOTOR CITY

Manufactured and distributed by PACIFIC, Pacific House, Vale Road, London N41 PQB. Later distributed by the now defuct Charly Records, 156/166, Ilderton Road, London 5E15. We added these specially recorded "soul disco" records, because of the artists involved. It appears that ex-Northern Soul DJ Ian Levine's intention was to record every living artist who had ever recorded for Motown. Whether he was aiming at the disco market or the Northern Soul market or both has never been clear. But the Northern Soul scene has resisted all attempts over the years to be infiltrated by outside forces. Any of the discs listed below, has the potential to have their day within the Rare Soul circuit, if any DJ cared to spin them. But there collectability as collector's items at present is questionable.

Please note: All the below were issued as 12" singles within Picture Sleeves, we have no definite information as to which release were pressed as a 7" release and which 7" releases were in picture sleeves. We are still researching this area, but one look at the artist listing will confirm that serious Motown fans will require these titles in their collection, and a quick glance through the titles will confirm how much Ian Levine's roots in Northern Soul influence his lyrics.

89	1	BILLY GRIFFIN	FIRST IN LINE	same: instrumental	6.00
89	2	MARY WELLS	YOU'RE THE ANSWER TO MY DREAMS	same: instrumental	6.00
89	3	SISTERS LOVE	NO MORE BROKEN HEARTS	same: instrumental	6.00
89	4	SYREETA	THE SHOE FITS	same: instrumental	6.00
89	5	SAMMY WARD	IF AT FIRST YOU DON'T SUCCEED	same: instrumental	6.00
89	6	MOTOR CITY ALL STARS	I CAN'T HELP MYSELF	same: instrumental	6.00
89	7	MARY WILSON	OOH CHILD	same: instrumental	6.00

89	8	FANTASTIC FOUR	WORKING ON A BUILDING OF LOVE	same: instrumental	6.00
89	9	CAROLYN CRAWFORD	TIMELESS	same: instrumental	6.00
89	10	EDWIN STARR	LET'S FALL IN LOVE TONIGHT	same: instrumental	6.00
89	11	MARTHA REEVES & the VANDELLAS	STEP INTO MY SHOES	same: instrumental	6.00
89	12	KIM WESTON	EMOTION	same: instrumental	6.00
89	13	JEAN, SCHRERRIE, LYNDA	CRAZY 'BOUT THE GUY	same: instrumental	6.00
89	14	VALADIERS	TRUTH HURTS	same: instrumental	6.00
89	15	CLAUDETTE ROBINSON	HURRY UP	same: instrumental	6.00
89	16	MARVELETTES	HOLDING ON WITH BOTH HANDS	same: instrumental	6.00
90	17	FREDDIE GORMAN	I JUST KEEP FALLING IN LOVE	same: instrumental	6.00
90	18	LEVI STUBBS	DESTINATION UNKNOWN	same: instrumental	6.00
90	19	G.C. CAMERON	IT'S A SHAME	same: instrumental	8.00
90	20	CONTOURS	FACE UP TO THE FACT	same: instrumental	8.00
90	21	JOHNNY BRISTOL	MAN UP IN THE SKY	same: instrumental	6.00
90	22	MONITORS	STANDING STILL	same: instrumental	6.00
90	23	FRANKIE GAYE	EXTRAORDINARY GIRL	same: instrumental	6.00
90	24	FRANCES NERO	FOOTSTEPS FOLLOWING ME	same: instrumental	5.00
90	25	J.J. BARNES	BUILD A FOUNDATION	same: instrumental	6.00
90	26	CHUCK JACKSON	RELIGHT MY FIRE	same: instrumental	6.00
90	28	LIZ LANDS	STARTING ALL OVER AGAIN	same: instrumental	6.00
90	29	HATTIE LITTLES	YOU'RE THE FIRST, MY LAST, MY EVERYTHING	same: instrumental	6.00
90	30	HERMAN GRIFFIN	NOT A CHANCE IN A MILLION	same: instrumental	6.00
90	33	DAVID RUFFIN	HURT THE ONE YOU LOVE	same: instrumental	10.00
90	35	RONNIE McNEIR	KEEP ON GIVING ME LOVE	same: instrumental	6.00
90	39	BETTYE LAVETTE	TIME WON'T CHANGE THIS LOVE	SURRENDER	6.00
90	41	EDWIN STARR	BREAKIN' DOWN THE WALLS OF HEARTACHE	same: instrumental	6.00
90	44	BEANS BOWLES & SWINGING TYGERS	MOTOR CITY MAGIC	same: diff. Mix	6.00
90	47	JOHNNY BRISTOL	KEEP THIS THOUGHT IN MIND	same: instrumental	6.00
91	69	FRANKIE GAYE	MY BROTHER	CROSS THAT BRIDGE	5.00
4502 test press		JEAN, SCHERRIE & LYNDA	BACK BY POPULAR DEMAND	YOUR LOVE KEEPS LIFTING ME	10.00

MOTOWN see Tamla Motown
MOVE

85	1	PERCY LARKINS	STRANGERS INTO LOVERS	MUSIC OF PASSION	6.00
85	2	DON EVANS	GONNA CARE FOR YOU	JUST CARE	4.00
85	3	OLIVER CHEATHAM	MAMA SAID	THE LOOK OF LOVE	4.00
85	4	HEPTONES	I SHOULD HAVE KNOWN BETTER	ONE STEP AHEAD	4.00
85	6	OLIVER CHEATHAM	TURNING POINT	PLAY ME, TRADE ME	5.00
85	7	JOHNNY DEAN	SITTING AT MY TABLE	SITTING AT MY TABLE part 2	6.00
86	9 PS	JIMMY SCOTT	THE MISSING LINK	THE HUNT	5.00
86	111 test press	BOBBY BOWENS	GONNA LOVE SOMEBODY	blank:	10.00

MOWEST

Subsidiary of the UK Tamla Motown label, started in the UK in 1972, during its 3 year life span it released around both soul and pop music in about equal amounts. The second release on the label in 1972 Mowest #3002 by Frankie Valli & the Four Seasons – "The Night" - sneeked onto the UK market unnoticed, but later achieved Northern Soul monster status. This 45 is the highlight of the label, with most collector not appreciating just how rare the first original press is. As the reissue 22 releases later is the one you always seem to see for sale. With no hits being generated on this label, UK Tamla Motown abandoned the label in 1975. Other 45's worth mentioning are the consecutive release #3009 & #3010 both are excellent examples of early 70s Northern Soul.

72	3001	THELMA HOUSTON	NO ONE'S GONNA BE A FOOL FOREVER	WHAT IF	8.00
72	3001 DJ	THELMA HOUSTON	NO ONE'S GONNA BE A FOOL FOREVER	WHAT IF	10.00
72	3002	FRANKIE VALLI & FOUR SEASONS	THE NIGHT	WHEN THE MORNING COMES	75.00
72	3002 DJ	FRANKIE VALLI & FOUR SEASONS	THE NIGHT	WHEN THE MORNING COMES	100.00
72	3003	FRANKIE VALLI & FOUR SEASONS	TOUCH THE RAINCHILD	WALK ON, DON'T LOOK BACK	15.00
72	3003 DJ	FRANKIE VALLI & FOUR SEASONS	TOUCH THE RAINCHILD	WALK ON, DON'T LOOK BACK	20.00
73	3004	THELMA HOUSTON	BLACK CALIFORNIA	I'M LETTING GO	15.00
73	3004 DJ	THELMA HOUSTON	BLACK CALIFORNIA	I'M LETTING GO	20.00
73	3005	THELMA HOUSTON	PIANO MAN	PART OF YESTERDAY	5.00
73	3005 DJ	THELMA HOUSTON	PIANO MAN	PART OF YESTERDAY	8.00
73	3006	SYREETA	TO KNOW YOU IS TO LOVE YOU	HAPPINESS	6.00
73	3006 DJ	SYREETA	TO KNOW YOU IS TO LOVE YOU	HAPPINESS	8.00
73	3007	HETHERINGTON	TEENAGE LOVE SONG	THAT GIRLS ALRIGHT	5.00
73	3007 DJ	HETHERINGTON	TEENAGE LOVE SONG	THAT GIRLS ALRIGHT	6.00
73	3008	PHIL CORDELL	CLOSE TO YOU	LONDONDERRY	5.00
73	3008 DJ	PHIL CORDELL	CLOSE TO YOU	LONDONDERRY	6.00
73	3009	SISTERS LOVE	I'M LEARNING TO TRUST MY MAN	TRY IT, YOU'LL LIKE IT	20.00
73	3009 DJ	SISTERS LOVE	I'M LEARNING TO TRUST MY MAN	TRY IT, YOU'LL LIKE IT	30.00
73	3010	DEVASTATING AFFAIR	THAT'S HOW IT WAS	IT'S SO SAD	30.00
73	3010 DJ	DEVASTATING AFFAIR	THAT'S HOW IT WAS	IT'S SO SAD	40.00
73	3011	PHIL CORDELL	ROADIE FOR THE BAND	TWISTIN' AND JIVIN'	5.00
73	3011 DJ	PHIL CORDELL	ROADIE FOR THE BAND	TWISTIN' AND JIVIN'	6.00
73	3012	ROCKITS	GIMME TRUE LOVE	I'M LOSING YOU	5.00
73	3012 DJ	ROCKITS	GIMME TRUE LOVE	I'M LOSING YOU	6.00
73	3013	TOM CLAY	WHAT THE WORLD NEEDS NOW IS LO	THE VICTORS	6.00
73	3013 DJ	TOM CLAY	WHAT THE WORLD NEEDS NOW IS LO	THE VICTORS	8.00
73	3014	BOBBY DARIN	BLUE MONDAY	MORIATI (MACK THE KNIFE)	6.00
73	3014 DJ	BOBBY DARIN	BLUE MONDAY	MORIATI (MACK THE KNIFE)	8.00
73	3015	PHIL CORDELL	LAUGHTER IN THE RAIN	IF I DON'T GET ALL THE LUCK	5.00
73	3015 DJ	PHIL CORDELL	LAUGHTER IN THE RAIN	IF I DON'T GET ALL THE LUCK	6.00

73	3016	ROCKITS	GIMME TRUE LOVE		I'M LOSING YOU	4.00
73	3016 DJ	ROCKITS	GIMME TRUE LOVE		I'M LOSING YOU	5.00
unissued						
74	3018	RIVER HEAD BAND	I CAN'T LET MAGGIE GO		THIS TIME AROUND	4.00
74	3018 DJ	RIVER HEAD BAND	I CAN'T LET MAGGIE GO		THIS TIME AROUND	5.00
74	3019	REUBEN HOWELL	RINGS		I BELIEVE (WHEN I FALL IN LOVE	6.00
74	3019 DJ	REUBEN HOWELL	RINGS		I BELIEVE (WHEN I FALL IN LOVE	8.00
74	3020	SEVERIN BROWN	LOVE SONG		SMOW FLAKES	4.00
74	3020 DJ	SEVERIN BROWN	LOVE SONG		SMOW FLAKES	6.00
74	3021	PHIL CORDELL	COOL CLEAR WATER		EVERYWHERE I GO	4.00
74	3021 DJ	PHIL CORDELL	COOL CLEAR WATER		EVERYWHERE I GO	5.00
74	3022	BOONE FAMILY	PLEASE MR. POSTMAN		FRIENDS	4.00
74	3022 DJ	BOONE FAMILY	PLEASE MR. POSTMAN		FRIENDS	5.00
74	3023	SEVERIN BROWN	ROMANCE		SWEET SOUND OF YOUR SONG	4.00
74	3023 DJ	SEVERIN BROWN	ROMANCE		SWEET SOUND OF YOUR SONG	5.00
75	3024	FRANKIE VALLI & FOUR SEASONS	THE NIGHT		WHEN THE MORNING COMES	10.00
75	3024 DJ	FRANKIE VALLI & FOUR SEASONS	THE NIGHT		WHEN THE MORNING COMES	15.00
75	3025	BOONES	WHEN THE LOVELIGHT STARTS THE NIGHTS		GAUDIO	5.00
75	3025 DJ	BOONES	WHEN THE LOVELIGHT STARTS THE NIGHTS		GAUDIO	6.00
75	3026	PHIL CORDELL	CHEVY VAN		STAY WITH ME BABY	4.00
75	3026 DJ	PHIL CORDELL	CHEVY VAN		STAY WITH ME BABY	5.00
75	3027	T.G. SHEPPARD	TRYIN' TO BEAT THE MORNING HOM		I'LL BE SATISFIED	4.00
75	3027 DJ	T.G. SHEPPARD	TRYIN' TO BEAT THE MORNING HOM		I'LL BE SATISFIED	5.00
75	3028	FRANKIE VALLI & FOUR SEASONS	TOUCH THE RAINCHILD		POOR FOOL	8.00
75	3028 DJ	FRANKIE VALLI & FOUR SEASONS	TOUCH THE RAINCHILD		same:	10.00
75	3029	ALLENS	HIGH TIDE		CALIFORNIA MUSIC	4.00
75	3029 DJ	ALLENS	HIGH TIDE		CALIFORNIA MUSIC	5.00
75	3030	FRANKIE VALLI	AND I WILL LOVE YOU		SUN COUNTRY	4.00
75	3030 DJ	FRANKIE VALLI	AND I WILL LOVE YOU		SUN COUNTRY	6.00
75	3031	T.G. SHEPPARD	SOLITARY MAN		PIGSKIN CHARADE	4.00
75	3031 DJ	T.G. SHEPPARD	SOLITARY MAN		PIGSKIN CHARADE	5.00
75	3032	JUD STRUNK	THE BIGGEST PARAKEETS IN TOWN		I WASN'T WRONG ABOUT YOU	4.00
75	3032 DJ	JUD STRUNK	THE BIGGEST PARAKEETS IN TOWN		I WASN'T WRONG ABOUT YOU	5.00
75	3033	T.G. SHEPPARD	MOTELS AND MEMORIES		PIGSKIN CHARADE	4.00
75	3033 DJ	T.G. SHEPPARD	MOTELS AND MEMORIES		PIGSKIN CHARADE	6.00
75	3034	FRANKIE VALLI	LIFE AND BREATH		THANK YOU	4.00
75	3034 DJ	FRANKIE VALLI	LIFE AND BREATH		THANK YOU	6.00
75	3035	T.G. SHEPPARD	SOLITARY MAN		PIGSKIN CHARADE	4.00
75	3035 DJ	T.G. SHEPPARD	SOLITARY MAN		PIGSKIN CHARADE	6.00

MUMS

73	1591	JACKSON SISTERS	(WHY CAN'T WE BE) MORE THAN JUST		ROCKIN' ON MY PORCH	8.00
73	1591 DJ	JACKSON SISTERS	(WHY CAN'T WE BE) MORE THAN JUST		ROCKIN' ON MY PORCH	10.00
73	1829	JACKSON SISTERS	I BELIEVE IN MIRACLES		DAY IN THE BLUE	75.00
73	1829 DJ	JACKSON SISTERS	I BELIEVE IN MIRACLES		DAY IN THE BLUE	100.00
75	2896	JACKSON SISTERS	BOY, YOU'RE DYNAMITE		SHAKE HER LOOSE	15.00
75	2896 DJ	JACKSON SISTERS	BOY, YOU'RE DYNAMITE		SAME:	15.00

MUSIC FACTORY

68	3	KRIS IFE	GIVE AND TAKE		SANDS OF TIME	10.00

MUSIC POWER

84	2	INTRIGUE	LET SLEEPING DOGS LIE		LIKE THE WAY YOU DO IT	10.00

NEMS

75	001	JIMMY & the LITTLE BRISCOE	I ONLY FEEL THIS WAY, WHEN I'M WITH		COUNTRY TO THE CITY (I'M COMIN	4.00
75	001 DJ	JIMMY & the LITTLE BRISCOE	I ONLY FEEL THIS WAY, WHEN I'M WITH		COUNTRY TO THE CITY (I'M COMIN	5.00
77	009	DORIS JONES	HE'S SO IRREPLACEABLE		NEVER GONNA GIVE HIM UP	5.00
77	009 DJ	DORIS JONES	HE'S SO IRREPLACEABLE		NEVER GONNA GIVE HIM UP	8.00
77	015	DORIS JONES	STRANDED IN THE WILDERNESS		THEME FROM THE WILDERNESS	5.00
77	015 DJ	DORIS JONES	STRANDED IN THE WILDERNESS		THEME FROM THE WILDERNESS	8.00
68	3500	CUPIDS INSPIRATION	YESTERDAY HAS GONE		DREAM	6.00
68	3500 DJ	CUPIDS INSPIRATION	YESTERDAY HAS GONE		DREAM	8.00
68	3702	CUPIDS INSPIRATION	MY WORLD		EVERYTHING IS MEANT TO BE	5.00
68	3702 DJ	CUPIDS INSPIRATION	MY WORLD		EVERYTHING IS MEANT TO BE	7.00

NEVIS

78	107	FESTIVAL	SOMETHING IN YOUR SMILE		LET'S MAKE LOVE	10.00
78	107 PS	FESTIVAL	SOMETHING IN YOUR SMILE		LET'S MAKE LOVE	15.00

NEW WAVE

68	001	DONNIE ELBERT	BABY PLEASE COME HOME		WITHOUT YOU	8.00

NIGHTMARE

See Motor City label comments: Both this label and Motor City were owned by Ian Levine, his productions were released through both labels. Note the influence the Northern Soul scene has on the values of these records. Very few Levine productions have ever been accepted by the Northern Soul scene, but Archie Bell "Look Back Over Your Shoulder" has recently been popular through its Achievement label reissue. Consequently the scarce original 1987 press is now highly collectable. With Chuck Jackson "All Over The World" being one of the few Levine productions to receive instant acceptance on release, and now considered somewhat a Northern Soul classic, with it's original Nightmare release on 7" being increasingly difficult to obtain.

86	1	EVELYN THOMAS	TIGHTROPE	same: instrumental	5.00
86	8	BARBARA PENNINGTON	DON'T STOP THE WORLD	same: instrumental	5.00
87	14	GRACE KENNEDY	TAKE OR LEAVE IT	same: instrumental	5.00
87	16	ARCHIE BELL & the DRELLS	LOOK BACK OVER YOUR SHOULDER	same: instrumental	30.00
87	31	EVELYN THOMAS	STANDING AT THE CROSSROADS	same: instrumental	5.00
88	33	MARY WELLS	DON'T BURN BRIDGES	same: instrumental	6.00
88	44	SHARON DEE CLARKE	AWESOME	same: instrumental	5.00
88	49	BARBARA PENNINGTON	BRIGHTER DAYS ARE HERE	same: instrumental	5.00
88	53	BRENDA HOLLOWAY	GIVE ME A LITTLE INSPIRATION	same: instrumental	8.00
89	103	CHUCK JACKSON	ALL OVER THE WORLD	same: instrumental	10.00
89	104	HATTIE LITTLES	RUNNING A FEVER	same: instrumental	8.00
89	105	MARV JOHNSON	RUN LIKE A RABBIT	same: instrumental	8.00
89	117	EARL VAN DYKE	DETROIT CITY	same: instrumental	5.00

NOW

70	1001	MASQUERADERS	LOVE, PEACE & UNDERSTANDING	TEL ME YOU LOVE ME	15.00
70	1002	O'JAYS	THAT'S ALRIGHT	DON'T YOU KNOW A TRUE LOVE	10.00
70	1003	LEN BARRY	NOW I'M ALONE	FUNKY NIGHT	6.00
70	19001	MASQUERADERS	LOVE, PEACE AND UNDERSTANDING	TELL ME YOU LOVE ME	15.00

OAK

64	131	BO STREET RUNNERS	BO STREET RUNNERS	1964 4 track EP	1000.00

OLGA

68	8	LENA JUNOFF	YESTERDAY HAS GONE	GOOD KIND OF HURT	50.00

OMNI

86	3	JEAN CARNE	CLOSER THAN CLOSE	LUCKY CHARM	5.00

OOTP see OUT OF THE PAST

OPIUM

87	1	CLEM CURTIS and the FOUNDATIONS	BABY NOW THAT I'VE FOUND YOU	same: instrumental	5.00
88	24	TONY JACKSON	SECRETLY IN LOVE	THE LOVE I LOST	20.00
88	24 PS	TONY JACKSON	SECRETLY IN LOVE	THE LOVE I LOST	25.00

ORANGE

72	208	JOHN MILES	YESTERDAY (WAS JUST THE BEGINNING)	ROAD TO FREEDOM	8.00
72	208 DJ	JOHN MILES	YESTERDAY (WAS JUST THE BEGINNING)	ROAD TO FREEDOM slt	10.00
73	213	JOHN MILES	ONE MINUTE EVERY HOUR	HOLLYWOOD QUEEN	8.00
73	213 DJ	JOHN MILES	ONE MINUTE EVERY HOUR	HOLLYWOOD QUEEN	25.00
71	508	JOHN MILES	WHY DON'T YOU LOVE ME	IF I COULD SEE THROUGH	8.00
71	508	JOHN MILES	WHY DON'T YOU LOVE ME	IF I COULD SEE THROUGH	12.00

ORBITONE

78	05	TIM CHANDELL	KEEP ME	LET'S MAKE LOVE	100.00

ORIOLE

60	1533	MAUREEN EVANS	THE BIG HURT	CAN'T BEGIN TO TELL YOU	6.00
60	1533 DJ	MAUREEN EVANS	THE BIG HURT	CAN'T BEGIN TO TELL YOU	10.00
61	1611	TITUS TURNER	PONY TRAIN	BLA BLA CHA CHA CHA	15.00
61	1611 DJ	TITUS TURNER	PONY TRAIN	BLA BLA CHA CHA CHA	20.00
62	1739	CHRISTINE QUAITE	GUILTY EYES	OH MY!	10.00
62	1739 DJ	CHRISTINE QUAITE	GUILTY EYES	OH MY!	15.00
62	1741	SUSAN SINGER	BOBBY'S LOVING TOUCH	JOHNNY SUMMERTIME	100.00
62	1741 DJ	SUSAN SINGER	BOBBY'S LOVING TOUCH	JOHNNY SUMMERTIME	150.00
62	1749	JACKIE TRENT	THE ONE WHO REALLY LOVES YOU	YOUR CONSCIENCE OR YOUR HEART	50.00
62	1749 DJ	JACKIE TRENT	THE ONE WHO REALLY LOVES YOU	YOUR CONSCIENCE OR YOUR HEART	70.00
62	1762	MARY WELLS	YOU BEAT ME TO THE PUNCH	OLD LOVE	100.00
62	1762 DJ	MARY WELLS	YOU BEAT ME TO THE PUNCH	OLD LOVE	130.00
62	1763	CONTOURS	DO YOU LOVE ME	MOVE, MR. MAN	40.00
62	1763 DJ	CONTOURS	DO YOU LOVE ME	MOVE, MR. MAN	85.00
62	1764	MARVELETTES	BEECHWOOD 4-5789	SOMEDAY SOMEWAY	130.00
62	1764 DJ	MARVELETTES	BEECHWOOD 4-5789	SOMEDAY SOMEWAY	175.00
62	1770	DONAYS	DEVIL IN HIS HEART	BAD BOY	**196.00**
62	1770 DJ	DONAYS	DEVIL IN HIS HEART	BAD BOY	200.00
62	1772	CHRISTINE QUAITE	YOUR NOSE IS GONNA GROW	OUR LAST CHANCE	15.00
62	1772 DJ	CHRISTINE QUAITE	YOUR NOSE IS GONNA GROW	OUR LAST CHANCE	22.00
62	1775	MIKE & THE MODIFIERS	I FOUND MYSELF A BRAND NEW BABY	IT'S TOO BAD	400.00
62	1775 DJ	MIKE & THE MODIFIERS	I FOUND MYSELF A BRAND NEW BABY	IT'S TOO BAD	500.00
62	1792	HUGO MONTENEGRO	SHERRY	GET OFF THE MOON (I WAS HERE FIRST)	30.00
62	1792 DJ	HUGO MONTENEGRO	SHERRY	GET OFF THE MOON	45.00
63	1795	MIRACLES	YOU REALLY GOT A HOLD ON ME	HAPPY LANDING	100.00
63	1795 DJ	MIRACLES	YOU REALLY GOT A HOLD ON ME	HAPPY LANDING	140.00
63	1796	MARY WELLS	TWO LOVERS	OPERATOR	40.00
63	1796 DJ	MARY WELLS	TWO LOVERS	OPERATOR	100.00
63	1799	CONTOURS	SHAKE SHERRY	YOU BETTER GET IN LINE	70.00
63	1799 DJ	CONTOURS	SHAKE SHERRY	YOU BETTER GET IN LINE	100.00

63	1799 PS	CONTOURS	SHAKE SHERRY	YOU BETTER GET IN LINE	100.00
63	1803	MARVIN GAYE	STUBBORN KIND OF FELLOW	IT HURT ME TO	130.00
63	1803 DJ	MARVIN GAYE	STUBBORN KIND OF FELLOW	IT HURT ME TO	160.00
63	1808	EDDIE HOLLAND	IF IT'S LOVE (IT'S ALL RIGHT)	IT'S NOT TOO LATE	**445.00**
63	1808 DJ	EDDIE HOLLAND	IF IT'S LOVE (IT'S ALL RIGHT)	IT'S NOT TOO LATE	600.00
63	1809	VALADIERS	I FOUND A GIRL	YOU'LL BE SORRY SOMEDAY	**950.00**
63	1809 DJ	VALADIERS	I FOUND A GIRL	YOU'LL BE SORRY SOMEDAY	1000.00+
63	1814	MARTHA & THE VANDELLAS	I'LL HAVE TO LET HIM GO	MY BABY WON'T COME BACK	**561.00**
63	1814 DJ	MARTHA & THE VANDELLAS	I'LL HAVE TO LET HIM GO	MY BABY WON'T COME BACK	600.00
63	1817	MARVELETTES	LOCKING UP MY HEART	FOREVER	300.00
63	1817 DJ	MARVELETTES	LOCKING UP MY HEART	FOREVER	400.00
63	1819	MARTHA & THE VANDELLAS	COME AND GET THESE MEMORIES	JEALOUS LOVER	175.00
63	1819 DJ	MARTHA & THE VANDELLAS	COME AND GET THESE MEMORIES	JEALOUS LOVER	250.00
63	1827	BUDDY BRITTEN & the REGENTS	MONEY	IF YOU GOTTA MAKE A FOOL OF SO	8.00
63	1827 DJ	BUDDY BRITTEN & the REGENTS	MONEY	IF YOU GOTTA MAKE A FOOL OF SO	10.00
63	1829	MARY WELLS	LAUGHING BOY	TWO WRONGS DON'T MAKE A RIGHT	75.00
63	1829 DJ	MARY WELLS	LAUGHING BOY	TWO WRONGS DON'T MAKE A RIGHT	120.00
63	1831	CONTOURS	DON'T LET HER BE YOUR BABY	IT MUST BE LOVE	85.00
63	1831 DJ	CONTOURS	DON'T LET HER BE YOUR BABY	IT MUST BE LOVE	130.00
63	1845	CHRISTINE QUAITE	MISTER HEARTACHE	WHISPER WONDERFUL WORDS	10.00
63	1845 DJ	CHRISTINE QUAITE	MISTER HEARTACHE	WHISPER WONDERFUL WORDS	15.00
63	1846	MARVIN GAYE	PRIDE AND JOY	ONE OF THESE DAYS	125.00
63	1846 DJ	MARVIN GAYE	PRIDE AND JOY	ONE OF THESE DAYS	200.00
63	1847	MARY WELLS	YOUR OLD STAND-BY	WHAT LOVE HAS JOINED TOGETHER	75.00
63	1847 DJ	MARY WELLS	YOUR OLD STAND-BY	WHAT LOVE HAS JOINED TOGETHER	120.00
63	1853	LITTLE STEVIE WONDER	FINGERTIPS	FINGER TIPS part 2	25.00
63	1853 DJ	LITTLE STEVIE WONDER	FINGER TIPS	FINGER TIPS part 2	60.00
63	1861	PLAYERS	MOCKINGBIRD	BIZET AS IT MAY	15.00
63	1861 DJ	PLAYERS	MOCKINGBIRD	BIZET AS IT MAY	20.00
63	1863	MIRACLES	MICKEY'S MONKEY	WHATEVER MAKES YOU HAPPY	85.00
63	1863 DJ	MIRACLES	MICKEY'S MONKEY	WHATEVER MAKES YOU HAPPY	130.00
63	1876	CHRISTINE QUAITE	IN THE MIDDLE OF THE FLOOR	TELL ME MAMA	20.00
63	1876 DJ	CHRISTINE QUAITE	IN THE MIDDLE OF THE FLOOR	TELL ME MAMA	30.00
63	1914	ERROL DIXON & the BLUEBEATERS	GIVE ME MORE TIME	ROCKS IN MY PILLOWS	100.00
63	1914 DJ	ERROL DIXON & the BLUEBEATERS	GIVE ME MORE TIME	ROCKS IN MY PILLOWS	130.00
63	1921	CHRISTINE QUAITE	I BELIEVE IN LOVE	HERE SHE COMES	10.00
63	1921 DJ	CHRISTINE QUAITE	I BELIEVE IN LOVE	HERE SHE COMES	15.00
64	1945	CHRISTINE QUAITE	WILL YOU BE THE SAME TOMORROW	MISTER STUCK UP	10.00
64	1945 DJ	CHRISTINE QUAITE	WILL YOU BE THE SAME TOMORROW	MISTER STUCK UP	15.00
64	1946	SONNY TERRY & BROWNIE McGEE	GOIN' DOWN SLOW	DISSATISFIED WOMAN	15.00
64	1946 DJ	SONNY TERRY & BROWNIE McGEE	GOIN' DOWN SLOW	DISSATISFIED WOMAN	20.00

OSCEOLA

81	2	JIMMY THOMAS	HANG RIGHT ON IN THERE	HANG RIGHT ON IN THERE part 2	10.00
81	2 PS	JIMMY THOMAS	HANG RIGHT ON IN THERE	HANG RIGHT ON IN THERE part 2	15.00
81	4	TONY COOK and the PARTY PEOPLE	REMEMBER YOU TOOK MY HEART	NEVER USE ME	10.00
81	4 PS	TONY COOK and the PARTY PEOPLE	REMEMBER YOU TOOK MY HEART	NEVER USE ME	15.00
83	5	DAVID GANPOT	GIVIN' IT UP FOR LOVE	LOVE'S SECRET	15.00
83	5 PS	DAVID GANPOT	GIVIN' IT UP FOR LOVE	LOVE'S SECRET	20.00

OUTASITE

66	120	JIMMY McCRACKLIN	CHRISTMAS TIME	CHRISTMAS TIME part 2	25.00
66	502	LOWELL FULSOM	STOP AND THINK	BABY	75.00

OUT OF THE PAST

Dubious UK based early 70s reissue label with a somewhat erratic numbering system. I believe the listing below is complete, any additions would be most welcome. Missing numbers were most probably never issued, there are also some duplicate numbers. Numbers 05 to 32 were made from vinyl and had green or sometimes blue labels. From duplicate number 32 Jerry Cook, the labels were white with the Out Of The Past logo being replaced by OOTP: These 45s were pressed in styrene. This series was a crucial part of the developing Northern Soul scene, as with many other later labels dedicated entirely to releasing Northern Soul classics we can not say whether any recording rights were owned or sought. But we felt this was a very influential early 70's label was too important to omit from this book on the grounds that they may or may not have been illegal pressings. We have taken this view, with all Northern Soul dedicated labels no matter how small or large the company is.

73	05	FRANK BEVERLY	IF THAT'S WHAT YOU WANTED	LOVE (YOUR PAIN GOES DEEP)	15..00
73	08	PATTI YOUNG	HEAD AND SHOULDERS	THE VALIANT KIND	20.00
73	09	INVITATIONS	SKIING IN THE SNOW	WHY DID MY BABY TURN BAD	10.00
73	09 duplicate #	MEL WILLIAMS	CAN IT BE ME	JET SET	15.00
73	10	NOLAN CHANCE	JUST LIKE THE WEATHER	DON'T USE ME	15..00
73	11	OLLIE JACKSON	JUST A LITTLE WHILE	THANK YOU NUMBER ONE	10.00
73	15	BILLY JOE ROYAL	HEART'S DESIRE	EVERYBODY'S GOTTA CRY	10.00
73	16	LYNNE RANDELL	STRANGER IN MY ARMS	CIAO BABY	10.00
73	17	HUGO MONTENEGRO	SHERRY	GET OFF THE MOON	10.00
73	18	CARL DOUGLAS	SERVING THE SENTENCE OF LIFE	NOBDY CRIES	20.00
73	23	MARKETTS	STIRRING UP SOME SOUL	TARZAN (TARZAN'S DANCE)	10.00
73	24	LITTLE JOHNNY BLAIR	MOMMAS GONE	EASIER TO SAY THAN DO	8.00
73	25 blue label	VELVET	I GOT TO FIND ME SOMEBODY	WHAT NOW MY LOVE	20.00
73	25 green label	VELVET	I GOT TO FIND ME SOMEBODY	WHAT NOW MY LOVE	15.00
73	26	DEBBIE DEAN	WHY AM I LOVING YOU	same:	15.00
73	27	BEN AIKEN	SATISFIED	THE LIFE OF A CLOWN	15.00
73	28	ROZETTA JOHNSON	CHAINED AND BOUND	HOLDING THE LOSING HAND	15.00
73	30	JERRY WILLIAMS	IF YOU ASK ME	YVONNE	15.00

73	31	SHALIMARS	STOP AND TAKE A LOOK AT YOURSELF	BABY	10.00
73	32	SHARON SOUL	HIS LOVE IS AMAZING	LET ME GET TO KNOW YOU	15.00
73	32 duplicate #	JERRY COOK	I HURT ON THE OTHER SIDE	TAKE WHAT I'VE GOT	15.00
73	33	DRAMATICS	INKY DINKY WANG DANG DO	BABY I NEED YOU	10.00
73	34	TRIUMPHS	MEMORIES	WORKIN'	10.00
73	35	RUFUS LUMLEY	I'M STANDING	LET'S HIDE AWAY (ME & YOU)	10.00
73	36	EXCITERS	NUMBER ONE	YOU GOT LOVE	10.00
73	37	KELLY BROTHES	LOVE TIME	FIRST STEP DOWN	10.00
73	38	LORRAINE CHANDLER	I CAN'T HOLD ON	SHE DON'T WANT YOU	10.00
73	39	DALTON BOYS	I'VE BEEN CHEATED	SOMETHING'S BOTHERING ME	10.00
73	40	BILL BLACK'S COMBO	LITTLE QUEENIE	BOO-RAY	10.00
73	41	CHUBBY CHECKER	YOU JUST DON'T KNOW WHAT YOU DO TO ME)	TWO HEARTS MAKE ONE LOVE	10.00
73	42	DUSTY SPRINGFIELD	WHAT'S IT GONNA BE	SMALL TOWN GIRL	10.00
73	43	RIGHTEOUS BROTHERS	RAT RACE	GREEN ONIONS	8.00
73	44	FUNKY SISTERS	DO IT TO IT	SOUL WOMAN	10.00
73	45	WONDERETTES	I FEEL STRANGE	WAIT UNTIL TONIGHT	10.00
73	46	TONY CLARKE	LANDSLIDE	YOU MADE ME A V.I.P.	10.00
73	48	MAJOR HARRIS	LOVING YOU MORE	JUST LOVE ME	10.00
73	49	PATTI & THE EMBLEMS	I'M GONNA LOVE YOU A LONG LONG TIME	MY HEART'S SO FULL OF YOU	20.00
73	50	SOUNDS OF LANE	TRACKS TO MY MIND	MY MY MAMA	10.00
73	51	SANDY WYNNS	THE TOUCH OF VENUS	A LOVER'S QUARREL	15.00
73	52	SHIRELLES	MARCH (YOU'LL BE SORRY)	EVERYBODY'S GOIN' MAD	10.00
73	53 not issued	MILTON WRIGHT	THE GALLOP	LIKE A ROLLING STONE	UN
73	53	DEAN PARRISH	I'M ON MY WAY	WATCHOUT!	25.00
73	54	THREE DEGREES	ARE YOU SATISFIED	LOVE OF MY LIFE	15.00

OVAL

75	1006	BARBARA LYNN	YOU'LL LOSE A GOOD THING	LETTER TO MOMMY AND DADDY	10.00

OYSTER

76	105 DJ	REFLECTIONS	WHEN EVER I'M AWAY FROM YOU	I CAN ONLY LOVE YOU	10.00

P4DB

00	P4DB1 DJ	ALFREDA BROCKINGTON	SPILT MILK	NICER GIRL	10.00

PAGE ONE

66	001	COL GARNETT	WITH A GIRL LIKE YOU	MONDAY MONDAY	15.00
66	001 DJ	COL GARNETT	WITH A GIRL LIKE YOU	MONDAY MONDAY	22.00
66	012	PATRON OF THE ARTS	THE TRUE PATRON OF THE ARTS	ELEANOR RIGBY	40.00
66	012 DJ	PATRON OF THE ARTS	THE TRUE PATRON OF THE ARTS	ELEANOR RIGBY	60.00
66	014	GRAHAM BOND	YOU'VE GOTTA HAVE LOVE BABE	I LOVE YOU	30.00
66	014 DJ	GRAHAM BOND	YOU'VE GOTTA HAVE LOVE BABE	I LOVE YOU	40.00
67	016	CHANTS	AIN'T NOBODY HOME	FOR YOU	8.00
67	016 DJ	CHANTS	AIN'T NOBODY HOME	FOR YOU	10.00
67	024	PIC & BILL	IT'S NOT YOU	ALL I WANT IS YOU	20.00
67	024 DJ	PIC & BILL	IT'S NOT YOU	ALL I WANT IS YOU	28.00
67	037	PIC & BILL	THIS IS IT	NOBODY BUT MY BABY	15.00
67	037 DJ	PIC & BILL	THIS IS IT	NOBODY BUT MY BABY	20.00
68	052	PIC & BILL	JUST A TEAR	SAD WORLD WITHOUT YOU	15.00
68	052 DJ	PIC & BILL	JUST A TEAR	SAD WORLD WITHOUT YOU	22.00
68	066	JUDI SCOTT	BILLY SUNSHINE	HAPPY SONG	25.00
68	066 DJ	JUDI SCOTT	BILLY SUNSHINE	HAPPY SONG	30.00
68	070	MEMPHIS THREE	SHE'S A YUM YUM	WILD THING	8.00
68	070 DJ	MEMPHIS THREE	SHE'S A YUM YUM	WILD THING	10.00
68	073	SETH MARTIN	LOOK AT ME	ANOTHER DAY GOES BY	20.00
68	073 DJ	SETH MARTIN	LOOK AT ME	ANOTHER DAY GOES BY	25.00
68	087	KEVIN KING LEAR	(YOU GOT) THE POWER OF LOVE	MR. PEARLY	25.00
68	087 DJ	KEVIN KING LEAR	(YOU GOT) THE POWER OF LOVE	MR. PEARLY	30.00
68	099	BILLY BUDD	WHY CAN'T IT RAIN	TIME	15.00
68	099 DJ	BILLY BUDD	WHY CAN'T IT RAIN	TIME	20.00
68	105	GLEN DALE	I'VE GOT SOMETHING TOO	SOMETHING'S GOTTEN HOLD OF MY	15.00
68	105 DJ	GLEN DALE	I'VE GOT SOMETHING TOO	SOMETHING'S GOTTEN HOLD OF MY	20.00
68	109	KEVIN KING LEAR	CRY ME A RIVER	SHOE SHINE SAM	10.00
68	109 DJ	KEVIN KING LEAR	CRY ME A RIVER	SHOE SHINE SAM	15.00
69	132	KEVIN KING LEAR	THE SNAKE	MAN IN THE FUNNIES	20.00
69	132 DJ	KEVIN KING LEAR	THE SNAKE	MAN IN THE FUNNIES	30.00
69	151	MURIEL DAY	NINE TIMES OUT OF TEN	OPTIMISTIC FOOL	85.00
69	151 DJ	MURIEL DAY	NINE TIMES OUT OF TEN	OPTIMISTIC FOOL	120.00
69	151 DJ + press sheet	MURIEL DAY	NINE TIMES OUT OF TEN	OPTIMISTIC FOOL	**154.00**
69	154	BUCHANAN BROTHERS	I'LL NEVER GET ENOUGH	SON OF A LOVIN' MAN	15.00
69	154 DJ	BUCHANAN BROTHERS	I'LL NEVER GET ENOUGH	SON OF A LOVIN' MAN	20.00
70	179	BIRDS OF A FEATHER	ALL GOD'S CHILDREN GOT SOUL	GET IT TOGETHER	4.00
70	179 DJ	BIRDS OF A FEATHER	ALL GOD'S CHILDREN GOT SOUL	GET IT TOGETHER	6.00

PALADIN

77	5021	JOKER	GONNA FIX YOU GOOD	PRAISE YOUR DJ	5.00

PAMA

67	706	RECO RODRIGUEZ	SOUL MAN	IT'S NOT UNUSUAL	10.00

68	716	BEVERLEY SIMMONS	THAT'S HOW STRONG MY LOVE IS	MR. PITIFUL	20.00
68	718	JOYCE BOND	BACK TO SCHOOL	THEY WISH	6.00
68	719 blue & silver	MOHAWKS	THE CHAMP	SOUND OF THE WITCHDOCTORS	40.00
68	719 purple & silver	MOHAWKS	THE CHAMP	SOUND OF THE WITCHDOCTORS	25.00
68	725	CROWNS	I KNOW, IT'S ALRIGHT	I SURRENDER	10.00
68	730	NORMAN T. WASHINGTON	SAME THING ALL OVER	YOU'VE BEEN CHEATING	10.00
68	731	LITTLE BEVERLEY	WHAT A GUY	YOU'RE MINE	8.00
68	732	MARTIN LUTHER KING	I HAVE A DREAM	TOP OF THE MOUNTAIN	15.00
68	733	MILWAUKEE COASTERS	SICK AND TIRED (OH BABE)	TREAT ME RIGHT	10.00
68	735	BOBBY PATTERSON	I MET MY MATCH	BROADWAY AIN'T FUNKY NO MORE	15.00
68	736	CROWNS	JERKING THE DOG	KEEP ME GOING	12.00
68	719	MOHAWKS	BABY HOLD ON	BABY HOLD ON part 2	15.00
68	741	NORMAN T. WASHINGTON	TIP TOE	DON'T HANG AROUND	10.00
68	742	BUTTERCUPS	IF I LOVE YOU	LOVING YOU	20.00
68	743	BOBBY PATTERSON	DON'T BE SO MEAN	THE GOOD OL DAYS	20.00
68	744	BEAS	WHERE DO I GO FROM YOU	DR. GOLDFOOT & HIS BIKINI MACH	20.00
68	745	CROWNS	SHE AIN'T GONNA DO RIGHT	I NEED YOUR LOVING	10.00
68	748	BETTY LAVETTE	ONLY YOUR LOVE CAN SAVE ME	I FEEL GOOD (ALL OVER)	30.00
68	748 test press	BETTY LAVETTE	ONLY YOUR LOVE CAN SAVE ME	I FEEL GOOD (ALL OVER)	45.00
69	750	ROY DOCKER	WHEN	GO	8.00
68	751	MOHAWKS	SWEET SOUL MUSIC	HIP HUGGER	20.00
68	754	BOBBY PATTERSON	BUSY BUST BEE	SWEET TASTE OF LOVE	15.00
68	755 uncomfirmed	VOLUMES	I JUST CAN'T HELP MYSELF	ONE WAY LOVER	1000.00+

A legend of a 45, since a photostat of the 4t appeared in a soul fanzine. It's existence is still unconfirmed, white label test press's may exist. The full label release most probably doesn't.

68	756	ROY DOCKER	EVERY DAY WILL BE LIKE A HOLIDAY	I'M AN OUTCAST	5.00
68	757	MOHAWKS	PEPSI	MONY MONY	50.00
69	758	MOHAWKS	RIDE YOUR PONY	WESTERN PROMISE	20.00
69	759	CROWNS	CALL ME	SINCE YOU BEEN GONE	10.00
69	760	BUTTERCUPS	IF I LOVE YOU	COME PUT MY LIFE IN ORDER	15.00
69	761	BILLY BASS	I'M COMING TO	I NEED YOUR LOVE SO BAD	25.00
69	762	WARREN LEE	UNDERDOG BACKSTREET	COME PUT MY LIFE IN ORDER	10.00
69	763	BOBBY PATTERSON	WHAT A WONDERFUL NIGHT FOR LOVE	T.C.B OR T.Y.A.	22.00
69	765	BILL MOSS	SOCK IT TO 'EM SOUL BROTHER	same: instrumental	15.00
69	766	SOUL PARTNERS	WALK ON JUDGE	LOSE THE ONE YOU LOVE	20.00
69	767	SHOWMEN	ACTION	WHAT WOULD IT TAKE	15.00
69	768	ANNA WALKER & the CROWNETTES	YOU DON'T KNOW	BILLY JOE	10.00
69	771	JOYCE BOND & LITTLE JOHN	MR. PITIFUL	LET'S GET MARRIED	8.00
69	772	PERSIANS	THE SUN GOTTA SHINE IN YOUR HEART	I ONLY HAVE EYES FOR YOU	10.00
69	773	BOBBY PATTERSON	MY THING IS YOUR THING (COME GET	KEEP IT IN THE FAMILY	15.00
69	774	ROOSEVELT GRIER	WHO'S GOT THE BALL Y'ALL	10.00	
69	775	CLYDE McPHATTER	A SHOT OF RHYTHM AND BLUES	I'M NOT GOING TO WORK TODAY	10.00
69	784 blue & silver	ROOSEVELT GRIER	C'MON CUPID	HIGH SOCIETY WOMAN	20.00
69	784 purple & silver	ROOSEVELT GRIER	C'MON CUPID	HIGH SOCIETY WOMAN	15.00
69	785	OTHER BROTHERS	LET'S GET TOGETHER	LITTLE GIRL	20.00
69	786	EMPERORS	KARATE	I'VE GOT TO HAVE HER	12.00
69	793	CLIFFORD CURRY	YOU TURN OUT THE LIGHT	GOOD HUMOUR MAN	10.00
69	794	SPENCER WIGGINS	I'M A POOR MAN'S SON	THAT'S HOW STRONG MY LOVE IS	20.00
70	795	BARBARA PERRY	UNLOVED	SAY YOU NEED ME	15.00
70	796	BILL MOSS	NUMBER ONE	LANDSCAPE (Mohawks)	6.00
70	797	CLIFFORD CURRY	I CAN'T GET A HOLD OF MYSELF	AIN'T NO DANGER	25.00
70	798	CHAMPS c/w RICO	SKINHEAD SHUFFLE	RED COW	15.00
70	810	OWEN GRAY	SUGAR DUMPLIN	I DON'T KNOW WHY	15.00
70	814	BLOSSOMS	STAND BY	SOUL AND INSPERATION	15.00

PAMA SUPREME

73	380	BEVERLEY SIMMONDS	YOU'RE MINE	WHAT A GUY	8.00

PARACHUTE

79	508	RANDY BROWN	USE IT	I THOUGHT OF YOU TODAY	5.00
79	508 DJ	RANDY BROWN	USE IT	I THOUGHT OF YOU TODAY	6.00

PARAMOUNT

72	3019	JAMES PHELPS	MY LOVER'S PRAYER	CHECK YOURSELF	10.00
72	3019 DJ	JAMES PHELPS	MY LOVER'S PRAYER	CHECK YOURSELF	15.00
72	3022	DETROIT with MITCH RYDER	IT AIN'T EASY	LONG NECK GOOSE	4.00
72	3022 DJ	DETROIT with MITCH RYDER	IT AIN'T EASY	LONG NECK GOOSE	5.00
72	3024	MARK RADICE	HEY MY LOVE	LOVE IS LIKE FIRE	6.00
72	3024 DJ	MARK RADICE	HEY MY LOVE	LOVE IS LIKE FIRE	8.00
72	3025	MARK RADICE	NEW DAY	TAKE ME TO THE PARK	6.00
72	3025 DJ	MARK RADICE	NEW DAY	TAKE ME TO THE PARK	8.00
73	3031	LEN BARRY	HEAVEN AND EARTH	I'M MARCHING TO THE MUSIC	4.00
73	3031 DJ	LEN BARRY	HEAVEN AND EARTH	I'M MARCHING TO THE MUSIC	5.00
73	3034	SURFARIS	SHAKE	WIPE OUT	4.00
73	3034 DJ	SURFARIS	SHAKE	WIPE OUT	5.00
73	3035	SAMUEL E. WRIGHT	THERE'S SOMETHING FUNNY GOING ON	300 POUNDS OF HUNGER	20.00
73	3035 DJ	SAMUEL E. WRIGHT	THERE'S SOMETHING FUNNY GOING ON	300 POUNDS OF HUNGER	28.00
73	3039	LEN BARRY	IT'S TIME TO FALL IN LOVE	TOUCHING HOLDING FEELING	4.00
73	3039 DJ	LEN BARRY	IT'S TIME TO FALL IN LOVE	TOUCHING HOLDING FEELING	5.00
74	3050	STEPHANIE MILLS	I KNEW IT WAS LOVE	THE PASSION AND THE PAIN	6.00

74	3050 DJ	STEPHANIE MILLS	I KNEW IT WAS LOVE	THE PASSION AND THE PAIN	8.00
74	3051	LINDA CLIFFORD	AFTER LOVING YOU	CHECK OUT YOUR HEART	6.00
74	3051 DJ	LINDA CLIFFORD	AFTER LOVING YOU	CHECK OUT YOUR HEART	8.00

PARLOPHONE

The Parlophone label first started in business before the first World War. Founded in Germany by Carl Lindstrom. The company's £ logo was long thought to be the sign for the British Pound but it is in fact a German capitol L for the founders surname. During the 1920's Parlophone masters were issued in the USA through Okeh Records. The British interest in Parlophone came in 1927 when Columbia & Graphophone acquired a controlling interest in Carl Lindstrom's company. In 1931, Columbia merged with Graphophone to form EMI. Under EMI, Parlophone released mainly spoken-word, novelty, and comedy label material, such as the comedy recordings of Spike Milligan, The Goon Shows etc. In 1962 that all changed when Parlopone's artist & repertoire manager George Martin signed The Beatles, this turned a once insignificant record label into one of the most important and certainly world renowned and sought-after record labels. The Hollies soon followed the Beatles onto Parlophone, they actually covered three soul standards which made the records more famous: I wonder how many music fans actually went the extra mile to seek out the original versions of "Stay" "Just One Look" "Searchin". I've not added the Hollies versions into this listing as they are as far removed from the "soul" versions as they could possibly get. Where as, The Fourmost's version of The Four Tops "Baby I Need Your Loving" is considered totally acceptable to file into your UK "Soul" collection. These artists soul releases turned Parlophone into one of the UK top best selling labels. The label name still carries weight today as they continue to release music under its banner.

For black music Parlophone had the rights to release Cincinnati's King / Federal label in the 50's and early 60's hence some very interesting transitional soul and R&B was introduced through this label to the more adventurous UK music collector. Today, some of the early Parlophone releases by black artists are considered extremely desirable.

After King moved UK distribution to Decca, Parlophone concentrated on home grown talent many of which turned out some wonderful Brit-Soul. Interesting to note after James Brown's – "Shout and Shimmy" – in 1962 every other 45 release was by a UK artist or a artist residing in the UK at the time.

56	4209	LITTLE WILLIE JOHN	FEVER	LETTER FROM MY DARLING	100.00
56	4231 gold	BILL DOGGETT	HONKY TONK	HONKY TONK part 2	15.00
58	4231 silver	BILL DOGGETT	HONKY TONK	HONKY TONK part 2	10.00
57	4265	BILL DOGGETT	SLOW WALK	PEACOCK ALLEY	15.00
57	4306	BILL DOGGETT	RAM-BUNK-SHUSH	BLUE LARGO	10.00
57	4379	BILL DOGGETT	HOT GINGER	SOFT	10.00
58	4396	LITTLE WILLIE JOHN	UH, UH, BABY	DINNER DATE	40.00
58	4397	TINY TOPSY and the CHARMS	COME ON, COME ON, COME ON	A RING AROUND MY FINGER	50.00
58	4403	DONNIE ELBERT	LET'S DO THE STROLL	WILD CHILD	100.00
58	4407	SILHOUETTES	GET A JOB	I AM LONELY	40.00
58	4413	BILL DOGGETT	LEAPS AND BOUNDS	LEAPS AND BOUNDS part 2	10.00
58	4427	TINY TOPSY and the CHARMS	YOU SHOCKED ME	WATERPROOF EYES	50.00
58	4432	LITTLE WILLIE JOHN	TALK TO ME, TALK TO ME	SPASMS	40.00
58	4472	LITTLE WILLIE JOHN	LET'S ROCK WHILE THE ROCKIN' GOOD	YOU'RE A SWEETHEART	40.00
58	4558	HANK BALLARD	TWIST	KANSAS CITY	30.00
59	4571	LITTLE WILLIE JOHN	LEAVE MY KITTEN ALONE	LET NOBODY LOVE YOU	40.00
59	4583	NINA SIMONE	I LOVES YOU PORGY	LOVE ME OR LEAVE ME	8.00
59	4629	BILL DOGGETT	SMOKIE	EVENING DREAMS	8.00
60	4667	JAMES BROWN	THINK	YOU'VE GOT THE POWER	30.00
60	4674	LITTLE WILLIE JOHN	HEARTBREAK (IT'S HURTIN' ME)	DO YOU LOVE ME	40.00
60	4682	HANK BALLARD	FINGER POPPIN' TIME	I LOVE YOU, I LOVE YOU SO-O-O	15.00
60	4684	BOBBY FREEMAN	(I DO THE) SHIMMY SHIMMY	YOU DON'T UNDERSTAND ME	10.00
60	4688	HANK BALLARD	TWIST	TEARDROPS ON YOUR LETTER	22.00
60	4699	LITTLE WILLIE JOHN	SLEEP	THERE'S A DIFFERENCE	25.00
60	4707	HANK BALLARD	LET'S GO LET'S GO LET'S GO	IF YOU'D FORGIVE ME	25.00
61	4728	HANK BALLARD c/w LITTLE WILLIE JOHN	HOOCHIE COOCHIE COO	WALK SLOW	30.00
61	4746	TITUS TURNER	SOUND-OFF	ME AND MY TELEPHONE	15.00
61	4762	HANK BALLARD	LET'S GO AGAIN	DEEP BLUE SEA	15.00
61	4771	HANK BALLARD	CONTINENTAL WALK	WHAT IS THIS I SEE	15.00
61	4777	FREDDIE KING	HIDEAWAY	I LOVE THE WOMAN	30.00
61	4794	BOBBY LEWIS	TOSSING AND TURNING	OH YES I LOVE YOU	20.00
61	4831	BOBBY LEWIS	ONE TRACK MIND	ARE YOU READY	15.00
61	4822	JIVE FIVE	MY TRUE STORY	WHEN I WAS SINGLE	100.00
61	4848	CHARLES BROWN	CHRISTMAS QUESTION	CHRISTMAS ALL YEAR ROUND	25.00
61	4867	CRYSTALS	THERE'S NO OTHER	OH YEAH, MAYBE BABY	60.00
61	4867 DJ	CRYSTALS	THERE'S NO OTHER	OH YEAH, MAYBE BABY	100.00
62	4922	JAMES BROWN	NIGHT TRAIN	WHY DOES EVERYTHING HAPPEN TO	85.00
62	4922 DJ	JAMES BROWN	NIGHT TRAIN	WHY DOES EVERYTHING HAPPEN TO	**228.00**
62	4952	JAMES BROWN	SHOUT AND SHIMMY	COME OVER HERE	30.00
62	4952 DJ	JAMES BROWN	SHOUT AND SHIMMY	COME OVER HERE	45.00
63	5093	PARAMOUNTS	POISON IVY	I FEEL GOOD ALL OVER	10.00
63	5093 DJ	PARAMOUNTS	POISON IVY	I FEEL GOOD ALL OVER	15.00
64	5111	DUFFY POWER	PARCHMAN FARM	TIRED, BROKE AND BUSTED	22.00
64	5111 DJ	DUFFY POWER	PARCHMAN FARM	TIRED, BROKE AND BUSTED	30.00
64	5119	CLIFF BENNETT & the REBEL ROUSERS	GOT MY MOJO WORKING	BEATIFUL DREAMER	10.00
64	5119 DJ	CLIFF BENNETT & the REBEL ROUSERS	GOT MY MOJO WORKING	BEATIFUL DREAMER	15.00
64	5154	MARGO & the MARVETTES	SAY YOU WILL	CHERRY PIE	15.00
64	5154 DJ	MARGO & the MARVETTES	SAY YOU WILL	CHERRY PIE	20.00
64	5155	PARAMOUNTS	I'M THE ONE WHO LOVES YOU	IT WON'T BE LONG	25.00
64	5155 DJ	PARAMOUNTS	I'M THE ONE WHO LOVES YOU	IT WON'T BE LONG	35.00
64	5173	CLIFF BENNETT & the REBEL ROUSERS	ONE WAY LOVE	SLOW DOWN	6.00
64	5173 DJ	CLIFF BENNETT & the REBEL ROUSERS	ONE WAY LOVE	SLOW DOWN	10.00
64	5189	BEVERLY JONES	HEATWAVE	HEAR YOU TALKING	20.00
64	5189 DJ	BEVERLY JONES	HEATWAVE	HEAR YOU TALKING	28.00
64	5194	FOURMOST	BABY I NEED YOUR LOVING	THAT'S ONLY WHAT THEY SAY	5.00
64	5194 DJ	FOURMOST	BABY I NEED YOUR LOVING	THAT'S ONLY WHAT THEY SAY	10.00
64	5206	ALEXIS KORNER'S BLUES INC.	I NEED YOUR LOVING	PLEASE PLEASE PLEASE	20.00
64	5206 DJ	ALEXIS KORNER'S BLUES INC.	I NEED YOUR LOVING	PLEASE PLEASE PLEASE	28.00

64	5218	ROULETTES	STUBBORN KIND OF FELLOW	MEBODY	8.00
64	5218 DJ	ROULETTES	STUBBORN KIND OF FELLOW	MEBODY	10.00
64	5227	MARGO & the MARVETTES	SO FINE	COPPER KETTLE	15.00
64	5227 DJ	MARGO & the MARVETTES	SO FINE	COPPER KETTLE	20.00
65	5229	CLIFF BENNETT & the REBEL ROUSERS	I'LL TAKE YOU HOME	DO YOU LOVE HIM	5.00
65	5229 DJ	CLIFF BENNETT & the REBEL ROUSERS	I'LL TAKE YOU HOME	DO YOU LOVE HIM	8.00
65	5247	ALEXIS KORNER'S BLUES INC	LITTLE BABY	ROBERTA	20.00
65	5247 DJ	ALEXIS KORNER'S BLUES INC	LITTLE BABY	ROBERTA	28.00
65	5259	CLIFF BENNETT & the REBEL ROUSERS	THREE ROOMS WITH RUNNING WATER	IF ONLY YOU'D REPLY	10.00
65	5259 DJ	CLIFF BENNETT & the REBEL ROUSERS	THREE ROOMS WITH RUNNING WATER	IF ONLY YOU'D REPLY	15.00
65	5261	EARL ROYCE & the OLYMPICS	GUESS THINGS HAPPEN THAT WAY	SURE TO FALL	20.00
65	5261 DJ	EARL ROYCE & the OLYMPICS	GUESS THINGS HAPPEN THAT WAY	SURE TO FALL	28.00
65	5264	BLUES COUNCIL	BABY DON'T LOOK DOWN	WHAT WILL I DO	75.00
65	5264 DJ	BLUES COUNCIL	BABY DON'T LOOK DOWN	WHAT WILL I DO	100.00
65	5271	CHANTELLES	I WANT THAT BOY	LONDON MY HOME TOWN	15.00
65	5271 DJ	CHANTELLES	I WANT THAT BOY	LONDON MY HOME TOWN	22.00
65	5272	PARAMOUNTS	BLUE RIBBONS	CUTTIN' IN	20.00
65	5272 DJ	PARAMOUNTS	BLUE RIBBONS	CUTTIN' IN	28.00
65	5274	REY ANTON & the PEPPERMINT MEN	GIRL, YOU DON'T KNOW ME	DON'T TREAT ME BAD	75.00
65	5274 DJ	REY ANTON & the PEPPERMINT MEN	GIRL, YOU DON'T KNOW ME	DON'T TREAT ME BAD	85.00
65	5276	IN CROWD	THAT'S HOW STRONG MY LOVE IS	THINGS SHE SAYS	100.00
65	5276 DJ	IN CROWD	THAT'S HOW STRONG MY LOVE IS	THINGS SHE SAYS	120.00
65	5283	LEWIS RICH	EVERYBODY BUT ME	THIS TIME IT'S REAL	40.00
65	5283 DJ	LEWIS RICH	EVERYBODY BUT ME	THIS TIME IT'S REAL	50.00
65	5290	JAMES ROYAL & the HAWKS	SHE'S ABOUT A MOVER	BLACK CLOUD	15.00
65	5290 DJ	JAMES ROYAL & the HAWKS	SHE'S ABOUT A MOVER	BLACK CLOUD	20.00
65	5296	JULIE DRISCOLL	DON'T DO IT NO MORE	I KNOW YOU	20.00
65	5296 DJ	JULIE DRISCOLL	DON'T DO IT NO MORE	I KNOW YOU	28.00
65	5300	MARIONETTES	UNDER THE BOARDWALK	WAS IT ME	10.00
65	5300 DJ	MARIONETTES	UNDER THE BOARDWALK	WAS IT ME	15.00
65	5303	CHANTELLES	STICKS AND STONES	THE SECRET OF MY SUCCESS	15.00
65	5303 DJ	CHANTELLES	STICKS AND STONES	THE SECRET OF MY SUCCESS	22.00
65	5310	REY ANTON & the PEPPERMINT MEN	NOTHING COMES EASY	BREAKOUT	15.00
65	5310 DJ	REY ANTON & the PEPPERMINT MEN	NOTHING COMES EASY	BREAKOUT	20.00
65	5321	SOUL BROTHERS	I CAN'T BELIEVE IT	YOU DON'T WANT TO KNOW	10.00
65	5321 DJ	SOUL BROTHERS	I CAN'T BELIEVE IT	YOU DON'T WANT TO KNOW	15.00
65	5334	SOULMATES	TOO LATE TO SAY YOU'RE SORRY	YOUR LOVE	150.00
65	5334 DJ	SOULMATES	TOO LATE TO SAY YOU'RE SORRY	YOUR LOVE	200.00
65	5350	CHANTELLES	GONNA GIVE HIM SOME LOVE	GONNA GET BURNED	20.00
65	5350 DJ	CHANTELLES	GONNA GIVE HIM SOME LOVE	GONNA GET BURNED	28.00
65	5354	ACTION	LAND OF ONE THOUSAND DANCES	IN MY LONELY ROOM	50.00
65	5354 DJ	ACTION	LAND OF ONE THOUSAND DANCES	IN MY LONELY ROOM	70.00
65	5355	NIGHT-TIMERS feat: HERBIE GOINS	THE MUSIC PLAYED ON	YIELD NOT TO TEMPTATION	50.00
65	5355 DJ	NIGHT-TIMERS feat: HERBIE GOINS	THE MUSIC PLAYED ON	YIELD NOT TO TEMPTATION	70.00
65	5356	MARIONETTES	RAINING IT POURING	PICK UP YOUR FEET	15.00
65	5356 DJ	MARIONETTES	RAINING IT POURING	PICK UP YOUR FEET	20.00
65	5369	CAROL FRIDAY	EVERYBODY I KNOW	WASTED DAYS	80.00
65	5369 DJ	CAROL FRIDAY	EVERYBODY I KNOW	WASTED DAYS	100.00
65	5374	MARIONETTES	AT THE END OF THE END	PICK UP YOUR FEET	8.00
65	5374 DJ	MARIONETTES	AT THE END OF THE END	PICK UP YOUR FEET	12.00
65	5383	JAMES ROYAL	THE WORK SONG	I CAN'T STAND IT	20.00
65	5383 DJ	JAMES ROYAL	THE WORK SONG	I CAN'T STAND IT	28.00
65	5396	FRIDAY BROWNE	AND (TO ME HE MEANT EVERYTHING)	GETTING NOWHERE	30.00
65	5396 DJ	FRIDAY BROWNE	AND (TO ME HE MEANT EVERYTHING)	GETTING NOWHERE	40.00
65	5403	BOBBY SHAFTO	THE SAME OLD ROOM	LONELY IS AS LONELY DOES	20.00
65	5403 DJ	BOBBY SHAFTO	THE SAME OLD ROOM	LONELY IS AS LONELY DOES	28.00
66	5407	SOULMATES	BRING YOUR LOVE BACK HOME	WHEN LOVE IS GONE	10.00
66	5407 DJ	SOULMATES	BRING YOUR LOVE BACK HOME	WHEN LOVE IS GONE	15.00
66	5410	ACTION	I'LL KEEP ON HOLDING ON	HEY-SAH-LO-NEY	50.00
66	5410 DJ	ACTION	I'LL KEEP ON HOLDING ON	HEY-SAH-LO-NEY	75.00
66	5416	MARIONETTES	LIKE A MAN	TONIGHT IT'S GOING TO STORM	20.00
66	5416 DJ	MARIONETTES	LIKE A MAN	TONIGHT IT'S GOING TO STORM	28.00
66	5423	MARK LOYD	WHEN I'M GONNA FIND HER	WHEN EVENING FALLS	300.00
66	5423 DJ	MARK LOYD	WHEN I'M GONNA FIND HER	WHEN EVENING FALLS	**409.00**
66	5432	STEVE ALDO	YOU'RE ABSOLUTELY RIGHT	EVERYBODY HAS TO CRY	40.00
66	5432 DJ	STEVE ALDO	YOU'RE ABSOLUTELY RIGHT	EVERYBODY HAS TO CRY	60.00
66	5434	LEWIS RICH	I DON'T WANT TO HEAR IT ANYMORE	SHEDDING TEARS	40.00
66	5434 DJ	LEWIS RICH	I DON'T WANT TO HEAR IT ANYMORE	SHEDDING TEARS	60.00
66	5444	JULIE DRISCOLL	I DIDN'T WANT TO HAVE TO DO IT	DON'T DO IT NO MORE	10.00
66	5444 DJ	JULIE DRISCOLL	I DIDN'T WANT TO HAVE TO DO IT	DON'T DO IT NO MORE	15.00
66	5446	BARRY BENSON	STAY A LITTLE WHILE	THAT'S FOR SURE	25.00
66	5446 DJ	BARRY BENSON	STAY A LITTLE WHILE	THAT'S FOR SURE	45.00
66	5448	PHILIP GOODHAND-TAIT	I'M GONNA PUT SOME HURT ON YOU	IT'S A LIE	15.00
66	5448 DJ	PHILIP GOODHAND-TAIT	I'M GONNA PUT SOME HURT ON YOU	IT'S A LIE	20.00
66	5455	JOHN ANDREWS & the LONELY ONES	IT'S JUST LOVE	A ROSE GROWING IN THE RUINS	75.00
66	5455 DJ	JOHN ANDREWS & the LONELY ONES	IT'S JUST LOVE	A ROSE GROWING IN THE RUINS	100.00
66	5466	CLIFF BENNETT & the REBEL ROUSERS	HOLD ON I'M COMING	EASY FOR YOU	10.00
66	5466 DJ	CLIFF BENNETT & the REBEL ROUSERS	HOLD ON I'M COMING	EASY FOR YOU	15.00
66	5468	DEREK LEE	GIRL	YOU'VE DONE SOMETHING TO MY HEART	25.00

66	5468 DJ	DEREK LEE	GIRL	YOU'VE DONE SOMETHING TO MY HEART	40.00
66	5474	ACTION	BABY YOU'VE GOT IT	SINCE I LOST MY BABY	60.00
66	5474 DJ	ACTION	BABY YOU'VE GOT IT	SINCE I LOST MY BABY	75.00
66	5478	HERBIE GOINS and the NIGHT-TIMERS	NO. 1 IN YOUR HEART	CRUSIN'	150.00
66	5478 DJ	HERBIE GOINS and the NIGHT-TIMERS	NO. 1 IN YOUR HEART	CRUSIN'	200.00
66	5506	SOULMATES	SAYIN' SOMETHING	MOOD MELANCHOLY	50.00
66	5506 DJ	SOULMATES	SAYIN' SOMETHING	MOOD MELANCHOLY	75.00
66	5518	FRANKIE & JOHNNY	I WANNA MAKE YO UNDERSTAND	CLIMB EVERY MOUNTAIN	20.00
66	5518 DJ	FRANKIE & JOHNNY	I WANNA MAKE YO UNDERSTAND	CLIMB EVERY MOUNTAIN	28.00
66	5526	MIA LEWIS	NOTHING LASTS FOREVER	(BABY) I'M FEELING GOOD	25.00
66	5526 DJ	MIA LEWIS	NOTHING LASTS FOREVER	(BABY) I'M FEELING GOOD	35.00
66	5527	OLIVER BONE and SOUNDS MAXIMUM	KNOCK ON WOOD	JUGGER TEA	10.00
66	5527 DJ	OLIVER BONE and SOUNDS MAXIMUM	KNOCK ON WOOD	JUGGER TEA	15.00
66	5529	JOHNNY CURTIS	OUR LOVE IS DISINTERGRATING	(I'D BE) A LEGEND IN MY OWN TI	40.00
66	5529 DJ	JOHNNY CURTIS	OUR LOVE IS DISINTERGRATING	(I'D BE) A LEGEND IN MY OWN TI	50.00
66	5533	HERBIE GOINS and the NIGHT-TIMERS	COMIN' HOME TO YOU	THE INCREDIBLE MISS BROWN	50.00
66	5533 DJ	HERBIE GOINS and the NIGHT-TIMERS	COMIN' HOME TO YOU	THE INCREDIBLE MISS BROWN	75.00
66	5551	INCAS	I'LL KEEP HOLDING ON	ONE NIGHT STAND	25.00
66	5551 DJ	INCAS	I'LL KEEP HOLDING ON	ONE NIGHT STAND	32.00
66	5565	CLIFF BENNETT & the REBEL ROUSERS	I'LL TAKE GOOD CARE OF YOU	I'M SORRY	10.00
66	5565 DJ	CLIFF BENNETT & the REBEL ROUSERS	I'LL TAKE GOOD CARE OF YOU	I'M SORRY	15.00
66	5572	ACTION	NEVER EVER	TWENTY FOUR HOUR	50.00
66	5572 DJ	ACTION	NEVER EVER	TWENTY FOUR HOUR	75.00
67	5580	MICHAEL COX	I'LL ALWAYS LOVE YOU	YOU NEVER CAN TELL	10.00
67	5580 DJ	MICHAEL COX	I'LL ALWAYS LOVE YOU	YOU NEVER CAN TELL	15.00
67	5582	JOHNNY CURTIS	GO ON BACK	JACK AND THE BEANSTALK	20.00
67	5582 DJ	JOHNNY CURTIS	GO ON BACK	JACK AND THE BEANSTALK	30.00
67	5588	JULIE DRISCOLL	I KNOW YOU LOVE ME NOT	IF YOU SHOULD EVER LEAVE ME	10.00
67	5588 DJ	JULIE DRISCOLL	I KNOW YOU LOVE ME NOT	IF YOU SHOULD EVER LEAVE ME	15.00
67	5601	SOULMATES	IS THAT YOU?	TIME'S RUN OUT	6.00
67	5601 DJ	SOULMATES	IS THAT YOU?	TIME'S RUN OUT	10.00
67	5610	ACTION	SHADOWS AND REFLECTIONS	SOMERTHING HAS HIT ME	40.00
67	5610 DJ	ACTION	SHADOWS AND REFLECTIONS	SOMERTHING HAS HIT ME	60.00
68	5688	DON CHARLES	THE DRIFTER	GREAT TO BE LIVIN'	75.00
68	5688 DJ	DON CHARLES	THE DRIFTER	GREAT TO BE LIVIN'	100.00
68	5718	LOCOMOTIVE	RUDI'S IN LOVE	NEVER SET ME FREE	15.00
68	5718 DJ	LOCOMOTIVE	RUDI'S IN LOVE	NEVER SET ME FREE	25.00
69	5773	JIMMY THOMAS	THE BEAUTIFUL NIGHT	ABOVE A WHISPER	**256.00**
69	5773 DJ	JIMMY THOMAS	THE BEAUTIFUL NIGHT	ABOVE A WHISPER	**210.00**

Parlophone 5773 as you can see from recent auction prices, this is one of the few cases where the stock copy is considered rarer and more desirable than the promo.

69	5787	VIRGIL BROTHERS	TEMPTATION 'BOUT TO GET ME	LOOK AWAY	20.00
69	5787 DJ	VIRGIL BROTHERS	TEMPTATION 'BOUT TO GET ME	LOOK AWAY	30.00
69	5800	GENE LATTER	HELP ME JUDY, HELP ME	ON THE HIGHWAY	4.00
69	5800 DJ	GENE LATTER	HELP ME JUDY, HELP ME	ON THE HIGHWAY	6.00
69	5802	VIRGIL BROTHERS	GOOD LOVE	WHEN YOU WALK AWAY	6.00
69	5802 DJ	VIRGIL BROTHERS	GOOD LOVE	WHEN YOU WALK AWAY	10.00
70	5833	GENE LATTER	SOMEDAY YOU'LL NEED MY LOVE	COME ON HOME	5.00
70	5833 DJ	GENE LATTER	SOMEDAY YOU'LL NEED MY LOVE	COME ON HOME	8.00
70	5896	GENE LATTER	CATCH MY SOUL	HAPPINESS	6.00
70	5896 DJ	GENE LATTER	CATCH MY SOUL	HAPPINESS	10.00
70	5909	EBONY KEYES	BROTHER JOE	UNDER THE APPLE TREE	6.00
70	5909 DJ	EBONY KEYES	BROTHER JOE	UNDER THE APPLE TREE	8.00
71	5913	GENE LATTER	TOO BUSY THINKING ABOUT MY BABY	SING A SONG OF FREEDOM	12.00
71	5913 DJ	GENE LATTER	TOO BUSY THINKING ABOUT MY BABY	SING A SONG OF FREEDOM	20.00
71	5915	LOCOMOTIVE	RUDI'S IN LOVE	YOU MUST BE JOKING	8.00
71	5915 DJ	LOCOMOTIVE	RUDI'S IN LOVE	YOU MUST BE JOKING	10.00
71	5931	COASTERS	LOVE POTION NUMBER NINE	D.W. WASHBURN	25.00
71	5931 DJ	COASTERS	LOVE POTION NUMBER NINE	D.W. WASHBURN	40.00
71	5958	MEL NIXON	EV'RY LITTLE BEAT TO YOUR HEART	PILLARS OF STRAW	8.00
71	5958 DJ	MEL NIXON	EV'RY LITTLE BEAT TO YOUR HEART	PILLARS OF STRAW	10.00
61	8844 EP PS	NINA SIMONE	MY BABY JUST CARES FOR ME	1961 4 track EP with cover	40.00
62	8864 EP PS	NINA SIMONE	INTIMATE NINA SIMONE	1962 4 track EP with cover	15.00

PATHEWAY

71	104	ILA VAN	NO GOOD JIM	FLYING SOLO TOMORROW	5.00

PENNY FARTHING

70	717	GEORGE BAKER SELECTION	LITTLE GREEN BAG	PRETTY LITTLE DREAMER	20.00

PEOPLE

73	101	BABY WASHINGTON & DON GARDNER	BABY LET ME GET CLOSE TO YOU	FOREVER	6.00
73	101 DJ	BABY WASHINGTON & DON GARDNER	BABY LET ME GET CLOSE TO YOU	FOREVER	8.00
73	102	DON DOWNING	LONELY DAYS LONELY NIGHTS	I'M SO PROUD OF YOU	6.00
73	102 DJ	DON DOWNING	LONELY DAYS LONELY NIGHTS	I'M SO PROUD OF YOU	8.00
73	103	GENTLE PERSUASION	DYNAMITE EXPLODES	BRING IT ON HOME TO ME	6.00
73	103 DJ	GENTLE PERSUASION	DYNAMITE EXPLODES	BRING IT ON HOME TO ME	8.00
73	104	WEE THREE	GET ON BOARD	same: instrumental	8.00
73	104 DJ	WEE THREE	GET ON BOARD	same: instrumental	10.00
73	105	BABY WASHINGTON	JUST CAN'T GET YOU OUT OF MIND	YOU JUST A DREAM	8.00

73	105 DJ	BABY WASHINGTON	JUST CAN'T GET YOU OUT OF MIND	YOU JUST A DREAM	10.00
73	106	DELLA REESE	IF LOVING YOU NIS WRONG, I DON'T	WHO IS SHE & WHAT IS SHE TO YO	5.00
73	106 DJ	DELLA REESE	IF LOVING YOU NIS WRONG, I DON'T	WHO IS SHE & WHAT IS SHE TO YO	6.00
74	107	BABY WASHINGTON	I'VE GOT TO BREAK AWAY	CAN'T GET OVER LOSING YOU	8.00
74	107 DJ	BABY WASHINGTON	I'VE GOT TO BREAK AWAY	CAN'T GET OVER LOSING YOU	10.00
74	108	DON DOWNING	DREAM WORLD	THE MIRACLE	6.00
74	108 DJ	DON DOWNING	DREAM WORLD	THE MIRACLE	8.00
74	109	REUBEN WILSON	I'LL TAKE YOU THERE	CISCO KID	8.00
74	109 DJ	REUBEN WILSON	I'LL TAKE YOU THERE	CISCO KID	10.00
74	110	KRISSI K	WHO DO YOU THINK YOU ARE	STICK UP	5.00
74	110 DJ	KRISSI K	WHO DO YOU THINK YOU ARE	STICK UP	6.00
74	111	WESTSIDE	RUNNING IN AND OUT OF MY LIFE	HIGHWEAY DEMON	15.00
74	111 DJ	WESTSIDE	RUNNING IN AND OUT OF MY LIFE	HIGHWEAY DEMON	20.00
74	112	DORIS TROY	STRETCHIN' OUT	DON'T TELL YOUR MAMA	8.00
74	112 DJ	DORIS TROY	STRETCHIN' OUT	DON'T TELL YOUR MAMA	10.00
74	113	J. KELLY and the PREMIERS	SHE CALLS ME BABY	SIGNED SEALED AND DELIVERED	8.00
74	113 DJ	J. KELLY and the PREMIERS	SHE CALLS ME BABY	SIGNED SEALED AND DELIVERED	10.00
74	114	BARRY SMITH	HOLD ON TO IT	HOLD ON TO IT part 2	20.00
74	114 DJ	BARRY SMITH	HOLD ON TO IT	HOLD ON TO IT part 2	25.00
74	115	DONNA SUMMER	THE HOSTAGE	LET'S WORK TOGETHER NOW	10.00
74	115 DJ	DONNA SUMMER	THE HOSTAGE	LET'S WORK TOGETHER NOW	15.00
74	116	WEE WILLIE & the WINNERS	I DON'T KNOW WHAT YOU GOT BUT I	same: Instrumental	10.00
74	116 DJ	WEE WILLIE & the WINNERS	I DON'T KNOW WHAT YOU GOT BUT I	same: Instrumental	15.00
74	117 unissued ?	JIMMY JAMES and the VAGABONDS	HELP YOURSELF	WHY	UN
74	118	BROTHERS	IN THE POCKET	EVERYBODY LOVES A WINNER	8.00
74	118 DJ	BROTHERS	IN THE POCKET	EVERYBODY LOVES A WINNER	10.00

PHEONIX

73	137	LINCOLN ROGERS	LET LOVE COME BETWEEN US	SHE LOOKED AT ME WITH LOVE	15.00

PHIL SPECTOR INTERNATIONAL

75	2010002	CRYSTALS	HE'S A REBEL	I LOVE YOU EDDIE	5.00
75	2010003	RONETTES	BE MY BABY	I LOVE YOU	5.00
76	2010004	BOB B. SOXX & the BLUES JEANS	ZIP A DEE DOO DAH	WHY DO LOVERS BREAK EACH OTHERS HEARTS	5.00
76	2010009	RONETTES	I'M A WOMAN IN LOVE	WHEN I SAW YOU	8.00
76	2010010	RONNETTES c/w DARLENE LOVE	FROSTY THE SNOWMAN	WHITE CHRISTMAS	5.00
77	2010017	RONETTES	I WONDER	WALKNG IN THE RAIN	8.00
77	2010019	DARLENE LOVE	LORD IF YOUR A WOMAN	JOHNNY (BABY PLEASE COME HOME)	15.00
77	2010020	CRYSTALS	ALL GROWN UP	THE TWIST	6.00
77	2010022	RIGHTEOUS BROTHERS BAND	RAT RACE	YOU'VE LOST THAT LOVIN' FEELIN	8.00

PHILADELPHIA INTERNATIONAL RECORDS.

Only the second label in the world, to have a sound named after it. First was Tamla Motown "The Motown Sound", second ten years later wAS Philadelphia International with the world DJ's quoting the term "The Philly Sound". Until late 1973 all Philadelphia International recording were released in the UK by CBS on their own CBS label or the subsidiary Epic Records. The success of Billy Paul's – "Me & Mrs Jones" on Epic, and the O'Jays – "Love Train" and Harold Melvin's –"If You Don't Know Me By Now" – on CBS persuaded UK CBS to launch Philadelphia International records under it's own label. The promo copies are particularly desirable, as most of the releases on this label sold in reasonable quantities, making most of the stock releases common. CBS's numbering system was not as straight forward as you find, 1983 releases with 2000 numbers which fall in-between 1973 releases. So collectors do find it difficult to know if they have completed the series. Below is perhaps the largest listing of UK releases put together; any additions are most welcome. Only Tamla Motown has out released soul 45's in the UK. This label is just full of quality 70's soul recordings and can only become more collectable as the years roll by.

81	1030	JONES GIRLS	AT PEACE WITH WOMAN	WHEN I'M GONE	5.00
81	1030 DJ	JONES GIRLS	AT PEACE WITH WOMAN	WHEN I'M GONE	6.00
81	1663	TEDDY PENDERGRASS	NINE TIMES OUT OF TEN	I CAN'T LEAVE YOUR LOVE ALONE	3.00
81	1663 DJ	TEDDY PENDERGRASS	NINE TIMES OUT OF TEN	I CAN'T LEAVE YOUR LOVE ALONE	4.00
73	1879	HAROLD MELVIN & the BLUENOTES	THE LOVE I LOST	THE LOVE I LOST PART2	4.00
73	1879 DJ	HAROLD MELVIN & the BLUENOTES	THE LOVE I LOST	THE LOVE I LOST PART2	6.00
73	1880	THREE DEGREES	DIRTY OLE MAN	CAN'T YOU SEE WHAT YOUR DOING TO ME	4.00
73	1880 DJ	THREE DEGREES	DIRTY OLE MAN	CAN'T YOU SEE WHAT YOUR DOING TO ME	5.00
73	1893	BUNNY SIGLER	FIVE FINGERS OF DEATH	REGINA	4.00
73	1893 DJ	BUNNY SIGLER	FIVE FINGERS OF DEATH	REGINA	5.00
73	1899	INTRUDERS	HANG ON IN THERE	I WANA KNOW YOUR NAME	5.00
73	1899 DJ	INTRUDERS	HANG ON IN THERE	I WANA KNOW YOUR NAME	6.00
73	1905	O'JAYS	PUT YOUR HANDS TOGETHER	THAT AIR THAT I BREATH	4.00
73	1905 DJ	O'JAYS	PUT YOUR HANDS TOGETHER	THAT AIR THAT I BREATH	5.00
73	1928	BILLY PAUL	THANKS FOR SAVING MY LIFE	I SEE THE LIGHT	4.00
73	1928 DJ	BILLY PAUL	THANKS FOR SAVING MY LIFE	I SEE THE LIGHT	5.00
73	1989	TRAMMPS	LOVE EPIDEMIC	I KNOW THAT FEEELING	4.00
73	1989 DJ	TRAMMPS	LOVE EPIDEMIC	same:	4.00
82	2031	JONES GIRLS	NIGHTS OVER EGYPT	LOVE DON'T EVER SAY GOODBYE	6.00
82	2031 DJ	JONES GIRLS	NIGHTS OVER EGYPT	LOVE DON'T EVER SAY GOODBYE	8.00
82	2047	TEDDY PENDERGRASS	I JUST CALL TO SAY	REACH OUT AND TOUCH	4.00
82	2047 DJ	TEDDY PENDERGRASS	I JUST CALL TO SAY	REACH OUT AND TOUCH	5.00
73	2073	THREE DEGREES	YEAR OF DECISION	I KNOW THAT FEELING	4.00
73	2073 DJ	THREE DEGREES	YEAR OF DECISION	I KNOW THAT FEELING	5.00
73	2149	INTRUDERS	I'LL ALWAYS LOVE MY MAMA	I'LL ALWAYS LOVE MY MAMA part 2	4.00
73	2149 DJ	INTRUDERS	I'LL ALWAYS LOVE MY MAMA	I'LL ALWAYS LOVE MY MAMA part 2	5.00
73	2155	THREE DEGREES	WHEN WILL I SEE YOU AGAIN	I DIDN'T KNOW	4.00
73	2155 DJ	THREE DEGREES	WHEN WILL I SEE YOU AGAIN	I DIDN'T KNOW	5.00
74	2186	O'JAYS	FOR THE LOVE OF MONEY	PEOPLE KEEP TELLING ME	6.00

74	2186 DJ	O'JAYS	FOR THE LOVE OF MONEY	PEOPLE KEEP TELLING ME	8.00
74	2187	HAROLD MELVIN & the BLUENOTES	SATISFACION GUARANTEED	I'M WEAK FOR YOU	5.00
74	2187 DJ	HAROLD MELVIN & the BLUENOTES	SATISFACION GUARANTEED	I'M WEAK FOR YOU	6.00
74	2210	HAROLD MELVIN & the BLUENOTES	IF YOU DON'T KNOW ME BY NOW	LET ME INTO YOUR WORLD	4.00
74	2210 DJ	HAROLD MELVIN & the BLUENOTES	IF YOU DON'T KNOW ME BY NOW	LET ME INTO YOUR WORLD	5.00
74	2212	INTRUDERS	WIN, PLACE OR SHOW (SHE'S A WINNER)	MEMORIES ARE HERE TO STAY	5.00
74	2212 DJ	INTRUDERS	WIN, PLACE OR SHOW (SHE'S A WINNER)	MEMORIES ARE HERE TO STAY	6.00
74	2213	O'JAYS	LOVE TRAIN	WHO AM I	4.00
74	2213 DJ	O'JAYS	LOVE TRAIN	WHO AM I	5.00
74	2214	BILLY PAUL	ME & MRS JONES	YOUR SONG	4.00
74	2214 DJ	BILLY PAUL	ME & MRS JONES	YOUR SONG	5.00
74	2219	MFSB feat: LEON HUFF	FAMILY AFFAIR	LAY IN LOW	3.00
74	2219 DJ	MFSB feat: LEON HUFF	FAMILY AFFAIR	LAY IN LOW	4.00
74	2225	BILLY PAUL	THE WHOLE TOWN'S TALKIN'	I WAS MARRIED	4.00
74	2225 DJ	BILLY PAUL	THE WHOLE TOWN'S TALKIN'	I WAS MARRIED	5.00
74	2247	O'JAYS	I JUST WANT TO SATIFY	DON'T WALK AWAY MAD	4.00
74	2247 DJ	O'JAYS	I JUST WANT TO SATIFY	DON'T WALK AWAY MAD	5.00
74	2289	MSFB feat: THREE DEEGREES	TSOP (THE SOUND OF PHILADELPHIA)	SOMETHING FOR NOTHING	4.00
74	2289 DJ	MSFB feat: THREE DEEGREES	TSOP (THE SOUND OF PHILADELPHIA)	SOMETHING FOR NOTHING	5.00
74	2363	EBONYS	SEXY WAYS	IT'S FOREVER	5.00
74	2363 DJ	EBONYS	SEXY WAYS	IT'S FOREVER	6.00
74	2376	BUNNY SIGLER	I LIED	PICTURE US	6.00
74	2376 DJ	BUNNY SIGLER	I LIED	PICTURE US	8.00
74	2382	TRAMMPS	WHERE DO WE GO FROM HERE	SHOUT	5.00
74	2382 DJ	TRAMMPS	WHERE DO WE GO FROM HERE	SHOUT	6.00
82	2427	O'JAYS	JUST WANT TO SATISFY YOU	DON'T WALK AWAY MAD	3.00
82	2427 DJ	O'JAYS	JUST WANT TO SATISFY YOU	DON'T WALK AWAY MAD	4.00
74	2441	HAROLD MELVIN & the BLUENOTES	I'M COMIN' HOME TOMORROW	I'M COMIN' HOME TOMORROW part 2	4.00
74	2441 DJ	HAROLD MELVIN & the BLUENOTES	I'M COMIN' HOME TOMORROW	I'M COMIN' HOME TOMORROW part 2	5.00
74	2536	MFSB feat: THREE DEGREES	LOVE IS THE MESSAGE	MY ONE AND ONLY LOVE	3.00
74	2536 DJ	MFSB feat: THREE DEGREES	LOVE IS THE MESSAGE	MY ONE AND ONLY LOVE	4.00
74	2563	SPIRITUAL CONCEPT	I DON'T WANT TO HEAR IT	LETS TAKE IT ALL	3.00
74	2563 DJ	SPIRITUAL CONCEPT	I DON'T WANT TO HEAR IT	LETS TAKE IT ALL	4.00
74	2564	PEOPLES CHOICE	THE BIG HURT	LOVE SHOP	4.00
74	2564 DJ	PEOPLES CHOICE	THE BIG HURT	LOVE SHOP	5.00
74	2577	O'JAYS	NOW THAT WE'VE FOUND LOVE	YOU'VE GOT YOUR HOOKS IN ME	4.00
74	2577 DJ	O'JAYS	NOW THAT WE'VE FOUND LOVE	YOU'VE GOT YOUR HOOKS IN ME	5.00
82	2628 EP	O'JAYS	LOVE TRAIN + I LOVE MUSIC	USED TO BE MY GIRL + DARLIN' DARLIN'	4.00
74	2637	BUNNY SIGLER	LOVE TRAIN	LOVE TRAIN part 2	4.00
74	2637 DJ	BUNNY SIGLER	LOVE TRAIN	LOVE TRAIN part 2	5.00
74	2652	ROBERT UPCHURCH	GLAD YOUR MINE	THE DEVIL MADE ME DO IT	4.00
74	2652 DJ	ROBERT UPCHURCH	GLAD YOUR MINE	THE DEVIL MADE ME DO IT	5.00
74	2662	DEREK & CYNDI	YOU BRING OUT THE BEST IN ME	I'LL DO FOR YOU THE IMPOSSIBLE	3.00
74	2662 DJ	DEREK & CYNDI	YOU BRING OUT THE BEST IN ME	I'LL DO FOR YOU THE IMPOSSIBLE	4.00
74	2722	TALK OF THE TOWN	BUMPIN' BOOGIE	BUMPIN' BOOGIE part 2	3.00
74	2722 DJ	TALK OF THE TOWN	BUMPIN' BOOGIE	BUMPIN' BOOGIE part 2	4.00
74	2737	THREE DEGREES	GET YOUR LOVE BACK	I LIKE BEING A WOMAN	3.00
74	2737 DJ	THREE DEGREES	GET YOUR LOVE BACK	I LIKE BEING A WOMAN	4.00
74	2740	INTRUDERS	A NICE GIRL LIKE YOU	TOP BE HAPPY IS THE REAL THING	25.00
74	2740 DJ	INTRUDERS	A NICE GIRL LIKE YOU	TOP BE HAPPY IS THE REAL THING	30.00
74	2819	HAROLD MELVIN & the BLUENOTES	WHERE ARE ALL MY FRIENDS	LET IT BE YOU	4.00
74	2819 DJ	HAROLD MELVIN & the BLUENOTES	WHERE ARE ALL MY FRIENDS	LET IT BE YOU	5.00
74	2835	TRAMMPS	TRUSTING HEART	DOWN THREE DARK STREETS	5.00
74	2835 DJ	TRAMMPS	TRUSTING HEART	DOWN THREE DARK STREETS	6.00
75	2950	O'JAYS	SUNSHINE	SUNSHINE part 2	4.00
75	2950 DJ	O'JAYS	SUNSHINE	SUNSHINE part 2	5.00
75	3035	LOVE COMMITTEE	ONE DOZEN ROSES	ONE DAY OF PEACE	4.00
75	3035 DJ	LOVE COMMITTEE	ONE DOZEN ROSES	ONE DAY OF PEACE	5.00
75	3177	THREE DEGREES	TAKE GOOD CARE OF YOURSELF	IF AND WHEN	3.00
75	3177 DJ	THREE DEGREES	TAKE GOOD CARE OF YOURSELF	IF AND WHEN	4.00
75	3202	HAROLD MELVIN & the BLUENOTES	BAD LUCK	BAD LUCK part 2	4.00
75	3202 DJ	HAROLD MELVIN & the BLUENOTES	BAD LUCK	BAD LUCK part 2	6.00
75	3274	BILLY PAUL	JULY JULY JULY	BE TRUTHFUL TO ME	3.00
75	3274 DJ	BILLY PAUL	JULY JULY JULY	BE TRUTHFUL TO ME	4.00
75	3296	O'JAYS	GIVE THE PEOPLE WHAT THEY WANT	WHAT AM I LIVING FOR	4.00
75	3296 DJ	O'JAYS	GIVE THE PEOPLE WHAT THEY WANT	WHAT AM I LIVING FOR	5.00
75	3352	THREE DEGREES	LONG LOST LOVER	LONELIER ARE THE FOOLS	4.00
75	3352 DJ	THREE DEGREES	LONG LOST LOVER	LONELIER ARE THE FOOLS	5.00
75	3381	MFSB	SEXY	HUMAN MACHINE	3.00
75	3381 DJ	MFSB	SEXY	HUMAN MACHINE	4.00
75	3500	PEOPLES CHOICE	DO IT ANY WAY YOU WANNA	THE BIG HURT	4.00
75	3500 DJ	PEOPLES CHOICE	DO IT ANY WAY YOU WANNA	THE BIG HURT	5.00
75	3566	HAROLD MELVIN & SHARON PAIGE	HOPE THAT WE CAN BE TOGETHER SOON	BE FOR REAL	5.00
75	3566 DJ	HAROLD MELVIN & SHARON PAIGE	HOPE THAT WE CAN BE TOGETHER SOON	BE FOR REAL	6.00
75	3624	INTRUDERS	I'LL ALWAYS LOVE MY MAMA	I'LL ALWAYS LOVE MY MAMA part 2	4.00
75	3624 DJ	INTRUDERS	I'LL ALWAYS LOVE MY MAMA	I'LL ALWAYS LOVE MY MAMA part 2	5.00
75	3635	MFSB	LET'S GO DISCO	MY MOOD	3.00
75	3635 DJ	MFSB	LET'S GO DISCO	MY MOOD	4.00
83	3642	O'JAYS	PUT OUR HEADS TOGETHER	LETTER TO MY FRIENDS	3.00

83	3642 PS	O'JAYS	PUT OUR HEADS TOGETHER	LETTER TO MY FRIENDS	4.00
83	3642 PS DJ	O'JAYS	PUT OUR HEADS TOGETHER	LETTER TO MY FRIENDS	5.00
79	3680	JONES GIRLS	YOU GONNA MAKE ME LOVE	I'M AT YOUR MERCY	5.00
79	3680 DJ	JONES GIRLS	YOU GONNA MAKE ME LOVE	same:	5.00
75	3743	O'JAYS	CHRISTMAS AIN'T CHRISTMAS NEW	JUST CAN'T GET ENOUGH	4.00
75	3743 DJ	O'JAYS	CHRISTMAS AIN'T CHRISTMAS NEW	JUST CAN'T GET ENOUGH	5.00
75	3751	BILLY PAUL	ME & MRS JONES	THIS IS YOUR LIFE	5.00
75	3751 DJ	BILLY PAUL	ME & MRS JONES	THIS IS YOUR LIFE	6.00
75	3752	HAROLD MELVIN the BLUENOTES	IF YOU DON'T KNOW ME BY NOW	I MISS YOU	4.00
75	3752 DJ	HAROLD MELVIN the BLUENOTES	IF YOU DON'T KNOW ME BY NOW	I MISS YOU	5.00
75	3753	O'JAYS	BACK STABBERS	992 ARGUMENTS	6.00
75	3753 DJ	O'JAYS	BACK STABBERS	992 ARGUMENTS	8.00
75	3815	PEOPLES CHOICE	A PARTY IS A GROOVY THING	DON'T SEND ME AWAY	4.00
75	3815 DJ	PEOPLES CHOICE	A PARTY IS A GROOVY THING	DON'T SEND ME AWAY	5.00
76	3851	ARCHIE BELL and the DRELLS	I COULD HAVE DANCED ALL NIGHT	KING OF THE CASTLE	4.00
76	3851 DJ	ARCHIE BELL and the DRELLS	I COULD HAVE DANCED ALL NIGHT	KING OF THE CASTLE	5.00
76	3866	HAROLD MELVIN the BLUENOTES	WAKE UP EVERYBODY	WAKE UP EVERYBODY part 2	5.00
76	3866 DJ	HAROLD MELVIN the BLUENOTES	WAKE UP EVERYBODY	WAKE UP EVERYBODY part 2	8.00
76	3879	O'JAYS	I LOVE MUSIC	I LOVE MUSIC PART2	5.00
76	3879 DJ	O'JAYS	I LOVE MUSIC	I LOVE MUSIC PART2	6.00
76	3943	O'JAYS	BACKSTABBERS	LOVE TRAIN	5.00
76	3943 DJ	O'JAYS	BACKSTABBERS	LOVE TRAIN	6.00
76	3951	THREE DEGREES	DIRTY OLE MAN	WHEN WILL I SEE YOU AGAIN	3.00
76	3951 DJ	THREE DEGREES	DIRTY OLE MAN	WHEN WILL I SEE YOU AGAIN	4.00
76	4064	PEOPLES CHOICE	NURSERY RHYMES	NURSERY RHYMES part 2	4.00
76	4064 DJ	PEOPLES CHOICE	NURSERY RHYMES	NURSERY RHYMES part 2	5.00
76	4144	BILLY PAUL	LET'S MAKE A BABY	MY HEAD'S ON STRAIGHT	4.00
76	4144 DJ	BILLY PAUL	LET'S MAKE A BABY	MY HEAD'S ON STRAIGHT	5.00
76	4189	O'JAYS	LIVIN' FOR THE WEEKEND	STAIRWAY TO HEAVEN	4.00
76	4189 DJ	O'JAYS	LIVIN' FOR THE WEEKEND	STAIRWAY TO HEAVEN	8.00
76	4191	ARCHIE BELL & the DRELLS	SOUL CITY WALK	I LOVE YOU	6.00
76	4191 DJ	ARCHIE BELL & the DRELLS	SOUL CITY WALK	I LOVE YOU	8.00
76	4238	HAROLD MELVIN the BLUENOTES	TELL THE WORLD HOW I FEEL ABOUT YOU	YOU KNOW HOW TO MAKE ME FEEL	4.00
76	4238 DJ	HAROLD MELVIN the BLUENOTES	TELL THE WORLD HOW I FEEL ABOUT YOU	YOU KNOW HOW TO MAKE ME FEEL	5.00
76	4250	ARCHIE BELL & the DRELLS	THE SOUL CITY WALK	LET'S GROOVE	5.00
76	4250 DJ	ARCHIE BELL & the DRELLS	THE SOUL CITY WALK	LET'S GROOVE	6.00
84	4287	O'JAYS	EXTRAORDINARY GIRL	I REALY NEED YOU NOW	4.00
84	4287 DJ	O'JAYS	EXTRAORDINARY GIRL	I REALY NEED YOU NOW	5.00
76	4291	INSTANT FUNK	FLOAT LIKE A BUTTERFLY	FLOAT LIKE A BUTTERFLY part 2	4.00
76	4291 DJ	INSTANT FUNK	FLOAT LIKE A BUTTERFLY	FLOAT LIKE A BUTTERFLY part 2	5.00
76	4351	CITY LIMITS	LOVE IS EVERYTHING	UNCLE JAMES	8.00
76	4351 DJ	CITY LIMITS	LOVE IS EVERYTHING	UNCLE JAMES	10.00
76	4372	LOU RAWLS	YOU'LL NEVER FIND ANOTHER LOVE LIKE MINE	LETS FALL IN LOVE ALL OVER AGAIN	4.00
76	4372 DJ	LOU RAWLS	YOU'LL NEVER FIND ANOTHER LOVE LIKE MINE	LETS FALL IN LOVE ALL OVER AGAIN	5.00
76	4410	PEOPLES CHOICE	HERE WE GO AGAIN	ICKEY D'S	5.00
76	4410 DJ	PEOPLES CHOICE	HERE WE GO AGAIN	ICKEY D'S	6.00
76	4461	BILLY PAUL	PEOPLE POWER	I WANTCHA BABY	4.00
76	4461 DJ	BILLY PAUL	PEOPLE POWER	I WANTCHA BABY	5.00
76	4598	O'JAYS	MESSAGE IN OUR MUSIC	SHE'S ONLY A WOMAN	3.00
76	4598 DJ	O'JAYS	MESSAGE IN OUR MUSIC	SHE'S ONLY A WOMAN	4.00
76	4614	PEOPLES CHOICE	MOVIN' IN ALL DIRECTIONS	MELLOW MOOD	3.00
76	4614 DJ	PEOPLES CHOICE	MOVIN' IN ALL DIRECTIONS	MELLOW MOOD	4.00
76	4663	DON COVAY	TRAVELLING IN HEAVY TRAFFIC	ONCE YOU HAD IT	4.00
76	4663 DJ	DON COVAY	TRAVELLING IN HEAVY TRAFFIC	ONCE YOU HAD IT	5.00
76	4674	LOU RAWLS	FROM NOW ON	YOU'RE THE ONE	3.00
76	4674 DJ	LOU RAWLS	FROM NOW ON	YOU'RE THE ONE	4.00
76	4803	ARCHIE BELL & the DRELLS	WHERE WILL YOU GO WHEN THE PARTY'S OVER	I SWEAR YOU'RE BEAUTIFUL	25.00
76	4803 DJ	ARCHIE BELL & the DRELLS	WHERE WILL YOU GO WHEN THE PARTY'S OVER	I SWEAR YOU'RE BEAUTIFUL	30.00
77	4834	O'JAYS	DARLIN' DARLIN' BABY (SWEET, TENDER	A PRAYER	5.00
77	4834 DJ	O'JAYS	DARLIN' DARLIN' BABY (SWEET, TENDER	A PRAYER	6.00
77	4881	HAROLD MELVIN & the BLUENOTES	THE LOVE I LOST	BAD LUCK	4.00
77	4881 blue vinyl	HAROLD MELVIN & the BLUENOTES	THE LOVE I LOST	BAD LUCK	5.00
77	4881 DJ	HAROLD MELVIN & the BLUENOTES	THE LOVE I LOST	BAD LUCK	5.00
77	4882	O'JAYS	BACK STABBERS	LOVE TRAIN	4.00
77	4882 blue vinyl	O'JAYS	BACK STABBERS	LOVE TRAIN	5.00
77	4882 DJ	O'JAYS	BACK STABBERS	LOVE TRAIN	5.00
77	4884	LOU RAWLS	YOU'LL NEVER FIND ANOTHER LOVE (LIKE MINE)	FROM NOW ON	4.00
77	4884 DJ	LOU RAWLS	YOU'LL NEVER FIND ANOTHER LOVE (LIKE MINE)	FROM NOW ON	6.00
77	4887	ARCHIE BELL & the DRELLS	I COULD HAVE DANCED ALL NIGHT	THE SOUL CITY WALK	5.00
77	4887 DJ	ARCHIE BELL & the DRELLS	I COULD HAVE DANCED ALL NIGHT	THE SOUL CITY WALK	6.00
77	4888	MFSB	TSOP	SEXY	4.00
77	4888 DJ	MFSB	TSOP	SEXY	5.00
77	4891	PEOPLES CHOICE	DO IT ANYWAY YOU WANNA	HERE WE GO AGAIN	4.00
77	4891 DJ	PEOPLES CHOICE	DO IT ANYWAY YOU WANNA	HERE WE GO AGAIN	5.00
77	4893	BILLY PAUL	ME & MRS JONES	LET'S MAKE A BABY	4.00
77	4893 DJ	BILLY PAUL	ME & MRS JONES	LET'S MAKE A BABY	5.00
77	4909	HAROLD MELVIN & the BLUENOTES	DON'T LEAVE ME THIS WAY	TO BE FREE TO BE WHO WE ARE	5.00
77	4909 DJ	HAROLD MELVIN & the BLUENOTES	DON'T LEAVE ME THIS WAY	TO BE FREE TO BE WHO WE ARE	8.00
77	4935	BUNNY SIGLER	CAN'T BELIEVE THAT YOU LOVE ME	WOMAN, WOMAN	8.00

77	4935 DJ	BUNNY SIGLER	CAN'T BELIEVE THAT YOU LOVE ME	WOMAN, WOMAN	10.00
77	4944	BILLY PAUL	I TRUST YOU	LOVE WON'T COME EASY	4.00
77	4944 DJ	BILLY PAUL	I TRUST YOU	LOVE WON'T COME EASY	5.00
77	5116	TEDDY PENDERGRASS	THE WHOLE TOWN'S LAUGHING AT ME	AND IF I HAD	4.00
77	5116 PS	TEDDY PENDERGRASS	THE WHOLE TOWN'S LAUGHING AT ME	AND IF I HAD	8.00
77	5116 DJ	TEDDY PENDERGRASS	THE WHOLE TOWN'S LAUGHING AT ME	AND IF I HAD	6.00
77	5143	BILLY PAUL	LET 'EM IN	I THINK I'LL STAY HOME TODAY	4.00
77	5143 DJ	BILLY PAUL	LET 'EM IN	I THINK I'LL STAY HOME TODAY	5.00
77	5179	ARCHIE BELL & the DRELLS	EVERYBODY HAVE A GOOD TIME	I BET I CAN DO THAT DANCE	4.00
77	5179 DJ	ARCHIE BELL & the DRELLS	EVERYBODY HAVE A GOOD TIME	I BET I CAN DO THAT DANCE	5.00
77	5232	LOU RAWLS	SOME FOLKS NEVER LEARN	EARLY MORNING LOVE	3.00
77	5232 DJ	LOU RAWLS	SOME FOLKS NEVER LEARN	EARLY MORNING LOVE	4.00
77	5237	PEOPLES CHOICE	IF YOU GONNA DO IT	IF YOU GONNA DO IT part 2	3.00
77	5237 DJ	PEOPLES CHOICE	IF YOU GONNA DO IT	IF YOU GONNA DO IT part 2	4.00
77	5244	LOU RAWLS	SEE YOU WHEN YOU GET THERE	SPRING AGAIN	4.00
77	5244 DJ	LOU RAWLS	SEE YOU WHEN YOU GET THERE	SPRING AGAIN	5.00
77	5337	O'JAYS	SO GLAD I GOT YOU GIRL	LET'S SPEND SOME TIME TOGETHER	4.00
77	5337 DJ	O'JAYS	SO GLAD I GOT YOU GIRL	LET'S SPEND SOME TIME TOGETHER	5.00
77	5391	BILLY PAUL	YOUR SONG	HOW GOOD IS YOUR GAME	4.00
77	5391 DJ	BILLY PAUL	YOUR SONG	HOW GOOD IS YOUR GAME	5.00
77	5444	TEDDY PENDERGRASS	I DON'T LOVE YOU ANYMORE	EASY, EASY, GOT TO TAKE IT EAS	4.00
77	5444 DJ	TEDDY PENDERGRASS	I DON'T LOVE YOU ANYMORE	EASY, EASY, GOT TO TAKE IT EAS	5.00
77	5451	MFSB	LET'S CLEAN UP THE GHETTO	same: instrumental	6.00
77	5451 DJ	MFSB	LET'S CLEAN UP THE GHETTO	same: instrumental	10.00
77	5451 ink	MFSB	LET'S CLEAN UP THE GHETTO	same: instrumental	4.00
77	5501	JEAN CARN	IF YOU WANNA GO BACK	YOU ARE ALL I NEED	10.00
77	5501 DJ	JEAN CARN	IF YOU WANNA GO BACK	YOU ARE ALL I NEED	15.00
77	5580	ARCHIE BELL & the DRELLS	I'VE BEEN MISSING YOU	DISCO SHOWDOWN	4.00
77	5580 DJ	ARCHIE BELL & the DRELLS	I'VE BEEN MISSING YOU	DISCO SHOWDOWN	5.00
77	5582	O'JAYS	WE'RE ALL IN THIS THING TOGETHER	FEELINGS	4.00
77	5582 DJ	O'JAYS	WE'RE ALL IN THIS THING TOGETHER	FEELINGS	5.00
77	5391	BILLY PAUL	YOUR SONG	HOW GOOD IS YOUR GAME	5.00
77	5391 DJ	BILLY PAUL	YOUR SONG	HOW GOOD IS YOUR GAME	6.00
77	5684	TEDDY PENDERGRASS	SOMEBODY TOLD ME	THE MORE I GET THE MORE I WANT	4.00
77	5684 DJ	TEDDY PENDERGRASS	SOMEBODY TOLD ME	THE MORE I GET THE MORE I WANT	5.00
77	5699	BILLY PAUL	ONLY THE STRONG SURVIVE	WHERE I BELONG	8.00
77	5699 DJ	BILLY PAUL	ONLY THE STRONG SURVIVE	WHERE I BELONG	10.00
77	5702	DEE DEE SHARP GAMBLE	NOBODY COULD TAKE YOUR PLACE	FLASHBACK	8.00
77	5702 DJ	DEE DEE SHARP GAMBLE	NOBODY COULD TAKE YOUR PLACE	FLASHBACK	10.00
77	5891	PEOPLES CHOICE	JAM JAM JAM (ALL NIGHT LONG)	COLD BLOODED AND DOWN RIGHT FU	4.00
77	5891 DJ	PEOPLES CHOICE	JAM JAM JAM (ALL NIGHT LONG)	COLD BLOODED AND DOWN RIGHT FU	5.00
78	5911	LOU RAWLS	LADY LOVE	NOT THE STAYING KIND	4.00
78	5911 DJ	LOU RAWLS	LADY LOVE	NOT THE STAYING KIND	5.00
78	5944	THREE DEGREES	DIRTY OLD MAN	CAN'T YOU SEE WHAT YOUR DOING	4.00
78	5944 DJ	THREE DEGREES	DIRTY OLD MAN	CAN'T YOU SEE WHAT YOUR DOING	5.00
78	5969	THREE DEGREES	WHEN WILL I SEE YOU AGAIN	DIRTY OL' MAN	4.00
78	5969 DJ	THREE DEGREES	WHEN WILL I SEE YOU AGAIN	DIRTY OL' MAN	5.00
78	5983	BILLY PAUL	ONE MAN'S JUNK	EVERYBODY'S BREAKIN' UP	6.00
78	5983 DJ	BILLY PAUL	ONE MAN'S JUNK	EVERYBODY'S BREAKIN' UP	8.00
78	6093	O'JAYS	I LOVE MUSIC	LOVE TRAIN	5.00
78	6093 DJ	O'JAYS	I LOVE MUSIC	LOVE TRAIN	6.00
78	6255	DEXTER WANSEL	ALL NIGHT LONG	DISCO LIGHTS	4.00
78	6255 DJ	DEXTER WANSEL	ALL NIGHT LONG	DISCO LIGHTS	5.00
78	6276	BILLY PAUL	DON'T GIVE UP ON US	TIME OF OUR LIVES	4.00
78	6276 DJ	BILLY PAUL	DON'T GIVE UP ON US	TIME OF OUR LIVES	5.00
78	6287	MFSB	K-JEE	MY MOOD	5.00
78	6287 DJ	MFSB	K-JEE	MY MOOD	6.00
78	6332	O'JAYS	USE TA BE MY GIRL	THIS TIME BABY	4.00
78	6332 DJ	O'JAYS	USE TA BE MY GIRL	THIS TIME BABY	6.00
78	6354	LOU RAWLS	TRADE WINDS	IF I COULDA WOULDA SHOULDA	4.00
78	6354 DJ	LOU RAWLS	TRADE WINDS	IF I COULDA WOULDA SHOULDA	5.00
78	6417	TEDDY PENDERGRASS	CLOSE THE DOOR	GET UP GET DOWN GET FUNKY	4.00
78	6417 DJ	TEDDY PENDERGRASS	CLOSE THE DOOR	GET UP GET DOWN GET FUNKY	5.00
78	6468	JEAN CARN	HAPPY TO BE WITH YOU	TOGETHER ONCE AGAIN	6.00
78	6468 DJ	JEAN CARN	HAPPY TO BE WITH YOU	TOGETHER ONCE AGAIN	8.00
78	6492	DEXTER WANSEL	I'M IN LOVE	SOLUTIONS	5.00
78	6492 DJ	DEXTER WANSEL	I'M IN LOVE	SOLUTIONS	6.00
78	6658	O'JAYS	BRANDY	TAKE ME TO THE STARS	4.00
78	6658 DJ	O'JAYS	BRANDY	TAKE ME TO THE STARS	6.00
78	6713	TEDDY PENDERGRASS	CLOSE THE DOOR	ONLY YOU	4.00
78	6713 DJ	TEDDY PENDERGRASS	CLOSE THE DOOR	ONLY YOU	5.00
78	6790	JERRY BUTLER	(I'M JUST THINKING ABOUT) COOLING	ARE YOU LONELY TONIGHT	4.00
78	6790 DJ	JERRY BUTLER	(I'M JUST THINKING ABOUT) COOLING	ARE YOU LONELY TONIGHT	5.00
79	7064	THREE DEGREES	TAKE GOOD CARE OF YOURSELF	IF AND WHEN	4.00
79	7064 DJ	THREE DEGREES	TAKE GOOD CARE OF YOURSELF	IF AND WHEN	5.00
79	7361	JONES GIRLS	YOU GONNA MAKE ME LOVE	WHO CAN I RUN TO	6.00
79	7361 DJ	JONES GIRLS	YOU GONNA MAKE ME LOVE	WHO CAN I RUN TO	10.00
79	7456	BILLY PAUL	BRING THE FAMILY BACK	IT'S CRITICAL	5.00
79	7456 DJ	BILLY PAUL	BRING THE FAMILY BACK	IT'S CRITICAL	8.00

79	7500	LOU RAWLS	TIME WILL TAKE CARE OF EVERYTHING	LOVER'S HOLIDAY		4.00
79	7500 DJ	LOU RAWLS	TIME WILL TAKE CARE OF EVERYTHING	LOVER'S HOLIDAY		5.00
79	7365	McFADDEN & WHITEHEAD	AIN'T NO STOPPING US NOW	I GOT THE LOVE		5.00
79	7365 DJ	McFADDEN & WHITEHEAD	AIN'T NO STOPPING US NOW	I GOT THE LOVE		6.00
79	7500	LOU RAWLS	TIME WILL TAKE CARE OF EVERYTHING	LOVER'S HOLIDAY		4.00
79	7500 DJ	LOU RAWLS	TIME WILL TAKE CARE OF EVERYTHING	LOVER'S HOLIDAY		5.00
79	7740	TEDDY PENDERGRASS	TURN OFF THE LIGHTS	IF YOU KNOW LIKE I KNOW		4.00
79	7740 DJ	TEDDY PENDERGRASS	TURN OFF THE LIGHTS	IF YOU KNOW LIKE I KNOW		5.00
79	7744	McFADDEN & WHITEHEAD	DO YOU WANT TO DANCE	I'VE BEEN PUSHED ASIDE		4.00
79	7744 DJ	McFADDEN & WHITEHEAD	DO YOU WANT TO DANCE	I'VE BEEN PUSHED ASIDE		5.00
79	7825	O'JAYS	SING A HAPPY SONG	ONE IN A MILLION (GIRL)		5.00
79	7825 DJ	O'JAYS	SING A HAPPY SONG	ONE IN A MILLION (GIRL)		6.00
79	7842	ARCHIE BELL & the DRELLS	STRATEGY	WE GOT 'EM DANCIN'		5.00
79	7842 DJ	ARCHIE BELL & the DRELLS	STRATEGY	WE GOT 'EM DANCIN'		6.00
79	7901	LOU RAWLS	WHAT'S THE MATTER WITH THE WORLD	TOMORROW		4.00
79	7901 DJ	LOU RAWLS	WHAT'S THE MATTER WITH THE WORLD	TOMORROW		5.00
79	7927	TEDDY PENDERGRASS	DO ME	I'LL NEVER SEE HEAVEN AGAIN		4.00
79	7927 DJ	TEDDY PENDERGRASS	DO ME	I'LL NEVER SEE HEAVEN AGAIN		5.00
79	8054	O'JAYS	IDENTIFY	HURRY UP AND COME BACK		4.00
79	8054 DJ	O'JAYS	IDENTIFY	HURRY UP AND COME BACK		5.00
79	8183	TEDDY PENDERGRASS	SHOUT AND SCREAM	CLOSE THE DOOR (live)		4.00
80	8183 DJ	TEDDY PENDERGRASS	SHOUT AND SCREAM	CLOSE THE DOOR (live)		5.00
80	8201	LOU RAWLS	SIT DOWN AND TALK TO ME	WHEN YOU GET HOME		4.00
80	8201 DJ	LOU RAWLS	SIT DOWN AND TALK TO ME	WHEN YOU GET HOME		5.00
80	8202	BILLY PAUL	YOU'RE MY SWEETNESS	ME & MRS JONRES		4.00
80	8202 DJ	BILLY PAUL	YOU'RE MY SWEETNESS	ME & MRS JONRES		5.00
80	8222	JOCKO	RHYTHM TALK	RHYTHM TALK part 2		5.00
80	8222 DJ	JOCKO	RHYTHM TALK	RHYTHM TALK part 2		6.00
80	8840	JEAN CARN	WAS THAT ALL IT WAS	WHAT'S ON YOUR MIND		5.00
80	8840 DJ	JEAN CARN	WAS THAT ALL IT WAS	WHAT'S ON YOUR MIND		6.00
80	8858	THREE DEGREES	WHEN WILL I SEE YOU AGAIN	TAKE GOOD CARE OF YOURSELF		3.00
80	8858 DJ	THREE DEGREES	WHEN WILL I SEE YOU AGAIN	TAKE GOOD CARE OF YOURSELF		4.00
80	8864	O'JAYS	LOVE TRAIN	BACK STABBERS		4.00
80	8864 DJ	O'JAYS	LOVE TRAIN	BACK STABBERS		5.00
80	8865	BILLY PAUL	ME & MRS JONES	LET THEM IN		3.00
80	8865 DJ	BILLY PAUL	ME & MRS JONES	LET THEM IN		4.00
80	8867	HAROLD MELVIN & the BLUENOTES	DON'T LEAVE ME THIS WAY	THE LOVE I LOST		4.00
80	8867 DJ	HAROLD MELVIN & the BLUENOTES	DON'T LEAVE ME THIS WAY	THE LOVE I LOST		5.00
80	8866	LOU RAWLS	YOU'LL NEVER FIND ANOTHER LOVE	LADY LOVE		4.00
80	8866 DJ	LOU RAWLS	YOU'LL NEVER FIND ANOTHER LOVE	LADY LOVE		5.00
80	8869	O'JAYS	I LOVE MUSIC	USED TO BE MY GIRL		4.00
80	8869 DJ	O'JAYS	I LOVE MUSIC	USED TO BE MY GIRL		5.00
80	8871	McFADDEN & WHITEHEAD	AIN'T NO STOPPING US NOW	DO YOU WANNA DANCE		4.00
80	8871 DJ	McFADDEN & WHITEHEAD	AIN'T NO STOPPING US NOW	DO YOU WANNA DANCE		6.00
80	8907	STYLISTICS	HURRY UP THIS WAY AGAIN	IT STARTED OUT		5.00
80	8907 DJ	STYLISTICS	HURRY UP THIS WAY AGAIN	IT STARTED OUT		6.00
80	8964	McFADDEN & WHITEHEAD	IT HEARD IT IN A LOVE SONG	ALWAYS ROOM FOR ONE MORE		4.00
80	8964 DJ	McFADDEN & WHITEHEAD	IT HEARD IT IN A LOVE SONG	ALWAYS ROOM FOR ONE MORE		5.00
81	9501	MFSB	MYSTERIES OF THE WORLD	MANHATTAN SKYLINE		3.00
81	9501 DJ	MFSB	MYSTERIES OF THE WORLD	MANHATTAN SKYLINE		4.00
75	JB 1	VARIOUS ARTISTS	PHILLY FREEBIE	4 track Promotional EP with cover		25.00
75	JB 1 flexi	VARIOUS ARTISTS	PHILLY FREEBIE	4 track Promotional EP flexi disc		5.00

The Philly Freebie EP came to the attention of Northern Soul enthusiast as one track – Billy Paul's –Let The Dollar Circulate – was played at Cleethorpes Pier All Nighter in 1975 not at the 33rpm it was designed for but at 38 rpm which transformed the mid-tempo male vocal protest song, into a furious up-tempo "female" vocal archetypical Philadelphia Sound dance tune. The EP was given to record shops to promote four different LPs. 1. Billy Paul – When Love Is New 2. O'Jays – Family Reunion 3. MFSB – Philadelphia Freedom 4. Harold Melvin & The Bluenotes – Wake Up Everybody. The felxidisc version of the same EP was given away in various 1975 Music publication New Musical Express etc.

PHILIPS

This UK giant released mostly UK recordings but had some fine USA labels in it's catalogue like it's parent company Philips i.e.: Bobby Hebb numerous 45's and the Chicago based Smash label, which boasted such obscure bands as The Daylighters, Spotlights, Swinging Medallions etc. Other USA labels like Double Shot also came under its umbrella as one of the 60's soul labels it could draw on for releases. But perhaps the most important releases on the label came from UK artists Madeline Bell, John Ford, etc. But without a doubt the most important artist to record and release product on the UK Philips label was Dusty Springfield, considered by many as the finest female vocalist ever to record in the UK. Amazingly a recent price guide listed this gargantuan artist as "Pop", just one listen to this lady will confirm to you, why USA Atlantic recorded her on numerous singles and later releasing her fabulous "Dusty in Memphis" LP. You'll find throughout this price guide white skinned artists singing and performing not only acceptable soul but sometimes even soul of the very highest calibre.

The late great Dusty's recordings rubber stamped the validity of white artists records being added to any Soul orientated collection. Thankfully, colour prejudice in record collecting is a minority practice. Philips released some of the best white vocal recording that became cornerstones for the largest vinyl-collecting scene in the world: Northern Soul.

Demo collectors will find Philips DJ copies hard to come by, the early 60's releases on Philips and sister label Mercury were stamped with a Yellow paint rubber stamp "Promotional Copy – Not For Sale" later white label with a two line capitol red A on the preferred side was issued. I've not noted the yellow rubber stamped promo copies unless there is a significant price difference, as many collectors don't consider rubber stamps or promo only sticker warranting a price difference.

61	1140	DON COVAY	SHAKE WID THE SHAKE	EVERY WHICH WAY	20.00
61	1195	FRANKIE VAUGHN	TOWER OF STRENGTH	RACHEL	6.00
64	12560 EP PS	DUSTY SPRINGFIELD	I ONLY WANT TO BE WITH YOU	1964 4 track EP with cover	15.00
64	12564 EP PS	DUSTY SPRINGFIELD	DUSTY: 4 track EP	can i get a witness + all cried	15.00
65	12572 EP PS	DUSTY SPRINGFIELD	DUSTY IN NEW YORK	1965 4 track EP with cover	15.00
65	12585 EP PS	NINA SIMONE	DON'T LET ME BE MISUNDERSTOOD	1965 4 track EP with cover	10.00
65	12589 EP PS	NINA SIMONE	STRANGE FRUIT	1965 4 track EP with cover	15.00
68	12605 EP PS	DUSTY SPRINGFIELD	IF YOU GO AWAY	1968 4 track EP with cover	15.00

63	1282	TONY WILLIAMS	HOW COME	WHEN I HAD YOU	100.00
63	1292	DUSTY SPRINGFIELD	I ONLY WANT TO BE WITH YOU	ONCE UNPON A TIME	4.00
64	1312	ANGELS	WOW WEE WEE	SNOWFLAKES AND TEARDROPS	8.00
64	1313	DUSTY SPRINGFIELD	STAY AWHILE	SOMETHING SPECIAL	6.00
64	1348	DUSTY SPRINGFIELD	I JUST DON'T KNOW WHAT TO DO WITH	MY COLOURING BOOK	6.00
64	1362	CHEETAHS	MECCA	THAT GOODNIGHT KISS	4.00
64	1363	SUSAN MAUGHN	THAT OTHER PLACE	LITTLE THINGS MEAN A LOT	25.00
64	1364	FOUR SEASONS	SAVE IT FOR ME	FUNNY FACE	4.00
64	1368	JAMES BROWN	OUT OF SIGHT	MAYBE THE LAST TIME	20.00
64	1369	DUSTY SPRINGFIELD	LOSING YOU	SUMMER IS OVER	6.00
64	1385	LEE CURTIS & the ALL STARS	ECSTASY	SHOT OF RHYTHM AND BLUES	15.00
64	1385 DJ stamped	LEE CURTIS & the ALL STARS	ECSTASY	SHOT OF RHYTHM AND BLUES	20.00
64	1388	NINA SIMONE	DON'T LET ME BE MISUNDERSTOOD	A MONSTER	6.00
64	1391	DAVID NELSON	SOMEBODY LOVES ME	WELL I HAVE	15.00
65	1396	DUSTY SPRINGFIELD	YOUR HURTIN' KINDA LOVE	DON'T SAY IT BABY	6.00
65	1402	ANNA KING & BOOBY BYRD	IF SOMEBODY TOLD YOU	BABY, BABY, BABY	10.00
65	1415	NINA SIMONE	I PUT A SPELL ON YOU	GIMME SOME	12.00
65	1418	DUSTY SPRINGFIELD	IN THE MIDDLE OF NOWHERE	BABY DON'T YOU KNOW	4.00
65	1430	DUSTY SPRINGFIELD	SOME OF YOUR LOVIN'	I'LL LOVE YOU FOR A WHILE	8.00
65	1432	CHARLIE RICH	MOHAIR SAM	I WASHED MY HANDS IN THE MUDDY	15.00
65	1439	4 SEASONS	LET'S HANG ON !	ON BROADWAY TONIGHT	3.00
65	1448	MADELINE BELL	I CAN'T WAIT UNTIL I SEE MY BABY'S	WHAT THE WORLD NEEDS NOW	15.00
65	1450	BOB HENRY	BUILT LIKE A MAN	I NEED ME SOMEONE	25.00
65	1454	WALKER BROTHERS	MY SHIP IS COMING IN	YOU'RE ALL AROUND ME	5.00
65	1458	JAMES BROWN	TRY ME	PAPA'S GOT A BRAND NEW BAG	15.00
65	1460	FRANKIE VAUGHN	THERE GOES THE FORGOTTEN MAN	WAIT	15.00
66	1465	NINA SIMONE	EITHER WAY I LOSE	BREAK DOWN AND LET IT OUT	15.00
66	1466	DUSTY SPRINGFIELD	LITTLE BY LITTLE	IF IT HADN'T BEEN FOR YOU	6.00
66	1467	FRANKIE VALLI	(YOU'RE GONNA) HURT YOURSELF	NIGHT HAWK	10.00
66	1474	FOUR SEASONS	WORKING MY WAY BACK TO YOU	TOO MANY MEMORIES	6.00
66	1476	ROBERT HENRY	WALK AWAY LIKE A WINNER	THAT'S ALL I WANT	45.00
66	1481	JAMES BROWN	NEW BREED	NEW BREED PART 2	20.00
66	1482	DUSTY SPRINGFIELD	YOU DON'T HAVE TO SAY YOU LOVE ME	EVERY ONCE OF STRENGTH	4.00
66	1483	FLAMINGOS	THE BOOGALOO PARTY	NEARNESS OF YOU	28.00
66	1485	SPOTLIGHTS	DAYFLOWER	BATMAN AND ROBIN	22.00
66	1493	FOUR SEASONS	OPUS 17 (DON'T YOU WORRY 'BOUT ME)	BEGGAR'S PARADE	10.00
66	1496	CHRISTINE EVANS	SOMEWHERE THERE'S LOVE	RIGHT OR WRONG	15.00
66	1500	SWINGING MEDALLIONS	DOUBLE SHOT OF MY BABY'S LOVE	HERE IT COMES AGAIN	30.00
66	1501	MADELINE BELL	DON'T COME RUNNING TO ME	I REALLY GOT CARRIED AWAY	15.00
66	1502	DUSTY SPRINGFIELD	GOIN' BACK	I'M GONNA LEAVE YOU	6.00
66	1503	BOBBY HEBB	SUNNY	BREAD	10.00
66	1508	HYLAND, BRIAN	THE JOKER WENT WILD	I CAN HEAR THE RAIN	15.00
66	1510	DUSTY SPRINGFIELD	ALL I SEE IS YOU	GO AHEAD ON	6.00
66	1510 PS	DUSTY SPRINGFIELD	ALL I SEE IS YOU	GO AHEAD ON	15.00
66	1512	FRANKIE VALLI	YOU'RE READY NOW	CRY FOR ME	22.00
66	1512 DJ stamped	FRANKIE VALLI	YOU'RE READY NOW	CRY FOR ME	40.00
66	1515	SWINGING MEDALLIONS	SHE DRIVES ME OUT OF MY MIND	YOU GOTTA HAVE FAITH	30.00
66	1517	LEFT BANKE	WALK AWAY RENEE	I HAVEN'T GOT THE NERVE	10.00
66	1522	BOBBY HEBB	LOVE LOVE LOVE	A SATISFIED MIND	22.00
66	1522 DJ stamped	BOBBY HEBB	LOVE LOVE LOVE	A SATISFIED MIND	40.00
66	1526	MADELINE BELL	ONE STEP AT A TIME	YOU WONT'T SEE ME	10.00
66	1529	FRANKIE VALLI	THE PROUD ONE	IVY	8.00
66	1538	FOUR SEASONS	TELL IT TO THE RAIN	SHOW GIRL	5.00
66	1541	BOBBY HEBB	LOVE ME	BABEE I'M CRAZEE (CRAZY BABY)	15.00
66	1541 DJ stamped	BOBBY HEBB	LOVE ME	BABEE I'M CRAZEE (CRAZY BABY)	20.00
66	1543	JIMMY CASTOR	HEY LEROY, YOUR MAMA'S CALLIN'	HAMHOCK'S ESPANOL	20.00
66	1553	DUSTY SPRINGFIELD	I'LL TRY ANYTHING	THE CORRUPT ONES	4.00
67	1556	FOUR SEASONS	BEGGIN'	DODY	6.00
67	1557	PEDDLERS	DELICIOUS LADY	WHAT'LL I DO	8.00
67	1563	TOYS	CIAO BABY	I GOT CARRIED AWAY	8.00
67	1567	FIVE CARD STUD	BEG ME	ONCE	15.00
67	1570	BOBBY HEBB	I LOVE EVERYTHING ABOUT YOU	SOME KINDA MAGIC	10.00
67	1575	LEFT BANKE	AND SUDDENLY	IVY IVY	12.00
67	1577	DUSTY SPRINGFIELD	GIVE ME TIME	THE LOOK OF LOVE	6.00
67	1579	BRENTON WOOD	OOGUM BOOGUM SONG	I LIKE THE WAY YOU LOVE ME	12.00
67	1580	FRANKIE VALLI	CAN'T TAKE MY EYES OFF YOU	THE TROUBLE WITH ME	5.00
67	1581	TOYS	MY LOVE SONATA	I CLOSE MY EYES	8.00
67	1586	FRANKIE & THE CLASSICALS	WHAT SHALL I DO	I ONLY HAVE EYES FOR YOU	**415.00**
67	1586 stamped	FRANKIE & THE CLASSICALS	WHAT SHALL I DO	I ONLY HAVE EYES FOR YOU	500.00
67	1590	JIMMY CASTOR	JUST YOU GIRL	MAGIC SAXOPHONE	30.00
67	1591	PAUL ELLY	SWEET SWEET LOVIN'	CRYIN' FOR MY BABY	45.00
67	1597	JAY & THE TECHNIQUES	APPLES, PEACHES, PUMPKIN PIE	STRONGER THAN DIRT	30.00
67	1600	WONDER WHO	LONESOME ROAD	AROUND AND AROUND	25.00
67	1603	FRANKIE VALLI	I MAKE A FOOL OF MYSELF	SEPTEMBER RAIN	5.00
67	1608	DUSTY SPRINGFIELD	WHAT'S IT GONNA BE	SMALLTOWN GIRL	15.00
67	1610	BOBBY HEBB	EVERYTHING IS COMING UP ROSES	BOUND BY LOVE	10.00
67	1611	MADELINE BELL	PICTURE ME GONE	GO AHEAD ON	20.00
67	1615	JERRY LEE LEWIS	SHOTGUN MAN	TURN ON YOUR LOVE LIGHT	10.00
67	1618	JAY & THE TECHNIQUES	KEEP THE BALL ROLLIN'	HERE WE GO AGAIN	20.00

67	1634	FRANKIE VALLI	TO GIVE (THE REASON I LIVE)	WATCH WHERE YOU WALK	5.00
67	1644	JAY & THE TECHNIQUES	STILL (IN LOVE WITH YOU)	STRAWBERRY SHORTCAKE	25.00
67	1648	EBONIES	NEVER GONNA BREAK YOUR HEART AGAIN	SHOE SHINE BOY	8.00
67	1656	MADELINE BELL	I'M GONNA MAKE YOU LOVE ME	I'M GONNA LEAVE YOU	6.00
68	1673	DUTCH	WHAT IS SOUL	DOWN HERE	8.00
68	1682	DUSTY SPRINGFIELD	I CLOSE MY EYES AND COUNT TO TEN	NO STRANGER AM I	5.00
68	1683	ECHOES	SEARCHING FOR YOU BABY	LISTEN TO ME BABY	15.00
68	1688	MADELINE BELL	THINKIN' (THROUGH MY TEARS)	DON'T GIVE YOUR LOVE AWAY	5.00
68	1690	JOHN FORD	A PLACE IN YOUR HEART	TWO'S COMPANY, THREE'S A CROWD	6.00
68	1702	BOBBY HEBB	YOU WANT TO CHANGE ME	DREAMY	50.00
68	1706	DUSTY SPRINGFIELD	I WILL COME TO YOU	THE COLOUR OF YOUR EYES	6.00
68	1709	ALAN SHELLY	LADY BLACK WIFE	GIVE ME TIME	18.00
68	1714	NOLA YORK	WE'LL GET TO HEAVEN	CIAO BABY	20.00
68	1721	MARION RYAN	BETTER USE YOUR HEAD	THE SEASON'S CHANGE	45.00
68	1726	MADELINE BELL	WHAT AM I SUPPOSED TO DO	HOLD IT	10.00
68	1730	DUSTY SPRINGFIELD	SON OF A PREACHER MAN	JUST A LITTLE LOVIN	5.00
69	1736	NINA SIMONE	I PUT A SPELL ON YOU	DON'T LET ME BE MISUNDERSTOOD	10.00
69	1738	FREE	SOUL PARTY	DOWN TO THE BONE	6.00
69	1754	FREE	TAKING IT AWAY (WOULD BE BREAKING MY HEART)	KEEP IN TOUCH	50.00
69	1754 DJ	FREE	TAKING IT AWAY (WOULD BE BREAKING MY HEART)	KEEP IN TOUCH	75.00
69	1786	FLAMINGOS	THE BOOGALOO PARTY	THE NEARNESS OF YOU	10.00
69	1786 solid center	FLAMINGOS	BOOGALOO PARTY	NEARNESS OF YOU	15.00
69	1786 large hole	FLAMINGOS	BOOGALOO PARTY	NEARNESS OF YOU	8.00
69	1786 DJ	FLAMINGOS	BOOGALOO PARTY	NEARNESS OF YOU	45.00
69	1786 DJ PS	FLAMINGOS	BOOGALOO PARTY	NEARNESS OF YOU	75.00
69	1786 ink	FLAMINGOS	THE BOOGALOO PARTY	THE NEARNESS OF YOU	6.00
69	1791	JOHN FORD	I KNOW IT'S LOVE	LOOK BEFORE YOU LEAP	6.00
69	1795	FRANKIE VALLI	THE GIRL I'LL NEVER KNOW	A FACE WITHOUT A NAME	5.00
69	1799	MADELINE BELL	WE'RE SO MUCH IN LOVE	HOW MUCH DO I LOVE YOU	4.00
69	1811	DUSTY SPRINGFIELD	AM I THE SAME GIRL	EARTHBOUND GYPSY	10.00
69	1826	DUSTY SPRINGFIELD	BRAND NEW ME	BAD CASE OF THE BLUES	10.00
69	1833	JOHN FORD	RUNNING AWAY	YESTERDAY WHEN WHEN I YOUNG	15.00
69	1833 DJ	JOHN FORD	RUNNING AWAY	YESTERDAY WHEN WHEN I YOUNG	12.00
72	320226	FRANKIE VALLI	YOU'RE READY NOW	CRY FOR ME	8.00
72	320226 DJ	FRANKIE VALLI	YOU'RE READY NOW	CRY FOR ME	20.00
62	326530	ANNE SHELTON	ROME (WASN'T BUILT IN A DAY)	I UNDERSTAND	30.00
72	600214	DUSTY SPRINGFIELD	YESTERDAY WHEN I WAS YOUNG	I START COUNTING	5.00
70	6006030	JOHN FORD	YOU'VE GOT ME WHERE YOU WANT ME	YOU'RE ALL ALONE TONIGHT	150.00
70	6006035 withdrawn	WAYNE FONTANA	GIVE ME JUST A LITTLE MORE TIME	I'M IN LOVE	200.00
70	6006035 DJ	WAYNE FONTANA	GIVE ME JUST A LITTLE MORE TIME	I'M IN LOVE	**185.00**
70	6006037	SUSAN SHIRLEY	REALLY INTO SOMETHIN'	MY FRIEND THE CLOWN	45.00
70	6006037	SUSAN SHIRLEY	REALLY INTO SOMETHIN'	MY FRIEND THE CLOWN	60.00
70	6006045	DUSTY SPRINGFIELD	SPOOKY	HOW CAN I BE SURE	5.00
70	6006045 DJ	DUSTY SPRINGFIELD	SPOOKY	HOW CAN I BE SURE	10.00
71	6006077	CLEO LAINE	NIGHT OWL	MODEL CITY'S PROGRAMME	10.00
71	6006082	MADELINE BELL	IF YOU DIDN'T HEAR ME THE FIRST TIME	YOU WALKED AWAY	5.00
71	6006083	RAY McVAY SOUND	THEY CALL ME MR. TIBBS	20.00	
72	6006196	MAYA FERNICK	GIVE ME YOUR LOVE AGAIN	FLOWERS IN THE CITY	30.00
72	6006225	CHAQUITO	HAWAII 5 - O	IRONSIDE	5.00
73	6006280 paper	LIFE	CAT'S EYES I	DEATH IN THE FAMILY	20.00
77	6006280 ink	LIFE	CAT'S EYES	DEATH IN THE FAMILY	6.00
73	6006291	ROZETTA HIGHTOWER	THE WALLS FELL DOWN	CAPTAIN'S ARMY	4.00
74	6006295	DUSTY SPRINGFIELD	WHO GETS YOUR LOVE	OF ALL THE THINGS	5.00
74	6006325	DUSTY SPRINGFIELD	LEARN TO SAY GOODBYE	EASY EVIL	5.00
74	6006350	DUSTY SPRINGFIELD	BRING HIM BACK	WHAT'S IT GONNA BE	15.00
75	6006446	DUSTY SPRINGFIELD	YESTERDAY WHEN I WAS YOUNG	THE LOOK OF LOVE	5.00
75	6006488	PLATTERS	DANCE TO THE MUSIC OF LOVE	FULL HEART EMPTY ARMS	4.00
75	6006464	5000 VOLTS	I'M ON FIRE	STILL ON FIRE	4.00
75	6006489	FAY HAUSER	YOU BRING THE SUN IN THE MORNING	YOU BRING THE SUN (DISCO MIX	6.00
76	6006492	L.J. JOHNSON	YOUR MAGIC PUT A SPELL ON ME	SPELLBOUND	5.00
76	6006597	JACKIE DARNELL	LEADING YOU ON	CAN LOVE BE THE SAME	8.00
73	6009316 paper	PAUL MAURIAT ORCH.	BLACK IS BLACK instrumental	UN HOMME ET UNE FEMME	5.00
75	6009633	CRYSTAL GRASS	CRYSTAL WORLD	CALIFORNIA SUMMER	8.00
72	6051011	FRANKIE VALLI	THE PROUD ONE	IVY	10.00
72	6051023 paper	BOBBY HEBB	LOVE LOVE LOVE	SUNNY	8.00
76	6051023 ink	BOBBY HEBB	LOVE LOVE LOVE	SUNNY	6.00
72	6051025	BOBBY HEBB	SOME KIND OF MAGIC	GOOD GOOD LOVIN'	8.00
73	6051027	SHANGRI-LAS	TRAIN FROM KANSAS	PAST PRESENT & FUTURE	5.00
73	6073705	GIL SCOTT-HERON	LADY DAY AND JOHN COLTRANE	WHEN YOU ARE WHO YOU ARE	20.00
73	6073707	LEON THOMAS	BOOM BOOM BOOM	LOVE	5.00
73	6073708	PRETTY PURDIE	GOOD LIVING	DAY DREAMING	4.00
73	6073808	SILVER BULLIT	WILLPOWER WEAK, TEMPTATION STRONG	HITTIN' ON YOU	22.00
75	6146300	BROTHER TO BROTHER	IN THE BOTTLE	MOTHER EARTH	8.00
	6160051	SHANGRI-LAS	PAST PRESENT AND FUTURE	GIVE HIM A GREAT BIG KISS + RE	4.00
	cut 114	FLAMINGOS c/w MITCH RYDER	THE BOOGALOO PARTY	JENNY TAKE A RIDE	6.00

PHILLY GROOVE

02	PG1	FIRST CHOICE	THIS IS THE HOUSE WHERE LOVE DIED	GONNA KEEP ON LOVING HIM	6.00
02	PG1 test press	FIRST CHOICE	THIS IS THE HOUSE WHERE LOVE DIED	GONNA KEEP ON LOVING HIM	10.00
02	PG2	ALFIE DAVISON c/w FLASHLIGHT	LOVE IS A SERIOUS BUSINESS	BEWARE SHE'S PULLING MY STRING	6.00
02	PG2 test press	ALFIE DAVISON c/w FLASHLIGHT	LOVE IS A SERIOUS BUSINESS	BEWARE SHE'S PULLING MY STRING	10.00
02	PG3	DELFONICS c/w CRUSADERS	YOU'LL GET ENOUGH	YOU PAY FOR LOVE	6.00
02	PG3 test press	DELFONICS c/w CRUSADERS	YOU'LL GET ENOUGH	YOU PAY FOR LOVE	10.00

PHOENIX

97	0001	ALESHURE c/w MIGHTY CLOUDS OF JOY	SHOWER THE WORLD	I'M READY	10.00

PHONOGRAM

33 RPM DJ EP	CISSY HOUSTON c/w DETROIT EMERALDS	I JUST DON'T KNOW WHAT TO DO WITH MYSELF	LONG LIVE THE KING	25.00

PICCADILLY

Subsidiary of Pye Records who originally sold televisions and radios. They entered the record business when it acquired Nixa Records in 1953 calling themselves Pye Nixa. In 1959 the name was changed to Pye Records when the television broadcasting company ATV bought 50% of the label completing the other 50% purchase in 1966.

The subsidiary Piccadilly was formed by Pye in 1961, exclusively releasing 45's by British or British based artists. Piccadilly boasted two of the UK's greatest soul bands of the era within its recording rosta. Jimmy James & the Vagabonds along with Geno Washington and the Ram Jam Band were filling dance halls and town halls up and down the country as the "Mod" movement gathered pace, and soul became the "in" sound of the day. These two bands must take some of the credit for creating the UK soul collecting foundations that would spawn the all night dance clubs during the mid-sixties that became the embryo of the biggest underground music movement in the world today- Northern Soul. But not just these two were travelling the country performing soul. The Timebox, Peter Jay & The Jaywalkers, Felders Orioles and single artists like Billie Davis, Antionette were doing their bit bringing the hip sound of soul to the sticks.

One look down the Piccadilly listing confirms Pye contribution through the label to soul music was considerable.

66	34049 EP PS	SOUNDS ORCHESTRAL	AIN'T THAT PECULIAR	1966 4 track EP with cover	10.00
66	34053 EP PS	JIMMY JAMES & the VAGABONDS	AIN'T LOVE GOOD AIN'T LOVE PROUD	1966 4 track EP with cover	30.00
66	34054 EP PS	GENO WASHINGTON & RAM JAM BAND	HI !	1966 4 track EP with cover	9.00
61	35035	DICK JORDAN	I WANT HER BACK	SOME OF THESE DAYS	100.00
61	35035 DJ	DICK JORDAN	I WANT HER BACK	SOME OF THESE DAYS	150.00
64	35165	JACKIE TRENT	ONLY ONE SUCH AS YOU	IF YOU LOVE ME	50.00
64	35165 DJ	JACKIE TRENT	ONLY ONE SUCH AS YOU	IF YOU LOVE ME	75.00
64	35171	TRENDS	ALL MY LOVING	SWEET LITTLE MISS LOVE	10.00
64	35171 DJ	TRENDS	ALL MY LOVING	SWEET LITTLE MISS LOVE	15.00
64	35199	PETER JAY and the JAYWALKERS	WHERE DID OUR LOVE GO	CAROLINE	10.00
64	35199 DJ	PETER JAY and the JAYWALKERS	WHERE DID OUR LOVE GO	CAROLINE	15.00
64	35205	PETER'S FACES	JUST LIKE ROMEO & JULIET	WAIT	12.00
64	35205 DJ	PETER'S FACES	JUST LIKE ROMEO & JULIET	WAIT	15.00
64	35206	SOUNDS ORCHESTRAL	CAST YOUR FATE TO THE WIND	TO WENDY WITH LOVE	6.00
64	35206 DJ	SOUNDS ORCHESTRAL	CAST YOUR FATE TO THE WIND	TO WENDY WITH LOVE	10.00
65	35220	PETER JAY and the JAYWALKERS	PARCHMAN FARM	WHAT'S EASY FOR TWO IS HARD FO	20.00
65	35220 DJ	PETER JAY and the JAYWALKERS	PARCHMAN FARM	WHAT'S EASY FOR TWO IS HARD FO	28.00
65	35226	SOUNDS ORCHESTRAL	HAVE FAITH IN YOUR LOVE	LIKE THE LONELY	6.00
65	35226 DJ	SOUNDS ORCHESTRAL	HAVE FAITH IN YOUR LOVE	LIKE THE LONELY	10.00
65	35227	BILLIE DAVIS	THE LAST ONE TO BE LOVED	YOU DON'T KNOW	10.00
65	35227 DJ	BILLIE DAVIS	THE LAST ONE TO BE LOVED	YOU DON'T KNOW	15.00
65	35235	KEITH RUSSELL	PEOPLE GET READY	PARADISE	8.00
65	35235 DJ	KEITH RUSSELL	PEOPLE GET READY	PARADISE	10.00
65	35236	ROCKIN' BERRIES	POOR MAN'S SON	FOLLOW ME	5.00
65	35236 DJ	ROCKIN' BERRIES	POOR MAN'S SON	FOLLOW ME	10.00
65	35237	VAL McKENNA	BABY DO IT	I BELIEVE IN LOVE	20.00
65	35237 DJ	VAL McKENNA	BABY DO IT	I BELIEVE IN LOVE	28.00
65	35239	DODIE WEST	IN THE DEEP OF THE NIGHT	ROVIN' BOY	30.00
65	35239 PS	DODIE WEST	IN THE DEEP OF THE NIGHT	ROVIN' BOY	50.00
65	35239 DJ	DODIE WEST	IN THE DEEP OF THE NIGHT	ROVIN' BOY	40.00
65	35241	BUDDY BRITTEN & the REGENTS	SHE'S ABOUT A MOVER	SINCE YOU'VE GONE	10.00
65	35241 DJ	BUDDY BRITTEN & the REGENTS	SHE'S ABOUT A MOVER	SINCE YOU'VE GONE	15.00
65	35246	BARBARA RUSKIN	YOU CAN'T BLAME A GIRL FOR TRYING	NO MORE TO FALL	15.00
65	35246 DJ	BARBARA RUSKIN	YOU CAN'T BLAME A GIRL FOR TRYING	NO MORE TO FALL	22.00
65	35256	VAL McKENNA	MIXED UP SHOOK UP GIRL	NOW THAT YOU'VE MADE UP YOUR M	15.00
65	35256 DJ	VAL McKENNA	MIXED UP SHOOK UP GIRL	NOW THAT YOU'VE MADE UP YOUR M	22.00
65	35262	JOHN SCHROEDER ORCH.	SOUL FOR SALE	LOVING YOU GIRL	30.00
65	35262 DJ	JOHN SCHROEDER ORCH.	SOUL FOR SALE	LOVING YOU GIRL	40.00
65	35268	SOUNDS ORCHESTRAL	GO HOME GIRL	A BOY AND A GIRL	10.00
65	35268 DJ	SOUNDS ORCHESTRAL	GO HOME GIRL	A BOY AND A GIRL	12.00
65	35269	FELDERS ORIOLES	TURN ON YOUR LOVELIGHT	DOWN HOME GIRL	15.00
65	35269 DJ	FELDERS ORIOLES	TURN ON YOUR LOVELIGHT	DOWN HOME GIRL	20.00
65	35271	JOHN SCHROEDER ORCH.	AGENT OO-SOUL	NIGHTRIDER	30.00
65	35271 DJ	JOHN SCHROEDER ORCH.	AGENT OO-SOUL	NIGHTRIDER	40.00
65	35272	CARNABY	JUMP AND DANCE	MY LOVE WILL STAY	75.00
65	35272 DJ	CARNABY	JUMP AND DANCE	MY LOVE WILL STAY	100.00
66	35275	KEITH POWELL	IT WAS EASIER TO HURT	GOODBYE GIRL	10.00
66	35275 DJ	KEITH POWELL	IT WAS EASIER TO HURT	GOODBYE GIRL	15.00
66	35285	JOHN SCHROEDER ORCH.	HUNGRY FOR LOVE	SOUL DESTROYER	20.00
66	35285 DJ	JOHN SCHROEDER ORCH.	HUNGRY FOR LOVE	SOUL DESTROYER	30.00
66	35292	BAND OF ANGELS	INVITATION	CHEAT AND LIE	50.00
66	35292 DJ	BAND OF ANGELS	INVITATION	CHEAT AND LIE	75.00
66	35293	ANTOINETTE	WHY DON'T I RUN AWAY FROM YOU	THERE'S NO ONE IN THE WHOLE WI	25.00

66	35293 DJ	ANTOINETTE	WHY DON'T I RUN AWAY FROM YOU	THERE'S NO ONE IN THE WHOLE WI	40.00
66	35298	JIMMY JAMES & the VAGABONDS	I WANNA BE YOUR EVERYTHNG	I FEEL ALRIGHT	20.00
66	35298 PS	JIMMY JAMES & the VAGABONDS	I WANNA BE YOUR EVERYTHNG	I FEEL ALRIGHT	100.00
66	35298 DJ	JIMMY JAMES & the VAGABONDS	I WANNA BE YOUR EVERYTHNG	I FEEL ALRIGHT	30.00
66	35303	BOBBY RIO	ASK THE LONELY	BE LONELY LITTLE GIRL	20.00
66	35303 DJ	BOBBY RIO	ASK THE LONELY	BE LONELY LITTLE GIRL	30.00
66	35307	NITA ROSSI	SOMETHING TO GIVE	HERE I GO AGAIN	45.00
66	35307 DJ	NITA ROSSI	SOMETHING TO GIVE	HERE I GO AGAIN	70.00
66	35310	ANTOINETTE	LULLABY OF LOVE	I'M FOR YOU	12.00
66	35310 DJ	ANTOINETTE	LULLABY OF LOVE	I'M FOR YOU	20.00
66	35312	GENO WASHINGTON & RAM JAM BAND	WATER	UNDERSTANDING	15.00
66	35312 DJ	GENO WASHINGTON & RAM JAM BAND	WATER	UNDERSTANDING	20.00
66	35316	DEE KING	SALLY GO ROUND THE ROSES	IT'S SO FINE	15.00
66	35316 DJ	DEE KING	SALLY GO ROUND THE ROSES	IT'S SO FINE	20.00
66	35317	DAVID GARRICK	LET'S GO SOMEWHERE	LADY JANE	6.00
66	35317 DJ	DAVID GARRICK	LET'S GO SOMEWHERE	LADY JANE	10.00
66	35320	JIMMY JAMES & the VAGABONDS	COME SOFTLY TO ME	HI DIDDLEY DEE DUM DUM	15.00
66	35320 DJ	JIMMY JAMES & the VAGABONDS	COME SOFTLY TO ME	HI DIDDLEY DEE DUM DUM	20.00
66	35321	KEITH POWELL & BILLIE DAVIS	YOU DON'T KNOW LIKE I KNOW	TWO LITTLE PEOPLE	10.00
66	35321 DJ	KEITH POWELL & BILLIE DAVIS	YOU DON'T KNOW LIKE I KNOW	TWO LITTLE PEOPLE	15.00
66	35329	GENO WASHINGTON & RAM JAM BAND	HI! HI! HAZEL	BEACH BASH	15.00
66	35329 DJ	GENO WASHINGTON & RAM JAM BAND	HI! HI! HAZEL	BEACH BASH	20.00
66	35330	BYSTANDERS	(YOU'RE GONNA) HURT YOURSELF	HAVE I OFFENDED THE GIRL	25.00
66	35330 DJ	BYSTANDERS	(YOU'RE GONNA) HURT YOURSELF	HAVE I OFFENDED THE GIRL	30.00
66	35331	JIMMY JAMES & the VAGABONDS	THIS HEART OF MINE	I DON'T WANNA CRY	75.00
66	35331 PS	JIMMY JAMES & the VAGABONDS	THIS HEART OF MINE	I DON'T WANNA CRY	200.00
66	35331 DJ	JIMMY JAMES & the VAGABONDS	THIS HEART OF MINE	I DON'T WANNA CRY	100.00
66	35332	FELDERS ORIOLES	BACK STREET	SOMETHING YOU GOT	25.00
66	35332 DJ	FELDERS ORIOLES	BACK STREET	SOMETHING YOU GOT	40.00
66	35342	LOVING KIND	AIN'T THAT PECULIAR	WITH RHYME AND REASON	15.00
66	35342 DJ	LOVING KIND	AIN'T THAT PECULIAR	WITH RHYME AND REASON	20.00
66	35346	GENO WASHINGTON & RAM JAM BAND	QUE SERA SERA	ALL I NEED	22.00
66	35346 DJ	GENO WASHINGTON & RAM JAM BAND	QUE SERA SERA	ALL I NEED	30.00
66	35349	JIMMY JAMES & the VAGABONDS	AIN'T LOVE GOOD AIN'T LOVE PROUD	DON'T KNOW WHAT I'M GONNA DO	15.00
66	35349 DJ	JIMMY JAMES & the VAGABONDS	AIN'T LOVE GOOD AIN'T LOVE PROUD	DON'T KNOW WHAT I'M GONNA DO	25.00
66	35350	BILLIE DAVIS	JUST WALK IN MY SHOES	EV'RY DAY	60.00
66	35350 DJ	BILLIE DAVIS	JUST WALK IN MY SHOES	EV'RY DAY	85.00
66	35358	EBONY KEYES	IF YOU KNEW	SITTING IN A RING	100.00
66	35358 DJ	EBONY KEYES	IF YOU KNEW	SITTING IN A RING	150.00
66	35359	GENO WASHINGTON & RAM JAM BAND	MICHAEL	(I GOTTA) HOLD ON TO MY LOVE	12.00
66	35359 DJ	GENO WASHINGTON & RAM JAM BAND	MICHAEL	(I GOTTA) HOLD ON TO MY LOVE	20.00
67	35360	JIMMY JAMES & the VAGABONDS	HUNGRY FOR LOVE	I CAN'T GET BACK HOME TO MY BA	10.00
67	35360 DJ	JIMMY JAMES & the VAGABONDS	HUNGRY FOR LOVE	I CAN'T GET BACK HOME TO MY BA	15.00
67	35363	BYSTANDERS	STUBBORN KIND OF FELLOW	98.6	15.00
67	35363 DJ	BYSTANDERS	STUBBORN KIND OF FELLOW	98.6	20.00
67	35364	SHIRLEY ABICAIR	AM I LOSING YOU	I WILL BE THERE	15.00
67	35364 DJ	SHIRLEY ABICAIR	AM I LOSING YOU	I WILL BE THERE	25.00
67	35366	STELLA STARR	BRING HIM BACK	SAY IT	75.00
67	35366 DJ	STELLA STARR	BRING HIM BACK	SAY IT	100.00
67	35369	TIMEBOX	I'LL ALWAYS LOVE YOU	SAVE YOUR LOVE	75.00
67	35369 DJ	TIMEBOX	I'LL ALWAYS LOVE YOU	SAVE YOUR LOVE	100.00
67	35374	JIMMY JAMES & the VAGABONDS	NO GOOD TO CRY	YOU SHOWED ME THE WAY	15.00
67	35374 DJ	JIMMY JAMES & the VAGABONDS	NO GOOD TO CRY	YOU SHOWED ME THE WAY	20.00
67	35375	EBONY KEYES	CUPID'S HOUSE	IF OUR LOVE SHOULD END	8.00
67	35375 DJ	EBONY KEYES	CUPID'S HOUSE	IF OUR LOVE SHOULD END	10.00
67	35379	TIMEBOX	SOUL SAUCE	I WISH I COULD JERK LIKE MY UNCLE	85.00
67	35379 DJ	TIMEBOX	SOUL SAUCE	I WISH I COULD JERK LIKE MY UNCLE	100.00
67	35381	NEW FORMULA	I'M ON THE OUTSIDE LOOKING IN	DO IT AGAIN A LITTLE BIT SLOWER	8.00
67	35381 DJ	NEW FORMULA	I'M ON THE OUTSIDE LOOKING IN	DO IT AGAIN A LITTLE BIT SLOWER	10.00
67	35387	MARGO & the MARVETTES	SEVEN LETTERS	THAT'S HOW LOVE GOES	10.00
67	35387 DJ	MARGO & the MARVETTES	SEVEN LETTERS	THAT'S HOW LOVE GOES	15.00
67	35390	EBONY KEYES	COUNTRY GIRL	HOW MANY TIMES	8.00
67	35390 DJ	EBONY KEYES	COUNTRY GIRL	HOW MANY TIMES	10.00
67	35392	GENO WASHINGTON & RAM JAM BAND	SHE SHOT A HOLE IN MY SOUL	I'VE BEEN HURT BY LOVE	15.00
67	35392 DJ	GENO WASHINGTON & RAM JAM BAND	SHE SHOT A HOLE IN MY SOUL	I'VE BEEN HURT BY LOVE	20.00
67	35394	RAY KING SOUL BAND	BEHOLD	SOON YOU'LL BE GONE	10.00
67	35394 DJ	RAY KING SOUL BAND	BEHOLD	SOON YOU'LL BE GONE	15.00
67	35401	NEW FORMULA	I WANT TO GO BACK THERE AGAIN	CAN'T YOU SEE THAT SHE LOVES ME	8.00
67	35401 DJ	NEW FORMULA	I WANT TO GO BACK THERE AGAIN	CAN'T YOU SEE THAT SHE LOVES ME	10.00
67	35403	GENO WASHINGTON & RAM JAM BAND	TELL IT LIKE IT IS	GIRL I WANT TO MARRY	10.00
67	35403 DJ	GENO WASHINGTON & RAM JAM BAND	TELL IT LIKE IT IS	GIRL I WANT TO MARRY	15.00
67	35407	EBONY KEYES	DON'T	SWEET MARY (SWEETER THAN A ROSE)	8.00
67	35407 DJ	EBONY KEYES	DON'T	SWEET MARY (SWEETER THAN A ROSE)	10.00

PINNACLE

79	73 PS	PEGGY SCOTT	YOU'VE GOT IT ALL	LET ME UNITE YOU	15.00

PLANET

A project by Philips Records who manufactured and distributed this label that lasted only 22 releases with all those being pressed in 1966. The Planet label is one of the UK's most prized 45 catalogues. Why this label only lasted for a year is a mystery but during it's short life the label released some of the country's most collectable 45's. The Untamed, The Thoughts, Gnomes Of Zurich, Corduroys to name a few, are extremely sought after by the British 60's Psyche collectors. Even the original white with the black logo company sleeves of Planet Records can sell for up to £10.00 each. So when evaluating a Planet 45, add at least £5 to the price it's it is still with its original release sleeve. The 45's listed below are the only ones I find that would interest the UK soul enthusiast.

66	104	JOHN LEE'S GROUNDHOGS	I'LL NEVER FALL IN LOVE AGAIN	OVER YOU BABY	75.00
66	114	JOHN LEE HOOKER	MAI LEE	DON'T BE MESSING AROUND WITH ME	40.00
66	115	PERTETUAL LANGLEY	SURRENDER	TWO BY TWO	50.00
66	116	CREATION	MAKING TIME	TRY AND STOP ME	25.00
66	117	ORLONS	SPINNIN' TOP	ANYONE WHO HAD A HEART	100.00
66	119	CREATION	PAINTER MAN	BIFF BANG POW	50.00

PLEXIUM

69	10	CLEMENTS, SOUL JOE	EVER, EVER	SMOKE AND ASHES	200.00
70	19	MIKE MORTON COMBINATION	YOU GOTTA BE MINE	BURNING BRIDGES	15.00

PLUM

	001	STORM	AIN'T TOO PROUD TO BEG	LET'S GO DANCING	4.00

POLO

76	10	IRMA THOMAS	SAFE WITH ME	DON'T STOP	5.00

POLYDOR

Polydor is another huge label that started its life in Germany. Originally it was part of Deutsche Grammophon. Later it became part of Polygram but currently is one of the many labels within the Universal Music Group. During the 60's it established itself firmly in the hearts of soul collectors, it's distinguishable red label inside that eye catching red sleeve with a world recognised logo was one of the delights you might find whilst hunting for 45's on market stalls and junk shops. Polydor actually released some of the UK's most sought after soul related 45's.#

Tony Middleton, Inspirations, Paradox, Bobby Paris and of course Edwin Starr etc. The most prized 45 on the label is perhaps the Edwin Starr classic "S.O.S. Stop On Sight" as a promotional copy. Polydor promotional copies are a mystery as not all 45's received a pressing as a white label with a full label length red A. I've only noted the DJ copies I know actually exist. All red and white Polydor soul DJ copies are extremely desirable and sought after.

	JB1	JAMES BROWN	PAPA'S GOT A BRAND NEW BAG	I GOT YOU I FEEL GOOD + OUT OF SIGHT	4.00
78	1	FIVE & A PENNY	YOU DON'T KNOW WHERE YOUR INTEREST LIES	MARY GO ROUND	8.00
79	26	JOE SIMON	LOVE VIBRATION	I.O.U.	4.00
81	375	LEVEL 42	EASIER SAID THAN DONE	LATE NIGHT FLIGHT	3.00
63	52158	SHAKERS	MONEY	MEMPHIS TENNESSEE	20.00
63	52213	SHAKERS	HIPPY HIPPY SHAKE	DR. FEELGOOD	20.00
63	52258	SHAKERS	MONEY	HIPPY HIPPY SHAKE	15.00
64	52264	ALEX HARVEY	I JUST WANNA MAKE LOVE TO YOU	LET THE GOOD TIMES ROLL	25.00
64	52907	ALEX HARVEY & HIS SOUL BAND	I GOT MY MOJO WORKIN'	I AIN'T WORRIED BABY	40.00
64	52930	JOHN LEE HOOKER	SHAKE IT BABY	LET'S MAKE IT BABY	20.00
65	56006	TOMMY BRUCE and the BRUISERS	BOOM BOOM	CAN YOUR MONKEY DO THE DOG	15.00
65	56009	PINKY	ALL CRIED OUT	BACK WHERE I BELONG	10.00
65	56012	SALINA JONES	LONGING	TOO LATE	10.00
65	56012 test press	SALINA JONES	LONGING	TOO LATE	15.00
65	56017	ALEX HARVEY & HIS SOUL BAND	AIN'T THAT JUST TOO BAD	MY KIND OF LOVE	30.00
65	56027	CAROLINES	BELIEVE IN ME	LOVE MADE A FOOL OF ME	15.00
65	56028	PYRAMIDS	BABY'S GONE AWAY	KISS AND DANCE WITH YOU	15.00
65	56031	GABRIELLI BRASS	CAT WALK	ANGEL CAKE	6.00
65	56043	JOHNNY GUSTAFSON	TAKE ME FOR A LITTLE WHILE	MAKE ME YOUR NUMBER ONE	15.00
65	56043 DJ	JOHNNY GUSTAFSON	TAKE ME FOR A LITTLE WHILE	MAKE ME YOUR NUMBER ONE	40.00
65	56047	GABRIELLI BRASS	RIDE YOUR PONY	ANYONE WHO HAD A HEART	10.00
65	56059	CON-CHORDS	YOU CAN'T TAKE IT AWAY	LET ME WALK WITH YOU	20.00
65	56064	DIANE LANCASTER	HOW I NEED HIM	SOMEONE LIKE YOU	10.00
65	56065	JOHN BULL BREED	CAN'T CHANCE A BREAKUP	I'M A MAN	150.00
65	56065 DJ	JOHN BULL BREED	CAN'T CHANCE A BREAKUP	I'M A MAN	200.00
66	56076	LINDA KENDRICK	IT'S THE LITTLE THINGS	WHEN YOUR LOVE IS WARM	75.00
66	56076 DJ	LINDA KENDRICK	IT'S THE LITTLE THINGS	WHEN YOUR LOVE IS WARM	125.00
66	56077	TRACY ROGERS	THROUGH THICK AND THIN	BABY	15.00
66	56081	CARROLS	SURRENDER YOUR LOVE	THE FOLK I LOVE	15.00
66	56081 DJ	CARROLLS	SURRENDER YOUR LOVE	THE FOLK I LOVE	15.00
66	56086	JACKSON & SMITH	PARTY '66	AND THAT'S IT	8.00
66	56087	JOHNNY & JOHN	SCRAPE MY BOOT	BUMPER TO BUMPER	15.00
66	56087 DJ	JOHNNY & JOHN	SCRAPE MY BOOT	BUMPER TO BUMPER	25.00
66	56088	BARRY MONROE	NEVER AGAIN	WORLD OF BROKEN HEARTS	10.00
66	56091	JACK HAMMER	LOVE LADDER	THANKS	15.00
66	56091 DJ	JACK HAMMER	LOVE LADDER	THANKS	30.00
66	56096	MIKE COTTON SOUND	HARLEM SHUFFLE	LIKE THAT	20.00
66	56108	SONNY CHILDE	TWO LOVERS	AIN'T THAT GOOD NEWS	20.00
66	56114	LUCAS	DANCE CHILDREN DANCE	I SAW PITY IN THE FACE OF A FR	15.00
66	56119	CHANTELLES	THERE'S SOMETHING ABOUT YOU	JUST ANOTHER FOOL	20.00
66	56134	GARY JAMES	YOU'RE GONE	NICOLE	10.00
66	56135	VALERIE MASTERS	DON'T EVER GO	SAY HELLO	30.00
66	56141	SONNY CHILDE	HEARTBREAK	I STILL LOVE YOU	10.00
66	56144	NORMIE ROWE	AIN'T NOBODY HOME	OOH LA LA	10.00
66	56146	LINDA KENDRICKS	A FRIEND OF MINE	I FALL APART	15.00
66	56152	KINGSIZE TAYLOR	LET ME LOVE YOU	THINKIN'	25.00
66	56164	MONOPOLY	HOUSE OF LORDS	MAGIC CARPET	8.00
67	56173	LINDA LEWIS	YOU TURNED MY BITTER INTO SWEET	DO YOU BELIEVE IN LOVE	125.00

67	56176	OLIVER NORMAN	DROWNING IN MY OWN DESPAIR	DOWN IN THE BASEMENT	40.00
67	56176 DJ	OLIVER NORMAN	DROWNING IN MY OWN DESPAIR	DOWN IN THE BASEMENT	75.00
67	56189	STUDIO SIX	I CAN'T SLEEP	TIMES WERE WHEN	10.00
67	56198	BEN BROWN	ASK THE LONELY	SIDEWINDER	30.00
67	56203	KEVIN KING LEAR	COUNT ME OUT	PRETTY WOMAN	20.00
67	56228	AMBOY DUKES	WHO'S FOOLING WHO	JUDY IN DISQUISE	10.00
68	56234	DONNIE ELBERT	IN BETWEEN THE HEARTACHES	TOO FAR GONE	15.00
68	56234 test press	DONNIE ELBERT	IN BETWEEN THE HEARTACHES	TOO FAR GONE	20.00
68	56247	OLIVER NORMAN	PEOPLE PEOPLE	YOU'LL FIND IT WILL COME	5.00
68	56252	GABRIELLI BRASS	WORKING MY WAY BACK TO YOU	CANTERBURY TALES THEME	20.00
68	56252 DJ	GABRIELI BRASS	WORKING MY WAY BACK TO YOU	THEME FROM CANTERBURY TALES	30.00
68	56265	DONNIE ELBERT	THIS OLD HEART OF MINE (IS WEAK FOR YOU)	RUN LITTLE GIRL	10.00
68	56275	PARADOX	RING THE CHANGES	THE WEDNESDAY THEME	150.00
68	56276	AYSHEA	ONLY LOVE CAN SAME ME NOW	CELEBRATION OF THE YEAR	45.00
68	56282	FIVE & A PENNY	YOU DON'T KNOW WHERE YOUR INTEREST	MARY GO ROUND	60.00
68	56290	JOHN DREVAR	WHAT GREATER LOVE	I'VE DECIDED	10.00
68	56295	ROBERT HENRY HENSLEY	YOU'RE GONNA SEE ME CRY	MONTAGE	10.00
69	56336	STUART SMITH	MY HEAD GORES AROUND	WHERE YOU ARE	10.00
69	56350	P.P. ARNOLD	BURY ME DOWN BY THE RIVER	GIVE A HAND, TAKE A HAND	5.00
70	56369	CANDY CHOIR	WHY DO YOU CRY MY LOVE	LUCKY JIM	8.00
65	56503	SHAMROCKS	LA LA LA LA LA	AND I NEED YOU	10.00
66	56506	IKETTES	I'M SO THANKFUL	DON'T FEEL SORRY FOR ME	10.00
66	56510	TRIBE	DANCIN' TO THE BEAT OF MY HEART	WOOFIN'	75.00
66	56510 DJ	TRIBE	DANCIN' TO THE BEAT OF MY HEART	WOOFIN'	100.00
66	56513	TONY McKAY	DETROIT	NOBODY'S PERFECT	10.00
66	56513 DJ	TONY McKAY	DETROIT	NOBODY'S PERFECT	20.00
66	56515	LOWELL FULSOM	LITTLE ANGEL	BLACK NIGHTS	20.00
66	56515 DJ	LOWELL FULSOM	LITTLE ANGEL	BLACK NIGHTS	40.00
66	56516	IKETTES	(NEVER MORE) LONELY FOR YOU	SALLY GO ROUND THE ROSES	15.00
66	56516 DJ	IKETTES	(NEVER MORE) LONELY FOR YOU	SALLY GO ROUND THE ROSES	40.00
66	56533	IKETTES	I'M SO THANKFUL	DON'T FEEL SORRY FOR ME	15.00
66	56533 DJ	IKETTES	I'M SO THANKFUL	DON'T FEEL SORRY FOR ME	40.00
66	56540	JAMES BROWN	THAT'S LIFE	PLEASE, PLEASE, PLEASE	8.00
66	56541	JAMES BROWN	SAY IT LOUD, I'M BLACK AND I'M PROUD	same: part 2	5.00
66	56702 lh	EDWIN STARR	I HAVE FAITH IN YOU	STOP HER ON SIGHT (S.O.S.)	20.00
66	56702 sh	EDWIN STARR	I HAVE FAITH IN YOU	STOP HER ON SIGHT (S.O.S.)	40.00
66	56702 DJ	EDWIN STARR	I HAVE FAITH IN YOU	STOP HER ON SIGHT (S.O.S.)	700.00
66	56704	TONY MIDDLETON	TO THE ENDS OF THE EARTH	DON'T EVER LEAVE ME	**509.00**
66	56704 DJ	TONY MIDDLETON	TO THE ENDS OF THE EARTH	DON'T EVER LEAVE ME	750.00
66	56709	JAMO THOMAS & his PARTY BROS	I SPY (FOR THE FBI)	SNAKE HIP MAMA	25.00
66	56709 DJ	JAMO THOMAS & his PARTY BROS	I SPY (FOR THE FBI)	SNAKE HIP MAMA	200.00
66	56711	MARVA JOSIE	CRAZY STOCKING	I'LL GET BY	10.00
66	56715	SUZIE & BIG DEE IRWIN	AIN'T THAT LOVIN' YOU BABY	I CAN'T GET OVER YOU	8.00
66	56715 DJ	SUZIE & BIG DEE IRWIN	AIN'T THAT LOVING YOU BABY	I CAN'T GET OVER YOU	15.00
66	56717	EDWIN STARR	HEADLINE NEWS	HARLEM	15.00
67	56718	J.J.JACKSON	BUT IT'S ALRIGHT	DO THE BOOGALOO	25.00
67	56720	HOLIDAYS	I'LL LOVE YOU FOREVER	MAKIN' UP TIME	125.00
67	56722	J.J.BARNES	DEEPER IN LOVE	DAY TRIPPER	30.00
67	56725	RODGE MARTIN	WHEN SHE TOUCHES ME	LOVIN' MACHINE	20.00
67	56726	EDWIN STARR	GIRLS ARE GETTING PRETTIER	IT'S MY TURN NOW	40.00
67	56728	HECTOR RIVERA	AT THE PARTY	DO IT TO ME	75.00
67	56728 DJ	HECTOR RIVERA	AT THE PARTY	DO IT TO ME	150.00
67	56730	INSPIRATIONS	TOCH ME, HOLD ME, KISS ME	WHAT AM I GONNA DO WITH YOU ?	**325.00**
67	56732	SOULRUNNERS	SPREADING HONEY	GRITS 'N CORNBREAD	20.00
67	56735	B.B. KING	THE JUNGLE	LONG GONE BABY	15.00
67	56738	MICKEY MURRAY	LONELY ROOM	SHOUT BAMA LAMA	15.00
68	56740	JAMES BROWN	THERE WAS A TIME	I CAN'T STAND MYSELF	8.00
68	56741	LARRY & TOMMY	YO-YO	YOU'VE GOT TO BEND A LITTLE	10.0
68	56743	JAMES BROWN	I GOT THE FEELIN'	IF I RULED THE WORLD	8.00
68	56744	JAMES BROWN	LICKING STICK - LICKING STICK	LICKING STICK - LICKING STICK	8.00
68	56745	PEGGY SCOTT & JO JO BENSON	LOVER'S HOLIDAY	HERE WITH ME	10.00
68	56747	BOBBY PARIS	PER-SO-NAL-LY	TRAGEDY	85.00
68	56750	PEGGY SCOTT & JO JO BENSON	PICKIN' WILD MOUNTAIN BERRIES	PURE LOVE AND PLEASURE	6.00
68	56752	JAMES BROWN	SAY IT LOUD I'M BLACK & I'M PROUD	SAY IT LOUD I'M BLACK & I'M P	6.00
68	56753 lh	EDWIN STARR	STOP HER ON SIGHT (S.O.S.)	HEADLINE NEWS	8.00
68	56753 sh	EDWIN STARR	STOP HER ON SIGHT (S.O.S.)	HEADLINE NEWS	10.00
69	56755	JAMO THOMAS & the PARTY BROS	I SPY (FOR THE FBI)	SNAKE HIP MAMA	15.00
69	56760	SWINGING SOUL MACHINE	SPOOKY'S DAY OFF	NOBODY WANT YOU	10.00
69	56761	PEGGY SCOTT & JO JO BENSON	SOULSHAKE	WE WERE MADE FOR EACH OTHER	10.00
69	56762	BOBBY PARIS	LET THE SUNSHINE IN (THE FLESH)	YOU	5.00
69	56766	NINA SIMONE	I LOVES YOU PORGY	HE NEEDS ME	4.00
69	56772	PEGGY SCOTT	EVERY LITTLE BIT HURTS	YOU CAN NEVER GET SOMETHING FO	10.00
69	56773	PEGGY SCOTT & JO JO BENSON	I WANT TO LOVE YOU BABY	WE GOT OUR BAG	6.00
69	56775	JOHNNY ADAMS	RECONSIDER ME	IF I COULD SEE YOU ONE MORE TI	15.00
69	56776 paper	JAMES BROWN	MOTHER POPCORN	MOTHER POPCORN part 2	8.00
69	56776 ink	JAMES BROWN	MOTHER POPCORN	MOTHER POPCORN part 2	6.00
69	56780 paper	JAMES BROWN	THE WORLD	THE WORLD part 2	6.00
72	56780 ink	JAMES BROWN	THE WORLD	THE WORLD part 2	5.00
69	56783	JAMES BROWN	LET A MAN COME IN AND DO THE	SOMETIME	5.00

70	56786	BETTY LAVETTE	HE MADE A WOMAN OUT OF ME	NEARER TO YOU	10.00
70	56787	JAMES BROWN	THERE WAS A TIME	I CAN'T STAND MYSELF	10.00
70	56788 lh	GLORIA TAYLOR	YOU GOTTA PAY THE PRICE	LOVING YOU AND BEING LOVED BY	10.00
70	56788 sh	GLORIA TAYLOR	YOU GOTTA PAY THE PRICE	LOVING YOU AND BEING LOVED BY	15.00
70	56793	JAMES BROWN	AIN'T IT FUNKY NOW	AIN'T IT FUNKY NOW part 2	8.00
70	5692	MARVA HODGE	THE GHETTO	SOMETIMES	5.00
70	2001018	JAMES BROWN	IT'S A NEW DAY	GEORGIA ON MY MIND	6.00
70	2001036	MARVA WHITNEY	THIS GIRL'S IN LOVE WITH YOU	HE'S THE ONE	30.00
70	2001071	JAMES BROWN	GET UP I FEEL LIKE BEING A SEX	SAME: PART 2	6.00
70	2001097paper	JAMES BROWN	CALL ME SUPER BAD	CALL ME SUPER BAD PART 2 & 3	6.00
70	2001097 ink	JAMES BROWN	CALL ME SUPER BAD (PART1 & 2)	CALL ME SUPER BAD (PART3)	5.00
70	2001116	STRANGE BROS. SHOW	SHAKEY JAKES	RIGHT ON	10.00
71	2001127	MOB	I DIG EVERYTHING ABOUT YOU	LOVE'S GOT A HOLD ON ME	20.00
71	2001163	JAMES BROWN	SOUL POWER	SOUL POWER part 2 & 3	8.00
71	2001169	MOB	GIVE IT TO ME	I'D LIKE TO SEE MORE OF YOU	10.00
71	2001190	JAMES BROWN	GET UP, GET INTO IT, GET INVOLVED	I CRIED	6.00
71	2001200	MOB	MONEY	ONCE A MAN TWICE A CHILD	5.00
71	2001210	TONY MICHAELS	OLD ENOUGH	IT ALL COUNTS AS NOTHING	30.00
71	2001213	JAMES BROWN	HOT PANTS PART1	HOT PANTS PART 2 & 3	6.00
71	2001223	JAMES BROWN	MAKE IT FUNKY	MAKE IT FUNKY 2	6.00
73	2001474	KOOL & THE GANG	FUNKY STUFF	MORE FUNKY STUFF	6.00
74	2001481	NEW YORK CITY	QUICK FAST IN A HURRY	REACH OUT	4.00
74	2001495	BROWN SUGAR	DON'T HOLD BACK	DIDN'T I	10.00
74	2001500	KOOL & THE GANG	JUNGLE BOOGIE	NORTH EAT SOUTH WEST	8.00
74	2001530	KOOL & THE GANG	DUJII	HOLLYWOOD SWINGING	8.00
74	2001541 paper	KOOL & THE GANG	HIGHER PLANE	WILD IS LOVE	5.00
74	2001541 ink	KOOL & THE GANG	HIGHER PLANE	WILD IS LOVE	4.00
74	2001544	JAMO THOMAS	I SPY (FOR THE F.B.I.)	SNAKE HIP MAMA	8.00
75	2001545	TIMMY THOMAS	YOU'RE THE SONG I'VE ALWAYS	I'VE GOT TO SEE YOU TONIGHT	3.00
75	2001558	KOOL & THE GANG	RHYME TIME PEOPLE	FATHER, FATHER	5.00
75	2001560	EBB TIDE	GIVE ME YOU'RE YOUR BEST SHOT-BABY	same: part 2	15.00
75	2001566	KOOL & THE GANG	SPIRIT OF THE BOOGIE	GET DOWN WITH THE BOOGIE	5.00
75	2001594	MUHAMMED ALI	PEOPLE'S CHOICE	ROPE A DOPE	8.00
75	2001596	JOHNNY WILLIAMS	YOU'RE SOMETHING KINDA MELLOW	YOU MAKE ME WANT TO LAST FOREV	10.00
75	2001597	EXECUITIVE SUITE	WHEN THE FUEL RUNS OUT	same: Instrumental	5.00
75	2001602	CROWN HEIGHTS AFFAIR	DREAMING A DREAM	same: instrumental	4.00
75	2001623	CROWN HEIGHTS AFFAIR	EVERY BEAT OF MY HEART	SAME: PT 2	5.00
75	2001645	KOOL & THE GANG	LOVE AND UNDERSTANDING	SUNSHINE AND LOVE	5.00
75	2001651	RHYTHM MAKERS	ZONE	PRIME CUT	10.00
75	2001664	CROWN HEIGHTS AFFAIR	FOXY LADY	PICTURE SHOW	4.00
75	2001675	KAY-GEES	HUSTLE WIT' EVERY MUSCLE	LET'S BOOGIE	4.00
75	2001686	KAY-GEES	WAITING AT THE BUS STOP	same: part 2	4.00
75	2001862	ARPEGGIO	LOVE AND DESIRE	LOVE AND DESIRE PART 2	5.00
72	2006098	JOE SIMON	HELP ME MAKE IT THROUGH THE NIGHT	MOST OF ALL	5.00
72	2025098	EDDIE FLOYD	YUM YUM YUM I WANT SOME	TEARS OF JOY	5.00
74	2050502	R. DEAN TAYLOR,	WINDOW SHOPPING	BONNIE	3.00
70	2058020	ZOOT ONEY'S BIG ROLL BAND	NO ONE BUT YOU	PRISONER	5.00
70	2058061	P.P. ARNOLD	LIKELY PIECE OF WORK	MAY THE WINDS BLOW	5.00
70	2058071	DEVOTIONS	DAWNING OF LOVE	SO GLAD YOU'RE HOME	15.00
70	2058077	DUPREES	CHECK YOURSELF	THE SKY'S THER LIMIT	75.00
71	2058090	VALENTINOS	DON'T RAISE UP YOURS HANDS IN	STAND UP AND BE COUNTED	5.00
71	2058152	CARROLLS	THE FOLK I LOVE	SURRENDER YOUR LOVE	8.00
71	2058167	FLIRTATIONS	LITTLE DARLING (I NEED YOU)	TAKE ME IN YOUR ARMS	14.00
72	2058236	TOMMY HUNT	MIND, BODY AND SOUL	ONE MORE MOUNTAIN TO CLIMB	4.00
72	2058241	GREAT EXPECTATIONS	TIME AND PLACE	I'M SO GLAD I'VE GOTCHA	15.00
72	2058249	FLIRTATIONS	LOVE A LITTLE LONGER	HOLD ON TO ME BABE	10.00
72	2058252	VERITY	BRIGHT SHINES THE LIGHT	THE WORLD'S A CLOCKWORK ORANGE	20.00
73	2058295	FLIRTATIONS	NO SUCH THING AS A MIRACLE	DIRTY WORK	5.00
73	2058313	DECOYS	YOU GAVE ME SOMETHIONG	CHRISTMAS TIME	5.00
74	2058341	SYMPHONICS	USING ME	HEAVEN MUST HAVE SENT YOU	15.00
74	2058348	GREAT EXPECTIONS	BIGGER AND BETTER	DEVILS GUN	15.00
74	2058401	JIMMY RUFFIN	THANK YOU GIRL	DO YOU KNOW ME	5.00
74	2058426	JOHN SCOTT and his ORCHESTRA	MIDWEEK	TIME FORGOTTEN	8.00
74	2058433	JIMMY RUFFIN	TELL ME WHAT YOU WANT	GOING HOME	5.00
74	2058495	FLIRTATIONS	DIRTY WORK	NO SUCHTHING AS A MIRACLE	4.00
75	2058542	EDDIE HOLMAN	DARLING TAKE ME BABCK (I'M SORRY)	I BELIEVE IN MIRACLES	10.00
75	2058545	TIMMY THOMAS	YOU'RE THE SONG	I'VE GGOT TO SEE YOU TONIGHT	4.00
75	2058609	NORTHERN SOUL INC.	SOMETHING KEEPS CALLING ME BACK	TRAVELLING MAN	5.00
76	2058661	CHOSEN FEW	YOU MEAN EVERYTHING TO ME	YES IT WON'T BE LONG	50.00
76	2058699	CHANTER SISTERS	BAND OF GOLD	BLUE JEAN DAYS	4.00
76	2058721	CHOSEN FEW	I CAN MAKE YOUR DREAMS COME TRUE	PRETTY FACE	20.00
76	2058765	SAMMY GORDON & the HIP HUGGERS	MAKING LOVE	MAKING LOVE part 2	4.00
76	2058784	JAMES WELLS	BABY I'M STILL THE SAME MAN	same: long version	8.00
76	2058814	JOHNNY BRISTOL	DO IT TO MY MIND	LOVE TO HAVE THE CHANCE	4.00
76	2058842	ARTHUR PRYSOCK	ALL I NEED IS YOU TONIGHT	WHEN LOVE IS NEW	15.00
77	2058872	CHOSEN FEW	THANK YOU	THANK YOU part 2	20.00
77	2058891	JAMES WELLS	MY DAYS ARE NUMBERED	MY DAYS ARE NUMBERED part 2	4.00
78	2058975	CHOSEN FEW	YOU MEAN EVERYTHING TO ME	IT WON'T BE LONG	40.00
78	2059035	BILL FREDERICKS	ALMOST	WIND OF CHANGE	10.00

70	2062009	TARA	HAPPY	THE LOVE OF A WOMAN	15.00
70	2066007	FLAMINGOS	BUFFALO SOLDIER	FOUNTAINEOUS COMBUSTION	8.00
70	2066009	TARA	HAPPY	EL AMOR DE UNA MUJER	40.00
71	2066013	AMERICAN YOUTH CHIOR	KEEP YOUR FINE SELF NEAR ME	TOGETHER WE CAN MAKE IT	75.00
71	2066036	BOYS IN THE BAND	BOYS IN THE BAND	SUMPIN' HEABY	10.00
71	2066063	LEE DORSEY	OCCAPELLA	YES WE CAN - PT 1	5.00
71	2066066	JOE SIMON	I LOVE YOU MORE (THAN ANYTHING)	YOUR TIME TO CRY	8.00
71	2066096	FLOWER SHOPPE	YOU'VE COME A LONG WAY BABY	KILL THE MONSTER	10.00
72	2066098	JOE SIMON	HELP ME MAKE IT THROUGH THE NIGHT	MOST OF ALL	4.00
72	2066153	JAMES BROWN	I'M A GREEDY MAN	I'M A GREDDY MAN PART2	5.00
73	2066156	JOE SIMON	DROWNING IN A SEA OF LOVE	LET ME BE THE ONE	5.00
72	2066185	JAMES BROWN	KING HEROIN	THEME FROM KING HEROIN	6.00
72	2066210	JAMES BROWN	THERE IT IS	THERE IT IS PART2	6.00
72	2066216	JAMES BROWN	HONKY TONK	HONKY TONK PART2	8.00
72	2066231	JAMES BROWN	GET ON THE GOOD FOOT	GET ON THE GOOD FOOT part 2	8.00
72	2066283	JAMES BROWN and LYNN COLLINS	WHAT MY BABY NEEDS NOW IS A LITTLE	THIS GUY'S IN LOVE WITH YOU	20.00
72	2066285	JAMES BROWN	I GOT A BAG OF MY OWN	I KNOW IT'S TRUE	6.00
72	2066296	JAMES BROWN	I GOT ANTS IN MY PANTS PART1	SAME: PART2	6.00
73	2066317	MILLIE JACKSON	BREAKAWAY	STRANGE THINGS	4.00
73	2066320	MANDRILL	MANDRILL	HANG LOOSE	5.00
73	2066322	FRED WESLEY & the J.B'S	DOING IT TO DEATH	EVERYBODY GOT SOME SOUL	8.00
73	2066329	JAMES BROWN	THINK	SOMETHING	6.00
73	2066357	MANDRILL	FENCEWALK	POLK STREET CARNIVAL	5.00
74	2066363	MILLIE JACKSON	HURTS SO GOOD	LOVE DOCTOR	5.00
74	2066365	BINGO	WE CAN'T GET ENOUGH	MUMBLIN' MAN	75.00
74	2066366	INVITATIONS	LOVE HAS TO GROW	LET'S LIVE AND LOVE TOGETHER	75.00
74	2066367	MANDRILL	FENCEWALK	POLK STREET CARNIVAL	4.00
74	2066370	JAMES BROWN	WOMAN	WOMAN part 2	6.00
74	2066411	JAMES BROWN	STONE TO THE BONE	SEXY, SEXY, SEXY	8.00
74	2066429	LAST WORD	KEEP ON BUMPING BEFORE YOU GIVE	FUNKY AND SOME	10.00
74	2066430	JOE SIMON	CARRY ME	DO YOU KNOW WHAT IT'S LIKE	4.00
74	2066390	JOE SIMON	RIVER	LOVE AIN'T NEVER HURT NOBODY	4.00
74	2066466	MILLIE JACKSON	HOW DO YOU FEEL THE MORNING AFTER	IN THE WASH	4.00
75	2066473	JAY & THE TECHNIQUES	THIS WORLD OF MINE	I FEEL LOVE COMIN' ON	8.00
75	2066478	JOE SIMON	BEST OF MY LIFE	WHAT WE GONNA DO NOW	5.00
75	2066485	JAMES BROWN	MY THANG	THE PAYBACK	6.00
75	2066490	LYN COLLINS	WIDE AWAKE IN A DREAM	ROCK ME AGAIN AND AGAIN AND AGAIN	25.00
75	2066494	FATBACK BAND	KEEP ON STEPPIN'	BREAKING UP IS HARD TO DO	5.00
75	2066513	JAMES BROWN	PAPA DON'T TAKE NO MESS	IT'S HELL	6.00
75	2066520	JAMES BROWN	FUNKY PRESIDENT	COLDBLOODED	6.00
75	2066524	FATBACK BAND	WICKI WACKY	CAN'T FIGHT THE FLAME	5.00
75	2066536	MILLIE JACKSON	IF LOVING YOU IS WRONG	THE RAP	4.00
75	2066551	JOE SIMON	GET DOWN GET DOWN	IN MY BABY'S ARMS	4.00
75	2066557	GARLAND GREEN	BUMPIN' AND STOMPIN'	NOTHING CAN TAKE YOU FROM ME	5.00
75	2066578	RONNIE WALKER	MAGIC IN THE AIR	JUST CAN'T SAY HELLO	5.00
75	2066584	JOE SIMON	FIRE BURNING	MUSIC IN MY BONES	15.00
75	2066590	FATBACK BAND	YUM YUM (GIMME SOME)	TROMPIN'	5.00
75	2066612	MILLIE JACKSON	LOVING ARMS	LEFT OVER	5.00
75	2066637	FATBACK BAND	(ARE YOU READY) DO THE BUS STOP	GOTTA LEARN HOW TO DANCE	4.00
75	2066642	JAMES BROWN	HOT (I NEED TO BE LOVED, LOVED,	SUPERBAD, SUPERSLICK	6.00
75	2066648	JAY & THE TECHNIQUES	DON'T ASK ME TO FORGET	NUMBER WONDERFUL	15.00
76	2066649	JOE SIMON	I NEED YOU, YOU NEED ME	I'LL TAKE CARE OF YOU	4.00
75	2066656 PS	FATBACK BAND	(DO THE) SPANISH HUSTLE	GROOVY KIND OF DAY	4.00
75	2066671	ROY AYERS	EVOLUTION	MYSTIC VOYAGE	10.00
75	2066680	CREATIVE SOURCE	DON'T BE AFRAID TO TAKE MY LOVE	PASS THE FELING ON	20.00
76	2066682	FATBACK BAND	PAR-R-RTY TIME	PUT YOUR LOVE IN MY TENDER CAR	4.00
76	2066687	JAMES BROWN	GET UP OFFA THAT THING	RELEASE THE PRESSURE	4.00
77	2066735	GLORIA GAYNOR	TALK TALK TALK	LET'S MAKE LOVE	4.00
77	2066763	JAMES BROWN	BODYHEAT	BODYHEAT PART2	5.00
77	2066834	JAMES BROWN	HONKY TONK	BROTHER RAP	8.00
77	2066842	ROY AYERS UBIQUITY	RUNNING AWAY	CINCINNATI GROWL	6.00
78	2066915	JAMES BROWN	EYESIGHT	I NEVER, NEVER, NEVER WILL FOR	5.00
78	2066922	GLORIA GAYNOR	THIS LOVE AFFAIR	FOR THE FIRST TIME IN MY LIFE	40.00
78	2066984	JAMES BROWN	NATURE	NATURE part 2	5.00
	2095017 paper	GLORIA GAYNOR	I WILL SURVIVE	ANYBODSY WANNA PARTY	5.00
78	2095017 ink	GLORIA GAYNOR	I WILL SURVIVE	ANYBODSY WANNA PARTY	4.00
78	2095026	ALTON McCLAIN and DESTINY	IT MUST BE LOVE	TAKING MY LOVE FOR GRANTED	5.00
72	2121064	CHAKACHAS	JUNGLE FEVER	CHA KA CHA	5.00
	2141008 PS	JAMES BROWN	PAPA'S GOT A BRAND NEW BAG + OUT	IT'S A MAN'S MAN'S WORLD	5.00
74	2391125	FRED WESLEY & the J.B'S	DAMN RIGHT, I AM SOMEBODY	1974 UK press	40.00
	2816011	VARIOUS ARTISTS	4 HUNKS OF FUNK:	4 track ep Fatback, Gloria Gaynor, Jamo Thomas + 1	4.00
70	580701 EP PS	JAMES BROWN	TURN IT LOOSE	4 track EP	25.00
69	583731	PEGGY SCOTT & JO JO BENSON	SOULSHAKE	1969 UK press	20.00
64	66990	KINGSIZE TAYLOR	MONEY	MEMPHIS TENNESSE	20.00
63	66991	SHAKERS	HIPPY HIPPY SHAKE	DR. FEELGOOD	15.00
64	66991	KINGSIZE TAYLOR	HIPPY HIPPY SHAKE	DR. FEELGOOD	15.00

PORTRAIT

82	2272	ANGELA CLEMMONS	GIVE ME JUST A LITTLE MORE TIME	WHEN YOU'RE THROUGH I'LL BE WA	6.00
82	2272 DJ	ANGELA CLEMMONS	GIVE ME JUST A LITTLE MORE TIME	WHEN YOU'RE THROUGH I'LL BE WA	10.00
85	6805	NICOLE with TIMMY THOMAS	NEW YORK EYES	ORDINARY EYES	6.00
76	7254	ARCHIE BELL & the DRELLS	DON'T LET LOVE GET YOU DOWN	WHERE WILL YOU GO WHEN THE PAR	10.00

POWER EXCHANGE

EMI distributed label, missing numbers are not soul related 45's. Strong connection with West Coast producer extraordinaire H.B.Barnum, several of his 70s productions are included in the list below. The USA East Coast connection was from Philadelphia with several Virtue label recordings issued. J.J. Barrie's –"No Charge" – was the biggest hit on the label, this was far from being a soul 45. But there are two highlights: Billy Cole's – "Extra Careful" UK only 1975 release has emerged over the years as not only a superb 70's Northern Soul dancer, but has become increasingly difficult to find. Also hidden on the flip side of "Reggae Disco" is The Main Ingredients version of Daybreak's highly sought after 45 – "Everything Man" #265 . Also 45's by Little Anthony's backing group, the Imperials releases seem to be under-valued, at the moment. So there is plenty to check out on this diverse label.

74	101	O'JAYS	PEACE	LITTLE BROTHER	5.00
74	101 DJ	O'JAYS	PEACE	LITTLE BROTHER	6.00
74	102	H.B. BARNUM	HAVING A PARTY	HAVING A PARTY part 2	5.00
74	102 DJ	H.B. BARNUM	HAVING A PARTY	HAVING A PARTY part 2	6.00
74	103	DYNAMIC CONCEPT	CALIFORNIA	CALIFORNIA part 2	5.00
74	103 DJ	DYNAMIC CONCEPT	CALIFORNIA	CALIFORNIA part 2	6.00
75	104	BILLY COLE	EXTRA CAREFUL	BUMP ALL NIGHT	40.00
75	104 DJ	BILLY COLE	EXTRA CAREFUL	BUMP ALL NIGHT	50.00
75	105	DYNAMIC CONCEPT	LA DA DA	PRESSURE	5.00
75	105 DJ	DYNAMIC CONCEPT	LA DA DA	PRESSURE	6.00
75	106	SOUL FOOD	BOOGIE BUMP	TOM THE PEEPER'S BROTHER JOHN	5.00
75	106 DJ	SOUL FOOD	BOOGIE BUMP	TOM THE PEEPER'S BROTHER JOHN	6.00
75	108	ANN BYERS	THIS MAN IS RATED - X	GOTTA GET YOU BACK	6.00
75	108 DJ	ANN BYERS	THIS MAN IS RATED - X	GOTTA GET YOU BACK	8.00
75	109	GENE FAITH	LOVE OF A WOMAN, SOUL OF A MAN	CALL THE FBI (MY BABY'S MISSIN	8.00
75	109 DJ	GENE FAITH	LOVE OF A WOMAN, SOUL OF A MAN	CALL THE FBI (MY BABY'S MISSIN	10.00
76	207	EDDIE SPENCER	IF THIS IS LOVE (I'D RATHER BE LONELY)	POWER OF LOVE	10.00
76	207 DJ	EDDIE SPENCER	IF THIS IS LOVE (I'D RATHER BE LONELY)	POWER OF LOVE	15.00
77	265	MAIN INGREDIENT	EVERYTHING MAN	REGGAE DISCO	40.00
77	265 DJ	MAIN INGREDIENT	EVERYTHING MAN	REGGAE DISCO	50.00
77	266	IMPERIALS	WHO'S GONNA LOVE ME	CAN YOU IMAGINE	4.00
77	266 DJ	IMPERIALS	WHO'S GONNA LOVE ME	CAN YOU IMAGINE	6.00
77	270	IMPERIALS	WHERE YOU GONNA FIND SOMEBODY	ANOTHER STAR	4.00
77	270 DJ	IMPERIALS	WHERE YOU GONNA FIND SOMEBODY	ANOTHER STAR	6.00
78	274	IMPERIALS	DO WHAT I GOTTA DO	DANCE WITH ME	8.00
78	274 DJ	IMPERIALS	DO WHAT I GOTTA DO	DANCE WITH ME	10.00
78	275	SUGAR	OCHO RIOS	MANHATTAN FEVER	8.00
78	275 DJ	SUGAR	OCHO RIOS	MANHATTAN FEVER	10.00
78	277	BLACK IVORY	PUSH COMES TO SHOVE	YOU TURNED MY WHOLE WORLD AROU	6.00
78	277 DJ	BLACK IVORY	PUSH COMES TO SHOVE	YOU TURNED MY WHOLE WORLD AROU	8.00

PRESIDENT

Independent label started in 1966 in the UK by music publisher Austrian born Edward Kassner; he was no ordinary music publisher and had the insight to publish such songs as "Rock Around The clock" allegedly the most performed song of all time. In 1991 the BBC broadcasted "The Edward Kassner Story" such was the man's reputation within the music industry. Escaping Austria during the start of Hitler's reign, Kassner ended up in Australia via England. He returned to England in 1939 to serve in the British Army. By the end of the war, Eddie Kassner after almost twenty years, England had again become the focal point of Eddie Kassner's business. With the arrival of the singer-songwriter limiting the traditional role of independent publishers, the need for an affiliated record company became apparent to Edward. In 1966 he set up President Records Ltd. Within a year, the label had achieved its first chart success with records by The Symbols and Felice Taylor, with the latter a top 20 entry for the Barry White written "I Feel Love Comin' On".

From a serious collectors viewpoint, it is important to note that President records would repress and keep available their best selling titles. The first press label design up until release number #275 the artists credit on the left hand side ran horizontal. Later issues of the same release the artist credit ran vertical. Soul classics like Johnny Wyatt are particularly rare on their first release design. See label scans for a better understanding of the label layout changes.

Kassner had the intuition to acquire the rights for UK release of some prolific soul label independents which included Chicago's Onederful/Mar-v-lus, Los Angeles – Bronco, Kent labels plus Fraternity, Excello, and Vee Jay etc. When the 70's arrived they secured the massive catalogue of Miami's TK. They constantly released surprisingly obscure soul 45's. Viola Wills for example was a total unknown artists outside Los Angeles but all her Bronco 45s released on President are now considered classics. In the late 60's with President gaining the rights to Mirwood, Mira, Keymen, Shout etc, Kassner decided their new Jay Boy label was a better vehicle for the soul market. With a large percentage of releases being soul, the Jay Boy attained that rare status of being a completists label.

President's policy of releasing all styles and types of music saw them rewarded in 1968 with their biggest hit. A young Eddy Grant was the driving force behind The Equals massive seller "Baby Come Back" which also received respectable sales when leased out to RCA in the USA. A testament to President's contribution to the music industry, is that they are still going strong today, when you consider some of the great labels like Stax, Soul City etc have long ceased trading. One glance at the relevant President soul related releases below and that of Jay Boy catalogue, confirms the collectability of the companies early 45's.

68	2 EP PS	EQUALS	I WON'T BE THERE	1968 4 track EP with cover	15.00
67	102	SYMBOLS	CANADIAN SUNSET	GENTLE ART OF LOVING	8.00
67	108	VIOLA WILLS	I GOT LOVE	LOST WITHOUT THE LOVE OF MY GU	20.00
69	108 2nd label design	VIOLA WILLS	I GOT LOVE	LOST WITHOUT THE LOVE OF MY GU	10.00
67	109	JOHNNY WYATT	THIS THING CALLED LOVE	TO WHOM IT MAY CONCERN	100.00
69	109 2nd label design	JOHNNY WYATT	THIS THING CALLED LOVE	TO WHOM IT MAY CONCERN	20.00
67	110	PAT HERVEY	CAN'T GET YOU OUT OF MY MIND	GIVIN' IN	20.00
68	113	SYMBOLS	CANADIAN SUNSET	GENTLE ART OF LOVING	5.00
68	115	ALVIN CASH	THE PHILLY FREEZE	NO DEPOSITS - NO RETURNS	10.00
70	115 2nd label design	ALVIN CASH	THE PHILLY FREEZE	NO DEPOSITS - NO RETURNS	8.00
68	117	EQUALS	I WON'T BE THERE	FIRE	5.00
68	118	JIMMY ROBINS	I CAN'T PLEASE HER	I MADE IT OVE	**194.00**
68	119	ALVIN CASH	LET'S DO SOME GOOD TIMING	ALVIN'S BOOGALOO	10.00
68	120	FELICE TAYLOR	IT MAY BE WINTER OUTSIDE	WINTER AGAIN	15.00

Year	Catalog	Artist	A-Side	B-Side	Price
70	120 2nd label design	FELICE TAYLOR	IT MAY BE WINTER OUTSIDE	Same: instrumental	8.00
68	121	OTIS CLAY	IT'S EASIER SAID THAN DONE	FLAME IN YOUR HEART	22.00
68	123	CASINOS	I STILL LOVE YOU	THEN YOU CAN TELL ME GOODBYE	10.00
68	124	TWO OF CLUBS	WALK TALL	SO BLUE IS FALL	75.00
68	125	McKINLEY MITCHELL	THE TOWN I LIVE IN	NO LOVE LIKE YOUR LOVE	20.00
68	129	ALVIN CASH & the REGISTERS	DOIN' THE ALI SHUFFLE	FEEL SO GOOD	8.00
68	130	HAROLD BURRAGE	YOU MADE ME SO HAPPY	TAKE ME NOW	25.00
68	132	OTIS CLAY	I'M SATISFIED	I TESTIFY	20.00
68	133	FELICE TAYLOR	I'M UNDER THE INFLUENCE OF LOVE	LOVE THEME	10.00
68	134	FIVE DU-TONES	SHAKE A TAIL FEATHER	DIVORCE COURT	8.00
68	135	EQUALS	BABY, COME BACK	HOLD ME CLOSER	5.00
68	136	YOUNG FOLK	LONELY GIRL	JOEY	22.00
68	137	ALBERT WASHINGTON & the KINGS	A WOMAN IS A FUNNY THING	DOGGIN' ME AROUND	10.00
68	139	BARRY WHITE	ALL IN THE RUN OF A DAY	DON'T TAKE YOUR LOVE FROM ME	45.00
68	140	CASINOS	TO BE LOVED	TAILOR MADE	5.00
68	142	LONNIE MACK	SNOW ON THE MOUNTAIN	SAVE YOUR MONEY	6.00
68	143	KELLY BROTHERS	HANGING IN THERE	YOU PUT YOUR TOUCH ON ME	25.00
68	144	SYMBOLS	BYE, BYE BABY	THE THINGS YOU DO TO ME	5.00
68	147	ALVIN CASH & the REGISTERS	CHARGE	DIFF'RENT STOKES FOR DIFF'RENT	10.00
68	148	OTIS CLAY	SHOW PLACE	THAT'S HOW IT IS	15.00
68	150	VIOLA WILLS	TOGETHER FOREVER	DON'T KISS HIM HELLOW AND MEAN	45.00
68	151	BOB KEENE	HIDEAWAY	PEAS AND CORN	6.00
68	152	VIOLA WILLS	I'VE GOT TO HAVE ALL OF YOU	NIGHT SCENE	10.00
68	154	VIOLA WILLS	YOU'RE OUT OF MY MIND	ANY TIME	20.00
68	155	FELICE TAYLOR	I FEEL LOVE COMIN' ON	COMIN' ON AGAIN	15.00
70	155 2nd label design	FELICE TAYLOR	I FEEL LOVE COMIN' ON	COMING ON AGAIN	6.00
68	156	CASINOS	WHEN I STOP DREAMING	PLEASE LOVE ME	5.00
68	158	EQUALS	GIVE LOVE A TRY	ANOTHER SAD AND LONELY NIGHT	4.00
68	163	KIP ANDERSON	YOU'LL LOSE A GOOD THING	I'M OUT OF LOVE	20.00
68	164	SLIM HARPO	I'M GONNA KEEP WHAT I'VE GOT	I'VE GOT TO BE WITH YOU TONIGH	10.00
68	166	SOUL MERCHANTS	WHOLE LOT OF LOVIN'	STORMY WEATHER	5.00
68	171	WILLIE PARKER	YOU GOT YOUR FINGER IN MY EYE	I LIVE THE LIFE I LOVE	15.00
68	173 DJ	SYMBOLS	(THE BEST PART OF) BREAKING UP	AGAIN	10.00
68	176	OTIS CLAY	A LASTING LOVE	GOT TO FIND A WAY	15.00
68	180	EQUALS	I GET SO EXCITED	SKIES ABOVE	4.00
68	182	ALBERT WASHINGTON & the KINGS	I'M THE MAN	THESE ARMS OF MINE	100.00
68	187	SLIM HARPO	TIP ON IN	TIP ON IN Part2	10.00
68	192	BUTTERFLIES	LOVE ME FOR EVER	HE'S GOT EVERYTHING	15.00
68	193	FELICE TAYLOR	I CAN FEEL YOUR LOVE (COMING DOWN)	CAPTURED BY YOUR LOVE	8.00
68	198	LONNIE MACK	SOUL EXPRESS	I FOUND A LOVE	6.00
68	200	EQUALS	LAUREL AND HARDY	GUY WHO MADE HER A STAR	4.00
68	201	LITTLE RICHARD	WHOLE LOTTA SHAKIN' GOIN' ON	LAWDY MISS CLAWDY	5.00
68	207	WATSON T. BROWN	SOME LOVIN'	HOME IS WHERE YOUR HEART LIES	5.00
68	214	BETTY EVERETT & JERRY BUTLER	LET IT BE ME	SMILE	7.00
68	214 2nd label design	BETTY EVERETT & JERRY BUTLER	LET IT BE ME	SMILE	5.00
68	215	BETTY EVERETT	GETTING MIGHTY CROWDED	IT'S IN HIS KISS	10.00
68	215 2nd label design	BETTY EVERETT	GETTING MIGHTY CROWDED	IT'S IN HIS KISS	8.00
68	220	FELICE TAYLOR	ALL I WANT TO DO IS LOVE YOU	SUREE-SURRENDER	20.00
68	221	WATSON T. BROWN	CRYING ALL NIGHT	CLOSE MY EYES	10.00
68	222	EQUALS	SOFTLY SOFTLY	LONELY RITA	4.00
68	223	DELLS	IT'S NOT UNUSUAL	STAY IN MY CORNER	25.00
68	226	LEE DORSEY	YA YA	GIVE ME YOU	10.00
68	227	ALBERT WASHINGTON & the KINGS	BRING IT ON UP	WOMAN LOVE	15.00

1969 President started making promo 45's with a large red A similar the the red A promo's on their subsidiary Jay Boy

Year	Catalog	Artist	A-Side	B-Side	Price
69	232	TERRY LINDSEY	IT'S OVER	ONE DAY UP, NEXT DAY DOWN	25.00
69	232 DJ	TERRY LINDSEY	IT'S OVER	ONE DAY UP, NEXT DAY DOWN	40.00
69	234	GENE CHANDLER	STAND BY ME	DUKE OF EARL	8.00
69	234 DJ	GENE CHANDLER	STAND BY ME	DUKE OF EARL	10.00
69	240	EQUALS	MICHAEL AND THE SLIPPER TREE	HONEY GUM	4.00
69	240 DJ	EQUALS	MICHAEL AND THE SLIPPER TREE	HONEY GUM	5.00
69	242	ALBERT WASHINGTON & the KINGS	TURN ON THE BRIGHT LIGHTS	LONELY MOUNTAIN	10.00
69	242 DJ	ALBERT WASHINGTON & the KINGS	TURN ON THE BRIGHT LIGHTS	LONELY MOUNTAIN	15.00
69	251	BETTY EVERETT	YOU'RE NO GOOD	HANDS OFF	6.00
69	251 DJ	BETTY EVERETT	YOU'RE NO GOOD	HANDS OFF	8.00
69	252	BETTY EVERETT & JERRY BUTLER	OUR DAY WILL COME	JUST BE TRUE	6.00
69	252 DJ	BETTY EVERETT & JERRY BUTLER	OUR DAY WILL COME	JUST BE TRUE	8.00
69	253	BETTY EVERETT	YOU'RE NO GOOD	HANDS OFF	6.00
69	253 DJ	BETTY EVERETT	YOU'RE NO GOOD	HANDS OFF	8.00
69	260	EQUALS	VIVA BOBBY JOE	I CAN'T LET GO	4.00
69	260 DJ	EQUALS	VIVA BOBBY JOE	I CAN'T LET GO	6.00
69	263	BILLY PRESTON	BILLY'S BAG	GOLDFINGER	10.00
69	263 2nd label design	BILLY PRESTON	BILLY'S BAG	GOLDFINGER	8.00
69	263 DJ	BILLY PRESTON	BILLY'S BAG	GOLDFINGER	15.00
69	263 alternate flipside	BILLY PRESTON	BILLY'S BAG	DON'T LET THE SUN CATCH YOU CRYING	10.00
69	270	DELLS	OH WHAT A NIGHT	MOVING ON	6.00
69	270 DJ	DELLS	OH WHAT A NIGHT	MOVING ON	8.00

President changes the Artist credit to read VERTICAL on the left hand side of the label. All pre #270 artist credits that read VERTICAL are second presses.

Year	Catalog	Artist	A-Side	B-Side	Price
69	275	EQUALS	RUB A DUB DUB	AFTER THE LIGHTS GO DOWN LOW	4.00
69	275 DJ	EQUALS	RUB A DUB DUB	AFTER THE LIGHTS GO DOWN LOW	5.00

69	288	EQUALS	SOUL BROTHER CLIFFORD	HAPPY BIRTHDAY GIRL	4.00
69	288 DJ	EQUALS	SOUL BROTHER CLIFFORD	HAPPY BIRTHDAY GIRL	5.00
70	295	JOHN LEE HOOKER	DIMPLES	BOOM BOOM	8.00
70	295 DJ	JOHN LEE HOOKER	DIMPLES	BOOM BOOM	25.00
70	299	JERRY BUTLER	MAKE IT EASY ON YOURSELF	MOON RIVER	5.00
70	299 DJ	JERRY BUTLER	MAKE IT EASY ON YOURSELF	MOON RIVER	6.00
70	311	BELLES	DON'T PRETEND	WORDS CAN'T EXPLAIN	22.00
70	311 DJ	BELLES	DON'T PRETEND	WORDS CAN'T EXPLAIN	40.00
70	312	WITCHES & the WARLOCK	BEHIND LOCKED DOORS	MY ROOM	15.00
70	312 DJ	WITCHES & the WARLOCK	BEHIND LOCKED DOORS	MY ROOM	30.00
70	317	DARLETTES	LOST	SWEET KIND OF LONLINESS	20.00
70	317 DJ	DARLETTES	LOST	SWEET KINDA OF LONLINESS	25.00
70	319	WILSON PICKETT	IF YOU NEED ME	I'M GONNA LOVE YOU	6.00
70	319 DJ	WILSON PICKETT	IF YOU NEED ME	I'M GONNA LOVE YOU	8.00
70	321	LLOYD PRICE	READY FOR BETTY	BEAT IN TRINIDAD	4.00
70	321 DJ	LLOYD PRICE	READY FOR BETTY	BEAT IN TRINIDAD	5.00
70	322	WILSON PICKETT	I CAN'T STOP	DOWN TO MY LAST HEARTBREAK	6.00
70	322 DJ	WILSON PICKETT	I CAN'T STOP	DOWN TO MY LAST HEARTBREAK	8.00
70	325	EQUALS	BLACK SKIN BLUE EYED BOYS	AIN'T GOT NOTHING TO GIVE	5.00
70	325 DJ	EQUALS	BLACK SKIN BLUE EYED BOYS	AIN'T GOT NOTHING TO GIVE	6.00
70	329	LITTLE RICHARD	WITHOUT LOVE	TAKLING 'BOUT SOUL	8.00
70	329 DJ	LITTLE RICHARD	WITHOUT LOVE	TAKLING 'BOUT SOUL	10.00
71	338	ROSE COLORED GLASS	CAN'T FIND THE TIME	MYSTIC TOUCH	20.00
71	338 DJ	ROSE COLORED GLASS	CAN'T FIND THE TIME	MYSTIC TOUCH	28.00
72	351	ALVIN CASH & the REGISTERS	TWINE TIME	TWINE AWHILE	8.00
72	351 DJ	ALVIN CASH & the REGISTERS	TWINE TIME	TWINE AWHILE	10.00
72	372	BETTY EVERETT	TROUBLE OVER THE WEEKEND	THE SHOE DOESN'T FIT	15.00
72	372 DJ	BETTY EVERETT	TROUBLE OVER THE WEEKEND	THE SHOE DOESN'T FIT	20.00
72	373	DONTELLS	IN YOUR HEART (YOU KNOW I'M RIGHT)	NOTHING BUT NOTHING	15.00
72	373 DJ	DONTELLS	IN YOUR HEART (YOU KNOW I'M RIGHT)	NOTHING BUT NOTHING	20.00
72	380	MATATA	WANNA DO MY THING	WILD RIVER	25.00
72	380 DJ	MATATA	WANNA DO MY THING	WILD RIVER	30.00
72	382	DU-ETTES	EVERY BEAT OF MY HEART	SUGAR DADDY	15.00
72	382 DJ	DU-ETTES	EVERY BEAT OF MY HEART	SUGAR DADDY	22.00
72	383	ALVIN CASH & the REGISTERS	BARACUDA	DO IT ONE MORE TIME	8.00
72	383 DJ	ALVIN CASH & the REGISTERS	BARACUDA	DO IT ONE MORE TIME	10.00
72	389	SHARPEES	DO THE 45	MAKE UP YOUR MIND	10.00
72	389 DJ	SHARPEES	DO THE 45	MAKE UP YOUR MIND	15.00
72	390	KENNY SMITH & the NITELITERS	LET'S TRY AGAIN	NIGHT BEAT	30.00
72	390 DJ	KENNY SMITH & the NITELITERS	LET'S TRY AGAIN	NIGHT BEAT	40.00
72	391	ALBERT WASHINGTON & the KINGS	ROME, GA	TELLING ALL YOUR FRIENDS	10.00
72	391 DJ	ALBERT WASHINGTON & the KINGS	ROME, GA	TELLING ALL YOUR FRIENDS	15.00
73	398	DU-ETTES	PLEASE FORGIVE ME	LONELY DAYS	10.00
73	398 DJ	DU-ETTES	PLEASE FORGIVE ME	LONELY DAYS	12.00
73	399	SHARPEES	TIRED OF BEING LONELY	JUST TO PLEASE YOU	15.00
73	399 DJ	SHARPEES	TIRED OF BEING LONELY	JUST TO PLEASE YOU	25.00
73	400	MATATA	NEED SOMEBODY	EMPTY WORLD	10.00
73	400 DJ	MATATA	NEED SOMEBODY	EMPTY WORLD	15.00
73	406	MATATA	I FEEL FUNKY	I WANT YOU	10.00
73	406 DJ	MATATA	I FEEL FUNKY	I WANT YOU	15.00
74	413	GWEN McCRAE	FOR YOUR LOVE	YOUR LOVE	4.00
74	413 DJ	GWEN McCRAE	FOR YOUR LOVE	YOUR LOVE	5.00
74	414	EQUALS	DIVERSION	HER TODAY GONE TOMORROW	4.00
74	414 DJ	EQUALS	DIVERSION	HER TODAY GONE TOMORROW	5.00
74	415	LATIMORE	STORMY MONDAY	THERE'S NO END	4.00
74	415 DJ	LATIMORE	STORMY MONDAY	THERE'S NO END	5.00
74	416	GWEN McCRAE	90% OF ME IS YOU	IT'S WORTH THE HURT	25.00
74	416 DJ	GWEN McCRAE	90% OF ME IS YOU	IT'S WORTH THE HURT	30.00
74	417	MATATA	RETURN TO YOU	SOMETHING IN MIND	8.00
74	417 DJ	MATATA	RETURN TO YOU	SOMETHING IN MIND	30.00
74	418	ARCHIE BELL & the DRELLS	GIRLS GROW UP FASTER	LOVES GONNA RAIN ON YOU	5.00
74	418 DJ	ARCHIE BELL & the DRELLS	GIRLS GROW UP FASTER	LOVES GONNA RAIN ON YOU	6.00
74	419	LATIMORE	IF YOU WERE MY WOMAN	PUT PRIDE ASIDE	4.00
74	419 DJ	LATIMORE	IF YOU WERE MY WOMAN	PUT PRIDE ASIDE	5.00
74	420	DOYLEY BROTHERS	LET IT BE ME	DANCE LITTLE SUZIE	4.00
74	420 DJ	DOYLEY BROTHERS	LET IT BE ME	DANCE LITTLE SUZIE	5.00
74	423	LITTLE BEAVER	PARTY DOWN	PARTY DOWN PART 2	5.00
74	423 DJ	LITTLE BEAVER	PARTY DOWN	PARTY DOWN PART 2	6.00
74	424	DOYLEY BROTHERS	GOD KNOWS I'VE TRIED	JUST THE GIRL FOR ME	4.00
74	424 DJ	DOYLEY BROTHERS	GOD KNOWS I'VE TRIED	JUST THE GIRL FOR ME	5.00
74	425	LATIMORE	JOLIE	TAKE ME TO THE PILOT	4.00
74	425 DJ	LATIMORE	JOLIE	TAKE ME TO THE PILOT	5.00
74	427	GWEN McCRAE	HE DON'T EVER LOSE HIS GROOVE	MOVE ME BABY	5.00
74	427 DJ	GWEN McCRAE	HE DON'T EVER LOSE HIS GROOVE	MOVE ME BABY	6.00
74	428	LATIMORE	LET'S STRAIGHTEN IT OUT	AIN'T NOBODY GONNA MAKE ME CHD	5.00
74	428 DJ	LATIMORE	LET'S STRAIGHTEN IT OUT	AIN'T NOBODY GONNA MAKE ME CHD	6.00
74	430	TOBY KING	FIRST MAN TO DIE OF THE BLUES	COUNTRY BUMP	3.00
74	430 DJ	TOBY KING	FIRST MAN TO DIE OF THE BLUES	COUNTRY BUMP	4.00
75	431	LITTLE BEAVER	LET THE GOOD TIMES ROLL	LET'S STICK TOGETHER	4.00

75	431 DJ	LITTLE BEAVER	LET THE GOOD TIMES ROLL	LET'S STICK TOGETHER	5.00
75	433	LATIMORE	KEEP THE HOME FIRE BURNING	THAT'S HOW IT IS	4.00
75	433 DJ	LATIMORE	KEEP THE HOME FIRE BURNING	THAT'S HOW IT IS	5.00
75	434	GWEN McCRAE	ROCKIN' CHAIR	I KEEPS ON RAINING	5.00
75	434 DJ	GWEN McCRAE	ROCKIN' CHAIR	I KEEPS ON RAINING	6.00
75	436	EQUALS	GEORGETOWN GIRL	WE'VE GOT IT ALL WORKERD OUT	4.00
75	436 DJ	EQUALS	GEORGETOWN GIRL	WE'VE GOT IT ALL WORKERD OUT	5.00
75	438	MATATA	GIMME SOME LOVIN'	GOOD GOOD UNDERSTANDING	8.00
75	438 DJ	MATATA	GIMME SOME LOVIN'	GOOD GOOD UNDERSTANDING	10.00
75	440	MARIA MORGAN	TELL THE WORLD	TOUCH ME BABY (REACHING OUT FOR YOUR LOVE)	15.00
75	440 DJ	MARIA MORGAN	TELL THE WORLD	TOUCH ME BABY (REACHING OUT FOR YOUR LOVE)	20.00
75	441	FAMILY PLANN	SEXY SUMMER	CAN YOU GET INTO THE MUSIC	4.00
75	441 DJ	FAMILY PLANN	SEXY SUMMER	CAN YOU GET INTO THE MUSIC	5.00
75	444	GWEN McCRAE	HE KEEPS SOMETHING GROOVY GOIN'	LOVE INSURANCE	8.00
75	444 DJ	GWEN McCRAE	HE KEEPS SOMETHING GROOVY GOIN'	LOVE INSURANCE	10.00
76	446	SHARON RIDLEY	TO MAKE A LONG STORY SHORT	I'M IN YOUR CORNER	25.00
76	446 DJ	SHARON RIDLEY	TO MAKE A LONG STORY SHORT	I'M IN YOUR CORNER	30.00
76	447	GEORGE & GWEN McCRAE	I'LL DO THE ROCKIN	I'M COMIN' AT YOU	4.00
76	447 DJ	GEORGE & GWEN McCRAE	I'LL DO THE ROCKIN	I'M COMIN' AT YOU	5.00
76	448	CONTROLLERS	IS THAT LONG ENOUGH FOR YOU	PICTURES AND MEMOROIES	10.00
76	448 DJ	CONTROLLERS	IS THAT LONG ENOUGH FOR YOU	PICTURES AND MEMOROIES	15.00
76	449	LATIMORE	THERE';S A REDNECK IN THE SOUL BAND	JUST ONE STEP	3.00
76	449 DJ	LATIMORE	THERE';S A REDNECK IN THE SOUL BAND	JUST ONE STEP	4.00
76	451	GEORGE & GWEN McCRAE	LET'S DANCE, DANCE, DANCE	MECHANICAL BODY	4.00
76	451 DJ	GEORGE & GWEN McCRAE	LET'S DANCE DANCE DANCE	MECHANICAL BODY	5.00
76	452	GWEN McCRAE	CRADLE OF LOVE	EASY ROCK	6.00
76	452 DJ	GWEN McCRAE	CRADLE OF LOVE	EASY ROCK	8.00
76	456	OTIS CLAY	SPECIAL KIND OF LOVE	ALL I NEED IS YOU	10.00
76	456 DJ	OTIS CLAY	SPECIAL KIND OF LOVE	ALL I NEED IS YOU	15.00
76	457	RUTH BROWN	SUGAR BABE	STOP KNOCKING	4.00
76	457 DJ	RUTH BROWN	SUGAR BABE	STOP KNOCKING	5.00
77	464	EQUALS	BEAUTIFUL CLOWN	DAILY LOVE	4.00
77	464 DJ	EQUALS	BEAUTIFUL CLOWN	DAILY LOVE	5.00
77	465	JOHN O'HARA'S PLAYBOYS	STARSKY AND HUTCH	SISTER RAE	5.00
77	465 DJ	JOHN O'HARA'S PLAYBOYS	STARSKY AND HUTCH	SISTER RAE	6.00
81	492	LENA ZAVARONI	RESCUE ME	ROSES AND RAINBOWS	6.00
81	492 DJ	LENA ZAVARONI	RESCUE ME	ROSES AND RAINBOWS	8.00
84	522	GEORGE McCRAE	ONE STEP CLOSER (TO LOVE)	IF IT WASN'T FOR YOU	4.00
84	522 DJ	GEORGE McCRAE	ONE STEP CLOSER (TO LOVE)	IF IT WASN'T FOR YOU	5.00
85	530	GEORGE McCRAE	OWN THE NIGHT	EVERYTIME YOU SAY GOODBYE	4.00
85	530 DJ	GEORGE McCRAE	OWN THE NIGHT	EVERYTIME YOU SAY GOODBYE	5.00
85	524	GEORGE McCRAE	LET'S DANCE	NEVER FORGET YOUR EYES	4.00
85	524 DJ	GEORGE McCRAE	LET'S DANCE	NEVER FORGET YOUR EYES	5.00
85	528	GEORGE McCRAE	LISTEN TO MY HEART	NOW THAT I HAVE YOU	4.00
85	528 DJ	GEORGE McCRAE	LISTEN TO MY HEART	NOW THAT I HAVE YOU	5.00
85	549	GEORGE McCRAE	LOVE'S BEEN GOOD TO ME	OUT OF NOWHERE	4.00
85	549 DJ	GEORGE McCRAE	LOVE'S BEEN GOOD TO ME	OUT OF NOWHERE	5.00
89	579 PS	MATATA	MBONGO (MONEY)	ULIMWENGU (UNIVERSE)	4.00

PRESTIGE

78	101 DJ	BILL SUMMERS & SUMMERS HEAT STRAIGHT TO THE BANK		YOUR LOVE	4.00

PRIVATE STOCK

75	13	DEE DEE WARWICK	FUNNY HOW WE CHANGED PLACES	GET OUT OF MY LIFE	30.00
75	13 DJ	DEE DEE WARWICK	FUNNY HOW WE CHANGED PLACES	GET OUT OF MY LIFE	40.00
75	22	WILD HONEY	A MOTHER FOR MY CHILDREN	HAVE A LITTLE MERCY	8.00
75	22 DJ	WILD HONEY	A MOTHER FOR MY CHILDREN	HAVE A LITTLE MERCY	10.00
76	35	ROBERT KNIGHT	SECOND CHANCE	GLITTER LADY	4.00
76	35 DJ	ROBERT KNIGHT	SECOND CHANCE	GLITTER LADY	5.00
76	39	PEARLS	THE CHEATER	I'M GONNA STEAL YOUR HEART AWA	5.00
76	39 DJ	PEARLS	THE CHEATER	I'M GONNA STEAL YOUR HEART AWA	6.00
76	54	JOY FLEMING	ARE YOU READY FOR LOVE	ALABAMA STAND BY	12.00
76	54 DJ	JOY FLEMING	ARE YOU READY FOR LOVE	ALABAMA STAND BY	15.00
76	59	WALTER MURPHY & BIG APPLE	A FIFTH OF BEETHOVEN	CALIFORNIA STRUT	5.00
76	59 DJ	WALTER MURPHY & BIG APPLE	A FIFTH OF BEETHOVEN	CALIFORNIA STRUT	5.00
77	97	BRYAN TAYLOR	THIS IS THE LAST TIME	FUNKY FEELING	20.00
77	97 DJ	BRYAN TAYLOR	THIS IS THE LAST TIME	FUNKY FEELING	25.00
77	106	CISSY HOUSTON	TOMORROW	LOVE IS HOLDING ON	4.00
77	106 DJ	CISSY HOUSTON	TOMORROW	LOVE IS HOLDING ON	5.00
77	109	MOB	LOVE CONNECTION	GEMINI LADY	6.00
77	109 DJ	MOB	LOVE CONNECTION	GEMINI LADY	8.00
77	126	CISSY HOUSTON	MORNING MUCH BETTER	IT NEVER REALLY ENDED	4.00
77	126 DJ	CISSY HOUSTON	MORNING MUCH BETTER	IT NEVER REALLY ENDED	5.00
78	136	CISSY HOUSTON	YOUR SONG	LOVE IS HOLDING ON	5.00
78	136 DJ	CISSY HOUSTON	YOUR SONG	LOVE IS HOLDING ON	6.00
78	166	CISSY HOUSTON	THINK IT OVER	AN UMBRELLA SONG	5.00
78	166 DJ	CISSY HOUSTON	THINK IT OVER	AN UMBRELLA SONG	6.00

PROBE

Part of the ABC / Dunhill family, this label was first pressed and distributed in the UK in 1971 until 1974. The label pulled recordings from the USA ABC and Dunhill catalogue. It has the distinction of having the very first Northern Soul 45 to hit the charts. With the UK's night club love affair with soul music becoming stronger and stronger and the demand created by the underground all nighter circuit for rare soul 45's. Probe reissued the previously seriously rare & unobtainable Tams – "Hey Girl Don't Bother Me." From 18/09/1971 it spent 3 weeks at #1 with a total of 17 weeks in the UK Pop charts. Although Probe tried to repeat its success with The Tams with other Northern Soul desirables like The Sapphires and The Shakers, the blossoming Northern Soul scene never again backed up their enthusiasm for the rare record by turning it into sales of the reissue, at the local record shop.

75	120	MIGHTY MARVELOWS	I DO	IN THE MORNING	8.00
71	515	GRASS ROOTS	TEMPTATION EYES	KEEPIN' ME DOWN	8.00
71	515 DJ	GRASS ROOTS	TEMPTATION EYES	KEEPIN' ME DOWN	10.00
71	516	B.B. KING	CHAINS AND THINGS	KINGS SPECIAL	5.00
71	516 DJ	B.B. KING	CHAINS AND THINGS	KINGS SPECIAL	6.00
71	526	JIMMY WITHERSPOON	HANDBAGS TO GLADRAGS	IT'S TIME TO LIVE	8.00
71	526 DJ	JIMMY WITHERSPOON	HANDBAGS TO GLADRAGS	IT'S TIME TO LIVE	10.00
71	528	B.B. KING	ASK ME NO QUESTIONS	HELP THE POOR + HUMMING BIRD	5.00
71	528 DJ	B.B. KING	ASK ME NO QUESTIONS	HELP THE POOR + HUMMING BIRD	6.00
71	531	GRASS ROOTS	SOONER OR LATER	I CAN TURN OFF THE RAIN	10.00
71	531 DJ	GRASS ROOTS	SOONER OR LATER	I CAN TURN OFF THE RAIN	10.00
71	532 pink	TAMS	HEY GIRL DON'T BOTHER ME	TAKE AWAY	6.00
71	532 pink DJ	TAMS	HEY GIRL DON'T BOTHER ME	TAKE AWAY	10.00
74	532 biege	TAMS	HEY GIRL DON'T BOTHER ME	TAKE AWAY	6.00
71	542 pink	TAMS	WHAT KIND OF FOOL (DO YOU THINK	LAUGH IT OFF	5.00
71	542 pink DJ	TAMS	WHAT KIND OF FOOL (DO YOU THINK	LAUGH IT OFF	7.00
71	543	GAYLE McCORMICK	IF ONLY YOU BELIEVE	IT'S A CRYING SHAME	10.00
71	543 DJ	GAYLE McCORMICK	IF ONLY YOU BELIEVE	IT'S A CRYING SHAME	15.00
71	551	EDDIE HOLMAN	HEY THERE LONELY GIRL	IT#S ALL IN THE GAME	6.00
71	551 DJ	EDDIE HOLMAN	HEY THERE LONELY GIRL	IT#S ALL IN THE GAME	8.00
72	556 pink	SAPPHIRES	GOTTA HAVE YOUR LOVE	GEE, I'M SORRY BABY	10.00
72	556 pink DJ	SAPPHIRES	GOTTA HAVE YOUR LOVE	GEE, I'M SORRY BABY	20.00
74	556 biege	SAPPHIRES	GOTTA HAVE YOUR LOVE	GEE, I'M SORRY BABY	8.00
72	559	THELMA HOUSTON	JUMPIN' JACK FLASH	SUNSHOWER	4.00
72	559 DJ	THELMA HOUSTON	JUMPIN' JACK FLASH	SUNSHOWER	5.00
72	567	DON GREGORY and the SOUL TRAIN	SOUL LINE	SOUL LINE instrumental	5.00
72	567 DJ	DON GREGORY and the SOUL TRAIN	SOUL LINE	SOUL LINE instrumental	6.00
72	573	B.B. KING	SUMMER IN THE CITY	FOUND WHAT I WANTED	4.00
72	573 DJ	B.B. KING	SUMMER IN THE CITY	FOUND WHAT I NEED	6.00
72	575	FOUR TOPS	KEEPER OF THE CASTLE	JUBILEE WITH SOUL	4.00
72	575 DJ	FOUR TOPS	KEEPER OF THE CASTLE	JUBILEE WITH SOUL	6.00
72	579	FOUR TOPS	(I THINK I MUST BE) DREAMING	THE GOOD LORD KNOWS	4.00
72	579 DJ	FOUR TOPS	(I THINK I MUST BE) DREAMING	THE GOOD LORD KNOWS	6.00
72	580	NOLAN PORTER	IF I COULD ONLY BE SURE	WORK IT OUT IN THE MORNING	75.00
72	580 DJ	NOLAN PORTER	IF I COULD ONLY BE SURE	WORK IT OUT IN THE MORNING	125.00
72	582 pink	SHAKERS	ONE WONDERFUL MOMENT	LOVE, LOVE, LOVE	10.00
72	582 pink DJ	SHAKERS	ONE WONDERFUL MOMENT	LOVE, LOVE, LOVE	20.00
74	582 biege	SHAKERS	ONE WONDERFUL MOMENT	LOVE, LOVE, LOVE	8.00
73	584	IMPRESSIONS	PEOPLE GET READY	WE'RE ROLLING ON	6.00
73	584 DJ	IMPRESSIONS	PEOPLE GET READY	WE'RE ROLLING ON	8.00
73	585	CHARLES MANN	I CAN FEEL IT	SAY YOU LOVE ME TOO	15.00
73	585 DJ	CHARLES MANN	I CAN FEEL IT	SAY YOU LOVE ME TOO	15.00
73	586	FOUR TOPS	AIN'T NO WOMAN (LIKE THE ONE I GOT)	PUT A LITTLE LOVE AWAY	5.00
73	586 DJ	FOUR TOPS	AIN'T NO WOMAN (LIKE THE ONE I GOT)	PUT A LITTLE LOVE AWAY	8.00
73	595	CHUCK JACKSON	I ONLY GET THE FEELING	SLOWLY BUT SURELY	15.00
73	595 DJ	CHUCK JACKSON	I ONLY GET THE FEELING	SLOWLY BUT SURELY	20.00
73	596	FOUR TOPS	ARE YOU MAN ENOUGH	PEACE OF MIND	6.00
73	596 DJ	FOUR TOPS	ARE YOU MAN ENOUGH	PEACE OF MIND	8.00
73	597	TRIBE	KOKE	KOKE part 2	6.00
73	597 DJ	TRIBE	KOKE	KOKE part 2	8.00
73	603	B.B. KING.	TO KNOW YOU IS TO LOVE YOU	I CAN'T LEAVE	4.00
73	603 DJ	B.B. KING.	TO KNOW YOU IS TO LOVE YOU	I CAN'T LEAVE	5.00
73	604	FOUR TOPS	SWEET UNDERSTANDING LOVE	MAIN STREET PEOPLE	6.00
73	604 DJ	FOUR TOPS	SWEET UNDERSTANDING LOVE	MAIN STREET PEOPLE	8.00
73	608	PATTI AUSTIN	MUSIC TO MY HEART	LOVE EM AND LEAVE EM KIND OF LOVE	15.00
73	608 DJ	PATTI AUSTIN	MUSIC TO MY HEART	LOVE EM AND LEAVE EM KIND OF LOVE	22.00
74	609	SAPPHIRES	THE SLOW FIZZ	OUR LOVE IS EVERYWHERE	10.00
74	609 DJ	SAPPHIRES	THE SLOW FIZZ	OUR LOVE IS EVERYWHERE	20.00
74	612	FOUR TOPS	I JUST CAN'T GET YOU OUT OF MY MIND	AM I MY BROTHE'S KEEPER	10.00
74	612 DJ	FOUR TOPS	I JUST CAN'T GET YOU OUT OF MY MIND	AM I MY BROTHE'S KEEPER	15.00
74	613	B.B. KING	I LIKE TO LIVE THE LOVE	LOVE	4.00
74	613 DJ	B.B. KING	I LIKE TO LIVE THE LOVE	LOVE	5.00
74	614	BO DONALDSON	DEEPER AND DEEEPER	DRIVE ME CRAZY	3.00
74	614 DJ	BO DONALDSON	DEEPER AND DEEEPER	DRIVE ME CRAZY	4.00
74	617	CHUCK JACKSON	JUST A LITTLE TEAR	I CAN'T BREAK AWAY	25.00
74	617 DJ	CHUCK JACKSON	JUST A LITTLE TEAR	I CAN'T BREAK AWAY	30.00
74	618	LAMONT DOZIER	TRYING TO HOLD ON TO MY WOMAN	WE DON'T WANT NOBODY TO COME	10.00
74	618 DJ	LAMONT DOZIER	TRYING TO HOLD ON TO MY WOMAN	WE DON'T WANT NOBODY TO COME	15.00
74	621	FOUR TOPS	ONE CHAIN DON'T MAKE NO PRISON	TURN ON THE LIGHT OF LOVE	4.00
74	621 DJ	FOUR TOPS	ONE CHAIN DON'T MAKE NO PRISON	TURN ON THE LIGHT OF LOVE	6.00

PRODIGAL

A ten release project from UK Tamla Motown with only Meatloaf's version of the Temptations hits being remotely related to soul, there is little interest in these releases unless you collect UK Tamla Motown.

76	1	DUNN & RUBINI	DIGGIN' IT	JUST KEEP LAUGHIN'	5.00
77	2	CHARLENE	IT AIN'T EASY COMING DOWN	ON MY WAY TO YOU	5.00
77	3	PHIL CORDELL	BACK IN YOUR ARMS	ONE MAN SHOW	5.00
77	4	CHARLENE	I'VE NEVER BEEN TO ME	FREDDIE	3.00
77	5	GRAFFITI ORCHESTRA	THEME FROM STAR WARS	THEME FROM STAR WARS part 2	5.00
77	6	PHIL CORDELL	DOIN' THE BEST I CAN	CHEATIN' IN THE DARK	5.00
77	7	RARE EARTH	IS YOUR TEACHER COOL	CRAZY LOVE	6.00
78	8	FRESH	JUST HOW DOES IT FEEL	LET YOURSELF GO	5.00
78	9	RARE EARTH	WARM RIDE	WOULD YOU LIKE TO COME ALONG	6.00
79	10	STONEY & MEATLOAF	THE WAY YOU DO THE THINGS YOU DO	WHAT YOU SEE IS WHAT YOU GET	8.00

PROJECT

	1	GOLDIE ALEXANDER	GO BACK	SHOW YOU MY LOVE	20.00

PRT

When the trading name for PYE expired in 1980. Pye metamorphoses itself into PRT. Although they reissued 45's by The Foundations, The Real Thing etc their commitment to any form of USA black music was non-existent. Perhaps the success in 1981 with The Tweets – The Birdie Song – steered them away from anything remotely associated with soul music. But surely the Tweets follow up – "Let's All Sing Like The Birdies Sing" - may have jolted them towards their former music policy, but no, Chuck Wood remains the new Pye's only contribution to this book. Oh, what a difference 15 years makes.

	111	CHUCK WOOD c/w CHOSEN FEW	SEVEN DAYS IS TOO LONG	FOOTSEE (instrumental)	6.00

PSYCHO

78	2603	FOUNDATIONS	CHANGE MY LIFE	CLOSER TO LOVING YOU	350.00

PYE

Pye Records of A.T.V. House Great Cumberland Place, London, W1 One of the UK most famous record labels. Pye originally sold televisions and radios. They entered the record business when it acquired Nixa Records in 1953 calling themselves Pye Nixa. In 1955 they acquire Petula Clark's fathers record Label Polygon. Petula Clark was to become Pye's major selling artist; she first released 45's on Pye Nixa. She switched labels in 1959 when the Nixa name was dropped after television broadcasting company ATV bought 50% of the label, completing the other 50% purchase in 1966. Two subsidiaries where created during the sixties: Pye Golden Guinea records who released budget LPs; some of which today are highly desirable Blues and Soul collectors items, Piccadilly was revamped into Dawn Records in the early seventies, a label devoid of soul but highly prized by rock collectors. When the rights to the name Pye expired at the end of 1979 the label changed its name to PRT.

More interesting to the Soul enthusiast is the 1959 Pye vehicle for overseas product, especially the USA R&B market The company distributed many American labels, including Chess/Argo A&M, Buddah, Kama Sutra & King Records see bio further along in this guide.

When you consider from the Pye listing below, every disc is a UK production, Pye stands as a glowing testament to Brit-Soul. Perhaps Pye had the finest selection of home grown product when it comes to collectable "soul".

62	15483	JULIE GRANT	UP ON THE ROOF	WHEN YOU ASK ABOUT LOVE	6.00
62	15483 DJ	JULIE GRANT	UP ON THE ROOF	WHEN YOU ASK ABOUT LOVE	10.00
63	15508	JULIE GRANT	THEN, ONLY THEN	COUNT ON ME	15.00
63	15508 DJ	JULIE GRANT	THEN, ONLY THEN	COUNT ON ME	28.00
63	15526	JULIE GRANT	THAT'S HOW HEARTACHES ARE MADE	CRUEL WORLD	15.00
63	15526 DJ	JULIE GRANT	THAT'S HOW HEARTACHES ARE MADE	CRUEL WORLD	28.00
63	15543	UNDERTAKERS	MASHED POTATOES	EVERYBODY LOVES A LOVER	15.00
63	15543 DJ	UNDERTAKERS	MASHED POTATOES	EVERYBODY LOVES A LOVER	22.00
63	15557	CHANTS	I DON'T CARE	COME GO WITH ME	8.00
63	15557 DJ	CHANTS	I DON'T CARE	COME GO WITH ME	10.00
63	15559	JOHNNY SANDON and the REMO FOUR	MAGIC POTION	YES	10.00
63	15559 DJ	JOHNNY SANDON and the REMO FOUR	MAGIC POTION	YES	18.00
63	15562	UNDERTAKERS	MONEY	WHAT ABOUT US	15.00
63	15562 DJ	UNDERTAKERS	MONEY	WHAT ABOUT US	20.00
63	15574	LAURIE JOHNSON ORCHESTRA	TWANGO	JENNY	10.00
63	15574 DJ	LAURIE JOHNSON ORCHESTRA	TWANGO	JENNY	15.00
63	15591	CHANTS	I COULD WRITE A BOOK	A THOUSAND STARS	8.00
63	15591 DJ	CHANTS	I COULD WRITE A BOOK	A THOUSAND STARS	10.00
64	15607	UNDERTAKERS	STUPIDITY	JUST A LITTLE BIT	15.00
64	15607 DJ	UNDERTAKERS	STUPIDITY	JUST A LITTLE BIT	22.00
64	15615	JULIE GRANT	EVERY DAY I HAVE TO CRY	WATCH WHAT YOU DO WITH MY BABY	6.00
64	15615 DJ	JULIE GRANT	EVERY DAY I HAVE TO CRY	WATCH WHAT YOU DO WITH MY BABY	10.00
64	15623	JIMMY NICOL and the SHUBDUBS	HUMPTY DUMPTY	NIGT TRAIN	20.00
64	15623 DJ	JIMMY NICOL and the SHUBDUBS	HUMPTY DUMPTY	NIGT TRAIN	28.00
64	15643	CHANTS	SHE'S MINE	THEN I'LL BE HOME	8.00
64	15643 DJ	CHANTS	SHE'S MINE	THEN I'LL BE HOME	10.00
64	15644	TRENDS	YOU'RE A WONDERFUL ONE	THE WAY YOU DO THE THINGS YOU	15.00
64	15644 DJ	TRENDS	YOU'RE A WONDERFUL ONE	THE WAY YOU DO THE THINGS YOU	22.00
64	15646	LEON YOUNG STRINGS	GLAD ALL OVER	THIS BOY	45.00
64	15646 DJ	LEON YOUNG STRINGS	GLAD ALL OVER	THIS BOY	70.00
64	15660	SOUL AGENTS	I JUST WANNA MAKE LOVE TO YOU	MEAN WOMAN BLUES	40.00
64	15660 DJ	SOUL AGENTS	I JUST WANNA MAKE LOVE TO YOU	MEAN WOMAN BLUES	60.00
64	15666	JIMMY NICOL	HUSKY	DON'T COME BACK	15.00
64	15666 DJ	JIMMY NICOL	HUSKY	DON'T COME BACK	22.00
64	15684	JULIE GRANT	CAN'T GET YOU OUT OF MY MIND	COME TO ME	6.00
64	15684 DJ	JULIE GRANT	CAN'T GET YOU OUT OF MY MIND	COME TO ME	8.00
64	15685	TONY JACKSON & the VIBRATIONS	BYE BYE BABY	WATCH YOUR STEP	20.00
64	15685 DJ	TONY JACKSON & the VIBRATIONS	BYE BYE BABY	WATCH YOUR STEP	28.00
64	15691	CHANTS	SWEET WAS THE WINE	ONE STAR	8.00
64	15691 DJ	CHANTS	SWEET WAS THE WINE	ONE STAR	10.00
64	15703	FIRST GEAR	A CERTAIN GIRL	LEAVE MY KITTEN ALONE	150.00

64	15703 DJ	FIRST GEAR	A CERTAIN GIRL	LEAVE MY KITTEN ALONE	175.00
64	15707	SOUL AGENTS	SEVENTH SON	LET'S MAKE IT PRETTY BABY	40.00
64	15707 DJ	SOUL AGENTS	SEVENTH SON	LET'S MAKE IT PRETTY BABY	50.00
64	15745	TONY JACKSON & the VIBRATIONS	YOU BEAT ME TO THE PUNCH	THIS LITTLE GIRL OF MINE	25.00
64	15745 DJ	TONY JACKSON & the VIBRATIONS	YOU BEAT ME TO THE PUNCH	THIS LITTLE GIRL OF MINE	30.00
65	15756	JULIE GRANT	BABY, BABY (I STILL LOVE YOU)	MY WORLD IS EMPTY WITHOUT YOU	15.00
65	15756 DJ	JULIE GRANT	BABY, BABY (I STILL LOVE YOU)	MY WORLD IS EMPTY WITHOUT YOU	22.00
65	15763	FIRST GEAR	THE IN CROWD	GOTTA MAKE THEIR FUTURE BRIGHT	30.00
65	15763 DJ	FIRST GEAR	THE IN CROWD	GOTTA MAKE THEIR FUTURE BRIGHT	40.00
65	15766	TONY JACKSON & the VIBRATIONS	LOVE POTION NO. 9	FORTUNE TELLER	30.00
65	15766 DJ	TONY JACKSON & the VIBRATIONS	LOVE POTION NO. 9	FORTUNE TELLER	45.00
65	15768	SOUL AGENTS	DON'T BREAK IT UP	GOSPEL TRAIN	40.00
65	15768 DJ	SOUL AGENTS	DON'T BREAK IT UP	GOSPEL TRAIN	50.00
65	15775	YVONNE PRENOSILOVA	WHEN MY BABY CRIES	COME ON HOME	75.00
65	15775 DJ	YVONNE PRENOSILOVA	WHEN MY BABY CRIES	COME ON HOME	100.00
65	15777	RAY McVAY SOUND	RAUNCHY	REVENGE	25.00
65	15777 DJ	RAY McVAY SOUND	RAUNCHY	REVENGE	30.00
65	15778	MARTHA SMITH	AS I WATCH YOU WALK AWAY	IT ALWAYS SEEMS LIKE SUMMER	25.00
65	15778 DJ	MARTHA SMITH	AS I WATCH YOU WALK AWAY	IT ALWAYS SEEMS LIKE SUMMER	35.00
65	15796	MAXINE DARREN	HOW CAN I HIDE IT FROM MY HEART	DON'T YOU KNOW	15.00
65	15796 DJ	MAXINE DARREN	HOW CAN I HIDE IT FROM MY HEART	DON'T YOU KNOW	25.00
65	15806	SHARON TANDY	NOW THAT YOU'VE GONE	HURTIN' ME	15.00
65	15806 DJ	SHARON TANDY	NOW THAT YOU'VE GONE	HURTIN' ME	22.00
65	15816	RAY McVAY SOUND	KINDA KINKY	KINKDOM COME	20.00
65	15816 DJ	RAY McVAY SOUND	KINDA KINKY	KINKDOM COME	28.00
65	15817	RIOT SQUAD	I WANNA TALK ABOUT MY BABY	GONNA MAKE YOU MINE	60.00
65	15817 DJ	RIOT SQUAD	I WANNA TALK ABOUT MY BABY	GONNA MAKE YOU MINE	75.00
65	15840	SANDRA BARRY	QUESTION	YOU CAN TAKE IT FROM ME	6.00
65	15840 DJ	SANDRA BARRY	QUESTION	YOU CAN TAKE IT FROM ME	10.00
65	15860	MARTHA SMITH	LOVE MEANS NOTHING TO YOU	THE SONG IS LOVE	6.00
65	15860 DJ	MARTHA SMITH	LOVE MEANS NOTHING TO YOU	THE SONG IS LOVE	10.00
65	15863	JIMMY JUSTICE	ONLY HEARTBREAKS FOR ME	EVERYTHING IN THE GARDEN	30.00
65	15863 DJ	JIMMY JUSTICE	ONLY HEARTBREAKS FOR ME	EVERYTHING IN THE GARDEN	45.00
65	15869	RIOT SQUAD	NEVERTHELESS	NOT A GREAT TALKER	40.00
65	15869 DJ	RIOT SQUAD	NEVERTHELESS	NOT A GREAT TALKER	50.00
65	15874	MIGIL FIVE	I'M IN LOVE AGAIN	ONE HUNDRED YEARS	20.00
65	15874 DJ	MIGIL FIVE	I'M IN LOVE AGAIN	ONE HUNDRED YEARS	28.00
65	15884	JULIE GRANT	AS LONG AS I KNOW HE'S MINE	LONELY WITHOUT YOU	10.00
65	15884 DJ	JULIE GRANT	AS LONG AS I KNOW HE'S MINE	LONELY WITHOUT YOU	15.00
65	15886	TONY COLTON and the BIG BOSS BAND	I STAND ACCUSED	FURTHER ON DOWN THE TRACK	**310.00**
65	15886 DJ	TONY COLTON and the BIG BOSS BAND	I STAND ACCUSED	FURTHER ON DOWN THE TRACK	**222.00**
65	15914	BARBARA KAY	YES I'M READY	SOMEONE HAS TO CRY (WHY MUST I	25.00
65	15914 DJ	BARBARA KAY	YES I'M READY	SOMEONE HAS TO CRY (WHY MUST I	35.00
65	15920	KENNY BERNARD	THE TRACKER	YOU GOTTA GIVE	10.00
65	15920 DJ	KENNY BERNARD	THE TRACKER	YOU GOTTA GIVE	15.00
65	15922	LORRAINE SILVER	LOST SUMMER LOVE	I KNOW YOU'LL BE THERE	150.00
65	15922 DJ	LORRAINE SILVER	LOST SUMMER LOVE	I KNOW YOU'LL BE THERE	200.00
65	15934	ALAN BOWN SET	I'M THE ONE	CAN'T LET HER GO	15.00
65	15934 DJ	ALAN BOWN SET	I'M THE ONE	CAN'T LET HER GO	22.00
65	15935	TAWNY REED	NEEDLE IN A HAYSTACK	I GOT A FEELING	30.00
65	15935 DJ	TAWNY REED	NEEDLE IN A HAYSTACK	I GOT A FEELING	50.00
65	15936	JAMES GALT	MY OWN WAY	COMES THE DAWN	10.00
65	15936 DJ	JAMES GALT	MY OWN WAY	COMES THE DAWN	15.00
65	15937	JULIE GRANT	STOP	WHEN THE LOVIN' ENDS	8.00
65	15937 DJ	JULIE GRANT	STOP	WHEN THE LOVIN' ENDS	15.00
65	15939	SHARON TANDY	I'VE FOUND LOVE	PERHAPS NOT FOREVER	10.00
65	15939 DJ	SHARON TANDY	I'VE FOUND LOVE	PERHAPS NOT FOREVER	18.00
65	15943	LEONARD WHITING	THAT'S WHAT MAMMA SAY	THE PIPER	50.00
65	15943 DJ	LEONARD WHITING	THAT'S WHAT MAMMA SAY	THE PIPER	75.00
65	15953	KIM D	THE REAL THING	COME ON BABY	25.00
65	15953 DJ	KIM D	THE REAL THING	COME ON BABY	35.00
65	15956	KAREN YOUNG	WE'LL START THE PARTY AGAIN	WONDERFUL SUMMER	20.00
65	15956 DJ	KAREN YOUNG	WE'LL START THE PARTY AGAIN	WONDERFUL SUMMER	28.00
65	15963	PEANUT	HOME OF THE BRAVE	I WANNA HEAR IT AGAIN	10.00
65	15963 DJ	PEANUT	HOME OF THE BRAVE	I WANNA HEAR IT AGAIN	15.00
65	15991	PETULA CLARK	GOTTA TELL THE WORLD	YOU'RE THE ONE	10.00
65	15991 DJ	PETULA CLARK	GOTTA TELL THE WORLD	YOU'RE THE ONE	18.00
65	17008	TONY KELLING	IT'S A CRYING SHAME	ANYTHING THAT PART OF YOU	15.00
65	17008 DJ	TONY KELLING	IT'S A CRYING SHAME	ANYTHING THAT PART OF YOU	22.00
65	17012	KOOBAS	TAKE ME FOR A LITTLE WHILE	SOMEWHERE IN THE NIGHT	30.00
65	17012 DJ	KOOBAS	TAKE ME FOR A LITTLE WHILE	SOMEWHERE IN THE NIGHT	45.00
66	17018	EPISODE SIX	PUT YOURSELF IN MY PLACE	THAT'S ALL I WANT	25.00
66	17018 DJ	EPISODE SIX	PUT YOURSELF IN MY PLACE	THAT'S ALL I WANT	35.00
65	17021	JAMES GALT	A MOST UNUSUAL FEELING	WITH MY BABY	75.00
65	17021 DJ	JAMES GALT	A MOST UNUSUAL FEELING	WITH MY BABY	100.00
66	17029	NEW FACES	LIKE A MAN	SHAKE UP THE PARTY (MYRA)	10.00
66	17029 DJ	NEW FACES	LIKE A MAN	SHAKE UP THE PARTY (MYRA)	18.00
66	17036	SANDIE SHAW	TOMORROW	HURTING YO	10.00
66	17036 DJ	SANDIE SHAW	TOMORROW	HURTING YO	15.00

66	17042	TAMMY ST. JOHN	NOBODY KNOWS WHAT'S GOIN' ON	STAY TOGETHER YOUNG LOVERS	60.00
66	17042 DJ	TAMMY ST. JOHN	NOBODY KNOWS WHAT'S GOIN' ON	STAY TOGETHER YOUNG LOVERS	100.00
66	17046	TONY COLTON	YOU'RE WRONG THERE BABY	FURTHER DOWN THE TRACK	18.00
66	17046 DJ	TONY COLTON	YOU'RE WRONG THERE BABY	FURTHER DOWN THE TRACK	25.00
66	17047	JACKIE TRENT	YOU BABY	SEND HER AWAY	30.00
66	17047 DJ	JACKIE TRENT	YOU BABY	SEND HER AWAY	75.00
66	17054	KENNY ROBERTS	RUN LIKE THE DEVIL	WHERE GOES MY HEART	50.00
66	17054 DJ	KENNY ROBERTS	RUN LIKE THE DEVIL	WHERE GOES MY HEART	75.00
66	17055	LORRAINE SILVER	WHEN THE LOVELIGHT STARTS SHINING	THE HAPPY FACES	15.00
66	17055 DJ	LORRAINE SILVER	WHEN THE LOVELIGHT STARTS SHINING	THE HAPPY FACES	20.00
66	17069	ANITA HARRIS	SOMETHING MUST BE DONE	FUNNY KIND OF FEELING	25.00
66	17069 DJ	ANITA HARRIS	SOMETHING MUST BE DONE	FUNNY KIND OF FEELING	40.00
66	17071	PETULA CLARK	A SIGN OF THE TIMES	TIME FOR LOVE	10.00
66	17071 DJ	PETULA CLARK	A SIGN OF THE TIMES	TIME FOR LOVE	20.00
66	17078	TAWNY REED	YOU CAN'T TAKE IT AWAY	MY HEART CRIES	20.00
66	17078 DJ	TAWNY REED	YOU CAN'T TAKE IT AWAY	MY HEART CRIES	30.00
66	17084	ALAN BOWN SET	EVERYTHING'S GONNA BE ALRIGHT	BABY DON'T PUSH ME	25.00
66	17084 DJ	ALAN BOWN SET	EVERYTHING'S GONNA BE ALRIGHT	BABY DON'T PUSH ME	40.00
66	17097	JAN PANTER	PUT YOURSELF IN MY PLACE	SCRATCH MY BACK	25.00
66	17097 DJ	JAN PANTER	PUT YOURSELF IN MY PLACE	SCRATCH MY BACK	35.00
66	17105	MALLY PAGE	THE LIFE AND SOUL OF THE PARTY	YOU CAN BE WRONG ABOUT BOYS	15.00
66	17105 DJ	MALLY PAGE	THE LIFE AND SOUL OF THE PARTY	YOU CAN BE WRONG ABOUT BOYS	22.00
66	17131	KENNY BERNARD	WHAT LOVE BRINGS	NOTHING CAN CHANGE THIS LOVE	75.00
66	17131 DJ	KENNY BERNARD	WHAT LOVE BRINGS	NOTHING CAN CHANGE THIS LOVE	150.00
66	17148	ALAN BOWN SET	HEADLINE NEWS	MR. PLEASURE	25.00
66	17148 DJ	ALAN BOWN SET	HEADLINE NEWS	MR. PLEASURE	35.00
66	17155	BLUE CHIPS	TELL HER	GOOD LOVIN' NEVER HURT	30.00
66	17155 DJ	BLUE CHIPS	TELL HER	GOOD LOVIN' NEVER HURT	45.00
66	17184	JOE BROWN	STAY A LITTLE WHILE	A SATISFIED MIND	10.00
66	17184 DJ	JOE BROWN	STAY A LITTLE WHILE	A SATISFIED MIND	15.00
66	17192	ALAN BOWN SET	EMERGENCY 999	SETTLE DOWN	15.00
66	17192 DJ	ALAN BOWN SET	EMERGENCY 999	SETTLE DOWN	22.00
66	17194	SHELIA CARTER and the EPIDSODE SIX	INCENSE	I WILL WARM YOUR HEART	45.00
66	17194 DJ	SHELIA CARTER and the EPIDSODE SIX	INCENSE	I WILL WARM YOUR HEART	60.00
66	17215	RAY FRENCH	SINCE I LOST MY BABY	GUN ME DOWN	10.00
66	17215 DJ	RAY FRENCH	SINCE I LOST MY BABY	GUN ME DOWN	18.00
67	17233	KENNY BERNARD	AIN'T NO SOUL (LEFT IN THESE OLD SHOES)	HEY WOMAN	50.00
67	17233 DJ	KENNY BERNARD	AIN'T NO SOUL (LEFT IN THESE OLD SHOES)	HEY WOMAN	75.00
67	17249	JACKIE TRENT	LOVE CAN GIVE	OPEN YOUR HEART	10.00
67	17249 DJ	JACKIE TRENT	LOVE CAN GIVE	OPEN YOUR HEART	18.00
67	17256	ALAN BOWN SET	GONNA FIX YOU GOOD (EVERY TIME YOUR BAD)	I REALLY REALLY CARE	30.00
67	17256 DJ	ALAN BOWN SET	GONNA FIX YOU GOOD (EVERY TIME YOUR BAD)	I REALLY REALLY CARE	45.00
67	17313	LUCAS & THE MIKE COTTON	STEP OUT OF LINE	AIN'T LOVE GOOD, AIN'T LOVE PR	30.00
67	17313 DJ	LUCAS & THE MIKE COTTON	STEP OUT OF LINE	AIN'T LOVE GOOD, AIN'T LOVE PR	40.00
67	17366	FOUNDATIONS	BABY, NOW THAT I'VE FOUND YOU	COME ON BACK TO ME	5.00
67	17366 DJ	FOUNDATIONS	BABY, NOW THAT I'VE FOUND YOU	COME ON BACK TO ME	10.00
67	17387	FERRIS WHEEL	NUMBER ONE GUY	I CAN'T BREAK THE HABIT	30.00
67	17387 DJ	FERRIS WHEEL	NUMBER ONE GUY	I CAN'T BREAK THE HABIT	40.00
67	17399	JASON KNIGHT	OUR LOVE IS GETTING STRONGER	STANDING IN MY SHOES	200.00
67	17399 DJ	JASON KNIGHT	OUR LOVE IS GETTING STRONGER	STANDING IN MY SHOES	**362.00**
68	17417	FOUNDATIONS	BACK ON MY FEET AGAIN	I CAN TAKE OR LEAVE YOUR LOVIN	5.00
68	17417 DJ	FOUNDATIONS	BACK ON MY FEET AGAIN	I CAN TAKE OR LEAVE YOUR LOVIN	10.00
68	17423	MARGO & the MARVETTES	WHEN LOVE SLIPS AWAY	I'LL BE HOME	50.00
68	17423 DJ	MARGO & the MARVETTES	WHEN LOVE SLIPS AWAY	I'LL BE HOME	75.00
68	17425	GENO WASHINGTON & RAM JAM BAND	DIFFERENT STROKES	YOU GOT ME HUMMIN'	8.00
68	17425 DJ	GENO WASHINGTON & RAM JAM BAND	DIFFERENT STROKES	YOU GOT ME HUMMIN'	15.00
68	17437	JACKIE TRENT	ALLES OKAY (SEND HER AWAY)	BYE BYE LOVE	8.00
68	17437 DJ	JACKIE TRENT	ALLES OKAY (SEND HER AWAY)	BYE BYE LOVE	10.00
68	17495	YOUNG BLOOD	GREEN LIGHT	DON'T LEAVE ME IN THE DARK	15.00
68	17495 DJ	YOUNG BLOOD	GREEN LIGHT	DON'T LEAVE ME IN THE DARK	22.00
68	17501	JACK DORSEY ORCHESTRA	SOUL COAXING	ELIZABETH'S WALTZ	8.00
68	17501 DJ	JACK DORSEY ORCHESTRA	SOUL COAXING	ELIZABETH'S WALTZ	10.00
68	17503	FOUNDATIONS	ANY OLD TIME YOU'RE LONELY AND	WE ARE PEOPLE	5.00
68	17503 DJ	FOUNDATIONS	ANY OLD TIME YOU'RE LONELY AND	WE ARE PEOPLE	6.00
68	17504	SANDIE SHAW	DON'T RUN AWAY	STOP	10.00
68	17504 DJ	SANDIE SHAW	DON'T RUN AWAY	STOP	15.00
68	17531	SATIN BELLS	BABY YOU'RE SO RIGHT FOR ME	WHEN YOU'RE READY	15.00
68	17531 DJ	SATIN BELLS	BABY YOU'RE SO RIGHT FOR ME	WHEN YOU'RE READY	22.00
68	17547	PAPER DOLLS	THERE'S NOBODY I'D SOONER LOVE	MY LIFE (IS IN YOUR HANDS)	8.00
68	17547 DJ	PAPER DOLLS	THERE'S NOBODY I'D SOONER LOVE	MY LIFE (IS IN YOUR HANDS)	15.00
68	17570	GENO WASHINGTON & RAM JAM BAND	I CAN'T QUIT HER	PUT OUT THE FIRE BABY	8.00
68	17570 DJ	GENO WASHINGTON & RAM JAM BAND	I CAN'T QUIT HER	PUT OUT THE FIRE	15.00
68	17579	JIMMY JAMES & THE VAGABONDS	RED RED WINE	WHO COULD BE LOVING YOU	15.00
68	17579 DJ	JIMMY JAMES & THE VAGABONDS	RED RED WINE	WHO COULD BE LOVING YOU	22.00
68	17588	YOUNG BLOOD	JUST HOW LOUD	MASQUERADE	15.00
68	17588 DJ	YOUNG BLOOD	JUST HOW LOUD	MASQUERADE	22.00
68	17608	SATIN BELLS	DA-DI-DA-DA	OH NO OH YES	6.00
68	17608 DJ	SATIN BELLS	DA-DI-DA-DA	OH NO OH YES	8.00
68	17620	CITY OF WESTMINSTER STRINGS	A TOUCH OF VELVET AND A STING OF	TOMMY TUCKER	10.00

68	17620 DJ	CITY OF WESTMINSTER STRINGS	A TOUCH OF VELVET AND A STING OF	TOMMY TUCKER	12.00
68	17625	BARRY GRAY ORCHESTRA	JOE 90 - TITLE THEME	JOE 90 - HIJACKED	25.00
68	17625 DJ	BARRY GRAY ORCHESTRA	JOE 90 - TITLE THEME	JOE 90 - HIJACKED	40.00
68	17636	FOUNDATIONS	BUILD ME UP BUTTERCUP	NEW DIRECTION	5.00
68	17636 DJ	FOUNDATIONS	BUILD ME UP BUTTERCUP	NEW DIRECTION	10.00
68	17649	GENO WASHINGTON & RAM JAM BAND	I CAN'T LET YOU GO	BRING IT TO ME BABY	8.00
68	17649 DJ	GENO WASHINGTON & RAM JAM BAND	I CAN'T LET YOU GO	BRING IT TO ME BABY	15.00
68	17682	DONIE COLLINS SHOWBAND	I CAN'T HELP MYSELF (SUGAR PIE	GET DOWN WITH IT	10.00
68	17682 DJ	DONIE COLLINS SHOWBAND	I CAN'T HELP MYSELF (SUGAR PIE	GET DOWN WITH IT	15.00
68	17687	SOUNDS ORCHESTRAL	SOUL COAXING	LOVE STORY	10.00
68	17687 DJ	SOUNDS ORCHESTRAL	SOUL COAXING	LOVE STORY	15.00
69	17702	FOUNDATIONS	IN THE BAD BAD OLD DAYS	GIVE ME LOVE	5.00
69	17702 DJ	FOUNDATIONS	IN THE BAD BAD OLD DAYS	GIVE ME LOVE	10.00
69	17711	STRAWBERRY JAM	PER-SO-NAL-LY	THIS IS TO A GIRL	20.00
69	17711 DJ	STRAWBERRY JAM	PER-SO-NAL-LY	THIS IS TO A GIRL	30.00
69	17719	JIMMY JAMES & THE VAGABONDS	CLOSE THE DOOR	WHY	6.00
69	17719 DJ	JIMMY JAMES & THE VAGABONDS	CLOSE THE DOOR	WHY	10.00
69	17745	GENO WASHINGTON & RAM JAM BAND	MY LITTLE CHICKADEE	SEVEN ELEVEN	6.00
69	17745 DJ	GENO WASHINGTON & RAM JAM BAND	MY LITTLE CHICKADEE	SEVEN ELEVEN	10.00
69	17759	RAINBOW PEOPLE	LIVING IN A DREAM WORLD	HAPPY TO SEE YOU AGAIN	50.00
69.	17759 DJ	RAINBOW PEOPLE	LIVING IN A DREAM WORLD	HAPPY TO SEE YOU AGAIN	75.00
69	17766	ARROWS	MERCY	SEE SAW	10.00
69	17766 DJ	ARROWS	MERCY	SEE SAW	15.00
69	17785	HELEN SHAPIRO	TAKE ME FOR AWHILE	YOU'VE GUESSED	20.00
69	17785 DJ	HELEN SHAPIRO	TAKE ME FOR A WHILE	YOU'VE GUESSED	30.00
69	17798	MAXINE NIGHTINGALE	DON'T PUSH ME BABY	THRU' LOVING YOU	8.00
69	17798 DJ	MAXINE NIGHTINGALE	DON'T PUSH ME BABY	THRU' LOVING YOU	10.00
69	17809	FOUNDATIONS	BORN TO LIVE, BORN TO DIE	WHY DID YOU CRY	5.00
69	17809 DJ	FOUNDATIONS	BORN TO LIVE, BORN TO DIE	WHY DID YOU CRY	8.00
69	17823	TINA TOTT	BURNING IN THE BACKGROUND OF MY MIND	TAKE AWAY THE EMPTINESS TOO	60.00
69	17823 DJ	TINA TOTT	BURNING IN THE BACKGROUND OF MY MIND	TAKE AWAY THE EMPTINESS TOO	75.00
69	17849	FOUNDATIONS	BABY I COULDN'T SEE	PENNY SIR	5.00
69	17849 DJ	FOUNDATIONS	BABY I COULDN'T SEE	PENNY SIR	6.00
69	17863	CRAIG DOUGLAS	DON'T MIND IF I CRY	RAINDROPS KEEP FALLING ON MY H	40.00
69	17863 DJ	CRAIG DOUGLAS	DON'T MIND IF I CRY	RAINDROPS KEEP FALLING ON MY H	50.00
70	17904	FOUNDATIONS	TAKE A GIRL LIKE YOU	I'M GONNA BE A RICH MAN	5.00
70	17904 DJ	FOUNDATIONS	TAKE A GIRL LIKE YOU	I'M GONNA BE A RICH MAN	6.00
70	17956	FOUNDATIONS	I'M GONNA BE A RICH MAN	WHO AM I	5.00
70	17956 DJ	FOUNDATIONS	I'M GONNA BE A RICH MAN	WHO AM I	6.00
65	24218 EP PS	SEARCHERS	BUMBLE BEE	4 track EP with cover inc: Magic Potion	10.00
68	24293 EP PS	GENO WASHINGTON & RAM JAM BAND	DIFFERENT STROKES	1968 4 track EP with cover	22.00
68	24297 EP PS	FOUNDATIONS	IT'S ALL RIGHT	1968 4 track EP with cover	20.00
68	24302 EP PS	GENO WASHINGTON & RAM JAM BAND	SMALL PACKAGE OF HIPSTERS	1968 4 track EP with cover	28.00
71	45019	GENO WASHINGTON & RAM JAM BAND	ALISON PLEASE	EACH AND EVERY PART OF ME	6.00
71	45019 DJ	GENO WASHINGTON & RAM JAM BAND	ALISON PLEASE	EACH AND EVERY PART OF ME	8.00
71	45085	GENO WASHINGTON & RAM JAM BAND	FEELING SO GOO	WOULD YOU BELIEVE + MY LITTLE	5.00
71	45085 DJ	GENO WASHINGTON & RAM JAM BAND	FEELING SO GOO	WOULD YOU BELIEVE + MY LITTLE	8.00
71	45111	PHOENIX	BEGGIN'	BLACK IS BLACK	4.00
71	45111 DJ	PHOENIX	BEGGIN'	BLACK IS BLACK	5.00
72	45148	POLLY BROWN	THE FEELINGS RIGHT	I CAN'T DO WITHOUT YOU	40.00
72	45148 DJ	POLLY BROWN	THE FEELINGS RIGHT	I CAN'T DO WITHOUT YOU	50.00
72	45150	GLEM CURTIS	POINT OF NO RETURN	I'VE NEVER FOUND A GIRL	40.00
72	45150 DJ	GLEM CURTIS	POINT OF NO RETURN	I'VE NEVER FOUND A GIRL	50.00
72	45187	WATSON T. BROWNE	WHAT CAN I SAY	YOU'RE THE ONE I LOVE	10.00
72	45187 DJ	WATSON T. BROWNE	WHAT CAN I SAY	YOU'RE THE ONE I LOVE	15.00
72	45212 blue	PLAYTHINGS	STOP! WHAT YOU'RE DOING	SAD SONGS	10.00
72	45212 yellow DJ	PLAYTHINGS	STOP! WHAT YOU'RE DOING	SAD SONGS	22.00
73	45212 white	PLAYTHINGS	STOP ! WHAT YOU'RE DOING	SAD SONGS	15.00
74	45212 purple fade	PLAYTHINGS	STOP ! WHAT YOU'RE DOING	SAD SONGS	6.00
72	45227	ANGELS ONE FIVE	TOODY	THAT WAS YESTERDAY	8.00
72	45227 DJ	ANGELS ONE FIVE	TOODY	THAT WAS YESTERDAY	12.00
73	45287	JASÓN KNIGHT	LOVE IS GETTING STRONGER	STANDING IN MY SHOES	15.00
73	45287 DJ	JASON KNIGHT	LOVE IS GETTING STRONGER	STANDING IN MY SHOES	25.00
74	45325	TOMMY HUNT	TIME ALONE WILL TELL	SLEEP TIGHT HONEY	4.00
74	45325 DJ	TOMMY HUNT	TIME ALONE WILL TELL	SLEEP TIGHT HONEY	5.00
74	45342	WILMA READING	I'M NO GOOD FOR YOU BABY	LOOKING FOR ANOTHER PURE LOVE	10.00
74	45342 DJ	WILMA READING	I'M NO GOOD FOR YOU BABY	LOOKING FOR ANOTHER PURE LOVE	15.00
74	45380	WILMER READING	TWO CAN HAVE A PARTY	PLAY IT AGAIN	8.00
74	45380 DJ	WILMER READING	TWO CAN HAVE A PARTY	PLAY IT AGAIN	10.00
74	45383	NOSMO KING	GOODBYE	TEENAGE LOVE	15.00
74	45383 DJ	NOSMO KING	GOODBYE	TEENAGE LOVE	30.00
74	45399	PLAYTHINGS	SURROUNDED BY A RAY OF SUNSHINE	DANCE THE NIGHT AWAY	5.00
74	45399 DJ	PLAYTHINGS	SURROUNDED BY A RAY OF SUNSHIN	DANCE THE NIOGHT AWAY	8.00
74	45421	SWEET SENSATION	PURELY BY COINCIDECE	TOUCHED BY MAGIC	4.00
74	45421 DJ	SWEET SENSATION	PURELY BY COINCIDENCE	TOUCHED BY MAGIC	5.00
74	5427	PAUL SABU	NOWHERE TO RUN	OUT IN THE COUNTRY	5.00
74	5427 DJ	PAUL SABU	NOWHERE TO RUN	OUT IN THE COUNTRY	6.00
74	45435	JAVELLS feat. NOSMO KING	LOVIN' YOU IS EASY	ONLY THE BEGINNING	4.00
74	45435 DJ	JAVELLS feat. NOSMO KING	LOVIN' YOU IS EASY	ONLY THE BEGINNING	5.00

74	45440	JIMMY HELMS	ROMEO AND JULIET	RAGTIME GIRL	150.00
74	45440 DJ	JIMMY HELMS	ROMEO AND JULIET	RAGTIME GIRL	175.00
75	45472	JIMMY JAMES & THE VAGABONDS	HEY GIRL	I AM SOMEBODY	25.00
75	45472 DJ	JIMMY JAMES & THE VAGABONDS	HEY GIRL	I AM SOMEBODY	30.00
75	45487	MAJOR LANCE	YOU'RE EVERYTHING I NEED	same: instrumental	10.00
75	45487 DJ	MAJOR LANCE	YOU'RE EVERYTHING I NEED	same: instrumental	15.00
75	45503	JIMMY HELMS	DON'T COOL YOUR LOVE	I DON'T WANNA LOSE YOU	4.00
75	45503 DJ	JIMMY HELMS	DON'T COOL YOUR LOVE	I DON'T WANNA LOSE YOU	5.00
75	45522	REAL THING	WATCH OUT CAROLINA	I WANT YOU BACK	4.00
75	45522 DJ	REAL THING	WATCH OUT CAROLINA	I WANT YOU BACK	5.00
75	45524	JIMMY JAMES & THE VAGABONDS	WHATEVER HAPPENED TO THE LOVE	LET'S HAVE FUN	5.00
75	45524 DJ	JIMMY JAMES & THE VAGABONDS	WHATEVER HAPPENED TO THE LOVE	LET'S HAVE FUN	6.00
75	45551	CARL DOUGLAS	I WANT TO GIVE YOU MY EVERYTHING	WITCHFINDER GENERAL	15.00
75	45551 DJ	CARL DOUGLAS	I WANT TO GIVE YOU MY EVERYTHING	WITCHFINDER GENERAL	22.00
76	45585	JIMMY JAMES	I'LL GO WHER THE MUSIC TAKES ME	same: disco version	4.00
76	45585 DJ	JIMMY JAMES	I'LL GO WHER THE MUSIC TAKES ME	same: disco version	5.00
76	45606	JIMMY JAMES	WANT YOU SO MUCH	NOW IS THE TIME	8.00
76	45606 DJ	JIMMY JAMES	WANT YOU SO MUCH	NOW IS THE TIME	10.00
76	45609	FAMILY AFFAIR	LOVE HUSTLE	CALL ME	10.00
76	45609 DJ	FAMILY AFFAIR	LOVE HUSTLE	CALL ME	15.00
76	45618	REAL THING	CAN'T GET BY WITHOUT YOU	HE'S JUST A MONEY MATTER	4.00
76	45618 DJ	REAL THING	CAN'T GET BY WITHOUT YOU	HE'S JUST A MONEY MATTER	5.00
76	45631	WILMA READING	DO ME WRONG, BUT DO ME	IT'S OVER	4.00
76	45631 DJ	WILMA READING	DO ME WRONG, BUT DO ME	IT'S OVER	5.00
77	45662	REAL THING	YOU'LL NEVER KNOW WHAT YOU'RE MISSING	LOVE IS A PLAYGROUND	3.00
77	45662 DJ	REAL THING	YOU'LL NEVER KNOW WHAT YOU'RE MISSING	LOVE IS A PLAYGROUND	4.00
77	45691	JIMMY JAMES & THE VAGABONDS	TILL I CAN'T TAKE IT ANYMORE	STAY WITH ME	4.00
77	45691 DJ	JIMMY JAMES & THE VAGABONDS	TILL I CAN'T TAKE IT ANYMORE	STAY WITH ME	5.00
77	45701	REAL THING	LOVE IS SUCH A BEAUTIFUL THING	TOPSY TURVY	3.00
77	45701 DJ	REAL THING	LOVE IS SUCH A BEAUTIFUL THING	TOPSY TURVY	4.00
77	46025	REAL THING	LIGHTNING STRIKES AGAIN	DANCE WITH ME	3.00
77	46025 DJ	REAL THING	LIGHTNING STRIKES AGAIN	DANCE WITH ME	4.00
78	46031	JIMMY HELMS	BLACK JOY	DON'T PULL YOUR LOVE	5.00
78	46031 DJ	JIMMY HELMS	BLACK JOY	DON'T PULL YOUR LOVE	6.00
78	46039	JIMMY JAMES & THE VAGABONDS	YOU MADE ME LOVE AGAIN	DREAMS	4.00
78	46039 DJ	JIMMY JAMES & THE VAGABONDS	YOU MADE ME LOVE AGAIN	DREAMS	5.00
78	46045	REAL THING	WHENEVER YOU WANT MY LOVE	STANHOPE STREET	3.00
78	46045 DJ	REAL THING	WHENEVER YOU WANT MY LOVE	STANHOPE STREET	4.00
78	46113	REAL THING	RAININ' THROUGH MY SUNSHINE	LADY I LOVE YOU ALL THE TIME	8.00
78	46113 DJ	REAL THING	RAININ' THROUGH MY SUNSHINE	LADY I LOVE YOU ALL THE TIME	10.00
79	46147	REAL THING	CAN YOU FEL THE FORCE	CHILDREN OF THE GHETTO	3.00
79	46147 DJ	REAL THING	CAN YOU FEL THE FORCE	CHILDREN OF THE GHETTO	4.00

PYE STUDIO ACETATES of scheduled but unissued 45's

All these acetates have the company label with Pye Recording Studios with a long microphone logo plus phone number 01-262-5495/6 curved around the top of the label. Featuring CUSTOM DISC CUT around the bottom of the label.

73	acetate	FIRST CHOICE	THIS IS THE HOUSE WHERE LOVE DIED	blank:	400.00
74	acetate	DARRYL STEWART	NAME IT AND CLAIM IT	blank:	**450.00**
74	acetate	MAJOR LANCE	RIGHT TO CRY	blank:	**466.00**
75	acetate	DANNY LEAKE	HUNG UP IN MID AIR	blank	450.00

PYE ADVANCE PRESSING

These 45's have a special stick on PYE ADVANCE label with typed or handwritten credits, all Pye 45's most probably went through this process. Below are two we have sold recently: Price is usually matched or slightly exceeds the DJ promotion copy.

65	15943	LEONARD WHITING	THAT'S WHAT MY MAMA SAY	THE PIPER	45.00
66	25375	T.V. and the TRIBESMEN	BARFOOTIN'	FAT MAN	30.00

PYE DISCO DEMAND

In 1974 Pye were the first UK record label to recognize the sensational rise of the underground music movement, which Dave Godin had recently christened Northern Soul. Pye had a huge source to pull Northern Soul recordings from, having the UK distribution rights to such labels as Calla, New Voice, and Roulette, 20th Century Fox, Scepter/Wand, etc. Dave McAleer of Pye sought the guidance of Blackpool Mecca's most prominent DJ Ian Levine to choose tracks for the very first LP dedicated to the Northern Soul movement "Solid Soul Sensation" hit the UK shops in 1974 as Pye set about cashing in on a scene playing and establishing a huge demand for obscure old soul recordings. They came up with the format of a new label called Pye Disco Demand to promote the music on 45. Ironically only a year before the "real" disco explosion was about to happen on the East Coast of the USA. Perhaps this was one of the reasons for the premature demise of the label after only 25 releases as the meaning of "disco" changed overnight.

But during its short life it did gain a status with collectors, as a label to fully complete. 90% of the releases were considered of good collectable quality and most of the releases were the first timers to the UK. The timing for the releases was well advised as the original USA 45's were packing the floors of Wigan Casino, Blackpool Mecca etc, resulting in very healthy sales making none of the releases up until # 118 particularly rare.

Then, in true character of the bigger record labels, they thought they could make there own recordings for the Northern Soul market. When 45's like the "Sounds Of Lancashire" and "The Jezebelles" hit the market, they were total flops and inevitably Pye lost faith in the rare soul scene with Pye Disco Demands last release in 1975. As you will recognize from the price difference from the regular release to the promo copies: Pye Disco Demand demos are particularly sought after and difficult to find

74	101	FRANKIE & THE CLASSICALS	WHAT SHALL I DO	GOODBYE LOVE, HELLO SADNESS	10.00
74	101 DJ	FRANKIE & THE CLASSICALS	WHAT SHALL I DO	GOODBYE LOVE, HELLO SADNESS	15.00
74	102 silver lettering	JERRY WILLIAMS	IF YOU ASK ME (BECAUSE I LOVE YOU)	YVONNE	10.00
74	102 black lettering	JERRY WILLIAMS	IF YOU ASK ME (BECAUSE I LOVE YOU)	YVONNE	15.00
74	102 DJ	JERRY WILLIAMS	IF YOU ASK ME (BECAUSE I LOVE)	YVONNE	15.00
74	103	CASUALEERS	DANCE DANCE DANCE	THERE'S SOMETHING ABOUT THIS G	10.00
74	103 DJ	CASUALEERS	DANCE, DANCE, DANCE	THERE'S SOMETHING ABOUT THIS G	20.00
74	104	FUZZ	I'M SO GLAD	ALL ABOUT LOVE	8.00

74	104 DJ	FUZZ	I'M SO GLAD	ALL ABOUT LOVE	15.00
74	105	WALLY COX	THIS MAN	I'VE HAD ENOUGH	8.00
74	105 DJ	WALLY COX	THIS MAN	I'VE HAD ENOUGH	15.00
74	106	LITTLE JOHNNY BLAIR	MOMMAS GONE	EASIER TO SAY THAN DO	8.00
74	106 DJ	LITTLE JOHNNY BLAIR	MOMMA'S GONE	EASIER TO SAY THAN DO	10.00
74	107	AL WILSON	HELP ME	same: Instrumental	8.00
74	107 DJ	AL WILSON	HELP ME	HELP ME (instrumental)	15.00
74	108	ILA VAN	CAN'T HELP LOVING THAT MAN	I'VE GOT THE FEELING	8.00
74	108 DJ	ILA VAN	CAN'T HELP LOVING THAT MAN	I'VE GOT A FEELING	15.00
74	109	VEL-VETS	I GOT TO FIND ME SOMEBODY	WHAT NOW MY LOVE	15.00
74	109 DJ	VEL-VETS	I GOT TO FIND ME SOMEBODY	WHAT NOW MY LOVE	20.00
74	110	JIMMY BREEDLOVE	I CAN'T HELP LOVIN' YOU	I SAW YOU	8.00
74	110 DJ	JIMMY BREEDLOVE	I CAN'T HELP LOVIN' YOU	I SAW YOU	10.00
74	111	CHUCK WOOD c/w CHOSEN FEW	SEVEN DAYS TOO LONG	FOOTSEE	8.00
74	111 PS	CHUCK WOOD c/w CHOSEN FEW	SEVEN DAYS TOO LONG	FOOTSEE	10.00
74	111 DJ	CHUCK WOOD c/w CHOSEN FEW	SEVEN DAYS TOO LONG	FOOTSEE	15.00
74	111 black to grey fade	CHUCK WOOD c/w CHOSEN FEW	SEVEN DAYS TOO LONG	FOOTSEE	20.00
74	112	FUGITIVES	HUMAN JUNGLE	DON'T PLAY THAT SONG (YOU LIED	8.00
74	112 DJ	FUGITIVES	HUMAN JUNGLE	DON'T PLAY THAT SONG (YOU LIED	10.00
75	113	MITCH RYDER & DETROIT WHEELS	YOU GET YOUR KICKS	BREAKOUT	8.00
75	113 DJ	MITCH RYDER & DETROIT WHEELS	YOU GET YOUR KICKS	BREAKOUT	15.00
75	114	FLINT-NIKS c/w SHA-NA-NETTS	THE FLINT-NIK ROCK	(JUST LIKE) ROMEO AND JULIET	15.00
75	114 DJ	FLINT-NIKS c/w SHA-NA-NETTS	THE FLINT-NIK ROCK	(JUST LIKE) ROMEO AND JULIET	25.00
75	115	SHIRELLES	LAST MINUTE MIRACLE	MARCH	15.00
75	115 DJ	SHIRELLES	LAST MINUTE MIRACLE	MARCH	30.00
75	116	CHUCK JACKSON	THESE CHAINS OF LOVE	ANY DAY NOW	8.00
75	116 DJ	CHUCK JACKSON	THESE CHAINS OF LOVE	ANY DAY NOW	20.00
75	117	MAXINE BROWN	ONE IN A MILLION	LET ME GIVE YOU MY LOVING	15.00
75	117 DJ	MAXINE BROWN	ONE IN A MILLION	LET ME GIVE YOU MY LOVING	30.00
75	118	CHUCK JONES AND CO	BOO ON YOU (SHAKIN' THE BABY'S	GROOVIN' ON	8.00
75	118 DJ	CHUCK JONES AND CO	BOO ON YOU (SHAKIN' THE BABY'S	GROOVIN' ON	10.00
75	2001	WAYNE GIBSON	UNDER MY THUMB	THE GAME	10.00
75	2001 blue vinyl	WAYNE GIBSON	UNDER MY THUMB	THE GAME	15.00
75	2001 DJ	WAYNE GIBSON	UNDER MY THUMB	THE GAME	15.00
75	2002	JOHN SCHROEDER ORCH.	SOUL FOR SALE	LOVIN' YOU GIRL	6.00
75	2002 DJ	JOHN SCHROEDER ORCH.	SOUL FOR SALE	LOVIN' YOU GIRL	8.00
75	2003	JAVELLS feat. NOSMO KING	GOODBYE NOTHIN' TO SAY	NOTHIN' TO SAY	5.00
75	2003 DJ	JAVELLS feat. NOSMO KING	GOODBYE NOTHING TO SAY	NOTHIN' TO SAY	8.00
75	2004	KENNY BERNARD c/w LEON YOUNG STRINGS	WHAT LOVE BRINGS	GLAD ALL OVER	8.00
75	2004 DJ	KENNY BERNARD c/w LEON YOUNG STRINGS	WHAT LOVE BRINGS	GLAD ALL OVER	10.00
75	2005	SOUNDS OF LANCASHIRE	SLICED TOMATOES	BACK TO BACH	5.00
75	2005 DJ	SOUNDS OF LANCASHIRE	SLICED TOMATOES	BACK TO BACH	8.00
75	2006	JEZEBELLES	TAINTED LOVE	THE TORCH IS BACK	6.00
75	2006 DJ	JEZEBELLES	TAINTED LOVE	THE TORCH IS BACK	8.00
75	2007	PLAYTHINGS	STOP WHAT YOU'RE DOING	SAD SONGS	8.00
75	2007 DJ	PLAYTHINGS	STOP WHAT YOU'RE DOING	SAD SONGS	10.00

PYE INTERNATIONAL

Pye International, along with London American and Stateside were the three main outlets in the UK for American black music in the 60's. Pye, London & Stateside plus their forerunner Top Rank all started life in the 50's, bringing mainly Pop and Rock 'n Roll to the British market. Pye Records had been going for ten years before Pye International was launched in 1959, using both 78rpm and the 45 rpm disc but had little success until The Marcels – "Blue Moon" – reached #1 in the charts in March 1961. Two releases further on saw Pye again dip into their R&B catalogue with Don Covay and the Goodtimers – "Pony Time" – but Pye still were not making waves, mainly because of the strangle hold of London American and Top Rank had on the USA releases. But the spring of 1961 would be the turning point, when Pye International obtained the rights to the Argo Label, instantly issuing R&B from Etta James, Clarence Frogman Henry, The Sensations etc and within four months they secured the rights to the remainder of the Chess / Checker portfolio including Chuck Berry and Bo Diddley (Bo was momentarily issued on Pye Jazz). Although Pye did have a few R&B contracts such as Excello, it was the Chess stable that provide the bulk of its R&B success.

Pye International's first early soul release arrived in October 1962 from Billy Stewart – "Reap What You Sow" – closely followed by the Dells, Jan Bradley but it was Detroit not Chicago that would give the label interest to soul's main stream buyers, with "Gonna Send You Back To Georgia" in March 1964. This broke into the changing all night "Jazz" club scene that was veering towards R&B and Soul.

From this point on scores of great soul records were issued on the logo, Tony Clarke "Ain't Love Good, Ain't Love Proud" Jackie Ross "Selfish One" Maxine Brown " Oh No Not My Baby" Chuck Jackson "Any Day Now" Nella Dodds " Come See About Me" and not forgetting Dobie Gray "See You At The Go Go" and all these within a space of ten months. This happening laid the foundations in the clubs and coffee bars that would evolve into the Northern Soul scene.

By now Pye had given Chess its own identity with its own label, so it was left to Scepter / Wand and King Records to take over as Pye's main supplier for soul. King's major representative was James Brown who had several excellent soulful releases but it is certainly arguable that the first two real Northern Soul style records were issued in September 1966 with Chuck Jackson's "Chains Of Love" and Roscoe Robinson's "That's Enough" closely followed by The Dynatones "The Fife Piper" and Ronnie Milsap's version of Major Lance's "Ain't No Soul (Left In These Old Shoes)" the seeds of Northern Soul were being sown in that most golden of years 1966. As with many other UK labels, 1966 proved to be the peak soul year for Pye International. In 1967 far fewer Soul 45's were issued, but one heralding the newer, harder USA Soul scene with Pheonix's Dyke & The Blazer's "Funky Broadway". Beyond 1967 apart from Dionne Warwick, virtually no black music was represented on the label until 1970 when it acquired the Westbound label's catalogue but only four 45's materialised. The label folded in 1979, some twenty years after its #1 hit "Blue Moon". It's famous Red and Yellow livery will remain immortal.

Keith Rylatt Pye International Collector & author of CENTRAL 1179 – THE STORY OF THE TWISTED WHEEL

59	25029	NINA SIMONE	SOLITAIRE	CHILLY WINDS DON'T BLOW	5.00
60	25052	RAY BRYANT TRIO	LITTLE SUSIE	LITTLE SUSIE part 4	6.00
61	25073	MARCELS	BLUE MOON	GOODBYE TO LOVE	6.00
61	25075	DON COVAY & the GOODTIMERS	PONY TIME	LOVE BOAT	15.00
61	25079	ETTA JAMES	I JUST WANT TO MAKE LOVE TO YOU	AT LAST	40.00
61	25080	ETTA JAMES	TRUST IN ME	ANYTHING TO SAY YOU'RE MINE	20.00
61	25083	MARCELS	SUMMERTIME	TEETER TOTTER LOVE	8.00
61	25088	MARATHONS	PEANUT BUTTER	DOWN IN NEW ORLEANS	15.00

61	25089	CLARANCE FROGMAN HENRY	YOU ALWAYS HURT THE ONE YOU LOVE	LITTLE SUZY	6.00
61	25098	SLIM HARPO	RAININ' IN MY HEART	DON'T STOP CRYING NOW	20.00
61	25101	HOWLIN' WOLF	LITTLE BABY	DOWN IN THE BOTTOM	15.00
61	25104	TINY TOPSY	WORKING ON ME BABY	AFTER MARRIAGE BLUES	30.00
61	25105	MARCELS	FIND ANOTHER FOOL	YOU ARE MY SUNSHINE	25.00
61	25107	VIBRATIONS	THE WATUSI	WALLFLOWER	25.00
61	25110	SENSATIONS feat. YVONNE	A PART OF ME	MUSIC,MUSIC, MUSIC	15.00
61	25113	ETTA JAMES	DREAM	FOOL THAT I AM	20.00
61	25114	MARCELS	HEARTACHES	MY LOVE FOR YOU	15.00
61	25119	TERRY TYLER	A THOUSAND FEET BELOW	ANSWER ME	10.00
62	25124	MARCELS	I REALLY NEED YOUR LOVE	MY MELANCHOLY BABY	25.00
62	25126	JAMES RAY	IF YOU'VE GOTTA MAKE A FOLL OF	IT'S BEEN A DRAG	15.00
62	25128	SENSATIONS	LET ME IN	OH YES I'LL BE TRUE	20.00
62	25131	ETTA JAMES	SOMETHING'S GOT A HOLD ON ME	WAITING FOR CHARLIE TO COME HO	20.00
62	25147	JAMES RAY	ITTY BITTY PIECES	YOU REMEMBER THE FACE	10.00
62	25150	ANGELS	EVERYBODY LOVES A LOVER	BLOW JOE	8.00
62	25157	CLAUDINE CLARK	PARTY LIGHTS	DISAPPOINTED	10.00
62	25159	DAVE BABY CORTEZ	RINKY DINK	GETTING RIGHT	22.00
62	25160	CHUBBY CHECKER	DANCIN' PARTY	GOTTA GET MYSELF TOGETHER	5.00
62	25161	STEVE ALAIMO	MY FRIENDS	GOING BACK TO MARTY	8.00
62	25162	ETTA JAMES	STOP THE WEDDING	STREET OF TEARS	15.00
62	25164	BILLY STEWART	FAT BOY	REAP WHAT YOU SOW	22.00
62	25165	BO DIDDLEY	I CAN TELL	YOU CAN'T JUDGE A BOOK BY THE	25.00
63	25174	STEVE ALAIMO	EVERY DAY I HAVE TO CRY SOME	LITTLE GIRL	25.00
63	25174 DJ	STEVE ALAIMO	EVERY DAY I HAVE TO CRY SOME	LITTLE GIRL	45.00
63	25178	DELLS	THE BOSSA NOVA BIRD	ETERNALLY	20.00
63	25178 DJ	DELLS	THE BOSSA NOVA BIRD	ETERNALLY	28.00
63	25182	JAN BRADLEY	MAMA DIDN'T LIE	LOVER'S LIKE ME	30.00
63	25182 DJ	JAN BRADLEY	MAMA DIDN'T LIE	LOVER'S LIKE ME	45.00
63	25186	CLAUDINE CLARK	WALK ME HOME FROM THE PARTY	WHO WILL HURT YOU	10.00
63	25186 DJ	CLAUDINE CLARK	WALK ME HOME FROM THE PARTY	WHO WILL HURT YOU	15.00
63	25191	SONNY BOY WILLIAMSON	HELP ME	BYE BYE BIRD	15.00
63	25191 DJ	SONNY BOY WILLIAMSON	HELP ME	BYE BYE BIRD	20.00
63	25192	HOWLIN' WOLF	JUST LIKE I TREAT YOU	I AIN'T SUPERSTITIOUS	15.00
63	25192 DJ	HOWLIN' WOLF	JUST LIKE I TREAT YOU	I AIN'T SUPERSTITIOUS	22.00
63	25193	BO DIDDLEY	WHO DO YOU LOVE	THE TWISTER	15.00
63	25193 DJ	BO DIDDLEY	WHO DO YOU LOVE	THE TWISTER	22.00
63	25194	CYRIL DAVIES	COUNTRY LINE SPECIAL	CHICAGO CALLING	22.00
63	25194 DJ	CYRIL DAVIES	COUNTRY LINE SPECIAL	CHICAGO CALLING	28.00
63	25199	STEVE ALAIMO	IT'S A LONG LONG WAY TO HAPPINESS	A LIFETIME OF LONELINESS	8.00
63	25199 DJ	STEVE ALAIMO	IT'S A LONG LONG WAY TO HAPPINESS	A LIFETIME OF LONELINESS	12.00
63	25201	MARCELS	GIVE ME BACK YOUR LOVE	I WANNA BE THE LEADER	25.00
63	25201 DJ	MARCELS	GIVE ME BACK YOUR LOVE	I WANNA BE THE LEADER	35.00
63	25205	ETTA JAMES	PUSHOVER	I CAN'T HOLD IT IN ANYMORE	30.00
63	25205 DJ	ETTA JAMES	PUSHOVER	I CAN'T HOLD IT IN ANYMORE	45.00
63	25210	BO DIDDLEY	BO DIDDLEY	DETOUR	15.00
63	25210 DJ	BO DIDDLEY	BO DIDDLEY	DETOUR	22.00
63	25212	MEL CARTER	WHEN A BOY FALLS IN LOVE	SO WONDERFUL	10.00
63	25212 DJ	MEL CARTER	WHEN A BOY FALLS IN LOVE	SO WONDERFUL	15.00
63	25217	BO DIDDLEY	PRETTY THING	ROAD RUNNER	10.00
63	25217 DJ	BO DIDDLEY	PRETTY THING	ROAD RUNNER	15.00
63	25219	GUITAR RED	JUST YOU AND I	OLD FASHIONED LOVE	30.00
63	25219 DJ	GUITAR RED	JUST YOU AND I	OLD FASHIONED LOVE	45.00
63	25220	SLIM HARPO	RAININ' IN MY HEART	DON'T START CRYIN' NOW	20.00
63	25220 DJ	SLIM HARPO	RAININ' IN MY HEART	DON'T START CRYIN' NOW	28.00
63	25222	BILLY STEWART	SUGAR AND SPICE	STRANGE FEELING	25.00
63	25222 DJ	BILLY STEWART	SUGAR AND SPICE	STRANGE FEELING	40.00
63	25223	DIONNE WARWICK	PLEASE LET HIM LOVE ME	MAKE THE MUSIC PLAY	6.00
63	25223 DJ	DIONNE WARWICK	PLEASE LET HIM LOVE ME	MAKE THE MUSIC PLAY	8.00
63	25227	BO DIDDLEY	BO DIDDLEY IS A LOVER	DOIN' THE JAGUAR	10.00
63	25227 DJ	BO DIDDLEY	BO DIDDLEY IS A LOVER	DOIN' THE JAGUAR	18.00
63	25229	SHIRELLES	IT'S A MAD, MAD, MAD WORLD	31 FLAVOURS	8.00
63	25229 DJ	SHIRELLES	IT'S A MAD, MAD, MAD WORLD	31 FLAVOURS	15.00
63	25231	KINGSMEN	LOUIE LOUIE	HAUNTED CASTLE	25.00
63	25231 DJ	KINGSMEN	LOUIE LOUIE	HAUNTED CASTLE	45.00
63	25232	LOCKETS	DON'T CHA KNOW	LIITLE BOY	15.00
63	25232 DJ	LOCKETS	DON'T CHA KNOW	LIITLE BOY	22.00
64	25233	SHIRELLES	TONIGHT YOU'RE GONNA FALL IN LOVE	20th. CENTURY ROCK AND ROLL	8.00
64	25233 DJ	SHIRELLES	TONIGHT YOU'RE GONNA FALL IN LOVE	20th. CENTURY ROCK AND ROLL	12.00
64	25234	DIONNE WARWICK	ANYONE WHO HAD A HEART	THE LOVE OF A BOY	5.00
64	25234 DJ	DIONNE WARWICK	ANYONE WHO HAD A HEART	THE LOVE OF A BOY	8.00
64	25235	BO DIDDLEY	MEMPHIS	MNKEY DIDDLE	10.00
64	25235 DJ	BO DIDDLEY	MEMPHIS	MNKEY DIDDLE	18.00
64	25236	CHUCK BERRY	NADINE (IS IT YOU)	O RANGUTANG	8.00
64	25236 DJ	CHUCK BERRY	NADINE (IS IT YOU)	O RANGUTANG	10.00
64	25238	TOMMY TUCKER	HI-HEEL SNEAKERS	I DON'T WANT CHA	22.00
64	25238 DJ	TOMMY TUCKER	HI-HEEL SNEAKERS	I DON'T WANT CHA	35.00
64	25239	TIMMY SHAW	GONNA SEND YOU BACK TO GEORGIA	I'M A LONELY MAN	20.00
64	25239 DJ	TIMMY SHAW	GONNA SEND YOU BACK TO GEORGIA	I'M A LONELY GUY	40.00

64	25240	SHIRELLES	HIS LIPS GET IN THE WAY	SHA LA LA	8.00
64	25240 DJ	SHIRELLES	HIS LIPS GET IN THE WAY	SHA LA LA	10.00
64	25241	DIONNE WARWICK	WALK ON BY	ANY OLD TIME OF DAY	5.00
64	25241 DJ	DIONNE WARWICK	WALK ON BY	ANY OLD TIME OF DAY	20.00
64	25242	CHUCK BERRY	NO PARTICULAR PLACE TO GO	LIVERPOOL DRIVE	5.00
64	25242 DJ	CHUCK BERRY	NO PARTICULAR PLACE TO GO	LIVERPOOL DRIVE	10.00
64	25243	BO DIDDLEY	MONA	GIMME GIMME	12.00
64	25243 DJ	BO DIDDLEY	MONA	GIMME GIMME	18.00
64	25244	HOWLIN' WOLF	SMOKESTACK LIGHTNIN'	GOING DOWN SOUTH	15.00
64	25244 DJ	HOWLIN' WOLF	SMOKESTACK LIGHTNIN'	GOING DOWN SOUTH	22.00
64	25245	DIXIE CUPS	CHAPEL OF LOVE	AIN'T THAT NICE	8.00
64	25245 DJ	DIXIE CUPS	CHAPEL OF LOVE	AIN'T THAT NICE	22.00
64	25246	TOMMY TUCKER	LONG TALL SHORTY	MO' SHORTY	20.00
64	25246 DJ	TOMMY TUCKER	LONG TALL SHORTY	MO' SHORTY	30.00
64	25247	CHUCK JACKSON	BEG ME	FOR ALL TIME	30.00
64	25247 DJ	CHUCK JACKSON	BEG ME	FOR ALL TIME	50.00
64	25248	ALVIN ROBINSON	SOMETHING YOU GOT	SEARCHIN'	20.00
64	25248 DJ	ALVIN ROBINSON	SOMETHING YOU GOT	SEARCHIN'	30.00
64	25249	SUGAR PIE DE SANTO	SOULFUL DRESS	USE WHAT YOU GOT	28.00
64	25249 DJ	SUGAR PIE DE SANTO	SOULFUL DRESS	USE WHAT YOU GOT	**78.00**
64	25250	JOHNNY NASH	LOVE AIN'T NOTHING	TALK TO ME	50.00
64	25250 DJ	JOHNNY NASH	LOVE AIN'T NOTHING	TALK TO ME	85.00
64	25251	TONY CLARKE	AIN'T LOVE GOOD, AIN'T LOVE PROUD	COMING BACK STRONG	20.00
64	25251 DJ	TONY CLARKE	AIN'T LOVE GOOD, AIN'T LOVE PROUD	COMING BACK STRONG	30.00
64	25252	JELLY BEANS	I WANNA LOVE HIM SO BAD	SO LONG	15.00
64	25252 DJ	JELLY BEANS	I WANNA LOVE HIM SO BAD	SO LONG	22.00
64	25254	JIMMY HUGHES	STEAL AWAY	LOLLOIPOPS, LACE AND LIPSTICK	20.00
64	25254 DJ	JIMMY HUGHES	STEAL AWAY	LOLLIPOPS, LACE AND LIPSTICK	28.00
64	25255	JOHN LEE HOOKER	HIGH PRICED WOMAN	SUGAR MAMA	15.00
64	25255 DJ	JOHN LEE HOOKER	HIGH PRICED WOMAN	SUGAR MAMA	22.00
64	25256	DIONNE WARWICK	YOU'LL NEVER GET TO HEAVEN (IF YOU BREAK MY HEART)	A HOUSE IS NOT A HOME	6.00
64	25256 DJ	DIONNE WARWICK	YOU'LL NEVER GET TO HEAVEN (IF YOU BREAK MY HEART)	A HOUSE IS NOT A HOME	15.00
64	25257	CHUCK BERRY	YOU NEVER CAN TELL	BRENDA LEE	8.00
64	25257 DJ	CHUCK BERRY	YOU NEVER CAN TELL	BRENDA LEE	15.00
64	25258	BO DIDDLEY	MAMA KEEP YOUR BIG MOUTH SHUT	JO-ANN	10.00
64	25258 DJ	BO DIDDLEY	MAMA KEEP YOUR BIG MOUTH SHUT	JO-ANN	18.00
64	25259	JACKIE ROSS	SELFISH ONE	EVERYTHING BUT LOVE	75.00
64	25259 DJ	JACKIE ROSS	SELFISH ONE	EVERYTHING BUT LOVE	**124.00**
64	25260	BOBBY FREEMAN	C'MON AND SWIM	C'MON AND SWIM Part2	30.00
64	25260 DJ	BOBBY FREEMAN	C'MON AND SWIM	C'MON AND SWIM Part2	45.00
64	25262	KINGSMEN	LITTLE LATIN LUPE LU	DAVID'S MOOD	10.00
64	25262 DJ	KINGSMEN	LITTLE LATIN LUPE LU	DAVID'S MOOD	15.00
64	25263	LITTLE WALTER	MY BABE	YOU BETTER WATCH YOURSELF	18.00
64	25263 DJ	LITTLE WALTER	MY BABE	YOU BETTER WATCH YOURSELF	28.00
64	25265	DIONNE WARWICK	REACH OUT FOR ME	HOW MANY DAYS OF SADNESS	8.00
64	25265 DJ	DIONNE WARWICK	REACH OUT FOR ME	HOW MANY DAYS OF SADNESS	20.00
64	25266	LITTLE LUTHER	EENIE MEENIE MINIE MOE	TWIRL	50.00
64	25266 DJ	LITTLE LUTHER	EENIE MEENIE MINIE MOE	TWIRL	65.00
64	25267	SUGAR PIE DESANTO	I DON'T WANNA FUSS	I LOVE YOU SO MUCH	25.00
64	25267 DJ	SUGAR PIE DESANTO	I DON'T WANNA FUSS	I LOVE YOU SO MUCH	50.00
64	25268	SONNY BOY WILLIAMSON	LONESOME CABIN	THE GOAT	15.00
64	25268 DJ	SONNY BOY WILLIAMSON	LONESOME CABIN	THE GOAT	20.00
64	25269	HOWLIN' WOLF	LITTLE GIRL	TAIL DAGGER	15.00
64	25269 DJ	HOWLIN' WOLF	LITTLE GIRL	TAIL DAGGER	20.00
64	25271	CHUCK BERRY	LITTLE MARIE	GO, BOBBY SOXER	8.00
64	25271 DJ	CHUCK BERRY	LITTLE MARIE	GO, BOBBY SOXER	12.00
64	25272	MAXINE BROWN	OH NO NOT MY BABY	YOU UPSET MY SOUL	25.00
64	25272 DJ	MAXINE BROWN	OH NO NOT MY BABY	YOU UPSET MY SOUL	45.00
64	25273	KINGSMEN	DEATH OF AN ANGEL	SEARCHING FOR LOVE	10.00
64	25273 DJ	KINGSMEN	DEATH OF AN ANGEL	SEARCHING FOR LOVE	15.00
64	25275	MITTY COLLIER	I HAD A TALK WITH MY MAN	FREE GIRL	40.00
64	25275 DJ	MITTY COLLIER	I HAD A TALK WITH MY MAN	FREE GIRL	75.00
64	25276	CHUCK JACKSON	ANY DAY NOW	THE PROPHET	25.00
64	25276 DJ	CHUCK JACKSON	ANY DAY NOW	THE PROPHET	40.00
65	25276	CHUCK JACKSON	THE PROPHET	ANY DAY NOW	25.00
65	25276 DJ	CHUCK JACKSON	THE PROPHET	ANY DAY NOW	45.00
64	25278	KOLETTES	WHO'S THAT GUY	JUST HOW MUCH (can one heart take)	40.00
64	25278 DJ	KOLETTES	WHO'S THAT GUY	JUST HOW MUCH (can one heart t	70.00
64	25279	SHIRELLES	MAYBE TONIGHT	LOST LOVE	15.00
64	25279 DJ	SHIRELLES	MAYBE TONIGHT	LOST LOVE	20.00
64	25280	BOBBY FREEMAN	S-W-I-M	THAT LITTLE OLD HEARTBREAKER M	20.00
64	25280 DJ	BOBBY FREEMAN	S-W-I-M	THAT LITTLE OLD HEARTBREAKER M	30.00
64	25281	NELLA DODDS	COME SEE ABOUT ME	YOU DON'T LOVE ME ANYMORE	30.00
64	25281 DJ	NELLA DODDS	COME SEE ABOUT ME	YOU DON'T LOVE ME ANYMORE	50.00
64	25283	HOWLIN' WOLF	LOVE ME DARLING	MY COUNTRY SUGAR MAMA	10.00
64	25283 DJ	HOWLIN' WOLF	LOVE ME DARLING	MY COUNTRY SUGAR MAMA	15.00
64	25284	LARKS	THE JERK	FORGET ME	25.00
64	25284 DJ	LARKS	THE JERK	FORGET ME	40.00
64	25287	CHUCK JACKSON	HAND IT OVER	SINCE I DON'T HAVE YOU	**157.00**

64	25287 DJ	CHUCK JACKSON	HAND IT OVER	SINCE I DON'T HAVE YOU	**300.00**
65	25288	SHIRELLES	ARE YOU STILL MY BABY	I SAW A TEAR	20.00
65	25288 DJ	SHIRELLES	ARE YOU STILL MY BABY	I SAW A TEAR	40.00
65	25289	LITTLE MILTON	BLIND MAN	BLUES IN THE NIGHT	20.00
65	25289 DJ	LITTLE MILTON	BLIND MAN	BLUES IN THE NIGHT	28.00
64	25290	DIONNE WARWICK	YOU CAN HAVE HIM	DON'T SAY I DIDN'T TELL YOU	8.00
64	25290 DJ	DIONNE WARWICK	YOU CAN HAVE HIM	DON'T SAY I DIDN'T TELL YOU	15.00
65	25291	NELLA DODDS	FINDERS KEEPERS, LOSERS WEEPERS	A GIRL'S LIFE	30.00
65	25291 DJ	NELLA DODDS	FINDERS KEEPERS, LOSERS WEEPERS	A GIRL'S LIFE	50.00
65	25292	KINGSMEN	THE JOLLY GREEN GIANT	LONG GREEN	10.00
65	25292 DJ	KINGSMEN	THE JOLLY GREEN GIANT	LONG GREEN	15.00
65	25297	RIGHTEOUS BROTHERS	BRING YOUR LOVE TO ME	TRY AND FIND ANOTHER MAN	10.00
65	25297 DJ	RIGHTEOUS BROTHERS	BRING YOUR LOVE TO ME	TRY AND FIND ANOTHER MAN	22.00
65	25299	MAXINE BROWN	IT'S GONNA BE ALRIGHT	YOU DO SOMETHING TO ME	20.00
65	25299 DJ	MAXINE BROWN	IT'S GONNA BE ALRIGHT	YOU DO SOMETHING TO ME	30.00
65	25301	CHUCK JACKSON	I NEED YOU	CHUCK'S SOUL BROTHERS TWIST	20.00
65	25301 DJ	CHUCK JACKSON	I NEED YOU	CHUCK'S SOUL BROTHER TWIST	40.00
65	25302	DIONNE WARWICK	WHO CAN I TURN TO	THAT'S NOT THE ANSWER	5.00
65	25302 DJ	DIONNE WARWICK	WHO CAN I TURN TO	THAT'S NOT THE ANSWER	10.00
65	25303	UNIQUES	NOT TOO LONG AGO	FAST WAY OF LIVING	100.00
65	25303 DJ	UNIQUES	NOT TOO LONG AGO	FAST WAY OF LIVING	150.00
65	25304	RIGHTEOUS BROTHERS	NIGHT OWL	SOMETHING'S GOT A HOLD ON ME	20.00
65	25304 DJ	RIGHTEOUS BROTHERS	NIGHT OWL	SOMETHING'S GOT A HOLD ON ME	28.00
65	25307	DOBIE GRAY	SEE YOU AT THE GO GO	WALK WITH LOVE	40.00
65	25307 DJ	DOBIE GRAY	SEE YOU AT THE GO GO	WALK WITH LOVE	75.00
65	25308	CHUCK JACKSON and MAXINE BROWN	BABY TAKE ME	SOMETHING YOU GOT	22.00
65	25308 DJ	CHUCK JACKSON and MAXINE BROWN	BABY TAKE ME	SOMETHING YOU GOT	40.00
65	25311	KINGSMEN	THE CLIMB	WAITING	10.00
65	25311 DJ	KINGSMEN	THE CLIMB	WAITING	15.00
65	25316	DIONNE WARWICK	HERE I AM	THEY LONG TO BE CLOSE TO YOU	6.00
65	25316 DJ	DIONNE WARWICK	HERE I AM	THEY LONG TO BE CLOSE TO YOU	10.00
65	25317	MAXINE BROWN	ONE STEP AT A TIME	ANYTHING FOR A LAUGH	30.00
65	25317 DJ	MAXINE BROWN	ONE STEP AT A TIME	ANYTHING FOR A LAUGH	45.00
65	25321	CHUCK JACKSON	IF I DIDN'T LOVE YOU	JUST A LITTLE BIT OF YOUR SOUL	25.00
65	25321 DJ	CHUCK JACKSON	IF I DIDN'T LOVE YOU	JUST A LITTLE BIT OF YOUR SOUL	45.00
65	25322	KINGSMEN	ANNIE FANNY	SOMETHING'S GOT A HOLD ON ME	8.00
65	25322 DJ	KINGSMEN	ANNIE FANNY	SOMETHING'S GOT A HOLD ON ME	15.00
65	25323	RIGHTEOUS BROTHERS	LET THE GOOD TIMES ROLL	B-FLAT BLUES	6.00
65	25323 DJ	RIGHTEOUS BROTHERS	LET THE GOOD TIMES ROLL	B-FLAT BLUES	10.00
65	25334	RIGHTEOUS BROTHERS	FOR YOUR LOVE	MY TEARS WILL GO AWAY	8.00
65	25334 DJ	RIGHTEOUS BROTHERS	FOR YOUR LOVE	MY TEARS WILL GO AWAY	10.00
65	25336	MOJO MEN	DANCE WITH ME	THE LONELIEST BOY IN TOWN	18.00
65	25336 DJ	MOJO MEN	DANCE WITH ME	THE LONELIEST BOY IN TOWN	28.00
65	25338	DIONNE WARWICK	ARE YOU THERE WITH ANOTHER GIRL	IF I EVER MAKE YOU CRY	6.00
65	25338 DJ	DIONNE WARWICK	ARE YOU THERE WITH ANOTHER GIRL	IF I EVER MAKE YOU CRY	15.00
65	25340	ROY HEAD	JUST A LITTLE BIT	TREAT ME RIGHT	20.00
65	25340 DJ	ROY HEAD	JUST A LITTLE BIT	TREAT ME RIGHT	28.00
65	25343	PACKERS	HOLE IN THE WALL	GO AHEAD ON	22.00
65	25343 DJ	PACKERS	HOLE IN THE WALL	GO AHEAD ON	35.00
66	25347	BOBBY FREEMAN	THE DUCK	CROSS MY HEART	30.00
66	25347 DJ	BOBBY FREEMAN	THE DUCK	THE DEVIL	40.00
66	25348	CHRIS MONTEZ	CALL ME	GO 'HEAD ON	8.00
66	25348 DJ	CHRIS MONTEZ	CALL ME	GO 'HEAD ON	10.00
66	25349	JUVENILES	YES I BELIEVE	BO DIDDLEY	100.00
66	25349 DJ	JUVENILES	YES I BELIEVE	BO DIDDLEY	150.00
66	25350	JAMES BROWN & THE FAMOUS FLAMES	I GOT YOU (I FEEL GOOD)	I CAN'T HELP IT (I JUST DO DO)	20.00
66	25350 DJ	JAMES BROWN & THE FAMOUS FLAMES	I GOT YOU (I FEEL GOOD)	I CAN'T HELP IT (I JUST DO DO)	40.00
66	25353	JOHNNY NASH	LET'S MOVE AND GROOVE TOGETHER	UNDERSTANDING	10.00
66	25353 DJ	JOHNNY NASH	LET'S MOVE AND GROOVE TOGETHER	UNDERSTANDING	15.00
66	25355	SAM and BILL	TREAT ME RIGHT	FLY ME TO THE MOON	15.00
66	25355 DJ	SAM and BILL	TREAT ME RIGHT	FLY ME TO THE MOON	20.00
66	25357	DIONNE WARWICK	IN BETWEEN THE HEARTACHES	LONG DAY, SHORT NIGHT	6.00
66	25357 DJ	DIONNE WARWICK	IN BETWEEN THE HEARTACHES	LONG DAY, SHORT NIGHT	10.00
66	25358	RIGHTEOUS BROTHERS	GEORGIA ON MY MIND	MY TEARS WILL GO AWAY	6.00
66	25358 DJ	RIGHTEOUS BROTHERS	GEORGIA ON MY MIND	MY TEARS WILL GO AWAY	10.00
66	25363	JOHNNY NASH	TRYIN' TO FIND HER	ONE MORE TIME	20.00
66	25363 DJ	JOHNNY NASH	TRYIN' TO FIND HER	ONE MORE TIME	30.00
66	25365	BOBBY COLEMAN	PLEASURE GIRL	(BABY) YOU DON'T HAVE TO TELL	60.00
66	25365 DJ	BOBBY COLEMAN	PLEASURE GIRL	(BABY) YOU DON'T HAVE TO TELL	85.00
66	25366	KINGSMEN	LOUIE LOUIE	LITTLE LATIN LUPE	20.00
66	25366 DJ	KINGSMEN	LOUIE LOUIE	LITTLE LATIN LUPE	40.00
66	25367	JAMES BROWN & THE FAMOUS FLAMES	AIN'T THAT A GROOVE	AIN'T THAT A GROOVE part 2	10.00
66	25367 DJ	JAMES BROWN & THE FAMOUS FLAMES	AIN'T THAT A GROOVE	AIN'T THAT A GROOVE part 2	20.00
66	25368	DIONNE WARWICK	A MESSAGE TO MICHAEL	HERE WHERE THERE IS LOVE	6.00
66	25368 DJ	DIONNE WARWICK	A MESSAGE TO MICHAEL	HERE WHERE THERE IS LOVE	8.00
66	25369	CHRIS MONTEZ	THE MORE I SEE YOU	YOU, I LOVE YOU	15.00
66	25369 DJ	CHRIS MONTEZ	THE MORE I SEE YOU	YOU, I LOVE YOU	25.00
66	25371	JAMES BROWN & THE FAMOUS FLAMES	IT'S A MAN'S MAN'S MAN'S WORLD	IS IT YES OR IS IT NO	15.00
66	25371 DJ	JAMES BROWN & THE FAMOUS FLAMES	IT'S A MAN'S MAN'S MAN'S WORLD	IS IT YES OR IS IT NO	25.00

66	25375	T.V. and the TRIBESMEN	BAREFOOTIN'	FAT MAN	30.00
66	25375 DJ	T.V. and the TRIBESMEN	BAREFOOTIN'	FAT MAN	40.00
66	25378	DIONNE WARWICK	TRAINS AND BOATS AND PLANES	DON'T GO BREAKING MY HEART	5.00
66	25378 DJ	DIONNE WARWICK	TRAINS AND BOATS AND PLANES	DON'T GO BREAKING MY HEART	8.00
66	25379	JAMES BROWN & THE FAMOUS FLAMES	MONEY WON'T CHANGE YOU	MONEY WON'T CHANGE YOU part 2	22.00
66	25379 DJ	JAMES BROWN & THE FAMOUS FLAMES	MONEY WON'T CHANGE YOU	MONEY WON'T CHANGE YOU part 2	45.00
66	25384	CHUCK JACKSON	CHAINS OF LOVE	I KEEP FORGETTIN'	75.00
66	25384 DJ	CHUCK JACKSON	CHAINS OF LOVE	I KEEP FORGETTIN'	150.00
66	25385	ROSCO ROBINSON	THAT'S ENOUGH	ONE MORE TIME	85.00
66	25385 DJ	ROSCO ROBINSON	THAT'S ENOUGH	ONE MORE TIME	125.00
66	25386	SHIRELLES	SHADES OF BLUE	WHEN THE BOYS TALK ABOUT THE G	10.00
66	25386 DJ	SHIRELLES	SHADES OF BLUE	WHEN THE BOYS TALK ABOUT THE G	15.00
66	25389	DYNATONES	THE FIFE PIPER	AND I ALWAYS WILL	60.00
66	25389 DJ	DYNATONES	THE FIFE PIPER	AND I ALWAYS WILL	100.00
66	25392	RONNIE MILSAP	AIN'T NO SOUL (LEFT IN THESE OLE SHOES)	ANOTHER BRANCH FROM THE OLD TR	85.00
66	25392 DJ	RONNIE MILSAP	AIN'T NO SOUL (LEFT IN THESE OLE SHOES)	ANOTHER BRANCH FROM THE OLD TR	**154.00**
66	25393	COUNT FIVE	PSYCHOTIC REATION	THEY'RE GONNA GET YOU	30.00
66	25393 DJ	COUNT FIVE	PSYCHOTIC REATION	THEY'RE GONNA GET YOU	40.00
66	25394	JAMES BROWN & THE FAMOUS FLAMES	DON'T BE A DROP-OUT	TELL ME THAT YOU LOVE ME	10.00
66	25394 DJ	JAMES BROWN & THE FAMOUS FLAMES	DON'T BE A DROP-OUT	TELL ME THAT YOU LOVE ME	15.00
66	25395	DIONNE WARWICK	ANOTHER NIGHT	GO WITH LOVE	5.00
66	25395 DJ	DIONNE WARWICK	ANOTHER NIGHT	GO WITH LOVE	8.00
66	25396	SANDPIPERS	LOUIE LOUIE	THINGS WE SAID TODAY	8.00
66	25396 DJ	SANDPIPERS	LOUIE LOUIE	THINGS WE SAID TODAY	10.00
66	25401	JOE CUBA SEXTET	BANG ! BANG !	PUSH, PUSH, PUSH	20.00
66	25401 DJ	JOE CUBA SEXTET	BANG ! BANG !	PUSH, PUSH, PUSH	28.00
67	25404	TRAITS	HARLEM SHUFFLE	STRANGE LIPS (START OLD MEMORI	25.00
67	25404 DJ	TRAITS	HARLEM SHUFFLE	STRANGE LIPS (START OLD MEMORI	40.00
67	25406	KINGSMEN	DAYTIME SHADOWS	TROUBLE	10.00
67	25406 DJ	KINGSMEN	DAYTIME SHADOWS	TROUBLE	15.00
67	25410	MAXINE BROWN	I'VE GOT A LOT OF LOVE LEFT IN ME	HOLD ON (I'M COMING)	45.00
67	25410 DJ	MAXINE BROWN	I'VE GOT A LOT OF LOVE LEFT IN ME	HOLD ON (I'M COMING)	60.00
67	25411	JAMES BROWN & THE FAMOUS FLAMES	BRING IT UP	NOBODY KNOWS	12.00
67	25411 DJ	JAMES BROWN & THE FAMOUS FLAMES	BRING IT UP	NOBODY KNOWS	20.00
67	25413	DYKE AND THE BLAZERS	FUNKY BROADWAY	FUNKY BROADWAY part 2	25.00
67	25413 DJ	DYKE AND THE BLAZERS	FUNKY BROADWAY	FUNKY BROADWAY part 2	40.00
67	25418	JAMES BROWN & THE FAMOUS FLAMES	STONE FOX	KANSAS CITY	15.00
67	25418 DJ	JAMES BROWN & THE FAMOUS FLAMES	STONE FOX	KANSAS CITY	25.00
67	25420	TOUSSAINT McCALL	NOTHING TAKES THE PLACE OF YOU	SHIMMY	20.00
67	25420 DJ	TOUSSAINT McCALL	NOTHING TAKES THE PLACE OF YOU	SHIMMY	30.00
67	25423	JAMES BROWN & THE FAMOUS FLAMES	LET YOURSELF GO	GOOD ROCKIN' TONIGHT	10.00
67	25423 DJ	JAMES BROWN & THE FAMOUS FLAMES	LET YOURSELF GO	GOOD ROCKIN' TONIGHT	15.00
67	25424	DIONNE WARWICK	ALFIE	THE BEGINNING OF LONELINESS	4.00
67	25424 DJ	DIONNE WARWICK	ALFIE	THE BEGINNING OF LONELINESS	6.00
67	25425	SHIRELLES	TOO MUCH OF A GOOD THING	BRIGHT SHINY COLORS	25.00
67	25425 DJ	SHIRELLES	TOO MUCH OF A GOOD THING	BRIGHT SHINY COLORS	40.00
67	25427	PETE. TERRACE	AT THE PARTY	NO! NO! NO!	30.00
67	25427 DJ	PETE. TERRACE	AT THE PARTY	NO! NO! NO!	45.00
67	25428	DIONNE WARWICK	THE WINDOWS OF THE WORLD	WALK LITTLE DOLLY	4.00
67	25428 DJ	DIONNE WARWICK	THE WINDOWS OF THE WORLD	WALK LITTLE DOLLY	6.00
67	25434	MAXINE BROWN	SINCE I FOUND YOU	GOTTA FIND A WAY	15.00
67	25434 DJ	MAXINE BROWN	SINCE I FOUND YOU	GOTTA FIND A WAY	22.00
67	25435	DIONNE WARWICK	I SAY A LITTLE PRAYER	WINDOW WISHIN'	5.00
67	25435 DJ	DIONNE WARWICK	I SAY A LITTLE PRAYER	WINDOW WISHIN'	8.00
67	25439	CHUCK JACKSON	CANDY	SHAME ON ME	20.00
67	25439 DJ	CHUCK JACKSON	CANDY	SHAME ON ME	28.00
67	25440	PETE TERRACE	SHOT GUN BOOGALOO	I'M GONNA MAKE IT	30.00
67	25440 DJ	PETE TERRACE	SHOT GUN BOOGALOO	I'M GONNA MAKE IT	45.00
67	25441	JAMES BROWN & THE FAMOUS FLAMES	GET IT TOGETHER	GET IT TOGETHER part 2	15.00
67	25441 DJ	JAMES BROWN & THE FAMOUS FLAMES	GET IT TOGETHER	GET IT TOGETHER part 2	20.00
68	25442	JOHN FRED and his PLAYBOY BAND	JUDY IN DISGUISE (WITH GLASSES)	WHEN THE LIGHTS GO OUT	6.00
68	25442 DJ	JOHN FRED and his PLAYBOY BAND	JUDY IN DISGUISE (WITH GLASSES)	WHEN THE LIGHTS GO OUT	10.00
68	25445	DIONNE WARWICK	(THEME FROM) THE VALLEY OF THE	ZIP-A-DEE-DOO-DAH	4.00
68	25445 DJ	DIONNE WARWICK	(THEME FROM) THE VALLEY OF THE	ZIP-A-DEE-DOO-DAH	5.00
68	25448	FIVE STAIRSTEPS & CUBIE	A MILLION TO ONE	SOMETHING'S MISSING	10.00
68	25448 DJ	FIVE STAIRSTEPS & CUBIE	A MILLION TO ONE	SOMETHING'S MISSING	15.00
68	25453	JOHN FRED and his PLAYBOY BAND	HEY HEY BUNNY	NO LETTER TODAY	10.00
68	25453 DJ	JOHN FRED and his PLAYBOY BAND	HEY HEY BUNNY	NO LETTER TODAY	20.00
68	25457	DIONNE WARWICK	DO YOU KNOW THE WAY TO SAN JOSE	LET ME BE LONELY	4.00
68	25457 DJ	DIONNE WARWICK	DO YOU KNOW THE WAY TO SAN JOSE	LET ME BE LONELY	10.00
68	25463	OTIS REDDING	SHE'S ALRIGHT	GAMA LAMA	10.00
68	25463 DJ	OTIS REDDING	SHE'S ALRIGHT	GAMA LAMA	20.00
68	25466	NINA SIMONE	THE OTHER WOMAN	EXACTLY LIKE YOU	5.00
68	25466 DJ	NINA SIMONE	THE OTHER WOMAN	EXACTLY LIKE YOU	8.00
66	25470	KINGSMEN	KILLER JOE	LITTLE GREEN THING	10.00
66	25470 DJ	KINGSMEN	KILLER JOE	LITTLE GREEN THING	15.00
68	25471	CAMEL DRIVERS	SUNDAY MORNING 6 O'CLOCK	GIVE IT A TRY	10.00
68	25471 DJ	CAMEL DRIVERS	SUNDAY MORNING 6 O'CLOCK	GIVE IT A TRY	15.00
68	25474	DIONNE WARWICK	THERE'S ALWAYS SOMETHING THERE TO REMIND ME	WHO IS GONNA LOVE ME?	5.00

68	25474 DJ	DIONNE WARWICK	THERE'S ALWAYS SOMETHING THERE TO REMIND ME	WHO IS GONNA LOVE ME?	10.00
68	25476 unissued	KASENETZ-KATZ	QUICK JOEY SMALL (RUN JOEY RUN)	RUMBLE '69	UN
69	25480	KASENETZ-KATZ	LATIN SKATE	WE CAN WORK IT OUT	15.00
69	25480 DJ	KASENETZ-KATZ	LATIN SKATE	WE CAN WORK IT OUT	22.00
69	25490	RONNIE MILSAP	DENVER	NOTHING IS AS GOOD AS IT USED	5.00
69	25490 DJ	RONNIE MILSAP	DENVER	NOTHING IS AS GOOD AS IT USED	10.00
69	25492	JESSE LEE FERGUSON	NEW SHOES	PUTTIN' IT ON, PUTTIN' IT OFF	20.00
69	25492 DJ	JESSE LEE FERGUSON	NEW SHOES	PUTTIN' IT ON, PUTTIN IT OFF	30.00
69	25493	WINSTONS	COLOR HIM FATHER	AMEN, BROTHER	30.00
69	25493 DJ	WINSTONS	COLOR HIM FATHER	AMEN, BROTHER	45.00
69	25500	WINSTONS	WHEEL OF FORTUNE	LOVE OF THE COMMON PEOPLE	6.00
69	25500 DJ	WINSTONS	WHEEL OF FORTUNE	LOVE OF THE COMMON PEOPLE	10.00
70	25519	FUNKADELIC	I GOT A THING, YOU GOT A THING,	FISH, CHIPS AND SWEAT	15.00
70	25519 DJ	FUNKADELIC	I GOT A THING, YOU GOT A THING,	FISH, CHIPS AND SWEAT	18.00
70	25522	BRENTON WOOD	GREAT BIG BUNDLE OF LOVE	CAN YOU DIG IT	15.00
70	25522 DJ	BRENTON WOOD	GREAT BIG BUNDLE OF LOVE	CAN YOU DIG IT	22.00
70	25530	EAGLE	KICKIN' IT BACK TO YOU	COME IN, IT'S ALL FREE	15.00
70	25530 DJ	EAGLE	KICKIN' IT BACK TO YOU	COME IN, IT'S ALL FREE	20.00
70	25537	CISSY HOUSTON	I JUST DON'T KNOW WHAT TO DO WITH MYSELF	THIS EMPTY PLACE	40.00
70	25537 DJ	CISSY HOUSTON	I JUST DON'T KNOW WHAT TO DO WITH MYSELF	THIS EMPTY PLACE	60.00
71	25544	DETROIT EMERALDS	DO ME RIGHT	JUST NOW AND THEN	10.00
71	25544 DJ	DETROIT EMERALDS	DO ME RIGHT	JUST NOW AND THEN	22.00
71	25545	CISSY HOUSTON	BE MY BABY	THE LONG AND WINDING ROAD	5.00
71	25545 DJ	CISSY HOUSTON	BE MY BABY	THE LONG AND WINDING ROAD	8.00
71	25546	INEZ FOXX	YOU SHOULDN'T HAVE SET MY SOUL	LIVE FOR TODAY	6.00
71	25546 DJ	INEZ FOXX	YOU SHOULDN'T HAVE SET MY SOUL	LIVE FOR TODAY	10.00
71	25548	FUNKADELIC	YOU AND YOUR FOLKS, ME AND MINE	FUNKY DOLLAR BILL	10.00
71	25548 DJ	FUNKADELIC	YOU AND YOUR FOLKS, ME AND MINE	FUNKY DOLLAR BILL	15.00
71	25550	JOE WILSON	WHEN A MAN CRIES	SWEETNESS	15.00
71	25550 DJ	JOE WILSON	WHEN A MAN CRIES	SWEETNESS	22.00
71	25559	PLATTERS	GOING BACK TO DETROIT	SWEET, SWEET LOVIN'	20.00
71	25559 DJ	PLATTERS	GOING BACK TO DETROIT	SWEET, SWEET LOVING	45.00
71	25561	INEZ & CHARLIE FOXX	TIGHTROPE	BABY TAKE IT ALL	10.00
71	25561 DJ	INEZ & CHARLIE FOXX	TIGHTROPE	BABY TAKE IT ALL	25.00
71	25564	GENE PITNEY	RUN, RUN ROADRUNNER	RAINMAKER GIRL	20.00
71	25564 DJ	GENE PITNEY	RUN, RUN ROADRUNNER	RAINMAKER GIRL	30.00
71	25569	PLATTERS	WITH THIS RING	WASHED ASHORE (ON A LONELY ISLAND IN THE	10.00
71	25569 DJ	PLATTERS	WITH THIS RING	WASHED ASHORE (ON A LONELY ISLAND IN THE	20.00
72	25570	CURLEY MOORE & KOOL	SHELLEY'S RUBBER BAND	FUNKY YEAH	8.00
72	25570 DJ	CURLEY MOORE & KOOL	SHELLEY'S RUBBER BAND	FUNKY YEAH	10.00
72	25571	MACEO & ALL THE KING'S	THANK YOU FOR LETTING ME BE MYSELF	GOT TO GET CHA	10.00
72	25571 DJ	MACEO & ALL THE KING'S	THANK YOU FOR LETTING ME BE MYSELF	GOT TO GET CHA	15.00
72	25580	NU-SOUND EXPRESS LTD	ONE MORE TIME, YOU ALL	A ROSE FOR A LADY	10.00
72	25580 DJ	NU-SOUND EXPRESS LTD	ONE MORE TIME, YOU ALL	A ROSE FOR A LADY	15.00
73	25592	PAT CARROLL	OUT OF MY MIND	TO THE SUN	10.00
73	25592 DJ	PAT CARROLL	OUT OF MY MIND	TO THE SUN	15.00
73	25601	BRIGHTER SIDE OF DARKNESS	LOVE JONES	I'M THE GUY	5.00
73	25601 DJ	BRIGHTER SIDE OF DARKNESS	LOVE JONES	I'M THE GUY	8.00
73	25610	BARRY WHITE	I'M GONNA LOVE YOU JUST A LITTLE	JUST A LITTLE MORE BABY	4.00
73	25610 DJ	BARRY WHITE	I'M GONNA LOVE YOU JUST A LITTLE	JUST A LITTLE MORE BABY	6.00
73	25611	LEON HAYWWOD	LA LA SONG	THERE AIN'T ENOUGH HATE AROUND	6.00
73	25611 DJ	LEON HAYWWOD	LA LA SONG	THERE AIN'T ENOUGH HATE AROUND	8.00
73	25612	INDEPENDANTS	I LOVE YOU,YES I DO	LEAVING ME	8.00
73	25612 DJ	INDEPENDANTS	I LOVE YOU,YES I DO	LEAVING ME	12.00
73	25613	FIRST CHOICE	THIS IS THE HOUSE WHERE LOVE DIED	ONE STEP AWAY	UN
73	25613 DJ	FIRST CHOICE	THIS IS THE HOUSE WHERE LOVE DIED	ONE STEP AWAY	400.00
73	25614	JIMMY RADCLIFFE	LONG AFTER TONIGHT IS ALL OVER	WHAT I WANT I CAN NEVER HAVE	10.00
73	25614 DJ	JIMMY RADCLIFFE	LONG AFTER TONIGHT IS ALL OVER	WHAT I WANT I CAN NEVER HAVE	20.00
73	25615	SOUTHSIDE MOVEMENT	I'VE BEEN WATCHIN' YOU	HAVE A LITTLE MERCY	6.00
73	25615 DJ	SOUTH SIDE MOVEMENT	HAVE A LITTLE MERCY	I'VE BEEN WATCHIN' YOU	8.00
73	25616	AFRIQUE	SOUL MAKOSSA	HOT MUD	8.00
73	25616 DJ	AFRIQUE	SOUL MAKOSSA	HOT MUD	10.00
73	25619	LOVE UNLIMITED	OH LOVE (WELL WE FINALLY MADE	YES, WE FINALLY MADE IT	4.00
73	25619 DJ	LOVE UNLIMITED	OH LOVE (WELL WE FINALLY MADE	YES, WE FINALLY MADE IT	5.00
73	25623	INDEPENDENTS	BABY I'VE BEEN MISSING YOU	COULDN'T HEAR NOBODY SAY	5.00
73	25623 DJ	INDEPENDENTS	BABY I'VE BEEN MISSING YOU	COULDN'T HEAR NOBODY SAY	6.00
73	25628	ULTRA HIGH FREQUENCY	WE'RE ON THE RIGHT TRACK	same: instrumental	10.00
73	25628 DJ	ULTRA HIGH FREQUENCY	WE'RE ON THE RIGHT TRACK	same: instrumental	15.00
73	25631	WESTWING	FALLING IN LOVE IS A NO NO BABY	NO NO LOVE	8.00
73	25631 DJ	WESTWING	FALLING IN LOVE IS A NO NO BABY	NO NO LOVE	10.00
73	25634	INDEPENDANTS	IT'S ALL OVER	SARA LEE	5.00
73	25634 DJ	INDEPENDANTS	IT'S ALL OVER	SARA LEE	6.00
73	25635	LOVE UNLIMITED ORCHESTRA	LOVE'S THEME	SWEET MOMENTS	4.00
73	25635 DJ	LOVE UNLIMITED ORCHESTRA	LOVE'S THEME	SWEET MOMENTS	5.00
73	25639	BARRY WHITE	HONEY PLEASE, CAN'T YOU SEE	same: instrumental	4.00
73	25639 DJ	BARRY WHITE	HONEY PLEASE, CAN'T YOU SEE	same: instrumental	5.00
73	25641	ECSTASY, PASSION & PAIN	I WOULDN'T GIVE YOU	DON'T BURN YOUR BRIDGES BEHIND	10.00
73	25641 DJ	ECSTASY, PASSION & PAIN	I WOULDN'T GIVE YOU	DON'T BURN YOUR BRIDGES BEHIND	15.00
73	25643	MAGIC NIGHT	BABY YOU BELONG TO ME	LOST AND LONELY BOY	8.00

73	25643 DJ	MAGIC NIGHT	BABY YOU BELONG TO ME	LOST AND LONELY BOY	10.00
74	25652	LEON HAYWOOD	LONG AS THERE'S YOU (I GOT LOVE)	KEEP IT IN THE FAMILY	5.00
74	25652 DJ	LEON HAYWOOD	LONG AS THERE'S YOU (I GOT LOVE)	KEEP IT IN THE FAMILY	6.00
74	25653	ELEVENTH HOUR	SO GOOD	MY BED	4.00
74	25653 DJ	ELEVENTH HOUR	SO GOOD	MY BED	5.00
74	35655	HODGES, JAMES & SMITH	LOVIN' MAN	LUCKY ONE	4.00
74	35655 DJ	HODGES, JAMES & SMITH	LOVIN' MAN	LUCKY ONE	5.00
74	25656	SHAWNE JACKSON	JUST AS BAD AS YOU	HE MAY BE YOUR MAN	6.00
74	25656 DJ	SHAWNE JACKSON	JUST AS BAD AS YOU	HE MAY BE YOUR MAN	8.00
74	25660	ECSTASY, PASSION & PAIN	GOOD THINGS DON'T LAST FOREVER	BORN TO LOSE YOU	8.00
74	25660 DJ	ECSTASY, PASSION & PAIN	GOOD THINGS DON'T LAST FOREVER	BORN TO LOSE YOU	10.00
74	25661	BARRY WHITE	CAN'T GET ENOUGH OF YOUR LOVE, BABE	JUST NOT ENOUGH	4.00
74	25661 DJ	BARRY WHITE	CAN'T GET ENOUGH OF YOUR LOVE, BABE	JUST NOT ENOUGH	5.00
74	25662	LOVE UNLIMITED	PEOPLE OF TOMORROW ARE THE	SO NICE TO HEAR	4.00
74	25662 DJ	LOVE UNLIMITED	PEOPLE OF TOMORROW ARE THE	SO NICE TO HEAR	5.00
74	25666	B.T.EXPRESS	DO IT ('TIL YOU'RE SATISFIED)	same: part 2	5.00
74	25666 DJ	B.T.EXPRESS	DO IT ('TIL YOU'RE SATISFIED)	same: part 2	6.00
74	25668	WILLIE HENDERSON	GANSTER BOOGIE BUMP	LET'S MERENQUE	4.00
74	25668 DJ	WILLIE HENDERSON	GANSTER BOOGIE BUMP	LET'S MERENQUE	5.00
74	25669	ECSTASY, PASSION & PAIN	ASK ME	I'L TAKE THE BLAME	10.00
74	25669 DJ	ECSTASY, PASSION & PAIN	ASK ME	I'L TAKE THE BLAME	15.00
75	25671	THREE DEGREES	SUGAR ON SUNDAY	MAYBE	5.00
75	25671 DJ	THREE DEGREES	SUGAR ON SUNDAY	MAYBE	6.00
75	25674	B.T.EXPRESS	EXPRESS	EXPRESS part 2	5.00
75	25674 DJ	B.T.EXPRESS	EXPRESS	EXPRESS part 2	6.00
75	25675	ECSTASY, PASSION & PAIN	ONE BEAUTIFUL DAY	TRY TO BELIEVE	6.00
75	25675 DJ	ECSTASY, PASSION & PAIN	ONE BEAUTIFUL DAY	TRY TO BELIEVE	8.00
75	25677	LIQUID SMOKE	DANCE, DANCE, DANCE	WHERE IS OUR LOVE	6.00
75	25677 DJ	LIQUID SMOKE	DANCE, DANCE, DANCE	WHERE IS OUR LOVE	8.00
75	25679	MOMENT OF TRUTH	HELPLESSLY	HELPLESSLY PART 2	6.00
75	25679 DJ	MOMENT OF TRUTH	HELPLESSLY	HELPLESSLY PART 2	8.00
75	25680	CHAPTER THREE	I'LL NEVER BE THE SAME	I'LL NEVER BE THE SAME part 2	10.00
75	25680 DJ	CHAPTER THREE	I'LL NEVER BE THE SAME AGAIN	same: part 2	15.00
75	25681	REAL THING	STONE COLD LOVE AFFAIR	A LOVE THAT'S REAL	4.00
75	25681 DJ	REAL THING	STONE COLD LOVE AFFAIR	A LOVE THAT'S REAL	5.00
75	25682	B.T.EXPRESS	ONCE YOU GET IT	THIS HOUSE IS SMOKIN'	5.00
75	25682 DJ	B.T.EXPRESS	ONCE YOU GET IT	THIS HOUSE IS SMOKIN'	6.00
75	25688	SOUTH SHORE COMMISSION	FREE MAN	same:disco mix	4.00
75	25688 DJ	SOUTH SHORE COMMISSION	FREE MAN	same:disco mix	5.00
75	25691	BOBBY MOORE	(CALL ME YOUR) ANYTHING MAN	same: disco version	8.00
75	25691 DJ	BOBBY MOORE	(CALL ME YOUR) ANYTHING MAN	same: disco version	10.00
75	25696	JONES BROS.	LUCKY LADY	GOOD OLD DAYS	**178.00**
75	25696 DJ	JONES BROS.	LUCKY LADY	GOOD OLD DAYS	150.00
75	25698	MAGIC NIGHT	IF YOU AND I HAD NEVER MET	same: instrumental	20.00
75	25698 DJ	MAGIC NIGHT	IF YOU AND I HAD NEVER MET	same: instrumental	28.00
75	25700	JACKIE ROBINSON	LET ME BE	MOVING LIKE A SUPERSTAR	10.00
75	25700 DJ	JACKIE ROBINSON	LET ME BE	MOVING LIKE A SUPERSTAR	15.00
76	25704	TYRONE ASHLEY	FEET START MOVING	MOVIN ON	5.00
76	25704 DJ	TYRONE ASHLEY	FEET START MOVING	MOVIN ON	6.00
76	25705	MAJOR LANCE	NOTHING CAN STOP ME	FOLLOW THE LEADER	10.00
76	25705 DJ	MAJOR LANCE	NOTHING CAN STOP ME	FOLLOW THE LEADER	15.00
76	25709	REAL THING	YOU TRO ME ARE EVERYTHING	KEEP AN EYE ON YOUR BEST FRIEND	4.00
76	25709 DJ	REAL THING	YOU TRO ME ARE EVERYTHING	KEEP AN EYE ON YOUR BEST FRIEND	5.00
76	25710	TYRONE ASHLEY	NOTHING SHORT OF A MIRACLE	MIRACLE WORKER	5.00
76	25710 DJ	TYRONE ASHLEY	NOTHING SHORT OF A MIRACLE	MIRACLE WORKER	6.00
76	25719	D.C. LaRUE	CA-THE-DRALS	same:long version	6.00
76	25719 DJ	D.C. LaRUE	CA-THE-DRALS	same:long version	8.00
76	25731	GENTLEMAN AND THEIR LADY	LIKE HER (Short Version)	LIKE HER (Complete)	10.00
76	25731 DJ	GENTLEMAN AND THEIR LADY	LIKE HER (Short Version)	LIKE HER (Complete)	15.00
76	25733	WHIRLWIIND	FULL TIME THING (BETWEEN DUSK AND	DON'T LET HIM GET THE BEST OF	8.00
76	25733 DJ	WHIRLWIIND	FULL TIME THING (BETWEEN DUSK AND	DON'T LET HIM GET THE BEST OF	10.00
76	25736	JOBELL & the ORCHESTRA	NEVER GONNA LET YOU GO	NEVER GONNA LET YOU GO (disco)	12.00
76	25736 DJ	JOBELL & the ORCHESTRA	NEVER GONNA LET YOU GO	NEVER GONNA LET YOU GO (disco)	18.00
76	25741	DESTINATIONS	I'VE GOT TO DANCE (TO KEEP FROM	THE HUSTLE AND THE BUS STOP	5.00
76	25741 DJ	DESTINATIONS	I'VE GOT TO DANCE (TO KEEP FROM	THE HUSTLE AND THE BUS STOP	6.00
77	25751	DORIS TROY	I'LL DO ANYTHING	HEARTACHES	10.00
77	25751 DJ	DORIS TROY	I'LL DO ANYTHING	HEARTACHES	15.00
77	25783	D.C. LaRUE	DO YOU WANT THE REAL THING	YOU CAN ALWAYS TELL A LADY	5.00
77	25783 DJ	D.C. LaRUE	DO YOU WANT THE REAL THING	YOU CAN ALWAYS TELL A LADY	6.00

PYE INTERNATIONAL EPs

61	44007 EP PS	CLARENCE FROGMAN HENRY	CLARENCE HENRY HIT PARADE	1963 4 track EP with cover	20.00
63	44009 EP PS	CHUCK BERRY & BO DIDDLEY	CHUCK & BO	1963 4 track EP with cover	15.00
63	44010 EP PS	MUDDY WATERS	MUDDY WATERS	1963 4 track EP with cover	40.00
63	44011 EP PS	CHUCK BERRY	CHUCK BERRY	1963 4 track EP with cover	15.00
63	44012 EP PS	CHUCK BERRY & BO DIDDLEY	CHUCK & BO volume 2.	1963 4 track EP with cover	15.00
63	44013 EP PS	CHUCK BERRY	THIS IS CHUCK BERRY	1963 4 track EP with cover	15.00
63	44014 EP PS	BO DIDDLEY	HEY, BO DIDDLEY	1963 4 track EP with cover	20.00
63	44015 EP PS	HOWLIN' WOLF	SMOKESTACK LIGHTNING	1963 4 track EP with cover	30.00
64	44017 EP PS	CHUCK BERRY & BO DIDDLEY	CHUCK & BO volume 3.	1964 4 track EP with cover	15.00

64	44019 EP PS	BO DIDDLEY	THE STORY OF BO DIDDLEY	1964 4 track EP with cover	25.00
64	44023 EP PS	KINGSMEN	LOUIE, LOUIE	1964 4 track EP with cover	40.00
64	44024 EP PS	DIONNE WARWICK	IT'S LOVE THAT REALLY COUNTS	1964 4 track EP with cover	15.00
64	44025 EP PS	CYRIL DAVIES & his R&B ALL STARS	THE SOUND OF CYRIL DAVIES	1964 4 track EP with cover	45.00
64	44026 EP PS	DIONNE WARWICK	DON'T MAKE ME OVER	1964 4 track EP with cover	15.00
64	44027 EP PS	TOMMY TUCKER	HI HEEL SNEAKERS	1964 4 track EP with cover	45.00
64	44028 EP PS	CHUCK BERRY	HITS	1964 4 track EP with cover	15.00
64	44029 EP PS	VARIOUS ARTISTS	THE BLUES vol. 1 part 1.	1964 4 track EP with cover	22.00
64	44030 EP PS	VARIOUS ARTISTS	A FESTIVAL OF BLUES # 1	1964 4 track EP with cover	20.00
64	44031 EP PS	BO DIDDLEY	BO DIDDLEY IS A LUMBERJACK	1964 4 track EP with cover	25.00
64	44032 EP PS	HOWLIN' WOLF	TELL ME	1964 4 track EP with cover	25.00
65	44033 EP PS	CHUCK BERRY	BLUE MOOD	1964 4 track EP with cover	15.00
64	44034 EP PS	JOHN LEE HOOKER	LOVE BLUES	1964 4 track EP with cover	25.00
65	44035 EP PS	VARIOUS ARTISTS	THE BLUES vol. 1 part 2	1964 4 track EP with cover	22.00
64	44036 EP PS	BO DIDDLEY	DIDDLIN'	1964 4 track EP with cover	20.00
64	44037 EP PS	SONNY BOY WILLIAMSON	SONNY BOY WILLIAMSON	1964 4 track EP with cover	25.00
65	44038 EP PS	VARIOUS ARTISTS	BLUES FESTIVAL	1965 4 track EP with cover inc: Sugar Pie DeSanto	25.00
65	44039 EP PS	DIONNE WARWICK	WISHIN' AND HOPIN'	1965 4 track EP with cover	15.00
65	44040 EP PS	KINGSMEN	MOJO WORKOUT	1965 4 track EP with cover	30.00
65	44043 EP PS	RIGHTEOUS BROTHERS	THE RIGHTEOUS BROTHERS	1965 4 tracks EP with cover	30.00
65	44044 EP PS	DIONNE WARWICK	DIONNE	1965 4 track EP with cover	10.00
65	44046 EP PS	DIONNE WARWICK	FOREVER MY LOVE	1965 4 track EP with cover	10.00
65	44049 EP PS	DIONNE WARWICK	WHO CAN I TURN TO?	1966 4 track EP with cover	10.00
66	44051 EP PS	DIONNE WARWICK	HERE I AM	1966 4 track EP with cover	10.00
66	45054 EP PS	VARIOUS ARTISTS	THE GREATEST ON STAGE	1966 4 track EP with cover USA Wand recordings	22.00
66	44059 EP PS	JAMES BROWN & THE FAMOUS FLAMES	I GOT YOU	1966 4 track EP with cover	30.00
66	44063 EP PS	KINGSMEN	FEVER	1966 4 track EP with cover	25.00
66	44067 EP PS	DIONNE WARWICK	MESSAGE TO MICHAEL	1966 4 track EP with cover	10.00
66	44068 EP PS	JAMES BROWN & THE FAMOUS FLAMES	I'LL GO CRAZY	1966 4 track EP with cover	20.00
66	44072 EP PS	JAMES BROWN & THE FAMOUS FLAMES	PRISONER OF LOVE	1966 4 track EP with cover	40.00
66	44073 EP PS	DIONNE WARWICK	WINDOW WISHIN'	1966 4 track EP with cover	10.00
66	44076 EP PS	JAMES BROWN & THE FAMOUS FLAMES	HOW LONG DARLING	1966 4 track EP with cover	30.00
66	44077 EP PS	DIONNE WARWICK	I JUST DON'T KNOW WHAT TO DO WITH	1966 4 track EP with cover	15.00
66	44078 EP PS	RONNIE MILSAP c/w ROSCOE ROBINSON	SOUL SENSATIONS	1966 4 track EP with cover	40.00
67	44083 EP PS	DIONNE WARWICK	I LOVE PARIS	1967 4 track EP with cover	8.00
67	44088 EP PS	JAMES BROWN & THE FAMOUS FLAMES	BRING IT UP	1967 4 track EP with cover	30.00
68	44090 EP PS	DIONNE WARWICK	DO YOU KNOW THE WAY TO SAN JOSE	1968 4 track EP with cover	10.00

PYTHON

69	701	MAGIC SAM	TWENTY ONE DAYS IN JAIL	EASY BABY	30.00

QUALITY

76	1	SWEET BLINDNESS	COWBOYS TO GIRLS	GIVE IT TO YOU RIGHT NOW	6.00
76	1 DJ	SWEET BLINDNESS	COWBOYS TO GIRLS	GIVE IT TO YOU RIGHT NOW	10.00

R&B

Two soul releases on a Ska/Reggae orientated label

63	112	JIMMY JAMES	TELL ME	JUMP CHILDREN	15.00
63	127	RONNIE GORDON	SHAKE SOME TIME	COMIN' HOME	150.00

R&B

London based label from Stamford Hill. The label name R&B didn't stand for Rhythm & Blues but were the initials of Rita and Benny King who also own the UK King label. The company chose a strange selection of tracks for their releases, first outing by Teen Queens was a mid 50's recording. Then came some early 60's USA Kent recordings from Jimmy McCracklin, Z.Z. Hill, Slim Willis. One of the most interesting releases was # 5003 by Bel Cantos was actually *Barry White* performing at his local Downey, Los Angeles studio. Their last soul release by Terry and Jerry is now being heralded as a great dancer on the emerging R&B Northern Soul scene and becoming in-demand.

63	5001	TEEN QUEENS	EDDIE MY LOVE	JUST GOOFED	50.00
65	5002	JIMMY McCRACKLIN	I GOT EYES FOR YOU	I'M GONNA TEEL YOUR MOTHER	20.00
65	5003	BEL CANTOS	FEEL AW RIGHT	FEEL AW RIGHT part 2	15.00
65	5004	SLIM WILLIS	RUNNING AROUND	NO FEELING FOR YOU	20.00
65	5005	Z.Z. HILL	HAVE MERCY SOMEONE	SOMEONE TO LOVE ME	15.00
65	5009	TERRY and JERRY	MAMA JULIE	PEOPLE ARE DOING IT EVERY DAY	30.00

R&B RECORDS

81	203	SAVANNA	I CAN'T TURN AWAY	same: instrumental	8.00

R.B. RECORDS

81	101	OMNI c/w VELVET HAMMER	KEYS TO THE CITY	HAPPY	10.00

RAINBOW

66	104	ERROL DIXON & the GOODTIME BAND	I NEED SOMEONE TO LOVE	I WANT	45.00

RAK

	204	GONZALEZ	HOLE IN MY SOUL	RE-SOULED	20.00

RARE EARTH

A Tamla Motown off shoot label launched in the UK September 1971. Created to cater for their white pop and rock artists, enabling the identity of Tamla Motown as a soul label to continue. The idea not to damage UK Tamla Motown's reputation for soul by releasing pop under the Tamla Motown logo, worked. Interestingly their first release was scheduled for Tamla Motown TMG 786 the Rare Earth pressing has TMG 786 matrix in the deadwax: As this number on Tamla Motown was left unissued it is a very important # in the series, with most collectors fitting the Rare Earth 101 into the missing TMG 786 slot in their collection: Rare Earth was the first UK Motown label to release UK produced recordings after release # 107 only numbers 109, 111, 114, 115 were USA productions all the others were UK recorded. This label ceased releasing 45's in July 1975 after 4 years and releasing twenty singles in the process. The label itself will hold little interest to pure soul collectors: but to scholars and serious collectors of UK Tamla Motown releases, this series is an essential part of UK Tamla Motown's history. All releases did have a promo copy preceeding it, add 20% to the values quoted for promo copies. Company sleeves, seem to be hard to come by, value of 45 with its original sleeve in mint minus condition add £2.00

71	101 (TMG786)	R.DEAN TAYLOR	AIN'T IT A SAD THING	BACK STREET	20.00
71	102	RARE EARTH	I JUST WANT TO CELEBRATE	THE SEED	5.00
72	103	STONEY & MEATLOAF	THE WAY YOU DO THE THINGS YOU	WHAT YOU SEE IS WHAT YOU GET	10.00
72	104	RARE EARTH	HEY BIG BROTHER	UNDER GODS LIGHT	3.00
72	105	RARE EARTH	BORN TO WANDER	HERE COMES THE NIGHT	6.00
72	106	R. DEAN TAYLOR	TAOS NEW MEXICO	SHADOW	5.00
72	106 c	R. DEAN TAYLOR	TAOS NEW MEXICO	SHADOW	6.00
72	107	XIT	I WAS RAISED	END	6.00
73	108	WOLFE	DANCING IN THE MOONLIGHT	SNARLIN' MAMA LION	6.00
73	109	RARE EARTH	GOOD TIMES SALLY	LOVE SHINES DOWN	5.00
73	110	DAN THE BANJO MAN	DAN THE BANJO MAN	EVERYTHING WILL RHYTHM	6.00
74	111	XIT	RESERVATION OF EDUCATION	YOUNG WARRIOR	5.00
74	112	DAVID ALEAXANDER	LOVE, LOVE, LOVE	MISSY	6.00
74	113	DAN THE BANJO MAN	BLACK MAGIC	LONDONDERRY	5.00
74	114	RAE EARTH	I KNOW I'M LOSING YOU	WHEN JOANNIE SMILES	8.00
74	115	MICHAEL EDWARD CAMPBELL	ROXANNE (YOU SURE GOT A FINE DESIGN)	ROLL IT OVER	8.00
74	116	SLOWBONE & THE WONDER BOYS	HAPPY BIRTHDAY SWEET SIXTEEN	TALES OF A CROOKED MAN	5.00
74	117	SONNY & THE SOVEREIGNS	SCHOOL IS OUT	WARM JETZ	6.00
74	118	ROUGH RIDERS	HOT CALIFORNIA BEACH	DO YOU SEE ME	6.00
74	119	SLOWBONE	OH MAN	GET WHAT YOU'RE GIVEN	6.00
74	120	FRIENDLY PERSUASION	REMEMBER (SHA LA LA)	I'LL ALWAYS DO THE BEST I CAN	4.00

RCA

The Radio Corporation Of America or RCA is one of the most collected labels for soul collectors, but not the UK RCA counterpart. The catalogue issued in the UK was mostly picked with a "play safe" policy. When you consider the collectable Soul and Northern Soul released on that most famous dog logo black 60's label, the mind boggles at the prospect of any of the Lorraine Chandler's, or the Roy Hamilton's. You can only guess at the response of the early young English soul vinyl pioneers, searching the record shops and market stalls, to come across a Michael & Raymond, Laura Greene, Sharon Scott or Willie Kendricks. You can only imagine what the reaction to any of these 45's would have induced to a Tamla Motown fed soul fan. But it was not to be, the UK RCA catalogue is almost devoid of the USA releases which would evolve into Northern Soul classics.

RCA is a success story of USA entrepreneur David Sarnoff. His drive and business acumen led to RCA becoming one of the largest companies in the world, successfully turning it into a highly respected record industry conglomerate. But when in 1970 David Sarnoff retired he handed the reigns to his son Robert, one year later David Sarnoff died, and unfortunately RCA's success died with him.

RCA was formed in 1919 as a public company owned by AT&T and GE. David Sarnoff was named as general manager, In 1928 RCA bought radio stations to form NBC Nation Broadcasting Company. One year later, driven by Sarnoff RCA then took control of the Victor Talking Machine, the world's largest manufacturer of gramophone records. Hence the name evolved to RCA Victor. In 1931 RCA were the first company to make the 33rpm record and in 1949 RCA Victor developed and released the very first 7" 45rpm record.

In 1965 RCA was the first company to launch the 8-track tape cartridge. Which was initially hugely successful, because the mechanics of the cartridge allowed it to play continuously. 10 years later the cassette tape took over, and the 8-track slowly died.

During the 70's RCA's decline began, Robert Sarnoff was replaced in a boardroom coup, and replaced by Anthony Conrad. But their fortunes only got worse when Conrad resigned after failing to make tax returns for six years. RCA forays into innovative technology, satellite, computers, NBC Radio and smaller consumer electronics were money losers. Which weakened the company, which was ultimately sold to GE, who broke RCA up.

Why RCA were not more adventurous with their catalogue in the UK we may never know, but one glance at the UK soul collectables below, and a quick flick through your mind to what was pressed in the USA will reveal the UK label as a very poor comparison.

74	0205	MAIN INGREDIENT	JUST DON'T WANT TO BE LONELY	GOODBYE MY LOVE	6.00
74	0205 DJ	MAIN INGREDIENT	JUST DON'T WANT TO BE LONELY	GOODBYE MY LOVE	8.00
74	0305	MAIN INGREDIENT	HAPPINESS IS JUST AROUND THE BEND	WHY CAN'T WE ALL UNITE	6.00
74	0305 DJ	MAIN INGREDIENT	HAPPINESS IS JUST AROUND THE BEND	WHY CAN'T WE ALL UNITE	8.00
74	0315	CHOICE FOUR	THE FINGERS POINTERS	THE FINGERS POINTERS part 2	8.00
74	0315 DJ	CHOICE FOUR	THE FINGERS POINTERS	THE FINGERS POINTERS part 2	10.00
76	0836	MEMPHIS HORNS	GET UP AND DANCE	DON'T ABUSE IT	6.00
76	0836 DJ	MEMPHIS HORNS	GET UP AND DANCE	DON'T ABUSE IT	8.00
79	1	JOE BATAAN	RAP-O-CLAP-O	same: instrumental	5.00
79	1 DJ	JOE BATAAN	RAP-O-CLAP-O	same: instrumental	6.00
80	23	ODYSSEY	HANG TOGETHER	DOWN BOY	4.00
80	23 DJ	ODYSSEY	HANG TOGETHER	DOWN BOY	5.00
81	77	THELMA HOUSTON	IF YOU FEEL IT	HOLLYWOOD	4.00
81	77 DJ	THELMA HOUSTON	IF YOU FEEL IT	HOLLYWOOD	5.00
81	78	ESTHER WILLIAMS	I'LL BE YOUR PLEASURE	MAKE IT WITH YOU	4.00
81	78 DJ	ESTHER WILLIAMS	I'LL BE YOUR PLEASURE	MAKE IT WITH YOU	5.00
81	93	KENI BURKE	LET SOMEBODY LOVE YOU	same: instrumental	15.00
81	93 DJ	KENI BURKE	LET SOMEBODY LOVE YOU	same: instrumental	20.00
81	95	EVELYN KING	THE OTHER SIDE OF LOVE	I'M IN LOVE	4.00
81	95 DJ	EVELYN KING	THE OTHER SIDE OF LOVE	I'M IN LOVE	5.00
81	146	ARTHUR ADAMS	YOU GOT THE FLOOR	STAY WITH ME TONIGHT	8.00
81	146 DJ	ARTHUR ADAMS	YOU GOT THE FLOOR	STAY WITH ME TONIGHT	10.00
82	249 PS	EVELYN KING	LOVE COME DOWN	DON'T HIDE OUR LOVE	4.00
82	249 DJ PS	EVELYN KING	LOVE COME DOWN	DON'T HIDE OUR LOVE	5.00
82	252	KENI BURKE	RISIN' TO THE TOP (GIVE IT ALL YOU	HANG TIGHT	8.00
82	252 DJ	KENI BURKE	RISIN' TO THE TOP (GIVE IT ALL YOU	HANG TIGHT	10.00
84	315 PS	EVELYN KING	I'M IN LOVE	GET LOOSE	4.00
84	315 PS DJ	EVELYN KING	I'M IN LOVE	GET LOOSE	5.00
84	357 PS	JB's ALLSTARS	ONE MINUTE EVERY HOUR	THE THEME FROM 903	5.00

84	357 PS DJ	JB's ALLSTARS	ONE MINUTE EVERY HOUR	THE THEME FROM 903	6.00
84	384 PS	JB's ALLSTARS	BACKFIELD IN MOTION	THEME FROM ABEAM	4.00
84	384 PS DJ	JB's ALLSTARS	BACKFIELD IN MOTION	THEME FROM ABEAM	5.00
78	1029	VICKIE SUE ROBINSON	TURN THE BEAT AROUND	HOLD TIGHT	6.00
78	1029 DJ	VICKIE SUE ROBINSON	TURN THE BEAT AROUND	HOLD TIGHT	10.00
78	1032	REGAL DEWY	WHERE WOULD I BE WITHOUT YOU	LOVE MUSIC	8.00
78	1032 DJ	REGAL DEWY	WHERE WOULD I BE WITHOUT YOU	LOVE MUSIC	10.00
58	1078 tri	BOOTS BROWN & the BLOCKBUSTERS	CERVEZA	JUICY	15.00
59	1114 tri	JOHNNY O'NEILL	SOMEBODY JUST LIKE YOU	WAGON TRAIN	20.00
79	1122	EVELYN CHAMPAGNE KING	SHAME	DANCIN' DACIN' DANCIN'	5.00
79	1122 DJ	EVELYN CHAMPAGNE KING	SHAME	DANCIN' DACIN' DANCIN'	6.00
79	1129	ODYSSEY	NATIVE NEW YORKER	EVER LOVIN' SAM	4.00
79	1129 DJ	ODYSSEY	NATIVE NEW YORKER	EVER LOVIN' SAM	5.00
59	1149	ISLEY BROTHERS	SHOUT	SHOUT part 2	15.00
59	1149 DJ	ISLEY BROTHERS	SHOUT	SHOUT part 2	20.00
60	1172	ISLEY BROTHERS	RESPECTABLE	I'M GONNA KNOCK ON YOUR DOOR	20.00
60	1172 DJ	ISLEY BROTHERS	RESPECTABLE	I'M GONNA KNOCK ON YOUR DOOR	28.00
60	1184	SAM COOKE	TEENAGE SONATA	YOU WERE THE ONLY GIRL	10.00
60	1184 DJ	SAM COOKE	TEENAGE SONATA	YOU WERE THE ONLY GIRL	20.00
60	1190	ISLEY BROTHERS	HOW DEEP IS THE OCEAN	HE'S GOT THE WHOLE WORLD IN HI	15.00
60	1190 DJ	ISLEY BROTHERS	HOW DEEP IS THE OCEAN	HE'S GOT THE WHOLE WORLD IN HI	20.00
60	1202	SAM COOKE	CHAIN GANG	I FALL IN LOVE EVERYDAY	10.00
60	1202 DJ	SAM COOKE	CHAIN GANG	I FALL IN LOVE EVERYDAY	28.00
60	1213	ISLEY BROTHERS	TELL ME WHO	SAY YOU LOVE ME TOO	15.00
60	1213 DJ	ISLEY BROTHERS	TELL ME WHO	SAY YOU LOVE ME TOO	20.00
61	1221	SAM COOKE	SAD MOOD	LOVE ME	15.00
61	1221 DJ	SAM COOKE	SAD MOOD	LOVE ME	25.00
61	1230	SAM COOKE	THAT'S IT, I QUIT, I'M MOVING ON	WHAT DO YOU SAY	10.00
61	1230 DJ	SAM COOKE	THAT'S IT - I QUIT - I'M MOVIN' ON	WHAT DO YOU SAY	20.00
61	1242	SAM COOKE	CUPID	FAREWELL, MY DARLING	10.00
61	1242 DJ	SAM COOKE	CUPID	FAREWELL, MY DARLING	30.00
61	1260	SAM COOKE	FEEL IT	IT'S ALRIGHT	10.00
61	1260 DJ	SAM COOKE	FEEL IT	IT'S ALRIGHT	20.00
62	1296	SAM COOKE	HAVIN' A PARTY	BRING IT ON HOME TO ME	10.00
62	1296 DJ	SAM COOKE	HAVIN' A PARTY	BRING IT ON HOME TO ME	30.00
62	1306	DELLA REESE	BLOW OUT THE SUN	I LOVE YOU SO MUCH IT HURTS	40.00
62	1306 DJ	DELLA REESE	BLOW OUT THE SUN	I LOVE YOU SO MUCH IT HURTS	75.00
62	1310	SAM COOKE	NOTHING CAN CHANGE THIS LOVE	SOMEBODY HAVE MERCY	10.00
62	1310	SAM COOKE	NOTHING CAN CHANGE THIS LOVE	SOMEBODY HAVE MERCY	20.00
63	1327 DJ	SAM COOKE	BABY, BABY, BABY	SEND ME SOME LOVIN'	10.00
63	1327 DJ	SAM COOKE	BABY, BABY, BABY	SEND ME SOME LOVIN'	20.00
63	1339	GRADISONS	ALL RIGHT	TRUE ROMANCE	10.00
63	1339 DJ	GRADISONS	ALL RIGHT	TRUE ROMANCE	15.00
63	1341	SAM COOKE	ANOTHER SATURDAY NIGHT	LOVE WILL FIND A WAY	10.00
63	1341 DJ	SAM COOKE	ANOTHER SATURDAY NIGHT	LOVE WILL FIND A WAY	40.00
63	1361	SAM COOKE	FRANKIE AND JOHNNY	COOL TRAIN	8.00
63	1361 DJ	SAM COOKE	FRANKIE AND JOHNNY	COOL TRAIN	15.00
63	1367	SAM COOKE	SHAKE RATTLE AND ROLL	LITTLE RED ROOSTER	15.00
63	1367 DJ	SAM COOKE	SHAKE RATTLE AND ROLL	LITTLE RED ROOSTER	20.00
64	1386	SAM COOKE	GOOD NEWS	BASIN STREET BLUES	10.00
64	1386 DJ	SAM COOKE	GOOD NEWS	BASIN STREET BLUES	20.00
64	1394	KETTY LESTER	SOME THINGS ARE BETTER LEFT UNSAID	THE HOUSE IS HAUNTED	100.00
64	1394 DJ	KETTY LESTER	SOME THINGS ARE BETTER LEFT UNSAID	THE HOUSE IS HAUNTED	**116.00**
64	1401	ARTHUR BIG BOY CRUDUP	MY BABY LEFT ME	I DON'T KNOW IT	30.00
64	1401 DJ	ARTHUR BIG BOY CRUDUP	MY BABY LEFT ME	I DON'T KNOW IT	40.00
64	1403	KETTY LESTER	PLEASE DON'T CRY ANYMORE	ROSES GROW WITH THORNS	50.00
64	1403 DJ	KETTY LESTER	PLEASE DON'T CRY ANYMORE	ROSES GROW WITH THORNS	75.00
64	1405	SAM COOKE	GOOD TIMES	TENNESSEE WALTZ	10.00
64	1405 DJ	SAM COOKE	GOOD TIMES	TENNESSEE WALTZ	20.00
64	1420	SAM COOKE	COUSIN OF MINE	THAT'S WHERE IT'S AT	10.00
64	1420 DJ	SAM COOKE	COUSIN OF MINE	THAT'S WHERE IT'S AT	20.00
64	1421	KETTY LESTER	I TRUST YOU BABY	THE LUCK OF GINGER COFFEY	10.00
64	1421 DJ	KETTY LESTER	I TRUST YOU BABY	THE LUCK OF GINGER COFFEY	20.00
64	1426	PEGGY MARCH	WATCH WHAT YOU DO WITH MY BABY	CAN'T STOP THINKIN' ABOUT HIM	8.00
64	1426 DJ	PEGGY MARCH	WATCH WHAT YOU DO WITH MY BABY	CAN'T STOP THINKIN' ABOUT HIM	10.00
65	1436	SAM COOKE	SHAKE	A CHANGE IS GONNA COME	15.00
65	1436 DJ	SAM COOKE	SHAKE	A CHANGE IS GONNA COME	30.00
65	1447	AFRICAN BEAVERS	FIND MY BABY	JUNGLE FEVER	25.00
65	1447 DJ	AFRICAN BEAVERS	FIND MY BABY	JUNGLE FEVER	30.00
65	1451	GALE GARNETT	I'LL CRY ALONE	WHERE DO YOU GO TO GO AWAY	75.00
65	1451 DJ	GALE GARNETT	I'LL CRY ALONE	WHERE DO YOU GO TO GO AWAY	100.00
65	1452	SAM COOKE	IT'S GOT THE WHOLE WORLD SHAKIN'	(SOMEBODY) EASE MY TROUBLIN MI	20.00
65	1452 DJ	SAM COOKE	IT'S GOT THE WHOLE WORLD SHAKIN'	(SOMEBODY) EASE MY TROUBLIN MI	45.00
79	1456	MACHINE	THERE BUT FOR THE GRACE OF GOD GO I	GET YOUR BODY READY	6.00
79	1456 DJ	MACHINE	THERE BUT FOR THE GRACE OF GOD GO I	GET YOUR BODY READY	8.00
65	1460	KETTY LESTER	LOOKING FOR A BETTER WORLD	PRETTY EYES	8.00
65	1460 DJ	KETTY LESTER	LOOKING FOR A BETTER WORLD	PRETTY EYES	10.00
65	1470	DAWN and the DEE JAYS	THESE ARE THE THINGS ABOUT YOU	I WILL THINK OF YOU	5.00
65	1470 DJ	DAWN and the DEE JAYS	THESE ARE THE THINGS ABOUT YOU	I WILL THINK OF YOU	10.00

65	1472	PEGGY MARCH	YOUR GIRL	LET HER GO	15.00
65	1472 DJ	PEGGY MARCH	YOUR GIRL	LET HER GO	22.00
65	1476	SAM COOKE	SUGAR DUMPLING	BRIDGE OF TEARS	75.00
65	1476 DJ	SAM COOKE	SUGAR DUMPLING	BRIDGE OF TEARS	100.00
79	1481	ENCHANTMENT	ANYWAY YOU WANT IT	OASIS OF LOVE	6.00
79	1481 DJ	ENCHANTMENT	ANYWAY YOU WANT IT	OASIS OF LOVE	8.00
65	1490	SYLVIE VARTAN	I MADE MY CHOICE	ONE MORE DAY	85.00
65	1490 DJ	SYLVIE VARTAN	I MADE MY CHOICE	ONE MORE DAY	100.00
65	1495	SYLVIE VARTAN	ANOTHER HEART	THINKING ABOUT YOU	35.00
65	1495 DJ	SYLVIE VARTAN	ANOTHER HEART	THINKING ABOUT YOU	50.00
66	1500	ROY HAMILTON	TORE UP OVER YOU	AND I LOVE HER	20.00
66	1500 DJ	ROY HAMILTON	TORE UP OVER YOU	AND I LOVE HER	28.00
66	1538	SIDEKICKS	UP ON THE ROOF	SUSPICIONS	10.00
66	1538 DJ	SIDEKICKS	UP ON THE ROOF	SUSPICIONS	15.00
67	1568	HENRY III	SO MUCH LOVE	SITTING IN THE PARK	15.00
67	1568 DJ	HENRY III	SO MUCH LOVE	SITTING IN THE PARK	22.00
67	1573	KING GEORGE	I'M GONNA BE SOMEBODY, SOMEDAY	DRIVE ON JAMES	30.00
67	1573 DJ	KING GEORGE	I'M GONNA BE SOMEBODY, SOMEDAY	DRIVE ON JAMES	45.00
67	1583	NINA SIMONE	DO I MOVE YOU?	DAY AND NIGHT	5.00
67	1583 DJ	NINA SIMONE	DO I MOVE YOU?	DAY AND NIGHT	8.00
67	1588	LEN BARRY	OUR LOVE	THE MOVING FINGER WRITES	20.00
67	1588 DJ	LEN BARRY	OUR LOVE	THE MOVING FINGER WRITES	28.00
68	1662	AL HIRT	KEEP THE BALL ROLLIN'	MANHATTAN SAFARI	8.00
68	1662 DJ	AL HIRT	KEEP THE BALL ROLLIN'	MANHATTAN SAFARI	10.00
68	1664	DAVID WALKER	RING THE CHANGES	KEEP A LITTLE LOVE	100.00
68	1664 DJ	DAVID WALKER	RING THE CHANGES	KEEP A LITTLE LOVE	125.00
68	1676	PAUL ANKA	WHEN WE GET THERE	CAN'T GET YOU OUT OF MY MIND	40.00
68	1676 DJ	PAUL ANKA	WHEN WE GET THERE	CAN'T GET YOU OUT OF MY MIND	75.00
68	1681	JIMMY JUSTICE	WALKING AWAY WITH MY HEART	I'M PASSED FORGETTING YOU	30.00
68	1681 DJ	JIMMY JUSTICE	WALKING AWAY WITH MY HEART	I'M PASSED FORGETTING YOU	40.00
68	1687	PEGGY MARCH	IF YOU LOVED ME (SOUL COAXING -	THINKING THROUGH MY TEARS	50.00
68	1687 DJ	PEGGY MARCH	IF YOU LOVED ME (SOUL COAXING -	THINKING THROUGH MY TEARS	75.00
68	1691	REPARATA & the DELRONS	I CAN HEAR THE RAIN	ALWAYS WAITIN'	10.00
68	1691 DJ	REPARATA & the DELRONS	I CAN HEAR THE RAIN	ALWAYS WAITIN'	15.00
68	1697	NINA SIMONE	WHY? (THE KING OF LOVE IS DEAD)	same: part 2	5.00
68	1697 DJ	NINA SIMONE	WHY? (THE KING OF LOVE IS DEAD)	same: part 2	6.00
68	1701	SAM COOKE c/w DUANE EDDY	ANOTHER SATURDAY NIGHT	DANCE WITH THE GUITAR MAN	10.00
68	1701 DJ	SAM COOKE c/w DUANE EDDY	ANOTHER SATURDAY NIGHT	DANCE WITH THE GUITAR MAN	15.00
68	1705	FOUR KENTS	THE MOVING FINGER WRITES	SEARCHIN'	20.00
68	1705 DJ	FOUR KENTS	THE MOVING FINGER WRITES	SEARCHIN'	28.00
68	1714	ELVIS PRESLEY	YOUR TIME HASN'T COME YET BABY	LET YOURSELF GO	20.00
68	1714 DJ	ELVIS PRESLEY	YOUR TIME HASN'T COME YET BABY	LET YOURSELF GO	75.00
68	1737	GRASS ROOTS	MIDNIGHT CONFESSIONS	WHO WILL YOU BE TOMORROW	15.00
68	1737 DJ	GRASS ROOTS	MIDNIGHT CONFESSIONS	WHO WILL YOU BE TOMORROW	20.00
68	1743	NINA SIMONE	AIN'T GOT NO - I GOT LIFE	DO WHAT YOU GOTTA DO	10.00
68	1743 DJ	NINA SIMONE	AIN'T GOT NO - I GOT LIFE	DO WHAT YOU GOTTA DO	15.00
68	1754	CHANTS	BABY I DON'T NEED YOUR LOVE	A MAN WITHOUT A FACE	60.00
68	1754 DJ	CHANTS	BABY I DON'T NEED YOUR LOVE	A MAN WITHOUT A FACE	85.00
68	1766	DAVE HUNTER	SHE'SA HEARTBREAKER	LOVE ME A LIFETIME	10.00
68	1766 DJ	DAVE HUNTER	SHE'SA HEARTBREAKER	LOVE ME A LIFETIME	15.00
68	1769	FELICIANO	HI HEEK SNEAKERS	HITCHCOCK RAILWAY	10.00
68	1769 DJ	FELICIANO	HI HEEK SNEAKERS	HITCHCOCK RAILWAY	15.00
68	1776	SHARKS	FUNKOLOGY	GOODBYE LORENE	10.00
68	1776 DJ	SHARKS	FUNKOLOGY	GOODBYE LORENE	15.00
68	1779	NINA SIMONE	TO LOVE SOMEBODY	I CAN'T SEE NOBODY	4.00
68	1779 DJ	NINA SIMONE	TO LOVE SOMEBODY	I CAN'T SEE NOBODY	5.00
69	1817	SAM COOKE	CUPID	FAREWELL, MY DARLING	6.00
69	1817 DJ	SAM COOKE	CUPID	FAREWELL, MY DARLING	8.00
69	1822	SUE LYNNE	DON'T PITY ME	YOU	**181.00**
69	1822 DJ	SUE LYNNE	DON'T PITY ME	YOU	200.00
69	1823	CHANTS	I GET THE SWEETEST FEELING	CANDY	15.00
69	1823 DJ	CHANTS	I GET THE SWEETEST FEELING	CANDY	22.00
69	1851	CAROLYN FRANKLIN	BOXER	I DON'T TO LOSE YOU	10.00
69	1851 DJ	CAROLYN FRANKLIN	BOXER	I DON'T TO LOSE YOU	15.00
69	1903	NINA SIMONE	SAVE ME	TO BE YOUNG GIFTED AND BLACK	25.00
69	1903 DJ	NINA SIMONE	SAVE ME	TO BE YOUNG, GIFTED & BLACK	30.00
69	1905	ANTHONY SWETE	BACKFIELD IN MOTION	SOUL DEEP	10.00
69	1905 DJ	ANTHONY SWETE	BACKFIELD IN MOTION	SOUL DEEP	15.00
70	1916	ELVIS PRESLEY	RUBBERNECKIN'	DON'T CRY DADDY	10.00
70	1916 DJ	ELVIS PRESLEY	RUBBERNECKIN'	DON'T CRY DADDY	30.00
70	1916 PS	ELVIS PRESLEY	RUBBERNECKIN'	DON'T CRY DADDY	15.00
70	1922	GREY & HANKS	NOW I'M FINE	LOVE'S IN COMMAND	5.00
70	1922 DJ	GREY & HANKS	NOW I'M FINE	LOVE'S IN COMMAND	6.00
70	1948	TERESA GRAVES	WE'RE ON OUR WAY	I SPENT MY LAST DREAM	5.00
70	1948 DJ	TERESA GRAVES	WE'RE ON OUR WAY	I SPENT MY LAST DREAM	6.00
70	1952	FRIENDS OF DISTINCTION	LOVE OR LET ME BE LONELY	THE GENERATION	5.00
70	1952 DJ	FRIENDS OF DISTINCTION	LOVE OR LET ME BE LONELY	THE GENERATION	6.00
70	1961	NINA SIMONE	DO WHAT YOU GOTTA DO	TURN ME ON	5.00
70	1961 DJ	NINA SIMONE	DO WHAT YOU GOTTA DO	TURN ME ON	6.00

70	2009	CAROLYN FRANKLIN	ALL I WANT IS TO BE YOUR WOMAN	YOU REALLY DIDN'T MEAN IT	8.00
70	2009 DJ	CAROLYN FRANKLIN	ALL I WANT IS TO BE YOUR WOMAN	YOU REALLY DIDN'T MEAN IT	10.00
70	2016	MANITOBA	SOMETHING IN YOU	YOU'LL NEVER GET BACK	10.00
70	2016 DJ	MANITOBA	SOMETHING IN YOU	YOU'LL NEVER GET BACK	15.00
70	2017	GLOBETROTTERS	CHEER ME UP	GRAVY	8.00
70	2017 DJ	GLOBETROTTERS	CHEER ME UP	GRAVY	10.00
70	2018	FRIENDS OF DISTINCTION	TIME WAIT FOR NO-ONE	NEW MOTHER NATURE	4.00
70	2018 DJ	FRIENDS OF DISTINCTION	TIME WAIT FOR NO-ONE	NEW MOTHER NATURE	5.00
71	2034	MAIN INGREDIENT	I'M BETTER OFF WITHOUT YOU	SOMEBODY'S BEEN SLEEPING	4.00
71	2034 DJ	MAIN INGREDIENT	I'M BETTER OFF WITHOUT YOU	SOMEBODY'S BEEN SLEEPING	6.00
71	2050	FRIENDS OF DISTINCTION	GRAZING IN THE GRASS	I NEED YOU	5.00
71	2050 DJ	FRIENDS OF DISTINCTION	GRAZING IN THE GRASS	I NEED YOU	8.00
71	2055	MANITOBA	COME ON DOWN TO MY BOAT	DEAD END STREET	15.00
71	2055 DJ	MANITOBA	COME ON DOWN TO MY BOAT	DEAD END STREET	20.00
71	2093	SAM COOKE	TWISTIN' THE NIGHT AWAY	ONLY SIXTEEN + CUPID	4.00
71	2093 DJ	SAM COOKE	TWISTIN' THE NIGHT AWAY	ONLY SIXTEEN + CUPID	6.00
72	2183	ROCK FLOWERS	MOTHER YOU, SMOTHER YOU	NUMBER WONDERFUL	8.00
72	2183 DJ	ROCK FLOWERS	MOTHER YOU, SMOTHER YOU	NUMBER WONDERFUL	10.00
72	2197	BIG BORIS	DEVIL'S DRIVE	BIG COUNTRY	6.00
72	2197 DJ	BIG BORIS	DEVIL'S DRIVE	BIG COUNTRY	10.00
72	2203	NITE-LITERS	K-JEE	TANGA BOO GONK	10.00
72	2203 DJ	NITE-LITERS	K-JEE	TANGA BOO GONK	12.00
72	2214	NITE-LITERS	K-JEE	TANGA BOO GONK	8.00
72	2214 DJ	NITE-LITERS	K-JEE	TANGA BOO GONK	10.00
72	2226	JIMMY CASTOR	TROGLODYTE	PROMISE TO REMEMBER	4.00
72	2226 DJ	JIMMY CASTOR	TROGLODYTE	PROMISE TO REMEMBER	5.00
72	2256	SAM COOKE	ANOTHER SATURDAY NIGHT	CHAIN GANG + YOU SEND ME	5.00
72	2256 DJ	SAM COOKE	ANOTHER SATURDAY NIGHT	CHAIN GANG + YOU SEND ME	6.00
72	2270	MAIN INGREDIENT	EVERYBODY PLAYS THE FOOL	WHO CAN I TURN TO	4.00
72	2270 DJ	MAIN INGREDIENT	EVERYBODY PLAYS THE FOOL	WHO CAN I TURN TO	8.00
72	2271	DONNIE ELBERT	ALONG CAME PRIDE	TIME HANGS ON MY MIND	6.00
72	2271 DJ	DONNIE ELBERT	ALONG CAME PRIDE	TIME HANGS ON MY MIND	10.00
73	2309	MONA RICHARDSON	STAY WITH ME	HEARTBEAT	6.00
73	2309	MONA RICHARDSON	STAY WITH ME	HEARTBEAT	8.00
73	2313	MAIN INGREDIENT	JUST DON'T WANNA BE LONELY	YOU'VE GOT TO TAKE IT	4.00
73	2313 DJ	MAIN INGREDIENT	JUST DON'T WANNA BE LONELY	YOU'VE GOT TO TAKE IT	6.00
73	2336	FRIENDS OF DISTINCTION	LOVE ME OR LET ME BE LONELY	THIS GENERATION	4.00
73	2336 DJ	FRIENDS OF DISTINCTION	LOVE ME OR LET ME BE LONELY	THIS GENERATION	6.00
73	2338	WILSON PICKET	MR. MAGIC MAN	I SHO' YOU	4.00
73	2338 DJ	WILSON PICKET	MR. MAGIC MAN	I SHO' YOU	6.00
73	2339	BARRABAS	WOMAN	WILD SAFARI	4.00
73	2339 DJ	BARRABAS	WOMAN	WILD SAFARI	5.00
73	2340	MONA RICHARDSON	CRUMBS OFF THE TABLE	YOU'RE NO GOOD	10.00
73	2340 DJ	MONA RICHARDSON	CRUMBS OFF THE TABLE	YOU'RE NO GOOD	15.00
73	2351	NEW YORK CITY	I'M DOING FINE NOW	AIN'T IT SO	5.00
73	2351 DJ	NEW YORK CITY	I'M DOING FINE NOW	AIN'T IT SO	8.00
73	2360	NEW BIRTH	I CAN UNDERSTAND IT	OH BABY I LOVE THE WAY	8.00
73	2360 DJ	NEW BIRTH	I CAN UNDERSTAND IT	OH BABY I LOVE THE WAY	10.00
73	2382	LABELLE	OPEN UP MY HEART	GOINMG ON HOLIDAY	4.00
73	2382 DJ	LABELLE	OPEN UP MY HEART	GOINMG ON HOLIDAY	5.00
73	2386	JOHNNY GRIFFITH INC.	GRAND CENTRAL SHUTTLE	MY LOVE	10.00
73	2386 DJ	JOHNNY GRIFFITH INC.	GRAND CENTRAL SHUTTLE	MY LOVE	12.00
73	2390	NEW BIRTH	UNTIL IT'S TIME FOR YOU TO GO	YOU ARE WHAT I'M ALL ABOUT	4.00
73	2390	NEW BIRTH	UNTIL IT'S TIME FOR YOU TO GO	YOU ARE WHAT I'M ALL ABOUT	5.00
73	2425	SWISS MOVEMENT	BRING BACK YOUR LOVE	IF YOU NEED SOMEBODY TO LOVE	6.00
73	2425 DJ	SWISS MOVEMENT	BRING BACK YOUR LOVE	IF YOU NEED SOMEBODY TO LOVE	10.00
73	2430	WILSON PICKETT	TAKE A CLOSER LOOK	TWO WOMEN AND A WIFE	4.00
73	2430 DJ	WILSON PICKETT	TAKE A CLOSER LOOK	TWO WOMEN AND A WIFE	5.00
74	2444	HUES CORPORATION	FREEDOM OF THE STALLION	GET OFF MY CLOUD	5.00
74	2444 DJ	HUES CORPORATION	FREEDOM OF THE STALLION	GET OFF MY CLOUD	6.00
74	2450	WILSON PICKETT	TAKE YOU PLEASURE WHERE YOU FIND IT	WHAT GOOD IS A LIE	4.00
74	2450	WILSON PICKETT	TAKE YOU PLEASURE WHERE YOU FIND IT	WHAT GOOD IS A LIE	5.00
74	2456	TYMES	YOU LITTLE TRUSTMAKER	THE NORTH HILLS	5.00
74	2456 DJ	TYMES	YOU LITTLE TRUSTMAKER	THE NORTH HILLS	6.00
74	2491	BETTY WRIGHT	SHOO-RAH ! SHOO-RAH !	TONIGHT IS THE NIGHT	4.00
74	2491 DJ	BETTY WRIGHT	SHOO-RAH ! SHOO-RAH !	TONIGHT IS THE NIGHT	5.00
74	2493	TYMES	M/S GRACE	THE CRUTCH	5.00
74	2493 DJ	TYMES	M/S GRACE	THE CRUTCH	8.00
74	2498	PAUL ANKA	I CAN'T HELP LOVING YOU	CAN'T GET ALONG VERY WELL WITH	10.00
74	2498 DJ	PAUL ANKA	I CAN'T HELP LOVING YOU	CAN'T GET ALONG VERY WELL WITH	15.00
74	2503	NELL CARTER	DREAMS	SEND HIM BACK TO ME	30.00
74	2503 DJ	NELL CARTER	DREAMS	SEND HIM BACK TO ME	40.00
75	2519	I.G.'S	THANK YOU, GIRL	HANG ON TO ME, BABY	30.00
75	2519 DJ	I.G.'S	THANK YOU, GIRL	HANG ON TO ME, BABY	40.00
75	2530	TYMES	SOMEWAY, SOMEHOW I'M KEEPIN' YOU	INTERLOOP	5.00
75	2530 DJ	TYMES	SOMEWAY, SOMEHOW I'M KEEPIN' YOU	same: long version	10.00
75	2534	DEAN COURTNEY	I'LL ALWAYS NEED YOU	TAMMY	10.00
75	2534 DJ	DEAN COURTNEY	I'LL ALWAYS NEED YOU	TAMMY	15.00
75	2543	CAROL DOUGLAS	A HURRICANE IS COMING TONITE	I FELL IN LOVE WITH LOVE	4.00

75	2543 DJ	CAROL DOUGLAS	A HURRICANE IS COMING TONITE	I FELL IN LOVE WITH LOVE	5.00
75	2548	BETTY WRIGHT	WHERE IS THE LOVE	MY BABY AIN'T MY BABY ANYMORE	5.00
75	2548 DJ	BETTY WRIGHT	WHERE IS THE LOVE	MY BABY AIN'T MY BABY ANYMORE	8.00
75	2553	BATAAN	THE BOTTLE (LA BOTELLA)	WHEN YOUR DOWN	8.00
75	2553 DJ	BATAAN	THE BOTTLE (LA BOTELLA)	WHEN YOUR DOWN	10.00
75	2554	FLIRTATIONS	MR. UNIVERSE	SOMEBODY CARED FOR ME	4.00
75	2554 DJ	FLIRTATIONS	MR. UNIVERSE	SOMEBODY CARED FOR ME	5.00
75	2560	I.G.'S	SHOW AND TELL	I CAN'T GET YOU OUTTA MY MIND	40.00
75	2560 DJ	I.G.'S	SHOW AND TELL	I CAN'T GET YOU OUTTA MY MIND	50.00
75	2568	LONNIE LITSON SMITH	EXPANSIONS	EXPANSIONS part 2	8.00
75	2568 DJ	LONNIE LITSON SMITH	EXPANSIONS	EXPANSIONS part 2	10.00
75	2573	VICKIE SUE ROBINSON	BABY, NOW THAT I'VE FOUND YOU	THANKS A MILLION	4.00
75	2573 DJ	VICKIE SUE ROBINSON	BABY, NOW THAT I'VE FOUND YOU	THANKS A MILLION	5.00
75	2585	JIMMY BO HORNE	GIMME SOME	GIMME SOME part 2	5.00
75	2585 DJ	JIMMY BO HORNE	GIMME SOME	GIMME SOME part 2	6.00
75	2591	FLIRTATIONS	ONE NIGHT OF LOVE	LOVER WHERE ARE YOU	4.00
75	2591 DJ	FLIRTATIONS	ONE NIGHT OF LOVE	LOVER WHERE ARE YOU	5.00
75	2592	CHOCOLATE MILK	ACTION SPEAKS LOUDER THAN WORDS	AIN'T NOTHING BUT A THING	8.00
75	2592 DJ	CHOCOLATE MILK	ACTION SPEAKS LOUDER THAN WORDS	AIN'T NOTHING BUT A THING	8.00
75	2596	BETTY WRIGHT	OOLA LA	TO LOVE AND BE LOVED	4.00
75	2596 DJ	BETTY WRIGHT	OOLA LA	TO LOVE AND BE LOVED	5.00
75	2605	PEARLY GATES	MAKJE IT MY BUSINESS	YOU'RE THE ONE FOR ME	6.00
75	2605 DJ	PEARLY GATES	MAKJE IT MY BUSINESS	YOU'RE THE ONE FOR ME	8.00
75	2618	BROTHERS	ARE YOU READY FOR THIS	ERVERYBODY LOVES A WINNER	30.00
75	2618 DJ	BROTHERS	ARE YOU READY FOR THIS	ERVERYBODY LOVES A WINNER	40.00
76	2626	TYMES	GOD'S GONNA PUNISH YOU	IF I CAN'T MAKE YOU SMILE	5.00
76	2626 DJ	TYMES	GOD'S GONNA PUNISH YOU	IF I CAN'T MAKE YOU SMILE	8.00
76	2651	VICKIE SUE ROBINSON	NEVER GONNA LET YOU GO	same: instrumental	4.00
76	2651 DJ	VICKIE SUE ROBINSON	NEVER GONNA LET YOU GO	same: instrumental	5.00
76	2655	BEVERLY ANN c/w EXCITERS + 1	YOU'VE GOT YOUR MIND ON OTHER THINGS BLOWING UP MY MIND + AIN'T NO SOUL		10.00
76	2655 DJ	BEVERLY ANN c/w EXCITERS + 1	YOU'VE GOT YOUR MIND ON OTHER THINGS BLOWING UP MY MIND + AIN'T NO SOUL		15.00
76	2658	TYMES	ONLY YOUR LOVE	GOIN' THROUGH THE MOTIONS	4.00
76	2658 DJ	TYMES	ONLY YOUR LOVE	GOIN' THROUGH THE MOTIONS	5.00
76	2667	SHAWNE JACKSON	GET OUT OF THE KITCHEN	DON'T WAIT FOR TOMORROW	8.00
76	2667 DJ	SHAWNE JACKSON	GET OUT OF THE KITCHEN	DON'T WAIT FOR TOMORROW	10.00
76	2668	LONNIE LITSON SMITH	A CHANCE FOR PEACE	SUNSET	5.00
76	2668 DJ	LONNIE LITSON SMITH	A CHANCE FOR PEACE	SUNSET	6.00
76	2673	VICKIE SUE ROBINSON	TURN THE BEAT AROUND	COMMON THIEF	5.00
76	2673 DJ	VICKIE SUE ROBINSON	TURN THE BEAT AROUND	COMMON THIEF	6.00
76	2688	BRENDA JONES with GROOVE	THIS IS THE ME ME (NOT THE YOU YOU)	MORNING CHILDREN	15.00
76	2688 DJ	BRENDA JONES with GROOVE	THIS IS THE ME ME (NOT THE YOU YOU)	MORNING CHILDREN	20.00
76	2718	MARTHA SMITH	OPEN UP THE YOUR HEART	GIVE ME ONE (JUST FOR FUN)	8.00
76	2718 DJ	MARTHA SMITH	OPEN UP THE YOUR HEART	GIVE ME ONE (JUST FOR FUN)	8.00
76	2719	MIKE HARPER	I'M CRYING	RIP OFF	8.00
76	2719 DJ	MIKE HARPER	I'M CRYING	RIP OFF	10.00
76	2720	GEORGE CHANDLER	ONE IN A MILLION	GAMES ARE FIOR CHILDREN	8.00
76	2720 DJ	GEORGE CHANDLER	ONE IN A MILLION	GAMES ARE FIOR CHILDREN	10.00
76	2720 PS	GEORGE CHANDLER	ONE IN A MILLION	GAMES ARE FIOR CHILDREN	10.00
76	2727	LONNIE LITSON SMITH	GET DOWN EVERYBODY	INNER BEAUTY	5.00
76	2727 DJ	LONNIE LITSON SMITH	GET DOWN EVERYBODY	INNER BEAUTY	6.00
76	2736	DR. BUZZARD'S ORIGINAL SAVANAH	I'LL PLAY THE FOOL	SUNSHOWER	5.00
76	2736 DJ	DR. BUZZARD'S ORIGINAL SAVANAH	I'LL PLAY THE FOOL	SUNSHOWER	8.00
76	2750	CHARLES DRAIN	IS THIS REALLY LOVE	ONLY YOU	10.00
76	2750 DJ	CHARLES DRAIN	IS THIS REALLY LOVE	ONLY YOU	15.00
76	2759	JACKIE MOORE	TIRED OF HIDING	DISCO BODY	4.00
76	2759 DJ	JACKIE MOORE	TIRED OF HIDING	DISCO BODY	5.00
76	2765	BETTY WRIGHT	IF I EVER DO WRONG	ROCK ON BABY, ROCK ON	4.00
76	2765 DJ	BETTY WRIGHT	IF I EVER DO WRONG	ROCK ON BABY, ROCK ON	5.00
76	2769	TYMES	I NEED YOU AND YOUR KIND OF	THE READER	4.00
76	2769 DJ	TYMES	I NEED YOU AND YOUR KIND OF	THE READER	5.00
86	49731 PS	SONYA GRIER	LOVE FLIGHT	same: dub version	10.00
77	5020	GEORGE CHANDLER	LITTLE GIRL	MAKE UP YOUR MIND	6.00
77	5020 DJ	GEORGE CHANDLER	LITTLE GIRL	MAKE UP YOUR MIND	8.00
79	5175	CLEM CURTIS	UNCHAINED MELODY	NEED YOUR LOVE	5.00
79	5175 DJ	CLEM CURTIS	UNCHAINED MELODY	NEED YOUR LOVE	6.00
63	7117 EP PS	SAM COOKE	HEART AND SOUL	1963 4 track EP with cover	40.00
64	7128 EP PS	SAM COOKE	SWING SWEETLY	1964 4 track EP with cover	45.00
64	7147 EP without cover H.B.BARNUM		THE GREAT H.B.BARNUM	Inc: IT HURTS TOO MUCH TO CRY + 3	75.00
64	7147 EP PS with cover H.B.BARNUM		THE GREAT H.B.BARNUM	Inc: IT HURTS TOO MUCH TO CRY + 3	**271.00**
64	7149 EP PS	ISLEY BROTHERS	THE ISLEY BROTHERS: EP	1963 4 track EP with cover	50.00
64	7163 EP PS	JOHNNY NASH	PRESENTING JOHNNY NASH	1964 4 track EP with cover	85.00
65	7165 EP PS	SYLVIE VARTAN	SYLVIE VARTAN	1965 4 track EP with cover	100.00
65	7166 EP PS	GWEN STACY	INTRODUCING	1965 4 track EP with cover	150.00
75	9066	CHOICE FOUR	BESIDE ME	YOU'RE MY HAPPINESS	5.00
75	9066 DJ	CHOICE FOUR	BESIDE ME	YOU'RE MY HAPPINESS	6.00
76	9116 DJ	LORRAINE FRISAURA	JIMMY MACK	IT'S REALLY ALRIGHT	5.00
76	9136 orange	MIKE McDONALD c/w DEREK & RAY	GOD KNOWS	INTERPLAY	10.00
76	9136 black	MIKE McDONALD c/w DEREK & RAY	GOD KNOWS	INTERPLAY	6.00
76	9136 DJ	MIKE McDONALD c/w DEREK & RAY	GOD KNOWS	INTERPLAY	12.00

86	9138 PS	STEVE MANCHA	IT'S ALL OVER THE GRAPEVINE	same: instrumental	4.00
77	9243	NITE-LITERS	K-JEE	TANGA BOO GONK	6.00
77	9243 DJ	NITE-LITERS	K-JEE	TANGA BOO GONK	6.00
78	9392	PEGGY MARCH	IF YOU LOVED ME	THINKING THROUGH MY TEARS	8.00
78	9392 DJ	PEGGY MARCH	IF YOU LOVED ME (SOUL COAXING)	THINKING THROUGH MY TEARS	10.00
78	9394	PAUL ANKA	I CAN'T HELP LOVING YOU	WHEN WE GET THERE	6.00
78	9394 DJ	PAUL ANKA	I CAN'T HELP LOVING YOU	WHEN WE GET THERE	8.00
79	9450	LONNIE LITSON SMITH	EXPANSIONS	A CHANCE FOR PEACE	8.00
79	9450 DJ	LONNIE LITSON SMITH	EXPANSIONS	A CHANCE FOR PEACE	10.00
80	9637	BANDA RIO BLACK	MISS CHERYL	MISS CHERYL diiferent mix	5.00
80	9637 DJ	BANDA RIO BLACK	MISS CHERYL	MISS CHERYL diiferent mix	6.00
78	11403	JAMES WALSH GYPSY BAND	CUZ IT'S YOU GIRL	BRING YOURSELF AROUND	100.00
78	11403 DJ	JAMES WALSH GYPSY BAND	CUZ IT'S YOU GIRL	BRING YOURSELF AROUND	150.00
78	41497 PS	RICK CLARKE	LOOKING OUT FOR YOU	PERFECT LADY	5.00
78	41497 DJ PS	RICK CLARKE	LOOKING OUT FOR YOU	PERFECT LADY	6.00
89	43073 PS	GINA FOSTER	LOVE IS A HOUSE remix	TAKE ME AWAY	5.00
89	43073 DJ PS	GINA FOSTER	LOVE IS A HOUSE remix	TAKE ME AWAY	6.00
89	43139 PS	SAM DEES	AFTER ALL	ALWAYS SOMETHING	6.00
89	43139 DJ PS	SAM DEES	AFTER ALL	ALWAYS SOMETHING	8.00
86	49563 PS	MERRY CLAYTON c/w FIVE SATINS	YES	IN THE STILL OF THE NIGHT	4.00
86	49563 DJ PS	MERRY CLAYTON c/w FIVE SATINS	YES	IN THE STILL OF THE NIGHT	6.00
86	49611	RUFFIN & KENDRICK	I COULDN'T BELIEVE IT	DON'T KNOW WHY YOU'RE DREAMING	10.00
86	49849	SAM COOKE	ANOTHER SATURDAY NIGHT	YOU SEND ME	5.00
86	49871	SAM COOKE	CHAIN GANG	WONDERFUL WORLD	4.00
80	9511 EP PS	SAM COOKE	SAM COOKE: ANOTHER SATURDAY	4 track EP with picture cover	6.00
91	gene 1 DJ PS	GENE RICE	IT'S TOO LATE	YOU'RE GONNA GET SERVED	10.00
87	monk 6 PS	BLOW MONKEYS with CURTIS MAYFIELD	(CELEBRATE) THE DAY AFTER YOU	BEAUTIFUL CHILD	4.00

REAL SIDE

02	101	LEONIE	SILLY LOVE GAMES	FOOL FOR YOUR LOVIN'	8.00
02	101 DJ	LEONIE	SILLY LOVE GAMES	FOOL FOR YOUR LOVIN'	10.00
04	102	JACQUI WILLIAMS	FAVOUR	blank:	6.00
04	103	LEONIE	AM I LOSING YOU	MR DREAM MAKER	5.00
04	103 DJ	LEONIE	AM I LOSING YOU	MR DREAM MAKER	6.00

RED BIRD

Pye distributed the UK Red Bird label from 1963 to 1966. All releases were USA recordings using releases from USA's Red Bird parent company's labels Blue Cat, Red Bird & Tiger: all of which are highly collectable in their own right. Legendary writers and producers Jerry Leiber and Mike Stoller formed the USA label. Specializing in the in vogue sound of girl groups and the big production big city sound of New York. From which they had a string of hits with the Ad Libs, Dixie Cups, Shangri-las etc. In the UK all three labels were released under one umbrella of the Red Bird label but Pye always used the same catalogue number of the original USA release. Hence missing numbers in the series were USA # not issued in the UK i.e. *Butterlys – "Gee Baby Gee"* was Red Bird 10016 in USA not released in the UK. Red Bird has remained one of the most attractive UK label labels with their attractive "Bird" logo. White promo copies in the same format as all the Pye distributed labels of the era, Cameo Parkway etc are particularly sought after.

64	10006	DIXIE CUPS	PEOPLE SAY	GIRLS CAN TELL	15.00
64	10006 DJ	DIXIE CUPS	PEOPLE SAY	GIRLS CAN TELL	22.00
64	10008	SHANGRI-LAS	REMEMBER (WALKIN' IN THE SAND)	IT'S EASIER TO CRY	10.00
64	10008 DJ	SHANGRI-LAS	REMEMBER (WALKIN' IN THE SAND)	IT'S EASIER TO CRY	18.00
64	10009	BUTTERFLYS	GOOD NIGHT BABY	THE SWIM	15.00
64	10009 DJ	BUTTERFLYS	GOOD NIGHT BABY	THE SWIM	22.00
64	10010	ALVIN ROBINSON	FEVER	DOWN HOME GIRL	20.00
64	10010 DJ	ALVIN ROBINSON	FEVER	DOWN HOME GIRL	28.00
64	10011	JELLY BEANS	THE KIND OF BOY YOU CAN'T FORGET	BABY BE MINE	15.00
64	10011 DJ	JELLY BEANS	THE KIND OF BOY YOU CAN'T FORGET	BABY BE MINE	22.00
64	10012	DIXIE CUPS	YOU SHOULD HAVE SEEN THE WAY HE LOOKED AT ME	NO TRUE LOVE	15.00
64	10012 DJ	DIXIE CUPS	YOU SHOULD HAVE SEEN THE WAY HE LOOKED AT ME	NO TRUE LOVE	22.00
64	10014	SHANGRI-LAS	LEADER OF THE PACK	WHAT IS LOVE	10.00
64	10014 DJ	SHANGRI-LAS	LEADER OF THE PACK	WHAT IS LOVE	20.00
64	10017	DIXIE CUPS	LITTLE BELL	ANOTHER BOY LIKE MINE	10.00
64	10017 DJ	DIXIE CUPS	LITTLE BELL	ANOTHER BOY LIKE MINE	15.00
65	10018	SHANGRI-LAS	GIVE HIM A GREAT BIG KISS	TWIST AND SHOUT	12.00
65	10018 DJ	SHANGRI-LAS	GIVE HIM A GREAT BIG KISS	TWIST AND SHOUT	22.00
65	10020	TRADE WINDS	NEW YORK IS A LONELY TOWN	CLUB SEVENTEEN	20.00
65	10020 DJ	TRADE WINDS	NEW YORK IS A LONELY TOWN	CLUB SEVENTEEN	28.00
65	10021	RODDIE JOY	COME BACK BABY	LOVE HIT ME LIKE A WALLOP	50.00
65	10021 DJ	RODDIE JOY	COME BACK BABY	LOVE HIT ME LIKE A WALLOP	70.00
65	10024	DIXIE CUPS	IKO IKO	GEE BABY GEE	10.00
65	10024 DJ	DIXIE CUPS	IKO IKO	GEE BABY GEE	25.00
65	10025	SHANGRI-LAS	OUT IN THE STREETS	THE BOY	10.00
65	10025 DJ	SHANGRI-LAS	OUT IN THE STREETS	THE BOY	20.00
65	10030	SHANGRI-LAS	HEAVEN ONLY KNOWS	GIVE US YOUR BLESSINGS	15.00
65	10030 DJ	SHANGRI-LAS	HEAVEN ONLY KNOWS	GIVE US YOUR BLESSINGS	25.00
65	10032	DIXIE CUPS	GEE THE MOON IS SHINING BRIGHT	I'M GONA GET YOU YET	15.00
65	10032 DJ	DIXIE CUPS	GEE THE MOON IS SHINING BRIGHT	I'M GONA GET YOU YET	20.00
65	10036	SHANGRI-LAS	RIGHT NOW AND NOT LATER	THE TRAIN FROM KANSAS CITY	30.00
65	10036 DJ	SHANGRI-LAS	RIGHT NOW AND NOT LATER	THE TRAIN FROM KANSAS CITY	45.00
66	10043	SHANGRI-LAS	BULL DOG	I CAN NEVER GO HOME ANYMORE	15.00
66	10043 DJ	SHANGRI-LAS	BULL DOG	I CAN NEVER GO HOME ANYMORE	28.00
66	10048	SHANGRI-LAS	LONG LIVE OUR LOVE	SOPHISTICATED BOOM BOOM	15.00

66	10048 DJ	SHANGRI-LAS	LONG LIVE OUR LOVE	SOPHISTICATED BOOM BOOM	22.00
66	10053	SHANGRI-LAS	HE CRIED	DRESSED IN BLACK	15.00
66	10053 DJ	SHANGRI-LAS	HE CRIED	DRESSED IN BLACK	22.00
66	10068	SHANGRI-LAS	PAST, PRESENT AND FUTURE	PARADISE	20.00
66	10068 DJ	SHANGRI-LAS	PAST, PRESENT AND FUTURE	PARADISE	30.00
65	40002 EP PS	SHANGRI-LAS	THE SHANGRI-LAS	1965 4 track EP with cover	100.00
64	10-102	AD LIBS	THE BOY FROM NEW YORK CITY	KICKED AROUND	30.00
64	10-102 DJ	AD LIBS	THE BOY FROM NEW YORK CITY	KICKED AROUND	45.00
64	10-106	BESSIE BANKS	GO NOW	IT SOUNDS LIKE MY BABY	50.00
64	10-106 DJ	BESSIE BANKS	GO NOW	IT SOUNDS LIKE MY BABY	85.00
65	10-118	EVIE SANDS	TAKE ME FOR A LITTLE WHILE	RUN HOME TO YOUR MAMA	40.00
65	10-118 DJ	EVIE SANDS	TAKE ME FOR A LITTLE WHILE	RUN HOME TO YOUR MAMA	60.00

The above 4 are UK Red Bird releases but using Blue Cat USA release #. Whilst one of the highlights of the label Bessie Banks – "Go Now" is usually associated with the Tiger label. It's first and ultimately rarer press was on Blue Cat 106.

RED LIGHTNIN

	450031 PS	TOMMY TUCKER	HI HEEL SNEAKERS	IS THAT THE WAY GOD PLANNED IT	6.00

RED ROOSTER

	1	KOFFIE	AND I'M TELLING YOU I'M NOT GOING	same: instrumental	6.00

REGAL ZONOPHONE

68	3010	JOHNNY NASH	HOLD ME TIGHT	LET'S MOVE AND GROOVE TOGETHER	6.00

REPLAY

	218	ROBERT PARKER	BAREFOOTIN'	LET THE GOOD TIMES ROLL / STAY	5.00

REPRISE

Reprise Records was formed in the late 1950's by the one and only Frank Sinatra, in a move to allow him more 'artistic freedom' for his own recordings. Fellow 'rat pack' members Dean Martin and Sammy Davis, Jr. followed him to the label. Reprise was sold to Warner Brothers in the early 1960's, and has been the distributor for Reprise ever since. In the 60's UK Reprise was distributed by Pye. In 1971 along with Warner Bros and Atlantic Records, Reprise was distributed in the UK by Kinney using the K matrix numbering starting with a K followed by a 1 and four other digits, these numbers were universal to cover other Kinney labels.
As far soul in the UK is concerned, the Reprise label had only a few to offer, but there are a few "sleepers" that could rise in price in the future. Mavis Rivers, Jimmy Bowen etc have yet to reach full exposure.

71	14124	LITTLE RICHARD	DANCING IN THE STREET	GREEN POWER	8.00
71	14124 DJ	LITTLE RICHARD	DANCING IN THE STREET	GREEN POWER	10.00
72	14150	LITTLE RICHARD	MONEY IS	MONEY RUNNER	5.00
72	14150 DJ	LITTLE RICHARD	MONEY IS	MONEY RUNNER	6.00
72	14195	LITTLE RICHARD	MOCKINGBIRD SALLY	ROCKIN ROCKIN BOOGIE + KING OF ROCK	4.00
72	14195 DJ	LITTLE RICHARD	MOCKINGBIRD SALLY	ROCKIN ROCKIN BOOGIE + KING OF ROCK	5.00
72	14200	TOUSSAINT	SOUL SISTER	SHE ONCE BELONGED TO ME	5.00
72	14200 DJ	TOUSSAINT	SOUL SISTER	SHE ONCE BELONGED TO ME	6.00
74	14367	METERS	PEOPLE SAY	AFRICA	8.00
74	14367 DJ	METERS	PEOPLE SAY	AFRICA	10.00
75	14405	METERS	FIRE ON THE BAYOU	THEY ALL ASK'D FOR YOU	8.00
75	14405 DJ	METERS	FIRE ON THE BAYOU	THEY ALL ASK'D FOR YOU	10.00
63	20115	MAVIS RIVERS	FOOTSTEPS OF A FOOL	SLIGHTLY OUT OF TUNE	30.00
63	20115 DJ	MAVIS RIVERS	FOOTSTEPS OF A FOOL	SLIGHTLY OUT OF TUNE	45.00
63	20198	TRINI LOPEZ	UNCHAIN MY HEART	IF I HAD A HAMMER	5.00
63	20198 DJ	TRINI LOPEZ	UNCHAIN MY HEART	IF I HAD A HAMMER	8.00
64	20227	SAMMY DAVIS JR.	IN THE SHELTER OF YOUR ARMS	FALLING IN LOVE WITH LOVE	25.00
64	20227 DJ	SAMMY DAVIS JR.	IN THE SHELTER OF YOUR ARMS	FALLING IN LOVE WITH LOVE	35.00
64	20289	SAMMY DAVIS JR.	NOT FOR ME	BAMG ! BANG !	20.00
64	20289 DJ	SAMMY DAVIS JR.	NOT FOR ME	BAMG ! BANG !	28.00
64	20291	BLENDELLS	LA LA LA LA LA LA	HUGGIES BUNNIES	20.00
64	20291 DJ	BLENDELLS	LA LA LA LA LA LA	HUGGIES BUNNIES	30.00
64	20328	TRINI LOPEZ	SAD TOMORROWS	I'VE LOST LOVE FOR YOU	10.00
64	20328 DJ	TRINI LOPEZ	SAD TOMORROWS	I'VE LOST LOVE FOR YOU	15.00
64	20340	BLENDELLS	DANCE WITH ME	GET YOUR BABY	20.00
64	20340 DJ	BLENDELLS	DANCE WITH ME	GET YOUR BABY	30.00
66	20486	MOJO MEN	HANKY PANKY	SHE'S MY BABY	20.00
66	20486 DJ	MOJO MEN	HANKY PANKY	SHE'S MY BABY	28.00
67	20606	MIRIAM MAKEBA	PATA PATA	THE BALLAD OF THE AD YOUNG MEN	5.00
67	20606 DJ	MIRIAM MAKEBA	PATA PATA	THE BALLAD OF THE AD YOUNG MEN	6.00
68	20690	DUANE EDDY	NICKI HOEKY	VELVET NIGHTS	15.00
68	20690 DJ	DUANE EDDY	NICKI HOEKY	VELVET NIGHTS	22.00
68	20696	FATS DOMINO	HONEST MAMAS LOVE PAPAS BETTER	ONE FOR THE HIGHWAY	15.00
68	20696 DJ	FATS DOMINO	HONEST MAMAS LOVE PAPAS BETTER	ONE FOR THE HIGHWAY	20.00
68	20763	FATS DOMINO	LADY MADONNA	ONE FOR THE HIGHWAY	8.00
68	20763 DJ	FATS DOMINO	LADY MADONNA	ONE FOR THE HIGHWAY	10.00
69	20810	FATS DOMINO	EVERYBODY'S GOT SOMETHING TO HIDE	SO SWELL WHEN YOU'RE WELL	8.00
69	20810 DJ	FATS DOMINO	EVERYBODY'S GOT SOMETHING TO HIDE	SO SWELL WHEN YOU'RE WELL	10.00
69	20850	ELLA FITZGERALD	GET READY	OPEN YOUR WINDOW	30.00
69	20850 DJ	ELLA FITZGERALD	GET READY	OPEN YOUR WINDOW	45.00
70	20907	LITTLE RICHARD	DEW DROP IN	FREEDOM BLUES	5.00
70	20907 DJ	LITTLE RICHARD	DEW DROP IN	FREEDOM BLUES	6.00
65	23043	JIMMY BOWEN	THE EAGLE	SPANISH CRICKET	40.00
65	23043 DJ	JIMMY BOWEN	THE GOLDEN EAGLE	SPANISH CRICKET	50.00
71	23507	ELLA FITZGERALD	I HEARD IT THROUGH THE GRAPEVINE	DAYS OF WINE & ROSES	5.00

71	23507 DJ	ELLA FITZGERALD	I HEARD IT THROUGH THE GRAPEVINE	DAYS OF WINE & ROSES		6.00
64	30038 EP PS	SAMMY DAVIS JR.	DON'T SHUT ME OUT	1964 UK 4 track EP with cover		15.00
G5	30063 EP PS	COUNT BASIE	IN OTHER WORDS	1965 UK 4 track EP with cover		8.00

RETREAT

75	264	MIKE HARPER	I'M CRYING	GOODBYE	15.00
75	264 DJ	MIKE HARPER	I'M CRYING	GOODBYE	20.00

RICE KRISPIES

All the below 7" discs were a 1975 promotion giveway's with the RICE KRISPIES cereal packs . If anybody retained an original cereal box and has a set of six expect the total value   to be £250+

75	no # 1	JACKSON 5	SUGAR DADDY	blank:	30.00
75	no # 2	JACKSON 5	GOIN' BACK TO INDIANA	blank:	30.00
75	no # 3	JACKSON 5	WHO'S LOVING YOU	blank:	30.00
75	no # 4	JACKSON 5	MAMA'S PEARL	blank:	30.00
75	no # 6	JACKSON 5	THE LOVE YOU SAVE	blank:	30.00
75	no. # 5	JACKSON 5	ABC	blank:	30.00

RIGHT ON

Soul journalist, collector and a major influence on Soul collectors Dave Godin launched this, his third UK exclusively soul label in 1975. Right On ran for almost two years, pressing seven releases in total. In that short time Dave Godin managed (as he did with his other two labels Soul City & Deep Soul) to release some 45's that would become highly collectable in the future. In those few releases the only the disco influenced songs have remained label fillers. Whilst Northern Soul classics like the Jelly Beans and The Crow have rocketed in value, particularly The Crow that has a very in-demand Deep Funk track on the flipside. His impeccable taste decided the first and only UK outing for Chris Bartley's – I See Your Name – an absolutely superb soul dance track that inexplicably never saw release in the USA. Release # 106 The Fantastic Puzzles – "Come Back" - a 1975 New York male group soul harmony band recording, is probably a jewel in the listing. Never sold in any quantities either side of the Atlantic and is now appreciated as a very hard to find of the highest quality. All three of Dave Godin's labels are now considered an essential part of any UK soul collection just like Action, Sue, Tamla Motown, all three must be bought and filed to the very last number:

Dave Godin born Lambeth, South London 21st. June 1936 sadly died 15th. October 2004 in Rotherham Yorkshire, Dave contributed more to the UK soul collector's scene than any other person involved in the music.

75	101	CROW	YOUR AUTUMN OF TOMORROW	UNCLE FUNK	30.00
75	101 DJ	CROW	YOUR AUTUMN OF TOMORROW	UNCLE FUNK	40.00
75	102	JELLY BEANS	YOU DON'T MEAN ME NO GOOD	I'M HIP TO YOU	15.00
75	102 DJ	JELLY BEANS	YOU DON'T MEAN ME NO GOOD	I'M HIP TO YOU	20.00
75	103	SAM NESBIT	KEEP ON HUSTLING BABY	same: instrumental	5.00
75	103 DJ	SAM NESBIT	KEEP ON HUSTLING BABY	same: instrumental	6.00
76	104	ROZAA & WINE	DISCO BOOGIE WOMAN	DISCO BOOGIE WOMAN part 2	4.00
76	104 DJ	ROZAA & WINE	DISCO BOOGIE WOMAN	DISCO BOOGIE WOMAN part 2	5.00
76	105	CHRIS BARTLEY	I SEE YOUR NAME	same: instrumental	8.00
76	105 DJ	CHRIS BARTLEY	I SEE YOUR NAME	same: instrumental	15.00
76	106	FANTASTIC PUZZLES	COME BACK	COME BACK part 2	40.00
76	106 DJ	FANTASTIC PUZZLES	COME BACK	COME BACK part 2	50.00
76	107	SANDRA PHILLIPS	WE GOT LOVE	WE GOT LOVE adult version	6.00
76	107 DJ	SANDRA PHILLIPS	WE GOT LOVE	WE GOT LOVE adult version	8.00

RISE RECORDS

86	1	COGNAC	DON'T BOTHER TO KNOCK	same: instrumental	5.00

RIVERSIDE

UK Philips release a few interesting and desirable 45's from this worldwide and highly respected jazz and blues catalogue.

60	3202 EP PS	JOHN LEE HOOKER	WEDNESDAY EVENIN'	1960 4 track EP with cover inc: no more doggin + 3	25.00
60	3207 EP PS	JOHN LEE HOOKER	DEMOCRAT MAN	1960 4 track EP with cover inc	25.00
63	106902	STAPLE SINGERS	HAMMER AND NAILS	GLORY LAND	10.00
63	106908	MARK MURPHY	WHY DON'T YOU DO RIGHT (GET ME	FLY ME TO THE MOON	100.00
63	106909	MONGO SANTAMARIA	WATERMELON MAN	DON'T BOTHER ME NO MORE	30.00

RIVERSIDE

76	100 DJ	CLEM CURTIS & the FOUNDATIONS	MAKE A WISH	AMANDA	4.00

RK

78	1004	VARIOUS ARTISTS	THREE BEFORE EIGHT	LONG AFTER TONIGHT IS ALL OVER	15.00
78	1004 PS	VARIOUS ARTISTS	TIME WILL PASS YOU BY + I'M ON MY	LONG AFTER TONIGHT IS ALL OVER	25.00

This now legendary 3 track EP of Wigan Casino's last three records to be played every week on one disc: Three recording on this 45 are 1. Tobi Legend – "Time Will Pass You By"
2. Jimmy Radcliffe – "Long After Tonight Is All Over" 3. Dean Parrish – "I'm on my way" First original presses were released in an art picture sleeve of the Wigan Casino All Niter logo. This sleeve is now very difficult to find in excellent condition. Add extra to the value if the sleeve & disc are mint. Most sleeves were discarded upon purchase:

78	1005	WILD HONEY	AT THE TOP OF THE STAIRS	AT THE TOP OF THE STAIRS part 2	6.00
78	1005	WILD HONEY	AT THE TOP OF THE STAIRS	AT THE TOP OF THE STAIRS part 2	6.00
79	1012	TOMMY HUNT	STOP THE BUS	SUSANNA BABY	4.00
79	1012 DJ	TOMMY HUNT	STOP THE BUS	SUSANNA BABY	5.00

ROCKET RECORD CO.

75	17	DONNY GERRARD	BABY DON'T LET IT MESS YOUR MIND	A WOMAN, A LOVER, A FRIEND	4.00
75	17 DJ	DONNY GERRARD	BABY DON'T LET IT MESS YOUR MIND	A WOMAN, A LOVER, A FRIEND	4.00

ROCKFIELD

75	7	CHUCK BEDFORD	RAY OF SUNSHINE	HAVE YOU TRIED LOVE	6.00

ROKEL

80	13	JIMMY SENYAH	WEAKNESS FOR YOUR SWEETNESS	same: instrumental	6.00

ROOSTER

69	707 EP	MAGIC SAM	MEAN MISTREATER	4 track EP	10.00

ROULETTE

68	500	JAMES, TOMMY & the SHONDELLS	SOMEBODY CARES	DO SOMETHING FOR ME	10.00
68	501	RICARDO RAY	NITTY GRITTY	MONY MONY	20.00
69	503	BRENDA JO HARRIS	PLAY WITH FIRE (AND YOU'LL GET	I CAN REMEMBER	15.00
69	504	SHADOW MANN	COME LIVE WITH ME	ONE BY ONE	25.00
69	505	ESTHER PHILIPS	TOO LATE TO WORRY, TOO BLUE TO CRY	I'M IN THE MOOD FOR LOVE	8.00
69	508	ESTHER PHILIPS	TONIGHT I'LL BE STAYING HERE WITH	SWEET DREAMS	6.00
69	509	FREDDIE SCOTT	SUGAR SUNDAY	JOHNNY'S HILL	6.00
69	510	LITTLE JIMMY GANDY	COOL THIRTEEN	I'M NOT LIKE THE OTHERS	25.00
69	514	CHANTELS	MAYBE	HE'S GONE	6.00
69	515	GERALDINE HUNT	NEVER NEVER LEAVE ME	PUSH SWEEP	20.00
66	7001	DAVE BABY CORTEZ	COUNTDOWN	SUMMERTIME	10.00

ROUTE

Launched in 1975 and distributed by Pye Records from ATV House. Route released an interesting handful of soul and soul related 45's. With five Northern Soul classics emerging from it's catalogue during the scenes peak in 1975. All these releases are becoming increasingly difficult to find, with the promo copies of the Northern Soul releases being particularly desirable. Route promo copies have the release date (20.6.75 in the case of Route 09) top left hand side of the label and a bold A sitting over the catalogue release number on the right hand side. Route was a short- lived label, as far as soul releases were concerned, it only lasted for 12 months.

75	06	HAROLD MELVIN & the BLUE NOTES	GET OUT (AND LET ME CRY)	YOU MAY NOT LOVE ME	10.00
75	06 DJ	HAROLD MELVIN & the BLUE NOTES	GET OUT (AND LET ME CRY)	YOU MAY NOT LOVE ME	15.00
75	09	JANINE DEXTER	I LOVE MAKING LOVE TO YOU	COME ON CLOSER TO ME	10.00
75	09 DJ	JANINE DEXTER	I LOVE MAKING LOVE TO YOU	COME ON CLOSER TO ME	15.00
75	10	SMOKEY & the FABULOUS	JERK, BABY JERK	CHARLIE'S THEME Part2	8.00
75	10 DJ	SMOKEY & the FABULOUS	JERK, BABY JERK	CHARLIE'S THEME	15.00
75	11	LENIS GUESS	JUST ASK ME	WORKIN' FOR MY BABY	8.00
75	11 DJ	LENIS GUESS	JUST ASK ME	WORKIN' FOR MY BABY	15.00
75	12	BOB & HONEY BEE	IF I EVER NEEDED YOU	same: instrumental	5.00
75	12 DJ	BOB & HONEY BEE	IF I EVER NEEDED YOU	same: instrumental	6.00
75	13	SHEILA ANTHONY	LIVIN' IN LOVE	WOMAN TO WOMAN	8.00
75	13 DJ	SHEILA ANTHONY	LIVIN' IN LOVE	WOMAN TO WOMAN	15.00
75	16	KEVIN KING LEAR	YOU GOT) THE POWER OF LOVE	MR. PEARLY	8.00
75	16 DJ	KEVIN KING LEAR	(YOU GOT) THE POWER OF LOVE	MR. PEARLY	12.00
75	19	DEZRO ORCHESTRA	WITCHUNT	REFLECTIONS (SUMMER '75)	8.00
75	19 DJ	DEZRO ORCHESTRA	WITCHUNT	REFLECTIONS (SUMMER '75)	10.00
75	20	JUDY GEE & the CLASSMATES	NINETY-NINE WAYS	LET ME IN	6.00
75	20 DJ	JUDY GEE & the CLASSMATES	NINETY - NINE WAYS	LET ME IN	10.00
75	26	L.J. WAITERS & the ELECTRIFIERS	IF YOU AIN'T GETTING YOUR THING	same: part 2	8.00
75	26 DJ	L.J. WAITERS & the ELECTRIFIERS	IF YOU AIN'T GETTING YOUR THING	same: part 2	10.00
75	30	MISTURA feat. LLOYD MICHAELS	THE FLASHER	LIFE IS A SONG WORTH SINGING	8.00
75	30 DJ	MISTURA feat. LLOYD MICHAELS	THE FLASHER	LIFE IS A SONG WORTH SINGING	10.00

RSO

74	2090140	FREDDIE KING	SHAKE YOUR BOOTY	PACK IT UP	4.00
75	2090167	REVELATION	GET READY FOR THIS	WHERE IT'S WARM	6.00
75	2090236	YVONNE ELLIMAN	HELLO STRANGER	GOOD SIGN	6.00
80	2090459	JIMMY RUFFIN	NIGHT OF LOVE	SONGBIRD	4.00
79	28	CURTIS MAYFIELD	THIS YEAR	same: instrumental	5.00
79	30	LINDA CLIFFORD	BRIDGE OVER TROUBLED WATER	HOLD ME CLOSE	4.00
79	37	LINDA CLIFFORD	DON'T GIVE IT UP	DON'T LET ME HAVE ANOTHER BAD NIGHT	4.00
79	43	CURTIS MAYFIELD & LINDA CLIFFORD	BETWEEN YOU BABY AND ME	YOU'RE SO GOOD TO ME	5.00
80	57	JIMMY RUFFIN	HOLD ON TO MY LOVE	same: instrumental	5.00
80	64	LINDA CLIFFORD	RED LIGHT	RALPH AND MONTY	4.00
80	67	FRED WESLEY & the J.B'S	HOUSE PARTY	I MAKE MUSIC	6.00
80	68	CURTIS MAYFIELD	IT'S ALRIGHT	SUPERFLY	5.00
80	69	LINDA CLIFFORD	SHOOT YOUR BEST SHOT	IF YOU LEFT ME	4.00
82	89	FOUR TOPS	BACK TO SCHOOL AGAIN	ROCK A HULA LUAU	3.00

S.C.S.C.

98	1	JOHNNY ROBINSON c/w SIDNEY JOE QUALLS	GONE BUT NOT FORGOTTEN	I DON'T DO THIS	25.00
99	2	RINGLEADERS c/w PURPLE MUNDI	ALL OF MY LIFE	STOP HURTING ME BABY	20.00
00	3	KENNY WELLS c/w CHANNEL 3	ISN'T IT JUST A SHAME	THE SWEETEST THING	15.00

S.W.O.N.S

All the below 45's are Ian Levine productions SWONS stands for The Strange World Of Northern Soul

00	1	TAMMI LAVETTE	YOU TORE APART MY HEART	same: instrumental	4.00
00	1	WATTS 103rd. STREET STRINGS	SOUL A GO GO	WEST COAST SHING A LING	5.00
00	1 PS	CHUCK JACKSON c/w EDDIE HOLMAN	ALL OVER THE WORLD	WHAT EVER HAPPENED TO OUR MELO	6.00
00	twirl 1	ROCQ-E HARRELL	MY HEART KEEPS BEATING FASTER	same: instrumental	6.00

SAFARI

76	1102	DOYLEY BROTHERS	SCAREDY CAT	LITTLE SMILE	8.00

SALSOUL

78	101	CHARO and the SALSOUL	DANCE A LITTLE BIT CLOSER	CUCHI-CUCHI	4.00
78	101 DJ	CHARO and the SALSOUL	DANCE A LITTLE BIT CLOSER	CUCHI-CUCHI	5.00
78	102	BUNNY SIGLER	LET ME PARTY WITH YOU	LET ME PARTY WITH YOU part 2	4.00

78	102 DJ	BUNNY SIGLER	LET ME PARTY WITH YOU	LET ME PARTY WITH YOU part 2	5.00
78	103	ANTHONY WHITE	I CAN'T TURN YOU LOSE	BLOCK PARTY	8.00
78	103 DJ	ANTHONY WHITE	I CAN'T TURN YOU LOSE	BLOCK PARTY	10.00
78	104	FIRST CHOICE	DOCTOR LOVE	I LOVE YOU MORE THAN BEFORE	4.00
78	104 DJ	FIRST CHOICE	DOCTOR LOVE	I LOVE YOU MORE THAN BEFORE	6.00
78	105	RIPPLE	FACTS OF LIFE	THE BEATS GOES ON AND ON	6.00
78	105 DJ	RIPPLE	FACTS OF LIFE	THE BEATS GOES ON AND ON	8.00
84	sal 105	LOLEATTA HOLLOWAY	LOVE SENSATION	HIT AND RUN	6.00
78	106	O.R.S.	MOON BOOTS	MOON BOOTS part 2	4.00
78	106 DJ	O.R.S.	MOON BOOTS	MOON BOOTS part 2	5.00
78	107	METROPLOLIS	I LOVE NEW YORK	same: instrumental	4.00
78	107 DJ	METROPLOLIS	I LOVE NEW YORK	same: instrumental	5.00
78	108	LOLEATTA HOLLOWAY	HIT AND RUN	IS IT JUST A MANS WAY	8.00
78	108 DJ	LOLEATTA HOLLOWAY	HIT AND RUN	IS IT JUST A MANS WAY	10.00
78	109	LOVE COMMITTEE	LAW AND ORDER	WHERE WILL IT END	6.00
78	109 DJ	LOVE COMMITTEE	LAW AND ORDER	WHERE WILL IT END	8.00
78	110	CHARO and the SALSOUL	YOU'RE JUST THE RIGHT SIZE	SPEEDY GONZALES	4.00
78	110 DJ	CHARO and the SALSOUL	YOU'RE JUST THE RIGHT SIZE	SPEEDY GONZALES	5.00
78	111	LOLEATTA HOLLOWAY & BUNNY SIGLER	YOU LIGHT UP MY LIFE	ONLY YOU	4.00
78	111 DJ	LOLEATTA HOLLOWAY & BUNNY SIGLER	YOU LIGHT UP MY LIFE	ONLY YOU	5.00
78	112	METROPOLIS	THE GREATEST SHOW ON EARTH	NEW YORK IS MY KIND OF TOWN	4.00
78	112 DJ	METROPOLIS	THE GREATEST SHOW ON EARTH	NEW YORK IS MY KIND OF TOWN	5.00
78	113	SALSOUL ORCHESTRA	LITTLE DRUMMER BOY	MERRY CHRISTMAS ALL	4.00
78	113 DJ	SALSOUL ORCHESTRA	LITTLE DRUMMER BOY	MERRY CHRISTMAS ALL	5.00
79	114	INSTANT FUNK	GOT MY MIND MADE UP	WIDE WORLD OF SPORTS	5.00
79	114 DJ	INSTANT FUNK	GOT MY MIND MADE UP	WIDE WORLD OF SPORTS	6.00
79	115	FIRST CHOICE	HOLD YOUR HORSES	NOW THAT YOU'VE THROWN IT ALL AWAY	5.00
79	115 DJ	FIRST CHOICE	HOLD YOUR HORSES	NOW THAT YOU'VE THROWN IT ALL AWAY	6.00
79	116	GAZ	SING SING	THE GOOD THE BAD AND THE UGLY	4.00
79	116 DJ	GAZ	SING SING	THE GOOD THE BAD AND THE UGLY	6.00
79	117	BUNNY SIGLER	BY THE WAY YOU DANCE	DON'T EVEN TRY (GIVE UP)	5.00
79	117 DJ	BUNNY SIGLER	BY THE WAY YOU DANCE	DON'T EVEN TRY (GIVE UP)	6.00
79	118	INSTANT FUNK	CRYING	DARK VADER	5.00
79	118 DJ	INSTANT FUNK	CRYING	DARK VADER	6.00
79	119	SKYY	FIRST TIME AROUND	DISCO DANCIN'	5.00
79	119 DJ	SKYY	FIRST TIME AROUND	DISCO DANCIN'	6.00
79	120 DJ	DOUBLE EXPOSURE	TEN PERCENT	I GOT THE HOTS FOR YA	8.00
79	120 DJ	DOUBLE EXPOSURE	TEN PERCENT	I GOT THE HOTS FOR YA	10.00
76	2011	SALSOUL ORCHESTRA	NICE N' NASTY	NIGHT CRAWLER	4.00
76	2011 DJ	SALSOUL ORCHESTRA	NICE N' NASTY	NIGHT CRAWLER	5.00
76	2013	DOUBLE EXPOSURE	GONNA GIVE MY LOVE AWAY	TEN PERCENT	8.00
76	2013 DJ	DOUBLE EXPOSURE	GONNA GIVE MY LOVE AWAY	TEN PERCENT	10.00
76	2015	SALSOUL ORCHESTRA	LITTLE DRUMMER BOY	CHRISTMAS MEDLEY	4.00
76	2015 DJ	SALSOUL ORCHESTRA	LITTLE DRUMMER BOY	CHRISTMAS MEDLEY	5.00
76	2017	SALSOUL ORCHESTRA	SALSOUL 3001	STANDING AND WAITING ON LOVE	4.00
76	2017 DJ	SALSOUL ORCHESTRA	SALSOUL 3001	STANDING AND WAITING ON LOVE	5.00
77	2021	CAROL WILLIAMS	LOVE IS YOU	JUST FEEL	5.00
77	2021 DJ	CAROL WILLIAMS	LOVE IS YOU	JUST FEEL	6.00
77	2022	LOLEATTA HOLLOWAY	DREAMIN'	IS IT JUST A MAN'S WAY	6.00
77	2022 DJ	LOLEATTA HOLLOWAY	DREAMIN'	IS IT JUST A MAN'S WAY	8.00
77	2025	MOMENT OF TRUTH	YOU GOT ME HUMMIN'	AT LONG LAST	4.00
77	2025	MOMENT OF TRUTH	YOU GOT ME HUMMIN'	AT LONG LAST	5.00
77	2026	EDDIE HOLMAN	TIME WILL TELL	THIS WILL BE A NIGHT TO REMEMB	15.00
77	2026 DJ	EDDIE HOLMAN	TIME WILL TELL	THIS COULD BE A NIGHT TO REME	20.00

SANTA PONSA

Subsiduary of and distributed by Pye. At the end of 1974 Pye replaced this label with Route.

73	4	GUY DARRELL	I'VE BEEN HURT	BLESSED	6.00
73	4 DJ	GUY DARRELL	I'VE BEEN HURT	BLESSED	8.00
74	14	ETTA THOMAS	JUST ASK ME	NINETY NINE WAYS	6.00
74	14 DJ	ETTA THOMAS	JUST ASK ME	NINETY NINE WAYS	6.00
74	19	GUY DARRELL	YOU'RE READY NOW	TURN TO ME	6.00
74	19 DJ	GUY DARRELL	YOU'RE READY NOW	TURN TO ME	8.00

SATRIL

73	8	RASTAFARI	FUNKY CITY	IN THE GARDEN	15.00

SERIOUS RECORDS

70	US1 PS	DARLEEN DAVIS	I FOUND LOVE	same: instrumental	8.00
70	US3	FIRST CHOICE	LET ME DOWN EASY	LET NO MAN PUT ASUNDER	6.00

SEVEN SUN

72	2	WATSON T. BROWNE	WHAT CAN I DO	SOMEBODY'S CHANGING MY SWEET BABY'S	15.00
72	2 DJ	WATSON T. BROWNE	WHAT CAN I DO	SOMEBODY'S CHANGING MY SWEET BABY'S	15.00
73	4	BLACK VELVET	CAN YOU FEEL IT	GROOVE ALONG	10.00
73	4 DJ	BLACK VELVET	CAN YOU FEEL IT	GROOVE ALONG	15.00

SEVENS

Part of Goldmine/Soul Supply Ltd. This label released rare Northern Soul and a few previously unissued tracks from their acquired "Groovesville" catalogue. The label concentrated on giving value for money by doing all releases as back to back "A-sides" During the 60 releases listed, it changed it's label design or colour 5 times, due to repressing of the more popular titles there are some releases on several different designs. To understand what label design refers to the first press of each release, we have listed the label changes before each number. Different designs that fall into these divided areas we presume are second presses. We can't definitely say if there is no "crossover" labeling, that occurs with so many labels. Although this label released some highly sought after recordings it is unlikely to become the next Grapevine in years to come, as availability is widespread.

	Number	Artist	Side A	Side B	Price
	0001 DJ	MELVIN DAVIS and STEVE MANCHA I	NEED MY BABY	HIT AND RUN (Pat Lewis)	10.00
	0002 DJ	SAM DEES c/w SAM FLETCHER	LONELY FOR YOU BABY	I'D THINK IT OVER	10.00
	0003 DJ	BOBBY HUTTON c/w LOU PRIDE	LEND A HAND	I'M COMUN' HOME IN THE MORNUN'	15.00

First label design is Blue left hand side, left blue right hand side, this design runs to # 26.

	Number	Artist	Side A	Side B	Price
	1	JIMMY RADCLIFFE c/w TOBI LEGEND	LONG AFTER TONIGHT IS ALL OVER	TIME WILL PASS U BY/I'M ON MY	6.00
	1 DJ	PAT LEWIS c/w MELVIN DAVIS	HIT AND RUN	I NEED MY BABY	10.00
	2	FRANK BEVERLY c/w EDDIE FOSTER	IF THAT'S WHAT YOU WANTED	I NEVER KNEW	5.00
	3	ANDERSON BROS c/w MEL BRITT	I CAN SEE HIM LOVING YOU	SHE'LL COME RUNNING BACK	8.00
	4	EDDIE HOLMAN and the LARKS	WHERE I'M NOT WANTED	YOU NEED LOVE	6.00
	5	ROSE BATISTE c/w GEORGE LEMONS	HIT AND RUN	FASCINATING GIRL	8.00
	6	J.J. BARNES c/w DARRELL BANKS	OUR LOVE IS IN THE POCKET	OPEN THE DOOR TO YOUR HEART	6.00
	7	DOBIE GRAY c/w AL WILSON	OUT ON THE FLOOR	THE SNAKE	5.00
	8	JIMMY SOUL CLARK c/w DYNAMICS	I'LL BE YOUR CHAMPION	YES I LOVE YOU BABY	6.00
	9	CHAPTER FIVE	YOU CAN'T MEAN IT	ONE IN A MILLION	6.00
	10	RUBY ANDREWS c/w JAMES FOUNTAIN	JUST LOVING YOU	SEVEN DAY LOVER	6.00
	11	MAJESTICS c/w EPITOME OF SOUND	I LOVE HER SO MUCH IT HURTS	YOU DON'T LOVE ME	8.00
	12	GWEN OWENS c/w ANDREA HENRY	I NEED YOU LIKE A BABY	JUST SAY YOU'RE WANTED & NEEDE	6.00
	13	DAYBREAK c/w BILLY WOODS	EVERYTHING MAN	LET ME MAKE YOU HAPPY	8.00
	14	L. ALLEN c/w HERB WARD	CAN WE TALK IT OVER	STRANGE CHANGE	6.00
	15	MELVIN DAVIS c/w JOHNNY HAMPTON	FIND A QUIET PLACE	NOT MY GIRL	6.00
	16	PEOPLES CHOICE c/w JIMMY MACK	SAVE MY LOVIN' FOR YOU	MY WORLD IS ON FIRE	6.00
	17	DAYBREAK c/w VOICES OF EAST HARLEM	I NEED LOVE	CASHING IN	6.00
	18	JIMMY McFARLAND c/w KURT HARRIS	LONELY LOVER	EMPEROR OF MY BABY'S HEART	6.00
	19	JEWEL AKENS c/w CONSTELLATIONS	MY FIRST LONELY NIGHT	I DIDN'T KNOW HOW TO	6.00
	20	TEMPOS c/w FREDDIE CHAVEZ	(COUNTDOWN) HERE I COME	THEY'LL NEVER KNOW WHY	6.00
	21	DARRELL BANKS	I'M THE ONE WHO LOVES YOU	HARDER YOU LOVE	8.00
	22	PARLIMENTS c/w BOB & FRED	HEART TROUBLE	I'LL BE ON MY WAY	6.00
97	23	L.V. JOHNSON c/w EDWIN STARR	RECIPE	YOU'RE MY MELLOW	6.00
	24	JON and the WEIRDEST	CAN'T GET OVER THESE MEMORIES	NOT TIME	10.00
	25	ERNEST MOSELY c/w SHEPPARDS	STUBBORN HEART	HOW DO YOU LIKE IT	6.00

label colours changes from blue / light blue to Green / light green with the same design

	Number	Artist	Side A	Side B	Price
	26	INNERSECTION c/w WILL COLLINS	LET ME LOVE YUH	IS THERE ANYTHING I CAN DO	6.00
	27	SALVADORS c/w MICKIE CHAMPION	STICK BY ME BABY	WHAT GOOD AM I	6.00
	28	PARIS c/w ARIN DEMAIN	SLEEPLESS NIGHTS	SILENT TREATMENT	6.00
	28 DJ	ARIN DEMAIN c/w PARIS	SILENT TREATMENT	SLEEPLESS NIGHTS	15.00
	29	RONNIE McNEIR c/w DETROIT EXCUTIVES	SITTIN' IN MY CLASS	COOL OFF	6.00
98	30	LEWIS, DIANE c/w J.J.BARNES	KEEP A HOLD ON ME	SWEET HONEY BABY	6.00
	31	CAPITALS c/w CELESTE HARDIE	I CAN'T DENY THAT I LOVE YOU	YOU'RE GONE	6.00
	32	LUTHER INGRAM	IF IT'S ALL THE SAME TO YOU BABE	EXUS TREK	6.00

complete label change of both colour and design. Top half of the label is brown bottom half light brown

	Number	Artist	Side A	Side B	Price
	33	ANTIQUES c/w UTOPIAS	GO FOR YOURSELF	GIRLS ARE AGAINST ME	6.00
	33 DJ	ANTIQUES c/w UTOPIAS	GO FOR YOURSELF	GIRLS ARE AGAINST ME	10.00
	34	SILHOUETTES c/w JAMES BOUNTY	NOT ME BABY	PROVE YOURSELF A LADY	6.00
	35	CAROL ANDERSON c/w VELVET HAMMER	SAD GIRL	HAPPY	6.00
	36	JOANN COURCEY c/w BOBBY SMITH	I GOT THE POWER	WALK ON INTO MY HEART	6.00
	37	FLEMONS, WADE c/w HANK JACOBS	JEANETTE	ELIJAH ROCKIN' WITH SOUL	8.00
	38	EMPIRES c/w DELITES	YOU'RE ON TOP GIRL	LOVER	6.00
	39	DANNY WOODS c/w TOKAYS	YOU HAD ME FOOLED	BABY BABY BABY	6.00
	40	DEL-LARKS	JOB OPENING	JOB OPENING PART 2	6.00
	41	PATTI & THE EMBLEMS c/w ANN BYERS	I'M GONNA LOVE YOU A LONG LONG	I'M HAPPY WITHOUT YOU	8.00
	41 test press	PATTI & THE EMBLEMS c/w ANN BYERS	I'M GONNA LOVE YOU A LONG LONG	I'M HAPPY WITHOUT YOU	10.00
	42	PROFILES c/w GEORGE SMITH	TAKE A GIANT STEP	I'VE HAD IT	6.00
	43	AL WILLIAMS c/w ROYAL PLAYBOYS	I AM NOTHING	ARABIA	6.00
	44	STANLEY MITCHELL c/w TONY HESTER	GET IT BABY	DOWN IN THE DUMPS	6.00
	44 test press	STANLEY MITCHELL c/w TONY HESTER	GET IT BABY	DOWN IN THE DUMPS	10.00
	45	HONEY & THE BEES	BE YOURSELF	TWO CAN PLAY THE SAME GAME	6.00

another label change left hand side left hand side dark blue with GOLDMINE in orange lettering. Right hand side is orange with SEVENS in white letters.

	Number	Artist	Side A	Side B	Price
	46	SUPERLATIVES c/w ROBBY LAWSON	I STILL LOVE YOU	BURNING SENSATION	6.00
	47	JUDY STREET c/w THE SHERRYS	WHAT	PUT YOUR ARMS AROUND ME	6.00
	48	GENE CHANDLER	MR. BIG SHOT	I CAN TAKE CARE OF MYSELF	6.00
	48 test press	GENE CHANDLER	MR. BIG SHOT	I CAN TAKE CARE OF MYSELF	10.00
	49	CHECKERBOARD SQUARES c/w CONNIE CLARK	DOUBLE COOKIN'	MY SUGAR BABY	6.00
	50	ROMONA COLLINS c/w MARTHA STARR	YOU'VE BEEN CHEATIN'	NO PART TIME LOVE FOR ME	6.00

Ref: Romona Collins most of the instrumental intro of the USA release is missing on this UK press.

	Number	Artist	Side A	Side B	Price
	51	VIVIAN CARROLL	OH YEAH YEAH YEAH	same: instrumental	6.00
	52	EXITS c/w BROTHERS GUIDING LIGHT	ANOTHER SUNDOWN IN WATTS	GETTING TOGETHER	6.00
	53	LONNIE LESTER	YOU CAN'T GO	I NEED MY BABY instrumental	6.00
	54	PATRINELLE STATEN.c/w DEBONAIRES	LITTLE LOVE AFFAIR	LOVING YOU TAKES ALL OF MY TIME	6.00
02	55	FOUR VANDALS	THE WRONG SIDE OF TOWN	ONE PICTURE IS WORTH A THOUSAND WORDS	6.00
	55 test press	FOUR VANDALS	WRONG SIDE OF TOWN	ONE PICTURE IS WORTH A THOUSAND WORDS	8.00

Confusingly the label design reverts back to the "Top half of the label is brown bottom half light brown"

	56	HARVEY & JOKERS c/w VENETIA WILSON	SOUL SOUND	THIS TIME I'M LOVING YOU	6.00
	57	JOHN BOWIE c/w NOMADS	YOU'RE GONNA MISS A GOOD THING	SOMETHING'S BAD	6.00
	58	FOUR TRACKS c/w FOUR VOICES	LIKE MY LOVE FOR YOU	WITH A LONELY HEART	6.00
	59	A.C. REED c/w INSPIRATIONS	MY BABY'S BEEN CHEATING (I KNOW)	YOUR WISH IS COMMAND	6.00
	60	JEANNIE TRACY c/w TOMMY NEAL	MAKING NEW FRIENDS	GOING TO A HAPPENING	5.00
97	T-2 DJ	JOHNNY TAYLOR c/w L.V. JOHNSON	LOVE ON A LEASE PLAN	GOT TO GET RID OF YOU	15.00

SEVILLE

Distributed in the UK by President Records, this disco orientated New York based label launched its UK label, with a Blackpool Mecca current play by Snoopy Dean. "Shake and Bump" which immediately brought the label to the attentions of the UK soul collectors. Although most of the releases are aimed at the disco market, there are a few highlights that amongst it's listing. Dooley Silverspoon is better know to soul enthusiasts as Little Dooley who had 7 releases on the label. Little Dooley has always been a collectable artist, particularly his 60's work with Johnny Baylor. Born in South Carolina in 1946, he started his professional career in 1952 working the gospel circuit with such legends as Five Blind Boys Of Alabama, Gospelaires etc. His touring took him to New York and at the age of 13 he settled there. In the Big Apple he recorded four highly sought after records with his group the Fabulous Tears on the Baylor & Koko labels. With other recordings for Red Ruby and North Bay he eventually ended up under the management of Sonny Cassella at Cotton Records, New York. Cassella wrote and produced his best know Northern Soul 45 "Game Players" which was introduced to the UK All Niter crowds at the famous Cleepthorpes Pier in 1975 played off the import Seville LP. Which was released in the UK in 1975 and the 45 soon followed. An interesting and mostly overlooked label.

75	1000	SNOOPY DEAN	SHAKE N' BUMP	SHAKE N' BUMP part 2	6.00
75	1000 DJ	SNOOPY DEAN	SHAKE N' BUMP	SHAKE N' BUMP part 2	8.00
75	1001	SMOKEY 007	NEVER ENDING SONG OF LOVE	GOOD OLD SONG	3.00
75	1001 DJ	SMOKEY 007	NEVER ENDING SONG OF LOVE	GOOD OLD SONG	4.00
75	1002	DOOLEY SILVERSPOON	BUMP ME BABY	BUMP ME BABY part 2	4.00
75	1002 DJ	DOOLEY SILVERSPOON	BUMP ME BABY	BUMP ME BABY part 2	5.00
75	1003	BOBBY BYRD	BACK FROM THE DEAD	THE WAY TO GET DOWN	6.00
75	1003 DJ	BOBBY BYRD	BACK FROM THE DEAD	THE WAY TO GET DOWN	8.00
75	1004	BLACK STASH	MIGHTY LOVE MAN PART 1	MIGHTY LOVE MAN PART2	8.00
75	1004 DJ	BLACK STASH	MIGHTY LOVE MAN PART 1	MIGHTY LOVE MAN PART2	10.00
75	1005	BOBBY BYRD	HEADQUARTERS	same: instrumental	6.00
75	1005 DJ	BOBBY BYRD	HEADQUARTERS	same: instrumental	8.00
75	1006	SNOOPY DEAN	STEPPIN' OUT	LADY, LADY, LADY	4.00
75	1006 DJ	SNOOPY DEAN	STEPPIN' OUT	LADY, LADY, LADY	6.00
75	1007	FUNKY PARTY BAND	CHOCOLATE AND VANILLA	FUNKY JAM	4.00
75	1007 DJ	FUNKY PARTY BAND	CHOCOLATE AND VANILLA	FUNKY JAM	5.00
75	1008	unissued?			
75	1009	RAINY DAYS	ANYTHING I WOULD DO FOR YOU	PARTY	4.00
75	1009 DJ	RAINY DAYS	ANYTHING I WOULD DO FOR YOU	PARTY	5.00
75	1010	JEANNIE BURTON	NOBODY LOVES ME LIKE YOU DO	NOBODY LOVES ME LIKE YOU DO part 2	5.00
75	1010 DJ	JEANNIE BURTON	NOBODY LOVES ME LIKE YOU DO	NOBODY LOVES ME LIKE YOU DO part 2	6.00
75	1011	BLACK ROCK	NEW YORK CITY BUMP	NEW YORK CITY BUMP part 2	4.00
75	1011 DJ	BLACK ROCK	NEW YORK CITY BUMP	NEW YORK CITY BUMP part 2	4.00
75	1012	BLACK STASH	MR. SADNESS	I'LL PROVIDE	4.00
75	1012 DJ	BLACK STASH	MR. SADNESS	I'LL PROVIDE	5.00
75	1013	unissued?			
76	1014	GEORGE FLAME	WHERE DID YOUR LOVE COME FROM	YOU'RE GONE	10.00
76	1014 DJ	GEORGE FLAME	WHERE DID YOUR LOVE COME FROM	YOU'RE GONE	15.00
76	1016	DEBRA ANDERSON	WHERE DO WE GO FROM HERE	I CAN SEE LEAVING IN YOUR EYES	6.00
76	1016 DJ	DEBRA ANDERSON	WHERE DO WE GO FROM HERE	I CAN SEE LEAVING IN YOUR EYES	8.00
76	1017	JEANNIE BURTON & DOOLEY SILVERSPOON	AMERICAN MUSIC	AMERICAN MUSIC part 2	4.00
76	1017 DJ	JEANNIE BURTON & DOOLEY SILVERSPOON	AMERICAN MUSIC	AMERICAN MUSIC part 2	5.00
76	1018	LITTLE MILTON	FRIEND OF MINE	same; instrumental	4.00
76	1018 DJ	LITTLE MILTON	FRIEND OF MINE	same; instrumental	5.00
76	1019	ERNIE MARESCA	SHOUT SHOUT	CRYING LIKE A BABY OVER YOU	3.00
76	1019 DJ	ERNIE MARESCA	SHOUT SHOUT	CRYING LIKE A BABY OVER YOU	4.00
76	1020	DOOLEY SILVERSPOON	LET ME BE THE NO. 1 (LOVE OF YOUR LIFE)	LET ME BE THE NO. 1 (LOVE OF YOUR LIFE) part 2	4.00
76	1020 DJ	DOOLEY SILVERSPOON	LET ME BE THE NO. 1 (LOVE OF YOUR LIFE)	LET ME BE THE NO. 1 (LOVE OF YOUR LIFE) part 2	5.00
76	1021	T-CONNECTION	DISCO MAGIC	MONDAY MORNING	4.00
76	1021 DJ	T-CONNECTION	DISCO MAGIC	MONDAY MORNING	5.00
76	1022	DOOLEY SILVERSPOON	GAME PLAYERS	BELIEVE IN ME	10.00
76	1022 DJ	DOOLEY SILVERSPOON	GAME PLAYERS	BELIEVE IN ME	15.00
76	1023	DOOLEY SILVERSPOON	WHAT IN THE WORLD	BUILDING MY WORLD AROUND YOUQ	6.00
76	1023 DJ	DOOLEY SILVERSPOON	WHAT IN THE WORLD	BUILDING MY WORLD AROUND YOUQ	8.00
77	1024	JEANNIE BURTON & DOOLEY SILVERSPOON	AM I LOSING YOU	AM I LOSING YOU part 2	5.00
77	1024 DJ	JEANNIE BURTON & DOOLEY SILVERSPOON	AM I LOSING YOU	AM I LOSING YOU part 2	6.00
77	1025	DOOLEY SILVERSPOON	CLOSER TO LOVING YOU	IT'S SERIOUS	6.00
77	1025 DJ	DOOLEY SILVERSPOON	CLOSER TO LOVING YOU	IT'S SERIOUS	8.00
77	1026	DENNY ST. GEORGE	TALK TALK TALKIN'	THERE AIN'T NOTHING LIKE BEING	3.00
77	1026 DJ	DENNY ST. GEORGE	TALK TALK TALKIN'	THERE AIN'T NOTHING LIKE BEING	4.00

SHRINE

03	101	CAIROS	STOP OVER LOOKING ME	DON'T FIGHT IT	10.00
03	102	EDDIE DAYE & 4 BARS	GUESS WHO LOVES YOU	WHAT AM I GONNA DO	10.00
03	105	LES CHANSONETTES	DON'T LET HIM HURT YOU	DEEPER	10.00
03	114	BOBBY REED	CALDONIA BROWN	BABY DON'T LEAVE ME	10.00
03	LSA2	CAIROS c/w CAUTIONS	STOP OVERLOOKING ME	WATCH YOUR STEP	25.00

SIDEWALK

79	102	GONZALEZ	HAVEN'T STOP DANCING YET	YOU'RE ALL I NEED	4.00
79	104	GLORIA JONES	WINDSTORM	BLUE LIGHT MICROPHONE	5.00
79	112	LA VELLE	PLAYGIRL	FINALLY I'M FREE	4.00

SIGNPOST

72	755 DJ	DEE ERWIN	DARLING PLEASE TAKE ME BACK	WILLIE PASS THE WATER	4.00

SILENT

81	3	BUBBA LOU & the HIGHBALLS	OVER YOU	LOVE ALL OVER THE PLACE	20.00

SKA BEAT

66	242	JIMMY JAMES	YOUR LOVE	SOME DAY	50.00

SMP

85	SKM1	JACKIE WILSON	I GET THE SWEETEST FEELING	LONELY TEARDROPS	4.00
85	SKM1 alt	JACKIE WILSON	I GET THE SWEETEST FEELING	WHISPERS + HIGHER AND HIGHER	4.00
85	SKM2	CHI-LITES	HAVE YOU SEEN HER	HOMELY GIRL + FOUND SUNSHINE	4.00
85	SKM3 no PS	JACKIE WILSON	I'M THE ONE TO DO IT + REET PETITE	YOU BROUGHT A CHANGE ABOUT IN	5.00
85	SKM3 lips PS	JACKIE WILSON	YOU BROUGHT ABOUT A CHANGE IN ME	I'M THE ONE TO DO IT + REET PE	6.00
85	SKM3 red PS	JACKIE WILSON	I'M THE ONE TO DO IT + REET PETITE	YOU BROUGHT A CHANGE ABOUT IN	6.00
85	SKM7	LEE DORSEY	WORKING IN A COAL MINE	RIDE YOUR PONY + HOLY COW	5.00
85	SKM9	BILLY BUTLER	RIGHT TRACK	same: instrumental	10.00
85	SKM10 PS	JACKIE WILSON	(YOUR LOVE KEEPS LIFTING ME) HIGHER	WHO WHO SONG	4.00

SNB

69	4142	FLAMMA SHERMAN	WHERE IS HE	MOVE ME	50.00
69	4142 DJ	FLAMMA SHERMAN	WHERE IS HE	MOVE ME	75.00

SOLENT

90	090	IAN LEE	JUST DON'T CARE	same: instrumental	15.00

SONET

69	608	JOHNNY OTIS SHOW	COUNTRY GIRL	SIGNIFYIN' MONKEY	5.00
69	608 DJ	JOHNNY OTIS SHOW	COUNTRY GIRL	SIGNIFYIN' MONKEY	6.00
68	2002	LITTLE JOE COOK	HOLD ON TO YOUR MONEY	DON'T YOU HAVE FEELINGS?	20.00
68	2002 DJ	LITTLE JOE COOK	HOLD ON TO YOUR MONEY	DON'T YOU HAVE FEELINGS?	25.00
74	2041	LITTLE JOE COOK	HOLD ON TO YOUR MONEY	DON'T YOU HAVE FEELINGS	8.00
74	2041 DJ	LITTLE JOE COOK	HOLD ON TO YOUR MONEY	DON'T YOU HAVE FEELINGS	10.00
78	2168	FATS DOMINO	SLEEPING ON THE JOB	AFTER HOURS	5.00
78	2168 DJ	FATS DOMINO	SLEEPING ON THE JOB	AFTER HOURS	6.00
83	2258	JAMES BROWN	BRING IT ON - BRING IT ON	THE NIGHT TIME IS THE RIGHT TI	4.00
83	2258 DJ	JAMES BROWN	BRING IT ON - BRING IT ON	THE NIGHT TIME IS THE RIGHT TI	5.00

SOS

84	001	BEVERLEY ANN c/w DYNATONES	HE'S COMING HOME	FIFE PIPER	15.00
84	002	VIBRATIONS c/w COUNT FIVE	CAUSE YOUR MINE	PSYCHOTIC REACTION	10.00
84	003	MAJOR LANCE c/w MATT PARSONS	YOU DON'T WANT ME NO MORE	BOOGALOO INVESTIGATOR	10.00
84	004	PARIS, BOBBY c/w CARNABY	I WALKED AWAY	JUMP & DANCE	8.00
85	005	MAJESTICS c/w BOBBY PARIS	I LOVE HER SO MUCH (IT HURTS)	NIGHT OWL	10.00
85	006	DEE DEE SHARP c/w DEREK & RAY	WHAT KIND OF LADY	INTERPLAY	10.00
85	007	DELCOS c/w PRESENT	ARABIA	MANY'S THE SLIP	10.00
85	008	PERRY, GREG c/w ALFIE DAVISON	IT TAKES HEART	LOVE IS A SERIOUS BUSINESS	10.00
85	009	VARIOUS ARTISTS EP	AM I COLD (AM I HOT) + HEAVEN IN THE AFTERNOON	HOW CAN I TELL HER + CASHING IN	10.00

Various Artist 4 track EP 1. Bill Harris 2. Lew Kirton 3. Curtis 4. Voices Of East Harlem

86	010	N.F. PORTER c/w RAY CHARLES	KEEP ON KEEPING ON	I DON'T NEED NO DOCTOR	8.00

SOUL BANDIT

3		JIMMY MACK c/w INVITATIONS	MY WORLD IS ON FIRE	SKIING IN THE SNOW	10.00

SOUL BEAT

1		EDDIE HOLMAN c/w ORIGINALS	WHEN I'M NOT WANTED	SUSPICION	10.00
2		RONNIE DYSON c/w SISTER SLEDGE LADY IN RED	LOVE DON'T GO THOUGH NO CHANGES	15.00	

SOUL BROTHER RECORDS

	7001 DJ	SIDE EFFECT feat: JIM GILSTRAP	RUN RUN RUN	SPEND IT ON LOVE	5.00

SOUL CAT

	1 EP	VARIOUS ARTISTS	WALKING UP A ONE WAY STREET	CONITION RED + PICTURE ME GONE	10.00

SOUL CITY

The Soul City concept was created in 1966 by soul enthusiast and writer Dave Godin, who was already a legendary soul man through his work with the Motown Appreciation Society, which did much to promote the "Motown Sound" in the UK. The Societies promo record and monthly booklets "Hitsville U.S.A." "Motown Appreciation Society" are now highly collectable in their own right, as they were the first publications to write exclusively about soul music in Britain.

In 1966 Dave opened a record the shop in the High Street of Deptford, South London assisted by David Nathan and Robert Blackmore the shop soon gained a reputation for the outlet that specialized in selling American release R&B and Soul records. With import vinyl being very much the "hip" item to own, the shop soon out grew itself. Soul City was so successful they moved to the big city address of 17 Monmouth Street, London, WC2. From this address Soul City elevated themselves to claim to be country's only 100% American Soul & R&B outlet.

In March 1968 it released the first of 19 singles. Each and every Soul City label carried the words "Soul as deep as you like... and then some"

A sentence that would be repeated many times in the years that followed, by collectors dedicated to American Black Music.

68	101	DON & DEE DEE GARDNER	DON'T YOU WORRY	I'M COMING HOPME TO STAY	20.00
68	102	GENE CHANDLER	NOTHING CAN STOP ME	THE BIG LIE	20.00
68	103	SYLVIA	I CAN'T HELP IT	IT'S A GOOD LIFE	20.00
68	104	CHUCK EDWARDS	I NEED YOU	DOWNTOWN SOULVILLE	20.00

68	104 DJ	CHUCK EDWARDS	I NEED YOU	DOWNTOWN SOULVILLE	**55.00**
68	105	BESSIE BANKS	GO NOW	IT SOUNDS LIKE MY BABY	25.00
68	106	VALENTINOS	IT'S ALL OVER NOW	TIRED OF LIVING IN THE COUNTRY	25.00
68	107	BILLY PRESTON	GREAZEE	GREAZEE Part2	15.00
68	107 DJ	BILLY PRESTON	GREAZEE	GREAZEE Part2	50.00
68	108	SHIRLEY LAWSON	ONE MORE CHANCE	THE STAR	**207.00**
69	109	SOUL CITY EXECUTIVES	HAPPY CHATTER	FALLING IN LOVE	30.00
69	110	THELMA JONES	THE HOUSE THAT JACK BUILT	GIVE IT TO ME STRAIGHT	20.00
69	111	PACKERS	HOLE IN THE WALL	GO AHEAD ON	15.00
69	112	CHRIS JACKSON	I'LL NEVER FORGET YOU	FOREVER I'LL STAY WITH YOU	40.00
69	113	BILLY BUTLER	THE RIGHT TRACK	BOSTON MONKEY	20.00
69	114	MAJOR LANCE	THE BEAT	YOU'LL WANT ME BACK	20.00
69	115	MIGHTY SAM	PAPA TRUE LOVE	I NEED A LOT OF LOVIN'	30.00
69	116	CHUCK BROOKS	BLACK SHEEP	I'VE GOT TO GET MYSELF TOGETHER	25.00
69	117	STAPLE SINGERS	FOR WHAT IT'S WORTH	ARE YOU SURE?	20.00
69	118	ERMA FRANKLIN	DON'T WAIT TOO LONG	TIME AFTER TIME	20.00
69	119	ALLEN TOUSSAINT	WE THE PEOPLE	TEQUILA	25.00
70	120 unissued	CHRIS JACKSON	SINCE THERE'S NO DOUBT	WE WILL BE TOGETHER	2000.00

Only known to exist on 444 acetate, if a test presses or a promos was found, expect a price tag of £2000+

The label was reactivated in the year 1999 under the new management, who replicated original label and sleeve design. Although many desirable titles have been issued on this label from release # 123 the mastering and sound quality has been inconsistent. Promo copies exist on all releases but were pressed in reasonable quantities. Test pressings with handwritten labels were also pressed, which seemed to be the policy of many of the more recent Soul labels as they could sell the promos for more money than the regular stock copies, this gave the record label owners two or three bites of the cherry, which made commercial sense. All titles were allegedly limited to a 500 copies press only. But they do seem to be readily available in all formats, which has lessened the appeal of collecting the later releases. Note: Some releases have poor sound quality and the DJ 45 prices apply to the handwritten test presses also.

00	123	BARBARA LYNN	MOVIN' ON A GROOVE	DISCO MUSIC	10.00
00	123 DJ	BARBARA LYNN	MOVIN' ON A GROOVE	DISCO MUSIC	15.00
00	124	JACK MONTGOMERY	MY DEAR BELOVED	DO YOU BELIEVE IT	10.00
00	124 DJ	JACK MONTGOMERY	MY DEAR BELOVED	DO YOU BELIEVE IT	20.00
00	125	MARIE KNIGHT	THAT'S NO WAY TO TREAT A GIRL	YOU LIE SO WELL	10.00
00	125 DJ	MARIE KNIGHT	THAT'S NO WAY TO TREAT A GIRL	YOU LIE SO WELL	10.00
00	126	DEAN PARRISH c/w JOHNNY MAESTRO	BRICKS, BROKEN BOTTLES AND STICKS	I'M STEPPING OUT OF THE PICTURE	10.00
00	126 DJ	DEAN PARRISH c/w JOHNNY MAESTRO	BRICKS, BROKEN BOTTLES AND STICKS	I'M STEPPING OUT OF THE PICTURE	15.00
00	127	IVORIES c/w JUST BROTHERS	PLEASE STAY	CARLENA	10.00
00	127 DJ	IVORIES c/w JUST BROTHERS	PLEASE STAY	CARLENA	10.00
00	128	CHUCK JACKSON	GOOD THINGS COME TO THOSE WHO WAIT	HAND IT OVER	10.00
00	128 DJ	CHUCK JACKSON	GOOD THINGS COME TO THOSE WHO WAIT	HAND IT OVER	15.00
00	129	J.D. BRYANT c/w PROPHETS	I WON'T BE COMING BACK	IF I HAD (ONE GOLD PIECE)	10.00
00	129 DJ	J.D. BRYANT c/w PROPHETS	I WON'T BE COMING BACK	IF I HAD (ONE GOLD PIECE)	10.00
00	129 mis-press	J.D. BRYANT c/w PROPHETS	I WON'T BE COMING BACK	IF I HAD (ONE GOLD PIECE)	10.00

This copy actually plays Jesse James – Love Is Alright

00	130	BARBARA LYNN	TRYING TO LOVE TWO	SUGAR COATED LOVE	10.00
00	130 DJ	BARBARA LYNN	TRYING TO LOVE TWO	SUGAR COATED LOVE	15.00
00	131	JESSE JAMES	LOVE IS ALL RIGHT	same:	15.00
00	131 DJ	JESSE JAMES	LOVE IS ALL RIGHT	same:	20.00
02	132	BAD WEATHER INC:	I NEVER NEVER KNEW	YOU REALLY GOT A HOLD ON ME	15.00
02	132 DJ	BAD WEATHER INC:	I NEVER NEVER KNEW	YOU REALLY GOT A HOLD ON ME	20.00
02	133	CASHMERES	SHOWSTOPPER	LET THE DOOR HIT YOUR BACK	10.00
02	133 DJ	CASHMERES	SHOWSTOPPER	LET THE DOOR HIT YOUR BACK	10.00
02	134	YVONNE VERNEE	JUST LIKE YOU DID ME	IT'S BEEN A LONG TIME	10.00
02	134 DJ	YVONNE VERNEE	JUST LIKE YOU DID ME	IT'S BEEN A LONG TIME	10.00
02	135	ADMIRATIONS	YOU LEFT ME	I WANT TO BE FREE	15.00
02	135 DJ	ADMIRATIONS	YOU LEFT ME	I WANT TO BE FREE	20.00
02	136	WALTER & THE ADMIRATIONS	MAN O MAN (WHAT CAN I DO)	LIFE OF TEARS	10.00
02	136 DJ	WALTER & THE ADMIRATIONS	MAN O MAN (WHAT CAN I DO)	LIFE OF TEARS	15.00
02	137	SAM DEES	LONELY FOR YOU BABY	I NEED YOU BABY	10.00
02	137 DJ	SAM DEES	LONELY FOR YOU BABY	I NEED YOU BABY	10.00
02	138	unissued?			
02	139	unissued?			
04	140	FABULOUS JADES	COME ON AND LIVE	PLANNING THE MOMENT	6.00
04	140 DJ	FABULOUS JADES	COME ON AND LIVE	PLANNING THE MOMENT	10.00
04	141	MR. FLOODS PARTY	COMPARED TO WHAT	UNBREAKABLE TOY	3.00

The above 45 is NOT the original Mr. Floods recording released on Ember or Bulldog. The origin and real artist are unconfirmed hence low price.

04	142	AD LIBS	I DON'T NEED NO FORTUNE (TELLER)	NEW YORK IN THE DARK	6.00
04	142 DJ	AD LIBS	I DON'T NEED NO FORTUNE (TELLER)	NEW YORK IN THE DARK	10.00
04	143	SOUL TWINS	QUICK CHANGE ARTIST	GIVE A MAN A CHANCE	6.00
03	143 DJ	SOUL TWINS	QUICK CHANGE ARTIST	GIVE A MAN A CHANCE	10.00
04	144	LEN JEWELL	BETTING ON LOVE	ALL MY GOOD LOVIN	6.00
04	144 DJ	LEN JEWELL	BETTIN' ON LOVE	ALL MY GOOD LOVIN	10.00
04	145	TEMPOS	A LITTLE TOGETHERNESS	COUNTDOWN HERE I COME	6.00
04	145 DJ	TEMPOS	A LITTLE TOGETHERNESS	COUNTDOWN HERE I COME	10.00
04	146	LYNN VERNADO	WASH AND WEAR LOVE	SECOND HAND LOVE	6.00
04	146 DJ	LYNN VERNADO	WASH AND WEAR LOVE	SECOND HAND LOVE	10.00
04	147	DENIS EDWARDS	JOHNNY ON THE SPOT	I DIDN'T HAVE TO	6.00
04	147 DJ	DENIS EDWARDS	JOHNNY ON THE SPOT	I DIDN'T HAVE TO	10.00
04	148	SHERRY'S c/w LITTLE JOE COOK	PUT YOUR ARMS AROUND ME	I'M FALLING IN LOVE WITH YOU B	6.00
04	148 DJ	SHERRY'S c/w LITTLE JOE COOK	PUT YOUR ARMS AROUND ME BABY	I'M FALLING IN LOVE WITH YOU B	10.00
04	149	MAGNIFICENTS	MY HEART IS CALLING YOU	ON MAIN STREET	6.00
04	149 DJ	MAGNIFICENTS	MY HEART IS CALLING YOU	ON MAIN STREET	10.00

04	150	AL WILSON	THE SNAKE	NOW I KNOW WHAT LOVE IS	6.00
04	150 DJ	AL WILSON	THE SNAKE	NOW I KNOW WHAT LOVE IS	10.00
04	151	DON VARNER	TEAR STAINED FACE	MOJO MAMA	6.00
04	151 DJ	DON VARNER	TEAR STAINED FACE	MOJO MAMA	10.00
04	152	JOE MATTHEWS	AIN'T NOTHING YOU CAN DO	YOU BETTER CHECK YOURSELF	6.00
04	152 DJ	JOE MATTHEWS	AIN'T NOTHING YOU CAN DO	YOU BETTER CHECK YOURSELF	10.00
04	153	LARRY SANTOS	YOU GOT ME WHERE YOU WANT ME	TOMORROW WITHOUT LOVE	6.00
04	153 DJ	LARRY SANTOS	YOU GOT ME WHERE YOU WANT ME	TOMORROW WITHOUT LOVE	10.00
04	154	JADES	I'M WHERE IT'S AT	MOTHERS ONLY DAUGHTER	6.00
04	154 DJ	JADES	I'M WHERE IT'S AT	MOTHERS ONLY DAUGHTER	10.00
04	155	BILLY WOODS	LET ME MAKE YOU HAPPY	THAT WAS THE LOVE THAT WAS	6.00
04	155 DJ	BILLY WOODS	LET ME MAKE YOU HAPPY	THAT WAS THE LOVE THAT WAS	10.00
04	156	JOHNNY WYATT	THIS THING CALLED LOVE	TO WHOM IT MAY CONCERN	3.00
04	156 DJ	JOHNNY WYATT	THIS THING CALLED LOVE	TO WHOM IT MAY CONCERN	6.00
04	157	APPRECIATIONS	I CAN'T HIDE IT	NO NO NO	6.00
04	157 DJ	APPRECIATIONS	I CAN'T HIDE IT	NO, NO, NO	10.00
04	158	DELIGHTS	LOVER	TELL ME WHY	6.00
04	158 DJ	DE-LITES	LOVER	TELL ME WHY	10.00
04	159	MICKIE CHAMPION	WHAT GOOD AM I	THE HURT STILL LINGERS ON	6.00
04	159 DJ	MICKIE CHAMPION	WHAT GOOD AM I	THE HURT STILL LINGERS ON	10.00
04	160	JOHNNY SAYLES	TELL ME (WHERE I STAND)	I CAN'T GET ENOUGH	6.00
04	160 DJ	JOHNNY SAYLES	TELL ME (WHERE I STAND)	I CAN'T GET ENOUGH	10.00

SOUL FOOD

02	001	JOE TEX	I WANNA BE FREE	UNDER YOUR POWERFUL LOVE	10.00

SOUL GALORE

	1 EP DJ	CHUCK JACKSON	CHAINS OF LOVE + GOOD THINGS COME	HAND IT OVER + ANY DAY NOW	10.00

SOUL HQ

99	1	CARSTAIRS	IT REALLY HURTS ME GIRL	blank:	8.00
99	2	DRIZA BONE	PRESSURE	blank:	6.00
99	3	TIMMY WILLIS	SUCH MISERY	blank:	10.00
99	4	JACKIE WILSON & ERMA FRANKLIN	(I GET THE) SWEETEST FEELING	blank:	10.00
01	5	FLASHLIGHT	SHE'S PULLING MY STRINGS	blank:	6.00
01	6	CLYDENE JACKSON	I NEED YOUR LOVE	blank:	10.00

SOUL POWER

69	001	WALTER JACKSON c/w BILLY BUTLER	WHERE HAVE ALL THE FLOWERS GONE	I CAN'T WORK NO LONGER	30.00

SOUL SERIES

97	101 DJ	SAPPHIRES	BABY YOU'VE GOT ME	'HOUSE PARTY instrumental	10.00
97	102 DJ	SPENCER WIGGINS c/w PERCY WIGGINS	LET'S TALK IT OVER	CALL ON ME	10.00
97	103 DJ	DEL LARKS c/ w EDDIE PARKER	JOB OPENING	I'M GONE	10.00
97	104 DJ	HESITATIONS	I'M NOT BUILT THAT WAY	THAT'S THE WAY LOVE IS	10.00
97	105 DJ	MAJOR LANCE	DON'T FIGHT IT	NOTHING CAN STOP ME	10.00

SOUL SOUNDS

Soul Sounds was the first ever label to reproduce rare soul 45's on a large scale. Jeff King soon latched onto the demand created for deleted soul dance records played at the All Night clubs like The Nite Owl in Leicester, Blue Orchid in Derby, Mojo in Sheffield, Beachcomber in Nottingham and of course the legendary Twisted Wheel in Manchester.

The pressing run was thought to be around 200/250 copies. Doing a little mail order from Spendlow Gardens, Leicester or selling through a Leicester market stall and various retail outlets like Ralphs Records in Manchester. 250 copies were quickly sold and easily absorbed into an insatiable and growing scene. Apparently Jeff would even travel to these clubs and sell the 45's out the back of his car. Eventually Jeff would even take his records into the clubs, to become the very first dealer to ever sell rare soul 45's inside a nightclub.

Jeff also had great contacts for USA import 45's, and would regularly mail shot sales lists of rare USA import soul 45's. Even though this label was pressed in quantities of around 250, every title is today, ironically much rarer than it's original UK counterpart.

I doubt at the time, that Jeff could have, in his wildest dreams have foreseen that taking his wares into an "all niter", could have evolved into what has become in the 21st. Century. In recent years this label has become increasingly collectable and much harder to find, and you can expect values to increase in the future, as the history surrounding this label played a crucial part in developing the soul scene even further.

70	1001	LEON HAYWOOD	BABY RECONSIDER	GOIN' BACK TO NEW ORLEANS	10.00
70	1002	DONALD HEIGHT	TALK OF THE GRAPEVINE	THERE'LL BE NO TOMORROW	15.00
70	1003	JIMMY & KING HOLIDAY	READY, WILLING AND ABLE	WE GOT A GOOD THING GOING	15.00
70	1004	SHIRLEY ELLIS	SOUL TIME	WAITIN'	20.00
70	1005	HUMAN BEINZ	NOBODY BUT ME	SUENO	10.00
70	1006	TAMI LYNN	I'M GONNA RUN AWAY FROM YOU	THE BOY NEXT DOOR	15.00
70	1007	GENE CHANDLER	THERE WAS A TIME	THOSE WERE THE GOOD OLD DAYS	12.00
70	1008	ROUND ROBIN	KICK THAT LITTLE FOOT SALLY AN	SLAUSON PARTY	15.00
70	1009	INVITATIONS	WHAT'S WRONG WITH ME BABY	WHY DID MY BABY TURN BAD	12.00
70	1010	EARL HARRISON	HUMPHREY STOMP	CAN YOU FORGIVE ME	15.00
70	1011	ALEXANDER PATTON	A LIL' LOVING SOMETIMES	NO MORE DREAMS	15.00
70	1012	CHUCK JACKSON	THERSE CHAINS OF LOVE	I KEEP FORGETTIN'	30.00
70	1013	DEAN PARRISH	DETERMINATION	TURN ON YOUR LOVELIGHT	25.00
70	1014	PEACHES & HERB	WE'RE IN THIS THING TOGETHER	LET'S FALL IN LOVE	15.00
70	1015	MARY LOVE	YOU TURNED MY BITTER INTO SWEET	I'M IN YOUR HANDS	30.00
70	1016	BARBARA LEWIS	SOMEDAY WE'RE GONNA LOVE AGAIN	THANKFUL FOR WHAT I GOT	20.00
70	1017	MITCH RYDER	BREAK OUT	I NEED HELP	10.00
70	1018	BLENDELLS	DANCE WITH ME	GET YOUR BABY	20.00
70	1019	SOUL SISTERS	GOOD TIME TONIGHT	FOOLISH DREAMER	20.00

70	1020	DEAN PARRISH	TELL HER	FALL ON ME	15.00
70	1021	LITTLE ANTHONY & the IMPERIALS	GONNA FIX YOU GOOD	YOU BETTER TAKE IT EASY BABY	20.00
70	1022	CHUBBY CHECKER	(AT THE) DISCOTHEQUE	CU MA LA BE - STAY	15.00
70	1023	SHARPEES	TIRED OF BEING LONELY	DO THE 45	25.00
70	1024	ROSCOE ROBINSON	THAT'S ENOUGH	ONE MORE TIME	20.00
70	1025	INCREDIBLES	THERE'S NOTHING ELSE TO SAY	ANOTHER DIRTY DEAL	20.00
70	1026	HOMER BANKS	HOOKED BY LOVE	LADY OF STONE	20.00
70	1027	MARGIE HENDRIX	RESTLESS	ON THE RIGHT TRACK	15.00
70	1028	BOBBY SHEEN	DOCTOR LOVE	SWEET, SWEET LOVE	20.00
70	1029	RONNIE MILSAP	AIN'T NO SOUL LEFT IN THESE OLD SHOES	ANOTHER BRANCH FROM THE OLD TREE	20.00
70	1030	DOBIE GRAY	OUT ON THE FLOOR	NO ROOM TO CRY	25.00

Memories of Keith Rylatt:

It was a Saturday in spring 1970 as I walked along Corporation Street, Manchester just about to swing into Todd Street and Victoria Street, the usually darkened Ralph's Record Shop caught my eye, the place was lit up. What could be going on at 7.00 am in the morning? John ("Zan") and Doreen were in there, so I knocked on the door and got let in. Zan was busy placing 45's into a "dinking" machine chopping out the center piece, as if to go on a juke box, while Doreen was packing them into 25 count boxes. Looking at the amount of boxes, I didn't need to ask, they had been there all night.

As I looked at the titles my jaw dropped, I had before me every record I could only dream of on the "Soul Sounds" label distributed by Soul-Wise Inc. N.Y. U.S.A. There was Leon Haywood "Baby Reconsider", Tammi Lynn "I'm Gonna Run Away From You" Invitations "What's Wrong With Me Baby" What's more they were only £1.00 each. As I was probably the first punter to see them, I decided to spend my train fare and what cash I had, on five copies of "Baby Reconsider" the rarest most desirable 45 any soul fan could own. What these records were, where they came from and other trivial details were of no concern, all I knew was that I was now hitching towards Huddersfield with five ingots of SOLID GOLD!

I headed straight to Wakefield Mecca, where I knew a couple of DJ's would be hanging out, they were interested in soul but at £1.50 they turned their noses up, with one of them eventually parting with £1.25. Deflated, I sold the others at Hernie's in Leeds that evening, for the same price. The thing was that everyone else realized that they weren't original presses and Yorkshire folk aren't too disposed to parting with money at the best of times, let alone on replica gear.

The 45s were the brain child of Jeff King from Leicester, who was fully aware of the growing Rare Soul scene having sold imports at various all nighters of the time and had decided to cash in by having all the top titles repressed in London, to be sold in the North and the Midlands, they were a raging success.

This was not the very first time the embryonic soul scene had been catered for with repro's. Mancunian DJ and record dealer the legendary Brian 45 Philips extracted a couple of Herbie Mann LP tracks, and re-christened him The Dynatones and pressed them on blank disc. Another small one off, was the repro of Walter Jackson's "Where Have All The Flowers Gone" on the Soul Power label from Lincolnshire. They were small times but they were first bootlegs or "Pressings" as they became known in the North. Almost simultaneously to King's venture, three other labels emerged, Magic, BJD and Greenlight could be obtained at that mystical cellar on Arkwright Street, Nottingham. With in-demand and impossible to find gems as Roscoe Robinson's "That's Enough", Band Of Angels "Invitation" Jackie Edwards "I Feel So Bad". The North's craving for virtually impossible to find classics, was now being satisfied by the hundred. All these early British repro labels are now keenly sought after and a huge part of Northern Soul history.

SOUL SPIN

86	101	JACKIE DAY	NAUGHTY BOY	YES I WILL	30.00

SOUL STOP

This Stamford, Lincolnshire based label's releases were aimed directly at the Northern Soul market. Owned by artist and venue promotor Ken Cox, he tried like so many others before him, to tap into the UK rare soul scene by producing his own "Northern" 45's. All failed to make an impact. Other than his first release, the reissuing of Page One's Muriel Day which sold in very respectable quantities. This perhaps gave him the confidence to try 9 more times, no pun intended. But nine times out of ten the releases sold in less and less quantities.

84	3001 red	MURIEL DAY	NINE TIMES OUT OF TEN	DO THE SKUNK	8.00
85	3001 black	MURIEL DAY	NINE TIMES OUT OF TEN	DO THE SKUNK	6.00
84	3002	CORRAINE GILLIES	YOU DON'T KNOW WHERE YOUR INTEREST LIES	KEEP ON DANCING	6.00
84	3003 red	JUDY STREET	WHAT	HI-FLY	10.00
84	3003 black	JUDY STREET	WHAT	HI-FLY	8.00
84	3004	JEANETTE HARPER	(PICK ME UP AND) PUT ME IN YOUR	FALLING	10.00
84	3005	BILLY DIAMOND	STOP	HULLABALOO	6.00
84	3006	unissued ?			
84	3007	SCOTT McKENZIE	SECRET HOME	OPEN SECRET	6.00
84	3008	LENNY HARRIS	LONG AFTER TONIGHT IS ALL OVER	IMPRESSIONS	8.00
84	3009	JUAN SPENCER BAND	I'M ON MY WAY	RECREATION	6.00
84	3010	GLORIA JONES	TAINTED LOVE	BIKING	15.00

SOUL SUPPLY

83	101 EP	VARIOUS ARTISTS	INVITATION + MICHAEL THE LOVER	EMERGENCY 999	6.00

4 track EP artists inc: 1. Band Of Angels 2. Geno Washington & the Ram Jam Band 3. Alan Bown Set

83	102	MOOD-MOSAIC	A TOUCH OF VELVET - A STING OF BRASS	BOND STREET P.M.	6.00
83	103	BARBARA MILLS	QUEEN OF FOOLS	MAKE IT LAST	10.00
84	104 EP	VARIOUS ARTISTS	A LITTLE TOGETHERNESS + I CAN'T HIDE IT	I NEVER KNEW + STRONGER THAN HER LOVE	10.00

4 track EP artists inc: 1. Younghearts 2. Appreciations 3. Eddie Foster 4. Flirtations

84	105 EP	VARIOUS ARTISTS	YOU DIDN'T HAVE TO LEAVE +HEY GIRL	I DON'T LIKE TO LOSE + SOMETHING'S BAD	15.00

4 track EP artists inc: 1. Ellusions 2. Topics 3. Cecil Washington 4. Nomads

85	106	MAJESTICS c/w SEQUINS	(I LOVER HER SO MUCH) IT HURTS ME	TRY MY LOVE	25.00

SOULTRAIN

77	775	WHISPERS	I'VE GOT A FEELING	LIVIN' TOGETHER IN SIN	10.00
77	885	SHALAMAR	UPTOWN FESTIVAL	UPTOWN FESTIVAL PART2	4.00
77	891	CARRIE LUCAS	GOTTA KEEP DANCIN'	WHAT'S THE QUESTION	4.00
77	996	WHISPERS	MAKE IT WITH YOU	YOU ARE NUMBER ONE	4.00
77	1310	CARRIE LUCAS	STREET CORNER SYMPHONY	STREET CORNER SYMPHONY part 2	4.00

SOURCE

85	1	CHUCK BROWN & the SOUL SEARCHES	BUSTIN' LOOSE	BUSTIN' LOOSE part 2	4.00
85	1 PS	CHUCK BROWN & the SOUL SEARCHES	BUSTIN' LOOSE	BUSTIN' LOOSE part 2	4.00
85	1 DJ	CHUCK BROWN & the SOUL SEARCHES	BUSTIN' LOOSE	BUSTIN' LOOSE part 2	5.00
86	2	HAROLD MELVIN & the BLUENOTES	PRAYIN' (1986 remix)	PRAYIN' (instrumental)	8.00

86	2 PS	HAROLD MELVIN & the BLUENOTES	PRAYIN' (1986 remix)	PRAYIN' (instrumental)	12.00
86	2 DJ	HAROLD MELVIN & the BLUENOTES	PRAYIN' (1986 remix)	PRAYIN' (instrumental)	15.00
80	100	LEE MOORE	REACHIN' OUT (FOR YOUR LOVE)	REACHIN' OUT (FOR YOUR LOVE) 2	5.00
80	100 DJ	LEE MOORE	REACHIN' OUT (FOR YOUR LOVE)	REACHIN' OUT (FOR YOUR LOVE) 2	6.00
80	102	HAROLD MELVIN & the BLUENOTES	PRAYIN'	YOUR LOVE IS TAKING ME ON A JOURNEY	25.00
80	102 DJ	HAROLD MELVIN & the BLUENOTES	PRAYIN'	YOUR LOVE IS TAKING ME ON A JOURNEY	35.00
80	103	SHARON PAIGE	TONIGHT'S THE NIGHT	same: instrumental	5.00
80	103 DJ	SHARON PAIGE	TONIGHT'S THE NIGHT	same: Instrumental	6.00
80	104	HAROLD MELVIN & the BLUENOTES	PRAYIN'	I SHOULD BE YOUR LOVER	20.00
80	104 DJ	HAROLD MELVIN & the BLUENOTES	PRAYIN'	I SHOULD BE YOUR LOVER	20.00

SPARK

68	1005	VAL McKENNA	HOUSE FOR SALE	I'LL BE SATIFIED	8.00
68	1005 DJ	VAL McKENNA	HOUSE FOR SALE	I'LL BE SATIFIED	10.00
68	1006	SCEPTRES	SOMETHING'S COIMG ALONG	WHAT'S THE MATTER WITH JULIE	15.00
68	1006 DJ	SCEPTRES	SOMETHING'S COIMG ALONG	WHAT'S THE MATTER WITH JULIE	20.00
70	1015	GENE LATTER	MY LIFE AIN'T EASY	ANGIE	8.00
70	1015 DJ	GENE LATTER	MY LIFE AIN'T EASY	ANGIE	10.00
70	1022 silver and red	GENE LATTER	SIGN ON THE DOTTED LINE	I LOVE YOU	20.00
70	1022 DJ	GENE LATTER	SIGN ON THE DOTTED LINE	I LOVE YOU	30.00
69	1023	VAL McKENNA	ITS ALL IN MY IMAGINATION	SWEET SWEET LOVIN'	10.00
70	1035	JIMMY THOMAS	(WE AIN'T LOOKING FOR) NO TROUBLE	SPRINGTIME	10.00
70	1038 blue & silver	VAL McKENNA	LOVE FEELING	IT'S ALL IN MY IMAGINATION	30.00
70	1038 blue & silver DJ	VAL McKENNA	LOVE FEELING	IT'S ALL IN MY IMAGINATION	40.00
75	1038 blue & yellow	VAL McKENNA	LOVE FEELING	IT'S ALL IN MY IMAGINATION	6.00
75	1038 blue & yellow DJ	VAL McKENNA	LOVE FEELING	IT'S ALL IN MY IMAGINATION	10.00
70	1040	JIMMY THOMAS	WHITE DOVE	YOU DON'T HAVE TO SAY GOODBYE	6.00
70	1051	MIGHTY DODOS	YOU DON'T LOVE ME	HONEY (I NEED YOUR LOVE)	6.00
70	1063 blue & silver	GENE LATTER	SIGN ON THE DOTTED LINE	I LOVE YOU	10.00
70	1063 blue & silver DJ	GENE LATTER	SIGN ON THE DOTTED LINE	I LOVE YOU	15.00
75	1063 blue & yellow	GENE LATTER	SIGN ON THE DOTTED LINE	I LOVE YOU	8.00
75	1063 blue & yellowDJ	GENE LATTER	SIGN ON THE DOTTED LINE	I LOVE YOU	10.00
72	1072	HONEYEND	HEARTBREAKER	BEAUTIFUL DOWNTOWN	10.00
72	1072 DJ	HONEYEND	HEARTBREAKER	BEAUTIFUL DOWNTOWN	15.00
73	1093	FIREBALL	BACHANALIA instrumental	I DUNNO	5.00
73	1093 DJ	FIREBALL	BACHANALIA instrumental	I DUNNO	6.00
73	1100	PEPPERS	PEPPER BOX	PINCH OF SALT	5.00
73	1100 DJ	PEPPERS	PEPPER BOX	PINCH OF SALT	6.00
75	1122	WIGANS OVATION	SKIING IN THE SNOW	NORTHERN SOUL DANCER	4.00
75	1122 DJ	WIGANS OVATION	SKIING IN THE SNOW	NORTHERN SOUL DANCER	5.00
75	1124	RUTH SWANN	TAINTED LOVE	BOY - YOU'D BETTA MOVE ON	5.00
75	1124 DJ	RUTH SWANN	TAINTED LOVE	BOY - YOU'D BETTA MOVE ON	6.00
75	1129	WIGANS OVATION	PER-SO-NAL-LY	BE WITH ME TONIGHT	4.00
75	1129 DJ	WIGANS OVATION	PER-SO-NAL-LY	BE WITH ME TONIGHT	5.00
75	1132	TOMMY HUNT	CRACKIN' UP	GET OUT	8.00
75	1132 DJ	TOMMY HUNT	CRACKIN' UP	GET OUT	10.00
75	1133	WIGANS OVATION	SUPER LOVE	STAND IN LINE	4.00
75	1133 DJ	WIGANS OVATION	SUPER LOVE	STAND IN LINE	5.00
76	1146	TOMMY HUNT	LOVING ON THE LOSING SIDE	SUNSHINE GIRL	6.00
76	1146 DJ	TOMMY HUNT	LOVING ON THE LOSING SIDE	SUNSHINE GIRL	8.00
76	1148	TOMMY HUNT	SIGN ON THE DOTTED LINE + LOVING	ONE FINE MORNING	5.00
76	1148 DJ	TOMMY HUNT	SIGN ON THE DOTTED LINE + LOVING	ONE FINE MORNING	6.00
76	1149	LINDA & THE FUNKY BOYS	CLIMBING THE STEPS OF LOVE	BABY, ARE YOU SATISFIED	8.00
76	1149 DJ	LINDA & THE FUNKY BOYS	CLIMBING THE STEPS OF LOVE	BABY, ARE YOU SATISFIED	10.00
78	1152	DUANE CLARK	STOP COME DOWN, COME AROUND	GETTIN' IT	40.00
78	1152 DJ	DUANE CLARK	STOP COME DOWN, COME AROUND	GETTIN' IT	50.00
78	1158	DUANE CLARK	FIND MY WAY	ROOTS ARE BETTER	8.00
78	1158 DJ	DUANE CLARK	FIND MY WAY	ROOTS ARE BETTER	10.00

SPECIAL AGENT

	9001	JEWELL BASS	OVERFLOWING (FOR YOU)	I DON'T TRUST MYSELF	8.00
	9002				
	9003	HERMAN HITSON	YOU ARE TOO MUCH FOR THE HUMAN	I GOT THAT WILL	8.00
	9004	JOHNNY ADAMS	STAIRWAY TO HEAVEN	BABY I LOVE YOU	5.00
	9005	CHARLES BRIMMER	GOD BLESS OUR LOVE	GOD BLESS OUR LOVE part 2	6.00

SPECIALTY

68	1000	KING CURTIS	NIGHT TRAIN	WIGGLE WOBBLE	10.00
67	1001	EDDIE FLOYD	BYE BYE BABY	NEVER GET ENOUGH OF YOUR LOVE	25.00
67	1003	PAC-KEYS	DIGGIN'	STONE FOX	20.00
68	1005	LOU LAWTON	WRAPPED IN A DREAM	I'M JUST A FOOL	75.00
73	5007	PERCY MAYFIELD	PLEASE SEND ME SOMEONE TO LOVE	THE RIVER'S INVITATION	5.00

SPLASH

79	004	BYRON BURNS	THAT'S WHEN YOU KNOW (YOUR	HERE WE GO AGAIN	20.00
79	004 DJ	BYRON BURNS	THAT'S WHEN YOU KNOW (YOUR	HERE WE GO AGAIN	25.00

SPRING

The USA parent label Spring is a most collectable label for it's 70's soul. The UK Spring label was not launched in the UK until 1976, before that the USA Spring releases

that were pressed in the UK were put out on the London or Polydor labels. Polygram gave Spring it's own identity which had some measure of success with The Fatback Band. The higher valued 45's on Spring are Northern soul dance orientated recordings.

78	26	JOE SIMON	I.O.U.	LOVE VIBRATION	10.00
78	29	MILLIE JACKSON	MY MAN IS A SWEET MAN	HERE YOU ARE AGAIN + ALL THE W	5.00
80	149	FATBACK	BACKSTROKIN'	GOTTA GET HANDS ON SOME (MONEY	4.00
81	196	FATBACK	LET'S DO IT AGAIN	CHILLIN' OUT	4.00
83	590	FATBACK	GIRL IS FINE (SO FINE)	GIRL IS FINE (SO FINE) par 2	4.00
75	2006551	JOE SIMON	IN MY BABY'S ARMS	GET DOWN GET DOWN	5.00
76	2066706	FATBACK BAND	NIGHT FEVER	NO MORE ROOM FOR DANCING	4.00
76	2006713 AA	MILLIE JACKSON	A HOUSE FOR SALE	THERE YOU ARE	30.00

first press with a large A on each side of the label

78	2066713 A	MILLIE JACKSON	A HOUSE FOR SALE	THERE YOU ARE	20.00

second press the same year on the label with the A on the "House For Sale" side only

77	2066777	FATBACK BAND	DOUBLE DUTCH	SPANK THE BABY	4.00
77	2066843	MILLIE JACKSON	IF YOU'RE NOT BACK IN MY LOVE BY	A LITTLE TASTE OF OUTSIDE LOVE	4.00
78	2066870	FATBACK BAND	MASTER BOOTY	ZODIAC MAN	4.00
78	2066900	FATBACK BAND	MILE HIGH	MIDNIGHT FREAK	4.00
78	2066923	FATBACK	I LIKE GIRLS	GET OUT ON THE DANCEFLOOR	4.00
80	2095234	BUSTER JONES	JUST A LITTLE MISUNDERSTANDING	TAKE ME BACK NOW	15.00

STATE

Hidden on this label is the work of one of Britain's great soul songwriters. Ken Gold's work with Delegation is at the moment not fully appreciated by the soul collector. Ken signed his first publishing deal in 1971, fully committed to writing and producing soul. He had to go to the USA to get fully appreciated with artists like Aretha Franklin, Jackie Wilson and Eugene Record all recording his compositions. Although he struggled in the early part of his career, Ken's fortunes turned when he met Tony Hall, who was managing The Real Thing at the time, Ken's soulful skills were highlighted to the full when "You To Me Are Everything" became a #1 hit in 1976 and is considered an all time classic of UK 70's soul.

His work with Delegation, really should be checked out I think many will be surprised how it fits perfectly into today's "Rare Soul" scene. Any 45 with the name Ken Gold in the credits should be taken seriously. UK "soul" duo Mac & Katie Kissoon had several releases on the State label but these recordings are pure pop, so I've omitted them from the listing.

76	22	DUPREES	DELICIOUS	THE SKY'S THE LIMIT	10.00
76	25	DELEGATION	PROMISE OF LOVE	IT ONLY HAPPENS	15.00
77	40	DELEGATION	WHERE IS THE LOVE (WE USED TO KNOW)	BACK DOOR LOVE	6.00
77	54	KATIE KISSOON	THIS THING CALLED LOVE	IF NOT FOR YOUR LOVE	5.00
77	55	DELEGATION	BABY YOU'RE MY MYSTERY	YOU'VE BEEN DOING ME WRONG	10.00
77	64	DELEGATION	PROMISE OF LOVE	BACK DOOR LOVE	10.00
77	75	DELEGATION	HONEY I'M RICH	LET ME TAKE YOU TO THE SUN	4.00
78	77	BROWN SUGAR	BABY COME BACK	OH NO LOOK WHAT YOU'VE DONE	5.00
78	82	DELEGATION	OH HONEY	LOVE IS LIKE A FIRE	10.00

STATESIDE

The Stateside label to all intentions was the illegitimate offspring of the Top Rank label which had been the main competitor to Decca's London American logo in the 50's and early 60's. When EMI took control of the Top Rank label, EMI decided a new identity was required for Top Rank. Ultimately they re-christened it Stateside, and in June 1962 EMI's new label was presented to the world. EMI's mission for Stateside was to directly compete with London American exclusively issuing USA releases only. Having inherited Top Rank's rights to several USA labels including Wand, Vee Jay, S.P.Q.R., Sar, Scepter, Fire, Lenox etc. a wealth of soul releases were about to hit the UK market from Stateside's launch pad.

Soul & R&B fans didn't have to wait long; with Stateside second release was the now classic Chuck Jackson's "Any Day Now". Either by design or coincidence each month saw at least one soul / R&B 45 releases from various US companies. Soon the names on the release sheets, and reviews in Music weeklies would become familiar making regular appearances were Gene Chandler, Maxine Brown, Jerry Butler etc. In October 1963 EMI acquired the Tamla Motown UK rights, within a year Motown had provided Stateside with their first number one. The Supremes "Baby Love" would make the whole country aware of the USA "soul" sound. EMI would continue to scour the Billboard charts for new material, which lead them to a deal with Chicago label Constellation and Mar-V-Lus, Golden World in Detroit, Musicor in New York along with the Motown deal, USA soul was really starting to "happen" for EMI and the UK music fans.

By the mid sixties certain USA soul release started to acquire a cult club following: Alvin Cash "Twine Time" and "Philly Freeze", C.O.D's "Michael". But in the summer of 1965 at the height of the British Mod scene, one record came along that blew the club and dance hall scene sky high. The UK Mods couldn't prepare themselves for the hipshakin' power from New Orleans. Lee Dorsey "Ride Your Pony" was Stateside's first major hit that was not Motown related. I can remember as a 13 year old, at our local youth club a young girl going wild to the previously unencountered chart sound being played by our DJ. A new awareness for Soul music was starting to stir wider than the club circuit. But in September 1966 Stateside issued a London label "reject" that would change the course of Soul record collecting in the UK. The Detroit sound of Darrell Banks's "Open The Door to Your Heart" was the very first cult soul 45 on the scene. So popular was this 45 that although it never ever hit the charts, EMI kept the 45 available from 1966 to 1973 as special orders were received daily from record shops up and down the country, EMI periodically repressed to meet demand, confirming how big the soul movement was becoming in the UK.

By 1967 soul was starting to become unfashionable for radio play but the soul underground scene was blossoming. The Sunday People newspaper even did an article on these strange teenagers who dance on their own to soul music, at Clubs open all night. . The underground soul scene was taking shape and Stateside were providing the soundtrack. Inez & Charlie Foxx "Tightrope" Fascinations "Girls Are Out To Get You" Mary Love "Lay This Burden Down" and 45's from Betty Lavette, James & Bobby Purify, Vernon Garrett, Spencer Wiggins and Hoagy Lands all available in the UK within 6 months. The second half of 1967 didn't let up either with 45's from the Incredibles, James Carr, Esquires, Moses & Joshua, Oscar Toney Jr., the "new" Platters, The O'Jays which all go on to become the bedrock of the Rare Soul scene. But remember almost NONE of these artists had ever appeared in the UK and most of them were previously unheard of as they debuted with outstanding soul recordings. It took "detective" work from these teenage enthusiasts weekly visits to the local record shops to scan release sheets, buying every music paper and fanzine to read new release review pages and intense Pirate Radio listening to be able to learn about a largely undocumented music. Every city and town in the UK had a "hip" soul fan base. It was underground, it was new, it was unobtainable unless you'd done your homework. And so as EMI deleted their releases and clubs continued to play these 45's. Demand to acquire a copy and the street credibility gained by owning it, just exploded to almost fashion status.

The summer of 1968 saw a marked decline in EMI's interest in Stateside and along with the general demise of Soul, hardly any of this style of music appeared on the label apart from a few ABC Paramount "leftovers" from EMI now defunct HMV label and the odd reissue or repress. The label folded in the spring of 1974 but today it lives on as one of the most collectable of all the UK labels that ever released soul. The promo copies are particularly sought after you will notice the DJ copies are usually much more expensive and in some cases three times the value. As with other EMI labels the early 60's the promotional 45's were presented with a large red A on a white background, later using a white A on a green background. Classic Northern Soul titles with clean labels and unmarked vinyl command the highest prices with the promotional copies being the very pinnacle of UK soul collecting.
A Manship and Rylatt collaboration.

62	102	CHUCK JACKSON	ANY DAY NOW	THE PROPHET	28.00
62	102 DJ	CHUCK JACKSON	ANY DAY NOW	THE PROPHET	50.00
62	103	JIMMY SOUL	I CAN'T HOLD OUT ANY LONGER	TWISTIN' MATILDA	5.00

62	103 DJ	JIMMY SOUL	I CAN'T HOLD OUT ANY LONGER	TWISTIN' MATILDA	10.00
62	104	GARY CRISS	WELCOME HOME TO MY HEART	OUT FAVOURITE MELODIES	25.00
62	104 DJ	GARY CRISS	WELCOME HOME TO MY HEART	OUT FAVOURITE MELODIES	35.00
62	107	JOHNNY MORISETTE	ANY TIME ANY DAY ANY WHERE	MEET ME AT THE TWISTIN' PLACE	10.00
62	107 DJ	JOHNNY MORISETTE	ANY TIME ANY DAY ANY WHERE	MEET ME AT THE TWISTIN' PLACE	15.00
62	111	GARY (U.S.) BONDS	SEVEN DAY WEEKEND	GETTING' A GROOVE	6.00
62	111 DJ	GARY (U.S.) BONDS	SEVEN DAY WEEKEND	GETTING' A GROOVE	10.00
62	112	ISLEY BROTHERS	TWIST AND SHOUT	SPANISH TWIST	10.00
62	112 DJ	ISLEY BROTHERS	TWIST AND SHOUT	SPANISH TWIST	15.00
62	114	DON GARDNER & DEE DEE FORD	I NEED YOUR LOVING	TELL ME	25.00
62	114 DJ	DON GARDNER & DEE DEE FORD	I NEED YOUR LOVING	TELL ME	40.00
63	116	KENNY CHANDLER	HEART	WAIT FOR ME	6.00
63	116 DJ	KENNY CHANDLER	HEART	WAIT FOR ME	10.00
62	119	SHIRELLES	WELCOME HOME BABY	MAMA, HERE COMES THE BRIDE	12.00
62	119 DJ	SHIRELLES	WELCOME HOME BABY	MAMA, HERE COMES THE BRIDE	20.00
62	121	JERRY BUTLER	MAKE IT EASY ON YOURSELF	IT'S TOO LATE	20.00
62	121 DJ	JERRY BUTLER	MAKE IT EASY ON YOURSELF	IT'S TOO LATE	28.00
62	122	FOUR SEASONS	SHERRY	I'VE CRIED BEFORE	8.00
62	122 DJ	FOUR SEASONS	SHERRY	I'VE CRIED BEFORE	15.00
62	124	SHAWN ELLIOTT	AIN'T THAT A SHAME	GOODBYE MY LOVE	10.00
62	124 DJ	SHAWN ELLIOTT	AIN'T THAT A SHAME	GOODBYE MY LOVE	15.00
62	126	BOBBY LEWIS	I'M TOSSIN' AND TURNIN'	NOTHING BUT THE BLUES	12.00
62	126 DJ	BOBBY LEWIS	I'M TOSSIN' AND TURNIN'	NOTHING BUT THE BLUES	18.00
62	127	CHUCK JACKSON	WHO'S GONNA PICK UP THE PIECES	I KEEP FORGETTIN'	20.00
62	127 DJ	CHUCK JACKSON	WHO'S GONNA PICK UP THE PIECES	I KEEP FORGETTIN'	45.00
62	129	SHIRELLES	STOP THE MUSIC	IT'S LOVE THAT REALLY COUNTS	10.00
62	129 DJ	SHIRELLES	STOP THE MUSIC	IT'S LOVE THAT REALLY COUNTS	20.00
62	130	DON GARDNER & DEE DEE FORD	DON'T YOU WORRY	I'M COMING HOME TO STAY	25.00
62	130 DJ	DON GARDNER & DEE DEE FORD	DON'T YOU WORRY	I'M COMING HOME TO STAY	40.00
62	132	ISLEY BROTHERS	TWISTIN' WITH LINDA	YOU BETTER COME HOME	10.00
62	132 DJ	ISLEY BROTHERS	TWISTIN' WITH LINDA	YOU BETTER COME HOME	15.00
62	133	JIVE FIVE	WHAT TIME IS IT	BEGGING YOU PLEASE	50.00
62	133 DJ	JIVE FIVE	WHAT TIME IS IT	BEGGING YOU PLEASE	70.00
62	135	BUNKER HILL and the RAYMEN	HIDE & SEEK	HIDE & SEEK part 2	15.00
62	135 DJ	BUNKER HILL and the RAYMEN	HIDE & SEEK	HIDE & SEEK part 2	25.00
62	140	ESTHER PHILLIPS	RELEASE ME	DON'T FEEL RAINED ON	20.00
62	140 DJ	ESTHER PHILLIP	RELEASE ME	DON'T FEEL RAINED ON	30.00
62	142	LES COOPER & the SOUL ROCKERS	WIGGLE WOBBLE	DIG YOURSELF	20.00
62	142 DJ	LES COOPER & the SOUL ROCKERS	WIGGLE WOBBLE	DIG YOURSELF	30.00
63	145	FOUR SEASONS	BIG GIRL'S DON'T CRY	CONNIE-O	8.00
63	145 DJ	FOUR SEASONS	BIG GIRL'S DON'T CRY	CONNIE-O	15.00
63	146	TAMS	UNTIE ME	DISILLUSIONED	40.00
63	146 DJ	TAMS	UNTIE ME	DISILLUSIONED	60.00
63	148	MARK VALENTINO	WALKING ALONE	THE PUSH AND KICK	30.00
63	148 DJ	MARK VALENTINO	WALKING ALONE	THE PUSH AND KICK	50.00
63	149	JOHNNY THUNDER	LOOP DE LOOP	DON'T BE ASHAMED	8.00
63	149 DJ	JOHNNY THUNDER	LOOP DE LOOP	DON'T BE ASHAMED	15.00
63	152	SHIRELLES	EVERYBODY LOVES A LOVER	I DON'T THINK SO	10.00
63	152 DJ	SHIRELLES	EVERYBODY LOVES A LOVER	I DON'T THINK SO	15.00
63	153	EARLS	REMEMBER THEN	LET'S WADDLE	30.00
63	153 DJ	EARLS	REMEMBER THEN	LET'S WADDLE	40.00
63	157	DIONNE WARWICK	DON'T MAKE ME OVER	SMILED YESTERDAY	20.00
63	157 DJ	DIONNE WARWICK	DON'T MAKE ME OVER	SMILED YESTERDAY	30.00
63	158	JERRY BUTLER	YOU CAN RUN BUT YOU CAN'T HIDE	I'M THE ONE	30.00
63	158 DJ	JERRY BUTLER	YOU CAN RUN BUT YOU CAN'T HIDE	I'M THE ONE	50.00
63	160	TIPPIE and the CLOVERS	MY HEART SAID	BOSSA NOVA BABY	20.00
63	160 DJ	TIPPIE and the CLOVERS	MY HEART SAID	BOSSA NOVA BABY	28.00
63	164	GARY CRISS	I MISS YOU SO	LONG LONELY NIGHTS	10.00
63	164 DJ	GARY CRISS	I MISS YOU SO	LONG LONELY NIGHTS	15.00
63	166	KENNY CHANDLER	HEART	WAIT FOR ME	8.00
63	166 DJ	KENNY CHANDLER	HEART	WAIT FOR ME	12.00
63	168	JOHNNY THUNDER	THE ROSY DANCE	ROCK-A-BYE MY DARLING	5.00
63	168 DJ	JOHNNY THUNDER	THE ROSY DANCE	ROCK-A-BYE MY DARLING	8.00
63	169	FOUR SEASONS	WALK LIKE A MAN	LUCKY LADYBUG	8.00
63	169 DJ	FOUR SEASONS	WALK LIKE A MAN	LUCKY LADYBUG	15.00
63	170	JERRY BUTLER	YOU GOT RIGHT THROUGH ME	THE WISHING STAR	12.00
63	170 DJ	JERRY BUTLER	YOU GO RIGHT THROUGHT ME	THE WISHING STAR	18.00
63	171	CHUCK JACKSON	TELL HIM I'M NOT HOME	GETTING READY FOR THE HEART	25.00
63	171 DJ	CHUCK JACKSON	TELL HIM I'M NOT HOME	GETTING READY FOR THE HEART	45.00
63	172	CHIFFONS	HE'S SO FINE	OH MY LOVER	8.00
63	172 DJ	CHIFFONS	HE'S SO FINE	OH MY LOVER	25.00
63	178	JIMMY SOUL	IF YOU WANNA BE HAPPY	DON'T RELEASE ME	8.00
63	178 DJ	JIMMY SOUL	IF YOU WANNA BE HAPPY	DON'T RELEASE ME	25.00
63	180	DEE CLARK	I'M A SOLDIER BOY	SHOOK UP OVER YOU	20.00
63	180 DJ	DEE CLARK	I'M A SOLDIER BOY	SHOOK UP OVER YOU	30.00
63	181	SHIRELLES	FOOLISH LITTLE GIRL	NOT FOR ALL THE MONEY IN THE W	10.00
63	181 DJ	SHIRELLES	FOOLISH LITTLE GIRL	NOT FOR ALL THE MONEY IN THE W	15.00
63	182	FURYS	NEVER MORE	ZING, WENT THE STRINGS OF MY H	40.00
63	182 DJ	FURYS	NEVER MORE	ZING, WENT THE STRINGS OF MY H	75.00

Tamla Motown Extended - Plays

HITSVILLE U.S.A. No.1.   mono

HITSVILLE U.S.A. No.1

Baby don't you do it—Marvin Gaye

I'll always love you—Brenda Holloway

Devil in his heart—Carolyn Crawford

Candy to me—Eddie Holland

YOU'VE BEEN IN LOVE TOO LONG
NOWHERE TO RUN + QUICKSAND   mono

Hittin'

MARTHA AND THE VANDELLAS

MY GUY • OH! LITTLE BOY
WHAT'S EASY FOR TWO
YOU LOST THE SWEETEST BOY   mono

Mary Wells

MY GIRL, I'LL BE IN TROUBLE
WHY YOU WANNA MAKE ME BLUE
THE GIRL'S ALRIGHT WITH ME   mono

The Temptations

A LITTLE MORE LOVE • ANOTHER TRAIN COMING
LOOKING FOR THE RIGHT GUY
GO AHEAD AND LAUGH   mono

KIM WESTON

CAN YOU JERK LIKE ME
THAT DAY WHEN SHE NEEDED ME • CAN YOU DO IT
I'LL STAND BY YOU   mono

THE CONTOURS

Tamla Motown Extended-Plays

Tamla Motown — mono

- BABY LOVE
- COME SEE ABOUT ME
- WHERE DID OUR LOVE GO
- WHEN THE LOVELIGHT STARTS SHINING THROUGH HIS EYES

THE SUPREMES

Tamla Motown — mono

- SHAKE AND FINGERPOP ★ DO THE BOOMERANG
- CLEO'S BACK ★ SHOTGUN

shake and fingerpop

Jr. walker and the all stars

Tamla Motown — mono

- DANCING IN THE STREET · LIVE WIRE
- WILD ONE · IN MY LONELY ROOM

Martha and the Vandellas

Tamla Motown — mono

- I CAN'T HELP MYSELF ★ ASK THE LONELY
- SOMETHING ABOUT YOU ★ IT'S THE SAME OLD SONG

Four Tops

Tamla Motown — mono

- MY BABY · SINCE I LOST MY BABY
- IT'S GROWING
- THE WAY YOU DO THE THINGS YOU DO

IT'S THE TEMPTATIONS

Tamla Motown — mono

- SHAKE · CHAIN GANG
- HAVIN' A PARTY · GOOD NEWS

SHAKE
THE SUPREMES

Tamla Motown Extended - Plays

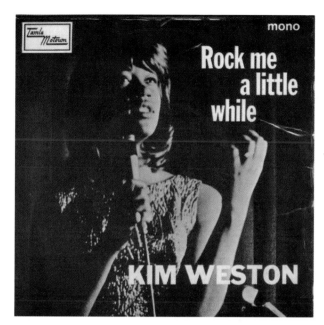

mono

Rock me a little while

KIM WESTON

AIN'T THAT PECULIAR • PRETTY LITTLE BABY
I'LL BE DOGGONE • HOW SWEET IT IS

mono

marvin gaye

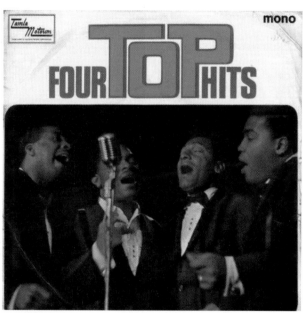

mono

FOUR TOP HITS

mono

originals from marvin gaye

FINGERTIPS • HAPPY STREET
HEY HARMONICA MAN • SQUARE

mono

Stevie Wonder

TOO MANY FISH IN THE SEA
HE'S A GOOD GUY • YOU'RE MY REMEDY
LITTLE GIRL BLUE

mono

the marvelettes

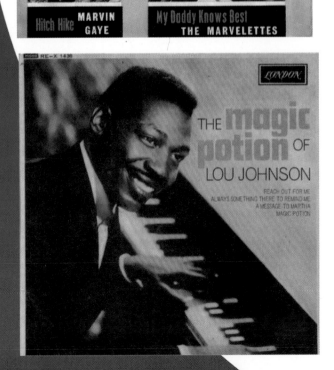

PYE

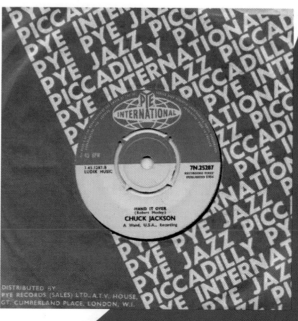

LONDON

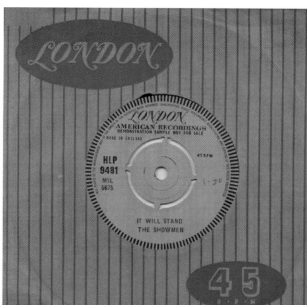

Beacon - Island - Direct - Fontana - Immediate - Planet

63	184	HARMONICA FATS	TORE UP	I GET SO TIRED		28.00
63	184 DJ	HARMONICA FATS	TORE UP	I GET SO TIRED		40.00
63	185	GENE CHANDLER	YOU THREW A LUCKY PUNCH	RAINBOW		30.00
63	185 DJ	GENE CHANDLER	YOU THREW A LUCKY PUNCH	RAINBOW		50.00
63	188	MAXINE BROWN	YESTERDAY'S KISSES	ASK ME		40.00
63	188 DJ	MAXINE BROWN	YESTERDAY'S KISSES	ASK ME		70.00
63	189	LORD NELSON	I GOT AN ITCH	PROBLEMS ON ME MIND		22.00
63	189 DJ	LORD NELSON	I GOT AN ITCH	PROBLEMS ON ME MIND		30.00
63	190	DAVID THORNE	DON'T LET IT GET AWAY	ONE MORE FOOL ONE MORE BROKEN HEART		15.00
63	190 DJ	DAVID THORNE	DON'T LET IT GET AWAY	ONE MORE FOOL ONE MORE BROKEN HEART		25.00
63	191	DIONNE WARWICK	THIS EMPTY PLACE	WISHIN' AND HOPIN'		25.00
63	191 DJ	DIONNE WARWICK	THIS EMPTY PLACE	WISHIN' AND HOPIN'		40.00
63	194	FOUR SEASONS	AIN'T THAT A SHAME	SOON (I'LL BE HOME AGAIN)		6.00
63	194 DJ	FOUR SEASONS	AIN'T THAT A SHAME	SOON (I'LL BE HOME AGAIN)		15.00
63	195	JERRY BUTLER	WHATEVER YOU WANT	YOU WON'T BE SORRY		15.00
63	195 DJ	JERRY BUTLER	WHATEVER YOU WANT	YOU WON'T BE SORRY		22.00
63	198	FOUR PENNIES	MY BLOCK	DRY YOUR EYES		30.00
63	198 DJ	FOUR PENNIES	MY BLOCK	DRY YOUR EYES		45.00
63	200	JOHNNY THUNDER	OUTLAW	JAILER, BRING ME WATER		20.00
63	200 DJ	JOHNNY THUNDER	OUTLAW	JAILER, BRING ME WATER		30.00
63	202	CHIFFONS	ONE FINE DAY	WHY AM I SO SHY		5.00
63	202 DJ	CHIFFONS	ONE FINE DAY	WHY AM I SO SHY		20.00
63	203	JOHN LEE HOOKER	BOOM BOOM	FRISCO BLUES		25.00
63	203 DJ	JOHN LEE HOOKER	BOOM BOOM	FRISCO BLUES		45.00
63	204	ROSCO GORDON	JUST A LITTLE BIT	WHAT I WOULDN'T DO		30.00
63	204 DJ	ROSCO GORDON	JUST A LITTLE BIT	WHAT I WOULDN'T DO		50.00
63	205	JIMMY REED	SHAME SHAME SHAME	LET'S GET TOGETHER		20.00
63	205 DJ	JIMMY REED	SHAME SHAME SHAME	LET'S GET TOGETHER		35.00
63	206	FIVE DU-TONES	SHAKE A TAIL FEATHER	DIVORCE COURT		25.00
63	206 DJ	FIVE DU-TONES	SHAKE A TAIL FEATHER	DIVORCE COURT		45.00
63	213	SHIRELLES	DON'T SAY GOODNIGHT AND MEAN	I DIDN'T MEAN TO HURT YOU		10.00
63	213 DJ	SHIRELLES	DON'T SAY GOODNIGHT AND MEAN	I DIDN'T MEAN TO HURT YOU		15.00
63	216	FOUR SEASONS	CANDY GIRL	MARLENA		8.00
63	216 DJ	FOUR SEASONS	CANDY GIRL	MARLENA		15.00
63	218	ISLEY BROTHERS	NOBODY BUT ME	I'M LAUGHING TO KEEP FROM CRYI		15.00
63	218 DJ	ISLEY BROTHERS	NOBODY BUT ME	I'M LAUGHING TO KEEP FROM CRYI		25.00
63	222 unissued	DIONNE WARWICK	PLEASE LET HIM LOVE ME	MAKE THE MUSIC PLAY		UN
63	223	SAPPHIRES	YOUR TRUE LOVE	WHERE IS JOHNNY		30.00
63	223 DJ	SAPPHIRES	YOUR TRUE LOVE	WHERE IS JOHNNY		45.00
63	224	SWANS	HE'S MINE	YOU BETTER BE A GOOD GIRL NOW		15.00
63	224 DJ	SWANS	HE'S MINE	YOU BETTER BE A GOOD GIRL NOW		25.00
63	227	JAYNETTS	SALLY GO ROUND THE ROSES	same: instrumental		10.00
63	227 DJ	JAYNETTS	SALLY GO ROUND THE ROSES	same: instrumental		20.00
63	228	MARTHA & THE VANDELLAS	HEAT WAVE	A LOVE LIKE YOURS		45.00
63	228 DJ	MARTHA & THE VANDELLAS	HEAT WAVE	A LOVE LIKE YOURS		125.00
63	229	JOHNNY THUNDER	EVERTYBODY LIKES TO DANCE WITH	HEY CHILD		8.00
63	229 DJ	JOHNNY THUNDER	EVERTYBODY LIKES TO DANCE WITH	HEY CHILD		15.00
63	230	CHIFFONS	A LOVE SO FINE	ONLY MY FRIEND		10.00
63	230 DJ	CHIFFONS	A LOVE SO FINE	ONLY MY FRIEND		25.00
63	232	SHIRELLES	WHAT DOES A GIRL DO	DON'T LET IT HAPPEN TO US		10.00
63	232 DJ	SHIRELLES	WHAT DOES A GIRL DO	DON'T LET IT HAPPEN TO US		15.00
63	237	EMOTIONS	A STORY UNTOLD	ONE LIFE ONE LOVE ONE YOU		20.00
63	237 DJ	EMOTIONS	A STORY UNTOLD	ONE LIFE ONE LOVE ONE YOU		28.00
63	238	LITTLE STEVIE WONDER	WORKOUT STEVIE, WORKOUT	MONKEY TALK		40.00
63	238 DJ	LITTLE STEVIE WONDER	WORKOUT STEVIE, WORKOUT	MONKEY TALK		100.00
63	242 DJ	MARY WELLS	YOU LOST THE SWEETEST BOY	WHAT'S EASY FOR TWO IS HARD FOR ONE		150.00

red A on the "You Lost The Sweetest Boy" side, first press

63	242	MARY WELLS	YOU LOST THE SWEETEST BOY	WHAT'S EASY FOR TWO IS HARD FOR ONE		30.00
63	242 DJ	MARY WELLS	WHAT'S EASY FOR TWO IS SO HARD FOR ONE	YOU LOST THE SWEETEST BOY		100.00

red A on the "What's Easy For Two.." side, second press

63	242	MARY WELLS	WHAT'S EASY FOR TWO IS SO HARD FOR ONE	YOU LOST THE SWEETEST BOY		22.00
63	243	MARVIN GAYE	CAN I GET A WITNESS	I'M CRAZY ABOUT MY BABY		30.00
63	243 DJ	MARVIN GAYE	CAN I GET A WITNESS	I'M CRAZY ABOUT MY BABY		100.00
63	244	FOUR PENNIES	WHEN THE BOYS HAPPY (THE GIRL'S	HOCKADAY part 1		25.00
63	244 DJ	FOUR PENNIES	WHEN THE BOYS HAPPY (THE GIRL'S	HOCKADAY part 1		35.00
63	246	LENA HORNE	NOW !	SILENT SPRING		5.00
63	246 DJ	LENA HORNE	NOW !	SILENT SPRING		8.00
64	249	DEAN & JEAN	TRA LA LA LA SUZY	I LOVE SUMMERTIME		10.00
64	249 DJ	DEAN & JEAN	TRA LA LA LA SUZY	I LOVE SUMMERTIME		15.00
64	250	MARTHA & THE VANDELLAS	QUICKSAND	DARLING, I HUM OUR SONG		30.00
64	250 DJ	MARTHA & THE VANDELLAS	QUICKSAND	DARLING, I HUM OUR SONG		100.00
64	251	MARVELETTES	AS LONG AS I KNOW HE'S MINE	LITTLE GIRL BLUE		40.00
64	251 DJ	MARVELETTES	AS LONG AS I KNOW HE'S MINE	LITTLE GIRL BLUE		100.00
64	252	JERRY BUTLER	NEED TO BELONG	GIVE ME YOUR LOVE		15.00
64	252 DJ	JERRY BUTLER	NEED TO BELONG	GIVE ME YOUR LOVE		25.00
64	254	CHIFFONS	I HAVE A BOYFRIEND	I'M GONNA DRY YOUR EYES		10.00
64	254 DJ	CHIFFONS	I HAVE A BOYFRIEND	I'M GONNA DRY YOUR EYES		15.00
64	257	SUPREMES	WHEN THE LOVELIGHT STARTS SHIN	STANDING AT THE CROSSROADS		45.00
64	257 DJ	SUPREMES	WHEN THE LOVELIGHT STARTS SHIN	STANDING AT THE CROSSROADS		100.00

64	259	BETTY EVERETT	YOU'RE NO GOOD	CHAINED TO YOUR LOVE	15.00
64	259 DJ	BETTY EVERETT	YOU'RE NO GOOD	CHAINED TO YOUR LOVE	30.00
64	260	FREDDY CANNON	THAT'S THE WAY GIRLS ARE	DO WHAT THE HIPPIES DO	15.00
64	260 DJ	FREDDY CANNON	THAT'S THE WAY GIRLS ARE	DO WHAT THE HIPPIES DO	22.00
64	261	BIG DEE IRWIN	DONKEY WALK	SOMEDAY YOU'LL UNDERSTAND WHY	10.00
64	261 DJ	BIG DEE IRWIN	DONKEY WALK	SOMEDAY YOU'LL UNDERSTAND WHY	15.00
64	262	FOUR SEASONS	PEANUTS	SILHOUETTES	10.00
64	262 DJ	FOUR SEASONS	PEANUTS	SILHOUETTES	15.00
64	263	MIRACLES	I GOTTA DANCE TO KEEP FROM CRYING	SUCH IS LOVE, SUCH IS LIFE	40.00
64	263 DJ	MIRACLES	I GOTTA DANCE TO KEEP FROM CRYING	SUCH IS LOVE, SUCH IS LIFE	100.00
64	267	SAPPHIRES	WHO DO YOU LOVE	OH SO SOON	20.00
64	267 DJ	SAPPHIRES	WHO DO YOU LOVE	OH SO SOON	30.00
64	270	DIANE RENAY	UNBELIEVABLE GUY	NAVY BLUE	15.00
64	270 DJ	DIANE RENAY	UNBELIEVABLE GUY	NAVY BLUE	20.00
64	271	GARY US BONDS	NEW ORLEANS	A QUARTER TO THREE	6.00
64	271 DJ	GARY US BONDS	NEW ORLEANS	A QUARTER TO THREE	10.00
64	272	MARTHA & THE VANDELLAS	LIVE WIRE	OLD LOVE (LET'S TRY IT AGAIN)	40.00
64	272 DJ	MARTHA & THE VANDELLAS	LIVE WIRE	OLD LOVE (LET'S TRY IT AGAIN)	100.00
64	273	MARVELETTES	HE'S A GOOD GUY (YES HE IS)	GODDESS OF LOVE	75.00
64	273 DJ	MARVELETTES	HE'S A GOOD GUY (YES HE IS)	GODDESS OF LOVE	125.00
64	274	JIMMY SOUL	I HATE YOU BABY	CHANGE PARTNERS	10.00
64	274 DJ	JIMMY SOUL	I HATE YOU BABY	CHANGE PARTNERS	15.00
64	275	BROTHER JACK McDUFF	SANCTIFIED SAMBA	WHISTLE WHILE YOU WORK	10.00
64	275 DJ	BROTHER JACK McDUFF	SANCTIFIED SAMBA	WHISTLE WHILE YOU WORK	15.00
64	277	LAZY LESTER	I'M A LOVER NOT A FIGHTER	SUGAR COATED LOVE	30.00
64	277 DJ	LAZY LESTER	I'M A LOVER NOT A FIGHTER	SUGAR COATED LOVE	40.00
64	278	TEMPTATIONS	THE WAY YOU DO THE THINGS YOU DO	JUST LET ME KNOW	45.00
64	278 DJ	TEMPTATIONS	THE WAY YOU DO THE THINGS YOU DO	JUST LET ME KNOW	100.00
64	280	BETTY EVERETT	THE SHOOP SHOOP SONG	HANDS OFF	22.00
64	280 DJ	BETTY EVERETT	THE SHOOP SHOOP SONG	HANDS OFF	35.00
64	281	LORD NELSON	PROUS WEST INDIAN	IT'S DELINQUENCY	15.00
64	281 DJ	LORD NELSON	PROUS WEST INDIAN	IT'S DELINQUENCY	22.00
64	282	MIRACLES	THE MAN IN YOU	HEARTBREAK ROAD	30.00
64	282 DJ	MIRACLES	THE MAN IN YOU	HEARTBREAK ROAD	85.00
64	283	DEAN & JEAN	HEY JEAN HEY DEAN	PLEASE DON'T TELL ME HOW	15.00
64	283 DJ	DEAN & JEAN	HEY JEAN HEY DEAN	PLEASE DON'T TELL ME HOW	20.00
64	284	MARVIN GAYE	YOU'RE A WONDERFUL ONE	WHEN I'M ALONE I CRY	30.00
64	284 DJ	MARVIN GAYE	YOU'RE A WONDERFUL ONE	WHEN I'M ALONE I CRY	**148.00**
64	285	LITTLE STEVIE WONDER	CASTLES IN THE SAND	THANK YOU	45.00
64	285 DJ	LITTLE STEVIE WONDER	CASTLES IN THE SAND	THANK YOU	85.00
64	287	TRACY DEY	GONNA GET ALONG WITHOUT YOU	GO AWAY	15.00
64	287 DJ	TRACY DEY	GONNA GET ALONG WITHOUT YOU	GO AWAY	20.00
64	288	MARY WELLS	MY GUY	OH LITTLE BOY	10.00
64	288 DJ	MARY WELLS	MY GUY	OH LITTLE BOY	100.00
64	290	DIANE RENAY	SOFT SPOKEN GUY	KISS ME SAILOR	10.00
64	290 DJ	DIANE RENAY	SOFT SPOKEN GUY	KISS ME SAILOR	15.00
64	294	REFLECTIONS	(JUST LIKE) ROMEO AND JULIET	CAN'T YOU TELL BY THE LOOK IN	45.00
64	294 DJ	REFLECTIONS	(JUST LIKE) ROMEO AND JULIET	CAN'T YOU TELL BY THE LOOK IN	125.00
64	297	JOHN LEE HOOKER	DIMPLES	I'M LEAVING	20.00
64	297 DJ	JOHN LEE HOOKER	DIMPLES	I'M LEAVING	40.00
64	299	CONTOURS	CAN YOU DO IT	I'LL STAND BY YOU	30.00
64	299 DJ	CONTOURS	CAN YOU DO IT	I'LL STAND BY YOU	100.00
64	300	JERRY BUTLER	GIVING UP ON LOVE	I'VE BEEN TRYING	25.00
64	300 DJ	JERRY BUTLER	GIVING UP ON LOVE	I'VE BEEN TRYING	40.00
64	302	BROTHER JACK McDUFF	ROCKY CANDY	A REAL GOOD 'UN	15.00
64	302 DJ	BROTHER JACK McDUFF	ROCKY CANDY	A REAL GOOD 'UN	20.00
64	304	JIMMY WITHERSPOON	MONEY IS GETTING' CHEAPER	EVENIN'	15.00
64	304 DJ	JIMMY WITHERSPOON	MONEY IS GETTING' CHEAPER	EVENIN'	20.00
64	305	MARTHA & THE VANDELLAS	IN MY LONELY ROOM	A TEAR FOR A GIRL	45.00
64	305 DJ	MARTHA & THE VANDELLAS	IN MY LONELY ROOM	A TEAR FOR THE GIRL	120.00
64	307	BRENDA HOLLOWAY	EVERY LITTLE BIT HURTS	LAND OF A THOUSAND BOYS	75.00
64	307 DJ	BRENDA HOLLOWAY	EVERY LITTLE BIT HURTS	LAND OF A THOUSAND BOYS	130.00
64	311	BERNADETTE CARROLL	PARTY GIRL	I DON'T WANNA KNOW	8.00
64	311 DJ	BERNADETTE CARROLL	PARTY GIRL	I DON'T WANNA KNOW	10.00
64	313	DEAN & JEAN	THREAD YOR NEEDLE	I WANNA BE LOVED	15.00
64	313 DJ	RONNIE DOVE	SWEETER THAN SUGAR	I BELIEVED IN YOU	5.00
64	314 DJ	RONNIE DOVE	SWEETER THAN SUGAR	I BELIEVED IN YOU	8.00
64	315	FOUR SEASONS	ALONE	LONG LONELY NIGHTS	8.00
64	315 DJ	FOUR SEASONS	ALONE	LONG LONELY NIGHTS	10.00
64	316	MARY WELLS and MARVIN GAYE	WHAT'S THE MATTER WITH YOU BABY	ONCE UPON A TIME	22.00
64	316 DJ	MARY WELLS and MARVIN GAYE	WHAT'S THE MATTER WITH YOU BABY	ONCE UPON A TIME	85.00
64	318	GLADYS KNIGHT & The PIPS	GIVING UP	MAYBE, MAYBE BABY	30.00
64	318 DJ	GLADYS KNIGHT & The PIPS	GIVING UP	MAYBE, MAYBE BABY	45.00
64	319	TEMPTATIONS	I'LL BE IN TROUBLE	THE GIRL'S ALRIGHT WITH ME	60.00
64	319 DJ	TEMPTATIONS	I'LL BE IN TROUBLE	THE GIRL'S ALRIGHT WITH ME	100.00
64	321	BETTY EVERETT	I CAN'T HEAR YOU	CAN I GET TO KNOW YOU	20.00
64	321 DJ	BETTY EVERETT	I CAN'T HEAR YOU	CAN I GET TO KNOW YOU	30.00
64	322	PATTY & THE EMBLEMS	MIXED-UP, SHOOK-UP, GIRL	ORDINARY GIRL	40.00
64	322 DJ	PATTY & THE EMBLEMS	MIXED-UP, SHOOK-UP, GIRL	ORDINARY GIRL	75.00

64	323	STEVIE WONDER	HEY HARMONICA MAN	THIS LITTLE GIRL	30.00
64	323 DJ	STEVIE WONDER	HEY HARMONICA MAN	THIS LITTLE GIRL	85.00
64	324	MIRACLES	I LIKE IT LIKE THAT	YOU'RE SO FINE AND SWEET	40.00
64	324 DJ	MIRACLES	I LIKE IT LIKE THAT	YOU'RE SO FINE AND SWEET	85.00
64	325	JIMMY WITHERSPOON	I WILL NEVER MARRY	I'M COMING DOWN WITH THE BLUES	15.00
64	325 DJ	JIMMY WITHERSPOON	I WILL NEVER MARRY	I'M COMING DOWN WITH THE BLUES	20.00
64	326	MARVIN GAYE	TRY IT BABY	IF MY HEART COULD SING	30.00
64	326 DJ	MARVIN GAYE	TRY IT BABY	IF MY HEART COULD SING	85.00
64	327	SUPREMES	WHERE DID OUR LOVE GO	HE MEANS THE WORLD TO ME	10.00
64	327 DJ	SUPREMES	WHERE DID OUR LOVE GO	HE MEANS THE WORLD TO ME	100.00
64	328	BROTHER JACK McDUFF	CARPETBAGGERS	THE PINK PANTHER	10.00
64	328 DJ	BROTHER JACK McDUFF	CARPETBAGGERS	THE PINK PANTHER	15.00
64	330	JIMMY REED	SHAME, SHAME,SHAME	LET'S GET TOGETHER	15.00
64	330 DJ	JIMMY REED	SHAME, SHAME,SHAME	LET'S GET TOGETHER	25.00
64	331	GENE CHANDLER	JUST BE TRUE	A SONG CALLED SOUL	15.00
64	331 DJ	GENE CHANDLER	JUST BE TRUE	A SONG CALLED SOUL	25.00
64	332	CHIFFONS	SAILOR BOY	WHEN SUMMER'S THROUGH	10.00
64	332 DJ	CHIFFONS	SAILOR BOY	WHEN SUMMER'S THROUGH	15.00
64	334	MARVELETTES	YOU'RE MY REMEDY	A LITTLE BIT OF SYMPATHY..	40.00
64	334 DJ	MARVELETTES	YOU'RE MY REMEDY	A LITTLE BIT OF SYMPATHY A LIT	85.00
64	335	PRINCE BUSTER	30 PIECES OF SILVER	EVERYBODY SKA	30.00
64	335 DJ	PRINCE BUSTER	30 PIECES OF SILVER	EVERYBODY SKA	40.00
64	336	FOUR TOPS	BABY I NEED YOUR LOVING	CALL ON ME	60.00
64	336 DJ	FOUR TOPS	BABY I NEED YOUR LOVING	CALL ON ME	**259.00**
64	337	JOHNNY THUNDER	MORE, MORE, MORE LOVE, LOVE, LOVE	SHOUT IT TO THE WORLD	8.00
64	337 DJ	JOHNNY THUNDER	MORE, MORE, MORE LOVE, LOVE, LOVE	SHOUT IT TO THE WORLD	12.00
64	339	BETTY EVERETT& JERRYBUTLER	LET IT BE ME	AIN'T THAT LOVING YOU BABY	10.00
64	339 DJ	BETTY EVERETT& JERRYBUTLER	LET IT BE ME	AIN'T THAT LOVING YOU BABY	15.00
64	340	LITTLE RICHARD	WHOLE LOTTA SHAKIN' GOIN' ON	GOODNIGHT IRENE	8.00
64	340 DJ	LITTLE RICHARD	WHOLE LOTTA SHAKIN' GOIN' ON	GOODNIGHT IRENE	10.00
64	341	JOHN LEE HOOKER	SEND ME YOUR PILLOW	I LOVE YOU HONEY	20.00
64	341 DJ	JOHN LEE HOOKER	SEND ME YOUR PILLOW	I LOVE YOU HONEY	30.00
64	342	JIMMY CLIFF	ONE EYED JACKS	KING OF KINGS	20.00
64	342 DJ	JIMMY CLIFF	ONE EYED JACKS	KING OF KINGS	30.00
64	343	FOUR SEASONS	SINCE I DON'T HAVE YOU	SINCERELY	8.00
64	343 DJ	FOUR SEASONS	SINCE I DON'T HAVE YOU	SINCERELY	10.00
64	344	LENA HORNE	BLOWING IN THE WIND	THE EAGLE AND ME	5.00
64	344 DJ	LENA HORNE	BLOWING IN THE WIND	THE EAGLE AND ME	6.00
64	345	MARTHA & THE VANDELLAS	DANCING IN THE STREET	THERE HE IS (AT MY DOOR)	20.00
64	345 DJ	MARTHA & THE VANDELLAS	DANCING IN THE STREET	THERE HE IS (AT MY DOOR)	100.00
64	348	TEMPTATIONS	WHY YOU WANNA MAKE ME BLUE	BABY, BABY I NEED YOU	75.00
64	348 DJ	TEMPTATIONS	WHY YOU WANNA MAKE ME BLUE	BABY, BABY I NEED YOU	**275.00**
64	350	SUPREMES	BABY LOVE	ASK ANY GIRL	10.00
64	350 DJ	SUPREMES	BABY LOVE	ASK ANY GIRL	100.00
64	352	GLADYS KNIGHT & The PIPS	LOVERS ALWAYS FORGIVE	ANOTHER LOVE	30.00
64	352 DJ	GLADYS KNIGHT & The PIPS	LOVERS ALWAYS FORGIVE	ANOTHER LOVE	50.00
64	353	MIRACLES	THAT'S WHAT LOVE IS MADE OF	WOULD I LOVE YOU	20.00
64	353 DJ	MIRACLES	THAT'S WHAT LOVE IS MADE OF	WOULD I LOVE YOU	85.00
64	354	MICKEY LEE LANE	SHAGGY DOG	OO OO	15.00
64	354 DJ	MICKEY LEE LANE	SHAGGY DOG	OO OO	22.00
64	355	DEE CLARK	WARM SUMMER BREEZES	HEARTBREAK	15.00
64	355 DJ	DEE CLARK	WARM SUMMER BREEZES	HEARTBREAK	25.00
64	357	EARL VAN DYKE	SOUL STOMP	HOT 'N' TOT	100.00
64	357 DJ	EARL VAN DYKE	SOUL STOMP	HON'N' TOT	150.00
64	359	KIM WESTON	A LITTLE MORE LOVE	GO AHEAD AND LAUGH	150.00
64	359 DJ	KIM WESTON	A LITTLE MORE LOVE	GO AHEAD AND LAUGH	200.00
64	360	MARVIN GAYE	HOW SWEET IT IS TO BE LOVED BY	FOREVER	40.00
64	360 DJ	MARVIN GAYE	HOW SWEET IT IS TO BE LOVED BY	FOREVER	135.00
64	361	VELVELETTES	NEEDLE IN A HAYSTACK	SHOULD I TELL THEM	45.00
64	361 DJ	VELVELETTES	NEEDLE IN A HAYSTACK	SHOULD I TELL THEM	**171.00**
64	362	JIMMY WITHERSPOON	YOU'RE NEXT	HAPPY BLUES	20.00
64	362 DJ	JIMMY WITHERSPOON	YOU'RE NEXT	HAPPY BLUES	30.00
64	363	MARVIN GAYE & KIM WESTON	I WANT YOU AROUND	WHAT GOOD AM I WITHOUT YOU	30.00
64	363 DJ	MARVIN GAYE & KIM WESTON	I WANT YOU AROUND	WHAT GOOD AM I WITHOUT YOU	85.00
64	364	GENE CHANDLER	BLESS OUR LOVE	LONDON TOWN	15.00
64	364 DJ	GENE CHANDLER	BLESS OUR LOVE	LONDON TOWN	20.00
64	369	MARVELETTES	TOO MANY FISH IN THE SEA	A NEED FOR LOVE	45.00
64	369 DJ	MARVELETTES	TOO MANY FISH IN THE SEA	A NEED FOR LOVE	100.00
64	370	JOHNNY THUNDER	SEND HER TO ME	EVERYBODY LIKES TO DANCE WITH	30.00
64	370 DJ	JOHNNY THUNDER	SEND HER TO ME	EVERYBODY LIKES TO DANCE WITH	45.00
64	371	FOUR TOPS	WITHOUT THE ONE YOU LOVE	LOVE HAS GONE	60.00
64	371 DJ	FOUR TOPS	WITHOUT THE ONE YOU LOVE	LOVE HAS GONE	120.00
64	372	MARY WELLS	AIN'T THAT THE TRUTH	STOP TAKIN' ME FOR GRANTED	20.00
64	372 DJ	MARY WELLS	AIN'T IT THE TRUTH	STOP TAKIN'ME FOR GRANTED	50.00
64	374	JIMMY RADCLIFFE	LONG AFTER TONIGHT IS ALL OVER	WHAT I WANT I CAN NEVER HAVE	60.00
64	374 DJ	JIMMY RADCLIFFE	LONG AFTER TONIGHT IS ALL OVER	WHAT I WANT I CAN NEVER HAVE	**288.00**
64	376	SUPREMES	COME SEE ABOUT ME	ALWAYS IN MY HEART	10.00
64	376 DJ	SUPREMES	COME SEE ABOUT ME	ALWAYS IN MY HEART	100.00
64	377	MIRACLES	COME ON DO THE JERK	BABY DON'T YOU GO	30.00

64	377 DJ	MIRACLES	COME ON DO THE JERK	BABY DON'T YOU GO	85.00
65	378	TEMPTATIONS	MY GIRL	NOBODY BUT MY BABY	30.00
65	378 DJ	TEMPTATIONS	MY GIRL	NOBODY BUT MY BABY	100.00
65	381	CONTOURS	CAN YOU JERK LIKE ME	THAT DAY WHEN SHE NEEDED ME	35.00
65	381 DJ	CONTOURS	CAN YOU JERK LIKE ME	THAT DAY WHEN SHE NEEDED ME	85.00
65	382	REPARATA & the DELRONS	HE'S MY GUY	WHENEVER A TEENAGER CRIES	15.00
65	382 DJ	REPARATA & the DELRONS	HE'S MY GUY	WHENEVER A TEENAGER CRIES	22.00
65	383	MARTHA & THE VANDELLAS	WILD ONE	DANCING SLOW	30.00
65	383 DJ	MARTHA & THE VANDELLAS	WILD ONE	DANCING SLOW	85.00
65	384	CAROLYN CRAWFORD	WHEN SOMEONE'S GOOD TO YOU	MY HEART	200.00
65	384 DJ	CAROLYN CRAWFORD	WHEN SOMEONE IS GOOD TO YOU	MY HEART	275.00
65	385	SAMMY AMBROSE	THIS DIAMOND RING	BAD NIGHT	100.00
65	385 DJ	SAMMY AMBROSE	THIS DIAMOND RING	BAD NIGHT	150.00
65	386	ALVIN CASH & the CRAWLERS	TWINE TIME	THE BUMP	30.00
65	386 DJ	ALVIN CASH & the CRAWLERS	TWINE TIME	THE BUMP	75.00
65	387	VELVELETTES	HE WAS REALLY SAYIN' SOMETHING	THROW A FAREWELL KISS	60.00
65	387 DJ	VELVELETTES	HE WAS REALLY SAYIN' SOMETHING	THROW A FAREWELL KISS	150.00
65	388	GENE CHANDLER	IF YOU CAN'T BE TRUE (FIND A PART TIME)	WHAT NOW	35.00
65	388 DJ	GENE CHANDLER	IF YOU CAN'T BE TRUE (FIND A PART TIME)	WHAT NOW	50.00
65	394	TONY MARTIN	TALKIN' TO YOUR PICTURE	OUR RHAPSODY	75.00
65	394 DJ	TONY MARTIN	TALKIN' TO YOUR PICTURE	OUR RAPSODY	100.00
65	396	MARY WELLS	USE YOUR HEAD	EVERLOVIN' BOY	22.00
65	396 DJ	MARY WELLS	USE YOUR HEAD	EVERLOVIN' BOY	50.00
65	399	SAMMY AMBROSE	WELCOME TO DREAMSVILLE	MONKEY SEE MONKEY DO	175.00
65	399 DJ	SAMMY AMBROSE	WELCOME TO DREAMSVILLE	MONKEY SEE - MONKEY DO	275.00
65	400	DEE CLARK	T.C.B.	IT'S IMPOSSIBLE	18.00
65	400 DJ	DEE CLARK	T.C.B.	IT'S IMPOSSIBLE	28.00
65	401	GENE CHANDLER	YOU CAN'T HURT ME NO MORE	EVERYBODY LET'S DANCE	20.00
65	401 DJ	GENE CHANDLER	YOU CAN'T HURT ME NO MORE	EVERYBODY LET'S DANCE	40.00
65	402	CHARLIE GRACIE	HE'LL NEVER LOVE YOU LIKE I DO	KEEP MY LOVE NEXT TO YOR HEART	85.00
65	402 DJ	CHARLIE GRACIE	HE'LL NEVER LOVE YOU LIKE I DO	KEEP MY LOVE NEXT TO YOR HEART	125.00
65	403	CANNIBAL and the HEADHUNTERS	LAND OF A THOUSAND DANCES	I'LL SHOW YOU HOW TO LOVE	25.00
65	403 DJ	CANNIBAL and the HEADHUNTERS	LAND OF A THOUSAND DANCES	I'LL SHOW YOU HOW TO LOVE	40.00
65	404	BOBBY SHARP	BLUES FOR MR. CHARLIE PART1	BLUES FOR MISTER CHARLIE PART2	12.00
65	404 DJ	BOBBY SHARP	BLUES FOR MR. CHARLIE PART1	BLUES FOR MISTER CHARLIE PART2	20.00
65	406	REFLECTIONS	COMING AT YOU	POOR MAN'S SOON	30.00
65	406 DJ	REFLECTIONS	COMING AT YOU	POOR MAN'S SOON	50.00
65	407	IKETTES	PEACHES 'N' CREAM	THE BIGGEST PLAYERS	30.00
65	407 DJ	IKETTES	PEACHES 'N' CREAM	THE BIGGEST PLAYERS	50.00
65	410	JIMMY CLANTON	HURTING EACH OTHER	DON'T KEEP YOUR FRIENDS AWAY	50.00
65	410 DJ	JIMMY CLANTON	HURTING EACH OTHER	DON'T KEEP YOUR FRIENDS AWAY	75.00
65	411	SHARON SOUL	HOW CAN I GET TO YOU	DON'T SAY GOODBYE LOVE	100.00
65	411 DJ	SHARON SOUL	HOW CAN I GET TO YOU	DON'T SAY GOODBYE LOVE	150.00
65	412	RONNIE DOVE	ONE KISS FOR OLD TIMES SAKE	BLUEBIRD	5.00
65	412 DJ	RONNIE DOVE	ONE KISS FOR OLD TIMES SAKE	BLUEBIRD	8.00
65	413	THREE DEGREES	GEE BABY I'M SORRY	DO WHAT YOU'RE SUPPOSED TO DO	25.00
65	413 DJ	THREE DEGREES	GEE BABY I'M SORRY	DO WHAT YOU'RE SUPPOSED TO DO	40.00
65	414	REPARATA & the DELRONS	TOMMY	MOMMA DON'T ALLOW	10.00
65	414 DJ	REPARATA & the DELRONS	TOMMY	MOMMA DON'T ALLOW	15.00
65	415	MARY WELLS	NEVER, NEVER LEAVE ME	WHY DON'T YOU LET YOURSELF GO	22.00
65	415 DJ	MARY WELLS	NEVER, NEVER LEAVE ME	WHY DON'T YOU LET YOURSELF GO	45.00
65	419	MARIE KNIGHT	CRY ME A RIVER	COMES THE NIGHT	20.00
65	419 DJ	MARIE KNIGHT	CRY ME A RIVER	COMES THE NIGHT	30.00
65	425	GENE CHANDLER	NOTHING CAN STOP ME	THE BIG LIE	75.00
65	425 DJ	GENE CHANDLER	NOTHING CAN STOP ME	THE BIG LIE	125.00
65	427	GARY CRISS	IF THIS IS GOODBYE	HANDS OF BUDDY	30.00
65	427 DJ	GARY CRISS	IF THIS IS GOODBYE	HANDS OF BUDDY	45.00
65	429	JIMMY WITHERSPOON	COME WALK WITH ME	OH HOW I LOVE YOU	15.00
65	429 DJ	JIMMY WITHERSPOON	COME WALK WITH ME	OH HOW I LOVE YOU	20.00
65	434	IKETTES	(HE'S GONNA BE) FINE, FINE, FINE	HOW COME	20.00
65	434 DJ	IKETTES	(HE'S GONNA BE) FINE, FINE, FINE	HOW COME	30.00
65	435	CHRISTINE QUAITE	IF YOU'VE GOT A HEART	SO NEAR SO FAR	15.00
65	435 DJ	CHRISTINE QUAITE	IF YOU'VE GOT A HEART	SO NEAR SO FAR	20.00
65	437	CHIFFONS	NOBODY KNOWS WHAT'S GOIN' ON	THE REAL THING	20.00
65	437 DJ	CHIFFONS	NOBODY KNOWS WHAT'S GOIN' ON	THE REAL THING	40.00
65	439	MARY WELLS	HE'S A LOVER	I'M LEARNIN'	20.00
65	439 DJ	MARY WELLS	HE'S A LOVER	I'M LEARNIN'	50.00
65	441	LEE DORSEY	RIDE YOUR PONY	THE KITTY CAT SONG	10.00
65	441 DJ	LEE DORSEY	RIDE YOUR PONY	THE KITTY CAT SONG	**74.00**
65	446	STRANGELOVES	I WANT CANDY	IT'S ABOUT MY BABY	20.00
65	446 DJ	STRANGELOVES	I WANT CANDY	IT'S ABOUT MY BABY	30.00
65	450	BIG DEE IRWIN	YOU SATISFY MY NEEDS	I WANNA STAY RIGHT HERE WITH YOU	150.00
65	450 DJ	BIG DEE IRWIN	YOU SATISFY MY NEEDS	I WANNA STAY RIGHT HERE WITH YOU	225.00
65	453	INVITATIONS	WRITTEN ON THE WALL	HALLELUJAH	40.00
65	453 DJ	INVITATIONS	WRITTEN ON THE WALL	HALLELUJAH	75.00
65	454	JOHNNY THUNDER	DEAR JOHN I'M GOING TO LEAVE YOU	SUZIE-Q	8.00
65	454 DJ	JOHNNY THUNDER	DEAR JOHN I'M GOING TO LEAVE YOU	SUZIE-Q	10.00
65	455	ERNESTINE ANDERSON	SOMEBODY TOLD YOU	HOW MANY TIMES	8.00
65	455 DJ	ERNESTINE ANDERSON	SOMEBODY TOLD YOU	HOW MANY TIMES	10.00

65	456	MICKEY LEE LANE	HEY SAH-LO-NEY	OF YESTERDAY	100.00
65	456 DJ	MICKEY LEE LANE	HEY SAH-LO-NEY	OF YESTERDAY	170.00
65	458	GENE CHANDLER	GOOD TIMES	NO ONE CAN LOVE YOU (LIKE I DO	30.00
65	458 DJ	GENE CHANDLER	GOOD TIMES	NO ONE CAN LOVE YOU (LIKE I DO	50.00
65	459	THREE DEEGREES	GOTTA DRAW THE LINE	CLOSE YOUR EYES	100.00
65	459 DJ	THREE DEEGREES	GOTTA DRAW THE LINE	CLOSE YOUR EYES	200.00
65	460	TOYS	A LOVER'S CONCERTO	THIS NIGHT	6.00
65	460 DJ	TOYS	A LOVER'S CONCERTO	THIS NIGHT	30.00
65	461	JIMMY WITHERSPOON	LOVE ME RIGHT	MAKE MY HEART SMILE AGAIN	15.00
65	461 DJ	JIMMY WITHERSPOON	LOVE ME RIGHT	MAKE MY HEART SMILE AGAIN	20.00
65	463	MARY WELLS	ME WITHOUT YOU	I'M SORRY	20.00
65	463 DJ	MARY WELLS	ME WITHOUT YOU	I'M SORRY	30.00
65	465	LEE DORSEY	WORK WORK WORK	CAN YOU HEAR ME	10.00
65	465 DJ	LEE DORSEY	WORK WORK WORK	CAN YOU HEAR ME	15.00
65	466	CAROL VENTURA	PLEASE SOMEBODY HELP ME	THE OLD LADY OF THREADNEEDLE STREET	40.00
65	466 DJ	CAROL VENTURA	PLEASE SOMEBODY HELP ME	THE OLD LADY OF THREADNEEDLE STREET	75.00
65	470	FIVE EMPREES	LITTLE MISS SAD	HEY LOVER	15.00
65	470 DJ	FIVE EMPREES	LITTLE MISS SAD	HEY LOVER	25.00
65	474	CLARA WARD	GONNA BUILD A MOUNTAIN	GOD BLESS THE CHILD	8.00
65	474 DJ	CLARA WARD	GONNA BUILD A MOUNTAIN	GOD BLESS THE CHILD	10.00
65	475	BETTY HARRIS	I'M EVIL TONIGHT	WHAT A SAD FEELING	30.00
65	475 DJ	BETTY HARRIS	I'M EVIL TONIGHT	WHAT A SAD FEELING	50.00
65	476	JOHNNY THUNDER	EVERYBODY DO THE SLOOPY	BEAUTIFUL	10.00
65	476 DJ	JOHNNY THUNDER	EVERYBODY DO THE SLOOPY	BEAUTIFUL	15.00
65	477	LITTLE EVA	STAND BY ME	THAT'S MY MAN	25.00
65	477 DJ	LITTLE EVA	STAND BY ME	THAT'S MY MAN	40.00
65	478	INVITATIONS	WHAT'S WRONG WITH ME BABY	WHY DID MY BABY TURN BAD	175.00
65	478 DJ	INVITATIONS	WHAT'S WRONG WITH ME BABY	WHY DID MY BABY TURN BAD	**412.00**
65	479	GEORGE STONE	HOLE IN THE WALL	MY BEAT	25.00
65	479 DJ	GEORGE STONE	HOLE IN THE WALL	MY BEAT	50.00
66	481	MITCH RYDER& DETROIT WHEELS	JENNY TAKE A RIDE!	BABY JANE (MO-MO JANE)	10.00
66	481 DJ	MITCH RYDER& DETROIT WHEELS	JENNY TAKE A RIDE!	BABY JANE (MO-MO JANE)	15.00
66	482	CHRISTINE QUAITE	LONG AFTER TONIGHT IS ALL OVER	I'M HOPING	100.00
66	482 DJ	CHRISTINE QUAITE	LONG AFTER TONIGHT IS ALL OVER	I'M HOPING	150.00
66	483	TOYS	ATTACK	SEE HOW THEY RUN	8.00
66	483 DJ	TOYS	ATTACK	SEE HOW THEY RUN	15.00
66	485	LEE DORSEY	GET OUT OF MY LIFE WOMAN	SO LONG	6.00
66	485 DJ	LEE DORSEY	GET OUT OF MY LIFE WOMAN	SO LONG	10.00
66	487	CLYDE McPHATTER	EVERYBODY'S SOMEBODY'S FOOL	I BELONG TO YOU	20.00
66	487 DJ	CLYDE McPHATTER	EVERYBODY'S SOMEBODY'S FOOL	I BELONG TO YOU	30.00
66	488	BOB KUBAN& THE IN-MEN	THE CHEATER	TRY ME BABY	60.00
66	488 DJ	BOB KUBAN& THE IN-MEN	THE CHEATER	TRY ME BABY	100.00
66	489	C.O.D'S	MICHAEL	CRY NO MORE	40.00
66	489 DJ	C.O.D'S	MICHAEL	CRY NO MORE	75.00
66	491	SLIM HARPO	BABY SCRATCH MY BACK	I'M GONNA MISS YOU (LIKE THE D	25.00
66	491 DJ	SLIM HARPO	BABY SCRATCH MY BACK	I'M GONNA MISS YOU (LIKE THE D	45.00
66	493	SHEEP	HIDE AND SEEK	TWELVE MONTHS LATER	25.00
66	493 DJ	SHEEP	HIDE AND SEEK	TWELVE MONTHS LATER	50.00
66	495	SHARPEES	TIRED OF BEING LONELY	JUST TO PLEASE YOU	75.00
66	495 DJ	SHARPEES	TIRED OF BEING LONELY	JUST TO PLEASE YOU	150.00
66	496	NORMA TANEGA	WALKING MY CAT NAMED DOG	IM THE SKY	5.00
66	496 DJ	NORMA TANEGA	WALKING MY CAT NAMED DOG	IM THE SKY	8.00
66	498	MITCH RYDER& DETROIT WHEELS	LITTLE LATIN LUPE LU	I HOPE	15.00
66	498 DJ	MITCH RYDER& DETROIT WHEELS	LITTLE LATIN LUPE LU	I HOPE	25.00
66	499	JOHNNY THUNDER	A BROKEN HEART	MY PRAYER	15.00
66	499 DJ	JOHNNY THUNDER	A BROKEN HEART	MY PRAYER	25.00
66	500	GENE CHANDLER	(I'M JUST A) FOOL FOR YOU	BUDDY AIN'T IT A SHAME	25.00
66	500 DJ	GENE CHANDLER	(I'M JUST A) FOOL FOR YOU	BUDDY AIN'T IT A SHAME	50.00
66	502	TOYS	MAY MY HEART BE CAST INTO STONE	ON BACKSTREET	10.00
66	502 DJ	TOYS	MAY MY HEART BE CAST INTO STONE	ON BACKSTREET	20.00
66	503	JIMMY WITHERSPOON	IF THERE WASN'T ANY YOU	I NEVERB THOUGHT I'D SE THE DA	10.00
66	503 DJ	JIMMY WITHERSPOON	IF THERE WASN'T ANY YOU	I NEVERB THOUGHT I'D SE THE DA	15.00
66	504	VAN DYKES	NO MAN IS AN ISLAND	I WON'T HOLD IT AGAINST YOU	40.00
66	504 DJ	VAN DYKES	NO MAN IS AN ISLAND	I WON'T HOLD IT AGAINST YOU	60.00
66	505	JAY W.KING	I'M SO AFRAID	I DON'T HAVE TO WORRY (NOT ANY	30.00
66	505 DJ	JAY W.KING	I'M SO AFRAID	I DON'T HAVE TO WORRY (NOT ANY	45.00
66	506	LEE DORSEY	CONFUSION	NEIGHBOUR'S DAUGHTER	6.00
66	506 DJ	LEE DORSEY	CONFUSION	NEIGHBOUR'S DAUGHTER	10.00
66	507	JAMES CARR	THAT'S WHAT I WANT TO KNOW	YOU'VE GOT MY MIND MESSED UP	85.00
66	507 DJ	JAMES CARR	THAT'S WHAT I WANT TO KNOW	YOU'VE GOT MY MIND MESSED UP	**175.00**
66	508	LITTLE RICHARD	BABY DON'T YOU WANT A MAN LIKE	HOLY MACKERAL	20.00
66	508 DJ	LITTLE RICHARD	BABY DON'T YOU WANT A MAN LIKE	HOLY MACKERAL	30.00
66	509	CAB CALLOWAY	AFTER TAXES	HISTORY REPEATS ITSELF	5.00
66	509 DJ	CAB CALLOWAY	AFTER TAXES	HISTORY REPEATS ITSELF	8.00
66	510	RONNIE DOVE	LET'S START ALL OVER AGAIN	THAT EMPTY FEELING	6.00
66	510 DJ	RONNIE DOVE	LET'S START ALL OVER AGAIN	THAT EMPTY FEELING	8.00
66	511	PLATTERS	HEAR NO EVIL, SPEAK NO EVIL, SEE NO	I LOVE YOU 1000 TIMES	30.00
66	511 DJ	PLATTERS	HEAR NO EVIL, SPEAK NO EVIL, SEE NO	I LOVE YOU 1000 TIMES	50.00
66	512	CHIFFONS	SWEET TALKIN' GUY	DID YOU EVER GO STEADY	6.00

66	512 DJ	CHIFFONS	SWEET TALKIN' GUY	DID YOU EVER GO STEADY	30.00
66	513	PEELS	JUANITA BANANA	FUN	5.00
66	513 DJ	PEELS	JUANITA BANANA	FUN	8.00
66	514	BOB KUBAN & THE IN-MEN	THE TEASER	ALL I WANT	15.00
66	514 DJ	BOB KUBAN & THE IN-MEN	THE TEASER	ALL I WANT	25.00
66	516	RUFUS LUMLEY	I'M STANDING	LET'S HIDE AWAY	200.00
66	516 DJ	RUFUS LUMLEY	I'M STANDING	LET'S HIDE AWAY	**486.00**
66	519	TOYS	CAN'T GET ENOUGH OF YOU BABY	SILVER SPOON	20.00
66	519 DJ	TOYS	CAN'T GET ENOUGH OF YOU BABY	SILVER SPOON	30.00
66	520	NORMA TANEGA	TREAT ME RIGHT	A STREET THAT RHYMES AT 6 A.M.	5.00
66	520 DJ	NORMA TANEGA	TREAT ME RIGHT	A STREET THAT RHYMES AT 6 A.M.	6.00
66	521	MITCH RYDER& DETROIT WHEELS	BREAK OUT	I NEED HELP	40.00
66	521 DJ	MITCH RYDER& DETROIT WHEELS	BREAK OUT	I NEED HELP	100.00
66	523	SYNDICATE OF SOUND	LITTLE GIRL	YOU	25.00
66	523 DJ	SYNDICATE OF SOUND	LITTLE GIRL	YOU	30.00
66	525	BUENA VISTAS	HOT SHOT	T.N.T.	25.00
66	525 DJ	BUENA VISTAS	HOT SHOT	T.N.T.	35.00
66	527	SLIM HARPO	SHAKE YOUR HIPS	MIDNIGHT BLUES	25.00
66	527 DJ	SLIM HARPO	SHAKE YOUR HIPS	MIDNIGHT BLUES	35.00
66	528	LEE DORSEY	WORKING IN A COAL MINE	MEXICO	10.00
66	528 DJ	LEE DORSEY	WORKING IN A COAL MINE	MEXICO	40.00
66	530	VAN DYKES	WHAT WILL I DO	I'VE GOTTA GO ON WITHOUT YOU	40.00
66	530 DJ	VAN DYKES	WHAT WILL I DO	I'VE GOTTA GO ON WITHOUT YOU	70.00
66	531	DEAN PARRISH	TELL HER	FALL ON ME	75.00
66	531 DJ	DEAN PARRISH	TELL HER	FALL ON ME	125.00
66	532	RAZOR'S EDGE	LET'S CALL IT A DAY GIRL	APRIL	18.00
66	532 DJ	RAZOR'S EDGE	LET'S CALL IT A DAY GIRL	APRIL	25.00
66	533	CHIFFONS	OUT OF THIS WORLD	JUST A BOY	8.00
66	533 DJ	CHIFFONS	OUT OF THIS WORLD	JUST A BOY	15.00
66	534	MIGHTY SAM	SWEET DREAMS	GOOD HUMOR MAN	15.00
66	534 DJ	MIGHTY SAM	SWEET DREAMS	GOOD HUMOR MAN	25.00
66	535	JAMES CARR	COMING BACK TO ME BABY	LOVE ATTACK	40.00
66	535 DJ	JAMES CARR	COMING BACK TO ME BABY	LOVE ATTACK	75.00
66	536 DJ mispelt title	DARRELL BANKS	OPEN THE DOOR **OF** YOUR HEART	OUR LOVE (IS IN THE POCKET)	500.00

Red and white promo label with mispelt title

66	536 DJ red and white	DARRELL BANKS	OPEN THE DOOR TO YOUR HEART	OUR LOVE (IS IN THE POCKET)	UN
66	536 sold subject to	DARRELL BANKS	OPEN THE DOOR TO YOUR HEART	OUR LOVE (IS IN THE POCKET)	35.00

die cut spine small hole center, with "sold in the UK subject to.." printed on the center piece

68	536 DJ green & white	DARRELL BANKS	OPEN THE DOOR TO YOUR HEART	OUR LOVE IS IN THE POCKET	120.00

Green & white promo with "sold in the UK subject to." on the center piece

68	536 solid center	DARRELL BANKS	OPEN THE DOOR TO YOUR HEART	OUR LOVE (IS IN THE POCKET)	30.00

solid center with small hole, "sold in the UK subject to.." printed on the center piece

70	536 test press	DARRELL BANKS	OPEN THE DOOR TO YOUR HEART	OUR LOVE (IS IN THE POCKET)	**104.00**
70	536 DJ green & white	DARRELL BANKS	OPEN THE DOOR TO YOUR HEART	OUR LOVE (IS IN THE POCKET)	85.00

 Green & white promo without "sold in the UK subject to" on the center piece

70	536 no sold subject to	DARRELL BANKS	OPEN THE DOOR TO YOUR HEART	OUR LOVE (IS IN THE POCKET)	20.00
66	537	NORMAN TANEGA	BREAD	WAVES	6.00
66	537 DJ	NORMAN TANEGA	BREAD	WAVES	10.00
66	538	SYNDICATE OF SOUND	RUMOURS	THE UPPER HAND	15.00
66	538 DJ	SYNDICATE OF SOUND	RUMOURS	THE UPPER HAND	20.00
66	539	TOYS	BABY TOYS	HAPPY BIRTHDAY BROKEN HEART	15.00
66	539 DJ	TOYS	BABY TOYS	HAPPY BIRTHDAY BROKEN HEART	20.00

 # 539 was the last Red & White Stateside promo with # 543 being the first green and white promo

66	543	ALVIN CASH & the REGISTERS	PHILLY FREEZE	NO DEPOSITS, NO RETURNS	25.00
66	543 DJ	ALVIN CASH & the REGISTERS	PHILLY FREEZE	NO DEPOSITS, NO RETURNS	45.00
66	544	MIGHTY SAM	FANNIE MAE	BADMOUTHIN'	15.00
66	544 DJ	MIGHTY SAM	FANNIE MAE	BADMOUTHIN'	22.00
66	545	JAMES CARR	YOU'RE POURING WATER ON A DROWNING	FORGETTING YOU	20.00
66	545 DJ	JAMES CARR	YOU'RE POURING WATER ON A DROWNING	FORGETTING YOU	30.00
66	547	JAMES & BOBBY PURIFY	I'M YOUR PUPPET	SO MANY REASONS	22.00
66	547 DJ	JAMES & BOBBY PURIFY	I'M YOUR PUPPET	SO MANY REASONS	50.00
66	549	MITCH RYDER& DETROIT WHEELS	DEVIL WITH A BLUE DRESS	I HAD IT MADE	15.00
66	549 DJ	MITCH RYDER& DETROIT WHEELS	DEVIL WITH A BLUE DRESS	I HAD IT MADE	25.00
66	550	DEAN PARRISH	DETERMINATION	TURN ON YOUR LOVELIGHT	100.00
66	550 DJ	DEAN PARRISH	DETERMINATION	TURN ON YOUR LOVELIGHT	**231.00**
66	551	IKE & TINA TURNER	GOODBYE, SO LONG	HURT IS ALL YOU GAVE ME	15.00
66	551 DJ	IKE & TINA TURNER	GOODBYE, SO LONG	HURT IS ALL YOU GAVE ME	25.00
66	552	LEE DORSEY	HOLY COW	OPERATION HEARTACHE	8.00
66	552 DJ	LEE DORSEY	HOLY COW	OPERATION HEARTACHE	40.00
66	553	DALE BROOKS	I WANNA BE YOUR GIRL	LIKE OTHER GIRLS DO	10.00
66	553 DJ	DALE BROOKS	I WANNA BE YOUR GIRL	LIKE OTHER GIRLS DO	15.00
66	555	GLORIA JONES	FINDERS KEEPERS	RUN ONE FLIGHT OF STAIRS	75.00
66	555 DJ	GLORIA JONES	FINDERS KEEPERS	RUN ONE FLIGHT OF STAIRS	100.00
66	556	INEZ & CHARLIE FOXX	NO STRANGER TO LOVE	COME BY HERE	20.00
66	556 DJ	INEZ & CHARLIE FOXX	NO STRANGER TO LOVE	COME BY HERE	45.00
66	557	SLIM HARPO	I'M A KING BEE	I GOT LOVE IF YOU WANT IT	22.00
66	557 DJ	SLIM HARPO	I'M A KING BEE	I GOT LOVE IF YOU WANT IT	30.00
66	559	CHIFFONS	STOP, LOOK AND LISTEN	MARCH	10.00
66	559 DJ	CHIFFONS	STOP LOOK AND LISTEN	MARCH	15.00

66	563	VIRGINIA WOLVES	STAY	B.L.T.	45.00
66	563 DJ	VIRGINIA WOLVES	STAY	B.L.T.	85.00
66	565	EMPERORS	KARATE	I'VE GOT TO HAVE HER	20.00
66	565 DJ	EMPERORS	KARATE	I'VE GOT TO HAVE HER	30.00
66	566	PERCY MILEM	CALL ON ME	CRYING BABY, BABY	100.00
66	566 DJ	PERCY MILEM	CALL ON ME	CRYING BABY, BABY	150.00
66	567	CLYDE McPHATTER	A SHOT OF RHYTHM AND BLUES	I'M NOT GOING TO WORK TODAY	15.00
66	567 DJ	CLYDE McPHATTER	A SHOT OF RHYTHM AND BLUES	I'M NOT GOING TO WORK TODAY	25.00
66	568	PLATTERS	(YOU'VE GOT) THE MAGIC TOUCH	I'LL BE HOME	15.00
66	568 DJ	PLATTERS	(YOU'VE GOT) THE MAGIC TOUCH	I'LL BE HOME	25.00
66	569	ELLA FITZGERALD	THESE BOOTS WERE MADE FOR WALKIN'	STAR DUST	8.00
66	569 DJ	ELLA FITZGERALD	THESE BOOTS WERE MADE FOR WALKIN'	STAR DUST	10.00
66	578	CHIFFONS	MY BOYFRIEND'S BACK	I GOT PLENTY O' NUTTIN'	10.00
66	578 DJ	CHIFFONS	MY BOYFRIEND'S BACK	I GOT PLENTY O' NUTTIN'	20.00
66	579	LARRY BANKS	I DON'T WANNA DO IT	I'M COMING HOME	30.00
66	579 DJ	LARRY BANKS	I DON'T WANNA DO IT	I'M COMING HOME	45.00
66	580	DEAN PARRISH	SKATE	SKATE PART2	30.00
66	580 DJ	DEAN PARRISH	SKATE	SKATE PART2	50.00
67	581	SLIM HARPO	I'M YOUR BREADMAKER, BABY	LOVING YOU (THE WAY I DO)	25.00
67	581 DJ	SLIM HARPO	I'M YOUR BREADMAKER BABY	LOVING YOU (THE WAY I DO)	45.00
67	582	BOB CREWE GENERATION	MUSIC TO WATCH GIRLS BY	GIRLS ON THE ROCKS	10.00
67	582 DJ	BOB CREWE GENERATION	MUSIC TO WATCH GIRLS BY	GIRLS ON THE ROCKS	15.00
67	584	AARON NEVILLE	TELL IT LIKE IT IS	WHY WORRY	15.00
67	584 DJ	AARON NEVILLE	TELL IT LIKE IT IS	WHY WORRY	30.00
67	585	SAMMIE JOHN	BOSS BAG	LITTLE JOHN	25.00
67	585 DJ	SAMMIE JOHN	BOSS BAG	LITTLE JOHN	40.00
67	586	INEZ & CHARLIE FOXX	TIGHTROPE	MY SPECIAL PRAYER	40.00
67	586 DJ	INEZ & CHARLIE FOXX	TIGHTROPE	MY SPECIAL PRAYER	85.00
67	588	BUCKINGHAMS	KIND OF A DRAG	YOU MAKE ME FEEL SO GOOD	15.00
67	588 DJ	BUCKINGHAMS	KIND OF A DRAG	YOU MAKE ME FEEL SO GOOD	25.00
67	589	LEE MEZA	ONE GOOD THING LEADS TO ANOTHER	IF IT HAPPENS	40.00
67	589 DJ	LEE MEZA	ONE GOOD THING LEADS TO ANOTHER	IF IT HAPPENS	70.00
67	591	EDDIE JEFFERSON	SOME OTHER TIME	WHEN YOU LOOK IN THE MIRROR	30.00
67	591 DJ	EDDIE JEFFERSON	SOME OTHER TIME	WHEN YOU LOOK IN THE MIRROR	50.00
67	592	CLYDE McPHATTER	LAVENDER LACE	SWEET AND INNOCENT	15.00
67	592 DJ	CLYDE McPHATTER	LAVENDER LACE	SWEET AND INNOCENT	25.00
67	593	LEE DORSEY	RAIN, RAIN GO AWAY	GOTTA FIND A JOB	8.00
67	593 DJ	LEE DORSEY	RAIN, RAIN GO AWAY	GOTTA FIND A JOB	15.00
67	594	FASCINATIONS	GIRLS ARE OUT TO GET YOU	YOU'LL BE SORRY	75.00
67	594 DJ	FASCINATIONS	GIRLS ARE OUT TO GET YOU	YOU'LL BE SORRY	125.00
67	595	JAMES & BOBBY PURIFY	YOU CAN'T KEEP A GOOD MAN DOWN	WISH YOU DIDN'T HAVE TO GO	10.00
67	595 DJ	JAMES & BOBBY PURIFY	YOU CAN'T KEEP A GOOD MAN DOWN	WISH YOU DIDN'T HAVE TO GO	15.00
67	596	MITCH RYDER& DETROIT WHEELS	SOCK IT TO ME - BABY	I NEVER HAD IT BETTER	16.00
67	596 DJ	MITCH RYDER& DETROIT WHEELS	SOCK IT TO ME - BABY !	I NEVER HAD IT BETTER	30.00

STATESIDE 1000 # series are collectable soul EP's with picture covers.

63	1008 EP PS	JIMMY REED c/w JOHN LEE HOOKER	RHYTHM AND BLUES	1963 4 track EP with cover	25.00
63	1009 EP PS	VARIOUS ARTISTS	R&B CHARTMAKERS	1963 4 track EP with cover	70.00
64	1009 EP PS	VARIOUS ARTISTS	R&B CHARTMAKERS	1964 4 track EP with cover	75.00
64	1010 EP PS	JIMMY SOUL	IF YOU WANT TO BE HAPPY	1964 4 track EP with cover	40.00
64	1011 EP PS	FOUR SEASONS	THE FOUR SEASONS SING	1964 4 track EP with cover	30.00
64	1012 EP PS	CHIFFONS	THEY'RE SO FINE	1964 4 track EP with cover	75.00
64	1014 EP PS	LITTLE STEVIE WONDER	I CALL IT PRETTY MUSIC BUT THE OLD	1964 4 track EP with cover	150.00
64	1016 EP PS	JIMMY REED	THE BLUES OF JIMMY REED	1964 4 track EP with cover	30.00
64	1018 EP PS	VARIOUS ARTISTS	R&B CHARTMAKERS vol. 2	1964 4 track EP with cover	85.00
64	1019 EP PS	JOHN LEE HOOKER	THE BLUES OF JOHN HOOKER	1964 4 track EP with cover	30.00
64	1022 EP PS	VARIOUS ARTISTS	R&B CHARTMAKERS No. 3	1964 4 track EP with cover	100.00
64	1022 EP PS	VARIOUS ARTISTS	R&B CHARTMAKERS vol. 3	1964 4 track EP with cover	125.00
64	1023 EP PS	JOHN LEE HOOKER	I'M JOHN LEE HOOKER	1964 4 track EP with cover	30.00
64	1025 EP PS	VARIOUS ARTISTS	R&B CHARTMAKERS vol. 4	1964 4 track EP with cover	100.00
64	1026 EP PS	JIMMY REED	I'M JIMMY REED	1964 4 track EP with cover	30.00
65	1033 EP PS	IKETTES	FINE FINE FINE	1965 4 track EP with cover	75.00
65	1034 EP PS	REFLECTIONS	POOR MAN'S SON	1965 4 track EP with cover	81.00
65	1038 EP PS	LEE DORSEY	RIDE YOUR PONY	1965 4 track EP with cover	18.00
66	1039 EP PS	MITCH RYDER& DETROIT WHEELS	RIDIN'	1966 4 track EP with cover	50.00
66	1042 EP PS	LITTLE RICHARD	DO YOU FEEL IT	1966 4 track EP with cover	40.00
66	1043 EP PS	LEE DORSEY	YOU'RE BREAKING ME UP	1966 4 track EP with cover	25.00
66	1044 EP PS	ELLA FITZGERALD	THESE BOOTS ARE MADE FOR WALKIN'	1966 4 track EP with cover	8.00

STATESIDE 2000 # series are 45's

67	2001	JAMES CARR	THE DARK END OF THE STREET	LOVEABLE GIRL	20.00
67	2001 DJ	JAMES CARR	THE DARK END OF THE STREET	LOVEABLE GIRL	30.00
67	2002	VONTASTICS	LADY LOVE	WHEN MY BABY COMES BACK HOME	30.00
67	2002 DJ	VONTASTICS	LADY LOVE	WHEN MY BABY COMES BACK HOME	50.00
67	2005	JOHNNY THUNDER & RUBY WINTERS	MAKE LOVE TO ME	TEACH ME TONIGHT	15.00
67	2005 DJ	JOHNNY THUNDER & RUBY WINTERS	MAKE LOVE TO ME	TEACH ME TONIGHT	20.00
67	2006	VERNON GARRETT	IF I COULD TURN BACK THE HHANDS OF	YOU AND ME TOGETHER	40.00
67	2006 DJ	VERNON GARRETT	IF I COULD TURN BACK THE HANDS OF	YOU AND ME TOGETHER	**106.00**
67	2007	PLATTERS	WITH THIS RING	IF I HAD A LOVE	12.00
67	2007 DJ	PLATTERS	WITH THIS RING	IF I HAD A LOVE	45.00
67	2009	MARY LOVE	LAY THIS BURDEN DOWN	THINK IT OVER BABY	60.00

67	2009 DJ	MARY LOVE	LAY THIS BURDEN DOWN	THINK IT OVER BABY	100.00
67	2011	BUCKINGHAMS	LAWDY MISS CLAWDY	MAKIN' UP AND BREAKING UP	5.00
67	2011 DJ	BUCKINGHAMS	LAWDY MISS CLAWDY	MAKIN' UP AND BREAKING UP	10.00
67	2015	BETTY LAVETTE	ONLY YOUR LOVE CAN SAVE ME	I FEEL GOOD (ALL OVER)	50.00
67	2015 DJ	BETTY LAVETTE	ONLY YOUR LOVE CAN SAVE ME	I FEEL GOOD (ALL OVER)	75.00
67	2016	JAMES & BOBBY PURIFY	SHAKE A TAIL FEATHER	GOODNESS GRACIOUS	30.00
67	2016 DJ	JAMES & BOBBY PURIFY	SHAKE A TAIL FEATHER	GOODNESS GRACIOUS	60.00
67	2017	LEE DORSEY	MY OLD CAR	WHY WAIT UNTIL TOMORROW	6.00
67	2017 DJ	LEE DORSEY	MY OLD CAR	WHY WAIT UNTIL TOMORROW	10.00
67	2023	MITCH RYDER& DETROIT WHEELS	TOO MANY FISH IN THE SEA	ONE GRAIN OF SAND	20.00
67	2023 DJ	MITCH RYDER& DETROIT WHEELS	TOO MANY FISH IN THE SEA	ONE GRAIN OF SAND	28.00
67	2024	SPENCER WIGGINS	UP TIGHT GOOD WOMAN	ANYTHING YOU DO IS ALRIGHT	20.00
67	2024 DJ	SPENCER WIGGINS	UP TIGHT GOOD WOMAN	ANYTHING YOU DO IS ALRIGHT	30.00
67	2025	GARY (U.S.) BONDS	WORKIN' FOR MY BABY	SEND HER TO ME	20.00
67	2025 DJ	GARY (U.S.) BONDS	WORKIN' FOR MY BABY	SEND HER TO ME	30.00
67	2026	VERNON GARRETT	SHINE IT ON	THINGS ARE LOOKIN' BETTER	60.00
67	2026 DJ	VERNON GARRETT	SHINE IT ON	THINGS ARE LOOKIN' BETTER	85.00
67	2028	MUSIC EXPLOSION	LITTLE BIT O'SOUL	I SEE THE LIGHT	10.00
67	2028 DJ	MUSIC EXPLOSION	LITTLE BIT O'SOUL	I SEE THE LIGHT	15.00
67	2030	HOAGY LANDS	THE NEXT IN LINE	PLEASE DON'T TALK ABOUT ME WHE	**337.00**
67	2030 DJ	HOAGY LANDS	THE NEXT IN LINE	PLEASE DON'T TALK ABOUT ME WHE	**587.00**
67	2032	BOB CREWE GENERATION	A LOVER'S CONCERTO	YOU ONLY LIVE TWICE	6.00
67	2032 DJ	BOB CREWE GENERATION	A LOVER'S CONCERTO	YOU ONLY LIVE TWICE	10.00
67	2033 sold subject to	OSCAR TONEY JR.	AIN'T THAT TRUE LOVE	FOR YOUR PRECIOUS LOVE	28.00
67	2033 DJsold subject to	OSCAR TONEY JR.	AIN'T THAT TRUE LOVE	FOR YOUR PRECIOUS LOVE	45.00
67	2033 no sold subject	OSCAR TONEY JR.	AIN'T THAT TRUE LOVE	FOR YOUR PRECIOUS LOVE	20.00
67	2033 DJ no sold subj	OSCAR TONEY JR.	AIN'T THAT TRUE LOVE	FOR YOUR PRECIOUS LOVE	30.00

 # 2033 EMI second press - without the –Sold Subject to price conditions etc on the centre piece

67	2033 DJ	OSCAR TONEY JR.	AIN'T THAT TRUE LOVE	FOR YOUR PRECIOUS LOVE	15.00
67	2034	FIFTH ESTATE	DING DONG THE WITCH IS DEAD	RUB A DUB	5.00
67	2034 DJ	FIFTH ESTATE	DING DONG THE WITCH IS DEAD	RUB A DUB	8.00
67	2037	MITCH RYDER& DETROIT WHEELS	JOY	I'D RATHER GO TO JAIL	8.00
67	2037 DJ	MITCH RYDER& DETROIT WHEELS	JOY	I'D RATHER GO TO JAIL	15.00
67	2038	JAMES CARR	A LOSING GAME	LET IT HAPPEN	30.00
67	2038 DJ	JAMES CARR	A LOSING GAME	LET IT HAPPEN	60.00
67	2039	JAMES & BOBBY PURIFY	I TAKE WHAT I WANT	SIXTEEN TONS	10.00
67	2039 DJ	JAMES & BOBBY PURIFY	I TAKE WHAT I WANT	SIXTEEN TONS	15.00
67	2041	JIMMY JONES	39 - 21 - 46 SHAPE	PERSONAL PROPERTY	20.00
67	2041 DJ	JIMMY JONES	39 - 21 - 46 SHAPE	PERSONAL PROPERTY	30.00
67	2042	PLATTERS	WASHED ASHORE (ON A LONELY	WHAT NAME SHALL I GIVE YOU MY	30.00
67	2042 DJ	PLATTERS	WASHED ASHORE (ON A LONELY	WHAT SHALL I GIVE YOU MY LOVE	**103.00**
67	2043	CORONADOS	SHOOK ME DOWN	JOHNNY B. GOODE	10.00
67	2043 DJ	CORONADOS	SHOOK ME DOWN	JOHNNY B. GOODE	15.00
67	2044	BOX TOPS	THE LETTER	HAPPY TIMES	8.00
67	2044 DJ	BOX TOPS	THE LETTER	HAPPY TIMES	20.00
67	2045	BETTY HARRIS	NEARER TO YOU	12 RED ROSES	22.00
67	2045 DJ	BETTY HARRIS	NEARER TO YOU	12 RED ROSES	35.00
67	2046	OSCAR TONEY JR.	ANY DAY NOW (MY WILD BEAUTIFUL	TURN ON YOUR LOVELIGHT	15.00
67	2046 DJ	OSCAR TONEY JR.	ANY DAY NOW	TURN ON YOUR LOVE LIGHT	25.00
67	2047	RONNIE DOVE	I WANT TO LOVE YOU FOR WHAT YOU	I THANK YOU FOR YOUR LOVE	6.00
67	2047 DJ	RONNIE DOVE	I WANT TO LOVE YOU FOR WHAT YOU	I THANK YOU FOR YOUR LOVE	8.00
67	2048	ESQUIRES	GET ON UP	LISTEN TO ME	20.00
67	2048 DJ	ESQUIRES	GET ON UP	LISTEN TO ME	35.00
67	2049	JAMES & BOBBY PURIFY	LET LOVE COME BETWEEN US	I DON'T WANT TO HAVE TO WAIT	15.00
67	2049 DJ	JAMES & BOBBY PURIFY	LET LOVE COME BETWEEN US	I DON'T WANT TO HAVE TO WAIT	25.00
67	2052	JAMES CARR	I'M A FOOL FOR YOU	GONNA SEND YOU BACK TO GEORGIA	15.00
67	2052 DJ	JAMES CARR	I'M A FOOL FOR YOU	GONNA SEND YOU BACK TO GEORGIA	25.00
67	2053	INCREDIBLES	THERE'S NOTHING ELSE TO SAY	HEART AND SOUL	**206.00**
67	2053 DJ	INCREDIBLES	THERE'S NOTHING ELSE TO SAY	HEART AND SOUL	300.00
67	2055	LEE DORSEY	GO-GO GIRL	I CAN HEAR YOU CALLIN	8.00
67	2055 DJ	LEE DORSEY	GO-GO GIRL	I CAN HEAR YOU CALLIN	15.00
67	2057	SOUL SURVIVORS	EXPRESSWAY TO YOUR HEART	HEY GYP	15.00
67	2057 DJ	SOUL SURVIVORS	EXPRESSWAY TO YOUR HEART	HEY GYP	30.00
67	2058	LINDA CARR	TRYING TO BE GOOD FOR YOU	EVERYTIME	40.00
67	2058 DJ	LINDA CARR	TRYING TO BE GOOD FOR YOU	EVERYTIME	70.00
67	2059	MOSES & JOSHUA DILLARD	MY ELUSIVE DREAMS	WHAT'S BETTER THAN LOVE	20.00
67	2059 DJ	MOSES & JOSHUA DILLARD	MY ELUSIVE DREAMS	WHAT'S BETTER THAN LOVE	70.00
67	2061	OSCAR TONEY JR	YOU CAN LEAD YOUR WOMAN TO THE	UNLUCKY GUY	20.00
67	2061 DJ	OSCAR TONEY JR	YOU CAN LEAD YOUR WOMAN TO THE	UNLUCKY GUY	30.00
67	2062	MITCH RYDER& DETROIT WHEELS	BLESSING IN DISGUISE	WHAT NOW MY LOVE	25.00
67	2062 DJ	MITCH RYDER& DETROIT WHEELS	BLESSING IN DISGUISE	WHAT NOW MY LOVE	40.00
67	2064	MARK BARKAN	A GREAT DAY FOR THE CLOWN	PITY THE WOMAN	10.00
67	2064 DJ	MARK BARKAN	A GREAT DAY FOR THE CLOWN	PITY THE WOMAN	15.00
67	2065	BALTIMORE & OHIO MARCHING BAND	CONDITION RED	LAPLAND	100.00
67	2065 DJ	BALTIMORE & OHIO MARCHING BAND	CONDITION RED	LAPLAND	150.00
67	2066	BRUCE CHANNEL	MR. BUS DRIVER	IT'S ME	10.00
67	2066 DJ	BRUCE CHANNEL	MR. BUS DRIVER	IT'S ME	15.00
67	2067	PLATTERS	SWEET, SWEET LOVIN'	SONATA	20.00
67	2067 DJ	PLATTERS	SWEET SWEET LOVIN'	SONATA	70.00

67	2068	FIFTH ESTATE	IT'S WAITING THERE FOR YOU	HEIGH-HO	20.00
67	2068 DJ	FIFTH ESTATE	IT'S WAITING THERE FOR YOU	HEIGH-HO	28.00
67	2069	LYNN ROMAN	THE PENTHOUSE	BORN TO LOSE	20.00
67	2069 DJ	LYNN ROMAN	THE PENTHOUSE	BORN TO LOSE	28.00
67	2070	BOX TOPS	SHE KNOWS HOW	NEON RAINBOW	15.00
67	2070 DJ	BOX TOPS	SHE KNOWS HOW	NEON RAINBOW	20.00
67	2071	RAY CHARLES	YESTERDAY	NEVER HAD ENOUGH OF NOTHING YET	4.00
67	2071 DJ	RAY CHARLES	YESTERDAY	NEVER HAD ENOUGH OF NOTHING YET	6.00
67	2073	O'JAYS	I DIG YOUR ACT	I'LL BE SWEETER TOMORROW	85.00
67	2073 DJ	O'JAYS	I DIG YOUR ACT	I'LL BE SWEETER TOMORROW	125.00
68	2075	MITCH RYDER& DETROIT WHEELS	YOU ARE MY SUNSHINE	WILD CHILD	8.00
68	2075 DJ	MITCH RYDER& DETROIT WHEELS	YOU ARE MY SUNSHINE	WILD CHILD	10.00
67	2076	MIGHTY SAM	WHEN SHE TOUCHES ME (NOTHING ELSE	JUST LIKE OLD TIMES	15.00
67	2076 DJ	MIGHTY SAM	WHEN SHE TOUCHES ME (NOTHING ELSE	JUST LIKE OLD TIMES	22.00
68	2077	ESQUIRES	AND GET AWAY	EVERYBODY'S LAUGHIN'	20.00
68	2077 DJ	ESQUIRES	AND GET AWAY	EVERYBODY'S LAUGHIN'	45.00
68	2078	AMERICAN BREED	BEND ME, SHAPE ME	MIND ROCKER	8.00
68	2078 DJ	AMERICAN BREED	BEND ME, SHAPE ME	MIND ROCKER	10.00
68	2079	AL GREENE & the SOUL MATES	DON'T LEAVE ME	BACK UP TRAIN	30.00
68	2079 DJ	AL GREENE & the SOUL MATES	DON'T LEAVE ME	BACK UP TRAIN	40.00
68	2080	ENCHANTED FOREST	YOU'RE NEVER GONNA GET MY LOVIN'	SUZANNE	10.00
68	2080 DJ	ENCHANTED FOREST	YOU'RE NEVER GONNA GET MY LOVIN'	SUZANNE	15.00
68	2083	IMPRESSIONS	WE'RE A WINNER	YOU'VE GOT ME RUNNIN'	10.00
68	2083 DJ	IMPRESSIONS	WE'RE A WINNER	YOU'VE GOT ME RUNNIN'	15.00
68	2085	HOAGY LANDS	I'M YOURS	ONLY YOU	25.00
68	2085 DJ	HOAGY LANDS	I'M YOURS	ONLY YOU	35.00
68	2087	TROY KEYES	LOVE EXPLOSIONS	I'M CRYING INSIDE	20.00
68	2087 DJ	TROY KEYES	LOVE EXPLOSIONS	I'M CRYING INSIDE	30.00
68	2088	BOBBI LYNN	EARTHQUAKE	OPPORTUNITY STREET	70.00
68	2088 DJ	BOBBI LYNN	EARTHQUAKE	OPPORTUNITY STREET	**105.00**
67	2090	RUBY WINTERS	BETTER	I WANT ACTION	**167.00**
67	2090 DJ	RUBY WINTERS	BETTER	I WANT ACTION	200.00
67	2092	TYRONE DAVIS	WHAT IF A MAN	BET YOU WIN	50.00
67	2092 DJ	TYRONE DAVIS	WHAT IF A MAN	BET YOU WIN	85.00
68	2093	JAMES & BOBBY PURIFY	DO UNTO ME	EVERYBODY NEEDS SOMEBODY	20.00
68	2093 DJ	JAMES & BOBBY PURIFY	DO UNTO ME	EVERYBODY NEEDS SOMEBODY	30.00
68	2094	SOUL SURVIVORS	EXPLOSION (IN YOUR SOUL)	DATHON'S THEME	15.00
68	2094 DJ	SOUL SURVIVORS	EXPLOSION (IN YOUR SOUL)	DATHON'S THEME	20.00
68	2096	MITCH RYDER& DETROIT WHEELS	(YOU'VE GOT) PERSONALITY/ CHANTILLY LACE	I MADE A FOOL OF MYSELF	10.00
68	2096 DJ	MITCH RYDER& DETROIT WHEELS	(YOU'VE GOT) PERSONALITY/ CHANTILLY LACE	I MADE A FOOL OF MYSELF	15.00
68	2099	RAY CHARLES	THAT'S A LIE	GO ON HOME	6.00
68	2099 DJ	RAY CHARLES	THAT'S A LIE	GO ON HOME	8.00
68	2108	LOVABLES	YOU'RE THE CAUSE OF IT	BEAUTIFUL IDEA	15.00
68	2108 DJ	LOVABLES	YOU'RE THE CAUSE OF IT	BEAUTIFUL IDEA	25.00
68	2110	KENNY CHANDLER	BEYOND LOVE	CHARITY	50.00
68	2110 DJ	KENNY CHANDLER	BEYOND LOVE	CHARITY	**79.00**
68	2111	MARY WELLS	THE DOCTOR	TWO LOVER'S HISTORY	15.00
68	2111 DJ	MARY WELLS	THE DOCTOR	TWO LOVER'S HISTORY	25.00
68	2112	B.B.KING	PAYING THE COST TO THE BOSS	HAVING MY SAY	8.00
68	2112 DJ	B.B.KING	PAYING THE COST TO THE BOSS	HAVING MY SAY	10.00
68	2113	FLORENCE BALLARD	IT DOESN'T MATTER HOW I SAY IT	GOIN' OUT OF MY HEAD	75.00
68	2113 DJ	FLORENCE BALLARD	IT DOESN'T MATTER HOW I SAY IT	GOIN' OUT OF MY HEAD	100.00
68	2114	JEAN CARTER	NO GOOD JIM	AND NONE	15.00
68	2114 DJ	JEAN CARTER	NO GOOD JIM	AND NONE	22.00
68	2115	FASHIONS	I.O.U (A LIFETIME OF LOVE)	WHEN LOVE SLIPS AWAY	22.00
68	2115 DJ	FASHIONS	I.O.U (A LIFETIME OF LOVE)	WHEN LOVE SLIPS AWAY	35.00
68	2119	RONNIE DOVE	MOUNTAIN OF LOVE	NEVER GONNA CRY THE WAY I CRIED	5.00
68	2119 DJ	RONNIE DOVE	MOUNTAIN OF LOVE	NEVER GONNA CRY THE WAY I CRIED	6.00
68	2123 sold subject	TAMS	BE YOUNG BE FOOLISH BE HAPPY	THAT SAME OLD SONG	30.00
68	2123 DJ with date	TAMS	BE YOUNG BE FOOLISH BE HAPPY	THAT SAME OLD SONG	45.00
70	2123 no sold subject	TAMS	BE YOUNG BE FOOLISH BE HAPPY	THAT SAME OLD SONG	15.00
68	2123 DJ no date	TAMS	BE YOUNG BE FOOLISH BE HAPPY	THAT SAME OLD SONG	30.00
68	2126	O'KAYSIONS	GIRL WATCHER	DEAL ME IN	40.00
68	2126 DJ	O'KAYSIONS	GIRL WATCHER	DEAL ME IN	85.00
68	2128	DELLA REESE	IT WAS A VERY GOOD YEAR	I HAD TO KNOW MY WAY AROUND	5.00
68	2128 DJ	DELLA REESE	IT WAS A VERY GOOD YEAR	I HAD TO KNOW MY WAY AROUND	8.00
68	2131	GENE PITNEY	SHE'S A HEARTBREAKER	YOURS UNTIL TOMORROW	10.00
68	2131 DJ	GENE PITNEY	SHE'S A HEARTBREAKER	YOURS UNTIL TOMORROW	25.00
68	2132	RAY CHARLES	SWEET YOUNG THING LIKE YOU	LISTEN, THEY'RE PLAYING MY SON	4.00
68	2132 DJ	RAY CHARLES	SWEET YOUNG THING LIKE YOU	LISTEN, THEY'RE PLAYING MY SON	5.00
68	2135	MARY LOVE	THE HURT IS JUST BEGINNING	IF YOU CHANGE YOUR MIND	30.00
68	2135 DJ	MARY LOVE	THE HURT IS JUST BEGINNING	IF YOU CHANGE YOUR MIND	50.00
68	2137	VALENTINOS	TIRED OF BEING NOBODY	THE DEATH OF LOVE	12.00
68	2137 DJ	VALENTINOS	TIRED OF BEING NOBODY	THE DEATH OF LOVE	20.00
68	2139 sold subject to	IMPRESSIONS	CAN'T SATISFY	YOU'VE BEEN CHEATING	22.00
68	2139 DJ with date	IMPRESSIONS	CAN'T SATISFY	YOU'VE BEEN CHEATING	35.00
70	2139 no sold subject to	IMPRESSIONS	CAN'T SATISFY	YOU'VE BEEN CHEATING	22.00
70	2139 DJ no date	IMPRESSIONS	CAN'T SATISFY	YOU'VE BEEN CHEATING	28.00

69	2140	METERS	SOPHISTICATED CISASY	SEHORN'S FARMS	15.00
69	2140 DJ	METERS	SOPHISTICATED CISASY	SEHORN'S FARMS	22.00
69	2141	B.B.KING	GET MYSELF SOMEBODY	DON'T WASTE MY TIME	10.00
69	2141 DJ	B.B.KING	GET MYSELF SOMEBODY	DON'T WASTE MY TIME	15.00
69	2143	TOMMY ROE	DIZZY	THE YOU I NEED	5.00
69	2143 DJ	TOMMY ROE	DIZZY	THE YOU I NEED	10.00
69	2147	SHEEP c/w THE HAWKS	HIDE AND SEEK	THE GRISSLE	15.00
69	2147 DJ	SHEEP c/w THE HAWKS	HIDE AND SEEK	THE GRISSLE	22.00
69	2149	TROY KEYES	LOVE EXPLOSIONS	I'M CRYING INSIDE	16.00
69	2149 DJ	TROY KEYES	LOVE EXPLOSION	I'M CRYING INSIDE	25.00
69	2150	PLATTERS	WITH THIS RING	IF I HAD A LOVE	18.00
69	2150 DJ	PLATTERS	WITH THIS RING	IF I HAD A LOVE	50.00
69	2151	RONNIE WALKER	IT'S A GOOD FEELING	PRECIOUS	20.00
69	2151 DJ	RONNIE WALKER	IT'S A GOOD FEELING	PRECIOUS	40.00
69	2155	RAY CHARLES	WE CAN MAKE IT	I CAN'T STOP LOVING YOU BABY	4.00
69	2155 DJ	RAY CHARLES	WE CAN MAKE IT	I CAN'T STOP LOVING YOU BABY	5.00
70	2160	EDDIE HOLMAN	(HEY THERE) LONELY GIRL	IT'S ALL THE GAME	8.00
70	2160 DJ	EDDIE HOLMAN	(HEY THERE) LONELY GIRL	IT'S ALL THE GAME	30.00
70	2161 DJ	B.B.KING	THE THRILL IS GONE	YOU'RE MEAN	8.00
70	2161 DJ	B.B.KING	THE THRILL IS GONE	YOU'RE MEAN	15.00
70	2162	ISLEY BROTHERS	WAS I GOOD TO YOU	I GOT TO GET MYSELF TOGETHER	8.00
70	2162 DJ	ISLEY BROTHERS	WAS I GOOD TO YOU	I GOT TO GET MYSELF TOGETHER	15.00
70	2169	B.B.KING	SO EXCITED	CONFESSIN' THE BLUES	6.00
70	2169 DJ	B.B.KING	SO EXCITED	CONFESSIN' THE BLUES	10.00
70	2170	EDDIE HOLMAN	SINCE I DON'T HAVE YOU	DON'T STOP NOW	8.00
70	2170 DJ	EDDIE HOLMAN	SINCE I DON'T HAVE YOU	DON'T STOP NOW	12.00
70	2176	B.B.KING	HUMMINGBIRD	ASK ME NO QUESTIONS	5.00
70	2176 DJ	B.B.KING	HUMMINGBIRD	ASK ME NO QUESTIONS	8.00
70	2178	RAY CHARLES	TILL I CAN'T IT ANYMORE	GOOD MORNING DEAR	4.00
70	2178 DJ	RAY CHARLES	TILL I CAN'T IT ANYMORE	GOOD MORNING DEAR	6.00
71	2188	ISLEY BROTHERS	WARPATH	I GOT TO FIND ME ONE	6.00
71	2188 DJ	ISLEY BROTHERS	WARPATH	I GOT TO FIND ME ONE	10.00
71	2193	ISLEY BROTHERS	LOVE THE ONE YOU WITH	HE'S GOT YOUR LOVE	6.00
71	2193 DJ	ISLEY BROTHERS	LOVE THE ONE YOU WITH	HE'S GOT YOUR LOVE	10.00
71	2198	HENRY SHED	SAVE THE LAST DANCE FOR ME	BEND ME, SHAPE ME	10.00
71	2198 DJ	HENRY SHED	SAVE THE LAST DANCE FOR ME	BEND ME, SHAPE ME	25.00
72	2201	COASTERS	COOL JERK	TALKIN' 'BOUT A WOMAN	40.00
72	2201 DJ	COASTERS	COOL JERK	TALKIN' 'BOUT A WOMAN	60.00
72	2204	JEAN CARTER& the CENTERPIECES	NO GOOD JIM	AND NONE	12.00
72	2204 DJ	JEAN CARTER& the CENTERPIECES	NO GOOD JIM	AND NONE	18.00
72	2205	CREATION	I GOT THE FEVER	SOUL CONTROL	15.00
72	2205 DJ	CREATION	I GOT THE FEVER	SOUL CONTROL	30.00
72	2207	JOHNNY JOHNSON & the BANDWAGON	I DON'T KNOW WHY	HONEY BEE	15.00
72	2207 DJ	JOHNNY JOHNSON & the BANDWAGON	I DON'T KNOW WHY	HONEY BEE	25.00
72	2209	JIMMY JAMES	A MAN LIKE ME	SURVIVAL	15.00
72	2209 DJ	JIMMY JAMES	A MAN LIKE ME	SURVIVAL	40.00
73	2214	AL CAPPS	MAGICIAN	SHANGRILA	20.00
73	2214 DJ	AL CAPPS	MAGICIAN	SHANGRILA	30.00

STATESIDE DUNHILL

69	8023	GRASS ROOTS	MIDNIGHT CONFESSIONS	WHO WILL YOU BE TOMORROW	8.00
69	8023 DJ	GRASS ROOTS	MIDNIGHT CONFESSIONS	WHO WILL YOU BE TOMORROW	18.00
69	8026	THELMA HOUSTON	JUMPIN' JACK FLASH	SUNSHOWER	4.00
69	8026 DJ	THELMA HOUSTON	JUMPIN' JACK FLASH	SUNSHOWER	5.00
69	8029	GRASS ROOTS	I'D WAIT A MILLION YEARS	FLY ME TO HAVANA	15.00
69	8029 DJ	GRASS ROOTS	I'D WAIT A MILLION YEARS	FLY ME TO HAVANA	20.00
70	8036	THELMA HOUSTON	SAVE THE COUNTRY	I JUST CAN'T STAY AWAY	4.00
70	8036 DJ	THELMA HOUSTON	SAVE THE COUNTRY	I JUST CAN'T STAY AWAY	6.00
70	8044	THELMA HOUSTON	I JUST WANNA BE ME	CRYING IN THE SUNSHINE	5.00
70	8044 DJ	THELMA HOUSTON	I JUST WANNA BE ME	CRYING IN THE SUNSHINE	6.00
70	8050	ROY HEAD	MAMA MAMA	I'M NOT A FOOL ANYMORE	8.00
70	8050 DJ	ROY HEAD	MAMA MAMA	I'M NOT A FOOL ANYMORE	10.00

STAX

The Stax label was named using the first two letters of the co-owners surnames Stewart & Axton. Jim Stewart a local Country & Western singer persuaded his sister to join him in forming a record label. At first the idea was to have an outlet for Jim's music. Starting in 1958 and working almost 25 miles outside the music cauldron of Memphis. The pair set about recording from a storage space. Leasing records through various established labels, with only limited success, the duo decided to start their own label Satellite Records. In 1959 they released their first 45 Satellite #100 by the Vel-tones and by 1960 they had moved their business to McLemore Ave, Memphis. Next release was a rockabilly shaker. But now based in the hot bed of R&B, by release # 103 this "Country & Western" orientated label had recorded father & daughter team Rufus & Carla Thomas. Steadily the label swung towards the R&B style, when in 1961 they had their first big hit with their studio group The Mar-Keys – "Last Night" – this group was to become the bedrock of the Memphis Sound. Original members were Tom Nix, Charles Axton, Charles Freeman and two musicians who would be credited with numerous Stax classics Duck Dunn and Steve Cropper. "Last Night" made its UK debut in 1961 through the London label. The same year they launched the STAX label. Over the next few years Stewart & Axton found themselves surrounded by a plethora of "Soul" talent adding Booker T. Jones, Isaac Hayes, David Porter, Al Bell, Al Jackson, to their already talent writing and producing team. In 1962 saw Otis Redding's first 45 on their new VOLT label
Gaining artists like Mable John from Motown, Eddie Floyd from Safice, Sam & Dave signing in 1964 after a few notable releases for Roulette. But of course Stax's major coup was Otis Redding walking into their studios in 1962 after an unsuccessful minor release in Denver, Colorado for Finer Arts label. He went to Memphis and requested an audition, the rest is history although Redding wasn't an instant success some believed him to be. After his debut "These Arms Of Mine" the follow-ups "That's What My Heart Needs" "Pain In My Heart" "Security" "You're One And Only Man" and "Come To Me" all had disappointing sales.
Stax was responsible for launching the careers of future soul legends like Otis Redding, Sam & Dave, William Bell, Eddie Floyd, Carla Thomas, plus making household

names of some of the more established R&B stars of the era, Rufus Thomas for an example. Even the in-house backing bands, became chartmakers with Bar-Kays and Booker T. & the M.G's (Memphis Group) selling huge quantities of vinyl on the strength of their unique sound. A glance at the artist listing below will confirm, that during its short life, Stax was a giant amongst soul labels, both in it's home country and in the UK.

From 1961 to 1966 this most famous of soul labels from Memphis was released in the UK by Decca Records first using the London and then the black Atlantic labels. In 1966 Polydor acquired the rights to release the Atlantic catalogue, which included the Stax label. Only one year later, with the "Memphis Sound" becoming one of the hippest sounds in the UK being played at all night clubs frequented by The Mods who were becoming heavily influence by Soul & R&B. Polydor rewarded the following for the music, by giving Stax it's very own label following the light blue background design of it's parent company, using the unmistakable "Stack of 45's" logo.

Starting in 1967 from # 601001 this design label only had 42 releases before being transformed in 1968 when Stax left the control of Atlantic records and was acquired by ABC Paramount, the label transformed it's label into the just as famous YELLOW label with the "finger click" logo. This transformation also took place in the UK adopting the same label design, as they left Polydor to be distributed by EMI.

EMI got off to a flying start with a hit with William Bell & Judy Clay's all time soul classic "Private Number" followed by another smash hit with Booker T. & the MG's "Soul Limbo". Their early elation was soon dampened as in two years and 57 releases they had only one more major hit with Rufus Thomas "Do The Funky Chicken".

For the UK serious soul collector EMI's releases may have been a little insignificant, but were spiced up with the USA Volt label's Groovesville productions: Stax #155 is considered by many, as the finest soul record ever to be released in the UK.

During the Stax label life in the UK the catalogue has been distributed by Polydor, EMI, RCA and PYE all these labels constantly reissued the classics. The listing below hopefully unravels the maze of release numbers, dates and label designs.

In 1976 USA Stax, as an independent label went out of business after putting 166 hits in the USA pop charts in less than 15 years. The labels driving force Estelle Axton died in February 20th. 2004. In 2003 a museum dedicated to the history of the Stax label was opened in Memphis on the site of the former Stax studios.

STAX   Light blue label with the "Stack of 45's" logo. Some releases had mid-blue shade labels, as noted. Distributed by Polydor.

67	601001	EDDIE FLOYD	RAISE YOUR HAND	I'VE JUST BEEN FEELING BAD	6.00
67	601002 blue	CARLA THOMAS	SOMETHING GOOD (IS GOING TO ME)	IT'S STARTING GROW	20.00
67	601002 light blue	CARLA THOMAS	SOMETHING GOOD (IS GOING TO ME)	IT'S STARTING TO GROW	15.00
67	601003	JOHNNIE TAYLOR	AIN'T THAT LOVIN' YOU	OUTSIDE LOVE	25.00
67	601004 blue	SAM and DAVE	SOOTHE ME	SWEET PAIN	25.00
67	601004 light blue	SAM and DAVE	SOOTHE ME	SWEET PAIN	20.00

The USA press of "Soothe Me" on blue Stax was a "LIVE" recording made in London. Ironically #601004 was the superior studio version, which was not issued in the USA

67	601005	OTIS REDDING	SHAKE	DAY TRIPPER	10.00
67	601006	SAM and DAVE	WHEN SOMETHING IS WRONG WITH MY	A SMALL PORTION OF YOUR LOVE	15.00
67	601007	OTIS REDDING	LET ME COME ON HOME	I LOVE YOU MORE THAN WORDS CAN	12.00
67	601008 blue	CARLA THOMAS	WHEN TOMORROW COMES	UNCHANGING LOVE	15.00
67	601009	BOOKER T. & THE MG'S	HIP HUG-HER	SUMMERTIME	6.00
67	601010	MABLE JOHN	BIGGER & BETTER	SAME TIME, SAME PLACE	15.00
67	601011	OTIS REDDING	SHAKE live	634-5789	10.00
67	601012	OTIS REDDING & CARLA THOMAS	TRAMP	OOH CARLA OOH OTIS	6.00
67	601013	RUFUS THOMAS	GREASY SPOON	SOPHISTICATED SISSY	10.00
67	601014	BAR-KAYS	SOUL FINGER	KNUCKLEHEAD	10.00
67	601015	ALBERT KING	BORN UNDER A BAD SIGN	PERSONAL MANAGER	10.00
67	601016	EDDIE FLOYD	THINGS GET BETTER	GOOD LOVE, BAD LOVE	10.00
67	601017	OTIS REDDING	GLORY OF LOVE	I'M COMING HOME	15.00
67	601018	BOOKER T. & THE MG'S	SLIM JENKINS' PLACE	GROOVIN'	8.00
67	601019	WILLIAM BELL	ELOISE (HANG ON IN THERE)	ONE PLUS ONE	5.00
67	601020	RUBY JOHNSON	KEEP ON KEEPING ON	IF I EVER NEEDED LOVE	25.00
67	601021	OTIS REDDING & CARLA THOMAS	KNOCK ON WOOD	LET ME BE GOOD TO YOU	8.00
67	601022	JUDY CLAY	YOU CAN'T RUN AWAY FROM YOUR	IT TAKES A LOT OF GOOD LOVE	10.00
67	601023	SAM and DAVE	SOUL MAN	MAY I BABY	5.00
67	601024	EDDIE FLOYD	ON SATURDAY NIGHT	UNDER MY NOSE	6.00
68	601025	BAR-KAYS	GIVE EVERYBODY SOME	DON'T DO THAT	10.00
68	601026	BOOKER T. & THE MG'S	CHINESE CHECKERS	PLUM NELLIE	8.00
68	601027	OTIS REDDING	(I CAN'T GET NO) SATISFACTION	I'VE BEEN LOVING YOU TOO LONG	10.00
68	601028	RUFUS THOMAS	DOWN TA MY HOUSE	STEADY HOLDING ON	8.00
68	601029	ALBERT KING	COLD FEET	YOU SURE DRIVE A HARD BARGAIN	10.00
68	601030	SAM and DAVE	I THANK YOU	WRAP IT UP	8.00
68	601031	OTIS REDDING	(SITTIN' ON) THE DOCK OF THE BAY	MY SWEET LORENE	6.00
68	601031 test press	OTIS REDDING	(SITTIN' ON) THE DOCK OF THE BAY	MY SWEET LORENE	40.00
68	601032	CARLA THOMAS	PICK UP THE PIECES	SEPARATION	8.00
68	601033 lh	OTIS REDDING & CARLA THOMAS	LOVEY DOVEY	NEW YEAR'S RESOLUTION	6.00
68	601033 sh	OTIS REDDING & CARLA THOMAS	LOVEY DOVEY	NEW YEAR'S RESOLUTION	8.00
68	601034	MABLE JOHN	ABLE MABLE	DON'T GET CAUGHT	15.00
68	601035	EDDIE FLOYD	BIG BIRD	HOLDING ON WITH BOTH HANDS	10.00
68	601036	BAR-KAYS	A HARD DAYS NIGHT	I WANT SOMEONE	10.00
68	601037	RUFUS THOMAS	THE MEMPHIS TRAIN	I THINK I MADE A BOO BOO	10.00
68	601038	WILLIAM BELL	A TRIBUTE TO A KING	EVERY MAN OUGHTA HAVE A WOMAN	6.00
68	601039	DEREK MARTIN	SLY GIRL	SOUL POWER	40.00
68	601040 lh	OTIS REDDING	THE HAPPY SONG (DUM-DUM)	OPEN THE DOOR	8.00
68	601040 sh	OTIS REDDING	THE HAPPY SONG (DUM-DUM)	OPEN THE DOOR	10.00
68	601041	LINDA LYNDELL	BRING YOUR LOVE BACK TO ME	HERE I AM	30.00
68	601042	ALBERT KING	(I LOVE) LUCY	YOU'RE GONNA NED ME	6.00

STAX Distribution rights move to EMI records. Label received a make-over to the now famous yellow label with "Finger Click" logo.

68	101	JUDY CLAY & WILLIAM BELL	PRIVATE NUMBER	LOVE-EYE-TIS	6.00
68	101 DJ	JUDY CLAY & WILLIAM BELL	PRIVATE NUMBER	LOVE-EYE-TIS	15.00
68	102	BOOKER T. & THE MG'S	SOUL LIMBO	HEADS OR TAILS	6.00
68	102 DJ	BOOKER T. & THE MG'S	SOUL LIMBO	HEADS OR TAILS	15.00
68	103	CARLA THOMAS	WHERE DO I GO	I'VE FALLEN IN LOVE	5.00
68	103 DJ	CARLA THOMAS	WHERE DO I GO	I'VE FALLEN IN LOVE	8.00
68	104	EDDIE FLOYD	I'VE NEVER FOUND A GIRL	I'M JUST THE KIND OF FOOL	15.00
68	104 DJ	EDDIE FLOYD	I'VE NEVER FOUND A GIRL	I'M JUST THE KIND OF FOOL	25.00
68	105	RUFUS THOMAS	FUNKY MISSISSIPPI	SP HARD TO GET ALONG WITH	8.00
68	105 DJ	RUFUS THOMAS	FUNKY MISSISSIPPI	SP HARD TO GET ALONG WITH	10.00

68	106	JOHNNIE TAYLOR	WHO'S MAKING LOVE	I'M TRYING	8.00
68	106 DJ	JOHNNIE TAYLOR	WHO'S MAKING LOVE	I'M TRYING	20.00
68	107	SOUTHWEST F.O.B.	SMELL OF INCENSE	GREEN SKIES	6.00
68	107 DJ	SOUTHWEST F.O.B.	SMELL OF INCENSE	GREEN SKIES	8.00
68	108	EDDIE FLOYD	BRING IT ON HOME TO ME	SWEET THINGS YOU DO	6.00
68	108 DJ	EDDIE FLOYD	BRING IT ON HOME TO ME	SWEET THINGS YOU DO	10.00
69	109	OLLIE and THE NIGHTINGALES	YOU'RE LEAVING ME	SHOWERED WITH LOVE	15.00
69	109 DJ	OLLIE and THE NIGHTINGALES	YOU'RE LEAVING ME	SHOWERED WITH LOVE	20.00
69	110	WILLIAM BELL	BRING THE CURTAIN DOWN	I FORGOT TO BE YOUR LOVER	10.00
69	110 DJ	WILLIAM BELL	BRING THE CURTAIN DOWN	I FORGOT TO BE YOUR LOVER	15.00
69	111	JOHNNY DAYE	STAY BABY STAY	I LOVE LOVE	15.00
69	111 DJ	JOHNNY DAYE	STAY BABY STAY	I LOVE LOVE	20.00
69	112	CARLA THOMAS	I LIKE WHAT YOU'RE DOING TO ME	STRUNG OUT	8.00
69	112 DJ	CARLA THOMAS	I LIKE WHAT YOU'RE DOING TO ME	STRUNG OUT	15.00
69	113	GOODEES	CONDITION RED	DIDN'T KNOW LOVE WAS SO GOOD	10.00
69	113 DJ	GOODEES	CONDITION RED	DIDN'T KNOW LOVE WAS SO GOOD	15.00
69	114	JOHNNIE TAYLOR	HOLD ON THIS TIME	TAKE CARE OF YOUR HOMEWORK	10.00
69	114 DJ	JOHNNIE TAYLOR	HOLD ON THIS TIME	TAKE CARE OF YOUR HOMEWORK	15.00
69	115	WILLIAM BELL & JUDY CLAY	MY BABY SPECIALIZES	LEFT OVER LOVE	8.00
69	115 DJ	WILLIAM BELL & JUDY CLAY	MY BABY SPECIALIZES	LEFT OVER LOVE	15.00
69	116	EDDIE FLOYD	GIRL I LOVE YOU	I'VE GOT TO HAVE YOUR LOVE	6.00
69	116 DJ	EDDIE FLOYD	GIRL I LOVE YOU	I'VE GOT TO HAVE YOUR LOVE	10.00
69	117	JIMMY HUGHES	SWEET THINGS YOU DO	LET 'EM DOWN BABY	6.00
69	117 DJ	JIMMY HUGHES	SWEET THINGS YOU DO	LET 'EM DOWN BABY	10.00
69	118	STAPLE SINGERS	THE GHETTO	I SEE IT	6.00
69	118 DJ	STAPLE SINGERS	THE GHETTO	I SEE IT	10.00
69	119	BOOKER T. & THE MG'S	TIME IS TIGHT	HANG 'EM HIGH	6.00
69	119 DJ	BOOKER T. & THE MG'S	TIME IS TIGHT	HANG 'EM HIGH	10.00
69	120	BILLY LEE RILEY	GOIN' BACK TO MEMPHIS	DOWN BY THE RIVERSIDE	6.00
69	120 DJ	BILLY LEE RILEY	GOIN' BACK TO MEMPHIS	DOWN BY THE RIVERSIDE	8.00
69	121	WILLIAM BELL	MY WHOLE WORLD IS FALLING DOWN	ALL GOD'S CHILDREN GOT SOUL	6.00
69	121 DJ	WILLIAM BELL	MY WHOLE WORLD IS FALLING DOWN	ALL GOD'S CHILDREN GOT SOUL	8.00
69	122	JOHNNIE TAYLOR	I HAD A FIGHT WITH LOVE	TESTIFY (I WONNA)	8.00
69	122 DJ	JOHNNIE TAYLOR	I HAD A FIGHT WITH LOVE	TESTIFY (I WONNA)	15.00

all the above from 101 to 122 promo copies were green with label length white A.

69	123	EMOTIONS	SO I CAN LOVE YOU	GOT TO BE THE MAN	8.00
69	123 DJ	EMOTIONS	SO I CAN LOVE YOU	GOT TO BE THE MAN	10.00
69	124	DARRELL BANKS	I'M THE ONE WHO LOVES YOU	JUST BECAUSE YOUR LOVE IS GONE	**180.00**
69	124 DJ	DARRELL BANKS	I'M THE ONE WHO LOVES YOU	JUST BECAUSE YOUR LOVE IS GONE	**211.00**
69	125	EDDIE FLOYD	DON'T TELL YOUR MAMA	CONSIDER ME	8.00
69	125 DJ	EDDIE FLOYD	DON'T TELL YOUR MAMA	CONSIDER ME	10.00
69	126	JIMMY HUGHES	CHAINS OF LOVE	I'M NOT ASHAMED TO BEG OR PLEAD	15.00
69	126 DJ	JIMMY HUGHES	CHAINS OF LOVE	I'M NOT ASHAMED TO BEG OR PLEAD	22.00
69	127	BOOKER T. & THE MG'S	SOUL CLAP '69	MRS. ROBINSON	6.00
69	127 DJ	BOOKER T. & THE MG'S	SOUL CLAP '69	MRS. ROBINSON	10.00
69	128	WILLIAM BELL	HAPPY	JOHNNY I LOVE YOU	20.00
69	128 DJ	WILLIAM BELL	HAPPY	JOHNNY I LOVE YOU	40.00
69	129	JOHNNIE TAYLOR	I COULD NEVER BE PRESIDENT	IT'S AMAZING	6.00
69	129 DJ	JOHNNIE TAYLOR	I COULD NEVER BE PRESIDENT	IT'S AMAZING	8.00
69	130	J.J. BARNES	BABY, PLEASSE COME BACK HOME	EASY LIVING	22.00
69	130 DJ	J.J. BARNES	BABY, PLEASSE COME BACK HOME	EASY LIVING	40.00
69	131	CARLA THOMAS	I'VE FALLEN IN LOVE	UNYIELDING	8.00
69	131 DJ	CARLA THOMAS	I'VE FALLEN IN LOVE	UNYIELDING	10.00
69	132	MAR-KEYS	BLACK	JIVE MAN	6.00
69	132 DJ	MAR-KEYS	BLACK	JIVE MAN	8.00
69	133	ISAAC HAYES	WALK ON BY	BY THE TIME I GET TO PHEONIX	6.00
69	133 DJ	ISAAC HAYES	WALK ON BY	BY THE TIME I GET TO PHEONIX	8.00
69	134	EMOTIONS	I LIKE IT	THE BEST PART OF A LOVE AFFAIR	8.00
69	134 DJ	EMOTIONS	I LIKE IT	THE BEST PART OF A LOVE AFFAIR	10.00
69	135	BAR-KAYS	A.J. THE HOUSE FLY	MIDNIGHT COWBOY	8.00
69	135 DJ	BAR-KAYS	A.J. THE HOUSE FLY	MIDNIGHT COWBOY	10.00
69	136	BOOKER T. & THE MG'S	THE HORSE	SLUM BABY	15.00
69	136 DJ	BOOKER T. & THE MG'S	THE HORSE	SLUM BABY	20.00
69	137	SOUL CHILDREN	THE SWEETER HE IS	THE SWEETER HE IS part 2	6.00
69	137 DJ	SOUL CHILDREN	THE SWEETER HE IS	THE SWEETER HE IS part 2	8.00
70	138	EDDIE FLOYD	WHY IS THE WINE SWEETER	PEOPLE, GET IT TOGETHER	6.00
70	138 DJ	EDDIE FLOYD	WHY IS THE WINE SWEETER	PEOPLE GET IT TOGETHER	8.00
70	139	DELANY & BONNIE	JUST PLAIN BEAUTIFUL	HARD TO SAY GOODBYE	6.00
70	139 DJ	DELANY & BONNIE	JUST PLAIN BEAUTIFUL	HARD TO SAY GOODBYE	8.00
70	141	JOHNNIE TAYLOR	LOVE BONES	SEPARATION LINE	8.00
70	141 DJ	JOHNNIE TAYLOR	LOVE BONES	SEPARATION LINE	10.00
70	142	LUTHER INGRAM	MY HONEY AND ME	PUTIN' GAME DOWN	8.00
70	142 DJ	LUTHER INGRAM	MY HONEY AND ME	PUTIN' GAME DOWN	10.00
70	143	WILLIAM BELL	BRING THE CURTAIN DOWN	BORN UNDER A BAD SIGN	10.00
70	143 DJ	WILLIAM BELL	BRING THE CURTAIN DOWN	BORN UNDER A BAD SIGN	15.00
70	144	RUFUS THOMAS	DO THE FUNKY CHICKEN	TURN YOUR DAMPER DOWN	6.00
70	144 DJ	RUFUS THOMAS	DO THE FUNKY CHICKEN	TURN YOUR DAMPER DOWN	10.00
70	145	EDDIE FLOYD	CALIFORNIA GIRL	WOODMAN	6.00
70	145 DJ	EDDIE FLOYD	CALIFORNIA GIRL	WOODMAN	8.00

70	146	BAR-KAYS	SANG AND DANCE	I THANK YOU	6.00
70	146 DJ	BAR-KAYS	SANG AND DANCE	I THANK YOU	8.00
70	147	STEVE CROPPER	FUNKY BROADWAY	CROP DUSTIN	8.00
70	147 DJ	STEVE CROPPER	FUNKY BROADWAY	CROP DUSTIN	10.00
70	148	LUTHER INGRAM	AIN'T THAT LOVING YOU? (FOR MORE REASONS THAN ONE)	HOME DON'T SEEM LIKE A HOME	8.00
70	148 DJ	LUTHER INGRAM	AIN'T THAT LOVING YOU? (FOR MORE REASONS THAN ONE)	HOME DON'T SEEM LIKE A HOME	10.00
70	149	RUFUS THOMAS	OLD McDONALD HAD A FARM	THE PREACHER AND THE BEAR	6.00
70	149 DJ	RUFUS THOMAS	OLD McDONALD HAD A FARM	THE PREACHER AND THE BEAR	8.00
70	150	JOHNNIE TAYLOR	FRIDAY NIGHT	STEAL AWAY	20.00
70	150 DJ	JOHNNIE TAYLOR	FRIDAY NIGHT	STEAL AWAY	40.00
70	152	BOOKER T. & THE MG'S	DOWN AT RALPH'S JOINT	SOMETHIMNG	6.00
70	152 DJ	BOOKER T. & THE MG'S	DOWN AT RALPH'S JOINT	SOMETHIMNG	10.00
70	153	EDDIE FLOYD	MY GIRL	LAURIE	6.00
70	153 DJ	EDDIE FLOYD	MY GIRL	LAURIE	10.00
70	154	ISAAC HAYES	I STAND ACCUSED	I JUST DON'T KNOW WHAT TO DO W	6.00
70	154 DJ	ISAAC HAYES	I STAND ACCUSED	I JUST DON'T KNOW WHAT TO DO W	8.00
70	155	DAVID PORTER	ONE PART TWO PARTS	CAN'T I SEE YOU WHEN I WANT TO	10.00
70	155 DJ	DAVID PORTER	ONE PART TWO PARTS	CAN'T I SEE YOU WHEN I WANT TO	15.00
70	156	JOHNNIE TAYLOR	I AM SOMEBODY	I AM SOMEBODY part 2	6.00
70	156 DJ	JOHNNIE TAYLOR	I AM SOMEBODY	I AM SOMEBODY part 2	8.00
70	157	ISREAL (POPPER) TOLBERT	BIG LEG WOMAN (WITH A SHORT MINI SKIRT)	I GOT LOVE	6.00
70	157 DJ	ISREAL (POPPER) TOLBERT	BIG LEG WOMAN (WITH A SHORT MINI SKIRT)	I GOT LOVE	8.00

all numbers in this series were preceded by STA

75	12	EDDIE FLOYD	BRING IT ON HOME TO ME	SWEET THING	4.00
75	13	BOOKER T. & THE MG'S	HANG 'EM HIGH	OVER EASY	4.00
75	15	WILLIAM BELL	I FORGOT TO BE YOUR LOVER	BRING THE CURTAIN DOWN	4.00
75	18	SOUL CHILDREN	I'LL UNDERSTAND	DOIN' OUR THING	4.00
75	23	JOHNNIE TAYLOR	TAKE CARE OF YOUR HOMEWORK	HOLD ON THIS TIME	4.00
75	33	JOHNNIE TAYLOR	TESTIFY	IHAD A FIGHT WITH LOVE	4.00
75	50	SOUL CHILDREN	SWEETER HE IS	SWEEETER HE IS part 2	4.00
75	55	JOHNNIE TAYLOR	LOVE BONES	MR. NOBODY IS SOMEBODY	4.00
75	59	RUFUS THOMAS	DO THE FUNKY CHICKEN	TURN YOUR DAMPER DOWN	4.00
75	60	EDDIE FLOYD	CALIFORNIA GIRL	WOODMAN	4.00
75	78	JOHNNIE TAYLOR	I AM SOMEBODY	I AM SOMEBODY part 2	4.00
75	82	BOOKER T. & THE MG'S	MELTING POT	KINDA EASY LIKE	4.00
75	83	STAPLE SINGERS	HEAVY MAKES YOU HAPPY (SHA NA BOOM)	LOVE IS PLENTIFUL	4.00
75	85	JOHNNIE TAYLOR	JODY'S GOT YOUR GIRL AND GONE	FOOL LIKER ME	4.00
75	88	JEAN KNIGHT	MR. BIG STUFF	WHY I KEEP LIVING THESE MEMORIES	4.00
75	89	JOHNNIE TAYLOR	I DON'T WANNA LOSE YOU	PARTY LIFE	4.00
75	96	JOHNNIE TAYLOR	HIJACKIN' LOVE	LOVE IN THE STREETS	4.00
75	98	RUFUS THOMAS	BREAKDOWN	BREAKDOWN part 2	4.00
75	100	LITTLE MILTON	MR. MAILMAN (I DON'T WANT NO MAIL)	IF THAT AIN'T A REASON	5.00
75	104	STAPLE SINGERS	RESPECT YOURSELF	YOU'RE GONNA MAKE ME CRY	4.00
75	111	LITTLE MILTON	THAT'S WHAT LOVE WILL MAKE YOU DO	I'M LIVING FOR THE LOVE YOU GAVE	5.00
75	114	JOHNNIE TAYLOR	STANDING IN FOR JODY	SHACKIN' UP	4.00
75	117	FREDERICK KNIGHT	I'VE BEEN LONELY FOR SO LONG	LEAN ON ME	4.00
75	119	SOUL CHILDREN	HEARSAY	DON'T TAKE MY SUNSHINE	5.00
75	125	STAPLE SINGERS	I'LL TAKE YOU THERE	I'M JUST ANOTHER SOLDIER	5.00

1000 distributed by RCA. The yellow label and original release dates were retained. IE #1003 dated 1968 released 1977. All release numbers are preceded by STAX

77	1001	WILLIAM BELL & JUDY CLAY	PRIVATE NUMBER	MY BABY SPECIALISES	4.00
77	1002	STAPLE SINGERS	I'LL TAKE YOU THERE	IF YOU'RE READYY	4.00
77	1003	BOOKER T. & THE MG'S	SOUL LIMBO	TIME IS TIGHT	4.00
77	1004	EDDIE FLOYD	KNOCK ON WOOD	I'VE NEVER FOUND A GIRL	5.00
77	1005 PS	JEAN KNIGHT c/w CARLA THOMAS	MR. BIG STUFF	I LIKE WHAT YOU'RE DOING TO ME	4.00
77	1006	MEL & TIM c/w DRAMATICS	STARTING ALL OVER AGAIN	IN THE RAIN	4.00
77	1007	VEDA BROWN	SHORT STOPPING	I KNOW IT'S NOT RIGHT	5.00
77	1008 PS	JOHNNIE TAYLOR	WHO'S MAKING LOVE	TAKE CARE OF YOUR HOMEWORK	4.00
77	1009	ISAAC HAYES	THEME FROM SHAFT	I DON'T WANT TO BE RIGHT	4.00
77	1010	SHIRLEY BROWN c/w FREDERICK KNIGHT	WOMAN TO WOMAN	I'VE BEEN LONELY FOR SO LONG	4.00
77	1011	BOOKER T. & THE MG'S	SOUL LIMBO	SOUL CLAP '69	4.00

2000 SERIES All release numbers are preceded by STXS distributed by PYE Records. Stax label was yellow with the "Finger Click" logo

74	2001	STAPLE SINGERS	CITY IN THE SKY	THAT'S WHAT FRIENDS ARE FOR	5.00
74	2001 DJ	STAPLE SINGERS	CITY IN THE SKY	THAT'S WHAT FRIENDS ARE FOR	6.00
74	2002	JOHNNIE TAYLOR	AT NIGHT TIME (MY PILLOW TELLS)	I'VE BEEN BORN AGAIN	5.00
74	2002 DJ	JOHNNIE TAYLOR	AT NIGHT TIME (MY PILLOW TELLS)	I'VE BEEN BORN AGAIN	6.00
74	2003	LITTLE MILTON	BEHIND CLOSED DOORS	BET YOU I WIN	5.00
74	2003 DJ	LITTLE MILTON	BEHIND CLOSED DOORS	BET YOU I WIN	6.00
74	2004	ISAAC HAYES	TITLE THEME	HUNG UP ON MY BABY	5.00
74	2004 DJ	ISAAC HAYES	TITLE THEME	HUNG UP ON MY BABY	6.00
74	2005	EDDIE FLOYD	SOUL STREET	THE HIGHWAY MAN	5.00
74	2005 DJ	EDDIE FLOYD	SOUL STREET	THE HIGHWAY MAN	8.00
74	2006	SOUL CHILDREN	LOVE MAKES IT RIGHT	LOVE MAKES IT RIGHT (RAP)	5.00
74	2006 DJ	SOUL CHILDREN	LOVE MAKES IT RIGHT	LOVE MAKES IT RIGHT (RAP)	6.00
74	2007	GENTRYS	LITTLE GOLD BAND	ALL HUNG UP ON YOU	8.00
74	2007 DJ	GENTRYS	LITTLE GOLD BAND	ALL HUNG UP ON YOU	10.00
74	2008	VEDA BROWN	SHORT STOPPING	I CAN SEE EVERY WOMAN'S MAN	5.00
74	2008 DJ	VEDA BROWN	SHORT STOPPING	I CAN SEE EVERY WOMAN'S MAN	8.00
74	2009	unissued?			
74	2010	ISAAC HAYES	THEME FROM SHAFT	CAFÉ REGIO'S	4.00

74	2010 DJ	ISAAC HAYES	THEME FROM SHAFT	CAFÉ REGIO'S	6.00
74	2011	WILLIAM BELL & JUDY CLAY	PRIVATE NUMBER	MY BASBY SPECIALIZES	5.00
74	2011 DJ	WILLIAM BELL & JUDY CLAY	PRIVATE NUMBER	MY BASBY SPECIALIZES	6.00
74	2012	RUFUS THOMAS c/w CARLA THOMAS	DO THE FUNKY CXHICKEN	GEE WHIZZ	5.00
74	2012 DJ	RUFUS THOMAS c/w CARLA THOMAS	DO THE FUNKY CXHICKEN	GEE WHIZZ	6.00
74	2013	JOHNNIE TAYLOR	WHO'S MAKING LOVE	JODY GOT YOUR GIRL AND GONE	5.00
74	2013 DJ	JOHNNIE TAYLOR	WHO'S MAKING LOVE	JODY GOT YOUR GIRL AND GONE	6.00
74	2014	BOOKER T. & THE MG'S	SOUL LIMBO	TIME IS TIGHT	5.00
74	2014 DJ	BOOKER T. & THE MG'S	SOUL LIMBO	TIME IS TIGHT	6.00
74	2015	unissued?			
74	2016	MARGIE ALEXANDER	KEEP ON SEARCHIN'	LOVE SLAVE	10.00
74	2016 DJ	MARGIE ALEXANDER	KEEP ON SEARCHIN'	LOVE SLAVE	15.00
74	2017	RUFUS THOMAS	BOOGIE AIN'T NUTTIN' (BUT GETTING'	THE FUNKY BIRD	5.00
74	2017 DJ	RUFUS THOMAS	BOOGIE AIN'T NUTTIN' BUT GETTING	FUNKY BIRD	6.00
75	2018	STAPLE SINGERS	MY MAIN MAN	WHO MADE THE MAN	4.00
75	2018 DJ	STAPLE SINGERS	MY MAIN MAN	WHO MADE THE MAN	5.00
75	2019	SHIRLEY BROWN	WOMAN TO WOMAN	YES SIR BROTHER	5.00
75	2019 DJ	SHIRLEY BROWN	WOMAN TO WOMAN	YES SIR BROTHER	6.00
75	2020	EMOTIONS	BABY I'M THROUGH	I WANNA COME BACK	5.00
75	2020 DJ	EMOTIONS	BABY I'M THROUGH	I WANNA COME BACK	6.00
75	2021	JOHNNIE TAYLOR	IT'S SEPTEMBER	JUST ONE MOMENT	5.00
75	2021 DJ	JOHNNIE TAYLOR	IT'S SEPTEMBER	JUST ONE MOMENT	6.00
75	2023	NEWCOMERS	KEEP AN EYE ON YOUT CLOSE FRIENDS	same: instrumental	6.00
75	2023 DJ	NEWCOMERS	KEEP AN EYE ON YOUT CLOSE FRIENDS	same: instrumental	6.00
75	2024	unissued?			
75	2025	JOHNNIE TAYLOR	FRIDAY NIGHT	I AIN'T PARTICULAR	10.00
75	2025 DJ	JOHNNIE TAYLOR	FRIDAY NIGHT	I AIN'T PARTICULAR	12.00
75	2026	RANCE ALLEN GROUP	AIN'T NO NEED OF CRYING	IF I COULD MAKE THE WORLD BETT	10.00
75	2026 DJ	RANCE ALLEN GROUP	AIN'T NO NEED OF CRYING	IF I COULD MAKE THE WORLD BETT	12.00
75	2027	TEMPREES	AT LAST	I'LL LIVE HER LIFE	8.00
75	2027 DJ	TEMPREES	AT LAST	I'LL LIVE HER LIFE	12.00
75	2028	FREDERICK KNIGHT	I BETCHA DIDN'T KNOW THAT	LET'S MAKE A DEAL	6.00
75	2028 DJ	FREDERICK KNIGHT	I BETCHA DIDN'T KNOW THAT	LET'S MAKE A DEAL	8.00
75	2029	RUFUS THOMAS	DO THE DOUBLE BUMP	DO THE DOUBLE BUMP part 2	4.00
75	2029 DJ	RUFUS THOMAS	DO THE DOUBLE BUMP	DO THE DOUBLE BUMP part 2	5.00
75	2030	WARP NINE	THEME FROM STAR TREK	PARA-SONG 1	6.00
75	2030 DJ	WARP NINE	THEME FROM STAR TREK	PARA-SONG 1	8.00
75	2031	BETTYE CRUTCHER	SUGAR DADDY	AS LONG AS YOU LOVE ME	8.00
75	2031 DJ	BETTYE CRUTCHER	SUGAR DADDY	AS LONG AS YOU LOVE ME	10.00
75	2032	SHIRLEY BROWN	I CAN'T GIVE YOU UP	AIN'T NO FUN	6.00
75	2032 DJ	SHIRLEY BROWN	I CAN'T GIVE YOU UP	AIN'T NO FUN	8.00
75	2033	JEAN KNIGHT	MR. BIG STUFF	WHY I KEEP LIVING THESE MEMORI	6.00
75	2033 DJ	JEAN KNIGHT	MR. BIG STUFF	WHY I KEEP LIVING THESE MEMORI	8.00
75	2034	ANNETTE THOMAS	YOU NEED A FRIEND LIKE MINE	WHAT GOOD IS A SONG	8.00
75	2034 DJ	ANNETTE THOMAS	YOU NEED A FROEND LIKE MINE	WHAT GOOD IS A SONG	10.00
75	2035	ISAAC HAYES	I'M GONNA HAVE TO TELL HER	GOOD LOVE 6-9969	4.00
75	2035 DJ	ISAAC HAYES	GOOD LOVE 6-9969	I'M GONNA HAVE TO TELL YOU	5.00
76	2036	KIM WESTON	GOODNESS GRACIOUS	WHEN SOMETHING IS WRONG WITH MY BABY	8.00
76	2036 DJ	KIM WESTON	GOODNESS GRACIOUS	WHEN SOMETHING IS WRONG WITH MY BABY	10.00
76	2037	RUFUS THOMAS	JUMP BACK 75	JUMP BACK 75 part 2	5.00
76	2037 DJ	RUFUS THOMAS	JUMP BACK 75	JUMP BACK 75 part 2	6.00
75	2038	WILLIAM BELL	HAPPY	BRING THE CURTAIN DOWN	10.00
75	2038 DJ	WILLIAM BELL	HAPPY	BRING THE CURTAIN DOWN	15.00
75	2039	FREDERICK KNIGHT	I WANNA PLAY WITH YOU	I MISS YOU	4.00
75	2039 DJ	FREDERICK KNIGHT	I WANNA PLAY WITH YOU	I MISS YOU	6.00
76	2040	unissued?			
76	2041	BOOKER T. & THE MG'S	SOUL LIMBO	MRS. ROBINSON	4.00
76	2041	BOOKER T. & THE MG'S	SOUL LIMBO	MRS. ROBINSON	5.00
76	2042	JUDY CLAY & WILLIAM BELL	PRIVATE NUMBER	SUCH A FEVER	4.00
76	2042 DJ	JUDY CLAY & WILLIAM BELL	PRIVATE NUMBER	SUCH A FEVER	5.00
76	2043	DRAMATICS	WHAT'CHA SEE IS WHAT'CHA GET	THANKFUL FOR YOUR LOVE	4.00
76	2043 DJ	DRAMATICS	WHATCHA SEE IS WHATCHA GET	NOW YOU GOT ME LOVING YOU	5.00

2000 series Distributed by EMI records with red labels later changing to plum to white fade label

77	2001	BOOKER T. & THE MG'S	TIME IS TIGHT	SOUL LIMBO	5.00
77	2002	ISAAC HAYES	THEME FROM SHAFT	CAFÉ REGIO'S	4.00
77	2003	RUFUS THOMAS	DO THE FUNKY CHICKEN	THE BREAKDOWN part 1	6.00
77	2004	STAPLE SINGERS	I'LL TAKE YOU THERE	IF YOU'RE READY	4.00
78	2005	JOHNNIE TAYLOR	WHO'S MAKING LOVE	TAKE CARE OF YOUR HOME WORK	5.00
78	2006	WILLIAM BELL & JUDY CLAY	PRIVATE NUMBER	MY BABY SPECIALISES	4.00
78	2007	VEDA BROWN c/w JEAN KNIGHT	SHORT STOPPPING	MR. BIG STUFF	6.00
78	2008	FREDERICK KNIGHT	I BETCHA DIDN'T KNOW THAT	I'VE BEEN LONELY FOR SO LONG	4.00
78	2009 DJ	SHIRLEY BROWN	WOMAN TO WOMAN	IT AIN'T NO FUN	6.00
78	2010	EDDIE FLOYD	KNOCK ON WOOD + GIRL I LOVE YOU	BRING IT ON HOME TO ME	4.00

2025 series Polydor distributed. Polydor release numbering policy covered releases worldwide. Missing numbers in this series were attributed to other labels within the Polydor group including overseas releases. Note in this series Polydor "dinked" some of the releases with a large hole center, I have noted some obvious ones to as examples. Small hole releases that have escaped the dinking process are more desirable and should be priced at about 20% more in value. The below values are for <u>large hole</u> releases.

71	2025016	RUFUS THOMAS	(DO THE) PUSH AND PULL	(DO THE) PUSH AND PULL part 2	5.00
71	2025019	STAPLE SINGERS	HEAVY MAKES YOU HAPPY (SHA NA	LOVE IS PLENTIFUL	5.00
71	2025020	ISAAC HAYES	YOU'VE LOST THAT LOVING FEELING	OUR DAY WILL COME	5.00

71	2025021	JOHNNIE TAYLOR	JODY GOT YOUR GIRL AND GONE	A FOOL LIKE ME	6.00
71	2025025	WILLIAM BELL	I FORGOT TO BE YOUR LOVER	WINDING WINDING ROAD	6.00
71	2025026	BOOKER T. & THE MG'S	MELTING POT	KINDA EASY LIKE	8.00
71	2025029	ISAAC HAYES	NEVER CAN SAY GOODBYE	I CAN'T HELP IT	5.00
72	2025133	FREDERICK KNIGHT	TROUBLE	FRIEND	6.00
71	2025049	JEAN KNIGHT	MR. BIG STUFF	WHY I KEEP LIVING THESE MEMORI	10.00
71	2025050	SOUL CHILDREN	GIVE ME ONE GOOD REASON	BRING IT HERE	5.00
71	2025052	MARGIE JOSEPH	MEDICINE BEND	SAME THING	8.00
71	2025053	DRAMATICS	WHATCHA SEE IS WHATCHA GET	THANKFUL FOR YOUR LOVE	5.00
72	2025060	RUFUS THOMAS	BREAKDOWN	BREAKDOWN part 2	10.00
72	2025063	NEWCOMERS	PIN THE TAIL ON THE DONKEY	MANNISH BOY	6.00
72	2025068	STAPLE SINGERS	RESPECT YOURSELF	YOU'RE GONNAMAKE ME CRY	5.00
72	2025069 sh	ISAAC HAYES	THEME FROM "SHAFT"	CAFÉ REGIO'S (inst.)	5.00
72	2025069 lh	ISAAC HAYES	THEME FROM "SHAFT"	CAFÉ REGIO'S (inst.)	4.00
72	2025074	M.G.'s	JAMAICA THIS MORNING	FUQUAWI	6.00
72	2025080	RUFUS THOMAS	DO THE FUNKY PENGUIN	SAME: PART2	5.00
72	2025082	CARLA THOMAS	YOU'VE GOT A CUSHION TO FALL ON	LOVE MEANS (NEVER HAVING TO SA	6.00
72	2025083	JOHNNIE TAYLOR	STANDING IN FOR JODY	SHAKIN' UP	5.00
73	2025186	WILLIAM BELL & JUDY CLAY	PRIVATE NUMBER	TESTIFY + MRS ROBINSON	5.00
73	2025089	EDDIE FLOYD	YUM YUM YUM	TEARS OF JOY	6.00
72	2025095	LITTLE MILTON	THAT'S WHAT LOVE WILL MAKE YOU	I'M LIVING OFF THE LOVE YOU GI	6.00
72	2025098 sh	FREDERICK KNIGHT	I'VE BEEN LONELY FOR SO LONG	LEAN ON ME	6.00
72	2025098 lh	FREDERICK KNIGHT	I'VE BEEN LONELY FOR SO LONG	LEAN ON ME	5.00
72	2025101	DRAMATICS	IN THE RAIN	GET UP AND GET DOWN	6.00
72	2025102	SOUL CHILDREN	HEARSAY	DON'T TAKE MY SUNSHINE	5.00
72	2025103	JEAN KNIGHT	CARRY ON	DO YOU THINK YOU'RE HOT STUFF	8.00
72	2025107	EMOTIONS	MY HONEY AND ME	SHOW ME HOW	5.00
72	2025110 sh	STAPLE SINGERS	I'LL TAKE YOU THERE	I'M JUST ANOTHER SOLDIER	5.00
72	2025110 lh	STAPLE SINGERS	I'LL TAKE YOU THERE	I'M JUST ANOTHER SOLDIER	6.00
72	2025117	DRAMATICS	TOAST TO THE FOOL	YOUR LOVE WAS STRANGE	5.00
73	2025123	WILLIAM BELL	SAVE US	LONELY FOR YOUR LOVE	4.00
73	2025124 sh	MAJOR LANCE	I WANNA MAKE UP (Before we break up)	THAT'S THE STORY OF MY LIFE	20.00
73	2025124 lh	MAJOR LANCE	I WANNA MAKE UP (Before we break up)	THAT'S THE STORY OF MY LIFE	15.00
73	2025125	MEL & TIM	STARTING ALL OVER AGAIN	IT HURTS TO WANT IT SO BAD	5.00
73	2051129	STAPLE SINGERS	THIS WORLD	ARE YOU SURE	5.00
73	2025133	FREDERICK KNIGHT	TROUBLE	FRIEND	5.00
73	2025146	ISAAC HAYES	THEME FROM THE MEN	TYPE THANG	4.00
73	2025147	CARLA THOMAS	SUGAR	I WAKE UP WANTING YOU	4.00
73	2025148	TEMPREES	EXPLAIN IT TO HER MAMA	(GIRL) I LOVE YOU	6.00
73	2025150	EDDIE FLOYD	YOU'RE GOOD ENOUGH (TO BE MY BABY)	SPEND ALL YOU HAVE ON LOVE	6.00
73	2025151	INEZ FOXX	YOU HURT ME FOR THE LAST TIME	WATCH THE DOG (THAT BRINGS THE	5.00
73	2025152	RANCE ALLEN GROUP	THERE'S GONNA BE A SHOWDOWN	THAT WILL BE GOOD ENOUGH FOR ME	8.00
73	2025161	JEAN KNIGHT	DO ME	SAVE THE LAST KISS FOR ME	8.00
73	2025162	ALBERT KING	BREAKING UP SOMEBODY'S HOME	LITTLE BROTHER (MAKE A WAY)	6.00
73	2025171	MEL & TIM	FREE FOR ALL	WHAT'S YOUR NAME	5.00
73	2025172	STAPLE SINGERS	WE THE PEOPLE	OH LA DE DA	4.00
73	2025177	ISAAC HAYES	(IF LOVING YOU IS WRONG) I DON'T	ROLLING DOWN A MOUNTAINSIDE	4.00
73	2025181	DRAMATICS	HEY YOU, GET OFF MY MOUNTAIN	DEVIL IS DOPE	15.00
73	2025185	STAPLE SINGERS	BE WHAT YOU ARE	LIKE THE THINGS ABOUT ME	4.00
73	2025186	WILLIAM BELL & JUDY CLAY	PRIVATE NUMBER	MRS. ROBINSON + (I WANNA) TEST	4.00
73	2025187	WILLIAM BELL & VARIOUS	HAPPY	DO THE FUNKY CHICKEN + HANG 'EM HIGH	5.00
73	2025188	JOHNNIE TAYLOR & VARIOUS	WHO'S MAKING LOVE	SOUL LIMBO + THE GHETTO	4.00
73	2025193	DON NIX	BLACK CAT MOAN	TRAIN DON'T STOP HERE NO MORE	8.00
73	2025194	JOHNNIE TAYLOR	I BELIEVE IN LOVE	LOVE DEPRESSION	6.00
73	2025199	RUFUS THOMAS c/w CARLA THOMAS	DO THE FUNKY CXHICKEN	GEE WHIZZ	5.00
74	2025207	BOOKER T. & VARIOUS ARTISTS	TIME IS TIGHT + BRING IT ON HOME TO ME	MY BABY BABY SPECIALISES	4.00
74	2025220	ISAAC HAYES	JOY	JOY part 2	4.00
74	2025224 paper	STAPLE SINGERS	IF YOU'RE READY (COME GO WITH ME)	TOUCH A HAND, MAKE A FRIEND	5.00
74	2025224 ink	STAPLE SINGERS	IF YOU'RE READY (COME GO WITH ME)	TOUCH A HAND, MAKE A FRIEND	4.00
77	501	EMOTIONS	SHOUTIN' OUT LOVE	BABY I'M THROUGH	8.00
77	502	FAT LARRY'S BAND	CASTLE OF JOY	SPARKLE	4.00
78	503	SOUL CHILDREN	CAN'T GIVE UP ON A GOOD THING	SIGNED SEALED DELIVERED I'M YOURS	5.00
78	504	BIG STAR	SEPTEMBER GIRLS	MOD LANG	6.00
79	505	BAR-KAYS	HOLY GHOST	MONSTER	4.00
79	505 DJ	BAR-KAYS	HOLY GHOST	MONSTER	5.00
79	506	RANCE ALLEN GROUP	SMILE	I BELONG TO YOU	5.00

800 series Yellow label with "finger Click" logo were pressed in Europe with the original release date on the label. IE Stax 806 release date on label 1974 actual release date 1987

87	801	JUDY CLAY & WILLIAM BELL	PRIVATE NUMBER + LEFT OVER LOVE	MY BABY SPECIALIZES	4.00
87	802	JOHNNIE TAYLOR	WHO'S MAKLING LOVE	I'M TRYING	4.00
87	803	BOOKER T. & THE MG'S	TIME IS TIGHT	JOHNNY I LOVE YOU	4.00
87	804 EP	JEAN KNIGHT	MR. BIG STUFF + CARRY ME + DO ME	YOU THINK YOUR HOT STUFF	4.00
87	805	STAPLE SINGERS	RESPECT YOURSELF	YOU'RE GONNA MAKE ME CRY	4.00
87	806	SHIRLEY BROWN	WOMAN TO WOMAN	YES SIR BROTHER	4.00
87	807	EDDIE FLOYD	KNOCK ON WOOD	BIG BIRD	5.00
87	808	BOOKER T. & THE MG'S	SOUL LIMBO	HEADS OR TAILS	4.00
87	809	DRAMATICS	IN THE RAIN	GOOD SOUL MUSIC	4.00
87	810	ISAAC HAYES	THEME FROM SHAFT	CAFÉ REGIO'S	4.00
87	811	FREDERICK KNIGHT	I'VE BEEN LONELY FOR SO LONG	LEAN ON ME	4.00
87	813	BOOKER T. & THE MG'S	HANG 'EM HIGH	OVER EASY	4.00

87	814	RUFUS THOMAS	DO THE FUNKY CHICKEN	TURN YOUR DAMPER DOWN	4.00
87	815	STAPLE SINGERS	I'LL TAKE YOU THERE	I'M JUST ANOTHER SOLDIER	4.00
87	816	MEL & TIM	STARTING ALL OVER AGAIN	IT HURT TO WANT IT SO BAD	4.00
87	817	STAPLE SINGERS	LONG WALK TO D.C.	STAY WITH US	4.00
87	818	WILLIAM BELL	I FORGOT TO BE YOUR LOVER	BRING THE CURTAIN DOWN	4.00
87	819	CARLA THOMAS	I LIKE WHAT YOU'RE DOING TO ME	STRUNG OUT	4.00
87	820	JOHNNIE TAYLOR	TESTIFY	I HAD A FIGHT WITH LOVE	4.00

STICKY

73	2	SOUL GENERATION	MILLION DOLLARS	SAILING	15.00

STIFF

81	114	BUBBA LOU & THE HIGHBALLS	OVER YOU	LOVE ALL OVER THE PLACE	22.00
81	114 DJ	BUBBA LOU & THE HIGHBALLS	OVER YOU	LOVE ALL OVER THE PLACE	30.00

STRAWBERRY

76	1	PHILADELPHIA BROWN	1 – 2 - 3	PHILADELPHIA ROCK	6.00
76	1 DJ	PHILADELPHIA BROWN	1 – 2 - 3	PHILADELPHIA ROCK	8.00

STREETWAVE

83	3	BARBARA MASON	ANOTHER MAN	ANOTHER MAN part 2	4.00
83	6	BLUE MAGIC	IN THE RAIN	MAGIC	5.00
83	8	ROZ RYAN	BOY WHERE HAVE YOU BEEN	WAITING FOR MY COVER	6.00
83	9	ARNIE'S LOVE	I'M OUT OF YOUR LIFE	same: instrumental	8.00
83	9 PS	ARNIE'S LOVE	I'M OUT OF YOUR LIFE	same: instrumental	10.00
84	12 PS	EDWIN STARR	MARVIN	HAPPY SONG	4.00
84	15	BARBARA MASON	DON'T I EVER CROSS YOUR MIND	same: instrumental	4.00
84	23 PS	CHERYL LYNN	ENCORE	GOT TO BE REAL	4.00
84	28	FONDA RAE	TOUCH ME	TOUCH ME part 2	4.00
84	29	MAJOR HARRIS	GOTTA MAKE UP YOUR MIND	same: instrumental	4.00
84	34	INTRUDERS	WHO DO YOU LOVE	WHO DO YOU LOVE part 2	8.00
85	66	VIOLA WILLS	DARE TO DREAM	BOTH SIDES NOW	4.00

STRIKE

66	329	J.J. JACKSON	COME SEE ME	TRY ME	30.00
66	302	JACKI BOND	TELL HIM TO GO AWAY	DON'T YOU WORRY	10.00
66	306	MIKI DALLON	CHEAT AND LIE	I'M GONNA FIND A CAVE	25.00
66	307	ALVIN ROBINSON	YOU BROUGHT MY HEART RIGHT DOW	WHATEVER YOU HAD YOU AIN'T GOT	20.00
66	309	JIMMY POWELL & the DIMENSIONS	I CAN GO DOWN	LOVE ME RIGHT	30.00
66	310	THIS N' THAT	GET DOWN WITH IT: SATISFACTION	I CARE ABOUT YOU	10.00
66	320	JACKI BOND	WHY CAN'T I LOVE HIM	HE SAY	75.00
67	329	J.J. JACKSON	COME SEE ME	TRY ME	30.00

STRIKE COLA

71	11	POETS	HEYLA HOLA	FUN BUGGY	50.00

SUE

Sue Records were more than a 7" music format; they were a cult object d'art. In the mid 60's it was important to be seen in the right clothes, stating some clear symbol as to your musical allegiance. The Tamla Motown label was dull and indistinguishable from other EMI distributed labels, Atlantic and Stax were maybe much better but the yellow and red of the Sue label topped the lot. To own a Sue 45, it showed that you were into the cool, obscure end of Soul music too, not just the chart and dance hall stuff and because they were notoriously difficult to obtain. Also it left your friends know, that you knew where to go for rare 45's. I supposed the Sue label cult was a forerunner to the Rare Soul scene of the 70's and beyond.

In my hometown of Wakefield they were unobtainable until owner Chris Blackwell struck a distribution deal with EMI and even then you got the distinct impression that the local record shops didn't like all the hassle of ordering "difficult" 45's. The nearest Sue friendly shop was Wood's in Bradford who seemed to stock them quite happily and in Leeds there was a place called Kennedy's who sold Sue deletions.

Sue Records could be categorised into two sections, those 45's you listened to at home and those you heard in the clubs. The former would be a long and varied list but the latter was surprisingly short including "Billy's Bag" Billy Preston, "A Little Piece Of Leather" Donnie Elbert, "Mockingbird" "Hurt By Love" and La De Da I Love You" by Inez & Charlie Fox and undoubtedly the biggest of the lot "Harlem Shuffle" by Bob and Earl. Still 40 years on, many revival nights are touted as "Harlem Shuffle" evenings.

In the mists of time Sue is regarded as an innovative label, presenting rare US recordings that would otherwise remained undiscovered. The most part it did just that but there were a couple of 45's that seemed to be issued more for their obscurity than their quality (it was "hip" to be obscure) and there were also a few release of recordings that had previously been released in the UK by larger British labels. These included Ike & Tina's "It's Gonna Work Out Fine" Bobby Hendricks "Itchy Twitchy Feeling" Bobby Parker "Watch Your Step" and of coarse James Brown's classic "Night Train but in well over 100 releases under it's belt these titles were a minor distraction.

Sue folded in 1968, remaining an underground cult label, it's final release, The Fascinations "Girls Are Out To Get You", although a reissue of an earlier Stateside outing, the Sue 45 still commands a high price solely because of the label. The label's momentum was continued almost immediately by B&C under the Action label banner, and I consider it much than a coincidence that B&C used the Sue team colours within their eye-catching graphics. Sue must be considered as the UK's most desirable and sought after of all 60's UK record labels.

60's Sue Scout Keith Rylatt

83	1 EP PS	IKE & TINA TURNER	SUE SESSIONS	1983 4 track EP	10.00
83	2 EP PS	INEZ & CHARLIE FOXX	MOCKINGBIRD	4 track ep. Reissue	10.00
83	3 EP PS	VARIOUS ARTISTS	THE SUE SOUL SISTERS:	UK 4 track EP with cover	10.00
83	4 EP PS	VARIOUS ARTISTS	THE SUE SOUL BROTHERS: 4 track EP	derek martin, prince la la, wi	10.00
83	5 EP PS	HANK JACOBS	SO FAR AWAY	1983 4 track EP with cover	10.00
83	6 EP PS	VARIOUS ARTISTS	SUE INSTRUMENTALS	1983 4 track EP with cover	10.00
64	301	INEZ.FOXX	MOCKINGBIRD	HE'S THE ONE YOU LOVE	25.00
64	302	BABY WASHINGTON	THAT'S HOW HEARTACHES ARE MADE	DOODLIN	75.00
64	303	JIMMY McGRIFF	ALL ABOUT MY GIRL	M.G. BLUES	40.00
64	304	INEZ.FOXX	JAYBIRDS	BROKEN HEARTED FOOL	30.00

64	305	RUSSELL BYRD	HITCHHIKE	HITCHHIKE part 2	40.00
64	306	IKE & KINGS OF TURNER	GONNA WORK OUT FINE	WON'T YOU FORGIVE ME	15.00
64	307	INEZ & CHARLIE FOXX	HERE WE GO ROUND THE MULBERRY	COMPETITION	30.00
64	308	DEREK MARTIN	DADDY ROLLIN' STONE	DON'T PUT ME DOWN LIKE THIS	45.00
64	309	ERNESTINE ANDERSON	KEEP AN EYE ON LOVE	CONTINENTAL MINDS	100.00
64	310	JIMMY McGRIFF	LAST MINUTE	LAST MINUTE part 2	30.00
64	311	MARY LOU WILLIAMS	CHUCK-A-LUNK JUG	CHUCK-A-LUNK JUG PART 2	30.00
64	312	SOUL SISTERS	I CAN'T STAND IT	BLUEBERRY HILL	40.00
64	313	HANK JACOBS	SO FAR AWAY	MONKEY, HIPS AND RICE	30.00
64	314	INEZ.FOXX	ASK ME	HI DIDDLE DIDDLE	30.00
64	315	BOBBY HENDRICKS	ITCHY TWITCHY FEELING	THOUSAND DREAMS	25.00
64	316	BARBARA GEORGE	SEND FOR ME	BLESS YOU	50.00
64	317	JIMMY McGRIFF	I'VE GOT A WOMAN PART1	I'VE GOT A WOMAN PART 2	20.00
64	318	TIM WHITSETT	MACKS BY THE TRACKS	SHINE	40.00
64	319	HOMESICK JAMES	CROSSROADS	MY BABY'S SWEET	30.00
64	320	WILLIE MABON	GOT TO HAVE SOME	WHY DID IT HAPPEN TO ME	20.00
64	321	BABY WASHINGTON	I CAN'T WAIT UNTIL I SEE MY BABY'S FACE	WHO'S GONNA TAKE CARE OF ME	100.00
64	322	IKE & TINA TURNER	POOR FOOL	THE ARGUMENT	40.00
64	323	INEZ.FOXX	CONFUSION	HURT BY LOVE	20.00
64	324	PATTI LABELLE & THE BLUEBELLES	DOWN THE AISLE	C'EST LA VIE	40.00
64	325	MEGATONS	SHIMMY SHIMMY WALK PART 1	SHIMMY SHIMMY WALK PART 2	45.00
64	326	BOBBY LEE TRAMMELL	NEW DANCE IN FRANCE	CAROLYN	20.00
	327	TONY WASHINGTON & the D.C.'s	SHOW ME HOW (TO MILK A COW)	BOOF SKA	30.00
64	328	ANITA WOOD	DREAM BOY	THIS HAPPENED BEFORE	20.00
64	329	JACKIE EDWARDS	STAGGER LEE	PRETTY GIRL	40.00
64	330	HOMESICK JAMES	SET A DATE	CAN'T AFFORD TO DO IT	30.00
64	331	WILLIE MABON	JUST GOT SOME	THAT'S NO BIG THING	25.00
64	332	DOUG SHELDON	TELL IT LIKE A MAN	LONELY BOY	25.00
64	333	JIMMY McGRIFF	'ROUND MIDNIGHT	LONELY AVENUE	30.00
64	334	WALLACE BROTHERS	PRECIOUS WORDS	YOU'RE MINE	40.00
64	335	ELMORE JAMES & the BROOM	DUST MY BLUES	HAPPY HOME	40.00
64	336	SOUL SISTERS	LOOP DE LOOP	LONG GONE	30.00
64	337	LOUISIANA RED	I DONE WOKE UP	I HAD A FEELING	40.00
64	338	unissued			
64	339	J.B. LENIOR	I SING UM THE WAY I FEEL	I FEEL SO GOOD	30.00
64	340	BOBBY PARKER	WATCH YOUR STEP	STEAL YOUR HEART AWAY	35.00
64	341	BIG AL DOWNING	YES I'M LOVING YOU	PLEASE COME HOME	50.00
64	342	BOBBY PETERSON	ROCKIN' CHARLIE	ROCKIN' CHARLIE part 2	25.00
64	343	DAYLIGHTERS	OH MOM	HARD HEADED GIRL	30.00
65	344	REVERE, PAUL & the RAIDERS	LIKE LONG HAIR	SHARON	25.00
65	345	WILLIE MAE THORNTON	TOM CAT	MONKEY IN THE BARN	150.00
65	346	BOBBY PETERSON	PIANO ROCK	ONE DAY	25.00
65	347	JUNE BATEMAN	I DON'T WANNA	NOBLES THEME	40.00
65	348	OLYMPICS	THE BOUNCE	FIREWORKS	30.00
65	349	FREDDY KING	DRIVING SIDEWAYS	HIDEAWAY	20.00
65	350	IKE & TINA TURNER	I CAN'T BELIEVE WHAT YOU SAY	MY BABY NOW	20.00
65	351	CHRIS KENNER	LAND OF A 1,000 DANCES	THAT'S MY GIRL	30.00
65	352	BETTY EVERETT	I'VE GOT A CLAIM ON YOU	YOUR LOVE IS IMPORTANT TO ME	30.00
65	353	HAROLD BURRAGE	I'LL TAKE ONE	A LONG WAYS TOGETHER	50.00
65	354	ROSCOE SHELTON	QUESTION	STRAIN ON MY HEART	30.00
65	355	WALLACE BROTHERS	LOVER'S PRAYER	LOVE ME LIKE I LOVE YOU	40.00
65	356	INEZ & CHARLIE FOXX	LA DE DA I LOVE YOU	YANKEE DOODLE DANDY	25.00
65	357	PLEASURES	MUSIC CITY	IF I HAD A LITTLE MONEY	30.00
65	358	B.B.KING	THE LETTER	YOU NEVER KNOW	35.00
65	359	ETTA JAMES	ROLL WITH ME HENRY	GOOD ROCKIN' DADDY	40.00
65	360	JAMES BROWN	NIGHT TRAIN	WHY DOES EVERYTHING HAPPEN TO	20.00
65	361	JOHN LEE HOOKER	I'M IN THE MOOD	BOOGIE CHILLUN	30.00
65	362	OTIS REDDING	SHOUT BAMALAMA	FAT GIRL	30.00
65	363	WILBERT HARRISON	LET'S STICK TOGETHER	KANSAS CITY TWIST	30.00
65	364	HUEY SMITH & the CLOWNS	IF IT AIN'T ONE THING IT'S ANOTHER	TU-BER-CU-LUCAS & THE SINUS BL	25.00
65	365	SONNY BOY WILLIAMSON	NO NIGHTS BY MYSELF	BOPPN' WITH SONNY BOY	30.00
65	366	FRANKIE FORD	SEA CRUISE	ROBERTA	20.00
65	367	LEE DORSEY	DO-RE-MI	YA YA	40.00
65	368	BUSTER BROWN	FANNIE MAE	LOST IN A DREAM	30.00
65	369	FRANKIE FORD	WHAT'S GOING ON?	WATCHDOG	30.00
65	370	JOE TEX	YUM YUM YUM	YOU LITTLE BABY FACE THING	30.00
65	371	LARRY WILLIAMS	STRANGE	CALL ON ME	30.00
65	372	IRMA THOMAS	DON'T MESS WITH MY MAN	SET ME FREE	45.00
65	373	BIG JAY McNEELEY	THERE IS SOMETHING ON YOUR MIND	BACK SHACK TRACK	30.00
66	374	BOB AND EARL	HARLEM SHUFFLE	I'LL KEEP RUNNING BACK	20.00
65	375	LOWELL FULSOM	KEY TO YOUR HEART	TOO MANY DRIVERS	40.00
65	376	IKE & TINA TURNER	PLEASE, PLEASE, PLEASE	AM I A FOOL IN LOVE	40.00
65	377	DONNIE ELBERT	A LITTLE PIECE OF LEATHER	DO WAT'CHA WANNA	20.00
65	378	HAROLD BETTERS	DO ANYTHING YOU WANNA	DO ANYTHING YOU WANNA Part2	20.00
65	379	SCREAMING JAY HAWKINS	I HEAR VOICES	JUST DON'T CARE	30.00
65	380	HUEY PIANO SMITH	ROCKIN' PNEUMONIA & THE BOOGIE WOOGIE FLU	same: part 2	20.00
65	381	LARRY WILLIAMS	TURN ON YOUR LOVELIGHT	DIZZY MISS LIZZY	25.00
65	382	WILLIE MABON	I'M THE FIXER	SOME MORE	40.00

65	383	ELMORE JAMES	IT HURTS ME TOO	BLEEDING HEART	35.00
65	384	MANHATTANS	I WANNA BE (YOUR EVERYTHING)	SEARCHIN' FOR MY BABY	40.00
65	385	LITTLE JOE COOK	STORMY MONDAY BLUES	STORMY MONDAY BLUES Part2	40.00
65	386	ALEXANDER JACKSON	THE WHIP	TELL IT LIKE IT IS	50.00
65	387	JIMMY JOHNSON	DON'T ANSWER THE DOOR	DON'T ANSWER THE DOOR part 2	40.00
65	388	BOBBY DAY	ROCKIN' ROBIN	OVER AND OVER	22.00
65	389	IKETTES	PRISONER OF LOVE	THOSE WORDS	40.00
65	390	TARHEEL SLIM & LITTLE ANN	YOU MAKE ME FEEL SO GOOD	GOT TO KEEP ON LOVIN'	30.00
65	391	DORSETS	PORK CHOPS	COOL IT	30.00
65	392	ELMORE JAMES	KNOCKING AT YOUR DOOR	CALLING THE BLUES	100.00
65	393	BOB AND EARL	BABY I'M SATISFIED	THE SISSY	30.00
65	394	GLADYS KNIGHT & The PIPS	LETTER FULL OF TEARS	YOU BROKE YOUR PROMISE	40.00
65	395	ESTHER PHILIPS	THE CHAINS	FEEL LIKE I WANNA CRY	50.00
65	396	DONNIE ELBERT	YOU CAN PUSH IT (OR PULL IT)	LILY LOU	25.00
65	397	PROFFESOR LONGHAIR	BABY LET ME HOLD YOUR HAND	LOOKA NO HAIR	35.00
65	398	BARON and his POUNDING PIANO	IS A BLUEBIRD BLUE	IN THE MOOD	25.00
66	399	LEE DORSEY	MESS AROUND	WHEN I MEET MY BABY	30.00
66	4001	LITTLE RICHARD	WITHOUT LOVE	DANCE WHAT YOU WANNA	35.00
66	4002	TOMMY DUNCAN	DANCE, DANCE, DANCE	LET'S TRY IT OVER AGAIN	30.00
66	4003	JERRY BUTLER	I STAND ACCUSED	I DON'T WANT TO HEAR IT	22.00
66	4004	JIMMY REED	ODDS AND ENDS	GOING DOWN BY THE RIVER PART 2	25.00
66	4005	PHIL UPCHURCH	YOU CAN'T SIT DOWN	YOU CAN'T SIT DOWN Part2	25.00
66	4006	JIMMY HUGHES	GOODBYE MY LOVE	IT WAS NICE	50.00
66	4007	ELMORE JAMES	MISTREATING MAMA	I NEED YOU	50.00
66	4008 unissued	SCREAMING JAY HAWKINS	I PUT A SPELL ON YOU	LITTLE DEMON	UN
66	4009	JERRY BUTLER	JUST FOR YOU	BELIEVE IN ME	20.00
66	4010	EFFIE SMITH	DIAL THAT TELEPHONE	DIAL THAT TELEPHONE part 2	25.00
66	4011	RITCHIE VALENS	DONNA	LA BAMBA	100.00
66	4012	BILLY PRESTON	BILLY'S BAG	DON'T LET THE SUN CATCH YOU CR	20.00
66	4013	JAYBIRDS	SOMEBODY HELP ME	THE RIGHT KIND	**209.00**
66	4014	BIRDLEGS & PAULINE	SPRING	IN SO MANY WAYS	20.00
66	4015	LITTLE RICHARD	IT AIN'T WATCHA DO (IT'S THE WAY	CROSSOVER	35.00
66	4016	THURSTON HARRIS	LITTLE BITTY PRETTY ONE	I HOPE YOU WON'T HOLD IT AGAIN	30.00
66	4017	PHIL UPCHURCH	NOTHING BUT SOUL	EVAD	15.00
66	4018	RIGHTEOUS BROTHERS	YOU CAN HAVE HER	JUSTINE	20.00
66	4019	SPIDELLS	FIND OUT WHAT'S HAPPENING	THAT'LL MAKE MY HEART BREAK	50.00
66	4020	SANTELLS	SO FINE	THESE ARE LOVE	30.00
66	4021	LITTLE MILTON	EARLY IN THE MORNING	BLESS YOUR HEART	30.00
66	4022	SHADES OF BLUE	OH! HOW HAPPY	LITTLE ORPHAN BOY	25.00
66	4023	LOWELL FULSOM	TALKING WOMAN	BLUES AROUND MIDNIGHT	50.00
66	4024	RAYMOND PARKER	RING AROUND THE ROSES	SHE'S COMING HOME	35.00
66	4025	LYDIA MARCELLE	ANOTHER KIND OF FELLOW	I'VE NEVER BEEN HURT LIKE THIS	50.00
66	4026 unissued	GERRI HALL	WHO CAN I RUN TO	I LOST A KEY	UN
67	4027	MR. DYNAMITE	SH'MON	SH'MON part 2	100.00
67	4028	BARBARA LYNN	SECOND FIDDLE GIRL	LETTER TO MOMMY AND DADDY	50.00
67	4029	SUGAR SIMONE	KING WITHOUT A THRONE	SUDDENLY	30.00
67	4030	BOB AND EARL	DON'T EVER LEAVE ME	FANCY FREE	30.00
67	4031	DANNY WHITE	KEEP MY WOMAN HOME	I'M DEDICATINGH MY LIFE	30.00
67	4032	DON & DEWEY	SOUL MOTION	STRETCHIN' OUT	25.00
67	4033 unissued	ANGLOS	INCENSE	YOU'RE FOOLING ME	UN
67	4034	KELLY BROTHERS	CRYING DAYS ARE OVER	FALLING IN LOVE AGAIN	100.00
67	4035	THEOLA KILGORE	I'LL KEEP TRYING	HE'S COMING BACK TO ME	40.00
67	4036	WALLACE BROTHERS	I'LL STEP ASIDE	HOLD MY HEART FOR AWHILE	40.00
67	4037	EDGEWOOD SMITH	AIN'T THAT LOVIN'	YEAH	50.00
67	4038	BARBARA LYNN	YOU'LL LOSE A GOOD THING	LONELY HEARTACHES	60.00
67	4039	CLAUDINE CLARK	THE STRENGTH TO BE STRONG	MOON MADNESS	40.00
67	4040	JACKIE DAY	BEFORE IT'S TOO LATE	WITHOUT A LOVE	200.00
67	4041	PAUL MARTIN	I'VE GOT A NEW LOVE	SNAKE IN THE GRASS	50.00
67	4042	JOHN ROBERTS	SOCKIN' 1, 2, 3, 4	SOPHISTICATED FUNK	30.00
68	4043	O.V.WRIGHT	WHAT ABOUT YOU	WHAT DID YOU TELL THIS GIRL OF	45.00
68	4044	BOBBY BLAND	THAT DID IT	A TOUCH OF THE BLUES	50.00
68	4045	AL KING	THINK TWICE BEFORE YOU SPEAK	THE WINNER	35.00
68	4046	JOE MATTHEWS	SORRY AIN'T GOOD ENOUGH	YOU BETTER MEND YOUR WAYS	75.00
68	4047	THELMA JONES	STRONGER	NEVER LEAVE ME	50.00
68	4048	LAMP SISTERS	A WOMAN WITH THE BLUES	I THOUGHT IT WAS ALL OVER	50.00
68	4049	FASCINATIONS	GIRLS ARE OUT TO GET YOU	YOU BE SORRY	30.00
64	706 EP PS	IKE & TINA TURNER	THE SOUL OF	1964 4 track EP with cover	150.00
66	710 EP PS	OTIS REDDING	EARLY OTIS REDDING	1966 4 track EP with cover	100.00
66	711 EP PS	Z.Z HILL. c/w INTENTIONS	GIMME GIMME	1966 4 track EP with cover	200.00

includes: 1. The Intentions - You Can't Have 2. Z.Z. Hill – Gimme Gimme 3. Jackie Day – Before It's Too Late 4. Bobby Day -

SUMMIT

77	100	FOUNDATIONS	WHERE WERE YOU WHEN I NEEDED	LOVE ME NICE N'EASY	5.00
64	2041 EP PS	MEMPHIS SLIM	THE WORLD'S FOREMOST BLUES SINGER	COLD-BLOODED WOMAN + 3	6.00

SUPREME

70	204	MOHAWKS	LET IT BE	LOOKING BACK	5.00

SURREY INTERNATIONAL

74	5003	OFFENBACH	JUDY IN DISGUISE	NO LETTER TODAY	8.00
74	5003 DJ	OFFENBACH	JUDY IN DISGUISE	NO LETTER TODAY	10.00
74	5011	BILLY JOE YOUNG	I'VE GOT YOU ON MY MIND AGAIN	STANDING AT THE EDGE OF PARADI	10.00
74	5011 DJ	BILLY JOE YOUNG	I'VE GOT YOU ON MY MIND AGAIN	STANDING AT THE EDGE OF PARADI	15.00
74	5013	REPARATA and the DELRONS	SHOES	SONG FOR YOU	4.00
74	5013 DJ	REPARATA and the DELRONS	SHOES	SONG FOR YOU	5.00

SURVIVAL

76	1 DJ	ESTHER BYRDE	TOUCH ME - TAKE ME	TRACKS OF LOVE	75.00

SUSSEX

74	1	CREATIVE SOURCE	WHO IS HE AND WHAT IS HE TO YOU	same: instrumental	6.00
74	1 DJ	CREATIVE SOURCE	WHO IS HE AND WHAT IS HE TO YOU	same: instrumental	8.00
74	2	SOUL SEARCHERS	BLOW YOUR WHISTLE	FUNK TO THE FOLKS	6.00
74	2 DJ	SOUL SEARCHERS	BLOW YOUR WHISTLE	FUNK TO THE FOLKS	8.00
74	3	MASTER FLEET	WELL PHASE	WELL PHASE part 2	6.00
74	3 DJ	MASTER FLEET	WELL PHASE	WELL PHASE part 2	8.00
75	4	LONETTE McKEE	SAVE IT (DON'T GIVE IT AWAY)	DO IT TO ME	8.00
75	4 DJ	LONETTE McKEE	SAVE IT (DON'T GIVE IT AWAY)	DO IT TO ME	10.00
75	5	CREATIVE SOURCE	MIGRATION	KEEP ON MOVIN'	5.00
75	5 DJ	CREATIVE SOURCE	MIGRATION	KEEP ON MOVIN'	6.00
75	6	DENNIS COFFEY	GETTING IT ON '75	CHICANO	6.00
75	6 DJ	DENNIS COFFEY	GETTING IT ON '75	same: xol	10.00

SUSU

01	13	KIM ENGLISH	SIMLPY GRATEFUL	SIMPLY GRATEFUL instrumental	6.00

SWAN

75	4240 DJ	GUYS FROM UNCLE	THE SPY	JAMMIN'	8.00
75	4243	MODERN REDCAPS	NEVER TOO YOUNG (TO FALL IN LOVE)	GOLDEN TEARDROPS	10.00
01	4275 DJ	TONY GALLA	IN LOVE	blank:	15.00

SYSTEM

1	MAXINE SINGLETON	DON'T YOU LOVE IT	same: instrumental	4.00

T.B. SUPER SOUL

T.B. stands for Tony Banks legendary DJ who made his name at Leeds, Central Club All Niter in the early 70's as a rare soul DJ. The Jimmy Thomas 45 was released on Parlophone, but was repressed due to demand created by Mr. Banks playing it. The T.B. Soul release is sadly poor sound quality. But it sold very well, as it was the only way most collectors could obtain a copy.

72	101	JIMMY THOMAS	A BEAUTIFUL NIGHT	ABOVE A WHISPER	15.00
2000	102	AL WILLIAMS c/w LEE ANDREWS	I AM NOTHING	I'VE HAD IT	25.00

The label credits Al Williams – I Am Nothing but actually plays Johnny Hampton – Not My Girl. B-side plays as titled

TAMLA MOTOWN

UK Tamla Motown is without doubt the best know of all the collectable Soul labels in the UK. Many, many collectors have set themselves the task of completing the series. The Tamla Motown company and it's music is so well documented, I feel I don't need to cover the history of the company or it's artists. But would like to cover a few points within this listing that will help Tamla Motown collectors purchase original first press 45's and file them in their correct sleeves. From release # 501 to #703 all first press UK Tamla Motown stock release copies had the standard "Sold in the UK subject to.. conditions" in silver lettering on the center piece. I've noted the 45rpm releases that EMI repressed and kept available past the TMG703 period, these ultimately had no reference of "Sold in the UK subject... From release # TMG 501 to TMG 629 they were issued in ORANGE sleeves with flipback seams. From release TMG 630 for a short.period, 45 releases were issued in special Tamla Motown "Advertising Sleeves" these had images of currently available Tamla Motown LPs. From release number TMG 668 EMI change the colour of the sleeves to Olive Green these sleeves continue all the way through to TMG 1053.

65	501	SUPREMES	STOP! IN THE NAME OF LOVE	I'M IN LOVE AGAIN	15.00
65	501 DJ	SUPREMES	STOP! IN THE NAME OF LOVE	I'M IN LOVE AGAIN	120.00
65	502	MARTHA & THE VANDELLAS	NOWHERE TO RUN	MOTORING	25.00
65	502 DJ	MARTHA & THE VANDELLAS	NOWHERE TO RUN	MOTORING	130.00
65	503	MIRACLES	OO BABY BABY	ALL THAT'S GOOD	50.00
65	503 DJ	MIRACLES	OO BABY BABY	ALL THAT'S GOOD	85.00
65	504	TEMPTATIONS	IT'S GROWING	WHAT LOVE HAS JOINED TOGETHER	30.00
65	504 DJ	TEMPTATIONS	IT'S GROWING	WHAT LOVE HAS JOINED TOGETHER	85.00
65	505	STEVIE WONDER	KISS ME BABY	TEARS IN VAIN	45.00
65	505 DJ	STEVIE WONDER	KISS ME BABY	TEARS IN VAIN	100.00
65	506	EARL VAN DYKE	ALL FOR YOU	TOO MANY FISH IN THE SEA	150.00
65	506 DJ	EARL VAN DYKE	ALL FOR YOU	TOO MANY FISH IN THE SEA	300.00
65	507	FOUR TOPS	ASK THE LONELY	WHERE DID YOU GO	45.00
65	507 DJ	FOUR TOPS	ASK THE LONELY	WHERE DID YOU GO	150.00
65	508	BRENDA HOLLOWAY	WHEN I'M GONE	I'VE BEEN GOOD TO YOU	100.00
65	508 DJ	BRENDA HOLLOWAY	WHEN I'M GONE	I'VE BEEN GOOD TO YOU	200.00
65	509	JR.WALKER & THE ALL STARS	SHOTGUN	HOT CHA	25.00
65	509 DJ	JR.WALKER & THE ALL STARS	SHOTGUN	HOT CHA	100.00
65	510	MARVIN GAYE	I'LL BE DOGGONE	YOU'VE BEEN A LONG TIME COMING	45.00
65	510 DJ	MARVIN GAYE	I'LL BE DOGGONE	YOU'VE BEEN A LONG TIME COMING	**118.00**
65	511	KIM WESTON	I'M STILL LOVING YOU	JUST LOVING YOU	200.00
65	511 DJ	KIM WESTON	I'M STILL LOVING YOU	JUST LOVING YOU	**310.00**
65	512	SHORTY LONG	OUT TO GET YOU	IT'S A CRYING SHAME	150.00
65	512 DJ	SHORTY LONG	OUT TO GET YOU	IT'S A CRYING SHAME	200.00
65	513	HIT PACK	NEVER SAY NO TO YOUR BABY	LET'S DANCE	85.00

65	513 DJ	HIT PACK	NEVER SAY NO TO YOUR BABY	LET'S DANCE	125.00
65	514	SPINNERS	SWEET THING	HOW CAN I	200.00
65	514 DJ	SPINNERS	SWEET THING	HOW CAN I	**526.00**
65	514	DETROIT SPINNERS	SWEET THING	HOW CAN I	200.00
65	514 DJ	DETROIT SPINNERS	SWEET THING	HOW CAN I	300.00
65	515	FOUR TOPS	I CAN'T HELP MYSELF	SAD SOUVENIRS	22.00
65	515 DJ	FOUR TOPS	I CAN'T HELP MYSELF	SAD SOUVENIRS	120.00
65	516	SUPREMES	BACK IN MY ARMS AGAIN	WHISPER YOU LOVE ME BOY	20.00
65	516 DJ	SUPREMES	BACK IN MY ARMS AGAIN	WHISPER YOU LOVE ME BOY	100.00
65	517	CHOKER CAMPBELL'S BIG BAND	MICKEY'S MONKEY	PRIDE AND JOY	100.00
65	517 DJ	CHOKER CAMPBELL'S BIG BAND	MICKEY'S MONKEY	PRIDE AND JOY	180.00
65	518	MARVELETES	I'LL KEEP ON HOLDING ON	NO TIME FOR TEARS	100.00
65	518 DJ	MARVELETTES	I'LL KEEP ON HOLDING ON	NO TIME FOR TEARS	220.00
65	519	BRENDA HOLLOWAY	I'LL BE AVAILABLE	OPERATOR	100.00
65	519 DJ	BRENDA HOLLOWAY	OPERATOR	I'LL BE AVAILABLE	**187.00**
65	520	JR.WALKER & THE ALL STARS	TUNE UP	DO THE BOOMERANG	85.00
65	520 DJ	JR.WALKER & THE ALL STARS	TUNE UP	DO THE BOOMERANG	150.00
65	521	VELVELETTES	LONELY LONELY GIRL AM I	I'M THE EXCEPTION TO THE RULE	150.00
65	521 DJ	VELVELETTES	LONELY LONELY GIRL AM I	I'M THE EXCEPTION TO THE RULE	250.00
65	522	MIRACLES	THE TRACKS OF MY TEARS	A FORK IN THE ROAD	75.00
65	522 DJ	MIRACLES	THE TRACKS OF MY TEARS	A FORK IN THE ROAD	100.00
65	523	SPINNERS	I'LL ALWAYS LOVE YOU	TOMORROW MAY NEVER COME	100.00
65	523 DJ	SPINNERS	I'LL ALWAYS LOVE YOU	TOMORROW MAY NEVER COME	150.00
65	523	DETROIT SPINNERS	I'LL ALWAYS LOVE YOU	TOMMORROW MAY NEVER COME	75.00
65	524	MARVIN GAYE	PRETTY LITTLE BABY	NOW THAT YOU'VE WON ME	25.00
65	524 DJ	MARVIN GAYE	PRETTY LITTLE BABY	NOW THAT YOU'VE WON ME	100.00
65	525	MARV JOHNSON	WHY DO YOU WEANT TO LET ME GO	I'M NOT A PLAYTHING	85.00
65	525 DJ	MARV JOHNSON	WHY DO YOU WEANT TO LET ME GO	I'M NOT A PLAYTHING	UN

Red and white promo copies of number 525 are unconfirmed and most probably don't exist.

65	526	TEMPTATIONS	SINCE I LOST MY BABY	YOU'VE GOT TO EARN IT	30.00
65	526 DJ	TEMPTATIONS	SINCE I LOST MY BABY	YOU'VE GOT TO EARN IT	100.00
65	527	SUPREMES	NOTHING BUT HEARTACHES	HE HOLDS HIS OWN	20.00
65	527 DJ	SUPREMES	NOTHING BUT HEARTACHES	HE HOLDS HIS OWN	100.00
65	528	FOUR TOPS	IT'S THE SAME SONG	YOUR LOVE IS AMAZING	22.00
65	528 DJ	FOUR TOPS	IT'S THE SAME SONG	YOUR LOVE IS AMAZING	120.00
65	529	JR.WALKER & THE ALL STARS	SHAKE AND FINGERPOP	CLEO'S BACK	25.00
65	529 DJ	JR.WALKER & THE ALL STARS	SHAKE AND FINGERPOP	CLEO'S BACK	100.00
65	530	MARTHA & THE VANDELLAS	YOU'VE BEEN IN LOVE TOO LONG	LOVE (MAKES ME DO FOOLISH THIN	30.00
65	530 DJ	MARTHA & THE VANDELLAS	YOU'VE BEEN IN LOVE TOO LONG	LOVE (MAKES ME DO FOOLISH THIN	100.00
65	531	CONTOURS	FIRST I LOOK AT THE PURSE	SEARCHING FOR A GIRL	40.00
65	531 DJ	CONTOURS	FIRST I LOOK AT THE PURSE	SEARCHING FOR A GIRL	100.00
65	532	STEVIE WONDER	HIGH HEEL SNEAKERS	MUSIC TALK	35.00
65	532 DJ	STEVIE WONDER	HIGH HEEL SNEEKERS	MUSIC TALK	85.00
65	533	BILLY ECKSTINE	HAD YOU BEEN AROUND	DOWN TO EARTH	100.00
65	533 DJ	BILLY ECKSTINE	HAD YOU BEEN AROUND	DOWN TO EARTH	130.00
65	534	DORSEY BURNETTE	JIMMY BROWN	EVERYBODY'S ANGEL	100.00
65	534 DJ	DORSEY BURNETTE	JIMMY BROWN	EVERYBODY'S ANGEL	130.00
65	535	MARVELETTES	DANGER HEARTBREAK DEAD AHEAD	YOUR CHEATING WAYS	40.00
65	535 DJ	MARVELETTES	DANGER HEARTBREAK DEAD AHEAD	YOUR CHEATING WAY	100.00
65	536	LEWIS SISTERS	YOU NEED ME	MOONLIGHT ON THE BEACH	100.00
65	536 DJ	LEWIS SISTERS	YOU NEED ME	MOONLIGHT ON THE BEACH	150.00
65	537	TONY MARTIN	THE BIGGER YOUR HEART IS	THE TWO OF US	75.00
65	537 DJ	TONY MARTIN	THE BIGGER YOUR HEART IS	THE TWO OF US	100.00
65	538	KIM WESTON	TAKE ME IN YOUR ARMS (ROCK ME A ..	DON'T COMPARE ME WITH HER	75.00
65	538 DJ	KIM WESTON	TAKE ME IN YOUR ARMS (ROCK ME A..	DON'T COMPARE ME WITH HER	150.00
65	539	MARVIN GAYE	AIN'T THAT PECULIAR	SHE'S GOT TO BE REAL	25.00
65	539 DJ	MARVIN GAYE	AIN'T THAT PECULIAR	SHE'S GOT TO BE REAL	150.00
65	540	MIRACLES	MY GIRL HAS GONE	SINCE YOU WON MY HEART	40.00
65	540 DJ	MIRACLES	MY GIRL HAS GONE	SINCE YOU WON MY HEART	100.00
65	541	TEMPTATIONS	MY BABY	DON'T LOOK BACK	30.00
65	541 DJ	TEMPTATIONS	MY BABY	DON'T LOOK BACK	100.00
65	542	FOUR TOPS	SOMETHING ABOUT YOU	DARLING, I HUM OUR SONG	20.00
65	542 DJ	FOUR TOPS	SOMETHING ABOUT YOU	DARLING, I HUM OUR SONG	125.00
65	543	SUPREMES	I HEAR A SYMPHONY	WHO COULD EVER DOUBT MY LOVE	20.00
65	543 DJ	SUPREMES	I HEAR A SYMPHONY	WHO COULD EVER DOUBT MY LOVE	85.00
65	544	BARBARA McNAIR	YOU'RE GONNA LOVE MY BABY	THE TOUCH OF TIME	200.00
65	544 DJ	BARBARA McNAIR	YOU'RE GONNA LOVE MY BABY	THE TOUCH OF TIME	350.00
65	545	STEVIE WONDER	UPTIGHT (EVERYTHING'S ALRIGHT)	PURPLE RAIN DROPS	20.00
65	545 DJ	STEVIE WONDER	UPTIGHT (EVERYTHING'S ALRIGHT)	PURPLE RAIN DROPS	125.00
65	546	MARVELETTES	DON'T MESS WITH BILL	ANYTHING YOU WANNA DO	30.00
65	546 DJ	MARVELETTES	DON'T MESS WITH BILL	ANYTHING YOU WANNA DO	**114.00**
66	547 sold subject	MIRACLES	GOING TO A GO GO	CHOOSEY BEGGAR	15.00
66	547 DJ	MIRACLES	GOING TO A GO GO	CHOOSEY BEGGAR	120.00
70	547 no sold subject	MIRACLES	GOING TO A GO GO	CHOOSEY BEGGAR	8.00
66	548	SUPREMES	MY WORLD IS EMPTY WITHOUT YOU	EVERYTHING IS GOOD ABOUT YOU	15.00
66	548 DJ	SUPREMES	MY WORLD IS EMPTY WITHOUT YOU	EVERYTHING IS GOOD ABOUT YOU	100.00
66	549	MARTHA & THE VANDELLAS	MY BABY LOVES ME	NEVER LEAVE YOUR BABY'S SIDE	45.00
66	549 DJ	MARTHA & THE VANDELLAS	MY BABY LOVES ME	NEVER LEAVE YOUR BABY'S SIDE	125.00
66	550	JR.WALKER & THE ALL STARS	CLEO'S MOOD	BABY YOU KNOW YOU AIN'T RIGHT	25.00

66	550 DJ	JR.WALKER & THE ALL STARS	CLEO'S MOOD	BABY YOU KNOW YOU AIN'T RIGHT	100.00
66	551	ELGINS	PUT YOURSELF IN MY PLACE	DARLING BABY	100.00
66	551 DJ	ELGINS	PUT YOURSELF IN MY PLACE	DARLING BABY	150.00
66	552	MARVIN GAYE	ONE MORE HEARTACHE	WHEN I HAD YOUR LOVE	25.00
66	552 DJ	MARVIN GAYE	ONE MORE HEARTACHE	WHEN I HAD YOUR LOVE	100.00
66	553	FOUR TOPS	SHAKE ME WAKE ME (WHEN IT'S OVER)	JUST AS LONG AS YOU NEEDED ME	20.00
66	553 DJ	FOUR TOPS	SHAKE ME WAKE ME (WHEN IT'S OVER)	JUST AS LONG AS YOU NEEDED ME	**174.00**
66	554	KIM WESTON	HELPLESS	A LOVE LIKE YOURS DON'T COME K	125.00
66	554 DJ	KIM WESTON	HELPLESS	A LOVE LIKE YOURS (DON'T COME	**409.00**
65	555 sold subject to	ISLEY BROTHERS	THIS OLD HEART OF MINE	THERE'S NO LOVE LEFT	15.00
66	555 DJ red & white	ISLEY BROTHERS	THIS OLD HEART OF MINE	THERE'S NO LOVE LEFT	150.00
70	555 no sold subject to	ISLEY BROTHERS	THIS OLD HEART OF MINE	THERE'S NO LOVE LEFT	15.00
66	555 DJ green & white	ISLEY BROTHERS	THIS OLD HEART OF MINE	THERE'S NO LOVE LEFT	45.00
66	556	BRENDA HOLLOWAY	TOGETHER 'TIL THE END OF TIME	SAD SONG	60.00
66	556 DJ	BRENDA HOLLOWAY	TOGETHER 'TIL THE END OF TIME	SAD SONG	100.00
66	557	TEMPTATIONS	GET READY	FADING AWAY	40.00
66	557 DJ	TEMPTATIONS	GET READY	FADING AWAY	100.00
66	558	STEVIE WONDER	NOTHING'S TOO GOOD FOR MY BABY	WITH A CHILD'S HEART	30.00
66	558 DJ	STEVIE WONDER	NOTHING'S TOO GOOD FOR MY BABY	WITH A CHILD'S HEART	**132.00**
66	559	JR.WALKER & THE ALL STARS	ROAD RUNNER	SHOOT YOUR SHOT	30.00
66	559 DJ	JR.WALKER & THE ALL STARS	ROAD RUNNER	SHOOT YOUR SHOT	120.00
65	560	SUPREMES	HE'S ALL I GOT	LOVE IS LIKE AN ITCHING IN MY	50.00
65	560 DJ	SUPREMES	HE'S ALL I GOT	LOVE IS LIKE AN ITCHING IN MY	175.00
66	561	TAMMI TERRELL	COME ON AND SEE ME	BABY DON'TCHA WORRY	75.00
66	561 DJ	TAMMI TERRELL	COME ON AND SEE ME	BABY DON'T CHA WORRY	175.00
66	562	MARVELETTES	YOU'RE THE ONE	PAPER BOY	45.00
66	562 DJ	MARVELETTES	YOU'RE THE ONE	PAPER BOY	100.00
66	563	MARVIN GAYE	TAKE THIS HEART OF MINE	NEED YOUR LOVIN' (WANT YOU BACK)	30.00
66	563 DJ	MARVIN GAYE	TAKE THIS HEART OF MINE	NEED YOUR LOVIN' (WANT YOU BACK)	100.00
66	564	CONTOURS	DETERMINATION	JUST A LITTLE MISUNDERSTANDING	50.00
66	564 DJ	CONTOURS	DETERMINATION	JUST ALITTLE MISUNDERSTANDING	150.00
66	565	TEMPTATIONS	AIN'T TOO PROUD TO BEG	YOU'LL LOSE A PRECIOUS LOVE	9.00
66	565 DJ	TEMPTATIONS	AIN'T TOO PROUD TO BEG	YOU'LL LOSE A PREVIOUS LOVE	100.00
66	566	ISLEY BROTHERS	TAKE SOME TIME OUT FOR LOVE	WHO COULD EVER DOUBT MY LOVE	30.00
66	566 DJ	ISLEY BROTHERS	TAKE SOME TIME OUT FOR LOVE	WHO COULD EVER DOUBT MY LOVE	100.00
66	567	MARTHA & THE VANDELLAS	WHAT AM I GOING TO DO WITHOUT	GO AHEAD AND LAUGH	40.00
66	567 DJ	MARTHA & THE VANDELLAS	WHAT AM I GOING TO DO WITHOUT	GO AHEAD AND LAUGH	125.00
66	568	FOUR TOPS	LOVING YOU IS SWEETER THAN EVER	I LIKE EVERYTHING ABOUT YOU	15.00
66	568 DJ	FOUR TOPS	LOVING YOU IS SWEETER THAN EVER	I LIKE EVERYTHING ABOUT YOU	100.00
66	569	MIRACLES	WHOLE LOT OF SHAKIN' IN MY HEART	OH BE MY LOVE	40.00
66	569 DJ	MIRACLES	WHOLE LOT OF SHAKIN' IN MY HEART	OH BE MY LOVE	120.00
66	570	STEVIE WONDER	AIN'T THAT ASKING FOR TROUBLE	BLOWIN' IN THE WIND	30.00
66	570 DJ	STEVIE WONDER	AIN'T THAT ASKING FOR TROUBLE	BLOWIN' IN THE WIND	100.00
66	571 sold subject to	JR.WALKER & THE ALL STARS	HOW SWEET IT IS (TO BE LOVED BY YOU)	NOTHING BUT SOUL	20.00
66	571 DJ red and white	JR.WALKER & THE ALL STARS	HOW SWEET IT IS (TO BE LOVED BY YOU)	NOTHING BUT SOUL	100.00
70	571 no sold subject to	JR.WALKER & THE ALL STARS	HOW SWEET IT IS (TO BE LOVED BY YOU)	NOTHING BUT SOUL	8.00
70	571 DJ green & white	JR.WALKER & THE ALL STARS	HOW SWEET IT IS (TO BE LOVED BY YOU)	NOTHING BUT SOUL	30.00
66	572	ISLEY BROTHERS	I GUESS I'LL ALWAYS LOVE YOU	I HEAR A SYMPHONY	30.00
66	572 DJ	ISLEY BROTHERS	I GUESS I'LL ALWAYS LOVE YOU	I HEAR A SYMPHONY mint unplayed copy	**325.00**
66	572 DJ	ISLEY BROTHERS	I GUESS I'LL ALWAYS LOVE YOU	I HEAR A SYMPHONY	150.00
66	573	SHORTY LONG	FUNCTION AT THE JUNCTION	CALL ON ME	30.00
66	573 DJ	SHORTY LONG	FUNCTION AT THE JUNCTION	CALL ON ME	100.00
66	574	MARVIN GAYE	LITTLE DARLING (I NEED YOU)	HEY DIDDLE DIDDLE	40.00
66	574 DJ	MARVIN GAYE	LITTLE DARLING (I NEED YOU)	HEY DIDDLE DIDDLE	175.00
66	575	SUPREMES	YOU CAN'T HURRY LOVE	PUT YOURSELF IN MY PLACE	10.00
66	575 DJ	SUPREMES	YOU CAN'T HURRY LOVE	PUT YOURSELF IN MY PLACE	100.00
66	576	GLADYS KNIGHT & The PIPS	JUST WALK IN MY SHOES	STEPPING CLOSER TO YOUR HEART	40.00
66	676 DJ	GLADYS KNIGHT & The PIPS	JUST WALK IN MY SHOES	STEPPING CLOSER TO YOUR HEART	150.00
66	577 sold subject to	JIMMY RUFFIN	WHAT BECOMES OF THE BROKENHEARTED	BABY I'VE GOT IT	10.00
66	577 DJ red & white	JIMMY RUFFIN	WHAT BECOMES OF THE BROKENHEARTED	BABY I'VE GOT IT	150.00
70	577 no sold subject to	JIMMY RUFFIN	WHAT BECOMES OF THE BROKENHEARTED	BABY I'VE GOT IT	5.00
70	577 DJ green & white	JIMMY RUFFIN	WHAT BECOMES OF THE BROKENHEARTED	BABY I'VE GOT IT	30.00
66	578	TEMPTATIONS	BEAUTY IS ONLY SKIN DEEP	YOU'RE NOT AN ORDINARY GIRL	15.00
66	578 DJ	TEMPTATIONS	BEAUTY IS ONLY SKIN DEEP	YOU'RE NOT AN ORDINARY GIRL	120.00

All promo copies from # 501 to 578 are white with a red A. # 579 is the first promo press using the green label with a white A. was TMG 579

66	579 sold subject to	FOUR TOPS	REACH OUT I'LL BE THERE	UNTIL YOU LOVE SOMEONE	6.00
66	579 DJ 66 date	FOUR TOPS	REACH OUT I'LL BE THERE	UNTIL YOU LOVE SOMEONE	85.00
70	579 no sold subject to	FOUR TOPS	REACH OUT I'LL BE THERE	UNTIL YOU LOVE SOMEONE	5.00
70	579 DJ no date	FOUR TOPS	REACH OUT I'LL BE THERE	UNTIL YOU LOVE SOMEONE	35.00
66	580	VELVELETTES	THESE THINGS WILL KEEP ME LOVING	SINCE YOU'VE BEEN LOVING ME	40.00
66	580 DJ	VELVELETTES	THESE THINGS WILL KEEP ME LOVING	SINCE YOU'VE BEEN LOVING ME	125.00
66	581	BRENDA HOLLOWAY	HURT A LITTLE EVERYDAY	WHERE WERE YOU	75.00
66	581 DJ	BRENDA HOLLOWAY	HURT A LITTLE EVERYDAY	WHERE WERE YOU	**83.00**
66	582	MARTHA & THE VANDELLAS	I'M READY FOR LOVE	HE DOESN'T LOVE HER ANYMORE	15.00
66	582 DJ	MARTHA & THE VANDELLAS	I'M READY FOR LOVE	HE DOESN'T LOVE HER ANYMORE	85.00
66	583	ELGINS	HEAVEN MUST HAVE SENT YOU	STAY IN MY LONELY ARMS	85.00
66	583 DJ	ELGINS	HEAVEN MUST HAVE SENT YOU	STAY IN MY LONELY ARMS	150.00
66	584	MIRACLES	SAVE ME	(COME ROUND HERE) I'M THE ONE	20.00
66	584 DJ	MIRACLES	SAVE ME	(COME ROUND HERE)I'M THE ONE Y	50.00

66	585	SUPREMES	YOU KEEP ME HANGING ON	REMOVE THIS DOUBT	12.00
66	585 DJ	SUPREMES	YOU KEEP ME HANGING ON	REMOVE THIS DOUBT	50.00
66	586	JR.WALKER & THE ALL STARS	MONEY (THAT'S WHAT I WANT)	MONEY (THAT'S WHAT I WANT) part 2	20.00
66	586 DJ	JR.WALKER & THE ALL STARS	MONEY (THAT'S WHAT I WANT)	MONEY (THAT'S WHAT I WANT) part 2	75.00
66	587	TEMPTATIONS	(I KNOW) I'M LOSING YOU	LITTLE MISS SWEETNESS	15.00
66	587 DJ	TEMPTATIONS	(I KNOW) I'M LOSING YOU	LITTLE MISS SWEETNESS	75.00
66	588	STEVIE WONDER	A PLACE IN THE SUN	SYLVIA	20.00
66	588 DJ	STEVIE WONDER	A PLACE IN THE SUN	SYLVIA	60.00
66	589	FOUR TOPS	STANDING IN THE SHADOWS OF LOVE	SINCE YOU'VE BEEN GONE	10.00
66	589	FOUR TOPS	STANDING IN THE SHADOWS OF LOVE	SINCE YOU'VE BEEN GONE	85.00
66	590 sold subject to	MARVIN GAYE & KIM WESTON	IT TAKES TWO	IT'S GOT TO BE A MIRACLE	15.00
66	590 DJ	MARVIN GAYE & KIM WESTON	IT TAKES TWO	IT'S GOT TO BE A MIRACLE	85.00
70	590 no sold subject to	MARVIN GAYE & KIM WESTON	IT TAKES TWO	IT'S GOT TO BE A MIRACLE	5.00
66	591	CHRIS CLARK	LOVE'S GONE BAD	PUT YOURSELF IN MY PLACE	75.00
66	591 DJ	CHRIS CLARK	LOVE'S GONE BAD	PUT YOURSELF IN MY PLACE	130.00
67	592	ORIGINALS	GOOD NIGHT IRENE	NEED YOUR LOVIN' (WANT YOU BACK)	75.00
67	592 DJ	ORIGINALS	GOOD NIGHT IRENE	NEED YOUR LOVIN' (WANT YOU BACK)	150.00
67	593	JIMMY RUFFIN	I'VE PASSED THIS WAY BEFORE	TOMORROW'S TEARS	10.00
67	593 DJ	JIMMY RUFFIN	I'VE PASSED THIS WAY BEFORE	TOMORROW'S TEARS	60.00
67	594	MARVELETES	THE HUNTER GETS CAPTURED BY THE GAME	THINK I CAN CHANGE YOU	20.00
67	594 DJ	MARVELETES	THE HUNTER GETS CAPTURED BY THE GAME	I THINK I CAN CHANGE U	85.00
67	595 sold subject to	VELVELETTES	HE WAS REALLY SAYING SOMETHIN'	NEEDLE IN A HAYSTACK	20.00
67	595 DJ	VELVELETTES	HE WAS REALLY SAYING SOMETHIN'	NEEDLE IN A HAYSTACK	75.00
70	595 no sold subject to	VELVELETTES	NEEDLE IN A HAYSTACK	HE WAS REALLY SAYING SOMETHING	6.00
67	596	JR.WALKER & THE ALL STARS	PUCKER UP BUTTERCUP	ANYWAY TO WANNTA'	22.00
67	596 DJ	JR.WALKER & THE ALL STARS	PUCKER UP BUTTERCUP	ANYWAY TO WANNTA'	75.00
67	597	SUPREMES	LOVE IS HERE AND NOW YOU'RE GONE	THERE'S NO STOPPING US NOW	15.00
67	597 DJ	SUPREMES	LOVE IS HERE AND NOW YOU'RE GONE	THERE'S NO STOPPING US NOW	70.00
67	598 sold subject	SMOKEY ROBINSON & MIRACLES	THE LOVE I SAW IN YOU WAS JUST A MIRAGE	SWEPT FOR YOU BABY	15.00
67	598 DJ	SMOKEY ROBINSON & MIRACLES	THE LOVE I SAW IN YOU WAS JUST A MIRAGE	SWEPT FOR YOU BABY	70.00
67	599 sold subject	MARTHA & THE VANDELLAS	THIRD FINGER, LEFT HAND	JIMMY MACK	15.00
67	599 DJ	MARTHA & THE VANDELLAS	THIRD FINGER, LEFT HAND	JIMMY MACK	75.00
70	599 DJ	MARTHA & THE VANDELLAS	JIMMY MACK	THIRD FINGER, LEFT HAND	30.00
72	599 DJ	MARTHA & THE VANDELLAS	THIRD FINGER LAFT HAND	JIMMY MACK	30.00
72	599 no sold subject to	MARTHA & THE VANDELLAS	THIRD FINGER, LEFT HAND	JIMMY MACK	6.00
76	599	MARTHA & THE VANDELLAS	JIMMY MACK	THIRD FINGER, LEFT HAND	4.00
67	600	SHORTY LONG	YOUR LOVE IS AMAZING	CHANTILLY LACE	15.00
67	600 DJ	SHORTY LONG	YOUR LOVE IS AMAZING	CHANTILLY LACE	75.00
67	601	FOUR TOPS	BERNADETTE	I GOT A FEELING	10.00
67	601 DJ	FOUR TOPS	BERNADETTE	I GOT A FEELING	60.00
67	602	STEVIE WONDER	TRAVLIN' MAN	HEY LOVE	20.00
67	602 DJ	STEVIE WONDER	TRAVLIN' MAN	HEY LOVE	40.00
67	603	JIMMY RUFFIN	GONNA GIVE HER ALL THE LOVE I'VE GOT	WORLD SO WIDE, NOWHERE TO HIDE	10.00
67	603 DJ	JIMMY RUFFIN	GONNA GIVE HER ALL THE LOVE I'VE GOT	WORLD SO WIDE, NOWHERE TO HIDE	50.00
67	604	GLADYS KNIGHT& The PIPS	TAKE ME IN YOUR ARMS AND LOVE	DO YOU LOVE ME JUST A LITTLE	10.00
67	604 DJ	GLADYS KNIGHT& The PIPS	TAKE ME IN YOUR ARMS AND LOVE	DO YOU LOVE ME JUST A LITTLE	30.00
67	605	CONTOURS	IT'S SO HARD BEING A LOSER	YOUR LOVE GROWS MORE PRECIOUS	30.00
67	605 DJ	CONTOURS	IT'S SO HARD BEING A LOSER	YOUR LOVE GROWS MORE PRECIOUS	100.00
67	606	ISLEY BROTHERS	GOT TO HAVE YOU BACK	JUST AIN'T ENOUGH LOVE	15.00
67	606 DJ	ISLEY BROTHERS	GOT TO HAVE YOU BACK	JUST AIN'T ENOUGH LOVE	50.00
67	607	SUPREMES	THE HAPPENING	ALL I KNOW ABOUT YOU	10.00
67	607 DJ	SUPREMES	THE HAPPENING	ALL I KNOW ABOUT YOU	50.00
67	608	BRENDA HOLLOWAY	JUST LOOK WHJAT YOU'VE DONE	STARTING THE HURT OVER AGAIN	40.00
67	608 DJ	BRENDA HOLLOWAY	JUST LOOK WHAT YOU'VE DONE	STARTING THE HURT OVER AGAIN	125.00
67	609	MARVELETTES	WHEN YOU'RE YOUNG AND IN LOVE	THE DAY YOU TAKE ONE	10.00
67	609 DJ	MARVELETTES	WHEN YOU'RE YOUNG AND IN LOVE	THE DAY YOU TAKE ONE	50.00
67	610	TEMPTATIONS	ALL I NEED	SORRY IS A SORRY WORD	15.00
67	610 DJ	TEMPTATIONS	ALL I NEED	SORRY IS A SORRY WORD	40.00
67	611	MARVIN GAYE & TAMMI TERRELL	AIN'T NO MOUNTAIN HIGH ENOUGH	GIVE A LITTLE LOVE	15.00
67	611 DJ	MARVIN GAYE & TAMMI TERRELL	AIN'T NO MOUNTAIN HIGH ENOUGH	GIVE A LITTLE LOVE	50.00
67	612	FOUR TOPS	7 ROOMS OF GLOOM	I'LL TURN TO STONE	10.00
67	612 DJ	FOUR TOPS	7 ROOMS OF GLOOM	I'LL TURN TO STONE	50.00
67	613	STEVIE WONDER	I WAS MADE TO LOVE HER	HOLD ME	8.00
67	613 DJ	STEVIE WONDER	I WAS MADE TO LOVE HER	HOLD ME	40.00
67	614 withdrawn b-side	SMOKEY ROBINSON &	MORE LOVE	COME SPY WITH ME	100.00
67	614 DJ	SMOKEY ROBINSON &	MORE LOVE	COME SPY WITH ME	UN
67	614	SMOKEY ROBINSON &	MORE LOVE	SWEPT FOR YOU BABY	20.00
67	614 DJ	SMOKEY ROBINSON &	MORE LOVE	SWEPT FOR YOU BABY	50.00
67	615	ELGINS	IT'S BEEN A LONG LONG TIME	I UNDERSTAND MY MAN	22.00
67	615 DJ	ELGINS	IT'S BEEN A LONG LONG TIME	I UNDERSTAND MY MAN	50.00
67	616	DIANA ROSS & the SUPREMES	GOING DOWN FOR THE THIRD TIME	REFLECTIONS	10.00
67	616 DJ	DIANA ROSS & the SUPREMES	GOING DOWN FOR THE THIRD TIME	REFLECTIONS	50.00
67	617	JIMMY RUFFIN	DON'T YOU MISS ME A LITTLE BIT BABY	I WANT HER LOVE	10.00
67	617 DJ	JIMMY RUFFIN	DON'T YOU MISS ME A LITTLE BIT BABY	I WANT HER LOVE	40.00
67	618	MARVIN GAYE	YOUR UNCHANGING LOVE	I'LL TAKE CARE OF YOU	10.00
67	618 DJ	MARVIN GAYE	YOUR UNCHANGING LOVE	I'LL TAKE CARE OF YOU	30.00
67	619	GLADYS KNIGHT & The PIPS	EVERYBODY NEEDS LOVE	SINCE I'VE LOST YOU	15.00
67	619 DJ	GLADYS KNIGHT & The PIPS	STEPPING CLOSER TO YOU HEART	EVERYBODY NEEDS LOVE	85.00
67	620	TEMPTATIONS	YOU'RE MY EVERYTHING	I'VE BEEN GOOD TO YOU	10.00
67	620 DJ	TEMPTATIONS	YOU'RE MY EVERYTHING	I'VE BEEN GOOD TO YOU	40.00
67	621	MARTHA REEVES & the VANDELLAS	ONE WAY OUT	LOVE BUG LEAVE MY HEART ALONE	25.00
67	621 DJ	MARTHA REEVES & the VANDELLAS	ONE WAY OUT	LOVE BUG LEAVE MY HEART ALONE	100.00
67	621test press	MARTHA REEVES & the VANDELLAS	ONE WAY OUT	LOVE BUG LEAVE MT HEART ALONE	**56.00**

white label with handwritten credits

67	622	BRENDA HOLLOWAY	YOU'VE MADE ME SO VERY HAPPY	I'VE GOT TO FIND IT	25.00
67	622 DJ	BRENDA HOLLOWAY	YOU'VE MADE ME SO VERY HAPPY	I'VE GOT TO FIND IT	40.00
67	623	FOUR TOPS	YOU KEEP RUNNING AWAY	IF YOU DON'T WANT MY LOVE	10.00
67	623 DJ	FOUR TOPS	YOU KEEP RUNNING AWAY	IF YOU DON'T WANT MY LOVE	40.00
65	624	CHRIS CLARK	FROM HEAD TO TOE	THE BEGINNING OF THE END	40.00
67	624 DJ	CHRIS CLARK	FROM HEAD TO TOE	THE BEGINNING OF THE END	85.00
67	625	MARVIN GAYE & TAMMI TERRELL	YOUR PRECIOUS LOVE	HOLD ME OH MY DARLING	15.00
67	625 DJ	MARVIN GAYE & TAMMI TERRELL	YOUR PRECIOUS LOVE	HOLD ME OH MY DARLING	40.00
67	626	STEVIE WONDER	EVERY TIME I SEE YOU I GO WILD	I'M WONDERING	20.00
67	626 DJ	STEVIE WONDER	EVERY TIME I SEE YOU I GO WILD	I'M WONDERING	60.00
67	627	DETROIT SPINNERS	I'LL ALWAYS LOVE YOU	FOR ALL WE KNOW	20.00
67	627 DJ	DETROIT SPINNERS	I'LL ALWAYS LOVE YOU	FOR ALL WE KNOW	50.00
67	628	BARBARA RANDOLF	I GOT A FEELING	YOU GOT ME HURTIN' ALL OVER	30.00
67	628 DJ	BARBARA RANDOLF	I GOT A FEELING	YOU GOT ME HURTIN' ALL OVER	75.00
67	629	GLADYS KNIGHT & The PIPS	I HEARD IT THROUGH THE GRAPEVINE	IT'S TIME TO GO NOW	20.00
67	629 DJ	GLADYS KNIGHT & The PIPS	I HEARD IT THROUGH THE GRAPEVINE	IT'S TIME TO GO NOW	40.00

all releases from this TMG 630 to TMG 650 came in Tamla Motown LP scan promo sleeves.

67	630	EDWIN STARR	I WANT MY BABY BACK	GONNA KEEP ON TRYING TILL I WIN YOUR LOVE	25.00
67	630 DJ	EDWIN STARR	I WANT MY BABY BACK	GONNA KEEP ON TRYING TILL I WIN YOUR LOV	75.00
67	631	SMOKEY ROBINSON & MIRACLES	I SECOND THAT EMOTION	YOU MUST BE LOVE	10.00
67	631 DJ	SMOKEY ROBINSON & MIRACLES	I SECOND THAT EMOTION	YOU MUST BE LOVE	40.00
67	632	DIANA ROSS & the SUPREMES	IN AND OUT OF LOVE	I GUESS I'LL ALWAYS LOVE YOU	8.00
67	632 DJ	DIANA ROSS & the SUPREMES	IN AND OUT OF LOVE	I GUESS I'LL ALWAYS LOVE YOU	40.00
67	633	TEMPTATIONS	I WANT A LOVE I CAN SEE	IT'S YOU THAT I NEED	30.00
67	633 DJ	TEMPTATIONS	I WANT A LOVE I CAN SEE	LONELINESS MADE ME REALIZE	**87.00**
67	634	FOUR TOPS	WALK AWAY RENEE	MAME	6.00
67	634 DJ	FOUR TOPS	WALK AWAY RENEE	MAME	40.00
67	635	MARVIN GAYE & TAMMI TERRELL	IF I COULD BUILD MY WHOLE WORLD	IF THIS WORLD WERE MINE	10.00
67	635 DJ	MARVIN GAYE & TAMMI TERRELL	IF I COULD BUILD MY WHOLE WORLD	IF THIS WORLD WERE MINE	40.00
67	636	MARTHA REEVES & THE VANDELLAS	SHOW ME THE WAY	HONEY CHILE	20.00
68	636 DJ	MARTHA REEVES & THE VANDELLAS	SHOW ME THE WAY	HONEY CHILE	50.00
68	637 sold subject	JR.WALKER & THE ALL STARS	COME SEE ABOUT ME	SWEET SOUL	10.00
68	637 DJ	JR.WALKER & THE ALL STARS	COME SEE ABOUT ME	SWEET SOUL	40.00
72	637 no sold subject to	JR.WALKER & THE ALL STARS	COME SEE ABOUT ME	SWEET SOUL	5.00
68	638	CHRIS CLARK	I LOVE YOU	I WANT TO GO BACK THERE AGAIN	25.00
68	638 DJ	CHRIS CLARK	I LOVE YOU	I WANT TO GO BACK THERE AGAIN	75.00
68	639	MARVELETTES	MY BABY MUST BE A MAGICIAN	I NEED SOMEONE	15.00
68	639 DJ	MARVELETTES	MY BABY MUST BE A MAGICIAN	I NEED SOMEONE	40.00
68	640	MARVIN GAYE	CHANGE WHAT YOU CAN	YOU	20.00
68	640 DJ	MARVIN GAYE	CHANGE WHAT YOU CAN	YOU	45.00
68	641	TEMPTATIONS	I WISH IT WOULD RAIN	I TRULY, TRULY BELIEVE	10.00
68	641 DJ	TEMPTATIONS	I WISH IT WOULD RAIN	I TRULY, TRULY BELIEVE	30.00
68	642	ELGINS	PUT YOURSELF IN MY PLACE	DARLING BABY	20.00
68	642 DJ	ELGINS	PUT YOURSELF IN MY PLACE	DARLING BABY	50.00
68	643	RITA WRIGHT	I CAN'T GIVE BACK THE LOVE I FEEL FOR YOU	SOMETHING ON MY MIND	20.00
68	643 DJ	RITA WRIGHT	I CAN'T GIVE BACK THE LOVE I FEEL FOR YOU	SOMETHING ON MY MIND	40.00
68	644	SHORTY LONG	NIGHT FO' LAST	same: instrumental	15.00
68	644 DJ	SHORTY LONG	NIGHT FO' LAST	same: instrumental	40.00
68	645	GLADYS KNIGHT & The PIPS	THE END OF OUR ROAD	DON'T LET HER TAKE YOUR LOVE FROM ME	10.00
68	645 DJ	GLADYS KNIGHT & The PIPS	THE END OF OUR ROAD	DON'T LET HER TAKE YOUR LOVE FROM ME	30.00
68	646	EDWIN STARR	MY WEAKNESS IS YOU	I AM THE MAN FOR YOU BABY	40.00
68	646 DJ	EDWIN STARR	MY WEAKNESS IS YOU	I AM THE MAN FOR YOU BABY	**253.00**
68	647	FOUR TOPS	YOUR LOVE IS WONDERFUL	IF I WERE A CARPENTER	20.00
68	647 DJ	FOUR TOPS	YOUR LOVE IS WONDERFUL	IF I WERE A CARPENTER	50.00
68	648	SMOKEY ROBINSON & MIRACLES	IF YOU CAN WANT	WHEN THE WORDS FROM YOUR HEART	10.00
68	648 DJ	SMOKEY ROBINSON & MIRACLES	IF YOU CAN WANT	WHEN THE WORDS FROM YOUR HEART	40.00
68	649	JIMMY RUFFIN	I'LL SAY FOREVER MY LOVE	EVERYBODY NEEDS LOVE	8.00
68	649 DJ	JIMMY RUFFIN	I'LL SAY FOREVER MY LOVE	EVERYBODY NEEDS LOVE	30.00
68	650	DIANA ROSS & the SUPREMES	FOREVER CAME TODAY	TIME CHANGES THINGS	8.00
68	650 DJ	DIANA ROSS & the SUPREMES	FOREVER CAME TODAY	TIME CHANGES THINGS	30.00
68	651	CHUCK JACKSON	GIRLS, GIRLS, GIRLS	THE MAN IN YOU	20.00
68	651 DJ	CHUCK JACKSON	GIRLS, GIRLS, GIRLS	THE MAN IN YOU	50.00
68	652	ISLEY BROTHERS	WHY WHEN LOVE IS GONE	TAKE ME IN YOUR ARMS (AND ROCK ME)	40.00
68	652 DJ	ISLEY BROTHERS	WHY WHEN LOVE IS GONE	TAKE ME IN YOUR ARMS (AND ROCK ME)	100.00
68	653	STEVIE WONDER	SHOO-BE-DOO-BE-DOO-DA-DAY	WHY DON'T YOU LEAD ME TO LOVE	6.00
68	653 DJ	STEVIE WONDER	SHOO-BE-DOO-BE-DOO-DA-DAY	WHY DON'T YOU LEAD ME TO LOVE	30.00
68	654	BOBBY TAYLOR & the VANCOUVERS	DOES YOUR MAMA KNOW ABOUT ME	FADING AWAY	50.00
68	654 DJ	BOBBY TAYLOR & the VANCOUVERS	DOES YOUR MAMA KNOW ABOUT ME	FADING AWAY	85.00
68	655	MARVIN GAYE & TAMMI TERRELL	AIN'T NOTHING LIKE THE REAL THING	LITTLE OLE BOY, LITTLE OLE GIRL	10.00
68	655 DJ	MARVIN GAYE & TAMMI TERRELL	AIN'T NOTHING LIKE THE REAL THING	LITTLE OLE BOY, LITTLE OLE GIRL	30.00
68	656	R.DEAN TAYLOR	GOTTA SEE JANE	DON'T FOOL AROUND	8.00
68	656 DJ	R.DEAN TAYLOR	GOTTA SEE JANE	DON'T FOOL AROUND	30.00
68	657	MARTHA REEVES & the VANDELLAS	I PROMISE TO WAIT MY LOVE	FORGET ME NOT	10.00
68	657 DJ	MARTHA REEVES & the VANDELLAS	I PROMISE TO WAIT MY LOVE	FORGET ME NOT	40.00
68	658	TEMPTATIONS	I COULD NEVER LOVE ANOTHER	GONNA GIVE HER ALL THE LOVE I'VE GOT	10.00
68	658 DJ	TEMPTATIONS	I COULD NEVER LOVE ANOTHER	GONNA GIVE HER ALL THE LOVE I'VE GOT	30.00
68	659	MARVELETTES	KEEP OFF, NO TRESPASSING	HERE I AM BABY	10.00
68	659 DJ	MARVELETTES	KEEP OFF, NO TRESPASSING	HERE I AM BABY	40.00
68	660	GLADYS KNIGHT & The PIPS	IT SHOULD HAVE BEEN ME	YOU DON'T LOVE ME NO MORE	15.00
68	660 DJ	GLADYS KNIGHT & The PIPS	IT SHOULD HAVE BEEN ME	YOU DON'T LOVE ME NO MORE	30.00
68	661	SMOKEY ROBINSON & MIRACLES	YESTER LOVE	MUCH BETTER OFF	10.00
68	661 DJ	SMOKEY ROBINSON & MIRACLES	YESTER LOVE	MUCH BETTER OFF	30.00
68	662	DIANA ROSS & the SUPREMES	YOU'VE BEEN SO WONDERFUL TO ME	SOME THINGS YOU NEVER GET USED TO	15.00
68	662 DJ	DIANA ROSS & the SUPREMES	YOU'VE BEEN SO WONDERFUL TO ME	SOME THINGS YOU NEVER GET USED TO	35.00
68	663	SHORTY LONG	HERE COME THE JUDGE	SING WHAT YOU WANNA	8.00
68	663 DJ	SHORTY LONG	HERE COME THE JUDGE	SING WHAT YOU WANNA	30.00

68	664	JIMMY RUFFIN	DON'T LET HIM TAKE YOUR LOVE FROM ME	LONELY LONELY MAN AM I	10.00
68	664 DJ	JIMMY RUFFIN	DON'T LET HIM TAKE YOUR LOVE FROM ME	LONELY LONELY MAN AM I	30.00
68	665	FOUR TOPS	YESTERDAY'S DREAMS	FOR ONCE IN MY LIFE	8.00
68	665 DJ	FOUR TOPS	YESTERDAY'S DREAMS	FOR ONCE IN MY LIFE	30.00
68	666	STEVIE WONDER	YOU MET YOUR MATCH	MY GIRL	15.00
68	666 DJ	STEVIE WONDER	YOU MET YOUR MATCH	MY GIRL	30.00
68	667	JR.WALKER & THE ALL STARS	HIP CITY	HIP CITY Part2	10.00
68	667 DJ	JR.WALKER & THE ALL STARS	HIP CITY	HIP CITY Part 2	30.00

The beginning of the olive green Company sleeves:

68	668 sold subject	MARVIN GAYE & TAMMI TERRELL	TWO CAN HAVE A PARTY	YOU'RE ALL I NEED TO GET BY	8.00
68	668 DJ	MARVIN GAYE & TAMMI TERRELL	TWO CAN HAVE A PARTY	YOU'RE ALL I NEED TO GET BY	45.00
72	668 no sold subject	MARVIN GAYE & TAMMI TERRELL	TWO CAN HAVE A PARTY	YOU'RE ALL I NEED TO GET BY	6.00
68	669	MARTHA REEVES & the VANDELLAS	I CAN'T DANCE TO THAT MUSIC YOUR PLAYING	I TRIED	10.00
68	669 DJ	MARTHA REEVES & the VANDELLAS	I CAN'T DANCE TO THAT MUSIC YOUR PLAYING	I TRIED	30.00
68	670	PAUL PETERSON	YOUR LOVE'S GOT ME BURNING ALIVE	A LITTLE BIT FOR SANDY	40.00
68	670 DJ	PAUL PETERSON	YOUR LOVE'S GOT ME BURNING ALIVE	A LITTLE BIT FOR SANDY	75.00
68	671	TEMPTATIONS	WHY DID YOU LEAVE ME DARLING	HOW CAN I FORGET	10.00
68	671 DJ	TEMPTATIONS	WHY DID YOU LEAVE ME DARLING	HOW CAN I FORGET	25.00
68	672 sold subject	EDWIN STARR	25 MILES	MIGHTY GOOD LOVIN'	8.00
72	672 DJ	EDWIN STARR	25 MILES	MIGHTY GOOD LOVIN'	40.00
72	672 no sold subject	EDWIN STARR	25 MILES	MIGHTY GOOD LOVIN'	6.00
68	673	SMOKEY ROBINSON & MIRACLES	SPECIAL OCCASION	GIVE HER UP	20.00
68	673 DJ	SMOKEY ROBINSON & MIRACLES	SPECIAL OCCASION	GIVE HER UP	30.00
68	674	GLADYS KNIGHT & The PIPS	I WISH IT WOULD RAIN	IT'S SUMMER	8.00
68	674 DJ	GLADYS KNIGHT & The PIPS	I WISH IT WOULD RAIN	IT'S SUMMER	22.00
68	675	FOUR TOPS	I'M IN A DIFFERENT WORLD	REMEMBER WHEN	8.00
68	675 DJ	FOUR TOPS	I'M IN A DIFFERENT WORLD	REMEMBER WHEN	30.00
68	676	MARVIN GAYE	CHAINED	AT LAST (I FOUND A LOVE)	8.00
68	676 DJ	MARVIN GAYE	CHAINED	AT LAST (I FOUND A LOVE)	25.00
68	677	DIANA ROSS & the SUPREMES	LOVE CHILD	WILL THIS BE THE DAY	8.00
68	677 DJ	DIANA ROSS & the SUPREMES	LOVE CHILD	WILL THIS BE THE DAY	40.00
68	678	FANTASTIC FOUR	I LOVE YOU MADLY	same: instrumental	20.00
68	678 DJ	FANTASTIC FOUR	I LOVE YOU MADLY	same: instrumental	40.00
68	679 sold subject to	STEVIE WONDER	FOR ONCE IN MY LIFE	ANGIE GIRL	6.00
68	679 DJ	STEVIE WONDER	FOR ONCE IN MY LIFE	ANGIE GIRL	25.00
73	679 no sold subject	STEVIE WONDER	FOR ONCE IN MY LIFE	ANGIE GIRL	4.00
68	680	MARV JOHNSON	YOU GOT THE LOVE I LOVE	I'LL PICK A ROSE FOR MY ROSE	15.00
68	680 DJ	MARV JOHNSON	YOU GOT THE LOVE I LOVE	I'LL PICK A ROSE FOR MY ROSE	50.00
69	681	MARVIN GAYE & TAMMI TERRELL	YOU AIN'T LIVIN' TILL YOU'RE LOVIN'	OH HOW I'D MISS YOU	8.00
69	681 DJ	MARVIN GAYE & TAMMI TERRELL	YOU AIN'T LIVIN' TILL YOU'RE LOVIN'	OH HOW I'D MISS YOU	30.00
69	682	JR. WALKER & THE ALL STARS	HOME COOKIN'	MUTINY	10.00
69	682 DJ	JR. WALKER & THE ALL STARS	HOME COOKIN'	MUTINY	25.00
69	683	ISLEY BROTHERS	I GUESS I'LL ALWAYS LOVE YOU	IT'S OUT OF THE QUESTION	8.00
69	683 DJ	ISLEY BROTHERS	I GUESS I'LL ALWAYS LOVE YOU	IT'S OUT OF THE QUESTION	25.00
69	684	MARTHA REEVES & the VANDELLAS	DANCING IN THE STREET	QUICKSAND	6.00
69	684 DJ	MARTHA REEVES & the VANDELLAS	DANCING IN THE STREET	QUICKSAND	25.00
69	685	DIANA ROSS & the SUPREMES	I'M GONNA MAKE YOU LOVE ME	A PLACE IN THE SUN	6.00
69	685 DJ	DIANA ROSS & the SUPREMES	I'M GONNA MAKE YOU LOVE ME	A PLACE IN THE SUN	22.00
69	686 sold subject to	MARVIN GAYE	I HEARD IT THROUGH THE GRAPEVINE	NEED SOMEBODY	10.00
73	686 DJ	MARVIN GAYE	I HEARD IT THROUGH THE GRAPEVINE	NEED SOMEBODY	40.00
73	686 no sold subject to	MARVIN GAYE	I HEARD IT THROUGH THE GRAPEVINE	NEED SOMEBODY	6.00
69	687	SMOKEY ROBINSON & MIRACLES	BABY, BABY DON'T CRY	YOUR MOTHER'S ONLY DAUGHTER	10.00
69	687 DJ	SMOKEY ROBINSON & MIRACLES	BABY, BABY DON'T CRY	YOUR MOTHER'S ONLY DAUGHTER	25.00
69	688	TEMPTATIONS	GET READY	MY GIRL	6.00
69	688 DJ	TEMPTATIONS	GET READY	MY GIRL	30.00
69	689	DAVID RUFFIN	MY WHOLE WORLD ENDED	I'VE GOT TO FIND MYSELF A BRAND	10.00
69	689 DJ	DAVID RUFFIN	MY WHOLE WORLD ENDED	I'VE GOT TO FIND MYSELF A BRAND	25.00
69	690 sold subject to	STEVIE WONDER	I DON'T KNOW WHY	MY CHERIE AMOUR	10.00
69	690 DJ	STEVIE WONDER	I DON'T KNOW WHY	MY CHERIE AMOUR	25.00
69	690 no sold subject to	STEVIE WONDER	MY CHERIE AMOUR	DON'T KNOW WHY I LOVE YOU	5.00
69	691 sold subject to	JR.WALKER & THE ALL STARS	ROAD RUNNER	SHOTGUN	8.00
73	691 DJ	JR.WALKER & THE ALL STARS	ROAD RUNNER	SHOT GUN	30.00
73	691 no sold subject to	JR.WALKER & THE ALL STARS	ROAD RUNNER	SHOT GUN	5.00
69	692	EDWIN STARR	WAY OVER THERE	IF MY HEART COULD TELL THE STORY	20.00
69	692 DJ	EDWIN STARR	WAY OVER THERE	IF MY HEART COULD TELL THE STORY	50.00
69	692 DJ single sided	EDWIN STARR	WAY OVER THERE	blank:	40.00
69	693 sold subject to	ISLEY BROTHERS	BEHIND THE PAINTED SMILE	ONE TOO MANY HEARTACHES	8.00
69	693 DJ	ISLEY BROTHERS	BEHIND THE PAINTED SMILE	ONE TOO MANY HEARTACHES	30.00
69	694 no sold subject to	MARTHA REEVES & the VANDELLAS	NOWHERE TO RUN	LIVE WIRE	8.00
69	694 DJ	MARTHA REEVES & the VANDELLAS	NOWHERE TO RUN	LIVE WIRE	25.00
69	695	DIANA ROSS & the SUPREMES	I'M LIVING IN SHAME	I'M SO GLAD I GOT SOMEBODY	6.00
69	695 DJ	DIANA ROSS & the SUPREMES	I'M LIVIN' IN SHAME	I'M SO GLAD I GOT SOMEBODY I	20.00
69	696 sold subject to	SMOKEY ROBINSON & MIRACLES	THE TRACKS OF MY TEARS	COME ON DO THE JERK	10.00
69	696 DJ	SMOKEY ROBINSON & MIRACLES	THE TRACKS OF MY TEARS	COME ON DO THE JERK	30.00
69	696 no sold subject to	SMOKEY ROBINSON & MIRACLES	THE TRACKS OF MY TEARS	COME ON DO THE JERK	6.00
69	697	MARVIN GAYE & TAMMI TERRELL	GOOD LOVIN AIN'T EASY TO COME BY	SATISFIED FEELIN'	8.00
69	697 DJ	MARVIN GAYE & TAMMI TERRELL	GOOD LOVIN AIN'T EASY TO COME BY	SATISFIED FEELIN'	25.00
69	698	FOUR TOPS	DON'T BRING BACK THE MEMORIES	WHAT IS A MAN	15.00
69	698 DJ	FOUR TOPS	DON'T BRING BACK THE MEMORIES	WHAT IS A MAN	30.00
69	699	TEMPTATIONS	AIN'T TOO PROUD TO BEG	FADING AWAY	6.00
69	699 DJ	TEMPTATIONS	AIN'T TOO PROUD TO BEG	FADING AWAY	20.00
69	700	BRENDA HOLLOWAY	JUST LOOK WHAT YOU'VE DONE	YOU'VE MADE ME SO VERY HAPPY	15.00
69	700 DJ	BRENDA HOLLOWAY	JUST LOOK WHAT YOU'VE DONE	YOU'VE MADE ME SO VERY HAPPY	25.00
69	701	MARVELETTES	REACHIN' FOR SOMETHING I CAN'T	DESTINATION, ANYWHERE	10.00
69	701 DJ	MARVELETTES	REACHIN' FOR SOMETHING I CAN'T	DESTINATION, ANYWHERE	30.00
69	702	ORIGINALS	GREEN GROW THE LILACS	YOU'RE THE ONE	15.00
69	702 DJ	ORIGINALS	GREEN GROW THE LILACS	YOU'RE THE ONE	25.00
69	703	JIMMY RUFFIN	I'VE PASSED THIS WAY BEFORE	TOMORROWS TEARS	6.00

69	703 DJ	JIMMY RUFFIN	I'VE PASSED THIS WAY BEFORE	TOMORROWS TEARS	20.00

Tamla Motown release # 703 was the last record to be released with "Sold in the U.K. subject to resale price conditions see price lists" printed on the centerpiece of the label. Releases before #703 without "Sold subject to" printed on the label are EMI second presses.

69	704	DIANA ROSS & the SUPREMES	NO MATTER WHAT SIGN YOU ARE	THE YOUNG FOLKS	8.00
69	704 DJ	DIANA ROSS & the SUPREMES	NO MATTER WHAT SIGN YOU ARE	THE YOUNG FOLKS	20.00
69	705	MARVIN GAYE	TOO BUSY THINKING ABOUT MY BABY	WHERE I LAY MY HAT	6.00
69	705 DJ	MARVIN GAYE	TOO BUSY THINKING ABOUT MY BABY	WHERE I LAY MY HAT	25.00
69	706	HONEST MEN	CHERIE	BABY	20.00
69	706 DJ	HONEST MEN	CHERIE	BABY	30.00
69	707	TEMPTATIONS	CLOUD NINE	WHY DID SHE HAVE TO LEAVE ME	6.00
69	707 DJ	TEMPTATIONS	CLOUD NINE	WHY DID SHE HAVE TO LEAVE ME	22.00
69	708	ISLEY BROTHERS	PUT YOURSELF IN MY PLACE	LITTLE MISS SWEETNESS	6.00
69	708 DJ	ISLEY BROTHERS	PUT YOURSELF IN MY PLACE	LITTLE MISS SWEETNESS	22.00
69	709	DIANA ROSS & the SUPREMES	I SECOND THAT EMOTION	THE WAY YOU DO THE THINGS YOU	6.00
69	709 DJ	DIANA ROSS & the SUPREMES	I SECOND THAT EMOTION	THE WAY YOU DO THE THINGS YOU	20.00
69	710	FOUR TOPS	CAN'T SEEM TO GET YOU OUT OF MY MIND	DO WHAT YOU GOTTA DO	20.00
69	710 DJ	FOUR TOPS	CAN'T SEEM TO GET YOU OUT OF MY MIND	DO WHAT YOU GOTTA DO	40.00
69	711	DAVID RUFFIN	I'VE LOST EVERYTHING I'VE EVER LOVED	WE'LL HAVE A GOOD THING GOING	10.00
69	711 DJ	DAVID RUFFIN	I'VE LOST EVERYTHING I'VE EVER LOVED	WE'LL HAVE A GOOD THING GOING	22.00
69	712	JR.WALKER & THE ALL STARS	WHAT DOES IT TAKE (TO WIN YOUR LOVE)	BRAINWASHER	8.00
69	712 DJ	JR.WALKER & THE ALL STARS	WHAT DOES IT TAKE (TO WIN YOUR LOVE)	BRAINWASHER	25.00
69	713	MARV JOHNSON	I MISS YOU BABY (HOW I MISS YOU)	BAD GIRL	8.00
69	713 DJ	MARV JOHNSON	I MISS YOU BABY (HOW I MISS YOU)	BAD GIRL	25.00
69	714	GLADYS KNIGHT & The PIPS	NITTY GRITTY	GOT MYSELF A GOOD MAN	10.00
69	714 DJ	GLADYS KNIGHT & The PIPS	NITTY GRITTY	GOT MYSELF A GOOD MAN	20.00
69	715	MARVIN GAYE & TAMMI TERRELL	THE ONION SONG	I CAN'T BELIEVE YOU LOVE ME	6.00
69	715 DJ	MARVIN GAYE & TAMMI TERRELL	THE ONION SONG	I CAN'T BELIEVE YOU LOVE ME	20.00
69	715 DJ PS	MARVIN GAYE & TAMMI TERRELL	THE ONION SONG	I CAN'T BELIEVE YOU LOVE ME	50.00
69	716	TEMPTATIONS	RUN AWAY CHILD, RUNNING WILD	I NEED YOUR LOVIN'	8.00
69	716 DJ	TEMPTATIONS	RUN AWAY CHILD, RUNNING WILD	I NEED YOUR LOVIN'	20.00
69	717	STEVIE WONDER	YESTER-ME, YESTER-YOU, YESTERDAY	I'D BE A FOOL RIGHT NOW	6.00
69	717 DJ	STEVIE WONDER	YESTER-ME, YESTER-YOU, YESTERDAY	I'D BE A FOOL RIGHT NOW	25.00
69	718	MARVIN GAYE	THAT'S THE WAY LOVE IS	GONNA KEEP ON TRYIN' TILL I WI	10.00
69	718 DJ	MARVIN GAYE	THAT'S THE WAY LOVE IS	GONNA KEEP ON TRYIN' TILL I WI	20.00
69	719	ISLEY BROTHERS	TAKE SOME TIME OUT FOR LOVE	WHO COULD EVER DOUBT MY LOVE	6.00
69	719 DJ	ISLEY BROTHERS	TAKE SOME TIME OUT FOR LOVE	WHO COULD EVER DOUBT MY LOVE	18.00
69	720 DJ	BLINKY & EDWIN STARR	OH HOW HAPPY	OOO BABY BABY	350.00

promo only stock release on TMG 748 has the # 720 crossed out in the deadwax

69	721	DIANA ROSS & the SUPREMES	SOMEDAY WE'LL BE TOGETHER	HE'S MY SUNNY BOY	6.00
69	721 DJ	DIANA ROSS & the SUPREMES	SOMEDAY WE'LL BE TOGETHER	HE'S MY SUNNY BOY	20.00
69	722	TEMPTATIONS	I CAN'T GET NEXT TO YOU	RUNNING AWAY (AIN'T GONNA HELP	6.00
69	722 DJ	TEMPTATIONS	I CAN'T GET NEXT TO YOU	RUNNING AWAY (AIN'T GONNA HELP	22.00
70	723	CONTOURS	JUST A LITTLE MISUNDERSTANDING	FIRST LOOK AT THE PURSE	10.00
70	723 DJ	CONTOURS	JUST A LITTLE MISUNDERSTANDING	FIRST LOOK AT THE PURSE	30.00
70	724	JACKSON 5	I WANT YOU BACK	WHO'S LOVIN' YOU	5.00
70	724 DJ	JACKSON 5	I WANT YOU BACK	WHO'S LOVING YOU	20.00
70	725	EDWIN STARR	TIME	RUNNING BACK AND FORTH	15.00
70	725 DJ	EDWIN STARR	TIME	RUNNING BACK AND FORTH	30.00
70	726	JIMMY RUFFIN	FAREWELL IS A LONELY SOUND	IF YOU WILL LET ME, I KNOW I CAN	5.00
70	726 DJ	JIMMY RUFFIN	FAREWELL IS A LONELY SOUND	IF YOU WILL LET ME, I KNOW I CAN	20.00
70	727	JR.WALKER & THE ALL STARS	THESE EYES	I'VE GOT TO FIND A WAY TO WIN	8.00
70	727 DJ	JR.WALKER & THE ALL STARS	THESE EYES	I'VE GOT TO FIND A WAY TO WIN	20.00
70	728	GLADYS KNIGHT & The PIPS	KEEP AN EYE	DIDN'T YOU KNOW (YOU'D HAVE TO CRY SOME	8.00
70	728 DJ	GLADYS KNIGHT & The PIPS	KEEP AN EYE	DIDN'T YOU KNOW (YOU'D HAVE TO CRY SOME	20.00
70	729	CHUCK JACKSON	WHAT AM I GONNA DO WITHOUT YOU	HONEY COME BACK	20.00
70	729 DJ	CHUCK JACKSON	WHAT AM I GONNA DO WITHOUT YOU	HONEY COME BACK	40.00
70	730	DIANA ROSS & the SUPREMES	WHY (MUST WE FALL IN LOVE)	UPTIGHT (EVERYTHING'S ALRIGHT)	6.00
70	730 DJ	DIANA ROSS & the SUPREMES	WHY (MUST WE FALL IN LOVE)	UPTIGHT (EVERYTHING'S ALRIGHT)	20.00
70	731	STEVIE WONDER	NEVER HAD A DREAM COME TRUE	SOMEBODY KNOWS, SOMEBODY CARES	5.00
70	731 DJ	STEVIE WONDER	NEVER HAD A DREAM COME TRUE	SOMEBODY KNOWS, SOMEBODY CARES	20.00
70	732	FOUR TOPS	I CAN'T HELP MYSELF	BABY I NEED YOUR LOVING	6.00
70	732 DJ	FOUR TOPS	I CAN'T HELP MYSELF	BABY I NEED YOUR LOVING	20.00
70	733	ORIGINALS	BABY I'M FOR REAL	MOMENT OF TRUTH	15.00
70	733 DJ	ORIGINALS	BABY I'M FOR REAL	MOMENT OF TRUTH	25.00
70	734	MARVIN GAYE	ABRAHAM, MARTIN AND JOHN	HOW CAN I FORGET	8.00
70	734 DJ	MARVIN GAYE	ABRAHAM, MARTIN AND JOHN	HOW CAN I FORGET	22.00
70	735	SUPREMES	UP THE LADDER TO THE ROOF	BILL, WHEN ARE YOU COMING BACK	6.00
70	735 DJ	SUPREMES	UP THE LADDER TO THE ROOF	BILL, WHEN ARE YOU COMING BACK	20.00
70	736	FOUR TOPS	IT'S ALL IN THE GAME	LOVE IS THE ANSWER	5.00
70	736 DJ	FOUR TOPS	IT'S ALL IN THE GAME	LOVE IS THE ANSWER	20.00
70	737	MARV JOHNSON	SO GLAD YOU CHOSE ME	I'M NOT A PLAYTHING	10.00
70	737 DJ	MARV JOHNSON	SO GLAD YOU CHOSE ME	I'M NOT A PLAYTHING	20.00
70	738	JACKSON 5	ABC	THE YOUNG FOLKS	6.00
70	738 DJ	JACKSON 5	ABC	THE YOUNG FOLKS	15.00
70	739	KIKI DEE	THE DAY WILL COME BETWEEN	MY WHOLE WORLD ENDED	15.00
70	739 DJ	KIKI DEE	THE DAY WILL COME BETWEEN	MY WHOLE WORLD ENDED	25.00
70	740	JIMMY RUFFIN	I'LL SAY FOREVER MY LOVE	EVERYBODY NEEDS LOVE	6.00
70	740 DJ	JIMMY RUFFIN	I'LL SAY FOREVER MY LOVE	EVERYBODY NEEDS LOVE	20.00
70	741	TEMPTATIONS	PSYCHEDELIC SHACK	THAT'S THE WAY LOVE IS	6.00
70	741 DJ	TEMPTATIONS	PSYCHEDELIC SHACK	THAT'S THE WAY LOVE IS	20.00
70	742	RARE EARTH	GET READY	MAGIC KEY	20.00
70	742 DJ	RARE EARTH	GET READY	MAGIC KEY	30.00
70	743	DIANA ROSS	REACH OUT AND TOUCH (SOMEBODY'S HAND)	DARK SIDE OF THE WORLD	6.00
70	743 DJ	DIANA ROSS	REACH OUT AND TOUCH (SOMEBODY'S HAND)	DARK SIDE OF THE WORLD	15.00
70	744	STEVIE WONDER	SIGNED, SEALED DELIVERED I'M YOURS	I'M MORE THAN HAPPY (I'M SATISFIED)	5.00
70	744 DJ	STEVIE WONDER	SIGNED, SEALED DELIVERED I'M YOURS	I'M MORE THAN HAPPY (I'M SATISFIED)	15.00
70	745 withdrawn	SMOKEY ROBINSON & MIRACLES	THE TEARS OF A CLOWN	YOU MUST BE LOVE	50.00

70	745	SMOKEY ROBINSON & MIRACLES	THE TEARS OF A CLOWN	WHO'S GONNA TAKE THE BLAME	5.00
70	745 DJ	SMOKEY ROBINSON & MIRACLES	THE TEARS OF A CLOWN	WHO'S GONNA TAKE THE BLAME	20.00
70	746	JACKSON 5	THE LOVE YOU SAVE	I FOUND THAT GIRL	5.00
70	746 DJ	JACKSON 5	THE LOVE YOU SAVE ·	I FOUND THAT GIRL	15.00
70	747	SUPREMES	EVERYBODY'S GOT THE RIGHT TO LOVE	BUT I LOVE YOU MORE	6.00
70	747 DJ	SUPREMES	EVERYBODY'S GOT THE RIGHT TO LOVE	BUT I LOVE YOU MORE	15.00
70	748	BLINKY & EDWIN STARR	OH HOW HAPPY	OO BABY BABY	15.00
70	748 DJ	BLINKY & EDWIN STARR	OH HOW HAPPY	OO BABY BABY	40.00
70	749	TEMPTATIONS	BALL OF CONFUSION	IT'S SUMMER	5.00
70	749 DJ	TEMPTATIONS	BALL OF CONFUSION	IT'S SUMMER	20.00
70	750	JR.WALKER & THE ALL STARS	DO YOU SEE MY LOVE (FOR YOU GROWING)	GROOVE AND MOOVE	8.00
70	750 DJ	JR.WALKER & THE ALL STARS	DO YOU SEE MY LOVE (FOR YOU GROWING)	GROOVE AND MOOVE	20.00
70	751	DIANA ROSS	AIN'T NO MOUNTAIN HIGH ENOUGH	CAN'T WAIT UNTIL TOMORROW	8.00
70	751 DJ	DIANA ROSS	AIN'T NO MOUNTAIN HIGH ENOUGH	CAN'T WAIT UNTIL TOMORROW	30.00
70	752	FOUR TOPS	STILL WATER (LOVE)	STILL WATER (PEACE)	5.00
70	752 DJ	FOUR TOPS	STILL WATER (LOVE)	STILL WATER (PEACE)	20.00
70	753	JIMMY RUFFIN	IT'S WONDERFUL (TO BE LOVED BY YOU)	MARIA (YOU WERE THE ONLY ONE)	6.00
70	753 DJ	JIMMY RUFFIN	IT'S WONDERFUL (TO BE LOVED BY YOU)	MARIA (YOU WERE THE ONLY ONE)	20.00
70	754	EDWIN STARR	WAR	HE WHO PICKS A ROSE	6.00
70	754 DJ	EDWIN STARR	WAR	HE WHO PICKS A ROSE	20.00
70	755	MOTOWN SPINNERS	SWEET THING	IT'S A SHAME	15.00
70	755 DJ unconfirmed	MOTOWN SPINNERS	SWEET THING	IT'S A SHAME	UN
70	756	GLADYS KNIGHT & The PIPS	FRIENDSHIP TRAIN	YOU NEED LOVE LIKE I DO	8.00
70	756 DJ	GLADYS KNIGHT & The PIPS	FRIENDSHIP TRAIN	YOU NEED LOVE LIKE I DO	20.00
70	757	STEVIE WONDER	HEAVEN HELP US ALL	I GOTTA HAVE A SONG	5.00
70	757 DJ	STEVIE WONDER	HEAVEN HELP US ALL	I GOTTA HAVE A SONG	15.00
70	758	JACKSON 5	I'LL BE THERE	ONE MORE CHANCE	5.00
70	758 DJ	JACKSON 5	I'LL BE THERE	ONE MORE CHANCE	15.00
70	759	EARL VAN DYKE	6 BY 6	ALL FOR YOU	10.00
70	759 DJ	EARL VAN DYKE	6 BY 6	ALL FOR YOU	40.00
70	760	SUPREMES	STONED LOVE	SHINE ON ME	6.00
70	760 DJ	SUPREMES	STONED LOVE	SHINE ON ME	25.00
70	761	SMOKEY ROBINSON & MIRACLES	(COME ROUND HERE) I'M THE ONE YOU	WE CAN MAKE IT WE CAN	4.00
70	761 DJ	SMOKEY ROBINSON & MIRACLES	(COME ROUND HERE) I'M THE ONE YOU	WE CAN MAKE IT WE CAN	20.00
70	762	MARTHA REEVES & the VANDELLAS	I GOTTA LET YOU GO	FORGET ME NOT	10.00
70	762 DJ	MARTHA REEVES & the VANDELLAS	I GOTTA LET YOU GO	FORGET ME NOT	25.00
71	763	R. DEAN TAYLOR	INDIANA WANT ME	LOVE'S YOUR NAME	5.00
71	763 DJ	R. DEAN TAYLOR	INDIANA WANT ME	LOVE'S YOUR NAME	15.00
71	764	EDWIN STARR	STOP THE WAR NOW	GONNA KEEP ON TRYING TILL I WIN YOUR LOVE	6.00
71	764 DJ unconfirmed	EDWIN STARR	STOP THE WAR NOW	GONNA KEEP ON TRYING TILL I WIN YOUR LOVE	UN
71	765	GLADYS KNIGHT & The PIPS	IF I WERE YOUR WOMAN	TRACKS OF MY TEARS	5.00
71	765 DJ	GLADYS KNIGHT & The PIPS	IF I WERE YOUR WOMAN	TRACKS OF MY TEARS	15.00
71	766	MOTOWN SPINNERS	TRULY YOURS	TOGETHER WE CAN MAKE SUCH SWEE	10.00
71	766 DJ	MOTOWN SPINNERS	TRULY YOURS	TOGETHER WE CAN MAKE SUCH SWEE	20.00
71	767	JIMMY RUFFIN	LET'S SAY GOODBYE TOMORROW	LIVING IN A WORLD I CREATED FOR	10.00
71	767 DJ	JIMMY RUFFIN	LET'S SAY GOODBYE TOMORROW	LIVING IN A WORLD I CREATED FOR	20.00
71	768	DIANA ROSS	REMEMBER ME	HOW ABOUT YOU	5.00
71	768 DJ	DIANA ROSS	REMEMBER ME	HOW ABOUT YOU	15.00
71	769	JACKSON 5	MAMA'S PEARL	DARLING DEAR	6.00
71	769 DJ	JACKSON 5	MAMA'S PEARL	DARLING DEAR	15.00
71	770	FOUR TOPS	JUST SEVEN NUMBERS	I WISH I WERE YOUR MIRROR	8.00
71	770 DJ	FOUR TOPS	JUST SEVEN NUMBERS	I WISH I WERE YOUR MIRROR	15.00
71	771	ELGINS	HEAVEN MUST HAVE SENT YOU	STAY IN MY LONELY ARMS	6.00
71	771 DJ	ELGINS	HEAVEN MUST HAVE SENT YOU	STAY IN MY LONELY ARMS	20.00
71	772	STEVIE WONDER	WE CAN WORK IT OUT	DON'T WONDER WHY	5.00
71	772 PS	STEVIE WONDER	WE CAN WORK IT OUT	DON'T WONDER WHY	25.00
71	772 DJ	STEVIE WONDER	WE CAN WORK IT OUT	DON'T WONDER WHY	15.00
71	772 DJ PS	STEVIE WONDER	WE CAN WORK IT OUT	DON'T WONDER WHY	30.00
71	773	TEMPTATIONS	JUST MY IMAGINATION	YOU MAKE YOUR OWN HEAVEN	6.00
71	773 DJ	TEMPTATIONS	JUST MY IMAGINATION	YOU MAKE YOUR OWN HEAVEN	20.00
71	774	SMOKEY ROBINSON & MIRACLES	I DON'T BLAME YOU AT ALL	THAT GIRL	6.00
71	774 DJ	SMOKEY ROBINSON & MIRACLES	I DON'T BLAME YOU AT ALL	THAT GIRL	15.00
71	775	MARVIN GAYE	WHAT'S GOING ON	GOD IS LOVE	6.00
71	775 DJ	MARVIN GAYE	WHAT'S GOING ON	GOD IS LOVE	30.00
71	776	UNDISPUTED TRUTH	SAVE MY LOVE FOR A RAINY DAY	SINCE I LOST YOU	8.00
71	776 DJ	UNDISPUTED TRUTH	SAVE MY LOVE FOR A RAINY DAY	SINCE I'VE LOST YOU	20.00
71	777	SUPREMES & FOUR TOPS	RIVER DEEP, MOUNTAIN HIGH	IT'S GOT TO BE A MIRACLE	6.00
71	777 DJ	SUPREMES & FOUR TOPS	RIVER DEEP - MOUNTAIN HIGH	IT'S GOT TO BE A MIRACLE	20.00
71	778	JACKSON 5	NEVER CAN SAY GOODBYE	SHE'S GOOD	6.00
71	778 DJ	JACKSON 5	NEVER CAN SAY GOODBYE	SHE'S GOOD	15.00
71	779	STEVIE WONDER	NEVER DREAMED YOU'D LEAVE ME IN SUMMER	IF YOU REALLY LOVE ME	10.00
71	779 DJ	STEVIE WONDER	NEVER DREAMED YOU'D LEAVE ME IN SUMMER	IF YOU REALLY LOVE ME	20.00
71	780	VELVELETTES	THESE THINGS WILL KEEP ME LOVING	SINCE YOU'VE BEEN GONE	10.00
71	780 DJ	VELVELETTES	THESE THINGS WILL KEEP ME LOVING	SINCE YOU'VE BEEN LOVING ME	30.00
71	781	DIANA ROSS	I'M STILL WAITING	REACH OUT I'LL BE THERE	5.00
71	781 DJ	DIANA ROSS	I'M STILL WAITING	REACH OUT I'LL BE THERE	20.00
71	782	SUPREMES	NATHAN JONES	HAPPY (IS A BUMPY ROAD)	6.00
71	782 DJ	SUPREMES	NATHAN JONES	HAPPY (IS A BUMPY ROAD)	20.00
71	783	TEMPTATIONS	IT'S SUMMER	UNITE THE WORLD	8.00
71	783 DJ	TEMPTATIONS	IT'S SUMMER	UNITE THE WORLD	18.00
71	783 DJ alternate title	TEMPTATIONS	IT'S SUMMER	UNGENA ZA ULIMWENGU (UNITE THE WORLD)	25.00
71	784	JIMMY RUFFIN	ON THE WAY OUT (ON THE WAY IN)	HONEY COME BACK	8.00
71	784 DJ	JIMMY RUFFIN	ON THE WAY OUT (ON THE WAY IN)	HONEY COME BACK	18.00
71	785	FOUR TOPS	SIMPLE GAME	YOU STOLE MY LOVE	6.00
71	785 DJ	FOUR TOPS	SIMPLE GAME	YOU STOLE MY LOVE	1500
71	786 test press	R. DEAN TAYLOR	AIN'T IT A SAD THING	BACKSTREET	UN

unissed #. later released to launch the new UK label Rare Earth on # 101 – TMG786 is in the deadwax. Test presses without the Rare Earth matrix may exist

71	787	ELGINS	PUT YOURSELF IN MY PLACE	IT'S GONNA BE HARD TIMES		10.00
71	787 DJ	ELGINS	PUT YOURSELF IN MY PLACE	IT'S GONNA BE HARD TIMES		20.00
71	788	BARBARA RANDOLF	I GOT A FEELING	YOU GOT ME HURTIN ALL OVER		10.00
71	788 DJ	BARBARA RANDOLF	I GOT A FEELING	YOU GOT ME HURTIN ALL OVER		20.00
71	789	UNDISPUTED TRUTH	YOU GOT THE LOVE I NEED	SMILING FACES SOMETIMES		15.00
71	789 DJ	UNDISPUTED TRUTH	YOU GOT THE LOVE I NEED	SMILING FACES SOMETIMES		25.00
71	790	EDWIN STARR	AGENT DOUBLE O SOUL	BACK STREET		6.00
71	790 DJ	EDWIN STARR	AGENT DOUBLE O SOUL	BACK STREET		22.00
71	791	RITA WRIGHT	I CAN'T GIVE BACK THE LOVE I FEEL FOR YOU	SOMETHING ON MY MIND		15.00
71	791 DJ unconfirmed	RITA WRIGHT	I CAN'T GIVE BACK THE LOVE I FEEL FOR YOU	SOMETHING ON MY MIND		UN
71	792	DIANA ROSS	SURRENDER	I'M A WINNER		5.00
71	792 DJ	DIANA ROSS	SURRENDER	I'M A WINNER		16.00
71	793	SUPREMES & FOUR TOPS	YOU GOTTA HAVE LOVE IN YOUR HEARTS	I'M GLAD ABOUT IT		6.00
71	793 DJ	SUPREMES & FOUR TOPS	YOU GOTTA HAVE LOVE IN YOUR HEARTS	I'M GLAD ABOUT IT		15.00
71	794	MARTHA REEVES & the VANDELLAS	BLESS YOU	HOPE I DON'T GET MY HEART BROKE		8.00
71	794 DJ	MARTHA REEVES & the VANDELLAS	BLESS YOU	HOPE I DON'T GET MY HEART BROKE		22.00
71	795	SAN REMO STRINGS	FESTIVAL TIME	ALL TURNED ON		8.00
71	795 DJ	SAN REMO STRINGS	FESTIVAL TIME	ALL TURNED ON		40.00
71	796	MARVIN GAYE	LITTLE DARLING (I NEED YOU)	SAVE THE CHILDREN		10.00
71	796 DJ	MARVIN GAYE	LITTLE DARLING (I NEED YOU)	SAVE THE CHILDREN		26.00
71	797	MICHAEL JACKSON	GOT TO BE THERE	MARIA (YOU WERE THE ONLY ONE)		5.00
71	797 DJ	MICHAEL JACKSON	GOT TO BE THERE	MARIA (YOU WERE THE ONLY ONE)		15.00
72	798	STEVIE WONDER	IF YOU REALLY LOVE ME	THINK OF ME AS YOUR SOLDIER		6.00
72	798 DJ	STEVIE WONDER	IF YOU REALLY LOVE ME	THINK OF ME AS YOUR SOLDIER		16.00
72	799	THELMA HOUSTON	I WANT TO GO BACK THERE AGAIN	PICK OF THE WEEK		10.00
72	799 DJ	THELMA HOUSTON	I WANT TO GO BACK THERE AGAIN	PICK OF THE WEEK		20.00
72	800	TEMPTATIONS	SUPERSTAR (REMEMBER HOW YOU GOT	GONNA KEEP ON TRYING TILL I WIN YOUR LOVE		6.00
72	800 DJ	TEMPTATIONS	SUPERSTAR (REMEMBER HOW YOU GOT	GONNA KEEP ON TRYING TILL I WIN YOUR LOVE		20.00
72	801	TOM CLAY	WHAT THE WORLD NEEDS NOW IS LOVE	THE VICTORS		10.00
72	801 DJ	TOM CLAY	WHAT THE WORLD NEEDS NOW IS LOVE	THE VICTORS		20.00
72	802	MARVIN GAYE	MERCY MERCY ME (THE ECOLOGY)	SAD TOMORROWS		6.00
72	802 DJ	MARVIN GAYE	MERCY MERCY ME (THE ECOLOGY)	SAD TOMORROWS		15.00
72	803	FOUR TOPS	IT'S THE SAME OLD SONG	I GOT A FEELING + BERNADETTE		5.00
72	803 DJ	FOUR TOPS	IT'S THE SAME OLD SONG	I GOT A FEELING + BERNADETTE		20.00
72	804	SUPREMES	FLOY JOY	THIS IS THE STORY		6.00
72	804 DJ	SUPREMES	FLOY JOY	THIS IS THE STORY		20.00
72	805	GLADYS KNIGHT & The PIPS	MAKE ME THE WOMAN THAT YOU GO HOME	I DON'T WANT TO DO WRONG		5.00
72	805 DJ	GLADYS KNIGHT & The PIPS	MAKE ME THE WOMAN THAT YOU GO HOME	I DON'T WANT TO DO WRONG		15.00
72	806	VELVELETTES	NEEDLE IN A HAYSTACK	I'M THE EXCEPTION TO THE RULE		6.00
72	806 DJ	VELVELETTES	NEEDLE IN A HAYSTACK	I'M THE EXCEPTION TO THE RULE		20.00
72	807	SAN REMO STRINGS	REACH OUT I'LL BE THERE	HUNGRY FOR LOVE		8.00
72	807 DJ	SAN REMO STRINGS	REACH OUT I'LL BE THERE	HUNGRY FOR LOVE		25.00
72	808	TEMPTATIONS	TAKE A LOOK AROUND	SMOOTH SAILING (FROM NOW ON)		6.00
72	808 DJ	TEMPTATIONS	TAKE A LOOK AROUND	SMOOTH SAILING (FROM NOW ON)		20.00
72	809	JACKSON 5	SUGAR DADDY	I'M SO HAPPY		6.00
72	809 DJ	JACKSON 5	SUGAR DADDY	I'M SO HAPPY		15.00
72	810	EDWIN STARR	FUNKY MUSIC SHO NUFF TURNS ME	CLOUD NINE		6.00
72	810 DJ	EDWIN STARR	FUNKY MUSIC SHO NUFF TURNS ME	CLOUD NINE		15.00
72	811	SMOKEY ROBINSON & MIRACLES	MY GIRL HAS GONE	CRAZY ABOUT THE LA LA		8.00
72	811 DJ	SMOKEY ROBINSON & MIRACLES	MY GIRL HAS GONE	CRAZY ABOUT THE LA LA		15.00
72	812	DIANA ROSS	DOOBEDOO'NDOOBE, DOOBEDOOD'NDB	KEEP AN EYE		5.00
72	812 DJ	DIANA ROSS	DOOBEDOO'NDOOBE, DOOBEDOOD'NDB	KEEP AN EYE		15.00
72	813	GLADYS KNIGHT & The PIPS	JUST WALK IN MY SHOES	(I KNOW) I'M LOSING YOU		8.00
72	813 DJ	GLADYS KNIGHT & The PIPS	JUST WALK IN MY SHOES	(I KNOW) I'M LOSING YOU		20.00
72	814	EARLVAN DYKE & the SOUL BROTHERS	I CAN'T HELP MYSELF	HOW SWEET IT IS (TO BE LOVED BY YOU)		10.00
72	814 DJ	EARLVAN DYKE & the SOUL BROTHERS	I CAN'T HELP MYSELF	HOW SWEET IT IS (TO BE LOVED BY YOU)		30.00
72	815	SUPREMES & FOUR TOPS	WITHOUT THE ONE YOU LOVE	LET'SMAKE LOVE NOW		8.00
72	815 DJ	SUPREMES & FOUR TOPS	WITHOUT THE ONE YOU LOVE	LET'S MAKE LOVE NOW		15.00
72	816	MICHAEL JACKSON	ROCKIN' ROBIN	LOVE IS HERE AND NOW YOUR GONE		4.00
72	816 DJ	MICHAEL JACKSON	ROCKIN' ROBIN	LOVE IS HERE AND NOW YOUR GONE		20.00
72	817	MARVIN GAYE	INNER CITY BLUES (MAKE ME WANNA HOLLER)	WHOLY HOLY		5.00
72	817 DJ	MARVIN GAYE	INNER CITY BLUES (MAKE WE WANNA HOLLER)	WHOLY HOLY		15.00
72	818	UNDISPUTED TRUTH	SUPERSTAR (REMEMBER HOW YOU GOT)	AIN'T NO SUN SINCE YOU'VE BEEN GONE		6.00
72	818 DJ	UNDISPUTED TRUTH	SUPERSTAR (REMEMBER HOW YOU GOT)	AIN'T NO SUN SINCE YOU'VE BEEN GONE		16.00
72	819	FRANKIE VALLI & the FOUR SEASONS	YOU'RE THE SONG (THAT I CAN'T SING)	SUN COUNTRY		8.00
72	819 DJ	FRANKIE VALLI & the FOUR SEASONS	YOU'RE THE SONG (THAT I CAN'T SING)	SUN COUNTRY		16.00
72	820	MARY WELLS	MY GUY + TWO LOVERS	YOU LOST THE SWEETEST BOY		6.00
72	820 DJ	MARY WELLS	MY GUY + TWO LOVERS	YOU LOST THE SWEETEST BOY		16.00
72	821	SUPREMES	AUTOMATICALLY SUNSHINE	PRECIOUS LITTLE THINGS		4.00
72	821 DJ	SUPREMES	AUTOMATICALLY SUNSHINE	PRECIOUS LITTLE THINGS		16.00
72	822	ORIGINALS	GOD BLESS WHOEVER SENT YOU	BABY I'M FOR REAL+ I LIKE YOUR STYLE		8.00
72	822 DJ	ORIGINALS	GOD BLESS WHOEVER SENT YOU	BABY I'M FOR REAL+ I LIKE YOUR STYLE		16.00
72	823	FOUR TOPS	WALK WITH ME, TALK WITH ME	L.A. (MY TOWN)		6.00
72	823 DJ	FOUR TOPS	WALK WITH ME, TALK WITH ME	L.A. (MY TOWN)		16.00
72	824	JR.WALKER & THE ALL STARS	WALK IN THE NIGHT	RIGHT ON BROTHERS AND SISTERS		6.00
72	824 DJ	JR.WALKER & THE ALL STARS	WALK IN THE NIGHT	RIGHT ON BROTHERS AND SISTERS		20.00
72	825	JACKSON 5	LITTLE BITTY PRETTY ONE	MAYBE TOMORROW		6.00
72	825 DJ	JACKSON 5	LITTLE BITTY PRETTY ONE	MAYBE TOMORROW		15.00
72	826	MICHAEL JACKSON	AIN'T NO SUNSHINE	I WANNA BE WHERE YOU ARE		5.00
72	826 DJ	MICHAEL JACKSON	AIN'T NO SUNSHINE	I WANNA BE WHERE YOU ARE		20.00
72	827	STEVIE WONDER	SUPERWOMAN	SEEMS SO LONG		5.00
72	827 DJ	STEVIE WONDER	SUPERWOMAN	SEEMS SO LONG		15.00
72	828	SISTERS LOVE	MR. FIX-IT MAN	YOU'VE GOT TO MAKE YOUR CHOICE		8.00
72	828 DJ	SISTERS LOVE	MR. FIX-IT MAN	YOU'VE GOT TO MAKE YOUR CHOICE		15.00
72	829	FOUR TOPS	LOVE FEELS LIKE FIRE	I'LL TURN TO STONE		10.00
72	829 DJ	FOUR TOPS	LOVE FEELS LIKE FIRE	I'LL TURN TO STONE		25.00
72	830	GLADYS KNIGHT & The PIPS	HELP ME MAKE IT THROUGH THE NIGHT	IF YOU GONNA LEAVE (JUST LEAVE		5.00

72	830 DJ	GLADYS KNIGHT & The PIPS	HELP ME MAKE IT THROUGH THE NIGHT	IF YOU GONNA LEAVE (JUST LEAVE	15.00
72	831	LAURA LEE	TO WIN YOUR HEART	SO WILL I	15.00
72	831 DJ	LAURA LEE	TO WIN YOUR HEART	SO WILL I	40.00
72	832	TEMPTATIONS	SMILING FACES SOMETIMES	MOTHER NATURE	6.00
72	832 DJ	TEMPTATIONS	SMILING FACES SOMETIMES	MOTHER NATURE	15.00
72	833	JACKSON 5	LOOKING THROUGH THE WINDOWS	LOVE SONG	6.00
72	833 DJ	JACKSON 5	LOOKING THROUGH THE WINDOWS	LOVE SONG	15.00
72	833 PS	JACKSON 5	LOOKING THROUGH THE WINDOWS	LOVE SONG	20.00
72	833 DJ PS	JACKSON 5	LOOKING THROUGH THE WINDOWS	LOVE SONG	30.00
72	834	MICHAEL JACKSON	BEN	YOU CAN CRY ON MY SHOULDER	5.00
72	834 DJ	MICHAEL JACKSON	BEN	YOU CAN CRY ON MY SHOULDER	20.00
72	835	SUPREMES	YOUR WONDERFUL SWEET, SWEET LOVE	LOVE IT CAN TO ME THIS TIME	6.00
72	835 DJ	SUPREMES	YOUR WONDERFUL SWEET, SWEET LOVE	LOVE IT CAN TO ME THIS TIME	16.00
72	836	SUPREMES & FOUR TOPS	REACH OUT AND TOUCH (SOMEBODYS HAND)	WHERE WOULD I BE WITHOUT YOU BABY	6.00
72	836 DJ	SUPREMES & FOUR TOPS	REACH OUT AND TOUCH (SOMEBODYS HAND)	WHERE WOULD I BE WITHOUT YOU BABY	15.00
72	837	JACKSON 5	SANTA CLAUS IS COMING TO TOWN	SOMEDAY AT CHRISTMAS + 1	5.00
72	837 DJ	JACKSON 5	SANTA CLAUS IS COMING TO TOWN	SOMEDAY AT CHRISTMAS + 1	15.00
72	838	JERMAINE JACKSON	THAT'S HOW LOVES GOES	I LOST MY LOVE IN THE BIG CITY	6.00
72	838 DJ	JERMAINE JACKSON	THAT'S HOW LOVE GOES	I LOST MY LOVE IN THE BIG CITY	12.00
72	839	TEMPTATIONS	PAPA WAS A ROLLING STONE	same: instrumental	6.00
72	839 DJ	TEMPTATIONS	PAPA WAS A ROLLING STONE	same: instrumental	16.00
72	840	JR.WALKER & THE ALL STARS	TAKE ME GIRL, I'M READY	I DON'T WANT TO DO WRONG	6.00
72	840 DJ	JR.WALKER & THE ALL STARS	TAKE ME GIRL, I'M READY	I DON'T WANT TO DO WRONG	15.00
72	841	STEVIE WONDER	SUPERSTITION	YOU'VE GOT IT BAD GIRL	5.00
72	841 DJ	STEVIE WONDER	SUPERSTITION	YOU'VE GOT IT BAD GIRL	15.00
72	842	JACKSON 5	DOCTOR MY EYES	MY LITTLE BABY	5.00
72	842 DJ	JACKSON 5	DOCTOR MY EYES	MY LITTLE BABY	15.00
72	843	MARTHA REEVES	NO ONE THERE	(I'VE GIVEN YOU) THE BEST YEAR	150.00
72	843 DJ	MARTHA REEVES	NO ONE THERE	(I'VE GIVEN YOU THE BEST) YEAR	**192.00**
72	844	GLADYS KNIGHT & The PIPS	THE LOOK OF LOVE	YOU'RE MY EVERYTHING	6.00
72	844 DJ	GLADYS KNIGHT & The PIPS	THE LOOK OF LOVE	YOU'RE MY EVERYTHING	12.00
72	845	EDDIE KENDRICKS	IF YOU LET ME	JUST MEMORIES	5.00
72	845 DJ	EDDIE KENDRICKS	IF YOU LET ME	JUST MEMORIES	15.00
72	846	MARVIN GAYE	TROUBLE MAN	DON'T MESS WITH MISTER T	6.00
72	846 DJ	MARVIN GAYE	TROUBLE MAN	DON'T MESS WITH MISTER "T"	12.00
72	847	SUPREMES	BAD WEATHER	IT'S SO HARD FOR ME TO SAY GOO	6.00
72	847 DJ	SUPREMES	BAD WEATHER	IT'S SO HARD FOR ME TO SAY GOO	15.00
72	848	MICHAEL LEGRAND	LOVE THEME FROM "LADY SINGS THE BLUES	ANY HAPPY HOME	10.00
72	848 DJ	MICHAEL LEGRAND	LOVE THEME FROM "LADY SINGS THE BLUES	ANY HAPPY HOME	15.00
72	848 DJ PS	MICHAEL LEGRAND	LOVE THEME FROM "LADY SINGS THE BLUES	ANY HAPPY HOME	30.00
72	849	DIANA ROSS	GOOD MORNING HEARTACHE	GOD BLESS THE CHILD	6.00
72	849 PS	DIANA ROSS	GOOD MORNING HEARTACHE	LADY SINGS THE BLUES	12.00
72	849 DJ PS	DIANA ROSS	GOOD MORNING HEARTACHE	LADY SINGS THE BLUES	20.00
72	850	FOUR TOPS	SO DEEP WITHIN YOU	HAPPY (IS A BUMPY ROAD)	6.00
72	850 DJ	FOUR TOPS	SO DEEP WITHIN YOU	HAPPY (IS A BUMPY ROAD)	12.00
72	851	JERMAINE JACKSON	DADDY'S HOME	TAKE ME IN YOUR ARMS	5.00
72	851 DJ	JERMAINE JACKSON	DADDY'S HOME	TAKE ME IN YOUR ARMS	10.00
72	852	STEVIE WONDER	YOU ARE THE SUNSHINE OF MY LIFE	LOOK AROUND	4.00
72	852 DJ	STEVIE WONDER	YOU ARE THE SUNSHINE OF MY LIFE	LOOK AROUND	15.00
72	853	SMOKEY ROBINSON & MIRACLES	WHOLE LOT OF SHAKIN' IN MY HEART	GOING TO A GO GO + YESTER LOVE	5.00
72	853 DJ	SMOKEY ROBINSON & MIRACLES	WHOLE LOT OF SHAKIN' IN MY HEART	GOING TO A GO GO + YESTER LOVE	12.00
72	854	TEMPTATIONS	MASTERPIECE	same: instrumental	5.00
72	854 DJ	TEMPTATIONS	MASTERPIECE	same: instrumental	12.00
72	855	GLADYS KNIGHT & The PIPS	NEITHER ONE OF US (WANTS TO BE THE FIRST)	CAN'T GIVE IT UP NO MORE	5.00
72	855 DJ	GLADYS KNIGHT & The PIPS	NEITHER ONE OF US (WANTS TO BE THE FIRST)	CAN'T GIVE IT UP NO MORE	12.00
72	856	JACKSON 5	HALLELUJAH DAY	TO KNOW	6.00
72	856 DJ	JACKSON 5	HALLELUJAH DAY	TO KNOW	12.00
72	857	JR.WALKER & THE ALL STARS	COUNTRY BOY	WAY BACK HOME vocal & instrumental	20.00
72	857	JR.WALKER & THE ALL STARS	WAY BACK HOME	same: instrumental	8.00
72	857 DJ	JR.WALKER & THE ALL STARS	WAY BACK HOME	same: instrumental	20.00
72	858	FOUR TOPS	I CAN'T QUIT YOUR LOVE	I AM YOUR MAN	6.00
72	858 DJ	FOUR TOPS	I CAN'T QUIT YOUR LOVE	I AM YOUR MAN	15.00
72	859	SUPREMES	TOSSIN' AND TURNIN'	OH BE MY LOVE	8.00
72	859 DJ	SUPREMES	TOSSIN' AND TURNIN'	OH BE MY LOVE	15.00
72	860	MARVELETTES	REACHIN' FOR SOMETHING I CAN'T	HERE I AM BABY	8.00
72	860 DJ	MARVELETTES	REACHIN' FOR SOMETHING I CAN'T	HERE I AM BABY	30.00
72	860 DJ	MARVELETTES	REACHIN' FOR SOMETHING I CAN'T	MY BABY MUST BE A MAGICIAN	75.00

mispress promo copy flipside title reads "Here I Am Baby" but plays "My Baby Must Be A Magician"

73	861	DIANA ROSS	TOUCH ME IN THE MORNING	BABY IT'S LOVE	6.00
73	861 DJ	DIANA ROSS	TOUCH ME IN THE MORNING	BABY, IT'S YOU	10.00
73	862	WILLIE HUTCH	I CHOOSE YOU	BROTHER'S GONNA WORK IT OUT	15.00
73	862 DJ	WILLIE HUTCH	I CHOOSE YOU	BROTHER'S GONNA WORK IT OUT	20.00
73	863	MICHAEL JACKSON	MORNING GLOW	MY GIRL	6.00
73	863 DJ	MICHAEL JACKSON	MORNING GLOW	MY GIRL	12.00
73	864	GLADYS KNIGHT & The PIPS	NO ONE COULD LOVE YOU MORE	TAKE ME IN YOUR ARMS AND LOVE	100.00
73	864 DJ	GLADYS KNIGHT & The PIPS	NO ONE COULD LOVE YOU MORE	TAKE ME IN YOUR ARMS AND LOVE	150.00
73	865	JACKSON FIVE	SKYWRITER	AIN'T NOTHING LIKE THE REAL THING	5.00
73	865 PS	JACKSON FIVE	SKYWRITER	AIN'T NOTHING LIKE THE REAL THING	15.00
73	865 DJ	JACKSON FIVE	SKYWRITER	AIN'T NOTHING LIKE THE REAL THING	15.00
73	865 DJ PS	JACKSON FIVE	SKYWRITER	AIN'T NOTHING LIKE THE REAL THING	20.00
73	866	TEMPTATIONS	FUNKY MUSIC SHO NUFF TURNS ME ON	LAW OF THE LAND	6.00
73	866 DJ	TEMPTATIONS	FUNKY MUSIC SHO NUFF TURNS ME ON	LAW OF THE LAND	15.00
73	867 DJ	MARTIN & FINLEY	IT'S ANOTHER SUNDAY	BEST FRIENDS	100.00

867 was a promo only press, stock copies are unconfirmed.

73	868	MARVIN GAYE	LET'S GET IN ON	I WISH IT WOULD RAIN	5.00
73	868 DJ	MARVIN GAYE	LET'S GET IT ON	I WISH IT WOULD RAIN	15.00
73	868 DJ PS	MARVIN GAYE	LET'S GET IT ON	I WISH IT WOULD RAIN	100.00

73	869	STEVIE WONDER	HIGHER GROUND	TOO HIGH	5.00
73	869 DJ	STEVIE WONDER	HIGHER GROUND	TOO HIGH	10.00
73	870	J.J. BARNES	REAL HUMDINGER	PLEASE LET ME IN + I AIN'T GONNA DO IT	10.00
73	870 DJ	J.J. BARNES	REAL HUMDINGER	PLEASE LET ME IN + I AIN'T GONNA DO IT	25.00
73	871	DETROIT SPINNERS	TOGETHER WE CAN MAKE SUCH SWEET MUSIC	BAD BAD WEATHER (TILL YOU COME	8.00
73	871 DJ	DETROIT SPINNERS	TOGETHER WE CAN MAKE SUCH SWEET MUSIC	BAD BAD WEATHER (TILL YOU COME	15.00
73	872	JR.WALKER & THE ALL STARS	WHOLLY HOLLY	PEACE AND UNDERSTANDING IS HARD	6.00
73	872 DJ	JR.WALKER & THE ALL STARS	HOLLY HOLY	PEACE AND UNDERSTANDING IS HAR	15.00
73	873	EDDIE KENDRICKS	KEEP ON TRUCKIN'	KEEP ON TRUCKIN' PART2	4.00
73	873 DJ	EDDIE KENDRICKS	KEEP ON TRUCKIN'	KEEP ON TRUCKIN' PART2	10.00
73	874	JERMAINE JACKSON	THE BIGGER YOU LOVE	I'M IN A DIFFERENT WORLD	8.00
73	874 DJ	JERMAINE JACKSON	THE BIGGER YOU LOVE	I'M IN A DIFFERENT WORLD	12.00
73	875	EDWIN STARR	LOVE (THE LONELY PEOPLE'S PRAY)	YOU'VE GOT MY SOUL ON FIRE	20.00
73	875 DJ	EDWIN STARR	LOVE (THE LONELY PEOPLE'S PRAY)	YOU'VE GOT MY SOUL ON FIRE	30.00
73	876	GLADYS KNIGHT & The Pips	DADDY COULD SWEAR, I DECLARE	FOR ONCE IN MY LIFE	6.00
73	876 DJ	GLADYS KNIGHT & The Pips	DADDY COULD SWEAR I DECLARE	FOR ONCE IN MY LIFE	10.00
73	877	ISLEY BROTHERS	TELL ME IT IS JUST A RUMOUR BABY	SAVE ME FROM THIS MISERY	10.00
73	877 DJ	ISLEY BROTHERS	TELL ME IT IS JUST A RUMOUR BABY	SAVE ME FROM THIS MISERY	30.00
73	878	JACKSON FIVE	GET IT TOGETHER	TOUCH	5.00
73	878 DJ	JACKSON 5	GET IT TOGETHER	TOUCH	15.00
73	879	DIANA ROSS & MARVIN GAYE	YOU'RE A SPECIAL PART OF ME	I'M FALLING IN LOVE WITH YOU	5.00
73	879 DJ	DIANA ROSS & MARVIN GAYE	YOU'RE A SPECIAL PART OF ME	I'M FALLING IN LOVE WITH YOU	10.00
73	880	DIANA ROSS	ALL OF MY LIFE	A SIMPLE THING LIKE CRY	4.00
73	880 DJ	DIANA ROSS	ALL OF MY LIFE	A SIMPLE THING LIKE CRY	10.00
73	881	STEVIE WONDER	LIVING FOR THE CITY	VISIONS	4.00
73	881 DJ	STEVIE WONDER	LIVING FOR THE CITY	VISIONS	10.00
73	882	MARVIN GAYE	COME GET TO THIS	DISTANT LOVER	15.00
73	882 DJ	MARVIN GAYE	COME GET TO THIS	DISTANT LOVER	25.00
73	883	SMOKEY ROBINSON	JUST MY SOUL RESPONDING	SWEET HARMONY	5.00
73	883 DJ	SMOKEY ROBINSON	JUST MY SOUL RESPONDING	SWEET HARMONY	10.00
73	884	SUPREMES	I GUESS I'LL MISS THE MAN	OVER AND OVER	6.00
73	884 DJ	SUPREMES	I GUESS I'LL MISS THE MAN	OVER AND OVER	10.00
73	886	CONTOURS	BABY HIT AND RUN	CAN YOU JERK LIKE ME	40.00
73	886 DJ	CONTOURS	BABY HIT AND RUN	CAN YOU JERK LIKE ME	75.00
73	887	TEMPTATIONS	I NEED YOU	HEY GIRL (I LIKE YOUR STYLE)	10.00
73	887 DJ	TEMPTATIONS	I NEED YOU	HEY GIRL (I LIKE YOUR STYLE)	15.00
73	888	EDDIE KENDRICKS	BOOGIE DOWN	EDDIE'S LOVE	5.00
73	888 DJ	EDDIE KENDRICKS	BOOGIE DOWN	EDDIE'S LOVE	10.00
73	889	JR.WALKER & THE ALL STARS	DON'T BLAME THE CHILDREN	SOUL CLAPPIN	8.00
73	889 DJ	JR.WALKER & THE ALL STARS	DON'T BLAME THE CHILDREN	SOUL CLAPPIN'	10.00
73	890	DIANA ROSS & MARVIN GAYE	YOU ARE EVERYTHING	INCLUDE ME IN YOUR LIFE	5.00
73	890 DJ	DIANA ROSS & MARVIN GAYE	YOU ARE EVERYTHING	INCLUDE ME IN YOUR LIFE	10.00
73	890 PS	DIANA ROSS & MARVIN GAYE	YOU ARE EVERYTHING	INCLUDE ME IN YOUR LIFE	8.00
73	891	MIRACLES	DON'T LET IT END	I WANNA BE WITH YOU	6.00
73	891 DJ	MIRACLES	DON'T LET IT END	I WANNA BE WITH YOU	10.00
73	892	STEVIE WONDER	HE'S MISSTRA KNOW IT ALL	YOU CAN'T JUDGE A BOOK BY IT'S COVER	4.00
73	892 DJ	STEVIE WONDER	HE'S MISSTRA KNOW IT ALL	YOU CAN'T JUDGE A BOOK BY IT'S COVER	10.00
73	893	DIANA ROSS	LAST TIME I SAW HIM	EVERYTHING IS EVERYTHING	4.00
73	893 DJ	DIANA ROSS	LAST TIME I SAW HIM	EVERYTHING IS EVERYTHING	10.00
73	894	JR.WALKER & THE ALL STARS	I AIN'T GOING NOWHERE	GOTTA HOLD ON TO THIS FEELING	10.00
73	894 DJ	JR.WALKER & THE ALL STARS	I AIN'T GOING NOWHERE	GOTTA HOLD ON TO THIS FEELING	22.00
74	895	JACKSON FIVE	THE BOOGIE MAN	DON'T LET YOUR BABY CATCH YOU	5.00
74	895 DJ	JACKSON FIVE	THE BOOGIE MAN	DON'T LET YOUR BABY CATCH YOU	7.00
74	896	R.DEAN TAYLOR	THERE'S A GHOST IN MY HOUSE	LET'S GO SOMEWHERE	8.00
74	896 DJ	R.DEAN TAYLOR	THERE'S A GHOST IN MY HOUSE	LET'S GO SOMEWHERE	15.00
74	897	UNDISPUTED TRUTH	HELP YOURSELF	WHAT IT IS?	6.00
74	897 DJ	UNDISPUTED TRUTH	HELP YOUSELF	WHAT IT IS?	10.00
74	898	SMOKEY ROBINSON	A SILENT PARTNER IN A THREE-WAY LOVE AFFAIR	BABY COME CLOSE	5.00
74	898 DJ	SMOKEY ROBINSON	A SILENT PARTNER IN A THREE-WAY LOVE AFFAIR	BABY COME CLOSE	10.00
74	899	CONTOURS	DO YOU LOVE ME	DETERMINATION	6.00
74	899 DJ	CONTOURS	DO YOU LOVE ME	DETERMINATION	10.00
74	900	MICHAEL JACKSON	MUSIC AND ME	JOHNNY RAVEN	8.00
74	900 DJ	MICHAEL JACKSON	MUSIC AND ME	JOHNNY RAVEN	10.00
74	901	EDDIE KENDRICKS	CAN'T HELP WHAT I AM	SON OF SAGITTARIUS	8.00
74	901 DJ	EDDIE KENDRICKS	CAN'T HELP WHAT I AM	SON OF SAGITTARIUS	15.00
74	902	COMMODORES	MACHINE GUN	THERE'S A SONG IN MY HEART	5.00
74	902 DJ	COMMODORES	MACHINE GUN	THERE'S A SONG IN MY HEART	8.00
74	903	GLADYS KNIGHT & The Pips	DIDN'T YOU KNOW (YOU'D HAVE TO	CLOUD NINE	5.00
74	903 DJ	GLADYS KNIGHT & The Pips	DIDN'T YOU KNOW (YOU'D HAVE TO	CLOUD NINE	8.00
74	904	JACKSON FIVE	DANCING MACHINE	IT'S TOO LATE TO CHANGE THE TIME	5.00
74	904 DJ	JACKSON FIVE	DANCING MACHINE	IT'S TOO LATE TO CHANGE THE TIME	10.00
74	905	EDWIN STARR	STOP HER ON SIGHT (S.O.S.)	HEADLINE NEWS	6.00
74	905 DJ	EDWIN STARR	STOP HER ON SIGHT (S.O.S.)	HEADLINE NEWS	10.00
74	906	DIANA ROSS & MARVIN GAYE	STOP, LOOK, LISTEN (TO YOUR HEART)	LOVE TWINS	4.00
74	906 DJ	DIANA ROSS & MARVIN GAYE	STOP, LOOK, LISTEN (TO YOUR HEART)	LOVE TWINS	8.00
74	907	REFLECTIONS	(JUST LIKE) ROMEO AND JULIET	CAN'T YOU TELL BY THE LOOK IN MY EYES	6.00
74	907 DJ	REFLECTIONS	(JUST LIKE) ROMEO AND JULIET	CAN'T YOU TELL BY THE LOOK IN MY EYES	15.00
74	908	STEVIE WONDER	DON'T YOU WORRY 'BOUT A THING	DO YOURSELF A FAVOUR	6.00
74	908 DJ	STEVIE WONDER	DON'T YOU WORRY 'BOUT A THING	DO YOURSELF A FAVOUR	8.00
74	909	R. DEAN TAYLOR	DON'T FOOL AROUND	POOR GIRL	5.00
74	909 DJ	R. DEAN TAYLOR	DON'T FOOL AROUND	POOR GIRL	10.00
74	910	GLORIA JONES	TIN CAN PEOPLE	SO TIRED (OF THE WAY YOU'VE TREATED ME)	8.00
74	910 DJ	GLORIA JONES	TIN CAN PEOPLE	SO TIRED (OF THE WAY YOU'VE TREATED ME)	15.00
74	911	JIMMY RUFFIN	WHAT BECOMES OF THE BROKENHEARTED	DON'T YOU MISS ME A LITTLE BIT	8.00
74	911 DJ	JIMMY RUFFIN	WHAT BECOMES OF THE BROKENHEARTED	DON'T YOU MISS ME A LITTLE BIT	10.00
74	912	SYREETA	SPINNIN' AND SPINNIN'	BLACK MAYBE	6.00
74	912 DJ	SYREETA	SPINNIN' AND SPINNIN'	BLACK MAYBE	8.00

74	913	YVONNE FAIR	FUNKY MUSIC SHO NUFF TURNS ME ON	LET YOUR HAIR DOWN	6.00
74	913 DJ	YVONNE FAIR	FUNKY MUSIC SHO NUFF TURNS ME ON	LET YOUR HAIR DOWN	8.00
74	914	MIRACLES	DO IT BABY	WIGS AND LASHES	6.00
74	914 DJ	MIRACLES	DO IT BABY	WIGS AND LASHES	10.00
74	915	DIANA ROSS & the SUPREMES	BABY LOVE	ASK ANY GIRL	5.00
74	915DJ	DIANA ROSS & the SUPREMES	BABY LOVE	ASK ANY GIRL	10.00
74	916	EDDIE KENDRICKS	GIRL YOU NEED A CHANGE OF MIND	GIRL YOU NEED A CHANGE OF MIND part 2	8.00
74	916 DJ	EDDIE KENDRICKS	GIRL YOU NEED A CHANGE OF MIND	GIRL YOU NEED A CHANGE OF MIND part 2	15.00
74	917	DIANA ROSS	LOVE ME	SAVE THE CHILDREN	5.00
74	917 DJ	DIANA ROSS	LOVE ME	SAVE THE CHILDREN	10.00
74	918	R. DEAN TAYLOR	GOTTA SEE JANE	CANDY APPLE RED	5.00
74	918 DJ	R.DEAN TAYLOR	GOTTA SEE JANE	CANDY APPLE RED	10.00
74	919	UNDISPUTED TRUTH	I'M A FOOL FOR YOU	MAMA I GOT A BRAND NEW THING	6.00
74	919 DJ	UNDISPUTED TRUTH	I'M A FOOL FOR YOU	MAMA GOT A BRAND NEW THING	10.00
74	920	DIANA ROSS & MARVIN GAYE	MY MISTAKE (WAS TO LOVE YOU)	JUST SAY, JUST SAY	5.00
74	920 DJ	DIANA ROSS & MARVIN GAYE	MY MISTAKE (WAS TO LOVE YOU)	JUST SAY, JUST SAY	10.00
74	921	STEVIE WONDER	YOU HAVEN'T DONE NOTHIN'	HAPPIER THAN THE MORNING SUN	5.00
74	921 DJ	STEVIE WONDER	YOU HAVEN'T DONE NOTHIN'	HAPPIER THAN THE MORNING SUN	10.00
74	922	JIMMY RUFFIN	I WILL NEVER LET YOU GET AWAY	FAREWELL IS A LONELY SOUND	30.00
74	922 DJ	JIMMY RUFFIN	I WILL NEVER LET YOU GET AWAY	FAREWELL IS A LONELY SOUND	45.00
74	923	MARVIN GAYE	I HEARD IT THROUGH THE GRAPEVINE	CHAINED	6.00
74	923 DJ	MARVIN GAYE	I HEARD IT THROUGH THE GRAPEVINE	CHAINED	8.00
74	924	COMMODORES	THE ZOO (THE HUMAN ZOO)	I'M LOOKING FOR LOVE	6.00
74	924 DJ	COMMODORES	THE ZOO (THE HUMAN ZOO)	I'M LOOKING FOR LOVE	15.00
74	925	DIANA ROSS & the SUPREMES	WHERE DID OUR LOVE GO	NOTHING BUT HEARTACHES	4.00
74	925 DJ	DIANA ROSS & the SUPREMES	WHERE DID OUR LOVE GO	NOTHING BUT HEARTACHES	10.00
74	926	SYREETA	I'M GOIN' LEFT	HEAVY DAY	5.00
74	926 DJ	SYREETA	I'M GOIN' LEFT	HEAVY DAY	10.00
74	927	JACKSON 5	THE LIFE OF THE PARTY	WHATEVER YOU GOT, I WANT	5.00
74	927 DJ	JACKSON 5	THE LIFE OF THE PARTY	WHATEVER YOU GOT I WANT	10.00
74	928	STEVIE WONDER	BOOGIE ON REGGAE WOMAN	EVIL	5.00
74	928 DJ	STEVIE WONDER	BOOGIE ON REGGAE WOMAN	EVIL	10.00
74	929	DYNAMIC SUPERIORS	SHOE SHOE SHINE	RELEASE ME	5.00
74	929 DJ	DYNAMIC SUPERIORS	SHOE SHOE SHINE	RELEASE ME	10.00
74	930	EDWIN STARR	WHO'S RIGHT OR WRONG	AIN'T IT HELL UP IN HARLEM	5.00
74	930 DJ	EDWIN STARR	WHO'S RIGHT OR WRONG	AIN'T IT HELL UP IN HARLEM	10.00
74	931	TEMPTATIONS	HAPPY PEOPLE	same: instrumental	5.00
74	931 DJ	TEMPTATIONS	HAPPY PEOPLE	same: instrumental	10.00
74	932	POPCORN WYLIE	FUNKY RUBBER BAND	same: instrumental	15.00
74	932 DJ	POPCORN WYLIE	FUNKY RUBBER BAND	same: instrumental	10.00
74	933	SYREETA	YOUR KISS IS SWEET	HOW MANY DAYS	4.00
74	933 DJ	SYREETA	YOUR KISS IS SWEET	HOW MANY DAYS	10.00
74	934	JIMMY RUFFIN	I'VE PASSED THIS WAY BEFORE	SAD AND LONESOME FEELING	5.00
74	934 DJ	JIMMY RUFFIN	I'VE PASSED THIS WAY BEFORE	SAD AND LONESOME FEELING	10.00
74	935	COMMODORES	SUPERMAN	IT IS AS GOOD AS YOU MAKE IT	5.00
74	935 DJ	COMMODORES	SUPERMAN	IT IS AS GOOD AS YOU MAKE IT	8.00
74	936	DAVID RUFFIN	TAKE ME CLEAR FROM HERE	BLOOD DONORS NEEDED (GIVE ALL YOU CAN)	6.00
74	936 DJ	DAVID RUFFIN	TAKE ME CLEAR FROM HERE	BLOOD DONORS NEEDED (GIVE ALL YOU CAN)	8.00
74	937	ISLEY BROTHERS	THIS OLD HEART OF MINE (IS WEAK FOR YOU) THERE'S NO LOVE LEFT		5.00
74	937 DJ	ISLEY BROTHERS	THIS OLD HEART OF MINE (IS WEAK FOR YOU) THERE'S NO LOVE LEFT		10.00
74	938	CASTON & MAJORS	CHILD OF LOVE	NO ONE WILL KNOW	6.00
74	938 DJ	CASTON & MAJORS	CHILD OF LOVE	NO ONE WILL KNOW	10.00
74	939	MARVELETTES	WHEN YOU'RE YOUNG AND IN LOVE	THE DAY YOU TAKE ONE	6.00
74	939 DJ	MARVELETTES	WHEN YOU'RE YOUNG AND IN LOVE	THE DAY YOU TAKE ONE	10.00
74	940	MIRACLES	WHERE ARE YOU GOING TO MY LOVE	UP AGAIN	8.00
74	940 DJ	MIRACLES	WHERE ARE YOU GOING TO MY LOVE	UP AGAIN	10.00
74	941	DIANA ROSS	SORRY DOESN'T ALWAYS MAKE IT	TOGETHER	5.00
74	941 DJ	DIANA ROSS	SORRY DOESN'T ALWAYS MAKE IT	TOGETHER	8.00
75	942	JACKSON 5	I AM LOVE	I AM LOVE part 2	6.00
75	942 DJ	JACKSON 5	I AM LOVE	I AM LOVE part 2	8.00
75	943	UNDISPUTED TRUTH	LAW OF THE LAND	LIL' RED RIDING HOOD	6.00
75	943 DJ	UNDISPUTED TRUTH	LAW OF THE LAND	LIL' RED RIDING HOOD	8.00
75	944	COMMODORES	DETERMINATION	I FEEL SANCTIFIED	6.00
75	944 DJ	COMMODORES	DETERMINATION	I FEEL SANCTIFIED	10.00
75	945	GLADYS KNIGHT & The PIPS	YOU'VE LOST THAT LOVIN' FEELIN'	THIS CHILD NEEDS IT'S FATHER	15.00
75	945 DJ	GLADYS KNIGHT & The PIPS	YOU'VE LOST THAT LOVIN' FEELIN	THIS CHILD NEEDS IT'S FATHER	20.00
75	946	MICHAEL JACKSON	ONE DAY IN YOUR LIFE	WITH A CHILD'S HEART	6.00
75	946 DJ	MICHAEL JACKSON	ONE DAY IN YOUR LIFE	WITH A CHILD'S HEART	8.00
75	947	EDDIE KENDRICKS	SHOESHINE BOY	HOOKED ON YOUR LOVE	5.00
75	947 DJ	EDDIE KENDRICKS	SHOESHINE BOY	HOOKED ON YOUR LOVE	10.00
75	948	TEMPTATIONS	MEMORIES	AIN'T NO JUSTICE	5.00
75	948 DJ	TEMPTATIONS	MEMORIES	AIN'T NO JUSTICE	10.00
75	948 DJ PS	TEMPTATIONS	MEMORIES	AIN'T NO JUSTICE	25.00
75	949	SMOKEY ROBINSON	BABY, THAT'S BACKATCHA	JUST PASSING THROUGH	5.00
75	949 DJ	SMOKEY ROBINSON	BABY, THAT'S BACKATCHA	JUST PASSING THROUGH	10.00
75	950	SUPREMES	HE'S MY MAN	GIVE OUT, BUT DON'T GIVE UP	5.00
75	950 DJ	SUPREMES	HE'S MY MAN	GIVE OUT, BUT DON'T GIVE UP	10.00
75	951	CASTON & MAJORS	SING	THERE'S FEAR	8.00
75	951 DJ	CASTON & MAJORS	SING	THERE'S FEAR	10.00
75	952	COMMODORES	SLIPPERY WHEN WET	THE BUMP	5.00
75	952 DJ	COMMODORES	SLIPPERY WHEN WET	THE BUMP	8.00
75	953	DIANA ROSS & MARVIN GAYE	DON'T KNOCK MY LOVE	I'M FALLING IN LOVE WITH YOU	4.00
75	953 DJ	DIANA ROSS & MARVIN GAYE	DON'T KNOCK MY LOVE	I'M FALLING IN LOVE WITH YOU	10.00
75	954	SYREETA	WHAT LOVE HAS JOINED TOGETHER	HARMOUR LOVE	10.00
75	954 DJ	SYREETA	WHAT LOVE HAS JOINED TOGETHER	HARMOUR LOVE	15.00
75	955	GLADYS KNIGHT & The PIPS	IF I WERE YOUR WOMAN	THE ONLY TIME YOU LOVE ME IS WHEN	6.00
75	955 DJ	GLADYS KNIGHT & The PIPS	IF I WERE YOUR WOMAN	THE ONLY TIME YOU LOVE ME IS WHEN	10.00

80	956 – 975 inclusive	VARIOUS ARTISTS	20th. ANNIVERSARY BOX SET	20 Back To Back 45's + enamel badge + tmg1000	175.00
80	956 - 975 DJ copies	VARIOUS ARTISTS	20th. ANNIVERSARY BOX SET	20 Back To Back 45's + enamel badge + tmg1000	250.00

at this number in the series UK Tamla Motown released a 25th. Anniversary box set with the numbers running from TMG 956 to TMG 975 individual prices noted:

80	956	DIANA ROSS & the SUPREMES	YOU CAN'T HURRY LOVE	THE HAPPENING	6.00
80	956 DJ	DIANA ROSS & the SUPREMES	YOU CAN'T HURRY LOVE	THE HAPPENING	8.00
80	957	SMOKEY ROBINSON & MIRACLES (COME ROUND HERE)	I'M THE ONE YOU NEED	I SECOND THAT EMOTION	6.00
80	957 DJ	SMOKEY ROBINSON & MIRACLES (COME ROUND HERE)	I'M THE ONE YOU NEED	I SECOND THAT EMOTION	8.00
80	958	FOUR TOPS	IF I WERE A CARPENTER	7-ROOMS OF GLOOM	6.00
80	958 DJ	FOUR TOPS	IF I WERE A CARPENTER	7-ROOMS OF GLOOM	8.00
80	959	STEVIE WONDER	I WAS MADE TO LOVE HER	NEVER HAD A DREAM COME TRUE	5.00
80	959 DJ	STEVIE WONDER	I WAS MADE TO LOVE HER	NEVER HAD A DREAM COME TRUE	8.00
80	960	DIANA ROSS & the SUPREMES	REFLECTIONS	LOVE CHILD	5.00
80	960 DJ	DIANA ROSS & the SUPREMES	REFLECTIONS	LOVE CHILD	8.00
80	961	JIMMY RUFFIN	I'LL SAY FOREVER MY LOVE	IT'S WONDERFUL (TO BE LOVED BY YOU)	5.00
80	961 DJ	JIMMY RUFFIN	I'LL SAY FOREVER MY LOVE	IT'S WONDERFUL (TO BE LOVED BY YOU)	8.00
80	962	JR.WALKER & THE ALL STARS	WHAT DOES IT TAKE (TO WIN LOVE	TAKE ME GIRL, I'M READY	5.00
80	962 DJ	JR.WALKER & THE ALL STARS	WHAT DOES IT TAKE (TO WIN LOVE	TAKE ME GIRL I'M READY	10.00
80	963	JACKSON 5	I WANT YOU BACK	THE LOVE YOU SAVE	5.00
80	963 DJ	JACKSON 5	I WANT YOU BACK	THE LOVE YOU SAVE	8.00
80	964	SUPREMES	UP THE LADDER TO THE ROOF	AUTOMATICALLY SUNSHINE	6.00
80	964 DJ	SUPREMES	UP THE LADDER TO THE ROOF	AUTOMATICALLY SUNSHINE	8.00
80	965	FOUR TOPS	BERNADETTE	IT'S ALL IN THE GAME	6.00
80	965 DJ	FOUR TOPS	BERNADETTE	IT'S ALL IN THE GAME	8.00
80	966	STEVIE WONDER	SIGNED, SEALED, DELIVERED, I'M YOURS	FINGERTIPS part 2	6.00
80	966 DJ	STEVIE WONDER	SIGNED, SEALED, DELIVERED, I'M YOURS	FINGERTIPS part 2	8.00
80	967	TEMPTATIONS	BALL OF CONFUSION (THAT'S WHAT THE WORLD IS TODAY)	TAKE A LOOK AROUND	6.00
80	967 DJ	TEMPTATIONS	BALL OF CONFUSION (THAT'S WHAT THE WORLD IS TODAY)	TAKE A LOOK AROUND	8.00
80	968	EDWIN STARR c/w R.DEAN TAYLOR	WAR	INDIANA WANTS ME	5.00
80	968 DJ	EDWIN STARR c/w R.DEAN TAYLOR	WAR	INDIANA WANTS ME	8.00
80	969	JACKSON 5	I'LL BE THERE	ABC	5.00
80	969 DJ	JACKSON 5	I'LL BE THERE	ABC	8.00
80	970	DIANA ROSS	REMEMBER ME	SURRENDER	5.00
80	970 DJ	DIANA ROSS	REMEMBER ME	SURRENDER	8.00
80	971	SUPREMES & the FOUR TOPS	RIVER DEEP – MOUNTAIN HIGH	YOU GOTTA HAVE LOVE IN YOUR HEART	5.00
80	971 DJ	SUPREMES & the FOUR TOPS	RIVER DEEP – MOUNTAIN HIGH	YOU GOTTA HAVE LOVE IN YOUR HEART	8.00
80	972	FOUR TOPS	SIMPLE GAME	STILL WATER (LOVE)	5.00
80	972 DJ	FOUR TOPS	SIMPLE GAME	STILL WATER (LOVE)	8.00
80	973	MARV JOHNSON c/w MICHAEL JACKSON	I MISS YOU BABY (HOW I MISS YOU)	GOT TO BE THERE	8.00
80	973 DJ	MARV JOHNSON c/w MICHAEL JACKSON	I MISS YOU BABY (HOW I MISS YOU)	GOT TO BE THERE	10.00
80	974	SUPREMES	FLOY JOY	BAD WEATHER	6.00
80	974 DJ	SUPREMES	FLOY JOY	BAD WEATHER	8.00
80	975	JACKSON 5	LOOKIN' THROUGH THE WINDOWS	DOCTOR MY EYES	5.00
80	975 DJ	JACKSON 5	LOOKIN' THROUGH THE WINDOWS	DOCTOR MY EYES	8.00

normal releases continue at # 976

81	976	MICHAEL JACKSON	ONE DAY IN YOUR LIFE	TAKE ME BACK	4.00
81	976 DJ	MICHAEL JACKSON	ONE DAY IN YOUR LIFE	TAKE ME BACK	6.00
81	977	MICHAEL JACKSON	WE'RE ALMOST THERE	WE'VE GOT A GOD THING GOING	4.00
81	977 DJ	MICHAEL JACKSON	WE'RE ALMOST THERE	WE'VE GOT A GOD THING GOING	6.00
82	978	FOUR TOPS	BABY I NEED YOUR LOVING	YESTERDAYS DREAMS	5.00
82	978 DJ	FOUR TOPS	BABY I NEED YOUR LOVING	YESTERDAYS DREAMS	6.00
83	979	ISLEY BROTHERS	I GUESS I'LL ALWAYS LOVE YOU	TAKE SOME TIME OUT FOR LOVE	5.00
83	979 DJ	ISLEY BROTHERS	I GUESS I'LL ALWAYS LOVE YOU	TAKE SOME TIME OUT FOR LOVE	8.00
83	980	SMOKEY ROBINSON & MIRACLES	I DON'T BLAME YOU AT ALL	OOH BABY BABY	5.00
83	980 DJ	SMOKEY ROBINSON & MIRACLES	I DON'T BLAME YOU AT ALL	OOH BABY BABY	6.00
83	981	DIANA ROSS & the SUPREMES	BACK IN MY ARMS AGAIN	LOVE IS HERE AND NOW YOU'RE GONE	5.00
83	981 DJ	DIANA ROSS & the SUPREMES	BACK IN MY ARMS AGAIN	LOVE IS HERE AND NOW YOU'RE GONE	6.00
83	982	TEMPTATIONS	CLOUD NINE	PSYCHEDELIC SHACK	5.00
83	982 DJ	TEMPTATIONS	CLOUD NINE	PSYCHEDELIC SHACK	6.00
83	983	MARTHA REEVES & the VANDELLAS	I'M READY FOR LOVE	FORGET ME NOT	5.00
83	983 DJ	MARTHA REEVES & the VANDELLAS	I'M READY FOR LOVE	FORGET ME NOT	6.00
83	984	MARVIN GAYE	WHAT'S GOING ON	GOD IS LOVE	5.00
83	984 DJ	MARVIN GAYE	WHAT'S GOING ON	GOD IS LOVE	6.00
83	985	EDDIE KENDRICKS	KEEP ON TRUCKIN	KEEP ON TRUCKIN part 2	4.00
83	985 DJ	EDDIE KENDRICKS	KEEP ON TRUCKIN	KEEP ON TRUCKIN part 2	6.00
83	986	MICHAEL JACKSON	HAPPY (love theme from LADY SING THE BLUES)	WE'RE ALMOST THERE	4.00
83	986 DJ	MICHAEL JACKSON	HAPPY (love theme from LADY SING THE BLUES)	WE'RE ALMOST THERE	5.00
83	986 pic disc	MICHAEL JACKSON	HAPPY (love theme from LADY SING THE BLUES)	WE'RE ALMOST THERE	15.00
83	987	MARVIN GAYE	WHAT'S GOING ON	I HEARD IT THROUGH THE GRAPEVINE	4.00
83	987 DJ	MARVIN GAYE	WHAT'S GOING ON	I HEARD IT THROUGH THE GRAPEVINE	6.00
83	987 PS	MARVIN GAYE	WHAT'S GOING ON	I HEARD IT THROUGH THE GRAPEVINE	6.00
84	988	DIANA ROSS c/w SUPREMES & FOUR TOPS	REACH OUT AND TOUCH (SOMEBODY'S HAND)	REACH OUT AND TOUCH	4.00
84	988 DJ	DIANA ROSS c/w SUPREMES & FOUR TOPS	REACH OUT AND TOUCH (SOMEBODY'S HAND)	REACH OUT AND TOUCH	6.00
85	989	STEVIE WONDER	I WAS MADE TO LOVE HER	FOR ONCE IN MY LIFE	5.00
85	989 DJ	STEVIE WONDER	I WAS MADE TO LOVE HER	FOR ONCE IN MY LIFE	6.00
85	990	TEMPTATIONS	LAW OF THE LAND	BEAUTY IS ONLY SKIN DEEP	5.00
85	990 DJ	TEMPTATIONS	LAW OF THE LAND	BEAUTY IS ONLY SKIN DEEP	6.00
85	991	DIANA ROSS & the SUPREMES with TEMPTATIONS	I'M GONNA MAKE YOU LOVE ME	I SECOND THAT EMOTION	6.00
85	991 DJ	DIANA ROSS & the SUPREMES with TEMPTATIONS	I'M GONNA MAKE YOU LOVE ME	I SECOND THAT EMOTION	6.00
85	992	DIANA ROSS & the SUPREMES	YOU KEEP ME HANGING ON	COME SEE ABOUT ME	4.00
85	992 DJ	DIANA ROSS & the SUPREMES	YOU KEEP ME HANGING ON	COME SEE ABOUT ME	6.00
85	993	MARVIN GAYE & TAMMI TERRELL	THE ONION SONG	YOU AIN'T LIVIN' TILL YOU'RE LOVIN'	4.00
85	993 DJ	MARVIN GAYE & TAMMI TERRELL	THE ONION SONG	YOU AIN'T LIVIN' TILL YOU'RE LOVIN'	6.00
85	994	MICHAEL JACKSON	GOT TO BE THERE	ROCKIN' ROBIN	4.00
85	994 DJ	MICHAEL JACKSON	GOT TO BE THERE	ROCKIN' ROBIN	6.00
85	995	FOUR TOPS	BERNADETTE	IF I WERE A CARPENTER	4.00
85	995 DJ	FOUR TOPS	BERNADETTE	IF I WERE A CARPENTER	6.00
85	996	JIMMY RUFFIN	GONNA GIVE HER ALL THE LOVE I GOT	I'VE PASSED THIS WAY BEFORE	4.00
85	996 DJ	JIMMY RUFFIN	GONNA GIVE HER ALL THE LOVE I GOT	I'VE PASSED THIS WAY BEFORE	6.00

85	997	TEMPTATIONS	BALL OF CONFUSION (THAT'S WHAT THE WORLD IS TODAY)	AIN'T TOO PROUD TO BEG	4.00
85	997 DJ	TEMPTATIONS	BALL OF CONFUSION (THAT'S WHAT THE WORLD IS TODAY)	AIN'T TOO PROUD TO BEG	6.00
85	998	DIANA ROSS & MARVIN GAYE	YOU ARE EVERYTHING	STOP LOOK LISTEN TO YOUR HEART	4.00
85	998 DJ	DIANA ROSS & MARVIN GAYE	YOU ARE EVERYTHING	STOP LOOK LISTEN TO YOUR HEART	6.00
85	999	DIANA ROSS & the SUPREMES	THE COMPOSER	TAKE ME WHERE YOU GO	15.00
85	999 DJ	DIANA ROSS & the SUPREMES	THE COMPOSER	TAKE ME WHERE YOU GO	20.00
75	1000	KIM WESTON c/w MARVELETTES	DO LIKE I DO	FINDERS KEEPERS LOSERS WEEPERS	100.00
75	1000 DJ	KIM WESTON c/w MARVELETTES	DO LIKE I DO	FINDERS KEEPERS LOSERS WEEPERS	150.00

TMG 1000 was the bonus 45 added to the set of 25 singles in the 25th. Anniversary Box set, this 45 was never commercially available on it's own. Both sides were selected from previously unreleased recordings from the vaults. Both are fine examples of mid-sixties Motown and both are Northern Soul style dancers.

75	1001	JACKSON 5	FOREVER CAME TODAY	I CAN'T QUIT YOUR LOVE	6.00
75	1001 DJ	JACKSON 5	FOREVER CAME TODAY	I CAN'T QUIT YOUR LOVE	10.00
75	1002	SISTERS LOVE	I'M LEARNING TO TRUST MY MAN	TRY IT YOU'LL LIKE IT	10.00
75	1002 DJ	SISTERS LOVE	I'M LEARNING TO TRUST MY MAN	TRY IT YOU'LL LIKE IT	20.00
75	1003	EDDIE KENDRICKS	IF ANYONE CAN	GET THE CREAM OFF THE TOP	6.00
75	1003 DJ	EDDIE KENDRICKS	IF ANYONE CAN	GET THE CREAM OFF THE TOP	8.00
75	1004	MAGIC DISCO MACHINE	SCRATCHIN'	CONTROL TOWER	15.00
75	1004 DJ	MAGIC DISCO MACHINE	SCRATCHIN'	CONTROL TOWER	20.00
75	1005	CASTON AND MAJORS	I'LL KEEP MY LIGHT IN MY WINDOW	SAY YOU LOVE ME TRUE	6.00
75	1005 DJ	CASTON AND MAJORS	I'LL KEEP MY LIGHT IN MY WINDOW	SAY YOU LOVE ME TRUE	8.00
75	1006	MICHAEL JACKSON	JUST A LITTLE BIT OF YOU	DEAR MICHAEL	6.00
75	1006 DJ	MICHAEL JACKSON	JUST A LITTLE BIT OF YOU	DEAR MICHAEL	8.00
75	1007	COMMODORES	LET'S DO IT RIGHT	THIS IS YOUR LIFE	5.00
75	1007 DJ	COMMODORES	LET'S DO IT RIGHT	THIS IS YOUR LIFE	8.00
75	1008	WILLIE HUTCH	LOVE POWER	GET READY FOR THE GET DOWN	8.00
75	1008 DJ	WILLIE HUTCH	LOVE POWER	GET READY FOR THE GET DOWN	10.00
75	1009	GLADYS KNIGHT & The PIPS	NEITHER ONE OF US (WANTS TO BE THE	EVERYBODY NEEDS LOVE + I WISH IT WOULD	5.00
75	1009 DJ	GLADYS KNIGHT & The PIPS	NEITHER ONE OF US (WANTS TO BE THE	EVERYBODY NEEDS LOVE + I WISH IT WOULD	6.00
75	1010	DIANA ROSS	DO YOU KNOW WHERE YOU'RE GOING TO	NO ONE'S GONNA BE A FOOL FOREV	5.00
75	1010 PS	DIANA ROSS	DO YOU KNOW WHERE YOU'RE GOING TO	NO ONE'S GONNA BE A FOOL FOREV	8.00
75	1010 DJ	DIANA ROSS	DO YOU KNOW WHERE YOU'RE GOING TO	NO ONE'S GONNA BE A FOOL FOREV	5.00
75	1011	FOUR TOPS	WALK AWAY RENEE	YOU KEEP RUNNING AWAY	5.00
75	1011 DJ	FOUR TOPS	WALK AWAY RENEE	YOU KEEP RUNNING AWAY	10.00
75	1012	SUPREMES	EARLY MORNING LOVE	WHERE IS IT I BELONG	6.00
75	1012 DJ	SUPREMES	EARLY MORNING LOVE	WHERE IS IT I BELONG	10.00
75	1013	YVONNE FAIR	IT SHOULD HAVE BEEN ME	YOU CAN'T JUDGE A BOOK BY IT'S	5.00
75	1013 DJ	YVONNE FAIR	IT SHOULD HAVE BEEN ME	YOU CAN'T JUDGE A BOOK BY IT'S	6.00
75	1014	UNDISPUTED TRUTH	HIGHER THAN HIGH	SPACED OUT	5.00
75	1014 DJ	UNDISPUTED TRUTH	HIGHER THAN HIGH	SPACED OUT	6.00
75	1015	MIRACLES	LOVE MACHINE	LOVE MACHINE part 2	4.00
75	1015 DJ	MIRACLES	LOVE MACHINE	LOVE MACHINE part 2	6.00
75	1016	DYNAMIC SUPERIORS	ONE - NIGHTER	DECEPTION	20.00
75	1016 DJ	DYNAMIC SUPERIORS	ONE-NIGHTER	DECEPTION	30.00
75	1017	DAVID RUFFIN	WALK AWAY FROM LOVE	LOVE CAN BE HAZARDOUS TO YOUR	10.00
75	1017 DJ	DAVID RUFFIN	WALK AWAY FROM LOVE	LOVE CAN BE HAZARDOUS TO YOUR	15.00
75	1018	COMMODORES	SWEET LOVE	BETTER NEVER THAN FOREVER	5.00
75	1018 DJ	COMMODORES	SWEET LOVE	BETTER NEVER THAN FOREVER	8.00
75	1019	SMOKEY ROBINSON	QUIET STORM	ASLEEP ON MY LOVE	5.00
75	1019 DJ	SMOKEY ROBINSON	QUIET STORM	ASLEEP ON MY LOVE	8.00
75	1020	STEPHANIE MILLS	THIS EMPTY PLACE	IF YOU CAN LEARN HOW TO FLY	10.00
76	1020 DJ	STEPHANIE MILLS	THIS EMPTY PLACE	IF YOU CAN LEARN HOW TO FLY	15.00
76	1020 DJ alternate title	STEPHANIE MILLS	I SEE YOU FOR THE FIRST TIME	THIS EMPTY PLACE	75.00
76	1021	EDDIE KENDRICKS	HE'S A FRIEND	ALL OF MY LOVE	6.00
76	1021 DJ	EDDIE KENDRICKS	HE'S A FRIEND	ALL OF MY LOVE	10.00
76	1022	DAVID RUFFIN	HEAVY LOVE	MEAND ROCK AND ROLL (ARE HERE	6.00
76	1022 DJ	DAVID RUFFIN	HEAVY LOVE	MEAND ROCK AND ROLL (ARE HERE	10.00
76	1023	MIRACLES	NIGHT LIFE	OVERTURE	6.00
76	1023 DJ	MIRACLES	NIGHT LIFE	OVERTURE	10.00
76	1024	DIANA ROSS	LOVE HANGOVER	KISS ME NOW	4.00
76	1024 DJ	DIANA ROSS	LOVE HANGOVER	KISS ME NOW	8.00
76	1025	YVONNE FAIR	IT'S BAD FOR ME TO SEE YOU	WALK OUT THE DOOR IF YOU WANN	6.00
76	1025 DJ	YVONNE FAIR	IT'S BAD FOR ME TO SEE YOU	WALK OUT THE DOOR IF YOU WANN	10.00
76	1026	MARVIN GAYE	I WANT YOU	same: instrumental	5.00
76	1026 DJ	MARVIN GAYE	I WANT YOU	same: instrumental	10.00
76	1027	JR. WALKER	I'M SO GLAD	DANCIN' LIKE THEY DO ON SOUL T	8.00
76	1027 DJ	JR. WALKER	I'M SO GLAD	DANCIN' LIKE THEY DO ON SOUL T	10.00
76	1028	EDWIN STARR	RUNNING BACK AND FORTH	TIME	15.00
76	1028 DJ	EDWIN STARR	RUNNING BACK AND FORTH	TIME	25.00
76	1029	SUPREMES	I'M GONNA LET MY HEART DO THE	COLOR MY WORLD BLUE	6.00
76	1029 DJ	SUPREMES	I'M GONNA LET MY HEART DO THE	COLOR MY WORLD BLUE	10.00
76	1030	BOONES	MY GUY	WHEN THE LOVELIGHT STARTS SHINING IN HIS	6.00
76	1030 DJ	BOONES	MY GUY	WHEN THE LOVELIGHT STARTS SHINING IN HIS	8.00
76	1031	EDDIE KENDRICKS	THE SWEETER YOU TREAT HER	HAPPY	5.00
76	1031 DJ	EDDIE KENDRICKS	THE SWEETER YOU TREAT HER	HAPPY	8.00
76	1032	DIANA ROSS	I THOUGHT IT TOOK A LITTLE TIME	AFTER YOU	5.00
76	1032 DJ	DIANA ROSS	I THOUGHT IT TOOK A LITTLE TIME	AFTER YOU	8.00
76	1033	G.C. CAMERON	ME AND MY LIFE	ACT LIKE A SHOTGUN	10.00
76	1033 DJ	G.C. CAMERON	ME AND MY LIFE	ACT LIKE A SHOTGUN	15.00
76	1034	COMMODORES	HIGH ON SUNSHINE	THUMPIN' MUSIC	6.00
76	1034 DJ	COMMODORES	HIGH ON SUNSHINE	THUMPIN' MUSIC	10.00
76	1035	MARVIN GAYE	AFTER THE DANCE	FEEL ALL MY LOVE INSIDE	6.00
76	1035 DJ	MARVIN GAYE	AFTER THE DANCE	FEEL ALL MY LOVE INSIDE	10.00
76	1036	DAVID RUFFIN	DISCOVER ME	SMILING FACES SOMETIMES	20.00
76	1036 DJ	DAVID RUFFIN	DISCOVER ME	SMILING FACES SOMETIMES	30.00
76	1037	ROSE BANKS	DARLING BABY	WHOLE NEW THING	8.00
76	1037 DJ	ROSE BANKS	DARLING BABY	WHOLE NEW THING	10.00
76	1038	ORIGINALS	DOWN TO LOVE TOWN	JUST TO BE CLOSE TO YOU	5.00
76	1038 DJ	ORIGINALS	DOWN TO LOVE TOWN	JUST TO BE CLOSE TO YOU	10.00

76	1039	JERRY BUTLER	THE DEVIL IN MRS. JONES	I DON'T WANNA BE REMINDED	5.00
76	1039 DJ	JERRY BUTLER	THE DEVIL IN MRS JONES	I DON'T WANNA BE REMINDED	8.00
76	1040	JERMAINE JACKSON	LET'S BE YOUNG TONIGHT	BASS ODYSSEY	6.00
76	1040 DJ	JERMAINE JACKSON	LET'S BE YOUNG TONIGHT	BASS ODYSSEY	8.00
76	1041	DIANA ROSS	TOUCH ME IN THE MORNING	I'M STILL WAITING	6.00
76	1041 DJ	DIANA ROSS	TOUCH ME IN THE MORNING	I'M STILL WAITING	8.00
76	1042	STEVIE WONDER	UPTIGHT (EVERYTHING'S ALRIGHT)	YESTER-ME, YESTER-YOU, YESTERD	6.00
76	1042 DJ	STEVIE WONDER	UPTIGHT (EVERYTHING'S ALRIGHT)	YESTER-ME, YESTER-YOU, YESTERD	8.00
76	1043	TEMPTATIONS	GET READY	JUST MY IMAGINATION	5.00
76	1043 DJ	TEMPTATIONS	GET READY	JUST MY IMAGINATION	10.00
76	1044	DIANA ROSS & the SUPREMES	BABY LOVE	STOP IN THE NAME OF LOVE	5.00
76	1044 DJ	DIANA ROSS & the SUPREMES	BABY LOVE	STOP IN THE NAME OF LOVE	8.00
76	1045	MARVIN GAYE c/w DIANA ROSS	I HEARD IT THROUGH THE GRAPEVINE	I'M GONNA MAKE YOU LOVE ME	5.00
76	1045 DJ	MARVIN GAYE c/w DIANA ROSS	I HEARD IT THROUGH THE GRAPEVINE	I'M GONNA MAKE YOU LOVE ME	8.00
76	1046	SUPREMES	STONED LOVE	NATHAN JONES	5.00
76	1046 DJ	SUPREMES	STONED LOVE	NATHAN JONES	8.00
76	1047	DIANA ROSS & MARVIN GAYE	YOU ARE EVERYTHING	THE ONION SONG	5.00
76	1047 DJ	DIANA ROSS & MARVIN GAYE	YOU ARE EVERYTHING	THE ONION SONG	8.00
76	1048	SMOKEY ROBINSON &	THE TEARS OF A CLOWN	THE TRACKS OF MY TEARS	5.00
76	1048 DJ	SMOKEY ROBINSON &	THE TEARS OF A CLOWN	THE TRACKS OF MY TEARS	0.00
76	1049	FOUR TOPS	STANDING IN THE SHADOWS OF LOVE	REACH OUT I'LL BE THERE	5.00
76	1049 DJ	FOUR TOPS	STANDING IN THE SHADOWS OF LOVE	REACH OUT I'LL BE THERE	8.00
76	1050	ISLEY BROTHERS	THIS OLD HEART OF MINE (IS WEAK FOR	BEHIND THE PAINTED SMILE	5.00
76	1050 DJ	ISLEY BROTHERS	THIS OLD HEART OF MINE (IS WEAK FOR	BEHIND THE PAINTED SMILE	8.00
76	1051	MARTHA REEVES & the	JIMMY MACK	DANCING IN THE STREET	6.00
76	1051 DJ	MARTHA REEVES & the	JIMMY MACK	DANCING IN THE STREET	8.00
76	1052	MARV JOHNSON c/w JIMMY RUFFIN	I'LL PICK A ROSE FOR MY ROSE	WHAT BECOMES OF THE BROKENHEARTED	6.00
76	1052 DJ	MARV JOHNSON c/w JIMMY RUFFIN	I'LL PICK A ROSE FOR MY ROSE	WHAT BECOMES OF THE BROKENHEARTED	10.00

Oct. 76 EMI changes Tamla Motown logo to MOTOWN 1st. release on the new MOTOWN label is TMG1053. The later re-issues used the old Tamla Motown design label these are noted

76	1053	TATA VEGA	TRY MY LOVE FROM THE INSIDE	JUST AS LONG AS THERE IS YOU	4.00
76	1053 DJ	TATA VEGA	TRY MY LOVE FROM THE INSIDE	JUST AS LONG AS THERE IS YOU	6.00
76	1054	STEVIE WONDER	I WISH	YOU AND I	3.00
76	1054 DJ	STEVIE WONDER	I WISH	YOU AND I	5.00
76	1055	WILLIAM GOLDSTEIN & the MAGIC DISCO MACHINE	MIDNIGHT RHAPSODY	MIDNIGHT RHAPSODY part 2	5.00
76	1055 DJ	WILLIAM GOLDSTEIN & the MAGIC DISCO MACHINE	MIDNIGHT RHAPSODY	MIDNIGHT RHAPSODY part 2	6.00
76	1056	DIANA ROSS	ONE LOVE IN MY LIFETIME	YOU'RE GOOD MY CHILD	5.00
76	1056 DJ	DIANA ROSS	ONE LOVE IN MY LIFETIME	YOU'RE GOOD MY CHILD	6.00
76	1057	TEMPTATIONS	WHO ARE YOU	LET ME COUNT THE WAYS (I LOVE	4.00
76	1057 DJ	TEMPTATIONS	WHO ARE YOU	LET ME COUNT THE WAYS (I LOVE	6.00
76	1058	COMMODORES	JUST TO BE CLOSE TO YOU	LOOK WHAT YOU'VE DONE TO ME	3.00
76	1058 DJ	COMMODORES	JUST TO BE CLOSE TO YOU	LOOK WHAT YOU'VE DONE TO ME	5.00
77	1060	THELMA HOUSTON	DON'T LEAVE ME THIS WAY	TODAY WILL SOON BE YESTERDAY	6.00
77	1060 DJ	THELMA HOUSTON	DON'T LEAVE ME THIS WAY	TODAY WILL SOON BE YESTERDAY	10.00
77	1061	EDDIE KENDRICKS	GOIN' UP IN SMOKE	GET IT WHILE IT'S HOT	6.00
77	1061 DJ	EDDIE KENDRICKS	GOIN' UP IN SMOKE	GET IT WHILE IT'S HOT	8.00
77	1062	COMMODORES	FANCY DANCER	CEBU	3.00
77	1062 DJ	COMMODORES	FANCY DANCER	CEBU	5.00
77	1063	TEMPTATIONS feat: DENNIS EDWARDS	SHAKEY GROUND	I'M A BACHELOR	5.00
77	1063 DJ	TEMPTATIONS feat: DENNIS EDWARDS	SHAKEY GROUND	I'M A BACHELOR	6.00
77	1064	SUPREMES	LOVE I NEVER KNEW YOU COULD FEEL	THIS IS WHY I BELIEVE IN YOU	6.00
77	1064 DJ	SUPREMES	LOVE I NEVER KNEW YOU COULD FEEL	THIS IS WHY I BELIEVE IN YOU	8.00
77	1065	SMOKEY ROBINSON	THEE WILL COME A DAY (I'M GONNA HAPPEN TO YOU)	OLD FASHIONED MAN	4.00
77	1065 DJ	SMOKEY ROBINSON	THEE WILL COME A DAY (I'M GONNA HAPPEN TO YOU)	OLD FASHIONED MAN	6.00
77	1066 unissued	ORIGINALS	CALL ON YOUR SIX MILLION DOLLAR MAN	MOTHER NATURE'S BEST	UN
77	1066 DJ unconfirmed	ORIGINALS	CALL ON YOUR SIX MILLION DOLLAR MAN	MOTHER NATURE'S BEST	400.00
77	1067	JENNIFER	DO IT FOR ME	BOOGIE BOOGIE LOVE	3.00
77	1067 PS	JENNIFER	DO IT FOR ME	BOOGIE BOOGIE LOVE	5.00
77	1067 DJ PS	JENNIFER	DO IT FOR ME	BOOGIE BOOGIE LOVE	6.00
77	1068	STEVIE WONDER	SIR DUKE	TUESDAY HEARTBREAK	3.00
77	1068 DJ	STEVIE WONDER	SIR DUKE	TUESDAY HEARTBREAK	5.00
77	1069	MARVIN GAYE	GOT TO GIVE IT UP	GOT TO GIVE IT UP part 2	5.00
77	1069 DJ	MARVIN GAYE	GOT TO GIVE IT UP	GOT TO GIVE IT UP part 2	8.00
77	1070	JR.WALKER & THE ALL STARS	I AIN'T GOING NOWHERE	WHAT DOES IT TAKE + 1	15.00
77	1070 DJ	JR.WALKER & THE ALL STARS	I AIN'T GOING NOWHERE	WHAT DOES IT TAKE + 1	20.00
77	1071	DYNAMIC SUPERIORS	STAY AWAY	SUPERSENSUOUSSENSATION	6.00
77	1071 DJ	DYNAMIC SUPERIORS	STAY AWAY	SUPERSENSUOUSSENSATION	8.00
77	1072	TATA VEGA	YOU'LL NEVER ROCK ALONE	JUST WHEN THINGS ARE GETTING G	4.00
77	1072 DJ	TATA VEGA	YOU'LL NEVER ROCK ALONE	JUST WHEN THINGS ARE GETTING G	5.00
77	1073	COMMODORES	EASY	MACHINE GUN + I FEEL SANCTIFIE	3.00
77	1073 DJ	COMMODORES	EASY	MACHINE GUN + I FEEL SANCTIFIE	6.00
77	1074	THELMA HOUSTON & JERRY BUTLER	IT'S A LIFETIME THING	ONLY THE BEGINNING	6.00
77	1074 DJ	THELMA HOUSTON & JERRY BUTLER	IT'S A LIFETIME THING	ONLY THE BEGINNING	8.00
77	1075	21ST. CREATION	TAILGATE	MR. DISCO RADIO	15.00
77	1075 DJ	21ST. CREATION	TAILGATE	MR. DISCO RADIO	20.00
77	1076	SMOKEY ROBINSON	VITAMIN U	HOLLY	4.00
77	1076 DJ	SMOKEY ROBINSON	VITAMIN U	HOLLY	5.00
77	1077	DYNAMIC SUPERIORS	NOWHERE TO RUN	NOWHERE TO RUN part 2	6.00
77	1077 DJ	DYNAMIC SUPERIORS	NOWHERE TO RUN	NOWHERE TO RUN part 2	8.00
77	1078	DAVID RUFFIN	I CAN'T STOP THE RAIN	MY WHOLE WORLD ENDED (THE MOMENT)	10.00
77	1078 DJ	DAVID RUFFIN	I CAN'T STOP THE RAIN	MY WHOLE WORLD ENDED (THE MOMENT)	15.00
77	1079	FLAVOR	DON'T FREEZE UP	same: Instrumental	10.00
77	1079 DJ	FLAVOR	DON'T FREEZE UP	same: instrumental	20.00
77	1080	DIANA ROSS & the SUPREMES	SOMEDAY WE'LL BE TOGETHER	YOU KEEP ME HANGING ON	6.00
77	1080 DJ	DIANA ROSS & the SUPREMES	SOMEDAY WE'LL BE TOGETHER	YOU KEEP ME HANGING ON	8.00
77	1080 PS	DIANA ROSS & the SUPREMES	SOMEDAY WE'LL BE TOGETHER	YOU KEEP ME HANGING ON	10.00
77	1081	JACKSON 5	SKYWRITER + I WANT YOU BACK	THE LOVE YOU SAVE	5.00

77	1081 DJ	JACKSON 5	SKYWRITER + I WANT YOU BACK	THE LOVE YOU SAVE	6.00
77	1081 PS	JACKSON 5	SKYWRITER + I WANT YOU BACK	THE LOVE YOU SAVE	6.00
77	1082	JERRY BUTLER	CHALK IT UP	I DON'T WANT NOBODY TO KNOW	8.00
77	1082 DJ	JERRY BUTLER	CHALK IT UP	I DON'T WANT NOBODY TO KNOW	10.00
77	1083	STEVIE WONDER	ANOTHER STAR	CREEPIN'	3.00
77	1083 DJ	STEVIE WONDER	ANOTHER STAR	CREEPIN'	5.00
77	1084	ALBERT FINNEY	THOSE OTHER MEN	WHAT HAVE THEY DONE (TO MY HOME TOWN)	8.00
77	1084 DJ	ALBERT FINNEY	THOSE OTHER MEN	WHAT HAVE THEY DONE (TO MY HOME TOWN)	10.00
77	1085	SMOKEY ROBINSON	THEME FROM BIG TIME	THEME FROM BIG TIME part 2	3.00
77	1085 DJ	SMOKEY ROBINSON	THEME FROM BIG TIME	THEME FROM BIG TIME part 2	5.00
77	1086	COMMODORES	BRICK HOUSE	SWEET LOVE	4.00
77	1086 DJ	COMMODORES	BRICK HOUSE	SWEET LOVE	6.00
77	1087	HIGH INERGY	YOU CAN'T TURN ME OFF (IN THE MIDDLE	LET ME GET CLOSE TO YOU	4.00
77	1087 DJ	HIGH INERGY	YOU CAN'T TURN ME OFF (IN THE MIDDLE	LET ME GET CLOSE TO YOU	5.00
77	1088	THELMA HOUSTON	I'M HERE AGAIN	SHARING SOMETHING PERFECT BEWTEEN OURS	5.00
77	1088 DJ	THELMA HOUSTON	I'M HERE AGAIN	SHARING SOMETHING PERFECT BEWTEEN OURS	6.00
77	1089	MANDRE	SOLAR FLIGHT (OPUS 1)	KEEP TRYIN'	5.00
77	1089 DJ	MANDRE	SOLAR FLIGHT (OPUS 1)	KEEP TRYIN'	6.00
77	1090	DIANA ROSS	GETTIN' READY FOR LOVE	STONE LIBERTY	4.00
77	1090 DJ	DIANA ROSS	GETTIN' READY FOR LOVE	STONE LIBERTY	5.00
77	1091	STEVIE WONDER	AS	CONFUSION	3.00
77	1091 DJ	STEVIE WONDER	AS	CONFUSION	5.00
77	1092	JERMAINE JACKSON	TAKE TIME	YOU NEED TO BE LOVED	5.00
77	1092 DJ	JERMAINE JACKSON	TAKE TIME	YOU NEED TO BE LOVED	6.00
77	1093	DAVID RUFFIN	RODE BY THE PLACE (WHERE WE USED	YOU'RE MY PEACE OF MIND	25.00
77	1093 DJ	DAVID RUFFIN	RODE BY THE PLACE (WHERE WE USED	YOU'RE MY PEACE OF MIND	35.00
77	1094	SYREETA & G.C.CAMERON	LET'S MAKE A DEAL	LET'S MAKE A DEAL part 2	6.00
77	1094 DJ	SYREETA & G.C.CAMERON	LET'S MAKE A DEAL	LET'S MAKE A DEAL part 2	5.00
77	1095	GLADYS KNIGHT & The PIPS	HELP ME MAKE IT THROUGH THE NIGHT	DADDY I COULD SWEAR I DECLARE	3.00
77	1095 DJ	GLADYS KNIGHT & The PIPS	HELP ME MAKE IT THROUGH THE NIGHT	DADDY I COULD SWEAR I DECLARE	5.00
78	1096	COMMODORES	ZOOM	TOO HOT TA TROT	3.00
78	1096 DJ	COMMODORES	ZOOM	TOO HOT TA TROT	5.00
78	1097	JERRY BUTLER	I WANNA DO IT TO YOU	LET'S GO GET OUT OF TOWN	8.00
78	1097 DJ	JERRY BUTLER	I WANNA DO IT TO YOU	LET'S GO GET OUT OF TOWN	10.00
78	1098	SCHERRIE PAYNE	FLY	WHEN I LOOK AT YOUR FACE	6.00
78	1098 DJ	SCHERRIE PAYNE	FLY	WHEN I LOOK AT YOUR FACE	8.00
78	1099	DIANA ROSS	TOP OF THE WORLD	TO SHY TO SAY	5.00
78	1099 DJ	DIANA ROSS	TOP OF THE WORLD	TO SHY TO SAY	6.00
78	1100	MARY WELS	MY GUY	WHAT'S EASY FOR TWO IS SO HARD FOR ONE	6.00
78	1100 DJ	MARY WELS	MY GUY	WHAT'S EASY FOR TWO IS SO HARD FOR ONE	8.00
78	1101	5TH. DIMENSION	YOU ARE THE REASON (I FEEL LIKE	SLIPPING INTO SOMETHING NEW	5.00
78	1101 DJ	5TH. DIMENSION	YOU ARE THE REASON (I FEEL LIKE	SLIPPING INTO SOMETHING NEW	6.00
78	1102	THELMA HOUSTON	I CAN'T GO ON LIVING WITHOUT YOUR	ANY WAY YOU LIKE IT	5.00
78	1102 DJ	THELMA HOUSTON	I CAN'T GO ON LIVING WITHOUT YOUR	ANY WAY YOU LIKE IT	6.00
78	1103	HIGH INERGY	LOVE IS ALL YOU NEED	SAVE IT FOR A RAINY DAY	4.00
78	1103 PS	HIGH INERGY	LOVE IS ALL YOU NEED	SAVE IT FOR A RAINY DAY	6.00
78	1103 DJ	HIGH INERGY	LOVE IS ALL YOU NEED	SAVE IT FOR A RAINY DAY	5.00
78	1104	DIANA ROSS	YOU'RE LOVE IS SO GOOD FOR ME	BABY IT'S ME	4.00
78	1104 DJ	DIANA ROSS	YOU'RE LOVE IS SO GOOD FOR ME	BABY IT'S ME	6.00
78	1105	3 OUNCES OF LOVE	STAR LOVE	I FOUND THE FEELING	4.00
78	1105 DJ	3 OUNCES OF LOVE	STAR LOVE	I FOUND THE FEELING	5.00
78	1106	SMOKEY ROBINSON	MADAME X	THE AGONY AND THE ECSTASY	4.00
78	1106 DJ	SMOKEY ROBINSON	MADAME X	THE AGONY AND THE ECSTASY	5.00
78	1107	CUBA GOODING	MIND PLEASER	AIN'T NOTHING TO IT	5.00
78	1107 DJ	CUBA GOODING	MIND PLEASER	AIN'T NOTHING TO IT	6.00
78	1108	CARL BEAN	I WAS BORN THIS WAY	same: instrumental	10.00
78	1108 DJ	CARL BEAN	I WAS BORN THIS WAY	same: instrumental	15.00
78	1109	MAJOR LANCE	I NEVER THOUGHT I'D BE LOSING YOU	CHICAGO DISCO	15.00
78	1109 DJ	MAJOR LANCE	I NEVER THOUGHT I'D BE LOSING YOU	CHICAGO DISCO	20.00
78	1110	RICK JAMES	YOU AND I	HOLLYWOOD	5.00
78	1110 DJ	RICK JAMES	YOU AND I	HOLLYWOOD	6.00
78	1111	COMMODORES	FLYING HIGH	FUNKY SITUATION	3.00
78	1111 DJ	COMMODORES	FLYING HIGH	FUNKY SITUATION	5.00
78	1112	DIANA ROSS	LOVIN', LIVIN' AND GIVIN'	YOU GOT IT	4.00
78	1112 DJ	DIANA ROSS	LOVIN', LIVIN' AND GIVIN'	YOU GOT IT	5.00
78	1113	COMMODORES	THREE TIMES A LADY	CAN'T LET YOU TEASE ME	3.00
78	1113 DJ	COMMODORES	THREE TIMES A LADY	CAN'T LET YOU TEASE ME	5.00
78	1114	SMOKEY ROBINSON	DAYLIGHT & DARKNESS	WHY YOU WANNA SEE MY BAD SIDE	4.00
78	1114 DJ	SMOKEY ROBINSON	DAYLIGHT & DARKNESS	WHY YOU WANNA SEE MY BAD SIDE	5.00
78	1115	PLATINUM HOOK	STANDING ON THE VERGE OF GETTING	TILL I MET YOU	3.00
78	1115 DJ	PLATINUM HOOK	STANDING ON THE VERGE OF GETTING	TILL I MET YOU	4.00
78	1116	MANDRE	FAIR GAME	LIGHT YEARS (OPUS IV)	5.00
78	1116 DJ	MANDRE	FAIR GAME	LIGHT YEARS	6.00
78	1117	THELMA HOUSTON	DON'T PITY ME	IT'S JUST ME FEELING GOOD	5.00
78	1117 DJ	THELMA HOUSTON	DON'T PITY ME	IT'S JUST ME FEELING GOOD	6.00
78	1118	JR.WALKER & THE ALL STARS	WALK IN THE NIGHT	I NEED YOU RIGHT NOW	5.00
78	1118 DJ	JR.WALKER & THE ALL STARS	WALK IN THE NIGHT	I NEED YOU RIGHT NOW	8.00
78	1118 DJ PS	JR.WALKER & THE ALL STARS	WALK IN THE NIGHT	I NEED YOU RIGHT NOW	15.00
78	1119	3 OUNCES OF LOVE	GIVE ME SOME FEELING	DON'T WORRY ABOUT MY LOVE	5.00
78	1119 DJ	3 OUNCES OF LOVE	GIVE ME SOME FEELING	DON'T WORRY ABOUT MY LOVE	6.00
78	1120	FOUR TOPS	I CAN'T HELP MYSELF	IT'S THE SAME OLD SONG	6.00
78	1120 PS	FOUR TOPS	I CAN'T HELP MYSELF	IT'S THE SAME OLD SONG	15.00
78	1120 DJ	FOUR TOPS	I CAN'T HELP MYSELF	IT'S THE SAME OLD SONG	8.00
78	1121	RICK JAMES	MARY JANE	DREAM MAKER	4.00
78	1121 DJ	RICK JAMES	MARY JANE	DREAM MAKER	6.00
78	1122	HIGH INERGY	LOVIN' FEVER	BEWARE	4.00
78	1122 DJ	HIGH INERGY	LOVIN' FEVER	BEWARE	5.00
78	1123	SWITCH	THERE'LL NEVER BE	YOU PULLED THE SWITCH	4.00

78	1123 DJ	SWITCH	THERE'LL NEVER BE	YOU PULLED THE SWITCH	5.00
78	1124	VELVELETTES	NEEDLE IN A HAYSTACK	HE WAS REALLY SAYING SOMETHING	8.00
78	1124 DJ	VELVELETTES	NEEDLE IN A HAYSTACK	HE WAS REALLY SAYING SOMETHING	10.00
78	1125	BONNIE POINTER	FREE ME FROM MY FREEDOM – TIE ME TO A TREE	same: instrumental	5.00
78	1125 DJ	BONNIE POINTER	FREE ME FROM MY FREEDOM – TIE ME TO A TREE	same: instrumental	6.00
78	1126	FINISHED TOUCH	I LOVE TO SEE YOU DANCE	STICKS AND STONES (BUT THE FUN	4.00
78	1126 DJ	FINISHED TOUCH	I LOVE TO SEE YOU DANCE	STICKS AND STONES (BUT THE FUN	5.00
78	1127	COMMODORES	JUST TO BE CLOSE TO YOU	X-RATED MOVIE	4.00
78	1127 DJ	COMMODORES	JUST TO BE CLOSE TO YOU	X-RATED MOVIE	5.00
78	1128	PLATINUM HOOK	GOTTA FIND A WOMAN	HOOKED FOR LIFE	4.00
78	1128 DJ	PLATINUM HOOK	GOTTA FIND A WOMAN	HOOKED FOR LIFE	5.00
78	1129	SMOKEY ROBINSON	SHOE SOUL	I'M LOVING YOU SOFTLY	6.00
78	1129 DJ	SMOKEY ROBINSON	SHOE SOUL	I'M LOVING YOU SOFTLY	8.00
79	1130	THELMA HOUSTON	SATURDAY NIGHT, SUNDAY MORNING	I'M NOT STRONG ENOUGH	10.00
79	1130 DJ	THELMA HOUSTON	SATURDAY NIGHT, SUNDAY MORNING	I'M NOT STRONG ENOUGH	15.00
79	1131	WASHINGTON JR, GROVER	REED SEED (TRIO TUNE)	DO DAT	4.00
79	1131 DJ	WASHINGTON JR, GROVER	REED SEED (TRIO TUNE)	DO DAT	6.00
79	1132	SWITCH	WE LIKE TO PARTY..COME ON	SOMEBODY'S WATCHING YOU	3.00
79	1132 DJ	SWITCH	WE LIKE TO PARTY..COME ON	SOMEBODY'S WATCHING YOU	5.00
79	1133	BARBARA RANDOLF	I GOT A FEELING	CAN I GET A WITNESS + YOU GOT ME HURTIN'	10.00
79	1133 DJ	BARBARA RANDOLF	I GOT A FEELING	CAN I GET A WITNESS + YOU GOT ME HURTIN'	15.00
79	1134	BONNIE POINTER	HEAVEN MUST HASVE SENT YOU	I WANNA MAKE IT (IN YOUR WORLD	6.00
79	1134 DJ	BONNIE POINTER	HEAVEN MUST HASVE SENT YOU	I WANNA MAKE IT (IN YOUR WORLD	8.00
79	1135	DIANA ROSS	WHAT YOU GAVE ME	AIN'T NO MOUNTAIN HIGH ENOUGH	4.00
79	1135 DJ	DIANA ROSS	WHAT YOU GAVE ME	AIN'T NO MOUNTAIN HIGH ENOUGH	5.00
79	1136	VARIOUS ARTISTS	POPS, WE LOVE YOU	same: instrumental	4.00
79	1136 DJ	VARIOUS ARTISTS	POPS, WE LOVE YOU	same: instrumental	6.00
79	1136 PS	VARIOUS ARTISTS	POPS, WE LOVE YOU	same: instrumental	6.00
79	1136 PS DJ	VARIOUS ARTISTS	POPS, WE LOVE YOU	same: instrumental	10.00
79	1136 heart shaped pic disc	VARIOUS ARTISTS	POPS, WE LOVE YOU	same: instrumental	20.00

TMG 1136 various artists are Diana Ross, Marvin Gaye, Smokey Robinson & Stevie Wonder singing a tribute to Berry Gordy Jr.

79	1137	RICK JAMES	HIGH ON YOUR LOVE SWEET	STONE CITY BAND, HI!	4.00
79	1137 DJ	RICK JAMES	HIGH ON YOUR LOVE SWEET	STONE CITY BAND, HI!	6.00
79	1138 DJ	MARVIN GAYE	A FUNKY SPACE REINCARNATION	A FUNKY SPACE REINCARNATION part 2	4.00
79	1138 DJ	MARVIN GAYE	A FUNKY SPACE REINCARNATION	A FUNKY SPACE REINCARNATION part 2	6.00
79	1139	BILLY PRESTON & SYREETA	GO FOR IT	WITH YOU I'M BORN AGAIN instrumental	5.00
79	1139 DJ	BILLY PRESTON & SYREETA	GO FOR IT	WITH YOU I'M BORN AGAIN instrumental	6.00
79	1140	TATA VEGA	I JUST KEEP THINKNG ABOUT YOU BABY	GET IT UP FOR LOVE	8.00
79	1140 DJ	TATA VEGA	I JUST KEEP THINKNG ABOUT YOU BABY	GET IT UP FOR LOVE	10.00
79	1141	APOLLO	ASTRO DISCO	ASTRO DISCO part 1	5.00
79	1141 DJ	APOLLO	ASTRO DISCO	ASTRO DISCO part 1	6.00
79	1142	HIGH INERGY	SHOULDA GONE DANCIN'	PEACELAND	4.00
79	1142 DJ	HIGH INERGY	SHOULDA GONE DANCIN'	PEACELAND	5.00
79	1143	MOTOWN SOUNDS	SPACE DANCE	BAD MOUTHIN'	4.00
79	1143 DJ	MOTOWN SOUNDS	SPACE DANCE	BAD MOUTHIN'	5.00
79	1144	MANDRE	SWANG	SPIRIT GROOVE	4.00
79	1144 DJ	MANDRE	SWANG	SPIRIT GROOVE	5.00
79	1145	BONNIE POINTER	HEAVEN MUST HAVE SENT YOU new mix	MY EVERYTHING	4.00
79	1145 DJ	BONNIE POINTER	HEAVEN MUST HAVE SENT YOU new mix	MY EVERYTHING	6.00
79	1146	TEENA MARIE	I'M JUST A SUCKER FOR YOUR LOVE	DE JA VU (I'VE BEEN HERE BEFOR	5.00
79	1146 DJ	TEENA MARIE	I'M JUST A SUCKER FOR YOUR LOVE	DE JA VU (I'VE BEEN HERE BEFOR	6.00
79	1147	RICK JAMES	BUSTIN' OUT	SEXY LADY	4.00
79	1147 PS	RICK JAMES	BUSTIN' OUT	SEXY LADY	5.00
79	1147 DJ	RICK JAMES	BUSTIN' OUT	SEXY LADY	6.00
79	1148	SWITCH	BEST BEAT IN TOWN	IT'S SO REAL	5.00
79	1148 DJ	SWITCH	BEST BEAT IN TOWN	IT'S SO REAL	6.00
79	1149	STEVIE WONDER	SEND ONE FOR LOVE	same: instrumental	4.00
79	1149 PS	STEVIE WONDER	SEND ONE FOR LOVE	same: instrumental	6.00
79	1149 DJ	STEVIE WONDER	SEND ONE FOR LOVE	same: instrumental	5.00
79	1150	DIANA ROSS	THE BOSS	I'M IN THE WORLD	4.00
79	1150 PS	DIANA ROSS	THE BOSS	I'M IN THE WORLD	6.00
79	1150 DJ	DIANA ROSS	THE BOSS	I'M IN THE WORLD	5.00
79	1151	FINISHED TOUCH	THE DOWN SOUND	same: part 2	5.00
79	1151 DJ	FINISHED TOUCH	THE DOWN SOUND	same: part 2	6.00
79	1152	SMOKEY ROBINSON	EVER HAD A DREAM	GET READY	8.00
79	1152 DJ	SMOKEY ROBINSON	EVER HAD A DREAM	GET READY	10.00
79	1153	GROVER WASHINGTON JR.	JUST THE WAY YOU ARE	LORAN'S DANCE	4.00
79	1153 DJ	GROVER WASHINGTON JR.	JUST THE WAY YOU ARE	LORAN'S DANCE	5.00
79	1154	MIRA WATERS	YOU HAVE INSPIRED ME	YOU HAVE INSPIRED ME long version	4.00
79	1154 DJ	MIRA WATERS	YOU HAVE INSPIRED ME	YOU HAVE INSPIRED ME long version	5.00
79	1155	COMMODORES	SAIL ON	CAPTAIN QUICK DRAW	4.00
79	1155 DJ	COMMODORES	SAIL ON	CAPTAIN QUICK DRAW	6.00
79	1156	RICK JAMES	FOOL ON THE STREET	JEFFERSON BALL	8.00
79	1156 DJ	RICK JAMES	FOOL IN THE STREET	JEFFERSON BALL	10.00
79	1157	TATA VEGA	IF LOVE MUST GO	COME IN HEAVEN (EARTH IS CALLI	5.00
79	1157 DJ	TATA VEGA	IF LOVE MUST GO	COME IN HEAVEN (EARTH IS CALLI	6.00
79	1158	TEENA MARIE	DON'T LOOK BACK	I'M GONNA MY CAKE (AND EAT IT TOO)	4.00
79	1158 PS	TEENA MARIE	DON'T LOOK BACK	I'M GONNA MY CAKE (AND EAT IT TOO)	6.00
79	1158 DJ	TEENA MARIE	DON'T LOOK BACK	I'M GONNA MY CAKE (AND EAT IT TOO)	5.00
79	1159	BILLY PRESTON & SYREETA	WITH YOU I'M BORN AGAIN	SOCK - IT, ROCKET	4.00
79	1159 PS	BILLY PRESTON & SYREETA	WITH YOU I'M BORN AGAIN	SOCK - IT, ROCKET	8.00
79	1159 DJ	BILLY PRESTON & SYREETA	WITH YOU I'M BORN AGAIN	SOCK - IT, ROCKET	5.00
79	1160	DIANA ROSS	NO ONE GETS THE PRIZE	NEVER SAY I DON'T LOVE YOU	4.00
79	1160 PS	DIANA ROSS	NO ONE GETS THE PRIZE	NEVER SAY I DON'T LOVE YOU	6.00
79	1160 DJ	DIANA ROSS	NO ONE GETS THE PRIZE	NEVER SAY I DON'T LOVE YOU	5.00
79	1161	PATRICK GAMMON	COP AN ATTITUDE	MY SONG IN - G -	5.00
79	1161 DJ	PATRICK GAMMON	COP AN ATTITUDE	MY SONG IN - G -	6.00
79	1162	STERLING	ROLL-HER SKATER	same: instrumental	4.00

79	1162 DJ	STERLING	ROLL-HER SKATER	same: instrumental	5.00
79	1163	MARY WILSON	RED HOT	MIDNIGHT DANCER	5.00
79	1163 DJ	MARY WILSON	RED HOT	MIDNIGHT DANCER	6.00
79	1164	SMOKEY ROBINSON	CRUSIN'	THE HUMMING SONG	4.00
79	1164 DJ	SMOKEY ROBINSON	CRUSIN'	THE HUMMING SONG	5.00
79	1164 DJ PS	SMOKEY ROBINSON	CRUSIN'	THE HUMMING SONG	10.00
79	1165	MICHAEL JACKSON c/w MARVIN GAYE	BEN	ABRAHAM, MARTIN AND JOHN	4.00
79	1165 DJ	MICHAEL JACKSON c/w MARVIN GAYE	BEN	ABRAHAM, MARTIN AND JOHN	5.00
79	1166	COMMODORES	STILL	SUCH A WOMAN	4.00
79	1166 PS	COMMODORES	STILL	SUCH A WOMAN	5.00
79	1166 DJ	COMMODORES	STILL	SUCH A WOMAN	5.00
79	1167	SCHERRIE & SUSAYE	LEAVING ME WAS THE BEST THING YOU'VE EVER DONE	SUCH A WOMAN	6.00
79	1167 DJ	SCHERRIE & SUSAYE	LEAVING ME WAS THE BEST THING YOU'VE EVER DONE	SUCH A WOMAN	8.00
79	1168	MARVIN GAYE	EGO TRIPPIN'	same: instrumental	4.00
79	1168 PS	MARVIN GAYE	EGO TRIPPIN'	same: instrumental	6.00
79	1168 DJ	MARVIN GAYE	EGO TRIPPIN'	same: instrumental	5.00
79	1169	DIANA ROSS	IT'S MY HOUSE	SPARKLE	4.00
79	1169 PS	DIANA ROSS	IT'S MY HOUSE	SPARKLE	5.00
79	1169 DJ	DIANA ROSS	IT'S MY HOUSE	SPARKLE	5.00
79	1170	FRANK WILSON	DO I LOVE YOU (INDEED I DO)	SWEETER AS THE DAYS GO BY	**181.00**
79	1170 DJ	FRANK WILSON	DO I LOVE YOU (INDEED I DO)	SWEETER AS THE DAYS GO BY	**241.00**
79	1170 DJ PS	FRANK WILSON	DO I LOVE YOU (INDEED I DO)	SWEETER AS THE DAYS GO BY	**405.00**

the above three 45 releases are the original presses from November 1979. Since 1979 UK Tamla Motown pressed and released this 45 on three more occasions using the same TMG 1170 number. See scans of all the Frank Wilson releases to evaluate.

79	1170 - 2	FRANK WILSON	DO I LOVE YOU (INDEED I DO)	SWEETER AS THE DAYS GO BY	85.00
79	1170 - 3	FRANK WILSON	DO I LOVE YOU (INDEED I DO)	SWEETER AS THE DAYS GO BY	50.00
79	1170 - 4	FRANK WILSON	DO I LOVE YOU (INDEED I DO)	SWEETER AS THE DAYS GO BY	30.00
04	1170 + special sleeve	FRANK WILSON c/w CHRIS CLARK	DO I LOVE YOU (INDEED I DO)	DO I LOVE YOU (INDEED I DO)	15.00
80	1171	BONNIE POINTER	I CAN'T HELP MYSELF (SUGAR PIE HONEY BUNCH)	WHEN I'M GONE	5.00
80	1171 DJ	BONNIE POINTER	I CAN'T HELP MYSELF (SUGAR PIE HONEY BUNCH)	WHEN I'M GONE	6.00
80	1172	COMMODORES	WONDERLAND	LOVIN' YOU	4.00
80	1172 PS	COMMODORES	WONDERLAND	LOVIN' YOU	5.00
80	1172 DJ	COMMODORES	WONDERLAND	LOVIN' YOU	5.00
80	1173	STEVIE WONDER	BLACK ORCHID	BLAME IT ON THE SUN	4.00
80	1173 PS	STEVIE WONDER	BLACK ORCHID	BLAME IT ON THE SUN	4.00
80	1173 DJ	STEVIE WONDER	BLACK ORCHID	BLAME IT ON THE SUN	5.00
80	1174	RICK JAMES	LOVE GUN	STORMY LOVE	4.00
80	1174 DJ	RICK JAMES	LOVE GUN	STORMY LOVE	5.00
80	1175	BILLY PRESTON & SYREETA	IT WILL COME IN TIME	ALL I WANTED WAS YOU	4.00
80	1175 PS	BILLY PRESTON & SYREETA	IT WILL COME IN TIME	ALL I WANTED WAS YOU	5.00
80	1175 DJ	BILLY PRESTON & SYREETA	IT WILL COME IN TIME	ALL I WANTED WAS YOU	5.00
80	1176	MARTHA REEVES & the VANDELLAS	HEATWAVE	DANCING IN THE STREET	5.00
80	1176 PS	MARTHA REEVES & the VANDELLAS	HEATWAVE	DANCING IN THE STREET	6.00
80	1176 DJ	MARTHA REEVES & the VANDELLAS	HEATWAVE	DANCING IN THE STREET	6.00
80	1177	MARY WILSON	PICK UP THE PIECES	YOU'RE THE LIGHT THAT GUIDES MY WAY	10.00
80	1177 DJ	MARY WILSON	PICK UP THE PIECES	YOU'RE THE LIGHT THAT GUIDES MY WAY	15.00
80	1178	TEENA MARIE	CAN IT BE LOVE	TOO MANY COLOURS (TEE'S INTERLUDE)	4.00
80	1178 DJ	TEENA MARIE	CAN IT BE LOVE	TOO MANY COLOURS (TEE'S INTERLUDE)	5.00
80	1179	STEVIE WONDER	OUTSIDE MY WINDOW	SAME OLD STORY	4.00
80	1179 DJ	STEVIE WONDER	OUTSIDE MY WINDOW	SAME OLD STORY	5.00
80	1180	DIANA ROSS & the SUPREMES	SUPREMES MEDLEY	SUPREMES MEDLEY part 2	4.00
80	1180 DJ	DIANA ROSS & the SUPREMES	SUPREMES MEDLEY	SUPREMES MEDLEY part 2	6.00
80	1181	STONE CITY BAND	STRUT YOUR STUFF	F.I.M.A. (FUNK IN MAMA AFRIKA)	4.00
80	1181 DJ	STONE CITY BAND	STRUT YOUR STUFF	F.I.M.A. (FUNK IN MAMA AFRIKA)	5.00
80	1182	SMOKEY ROBINSON	LET ME BE THE CLOCK	TRAVELIN' THROUGH	4.00
80	1182 DJ	SMOKEY ROBINSON	LET ME BE THE CLOCK	TRAVELIN' THROUGH	5.00
80	1183	JERMAINE JACKSON	JE VOUS AIME BEAUCOUP (I LOVE YOU)	LET'S GET SERIOUS	8.00
80	1183 DJ	JERMAINE JACKSON	JE VOUS AIME BEAUCOUP (I LOVE YOU)	LET'S GET SERIOUS	10.00
80	1184	BONNIE POINTER	DEEP INSIDE MY SOUL	I LOVE TO SING TO YOU	5.00
80	1184 PS	BONNIE POINTER	DEEP INSIDE MY SOUL	I LOVE TO SING TO YOU	6.00
80	1184 DJ	BONNIE POINTER	DEEP INSIDE MY SOUL	I LOVE TO SING TO YOU	6.00
80	1185	TEENA MARIE	BEHIND THE GROOVE	YOU'RE ALL THE BOOGIE I NEED	4.00
80	1185 DJ	TEENA MARIE	BEHIND THE GROOVE	YOU'RE ALL THE BOOGIE I NEED	5.00
80	1186	TEMPTATIONS	POWER	same: instrumental	4.00
80	1186 DJ	TEMPTATIONS	POWER	same: instrumental	5.00
80	1187	SWITCH	DON'T TAKE MY LOVE AWAY	same: instrumental	4.00
80	1187 DJ	SWITCH	DON'T TAKE MY LOVE AWAY	same: instrumental	5.00
80	1188	BILLY PRESTON & SYREETA	ONE MORE TIME FOR LOVE	DANCE FOR ME CHILDREN	4.00
80	1188 DJ	BILLY PRESTON & SYREETA	ONE MORE TIME FOR LOVE	DANCE FOR ME CHILDREN	5.00
80	1189	DETROIT SPINNERS	SWEET THING	IT'S A SHAME	8.00
80	1189 DJ	DETROIT SPINNERS	SWEET THING	IT'S A SHAME	10.00
80	1190	DR. STRUT	STRUTTIN'	BLUE LODGE	4.00
80	1190 DJ	DR. STRUT	STRUTTIN'	BLUE LODGE	5.00
80	1191	SMOKEY ROBINSON	HEAVY ON PRIDE (LIGHT ON LOVE)	I LOVE THE NEARNESS OF YOU	4.00
80	1191 DJ	SMOKEY ROBINSON	HEAVY ON PRIDE (LIGHT ON LOVE)	I LOVE THE NEARNESS OF YOU	5.00
80	1192	OZONE	WALK ON	I LOVE THE NEARNESS OF YOU	4.00
80	1192 DJ	OZONE	WALK ON	I LOVE THE NEARNESS OF YOU	5.00
80	1193	COMMODORES	OLD FASHIONED LOVE	SEXY LADY	4.00
80	1193 DJ	COMMODORES	OLD FASHIONED LOVE	SEXY LADY	5.00
80	1194	JERMAINE JACKSON	BURNIN' HOT	CASTLES OF SAND	4.00
80	1194 DJ	JERMAINE JACKSON	BURNIN' HOT	CASTLES OF SAND	5.00
80	1195	DIANA ROSS	UPSIDE DOWN	FRIEND TO FRIEND	4.00
80	1195 PS	DIANA ROSS	UPSIDE DOWN	FRIEND TO FRIEND	5.00
80	1195 DJ	DIANA ROSS	UPSIDE DOWN	FRIEND TO FRIEND	5.00
80	1196	TEENA MARIE	LONELY DESIRE	ALADDIN'S LAMP	4.00
80	1196 DJ	TEENA MARIE	LONELY DESIRE	ALADDIN'S LAMP	5.00
80	1197	TEMPTATIONS	STRUCK BY LIGHTNING TWICE	I'M COMING HOME	5.00

Year	Cat. No.	Artist	A-Side	B-Side	Price
80	1197 DJ	TEMPTATIONS	STRUCK BY LIGHTNING TWICE	I'M COMING HOME	6.00
80	1198	RICK JAMES	BIG TIME	ISLAND LADY	4.00
80	1198 DJ	RICK JAMES	BIG TIME	ISLAND LADY	5.00
80	1199	BLACK RUSSIAN	MYSTIFIED	LOVE'S ENOUGH	5.00
80	1199 DJ	BLACK RUSSIAN	MYSTIFIED	LOVE'S ENOUGH	6.00
80	1200	SYREETA	HE'S GONE	HERE'S MY LOVE	5.00
80	1200 DJ	SYREETA	HE'S GONE	HERE'S MY LOVE	6.00
80	1201	JERMAINE JACKSON	YOU'RE SUPPOSED TO KEEP LOVE FOR ME	LET IT RIDE	5.00
80	1201 DJ	JERMAINE JACKSON	YOU'RE SUPPOSED TO KEEP LOVE FOR ME	LET IT RIDE	6.00
80	1202	DIANA ROSS	MY OLD PIANO	WHERE DID WE GO WRONG	4.00
80	1202 PS	DIANA ROSS	MY OLD PIANO	WHERE DID WE GO WRONG	5.00
80	1202 DJ	DIANA ROSS	MY OLD PIANO	WHERE DID WE GO WRONG	5.00
80	1203	TEENA MARIE	I NEED YOUR LOVIN'	IRONS IN THE FIRE	4.00
80	1203 DJ	TEENA MARIE	I NEED YOUR LOVIN'	IRONS IN THE FIRE	5.00
80	1204 PS	STEVIE WONDER	MASTER BLASTER (JAMMIN')	MASTER BLASTER (DUB)	3.00
80	1204 PS DJ	STEVIE WONDER	MASTER BLASTER (JAMMIN')	MASTER BLASTER (DUB)	4.00
80	1205	HIGH INERGY	MAKE ME YOURS	I LOVE MAKIN' LOVE (TO THE MUS	8.00
80	1205 DJ	HIGH INERGY	MAKE ME YOURS	I LOVE MAKIN' LOVE (TO THE MUS	10.00
80	1206	COMMODORES	HEROES	DON'T YOU BE WORRIED	4.00
80	1206 DJ	COMMODORES	HEROES	DON'T YOU BE WORRIED	5.00
80	1207	LYNDA CARTER	THE LAST SONG	WHAT'S A LITTLE LOVE BETWEEN FRIENDS	6.00
80	1207 PS	LYNDA CARTER	THE LAST SONG	WHAT'S A LITTLE LOVE BETWEEN FRIENDS	8.00
80	1207 DJ	LYNDA CARTER	THE LAST SONG	WHAT'S A LITTLE LOVE BETWEEN FRIENDS	8.00
80	1208	MICHAEL URBANIAK	NANAVA	JOY	5.00
80	1208 DJ	MICHAEL URBANIAK	NANAVA	JOY	6.00
80	1209	RICK JAMES	SUMMER LOVE	GETTING' IT ON (IN THE SUNSHINE)	4.00
80	1209 DJ	RICK JAMES	SUMMER LOVE	GETTING' IT ON (IN THE SUNSHINE)	5.00
80	1210	DIANA ROSS	I'M COMING OUT	GIVE UP	4.00
80	1210 DJ	DIANA ROSS	I'M COMING OUT	GIVE UP	5.00
80	1211	BILLY PRESTON & SYREETA	PLEASE STAY	SIGNED SEALED DELIVERED I'M YOURS	4.00
80	1211 DJ	BILLY PRESTON & SYREETA	PLEASE STAY	SIGNED SEALED DELIVERED I'M YOURS	5.00
80	1212	JERMAINE JACKSON	LITTLE GIRL DON'T YOU WORRY	WE CAN PUT IT BACK TOGETHER	4.00
80	1212 DJ	JERMAINE JACKSON	LITTLE GIRL DON'T YOU WORRY	WE CAN PUT IT BACK TOGETHER	5.00
80	1213	DAZZ BAND	SHAKE IT UP	ONLY LOVE	4.00
80	1213 DJ	DAZZ BAND	SHAKE IT UP	ONLY LOVE	5.00
80	1214	HIGH INERGY	HOLD ON TO MY LOVE	IF I LOVE YOU TONIGHT	4.00
80	1214 DJ	HIGH INERGY	HOLD ON TO MY LOVE	IF I LOVE YOU TONIGHT	5.00
80	1215	STEVIE WONDER	I AIN'T GONNA STAND FOR IT	KNOCKS ME OFF MY FEET	4.00
80	1215 PS	STEVIE WONDER	I AIN'T GONNA STAND FOR IT	KNOCKS ME OFF MY FEET	5.00
80	1215 DJ	STEVIE WONDER	I AIN'T GONNA STAND FOR IT	KNOCKS ME OFF MY FEET	5.00
81	1216	TEMPTATIONS	TAKE ME AWAY	THERE'S MORE WHERE THAT CAME FROM	5.00
80	1216 DJ	TEMPTATIONS	TAKE ME AWAY	THERE'S MORE WHERE THAT CAME FROM	6.00
81	1217	DIANA ROSS	IT'S MY TURN	SLEEPIN'	4.00
81	1217 PS	DIANA ROSS	IT'S MY TURN	SLEEPIN'	6.00
80	1217 PS DJ	DIANA ROSS	IT'S MY TURN	SLEEPIN'	8.00
80	1218	COMMODORES	JESUS IS LOVE	MIGHTY SPIRIT	4.00
80	1218 DJ	COMMODORES	JESUS IS LOVE	MIGHTY SPIRIT	5.00
81	1219	TATA VEGA	YOU KEEP ME HANGIN' ON	YOU BETTER WATCH OUT	4.00
81	1219 DJ	TATA VEGA	YOU KEEP ME HANGIN' ON	YOU BETTER WATCH OUT	5.00
81	1220	BLACK RUSSIAN	LEAVE ME NOW	MOVE TOGETHER	6.00
81	1220 DJ	BLACK RUSSIAN	LEAVE ME NOW	MOVE TOGETHER	7.00
81	1221	STONE CITY BAND	ALL DAY AND ALL OF THE NIGHT	same: vamp version	4.00
81	1221 DJ	STONE CITY BAND	ALL DAY AND ALL OF THE NIGHT	same: vamp version	5.00
81	1222	JERMAINE JACKSON	YOU LIKE ME DON'T YOU	same: instrumental	4.00
81	1222 green vinyl	JERMAINE JACKSON	YOU LIKE ME DON'T YOU	same: instrumental	25.00
81	1222 DJ	JERMAINE JACKSON	YOU LIKE ME DON'T YOU	same: instrumental	5.00
81	1223	SMOKEY ROBINSON	BEING WITH YOU	WHAT'S IN YOUR LIFE FOR ME	4.00
81	1223 DJ	SMOKEY ROBINSON	BEING WITH YOU	WHAT'S IN YOUR LIFE FOR ME	5.00
81	1224	BILLY PRESTON	HOPE	GIVE IT UP, HOT	5.00
81	1224 DJ	BILLY PRESTON	HOPE	GIVE IT UP, HOT	6.00
81	1225	MARVIN GAYE	PRAISE	FUNK ME	4.00
81	1225 PS	MARVIN GAYE	PRAISE	FUNK ME	6.00
81	1225 DJ	MARVIN GAYE	PRAISE	FUNK ME	5.00
80	1226	STEVIE WONDER	LATELY	IF IT'S MAGIC	3.00
80	1226 PS	STEVIE WONDER	LATELY	IF IT'S MAGIC	4.00
80	1226 DJ	STEVIE WONDER	LATELY	IF IT'S MAGIC	4.00
81	1227	DIANA ROSS	ONE MORE CHANCE	CONFIDE IN ME	4.00
81	1227 PS	DIANA ROSS	ONE MORE CHANCE	CONFIDE IN ME	8.00
81	1227 DJ	DIANA ROSS	ONE MORE CHANCE	CONFIDE IN ME	6.00
81	1228	SYREETA	LOVE FIRE	CAUSE WE'VE ENDED AS LOVERS	**177.00**
81	1228 DJ unconfirmed	SYREETA	LOVE FIRE	CAUSE WE'VE ENDED AS LOVERS	UN
81	1229	RICK JAMES	GIVE IT TO ME BABY	DON'T GIVE UP ON LOVE	4.00
81	1229 DJ	RICK JAMES	GIVE IT TO ME BABY	DON'T GIVE UP ON LOVE	5.00
81	1230	TATA VEGA	LOVE YOUR NEIGHBOR	THERE'S LOVE IN THE WORLD	4.00
81	1230 DJ	TATA VEGA	LOVE YOUR NEIGHBOR	THERE'S LOVE IN THE WORLD	5.00
81	1231	BILLY PRESTON	A CHANGE IS GONNA COME	YOU	5.00
81	1231 DJ	BILLY PRESTON	A CHANGE IS GONNA COME	YOU	6.00
81	1232	MARVIN GAYE	HEAVY LOVE AFFAIR	FAR CRY	6.00
81	1232 DJ	MARVIN GAYE	HEAVY LOVE AFFAIR	FAR CRY	8.00
81	1233	DIANA ROSS	CRYIN' MY HEART OUT FOR YOU	TO LOVE AGAIN	5.00
81	1233 PS	DIANA ROSS	CRYIN' MY HEART OUT FOR YOU	TO LOVE AGAIN	6.00
81	1233 DJ	DIANA ROSS	CRYIN' MY HEART OUT FOR YOU	TO LOVE AGAIN	6.00
81	1234	HIGH INERGY	I JUST WANNA DANCE WITH YOU	TAKE MY LIFE	4.00
81	1234 DJ	HIGH INERGY	I JUST WANNA DANCE WITH YOU	TAKE MY LIFE	5.00
81	1235 PS	STEVIE WONDER	HAPPY BIRTHDAY	HAPPY BIRTHDAY (SING-A-LONG)	3.00
81	1235 DJ	STEVIE WONDER	HAPPY BIRTHDAY	HAPPY BIRTHDAY (SING-A-LONG)	5.00
81	1236	TEENA MARIE	SQUARE BIZ	OPUS III(DOES ANYBODY CARE)	4.00

81	1236 PS	TEENA MARIE	SQUARE BIZ	OPUS III(DOES ANYBODY CARE)	6.00
81	1236 DJ	TEENA MARIE	SQUARE BIZ	OPUS III(DOES ANYBODY CARE)	5.00
81	1237	SMOKEY ROBINSON	YOU ARE FOREVER	I HEAR THE CHILDREN SINGING	4.00
81	1237 PS	SMOKEY ROBINSON	YOU ARE FOREVER	I HEAR THE CHILDREN SINGING	5.00
81	1237 DJ	SMOKEY ROBINSON	YOU ARE FOREVER	I HEAR THE CHILDREN SINGING	5.00
81	1238 PS	COMMODORES	LADY (YOU BRING ME UP)	GETTING' IT	4.00
81	1238 PS DJ	COMMODORES	LADY (YOU BRING ME UP)	GETTING' IT	5.00
81	1239	STONE CITY BAND	FUNKY REGGAE	GANJA	4.00
81	1239 DJ	STONE CITY BAND	FUNKY REGGAE	GANJA	5.00
81	1240	DIANA ROSS & LIONEL RICHIE	ENDLESS LOVE	same: instrumental	3.00
81	1240 PS	DIANA ROSS & LIONEL RICHIE	ENDLESS LOVE	same: instrumental	4.00
81	1240 DJ	DIANA ROSS & LIONEL RICHIE	ENDLESS LOVE	same: instrumental	5.00
81	1241 PS	RICK JAMES	SUPER FREAK	SUPER FREAK part 2	5.00
81	1241 PS DJ	RICK JAMES	SUPER FREAK	SUPER FREAK part 2	6.00
81	1242 PS	JERMAINE JACKSON	I'M JUST TO SHY	ALL BECAUSE OF YOU	5.00
81	1242 PS DJ	JERMAINE JACKSON	I'M JUST TO SHY	ALL BECAUSE OF YOU	6.00
81	1243	TEMPTATIONS	AIMING AT YOUR HEART	THE LIFE OF A COWBOY	15.00
81	1243 PS	TEMPTATIONS	AIMING AT YOUR HEART	THE LIFE OF A COWBOY	20.00
81	1243 PS DJ	TEMPTATIONS	AIMING AT YOUR HEART	THE LIFE OF A COWBOY	25.00
81	1244	JOSE FELICIANO	EVERYBODY LOVES ME	THE DROUGHT IS OVER	5.00
81	1244 DJ	JOSE FELICIANO	EVERYBODY LOVES ME	THE DROUGHT IS OVER	6.00
81	1245	COMMODORES	OH NO	ARE YOU HAPPY	4.00
81	1245 DJ	COMMODORES	OH NO	ARE YOU HAPPY	5.00
81	1246	TEENA MARIE	I MUST BE MAGIC	YES INDEED	4.00
81	1246 PS	TEENA MARIE	I MUST BE MAGIC	YES INDEED	5.00
81	1246 DJ	TEENA MARIE	I MUST BE MAGIC	YES INDEED	5.00
81	1247	SYREETA	QUICK SLICK	I DON'T KNOW	8.00
81	1247 DJ	SYREETA	QUICK SLICK	I DON'T KNOW	10.00
81	1248 PS	DIANA ROSS	TENDERNESS	SUPREMES MEDLEY: 4 songs	5.00
81	1248 PS DJ	DIANA ROSS	TENDERNESS	SUPREMES MEDLEY: 4 songs	6.00
81	1248 pic disc	DIANA ROSS	TENDERNESS	SUPREMES MEDLEY: 4 songs	10.00
81	1249	OZONE	GIGOLETTE	same: instrumental	4.00
81	1249 DJ	OZONE	GIGOLETTE	same: instrumental	5.00
82	1250	RICK JAMES	GHETTO LIFE	BELOW THE FUNK (PASS THE J)	4.00
82	1250 PS	RICK JAMES	GHETTO LIFE	BELOW THE FUNK (PASS THE J)	5.00
82	1250 DJ	RICK JAMES	GHETTO LIFE	BELOW THE FUNK (PASS THE J)	5.00
82	1251	TEENA MARIE	PORTUGUESE LOVE	THE BALLAD OF CRADLE ROB	4.00
82	1251 PS	TEENA MARIE	PORTUGUESE LOVE	THE BALLAD OF CRADLE ROB	5.00
82	1251 DJ	TEENA MARIE	PORTUGUESE LOVE	THE BALLAD OF CRADLE ROB	5.00
82	1252	JOSE FELICIANO	I WANNA BE WHERE YOU ARE	LETS MAKE LOVE OVER THE TELEPH	5.00
82	1252 DJ	JOSE FELICIANO	I WANNA BE WHERE YOU ARE	LETS MAKE LOVE OVER THE TELEPH	6.00
82	1253	JERMAINE JACKSON	PARADISE IN YOUR EYES	I'M MY BROTHER'S KEEPER	5.00
82	1253 PS	JERMAINE JACKSON	PARADISE IN YOUR EYES	I'M MY BROTHER'S KEEPER	8.00
82	1253 DJ	JERMAINE JACKSON	PARADISE IN YOUR EYES	I'M MY BROTHER'S KEEPER	6.00
82	1254	STEVIE WONDER	THAT GIRL	ALL I DO	4.00
82	1254 PS	STEVIE WONDER	THAT GIRL	ALL I DO	5.00
82	1254 DJ	STEVIE WONDER	THAT GIRL	ALL I DO	5.00
82	1255 PS	SMOKEY ROBINSON	TELL ME TOMORROW	TELL ME TOMORROW part 2	15.00
82	1255 PS DJ	SMOKEY ROBINSON	TELL ME TOMORROW	TELL ME TOMORROW part 2	20.00
82	1256	COMMODOES	WHY YOU WANNA TRY ME	CELEBRATE	4.00
82	1256 PS	COMMODOES	WHY YOU WANNA TRY ME	CELEBRATE	4.00
82	1256 DJ	COMMODOES	WHY YOU WANNA TRY ME	CELEBRATE	5.00
82	1257	BETTY LAVETTE	YOU SEEN ONE YOU SEEN 'EM ALL	RIGHT IN THE MIDDLE (OF FALLIN	8.00
82	1257 PS	BETTY LAVETTE	YOU SEEN ONE YOU SEEN 'EM ALL	RIGHT IN THE MIDDLE (OF FALLIN	10.00
82	1257 DJ PS	BETTY LAVETTE	YOU SEEN ONE YOU SEEN 'EM ALL	RIGHT IN THE MIDDLE (OF FALLIN	15.00
82	1258	SYREETA	I MUST BE IN LOVE	OUT OF THE BOX	4.00
82	1258 PS	SYREETA	I MUST BE IN LOVE	OUT OF THE BOX	6.00
82	1258 DJ	SYREETA	I MUST BE IN LOVE	OUT OF THE BOX	5.00
82	1259	OZONE	DO WHAT YOU WANNA	COME ON IN	4.00
82	1259 PS	OZONE	DO WHAT YOU WANNA	COME ON IN	6.00
82	1259 DJ	OZONE	DO WHAT YOU WANNA	COME ON IN	5.00
82	1260	CHARLENE	I'VE NEVER BEEN TO ME	SOMEWHJERE IN MY LIFE	4.00
82	1260 PS	CHARLENE	I'VE NEVER BEEN TO ME	SOMEWHJERE IN MY LIFE	5.00
82	1260 PS DJ	CHARLENE	I'VE NEVER BEEN TO ME	SOMEWHJERE IN MY LIFE	6.00
82	1261	NOLEN & CROSSLEY	READY OR NOT	A PLACE IN MY HEART	5.00
82	1261 PS	NOLEN & CROSSLEY	READY OR NOT	A PLACE IN MY HEART	6.00
82	1261 DJ	NOLEN & CROSSLEY	READY OR NOT	A PLACE IN MY HEART	6.00
82	1262	SMOKEY ROBINSON	OLD FASHIONED LOVE	DESTINY	4.00
82	1262 PS	SMOKEY ROBINSON	OLD FASHIONED LOVE	DESTINY	5.00
82	1262 DJ	SMOKEY ROBINSON	OLD FASHIONED LOVE	DESTINY	5.00
82	1263	TEMPTATIONS feat: RICK JAMES	STANDING ON THE TOP	STANDING ON THE TOP part 2	5.00
82	1263 PS	TEMPTATIONS feat: RICK JAMES	STANDING ON THE TOP	STANDING ON THE TOP part 2	6.00
82	1263 DJ	TEMPTATIONS feat: RICK JAMES	STANDING ON THE TOP	STANDING ON THE TOP part 2	6.00
82	1264	JOSE FELICIANO	I SECOND THAT EMOTION	FREE ME FROM MY FREEDOM	4.00
82	1264 PS	JOSE FELICIANO	I SECOND THAT EMOTION	FREE ME FROM MY FREEDOM	5600
82	1264 PS DJ	JOSE FELICIANO	I SECOND THAT EMOTION	FREE ME FROM MY FREEDOM	6.00
82	1265	BETTY LAVETTE	I CAN'T STOP	EITHER WAY I LOSE	8.00
82	1265 PS	BETTY LAVETTE	I CAN'T STOP	EITHER WAY I LOSE	10.00
82	1265 DJ	BETTY LAVETTE	I CAN'T STOP	EITHER WAY I LOSE	10.00
82	1266	RICK JAMES	DANCE WIT ME	DANCE WIT ME part 2	4.00
82	1266 PS	RICK JAMES	DANCE WIT ME	DANCE WIT ME part 2	5.00
82	1266 picture disc	RICK JAMES	DANCE WIT ME	DANCE WIT ME part 2	10.00
82	1266 DJ	RICK JAMES	DANCE WIT ME	DANCE WIT ME part 2	6.00
82	1267	BOBBY WOMACK	SO MANY SIDES OF YOU	JUST MY IMAGINATION	**127.00**
82	1267 DJ	BOBBY WOMACK	SO MANY SIDES OF YOU	JUST MY IMAGINATION	125.00
82	1267 PS	BOBBY WOMACK	SO MANY SIDES OF YOU	JUST MY IMAGINATION	125.00
82	1267 DJ PS	BOBBY WOMACK	SO MANY SIDES OF YOU	JUST MY IMAGINATION	150.00

82	1268	HIGH INERGY	FIRST IMPRESSIONS	COULD THIS BE LOVE	15.00
82	1268 PS	HIGH INERGY	FIRST IMPRESSIONS	COULD THIS BE LOVE	20.00
82	1268 DJ	HIGH INERGY	FIRST IMPRESSIONS	COULD THIS BE LOVE	20.00
82	1269	STEVIE WONDER	DO I DO	ROCKET LOVE	3.00
82	1269 PS	STEVIE WONDER	DO I DO	ROCKET LOVE	4.00
82	1269 PS DJ	STEVIE WONDER	DO I DO	ROCKET LOVE	5.00
82	1270	DAZZ BAND	LET IT WHIP	EVERYDAY LOVE	4.00
82	1270 DJ	DAZZ BAND	LET IT WHIP	EVERYDAY LOVE	5.00
82	1271	JEAN CARN	IF YOU DON'T KNOW ME BY NOW	COMPLETENESS	5.00
82	1271 DJ	JEAN CARN	IF YOU DON'T KNOW ME BY NOW	COMPLETENESS	6.00
82	1272	CHARLENE	IT AIN'T EASY COMIN' DOWN	IF I COULD SEE MYSELF + NUNCA	3.00
82	1272 PS	CHARLENE	IT AIN'T EASY COMIN' DOWN	IF I COULD SEE MYSELF + NUNCA	5.00
82	1272 PS DJ	CHARLENE	IT AIN'T EASY COMIN' DOWN	IF I COULD SEE MYSELF + NUNCA	6.00
82	1273	DIANA ROSS	THE BOSS	OLD FUNKY ROLLS	4.00
82	1273 DJ	DIANA ROSS	THE BOSS	OLD FUNKY ROLLS	5.00
82	1274	SMOKEY ROBINSON	CRUSIN'	THE ONLY GAME IN TOWN	4.00
82	1274 DJ	SMOKEY ROBINSON	CRUSIN'	THE ONLY GAME IN TOWN	5.00
82	1275	SYREETA	CAN'T SHAKE YOUR LOVE	WISH UPON A STAR	5.00
82	1275 DJ	SYREETA	CAN'T SHAKE YOUR LOVE	WISH UPON A STAR	6.00
82	1276	JERMAINE JACKSON	LET ME TICKLE YOUR FANCY	MAYBE NEXT TIME	4.00
82	1276 DJ	JERMAINE JACKSON	LET ME TICKLE YOUR FANCY	MAYBE NEXT TIME	5.00
82	1277	RICK JAMES	HARD TO GET	MY LOVE	5.00
82	1277 PS	RICK JAMES	HARD TO GET	MY LOVE	6.00
82	1277 DJ	RICK JAMES	HARD TO GET	MY LOVE	6.00
82	1278	BOBBY WOMACK	SECRETS	STAND UP	8.00
82	1278 DJ	BOBBY WOMACK	SECRETS	STAND UP	10.00
82	1279 unissued	DAZZ BAND	KEEP IT LIVE (ON THE K.I.L.)	THIS TIME IT'S FOREVER	UN
82	1280	STEVIE WONDER	RIBBON IN THE SKY	THE SECRET LIFE OF PLANTS	3.00
82	1280 PS	STEVIE WONDER	RIBBON IN THE SKY	THE SECRET LIFE OF PLANTS	4.00
82	1280 DJ	STEVIE WONDER	RIBBON IN THE SKY	THE SECRET LIFE OF PLANTS	4.00
82	1281 latino label	JOSE FELICIANO	SAMBA PA TI	NO HAY SOMBRE QUE ME	4.00
82	1281 DJ latino label	JOSE FELICIANO	SAMBA PA TI	NO HAY SOMBRE QUE ME	5.00
82	1282	COMMODORES	LUCY	HEAVEN KNOWS	3.00
82	1282 PS	COMMODORES	LUCY	HEAVEN KNOWS	4.00
82	1282 DJ	COMMODORES	LUCY	HEAVEN KNOWS	4.00
82	1283	BILLY PRESTON	I'M NEVER GONNA SAY GOODBYE	I LOVE YOU SO	5.00
82	1283 DJ	BILLY PRESTON	I'M NEVER GONNA SAY GOODBYE	I LOVE YOU SO	6.00
82	1284	LIONEL RICHIE	TRULY	JUST PUT SOME LOVE IN YOUR HEART	3.00
82	1284 PS	LIONEL RICHIE	TRULY	JUST PUT SOME LOVE IN YOUR HEA	4.00
82	1284 PS DJ	LIONEL RICHIE	TRULY	JUST PUT SOME LOVE IN YOUR HEA	5.00
82	1285	WILLIE HUTCH	THE GIRL (CAN'T HELP IT)	IN AND OUT	6.00
82	1285 DJ	WILLIE HUTCH	THE GIRL (CAN'T HELP IT)	IN AND OUT	8.00
82	1286	JERMAINE JACKSON	VERY SPECIAL PART	YOU'RE GIVING ME THE RUN AROUND	5.00
82	1286 PS	JERMAINE JACKSON	VERY SPECIAL PART	YOU'RE GIVING ME THE RUN AROUND	8.00
82	1286 DJ	JERMAINE JACKSON	VERY SPECIAL PART	YOU'RE GIVING ME THE RUN AROUND	6.00
82	1287	CHARLENE & STEVIE WONDER	USED TO BE	I WANT TO COME BACK AS A SONG	3.00
82	1287 PS	CHARLENE & STEVIE WONDER	USED TO BE	I WANT TO COME BACK AS A SONG	4.00
82	1287 DJ	CHARLENE & STEVIE WONDER	USED TO BE	I WANT TO COME BACK AS A SONG	4.00
83	1288 Gordy label	BOBBY M feat: JEAN CARN	LETS STAY TOGTHER	CHARLIE'S BACK BEAT	15.00
83	1288 DJ Gordy label	BOBBY M feat: JEAN CARN	LETS STAY TOGTHER	CHARLIE'S BACK BEAT	20.00

first in the series on TMG # to be released on the GORDY label.

83	1289	STEVIE WONDER	FRONT LINE	same: instrumental	3.00
83	1289 PS	STEVIE WONDER	FRONT LINE	same: instrumental	4.00
83	1289 DJ	STEVIE WONDER	FRONT LINE	same: instrumental	4.00
83	1290	LIONEL RICHIE	YOU ARE	YOU MEAN MORE TO ME	3.00
83	1290 PS	LIONEL RICHIE	YOU ARE	YOU MEAN MORE TO ME	4.00
83	1290 DJ	LIONEL RICHIE	YOU ARE	YOU MEAN MORE TO ME	4.00
83	1291	BILLY PRESTON & SYREETA	A NEW WAY TO SAY I LOVE YOU	HEY YOU	4.00
83	1291 DJ	BILLY PRESTON & SYREETA	A NEW WAY TO SAY I LOVE YOU	HEY YOU	5.00
83	1291 PS	BILLY PRESTON & SYREETA	A NEW WAY TO SAY I LOVE YOU	HEY YOU	5.00
83	1292	COMMODORES	REACH HIGH	same: instrumental	3.00
83	1292 PS	COMMODORES	REACH HIGH	same: instrumental	4.00
83	1292 DJ	COMMODORES	REACH HIGH	same: instrumental	5.00
83	1293	WILLIE HUTCH	PART DOWN	SLICK	5.00
83	1293 DJ	WILLIE HUTCH	PART DOWN	SLICK	6.00
83	1294 Gordy label	HIGH INERGY	HE'S A PRETENDER	DON'T LET UP ON THE GROOVE	4.00
83	1294 DJ Gordy label	HIGH INERGY	HE'S A PRETENDER	DON'T LET UP ON THE GROOVE	5.00
83	1295	SMOKEY ROBINSON	I MADE LOVE TO YOU A THOUSAND TIMES	INTO EACH RAIN SOME LIFE MUST FALL	4.00
83	1295 DJ	SMOKEY ROBINSON	I MADE LOVE TO YOU A THOUSAND TIMES	INTO EACH RAIN SOME LIFE MUST FALL	5.00
83	1296 Gordy label	DeBARGE	I LIKE IT	HESITATED	4.00
83	1296 PS Gordy label	DeBARGE	I LIKE IT	HESITATED	5.00
83	1296 DJ Gordy label	DeBARGE	I LIKE IT	HESITATED	5.00
83	1297	TEMPTATIONS	LOVE ON MY MIND TONIGHT	BRING YOUR BODY HERE	5.00
83	1297 PS	TEMPTATIONS	LOVE ON MY MIND TONIGHT	BRING YOUR BODY HERE	6.00
83	1297 DJ	TEMPTATIONS	LOVE ON MY MIND TONIGHT	BRING YOUR BODY HERE	6.00
83	1298	ROBERT JOHN	BREAD AND BUTTER	IF YOU DON'T WANT MY LOVE	5.00
83	1298 DJ	ROBERT JOHN	BREAD AND BUTTER	IF YOU DON'T WANT MY LOVE	6.00
83	1299	DAZZ BAND	ON THE ONE	JUST BELIEVEIN LOVE	4.00
83	1299 DJ	DAZZ BAND	ON THE ONE	JUST BELIEVEIN LOVE	5.00
83	1300	LIONEL RICHIE	MY LOVE	ROUND AND ROUND	3.00
83	1300 PS	LIONEL RICHIE	MY LOVE	ROUND AND ROUND	4.00
83	1300 DJ	LIONEL RICHIE	MY LOVE	ROUND AND ROUND	4.00
83	1300 poster sleeve	LIONEL RICHIE	MY LOVE	ROUND AND ROUND	6.00
83	1301 Gordy label	MARY JANE GIRLS	CANDY MAN	same: instrumental	5.00
83	1301 DJ Gordy label	MARY JANE GIRLS	CANDY MAN	same: instrumental	6.00
83	1302	MONALISA YOUNG	DANCING MACHINE	I'LL BE THERE	3.00
83	1302 DJ	MONALISA YOUNG	DANCING MACHINE	I'LL BE THERE	4.00

83	1303	JERMAINE JACKSON	YOU MOVED A MOUNTAIN	RUNNING	4.00
83	1303 DJ	JERMAINE JACKSON	YOU MOVED A MOUNTAIN	RUNNING	5.00
83	1304	FINIS HENDERSON	SKIP TO MY LOU	I'D RATHER BE GONE	4.00
83	1304 DJ	FINIS HENDERSON	SKIP TO MY LOU	I'D RATHER BE GONE	5.00
83	1305	JOSE FELICIANO	LONELY TEARDROPS	CUIDADO	4.00
83	1305 DJ	JOSE FELICIANO	LONELY TEARDROPS	CUIDADO	5.00
83	1306	SYREETA	FOREVER IS NOT ENOUGH	SHE'S LEAVING HOME	4.00
83	1306 PS	SYREETA	FOREVER IS NOT ENOUGH	SHE'S LEAVING HOME	5.00
83	1306 DJ	SYREETA	FOREVER IS NOT ENOUGH	SHE'S LEAVING HOME	5.00
83	1307	SMOKEY ROBINSON	TOUCH THE SKY	ALL MY LIFE'S A LIE	4.00
83	1307 DJ	SMOKEY ROBINSON	TOUCH THE SKY	ALL MY LIFE'S A LIE	5.00
83	1308 Gordy label	DeBARGE	ALL THIS LOVE	I'M IN LOVE WITH LOVE	4.00
83	1308 DJ Gordy label	DeBARGE	ALL THIS LOVE	I'M IN LOVE WITH LOVE	5.00
83	1309 Gordy label	MARY JANE GIRLS	ALL NIGHT LONG	MUSICAL LOVE	4.00
83	1309 PS Gordy label	MARY JANE GIRLS	ALL NIGHT LONG	MUSICAL LOVE	5.00
83	1309 DJ Gordy label	MARY JANE GIRLS	ALL NIGHT LONG	MUSICAL LOVE	5.00
83	1310	CHARLENE	IF YOU TAKE AWAY THE PAIN UNTIL THE MORNING	RICHIE'S SONG (FOR RICHARD OLIVER)	4.00
83	1310 DJ	CHARLENE	IF YOU TAKE AWAY THE PAIN UNTIL THE MORNING	RICHIE'S SONG (FOR RICHARD OLIVER)	5.00
83	1311	MICHAEL LOVESMITH	BABY I WILL	WHAT'S THE BOTTOM LINE	6.00
83	1311 DJ	MICHAEL LOVESMITH	BABY I WILL	WHAT'S THE BOTTOM LINE	8.00
83	1312 not issued	GARY BYRD & the GB EXPERIENCE	THE CROWN	same: instrumental	UN
83	1313	SMOKEY ROBINSON & BARBARA MITCHELL	BLAME IT ON LOVE	EVEN THO'	4.00
83	1313 PS	SMOKEY ROBINSON & BARBARA MITCHELL	BLAME IT ON LOVE	EVEN THO'	5.00
83	1313 DJ	SMOKEY ROBINSON & BARBARA MITCHELL	BLAME IT ON LOVE	EVEN THO'	5.00
83	1314 Gordy label	RICK JAMES	COLD BLOODED	same: instrumental	4.00
83	1314 DJ Gordy label	RICK JAMES	COLD BLOODED	same: instrumental	5.00
83	1315 Gordy label	MARY JANE GIRLS	BOYS	YOU ARE MY HEAVEN	4.00
83	1315 PS Gordy label	MARY JANE GIRLS	BOYS	YOU ARE MY HEAVEN	5.00
83	1315 DJ Gordy label	MARY JANE GIRLS	BOYS	YOU ARE MY HEAVEN	5.00
83	1316 Gordy label	STONE CITY BAND	LADIES CHOICE	same: instrumental	4.00
83	1316 DJ Gordy label	STONE CITY BAND	LADIES CHOICE	same: instrumental	5.00
83	1317	COMMODORES	ONLY YOU	CEBU	3.00
83	1317 PS	COMMODORES	ONLY YOU	CEBU	4.00
83	1317 DJ	COMMODORES	ONLY YOU	CEBU	5.00
83	1318	JUNIOR WALKER	BLOW THE HOUSE DOWN	BALL BABY	4.00
83	1318 PS	JUNIOR WALKER	BLOW THE HOUSE DOWN	BALL BABY	6.00
83	1318 DJ	JUNIOR WALKER	BLOW THE HOUSE DOWN	BALL BABY	5.00
83	1319	LIONEL RICHIE	ALL NIGHT LONG (ALL NIGHT)	WANDERING STRANGER	3.00
83	1319 PS	LIONEL RICHIE	ALL NIGHT LONG (ALL NIGHT)	WANDERING STRANGER	4.00
83	1319 DJ	LIONEL RICHIE	ALL NIGHT LONG (ALL NIGHT)	WANDERING STRANGER	5.00
83	1320 Tamla Motown	TEMPTATIONS & FOUR TOPS	MEDLEY	PAPA WAS A ROLLING STONE	4.00
83	1320 DJ Tamla Motown	TEMPTATIONS & FOUR TOPS	MEDLEY	PAPA WAS A ROLLING STONE	6.00
83	1321	FOUR TOPS	I JUST CAN'T WALK AWAY	HANG	5.00
83	1321 PS	FOUR TOPS	I JUST CAN'T WALK AWAY	HANG	6.00
83	1321 DJ	FOUR TOPS	I JUST CAN'T WALK AWAY	HANG	6.00
83	1322	COMMODORES	TURN OFF THE LIGHTS	PAINTED PICTURE	3.00
83	1322 PS	COMMODORES	TURN OFF THE LIGHTS	PAINTED PICTURE	3.00
83	1322 DJ	COMMODORES	TURN OFF THE LIGHTS	PAINTED PICTURE	5.00
84	1323	BOBBY NUNN	ON'T KNOCK IT (UNTIL YOU TRY IT)	PRIVATE PARTY	5.00
84	1323 DJ	BOBBY NUNN	ON'T KNOCK IT (UNTIL YOU TRY IT)	PRIVATE PARTY	6.00
84	1324	LIONEL RICHIE	RUNNING WITH THE NIGHT	SERVES YOU RIGHT	3.00
84	1324 PS	LIONEL RICHIE	RUNNING WITH THE NIGHT	SERVES YOU RIGHT	4.00
84	1324 DJ	LIONEL RICHIE	RUNNING WITH THE NIGHT	SERVES YOU RIGHT	5.00
84	1325 12" only	MOTOR CITY CREW	SCRATCH BREAK (GLOVE STYLE)	LET'S BREAK	8.00
84	1326 12" only	STEVIE WONDER c/w REV. MARTIN LUTHER KING	HAPPY BIRTHDAY	I HAVE A DREAM speech	4.00
84	1327 Gordy label	RICK JAMES & FRIEND	EBONY EYES	1, 2, 3 (YOU, HER AND ME)	4.00
84	1327 PS Gordy label	RICK JAMES & FRIEND	EBONY EYES	1, 2, 3 (YOU, HER AND ME)	5.00
84	1327 DJ Gordy label	RICK JAMES & FRIEND	EBONY EYES	1, 2, 3 (YOU, HER AND ME)	5.00
84	1328 **12" only**	DAZZ BAND	JOYSTICK	DON'T GET CAUGHT IN THE MIDDLE	6.00
84	1329 Gordy label	DeBARGE	TIME WILL REVEAL	I'LL NEVER FALL IN LOVE AGAIN	4.00
84	1329 PS Gordy label	DeBARGE	TIME WILL REVEAL	I'LL NEVER FALL IN LOVE AGAIN	5.00
84	1329 DJ Gordy label	DeBARGE	TIME WILL REVEAL	I'LL NEVER FALL IN LOVE AGAIN	5.00
84	1330	LIONEL RICHIE	HELLO	ALL NIGHT LONG instrumental	3.00
84	1330 PS	LIONEL RICHIE	HELLO	ALL NIGHT LONG instrumental	4.00
84	1330 DJ	LIONEL RICHIE	HELLO	ALL NIGHT LONG instrumental	5.00
84	1331	ROCKWELL	SOMEBODY'S WATCHING ME	same: instrumental	3.00
84	1331 DJ	ROCKWELL	SOMEBODY'S WATCHING ME	same: instrumental	4.00
84	1332	KEITH & DARRELL	THE THINGS YOU'RE MADE OF	WORK THAT BODY	20.00
84	1332 DJ	KEITH & DARRELL	THE THINGS YOU'RE MADE OF	WORK THAT BODY	30.00
84	1333 PS	TIGGI CLAY	THE WINNER GETS THE HEART	WHO SHOT ZORRO	4.00
84	1333 PS DJ	TIGGI CLAY	THE WINNER GETS THE HEART	WHO SHOT ZORRO	5.00
84	1334 Gordy label	DENNIS EDWARDS	I THOUGHT I COULD HANDLE IT	DON'T LOOK ANY FURTHER	6.00
84	1334 DJ Gordy label	DENNIS EDWARDS	I THOUGHT I COULD HANDLE IT	DON'T LOOK ANY FURTHER	8.00
84	1335	BOBBY KING & SILVER FOXX	LOVEQUAKE	FALL IN LOVE	5.00
84	1335 DJ	BOBBY KING & SILVER FOXX	LOVEQUAKE	FALL IN LOVE	8.00
84	1336	BOBBY KING	LOVEQUAKE	FALL IN LOVE	5.00
84	1336 DJ	BOBBY KING	LOVEQUAKE	FALL IN LOVE	6.00
84	1337	KIDD GLOVE	GOOD CLEAN FUN	STREET ANGEL	3.00
84	1337 PS	KIDD GLOVE	GOOD CLEAN FUN	STREET ANGEL	4.00
84	1337 DJ	KIDD GLOVE	GOOD CLEAN FUN	STREET ANGEL	4.00
84	1338	DAZZ BAND	SWOOP (I'M YOURS	BAD GIRL	4.00
84	1338 DJ	DAZZ BAND	SWOOP (I'M YOURS)	BAD GIRL	5.00
84	1339	BOBBY WOMACK & PATI LABELLE	TELL ME WHY	THROUGH THE EYES OF A CHILD	6.00
84	1339 PS DJ	BOBBY WOMACK & PATI LABELLE	TELL ME WHY	THROUGH THE EYES OF A CHILD	8.00
84	1340 Gordy label	DENNIS EDWARDS	(YOU'RE MY) APHRODISIAC	SHAKE HANDS (COME OUT DANCING	4.00
84	1341	LIONEL RICHIE	STUCK ON YOU	ROUND AND ROUND	3.00
84	1341 PS	LIONEL RICHIE	STUCK ON YOU	ROUND AND ROUND	3.00
84	1341 DJ	LIONEL RICHIE	STUCK ON YOU	ROUND AND ROUND	5.00

84	1342 PS	MICHAEL JACKSON	FAREWELL MY SUMMER LOVE	CALL ON ME	4.00
84	1342 PS DJ	MICHAEL JACKSON	FAREWELL MY SUMMER LOVE	CALL ON ME	5.00
84	1343	DUKE JUPITER	LITTLE LADY	I'VE GOT A LITTLE BLACK BOOK	4.00
84	1343 PS	DUKE JUPITER	LITTLE LADY	I'VE GOT A LITTLE BLACK BOOK	5.00
84	1343 DJ	DUKE JUPITER	LITTLE LADY	I'VE GOT A LITTLE BLACK BOOK	5.00
84	1344	SMOKEY ROBINSON	AND I DON'T LOVE YOU	DYNAMITE	4.00
84	1344 PS	SMOKEY ROBINSON	AND I DON'T LOVE YOU	DYNAMITE	5.00
84	1344 DJ	SMOKEY ROBINSON	AND I DON'T LOVE YOU	DYNAMITE	5.00
84	1345	ROCKWELL	TAX MAN	WASTING TIME	4.00
84	1345 DJ	ROCKWELL	TAX MAN	WASTING TIME	5.00
84	1346	WOLF & WOLF	DON'T TAKE THE CANDY	WAR OF NERVES	4.00
84	1346 PS	WOLF & WOLF	DON'T TAKE THE CANDY	WAR OF NERVES	5.00
84	1346 DJ	WOLF & WOLF	DON'T TAKE THE CANDY	WAR OF NERVES	5.00
84	1347	BOBBY KINGfeat: ALFIE SILAS	CLOSE TO ME	LOVE IN THE FIRE	4.00
84	1347 PS	BOBBY KINGfeat: ALFIE SILAS	CLOSE TO ME	LOVE IN THE FIRE	5.00
84	1347 PS DJ	BOBBY KINGfeat: ALFIE SILAS	CLOSE TO ME	LOVE IN THE FIRE	6.00
84	1348 gordy label	RICK JAMES	17	same: instrumental	4.00
84	1348 PS gordy label	RICK JAMES	17	same: instrumental	5.00
84	1348 DJ gordy label	RICK JAMES	17	same: instrumental	5.00
84	1349 PS	STEVIE WONDER	I JUST CALLED TO SAY I LOVE YOU	same: instrumental	3.00
84	1349 PS DJ	STEVIE WONDER	I JUST CALLED TO SAY I LOVE YOU	same: instrumental	4.00
84	1350	COYOTE SISTERS	STRAIGHT FROM THE HEART	ECHO	5.00
84	1350 DJ	COYOTE SISTERS	STRAIGHT FROM THE HEART	ECHO	6.00
84	1351	SAMMY DAVIS JR.	HELLO DETROIT	same: instrumental	4.00
84	1351 PS	SAMMY DAVIS JR.	HELLO DETROIT	same: instrumental	5.00
84	1351 DJ	SAMMY DAVIS JR.	HELLO DETROIT	same: instrumental	5.00
84	1352	CHARLENE	WE'RE BOTH IN LOVE WITH YOU	RICHIE'S SONG (FOR RICHARD OLIVER)	4.00
84	1352 PS	CHARLENE	WE'RE BOTH IN LOVE WITH YOU	RICHIE'S SONG (FOR RICHARD OLIVER)	5.00
84	1352 DJ	CHARLENE	WE'RE BOTH IN LOVE WITH YOU	RICHIE'S SONG (FOR RICHARD OLIVER)	5.00
84	1353	BOBBY WOMACK	SURPRISE SURPRISE	AMERICAN DREAM	5.00
84	1353 PS	BOBBY WOMACK	SURPRISE SURPRISE	AMERICAN DREAM	6.00
84	1353 DJ	BOBBY WOMACK	SURPRISE SURPRISE	AMERICAN DREAM	6.00
84	1354	SAM HARRIS	SUGAR DON'T BITE	YOU KEEP ME HANGING ON	4.00
84	1354 PS	SAM HARRIS	SUGAR DON'T BITE	YOU KEEP ME HANGING ON	5.00
84	1354 DJ	SAM HARRIS	SUGAR DON'T BITE	YOU KEEP ME HANGING ON	5.00
84	1355	MICHAEL JACKSON	GIRL YO'RE SO TOGETHER	TOUCH THE ONE YOU LOVE	3.00
84	1355 PS	MICHAEL JACKSON	GIRL YO'RE SO TOGETHER	TOUCH THE ONE YOU LOVE	5 00
84	1355 DJ	MICHAEL JACKSON	GIRL YO'RE SO TOGETHER	TOUCH THE ONE YOU LOVE	5.00
84	1356	LIONEL RICHIE	PENNY LOVER	YOU ARE	4.00
84	1356 PS	LIONEL RICHIE	PENNY LOVER	YOU ARE	5.00
84	1356 DJ	LIONEL RICHIE	PENNY LOVER	YOU ARE	5.00
84	1357	JAKATA	HELL IS ON THE RUN	DON'T EVER LET GO	4.00
84	1357 PS	JAKATA	HELL IS ON THE RUN	DON'T EVER LET GO	5.00
84	1357 DJ	JAKATA	HELL IS ON THE RUN	DON'T EVER LET GO	5.00
84	1358	PHYLISS ST. JAMES	CANDLELIGHT AFTERNOON	BACK IN THE RACE	5.00
84	1358 DJ	PHYLISS ST. JAMES	CANDLELIGHT AFTERNOON	BACK IN THE RACE	6.00
84	1359 Gordy label	RICK JAMES	YOU TURN ME ON	FIRE AND DESIRE	4.00
84	1359 PS Gordy label	RICK JAMES	YOU TURN ME ON	FIRE AND DESIRE	5.00
84	1359 DJ Gordy label	RICK JAMES	YOU TURN ME ON	FIRE AND DESIRE	5.00
84	1360	VANITY	PRETTY MESS	same: instrumental	4.00
84	1360 PS	VANITY	PRETTY MESS	same: instrumental	5.00
84	1360 DJ	VANITY	PRETTY MESS	same: instrumental	5.00
84	1361	DAZZ BAND	LET IT ALL BLOW	NOW THAT I HAVE YOU	4.00
84	1361 DJ	DAZZ BAND	LET IT ALL BLOW	NOW THAT I HAVE YOU	5.00
84	1362	COYOTE SISTERS	I'VE GOT A RADIO	I'LL DO IT	4.00
84	1362 DJ	COYOTE SISTERS	I'VE GOT A RADIO	I'LL DO IT	5.00
84	1363	KOKO-POP	I'M IN LOVE WITH YOU	ON THE BEACH	4.00
84	1363 DJ	KOKO-POP	I'M IN LOVE WITH YOU	ON THE BEACH	5.00
84	1364	STEVIE WONDER	LOVE LIGHT IN FLIGHT	IT'S MORE THAN YOU	3.00
84	1364 PS	STEVIE WONDER	LOVE LIGHT IN FLIGHT	IT'S MORE THAN YOU	4.00
84	1364 DJ	STEVIE WONDER	LOVE LIGHT IN FLIGHT	IT'S MORE THAN YOU	4.00
84	1365	TEMPTATIONS	TREAT HER LIKE A LADY	ISN'T THE NIGHT FANTASTIC	4.00
84	1365 PS	TEMPTATIONS	TREAT HER LIKE A LADY	ISN'T THE NIGHT FANTASTIC	5.00
84	1365 DJ	TEMPTATIONS	TREAT HER LIKE A LADY	ISN'T THE NIGHT FANTASTIC	6.00
84	1366	THOMAS McCLARY	THIN WALLS	LOVE WILL FIND A WAY	4.00
84	1366 PS	THOMAS McCLARY	THIN WALLS	LOVE WILL FIND A WAY	5.00
84	1366 DJ	THOMAS McCLARY	THIN WALLS	LOVE WILL FIND A WAY	5.00
85	1367 not released	PHYLISS ST. JAMES	AIN'T NO TURNING BACK	RULER OF THE HUNT	UN
85	1368	DAZZ BAND	HEARTBEAT	ROCK WITH ME	4.00
85	1368 PS	DAZZ BAND	HEARTBEAT	ROCK WITH ME	5.00
85	1368 DJ	DAZZ BAND	HEARTBEAT	ROCK WITH ME	5.00
85	1369	VANITY	MECHANICAL EMOTION	CRAZY MAYBE	4.00
85	1369 DJ	VANITY	MECHANICAL EMOTION	CRAZY MAYBE	5.00
85	1370	SAM HARRIS	HEART'S ON FIRE	OVER THE RAINBOW	3.00
85	1370 PS	SAM HARRIS	HEART'S ON FIRE	OVER THE RAINBOW	4.00
85	1370 PS DJ	SAM HARRIS	HEART'S ON FIRE	OVER THE RAINBOW	4.00
85	1371	COMMODORES	NIGHT SHIFT	I KEEP RUNNING	3.00
85	1371 DJ	COMMODORES	NIGHT SHIFT	I KEEP RUNNING	5.00
85	1372	STEVIE WONDER	DON'T DRIVE DRUNK	same: instrumental	4.00
85	1372 PS	STEVIE WONDER	DON'T DRIVE DRUNK	same: instrumental	5.00
85	1372 DJ	STEVIE WONDER	DON'T DRIVE DRUNK	same: instrumental	5.00
85	1373	TEMPTATIONS	MY LOVE ISTRUE (TRULY FOR YOU)	I'LL KEEP MY LIGHT IN MY WINDOW	6.00
85	1373 PS	TEMPTATIONS	MY LOVE ISTRUE (TRULY FOR YOU)	I'LL KEEP MY LIGHT IN MY WINDOW	8.00
85	1373 DJ	TEMPTATIONS	MY LOVE ISTRUE (TRULY FOR YOU)	I'LL KEEP MY LIGHT IN MY WINDOW	8.00
85	1374	ROCKWELL	HE'S A COBRA	CHANGE YOUR WAYS	4.00
85	1374 PS	ROCKWELL	HE'S A COBRA	CHANGE YOUR WAYS	5.00
85	1374 DJ	ROCKWELL	HE'S A COBRA	CHANGE YOUR WAYS	5.00
85	1375	THOMAS McCLARY	MAD IN THE MIDDLE	same: instrumental	4.00

85	1375 DJ	THOMAS McCLARY	MAD IN THE MIDDLE	same: instrumental	5.00
85	1376 Gordy label	DeBARGE	RHYTHM OF THE NIGHT	QUEEN OF THE NIGHT	4.00
85	1376 PS Gordy label	DeBARGE	RHYTHM OF THE NIGHT	QUEEN OF THE NIGHT	5.00
85	1377 Gordy label	MARY JANE GIRLS	IN MY HOUSE	same: instrumental	5.00
85	1377 PS Gordy label	MARY JANE GIRLS	IN MY HOUSE	same: instrumental	6.00
85	1378 Gordy label	RICK JAMES	CAN'T STOP	OH WHAT A NIGHT (4 LUV)	4.00
85	1378 PS Gordy label	RICK JAMES	CAN'T STOP	OH WHAT A NIGHT (4 LUV)	5.00
85	1379	JAKATA	GOLDEN GIRL	LIGHT AT THE END OF THE TUNNEL	4.00
85	1379 PS	JAKATA	GOLDEN GIRL	LIGHT AT THE END OF THE TUNNEL	5.00
85	1379 DJ	JAKATA	GOLDEN GIRL	LIGHT AT THE END OF THE TUNNEL	5.00
85	1380 t. motown	DIANA ROSS	LOVE HANGOVER	REMEMBER ME	4.00
85	1380 DJ t. motown	DIANA ROSS	LOVE HANGOVER	REMEMBER ME	5.00
85	1381 t. motown	MARVIN GAYE	HOW SWEET IT IS (TO BE LOVED BY YOU)	GOT TO GIVE IT UP	4.00
85	1381 DJ t. motown	MARVIN GAYE	HOW SWEET IT IS (TO BE LOVED BY YOU)	GOT TO GIVE IT UP	6.00
85	1382	THELMA HOUSTON	DON'T LEAVE ME THIS WAY	JUMPIN' JACK FLASH	4.00
85	1382 DJ	THELMA HOUSTON	DON'T LEAVE ME THIS WAY	JUMPIN' JACK FLASH	6.00
85	1383	BONNIE POINTER	HEAVEN MUST HAVE SENT YOU	DEEP INSIDE MY SOUL	4.00
85	1383 DJ	BONNIE POINTER	HEAVEN MUST HAVE SENT YOU	DEEP INSIDE MY SOUL	5.00
85	1384	STEVIE WONDER	I WISH	SIR DUKE	3.00
85	1384 DJ	STEVIE WONDER	I WISH	SIR DUKE	4.00
85	1385	TEENA MARIE	BEHIND THE GROOVE	I NEED YOR LOVIN'	4.00
85	1385 DJ	TEENA MARIE	BEHIND THE GROOVE	I NEED YOR LOVIN'	5.00
85	1386	STEVIE WONDER	DO I DO	I AIN'T GONNA STAND FOR IT	4.00
85	1386 DJ	STEVIE WONDER	DO I DO	I AIN'T GONNA STAND FOR IT	4.00
85	1387	DIANA ROSS	MY OLD PIANO	I'M COMING OUT	4.00
85	1387 DJ	DIANA ROSS	MY OLD PIANO	I'M COMING OUT	4.00
85	1388	STEVIE WONDER	HE'S MISSTRA KNOW –IT-ALL	BOOGIE ON REGGAE WOMAN	4.00
85	1388 DJ	STEVIE WONDER	HE'S MISSTRA KNOW –IT-ALL	BOOGIE ON REGGAE WOMAN	4.00
85	1389 not released	STEVIE WONDER	UPSET STOMACH		NR
85	1390	ALFIE (SILAS)	STAR	KEEP ON SMILIN'	4.00
85	1390 PS	ALFIE (SILAS)	STAR	KEEP ON SMILIN'	5.00
85	1390 DJ	ALFIE (SILAS)	STAR	KEEP ON SMILIN'	5.00
92	1411 PS	BOYZ II MEN	END OF THE ROAD	same: instrumental	4.00
93	1426	MARVIN GAYE	LUCKY LUCKY ME (RADIO EDIT)	LUCKY LUCK ME (PURE SOUL MIX)	20.00
93	1426 PS	MARVIN GAYE	LUCKY LUCKY ME (RADIO EDIT)	LUCKY LUCK ME (PURE SOUL MIX)	30.00

4000 series were released across Europe using the same release numbers. All numbers preceded by ZB

85	40097 PS	COMMODORES	ANIMAL INSTINCT	LIGHTIN' UP THE NIGHT	4.00
85	40099 PS	ROCKWELL	PEEPING TOM	TOKYO	4.00
85	40113 PS	EMOTIONS	MISS YOUR LOVE	I CAN'T WAIT TO MAKE YOU MINE	4.00
85	40159 PS	MAUREEN STEELE	SAVE THE NIGHT FOR ME	ROCK MY HEART	4.00
85	40173 PS	WILLIE HUTCH	KEEP ON JAMMING	THE GLOW	4.00
85	40201 PS	JAKE JACAS	HOLD ME	same: instrumental	4.00
85	40213 PS	DeBARGE	WHO'S HOLDING DONNA NOW	BE MY LADY	4.00
85	40223 PS	RICK JAMES	GLOW	same: instrumental	4.00
85	40271 PS	MARY JANE GIRLS	WILD AND CRAZY LOVE	same: instrumental	4.00
85	40273 PS	MICHAEL LOVESMITH	BREAK THE OCE	LUCKY IN LOVE	4.00
85	40307 PS	DAZZ BAND	HOT SPOT	I'VE BEEN WAITING	4.00
85	40311 PS	COMMODORES	JANET	I'M IN LOVE	4.00
85	40343 PS	MAUREEN STEELE	BOYS WILL BE BOYS	ROCK MY HEART	4.00
85	40345 PS Gordy label	EL DeBARGE with DeBARGE	YOU WEAR IT WELL	BABY WON'TCHA COME QUICK	4.00
85	40351 PS	STEVIE WONDER	PART-TIME LOVER	same: instrumental	4.00
85	40369 PS	MICHAEL LOVESMITH	AIN'T NOTHING LIKE IT	FAST GIRLS	6.00
85	40401 PS	KOKO POP	BRAND NEW BREED	BRAND NEW BREED part 2	4.00
85	40419 PS gordy 12"	VAL YOUNG	SEDUCTION	same: instrumental	4.00
85	40421 PS	LIONEL RICHIE	SAY YOU SAY ME	CAN'T SLOW DOWN	4.00
85	40453 PS	TEMPTATIONS	DO YOU REALLY LOVE YOUR BABY	I'LL KEEP MY LIGHT IN MY WINDOW	4.00
85	40497 PS Gordy label	EL DeBARGE with DeBARGE	THE HEART IS NOT SO SMART	SHARE MY WORLD	4.00
85	40501 PS	STEVIE WONDER	GO HOME	same: instrumental	4.00
86	40503 PS	WARP 9	SKIPS A BEAT	same: dub version	4.00
86	40553 PS	SMOKEY ROBINSON	HOLD ON TO YOUR LOVE	TRAIN OF THOUGHT	4.00
86	40554 PS	PAL	TALK WE DON'T	same: instrumental	4.00
86	40567 PS	STEVIE WONDER	OVERJOYED	same: instrumental	4.00
86	40571 PS *	SAM HARRIS	DO IT ALL AGAIN	THE RESCUE	4.00
86	40577 PS Gordy label	VAL YOUNG	IF I SHOULD EVER BE LONELY	same: instrumental	4.00
86	40609 PS	VANITY	UNDER THE INFLUENCE	same: instrumental	4.00
86	40621 PS	TEMPTATIONS	I'M FASCINATED	HOW CAN YOU SAY THAT IT'S OVER	4.00
86	40701 Tamla Motown	MARVIN GAYE	I HEARD IT THROUGH THE GRAPEVINE	CAN I GET A WITNESS	4.00
86	40709 Tamla Motown	DIANA ROSS & the SUPREMES	YOU KEEP ME HANGING ON	COME SEE ABOUT ME	4.00
86	40717 PS	SMOKEY ROBINSON	SLEEPLESS NIGHTS	CLOSE ENCOUNTERS OF THE FIRST KIND	4.00
86	40721 PS *	LIONEL RITCHIE	DANCING ON THE CEILING	LOVE WILL FIND A WAY	4.00
86	40723 PS	EL DeBARGE with DeBARGE	WHO'S JOHNNY	LOVE ME IN A SPECIAL WAY	4.00
86	40743 PS Tamla Motown	TEMPTATIONS	MY GIRL	WHERE EVER I LAY MY HAT (THAT'S MY HOME)	5.00
86	40747 PS *`	STEVIE WONDER	LAND OF LA LA	same: instrumental	4.00
86	40755 PS Gordy label	RICK JAMES	SWEET AND SEXY THING	same: instrumental	4.00
86	40767 PS	MARVIN GAYE	LONELY LOVER	THE WORLD IS RATED X	40.00
86	40767	MARVIN GAYE	LONELY LOVER	THE WORLD IS RATED X	30.00
86	40777 PS	ROCKWELL	CARME ·	CARME part 2	4.00
86	40795 PS	MARY JANE GIRLS	WALK LIKE A MAN	SHADOW LOVER	4.00
86	40803 Tamla Motown	DIANA ROSS	AIN'T NO MOUNTAIN HIGH ENOUGH	IT'S MY HOUSE	4.00
86	40845 PS *	EL DeBARGE with DeBARGE	LOVE ALWAYS	THE WALLS (COME TUMBLING DOWN)	4.00
86	40847 PS	FOUR TOPS	HOT NIGHTS	AGAIN	4.00
86	40849 PS	TEMPTATIONS	LADY SOUL	A FINE MESS	15.00
86	40849	TEMPTATIONS	LADY SOUL	A FINE MESS	10.00
86	40885 PS	STACY LATTISAW	NAIL IT TO THE WALL	same: instrumental	4.00
86	40887 PS	CHICO DeBARGE	TALK TO ME	IF IT TAKES ALL NIGHT	4.00
87	41033 PS	GENERAL KANE	HAIRDOOZ	CRACK KILLED APPLEJACK	4.00
87	41109 PS	STACY LATTISAW	JUMP INTO MY LIFE	LONGSHOT	4.00
87	41117 PS	BRUCE WILLIS	RESPECT YOURSELF	FUN TIME	4.00

Year	Catalog #	Artist	Title	Notes / B-side	Price
87	41123 PS	CHICO DeBARGE	THE GIRL NEXT DOOR	YOU'RE MUCH TO FAST	4.00
87	41147 PS	SMOKEY ROBINSON	JUST TO SEE HER	TE QUIERO COMO SI HUBIERA UN	4.00
87	41147 PS	SMOKEY ROBINSON	THE TRACKS OF MY TEARS	JUST TO SEE HER +TE QUIERO COMO SI HUBIERA	8.00
87	41209 PS	GEORGIO	SEXAPPEAL	same: instrumental	4.00
88	41273 PS	BRUCE WILLIS	YOUNG BLOOD	FLIRTING WITH DISASTER	4.00
87	41277 PS	DARRYL DUNCAN	ROCK THE HOUSE	same: instrumental	4.00
87	41349 PS	BRUCE WILLIS	UNDER THE BOARDWALK	JACKPOT (BRUNO'S BOP)	4.00
87	41373	SMOKEY ROBINSON & the MIRACLES	THE TRACKS OF MY TEARS	I SECOND THAT EMOTION	4.00
87	41411 PS	KIM O'LEARY	PUT THE PIECES BACK	THE KIDS DOWNTOWN	NR
87	41431 PS	TEMPTATIONS	PAPA WAS A ROLLING STONE (remix)	AIN'T TOO PROUD TO BEG	4.00
87	41433 PS	GENERAL KANE	GIRL PULLED THE DOG	CUTTIN' IT UP	4.00
87	41437 PS	BRUCE WILLIS	SECRET AGENT MAN/JAMES BOND IS	LOSE MYSELF	4.00
87	41439 PS	STEVIE WONDER	SKELETONS	same: instrumental	4.00
87	41501 PS	CARRIE McDOWELL	UH UH, NO NO CASUAL SEX	UH UH, NO NO CASUAL SEX part 2	4.00
87	41525 PS	SMOKEY ROBINSON	ONE HEARTBEAT	LOVE WILL SET YOU FREE	4.00
87	41547 PS	TEMPTATIONS	I WONDER WHO SHE'S SEEING NOW	GIRL (THEY LIKE IT)	4.00
87	41555 PS	GEORGIO	TINA CHERRY	same: bonus beats	4.00
87	41583	WILSON PICKETT	IN THE MIDNIGHT HOUR	same: instrumental	5.00
87	41611 PS	GEORGIO	LOVER'S LANE	LOVERS LANE after hous mix	4.00
87	41651 PS	CARRIE McDOWELL	WHEN A MAN LOVES A WOMAN	THE TRACKS OF MY TEARS	4.00
87	41653 PS	BRUCE WILLIS	COMIN' RIGHT UP	DOWN IN HOLLYWOOD	4.00
87	41655 EP	JACKSON 5	THE CHRISTMAS EP:	3 track EP	4.00
88	41723 PS	STEVIE WONDER	YOU WILL KNOW	same: instrumental	4.00
88	41733	TEMPTATIONS	LOOK WHAT YOU STARTED	same: radio edit	4.00
88	41739 PS	DARRYL DUNCAN	JAMES BROWN	JAMES BROWN part 2	4.00
88	41783 PS	SMOKEY ROBINSON	LOVE DON'T GIVE NO REASON	same: radio mix	4.00
88	41903	BARRETT STRONG c/w CONTOURS	MONEY (THAT'S WHAT I WANT)	DO YOU LOVE ME	5.00
88	41911	BRENDA HOLLOWAY	WHEN I'M GONE	JUST LOOK WHAT YOU'VE DONE	6.00
88	41913	JACKSON 5	I WANT YOU BACK	NEVER CAN SAY GOODBYE	4.00
88	41915 PS	SHORTY LONG	HERE COMES THE JUDGE	FUNCTION AT THE JUNCTION	4.00
88	41929	DETROIT SPINNERS c/w EDDIE KENDRICKS	IT'S A SHAME	KEEP ON TRUCKIN'	3.00
88	41943 PS	FOUR TOPS	REACH OUT I'LL BE THERE extra producion	STANDING IN THE SHADOWS OF LOVE	4.00
88	42307 PS	DIANA ROSS	LOVE HANGOVER pwl 88 remix	same: instrumental	4.00
89	43233 PS	TEMPTATIONS	ALL I WANT FROM YOU	same: instrumental	5.00
86	ELD 1 PS	EL DeBARGE with DeBARGE	WHO'S JOHNNY	LOVE ME IN A SPECIAL WAY	4.00
86`	ELD 2 PS*	EL DeBARGE with DeBARGE	LOVE ALWAYS	THE WALLS (COME TUMBLING DOWN)	4.00

* release # transferred to ZB40845

Year	Catalog #	Artist	Title	Notes / B-side	Price
86	GUINN 1 PS	GUINN	OPEN YOUR DOOR	SINCERELY	4.00
86	GUINN 2 PS	GUINN	PEOPLE WILL BE PEOPLE	DREAMIN'	4.00
86	LIO 1 PS	LIONEL RICHIE	DANCING ON THE CEILING	LOVE WILL FIND A WAY	4.00
86	LIO 2 PS	LIONEL RICHIE	LOVE WILL CONQUER ALL	THE ONLY ONE	4.00
86	LIO 3 PS	LIONEL RICHIE	BALLERINA GIRL	DEEP RIVER WOMAN	4.00
86	LIO 4 PS	LIONEL RICHIE	SE LA	SERVES YOU RIGHT	4.00
86	SAMMY 1 PS	SAM HARRIS	I'D DO IT ALL AGAIN	THE RESCUE	4.00
86	WOND 1 PS*	STEVIE WONDER	LAND OF LA LA	same: instrumental	4.00

* release # transferred to ZB40747

Year	Catalog #	Artist	Title	Notes / B-side	Price
86	WOND 2 PS	STEVIE WONDER	STRANGER ON THE SHORE OF LOVE	DID HEAR YOU SAY YOU LOVE ME	4.00
75	982160	TEMPTATIONS	AIN'T TOO PROUD TO BEG	MY GIRL	4.00

Tamla Motown 2000 series EP's with Picture Covers

Year	Catalog #	Artist	Title	Notes	Price
65	2001 EP PS	VARIOUS ARTISTS	HITSVILLE U.S.A.	1965 4 track EP with cover	100.00
65	2002 EP PS	CONTOURS	THE CONTOURS	1965 4 track EP with cover	100.00
65	2003 EP PS	MARVELETTES	TOO MANY FISH IN THE SEA	1965 4 track EP with cover	85.00
65	2004 EP PS	TEMPTATIONS	THE TEMPTATIONS	1965 4 track EP with cover	45.00
65	2005 EP PS	KIM WESTON	KIM WESTON	1965 4 track EP with cover	100.00
65	2006 EP PS	LITTLE STEVIE WONDER	LITTLE STEVIE WONDER	1965 4 track EP with cover	100.00
65	2007 EP PS	MARY WELLS	MARY WELLS	1965 4 track EP with cover	100.00
65	2008 EP PS sold subject	SUPREMES	SUPREMES HITS	first press with flipback seam	30.00
69	2008 EP PS no sold subject	SUPREMES	SUPREMES HITS	2nd. Press clean seam fold cover	15.00
65	2009 EP PS	MARTHA & THE VANDELLAS	MARTHA AND THE VANDELLAS	1965 4 track EP with cover	150.00
66	2010 EP PS	TEMPTATIONS	IT'S THE TEMPTATIONS	1965 UK 4 track ep	30.00
66	2011 EP PS	SUPREMES	SHAKE	1966 4 track EP with cover	85.00
66	2012 EP PS sold subject	FOUR TOPS	FOUR TOPS	first press with flipback seam	22.00
66	2012 EP PS no sold subjec	FOUR TOPS	FOUR TOPS	2nd. Press clean seam fold cover	10.00
66	2013 EP PS	JR. WALKER & THE ALL STARS	JR. WALKER & THE ALL STARS	1966 4 track EP with cover	45.00
66	2014 EP PS	VARIOUS ARTISTS	NEW FACES FROM HITSVILLE	1966 4 track EP with cover	300.00
66	2015 EP PS	KIM WESTON	ROCK ME A LITTLE WHILE	1966 4 track EP with cover	250.00
66	2016 EP PS	MARVIN GAYE	AIN'T THAT PECULIAR + HOW SWEET	1966 4 track EP with cover	45.00
66	2017 EP PS	MARTHA & THE VANDELLAS	HITTIN'	1965 4 track EP with cover	100.00
66	2018 EP PS	FOUR TOPS	FOUR TOP HITS	first press with flipback seam	22.00
66	2018 EP PS	FOUR TOPS	FOUR TOP HITS	2nd. Press clean fold cover	20.00
66	2019 EP PS	MARVIN GAYE	ORIGINALS FROM MARVIN GAYE	6 track EP with cover	25.00
	3024	FRANKIE VALLI & FOUR SEASONS	THE NIGHT	WHEN THE MORNING COMES	8.00
73	209 DJ PS	VARIOUS ARTISTS	TAMLA TRIPLE-PACK	PROMO ONLY 8 TRACK SAMPLER	40.00
66	PSRS 319 DJ	DAINA ROSS & THE SUPREMES	PARTY INVITATION DISC	blank:	200.00
	PRS 352 DJ	VARIOUS ARTISTS	OH PRETTY LADY - AL KENT + SLICK -	WE'LL HAVE IT MADE - SPINNERS	25.00

Various artists special promo 45 tracks include Al Kent – Oh Pretty Lady, Willie Hutch – Slick, Motown Spinners – We'll have it made

Year	Catalog #	Artist	Title	Notes	Price
73	PSR 353 DJ	VARIOUS ARISTS	MARVIN GAYE – LET'S GET IT ON	UNDISPUTED TRUTH + RARE EARTH + J.JACKSON	25.00
73	PSR 357 EP DJ	VARIOUS ARTISTS	BAD WEATHER (SUPREMES)	STANDIN IN THE SHADOWS (4 TOPS	25.00
73	PSR 360	TEMPTATIONS	THE WAY YOU DO THE THINGS YOU DO	SINCE I LOST MY BABY +	30.00
73	PRS 361 DJ	SMOKEY ROBINSON & MIRACLES	I GOTTA DANCE TO KEEP FROM CRYING	4 track promo only EP	30.00
73	PSR 362 DJ	GLADYS KNIGHT & the PIPS	JUST WALK IN MY SHOES	I HEARD IT THROUGH THE GRAPEVINE + 2	30.00
73	PSR 365 DJ	DIANA ROSS & the SUPREMES	BABY LOVE + YOU CAN'T HURRY LOVE	THE HAPPENING + LOVE CHILD	30.00
	PSR 370 DJ	JR. WALKER & THE ALL STARS	WHAT DOES IT TAKE + DO YOU SEE MY	THESE EYES + TAKE ME GIRL I'M	30.00
	PSR 378 DJ	COMMODORES	WIDE OPEN + THE BUMP	SLIPPERY WHEN WET	20.00
	PSR 399 DJ	DIANA ROSS	LOVE HANGOVER	spoken intro promo	30.00
77	PSR 417 DJ PS	VARIOUS ARTISTS	CHRISTMAS GREETINGS FROM MOTOWN	Ruffin, Hutch, Wonder, Commodores	20.00
70	SFI 66	VARIOUS ARTISTS	CHARTBUSTERS volume 5	33 1/3 rpm 5 track flexi disc	10.00

	SPSEP 209 DJ	VARIOUS ARTISTS	EXTRACTS FROM "SKYWRITER" LP	EXTRACTS FROM "LAW OF THE LAND	20.00

Below are some other 45's for UK Tamla Motown Collectors to consider adding to their collection:

HARRY J

70	6605 white	BOB & MARCIA	YOUNG, GIFTED AND BLACK	same: instrumental	8.00
70	6605 green	BOB & MARCIA	YOUNG, GIFTED AND BLACK	same: instrumental	6.00

release in July 1970 on USA Tamla 54197

ISLAND

70	6040	SOUL PURPOSE	HUMMIN'	SOUL DRINK	15.00

1968 UK press of a Chisa recording: Chisa became part of USA Motown in September 1969

PARLOPHONE

69	5787	VIRGIL BROTHERS	TEMPTATION 'BOUT TO GET ME	LOOK AWAY	20.00

released in 1969 on USA Rare Earth # 5006

POLYDOR

66	56702 lh	EDWIN STARR	I HAVE FAITH IN YOU	STOP HER ON SIGHT (S.O.S.)	20.00
66	56702 sh	EDWIN STARR	I HAVE FAITH IN YOU	STOP HER ON SIGHT (S.O.S.)	40.00
66	56702 DJ	EDWIN STARR	I HAVE FAITH IN YOU	STOP HER ON SIGHT (S.O.S.)	700.00

released 1966 Ric-Tic 109

66	56717	EDWIN STARR	HEADLINE NEWS	HARLEM	15.00

released 1966 1966 Ric-Tic 114

67	56726	EDWIN STARR	GIRLS ARE GETTING PRETTIER	IT'S MY TURN NOW	40.00

released 1967 Ric-Tic 118

67	56720	HOLIDAYS	I'LL LOVE YOU FOREVER	MAKIN' UP TIME	125.00

released Golden World 36

67	56722	J.J.BARNES	DEEPER IN LOVE	DAY TRIPPER	30.00

released 1966 Ric-Tic 117

STATESIDE

64	294	REFLECTIONS	(JUST LIKE) ROMEO AND JULIET	CAN'T YOU TELL BY THE LOOK IN	45.00

released 1964 on Golden World 9

65	406	REFLECTIONS	COMING AT YOU	POOR MAN'S SOON	30.00

released 1965 Golden World 20

65	1034 EP PS	REFLECTIONS	POOR MAN'S SON	1965 4 track EP with cover	**81.00**

4 tracks are a combination of the two releases above

YOUNGBLOOD

71	1023	JACK HAMMER	COLOUR COMBINATION	SWIM	15.00
71	1023 DJ	JACK HAMMER	COLOUR COMBINATION	SWIM	20.00

released in September 1971 on USA Soul 35088

TAMMI RECORDS

79	101	IMPERIALS	I JUST WANNA BE YOUR LOVIN' MAN	GOIN' OUT OF MY HEAD	5.00
79	101 DJ	IMPERIALS	I JUST WANNA BE YOUR LOVIN' MAN	GOIN' OUT OF MY HEAD	6.00
79	102	RAY MUNNINGS	IT COULD HAPPEN TO YOU	LET'S BOOGIE	50.00
79	102 DJ	RAY MUNNINGS	IT COULD HAPPEN TO YOU	LET'S BOOGIE	75.00
79	103	RAY MUNNINGS	FUNKY NASSAU	JUMP IN THE WATER	30.00
79	103 DJ	RAY MUNNINGS	FUNKY NASSAU	JUMP IN THE WATER	40.00

TANGERINE

71	6121001	RAY CHARLES	BOOTY BOOT	ZIG ZAG	15.00
71	6121002	RAELETTES	BAD WATER	THAT GOES TO SHOW	8.00
71	6121003	RAELETTES	HERE I GO AGAIN	LEAVE MY MAN (WOMAN) ALONE	8.00

TANGSONG

75	101	FOOTSIE	CONDITION RED	CABBAGE PATCH	10.00

TIFFANY

74	6121507	VELICIA	STOP THE WORLD	same: instrumental	6.00

TK

Miami, Florida based label is a soul and disco giant. Its artist rosta reads like a who's who of the disco scene. Missing numbers in the series were released out of the UK using the same numbering system. Very few of this late 70's label are valuable on UK releases, but this guide would certainly be poorer if this label was not documented properly.

88	1	TIMMY THOMAS	WHY CAN'TWE LIVE TOGETHER	same: war & peace edit version	4.00
77	2151	LATIMORE	SWEET VIBRATIONS	SOMETHIN' 'BOUT CHA	8.00
77	2167	K.C. and the SUNSHINE BAND	I'M YOUR BOOGIE MAN	WRAP YOUR ARMS AROUND ME	3.00
77	2173	JIMMY BO HORNE	GET HAPPY	IT'S YOUR SWEET LOVE	4.00
77	2180	FACTS OF LIFE	SOMETIMES	LOVE IS THE FINAL TRUTH	5.00
77	2182	CELI BEE	SUPERMAN	HURT ME, HURT ME	3.00
77	2183	PETER BROWN	DO YA WANNA GET FUNKY WITH ME	BURNING LOVE BREAKDOWN	4.00
77	6005	GEORGE McCRAE	KISS ME THE WAY I LIKE IT	same: different mix	3.00
77	6006	T-CONNECTION	ON FIRE	CRUSH	4.00
78	6009	PETER BROWN	DO YA WANNA GET FUNKY WITH ME	WITHOUT LOVE	4.00
78	6011	CHI COLTRANE	OOH BABY	BELLA AMI	4.00
78	6016	CONTROLLERS	SOMEBODY'S GOTTA WIN, SOMEBODY'S	FEELING A FEELING	5.00
78	6017	TIMMY THOMAS	TOUCH TO TYOUCH	WHEN A HOUSE HAS GOT MUSIC	4.00
78	6021	LONNIE LITSON SMITH	FUNK REACTION	WHEN THE NIGHT IS RIGHT	4.00
78	6024	T-CONNECTION	LET YOURSELF GO	GROOVE TO GET DOWN	4.00
78	6025	K.C. and the SUNSHINE BAND	BOOGIE SHOES	I GET LIFTED	3.00
78	6026	GEORGE McCRAE	LET'S DANCE	LET GEORGE DO IT	3.00
78	6027	PETER BROWN	DANCE WITH ME	FOR YOUR LOVE	3.00
78	6028	JIMMY BO HORNE	DANCE ACROSS THE FLOOR	IT'S YOUR SWEET LOVE	4.00
78	6032	CELI BEE	HOLD YOUR HORSES BABY	ALTERNATING CURRENTS	3.00
78	6034	USA EUROPEAN CONNECTION	COME INTO MY HEART	GOOD LOVIN'	4.00
78	6035	RALPH McDONALD	WHERE IS THE LOVE	CALYPSO BREAKDOWN	5.00
78	6036	SUNSHINE BAND	BLACK WATER GOLD	BLACK WATER GOLD 2	4.00
78	6037	K.C. and the SUNSHINE BAND	IT'S THE SAME OLD SONG	LET'S GO BABY	3.00
78	6038	FIRE	LET'S MAKE IT LAST	IT'S BEEN SO LONG	4.00
78	6040	FOXY	GET OFF	YOU MAKE ME HOT	3.00
78	6048	PETER BROWN	YOU SHOULD DO IT	WITHOUT LOVE	4.00
78	6049	JOE THOMAS	PLATO'S RETREAT	PLACE IN SPACE	4.00

78	6050	K.C. and the SUNSHINE BAND	DO YOU FEEL ALRIGHT	SHO' NUFF	3.00
79	7068	GEORGE McCRAE	ROCK YOUR BABY	IT'S BEEN SO LONG	3.00
79	7074	K.C. and the SUNSHINE BAND	QUEEN OF CLUBS	THAT'S THE WAY I LIKE IT	4.00
78	7505	TIMMY THOMAS	FREAK IN, FREAK OUT	SAY LOVE, CAN YOU CHASE MY BLUES AWAY	3.00
78	7509	CELI BEE	BOOMERANG	CAN'T LET YOU GO	4.00
78	7511	GREG DIAMOND	THIS SIDE OF MIDNIGHT	STAR CRUISER	3.00
78	7512	BEAUTIFUL BEND	BOOGIE MOTION	MAKE THAT FEELING COME AGAIN	3.00
79	7514	K.C. and the SUNSHINE BAND	WHO DO YOU LOVE	SO GLAD	3.00
79	7515	BOBBY CALDWELL	DOWN FOR THE THIRD TIME	MY FLAME	4.00
79	7517	T-CONNECTION	AT MIDNIGHT	PLAYING GAMES	5.00
79	7524	LATIMORE	TOO HOT TO HANDLE	LET ME GO	4.00
79	7529	BOBBY CALDWELL	WHAT YOU WON'T DO FOR LOVE	LOVE WON'T WAIT	8.00
79	7532	FOXY	HOT NUMBER	CALL IT LOVE	3.00
79	7534	GREGG DIAMOND	HOLDING BACK	DOING THAT (FANCY DANCER)	4.00
79	7536	T-CONNECTION	SATURDAY NIGHT	PRISONER OF MY MIND	4.00
79	7539	K.C. and the SUNSHINE BAND	DO YOU WANNA GO PARTY	COME TO MY ISLAND	3.00
79	7540	ISH	FASTER THAN A SPEEDING BULLET	DON'T STOP	3.00
79	7541	K.C. and the SUNSHINE BAND	I WILL LOVE YOU TOMORROW	COME TO MY ISLAND	3.00
79	7543	ANITA WARD	RING MY BELL	IF I COULD FEEL THAT OLD FEELING	3.00
79	7544	JOE THOMAS	MAKE YOUR MOVE	GET ON BACK	4.00
79	7545	PETER BROWN	CRANK IT UP (FUNK TOWN)	CRANK IT UP (FUNK TOWN) part 2	4.00
79	7550	FOXY	HEADHUNTER	LADY OF THE STREET	3.00
79	7551	ANITA WARD	MAKE BELIEVE LOVERS	SPOILED BY OUR LOVE	5.00
79	7554	GEORGE McCRAE	DO YOU FEEL MY LOVE	YOU GOT ME CRAZY	3.00
79	7558	K.C. and the SUNSHINE BAND	PLEASE DON'T GO	I BETCHA DIDN'T KNOW THAT	4.00
79	7559	RALPH McDONALD	I NEED SOMEONE	DISCOLYPSO	4.00
79	7562	ANITA WARD	DON'T DROP MY LOVE	YOU LIED	4.00
79	7564	JOE TEX	DISCOMANIA	FAT PEOPLE	3.00
79	7571	T-CONNECTION	DANGER ZONE	DANGER ZONE part 2	4.00
79	7572	PETER BROWN	LOVE IN OUR HEARTS	PENGUIN	3.00
79	7574	K.C. and the SUNSHINE BAND	I'VE GOT THE FEELING	LET'S GO ROCK AND ROLL	3.00
79	7575	JIMMY BO HORNE	WITHOUT YOU	GOIN' HOME FOR LOVE	4.00
79	7577	BOBBY CALDWELL	COMING DOWN FROM LOVE	OPEN YOUR EYES	4.00
79	7579	PETER BROWN	STARGAZER	WEST OF THE NORTH STAR	3.00
79	7580	PETER BROWN	CAN'T BE LOVE, DO IT ANYWAY	CAN'T BE LOVE, DO IT ANYWAY part 2	3.00
80	7583	DAVID HUDSON	HONEY, HONEY	COME ON BACK BABY	6.00
80	7586	JIMMY BO HORNE	IS IT IN	SPANK	4.00
80	7587	WILLIE BEAVER HALE	GROOVE ON	PARTY TIMES	6.00
77	9052	TIMMY THOMAS	THE MAGICIAN	DON'T PULL IT DOWN	4.00

TMW

White label handwritten credits, both are Ian Levine productions

00	101	BRENDA HOLLOWAY	GIVE ME A LITTLE INSPIRATION	Blank: test press promo omly	10.00
00	102	PAT LEWIS	I'M NOT OVER YOU YET	SOMETHING NEW TO DO	6.00

TOAST

68	500	STOCKING TOPS	YOU'RE NEVER GONNA GET MY LOVING	YOU DON'T KNOW WHAT LOVE IS	15.00
68	501	NINO FERRER	THE TELEPHONE	LOOKING FOR A LOVE	6.00
68	502	JOE E. YOUNG and the TONIKS	FLOWER IN MY HAND	LIFE TIME OF LOVIN'	70.00
68	503	CAMEOS	PRETTY SHADE OF BLUE	YOU DIDN'T HAVE TO BE SO NICE	8.00
68	504	EDDIE ELWELL	DON'T KNOCK IT	DON'T SAY YOU'RE GONNA LEAVE ME	6.00
68	505	SANDPEBBLES	IF YOU DON'T HEAR ME THE FIRST TIME	FLOWER POWER	6.00
68	506	ROZETTA HIGHTOWER	PRETTY RED BALLOONS	HOW CAN YOU MISTREAT THE ONE U	15.00
68	507	DORIS TROY	I'LL DO ANYTHING	HEARTACHES	15.00
68	508	CAMEOS	THE LOVE OF A BOY	ON THE GOOD SHIP LOLLIPOP	8.00
68	509	ROZETTA HIGHTOWER	BIG BIRD	I CAN'T GIVE BCK THE LOVE I FE	15.00
68	510 unissued?				
68	511	HAMILTON KING	THIS LOVE OF MINE	CUPIS FULLER	6.00
68	512 unissued?				
68	513	COINS	LOVE POWER	YOU CAN'T GET AWAY FROM IT	10.00
69	514	JOE E. YOUNG and the TONIKS	LIFE TIME OF LOVIN'	GOOD DAY SUNSHINE	8.00
69	515	COINS	CRYING OVER YOU	DON'T YOU KNOW IT'S JUST A LOVE	10.00

TOMORROW

76	001	EVELYN THOMAS	DOOMSDAY	same: instrumental	15.00
76	002	DORIS JONES	HE'S SO IRREPLACEABLE	same: instrumental	15.00
76	003	CAROL WOODS	HEADING DOWN FOOLS ROAD	same: instrumental	15.00
76	004	TYRONE ASHLEY	FEET START MOVING	same: instrumental	15.00
76	005	EXCITERS	SWALLOW YOUR PRIDE	same: instrumental	15.00
76	006	BARBARA PENNINGTON	I CAN'T ERASE THE THOUGHTS OF YOU	same:instrumental	15.00
76	007	L.J. JOHNSON	DANCING ON THE EDGE OF A DREAM	same: instrumental	15.00
76	008	DORIS JONES	STRANDED IN THE WILDNESS	STRANDED IN THE WILDERNESS	15.00
76	009	EXCITERS	HEAVEN IS WHEREVER YOU ARE	same: instrumental	15.00
76	010	TYRONE ASHLEY	NOTHING SHORT OF A MIRACLE	same: Instrumental	10.00
76	011				
76	012	CAROL WOODS	YOUR FACE KEEPS HAUNTING ME	same: instrumental	15.00
98	mecca 1	EXCITERS	REACHING FOR THE BEST	I'M GONNA MAKE YOU LOVE ME	6.00

TOP DOG

98	1	CODY BLACK c/w JIMMY BURNS	MR. BLUE	I REALLY LOVE YOU	10.00

TOP RANK

59	132	WILBERT HARRISON	KANSAS CITY	LISTEN, MY DARLING	10.00
59	154	CHUBBY CHECKER	THE CLASS	SCHOOLDAYS, OH, SCHOOLDAYS1	40.00
59	169	BIG JAY McNEELEY	THERE IS SOMETHING ON YOUR MIND	BACK SHAC TRACK	30.00
59	196	DEE CLARK	HEY LITTLE GIRL	IF IT WASN'T FOR LOVE	20.00
59	213	FLAMINGOS	LOVE WALKED IN	YOURS	30.00

59	232	BOBBY PETERSON QUINTET	THE HUNCH	LOVE YOU PRETTY BABY	20.00
59	256	LITTLE ANTHONY & the IMPERIALS	SHIMMY, SHIMMY, KO-KO, POP	I'M STILL IN LOVE WITH YOU	30.00
60	261	TONI FISHER	THE BIG HURT	MEMPHIS BELLE	10.00
60	284	DEE CLARK	HOW ABOUT THAT	BLUES GET OFF MY SHOULDER	15.00
60	332	ROSCO GORDON	JUST A LITTLE BIT	GOIN' HOME	30.00
60	333	JIMMY REED	BABY WHAT YOU WANT ME TO DO	CARESS ME BABY	20.00
60	351	NAT KENDRICK and the SWANS	(DO THE) MASHED POTATOES	(DO THE) MASHED POTATOES part 2	22.00
60	366	LITTLE ANTHONY & the IMPERIALS	MY EMPTY ROOM	BAYOU, BABY	20.00
60	367	FLAMINGOS	NOBODY LOVES ME LIKE YOU DO	YOU, ME AND THE SEA	30.00
60	373	DEE CLARK	AT MY FRONT	CLING-A-LING	20.00
60	387	NAT KENDRICK and the SWANS	DISH RAG	DISH RAG part 2	22.00
60	389	JERRY BUTLER	I FOUND A LOVE	A LONELY SOLDIER	20.00
60	394	JIMMY REED	FOUND LOVE	WHERE CAN YOU BE	15.00
60	501	DEE CLARK	GLORIA	YOU'RE LOOKING GOOD	8.00
60	519	FLAMINGOS	MIO AMORE	AT NIGHT	30.00
60	526	MAURICE WILLIAMS and the ZODIACS	STAY	DO YOU BELIVE	10.00
60	531	JERRY BUTLER	HE WILL BREAK YOUR HEART	THANKS TO YOU	50.00
60	533	JIMMY REED	HUSH-HUSH	GOING BY THE RIVER	15.00
61	538	BOBBY DAY	GEE WHIZ	OVER AND OVER	15.00
61	540	SHIRELLES	WILL YOU STILL LOVE ME TOMORROW	BOYS	8.00
61	546	LENNY MILES	DON'T BELIEVE HIM DONNA	INVISIBLE	30.00
61	549	SHIRELLES	DEDICATED TO THE ONE I LOVE	LOOK-A-HERE BABY	10.00
61	550	MAURICE WILLIAMS and the ZODIACS	I REMEMBER	ALWAYS	15.00
61	551	DEE CLARK	YOUR FRIENDS	BECAUSE I LOVE YOU	8.00
61	555	CRAIG DOUGLAS	A HUNDRED POUNDS OF CLAY	HELLO SPRING	10.00
61	556 PS	CRAIG DOUGLAS	A HUNDRED POUNDS OF CLAY	HELLO SPRING	20.00
61	560	JARMELS	SHE LOVES TO DANCE	LITTLE LONELY ONE	20.00
61	562	JERRY BUTLER	FIND ANOTHER GIRL	WHEN TROUBLE CALLS	25.00
61	563	MAURICE WILLIAMS and the ZODIACS	COME ALONG	DO I	18.00
61	564	CHUCK JACKSON	I DON'T WANT TO CRY	JUST ONCE	40.00
61	566	U.S. BONDS	GIVE ME ONE MORE CHANCE	NOT ME	8.00
61	567	SHIRELLES	MAMA SAID	BLUE HOLIDAY	10.00
61	570	DEE CLARK	RAINDROPS	I WANT TO LOVE YOU	10.00
61	574	PIPS	EVERY BEAT OF MY HEART	ROOM IN YOUR HEART	40.00
61	575	U.S. BONDS	QUARTER TO THREE	TIME OLE STORY	8.00
61	578	SHIRELLES	WHAT A SWEET THING THAT WAS	A THING OF THE PAST	10.00
61	580	JARMELS	A LITTLE BIT OF SOAP	THE WAY YOU LOOK TONIGHT	40.00
61	588	PARIS SISTERS	I LOVE HOW YOU LOVE ME	I'LL BE CRYING TOMORROW	10.00
61	590	SHIRELLES	BIG JOHN	TWENTY ONE	10.00
62	601	SHIRELLES	BABY IT'S YOU	THE THINGS I WANT TO HEAR	10.00
62	605	TOMMY HUNT	THE DOOR IS OPEN	I'M WONDERING	20.00
62	606	LEE DORSEY	DO-RE-MI	PEOPLE GONNA TALK	20.00
62	607	CHUCK JACKSON	THE BREAKING POINT	MY WILLOW TREE	20.00
62	617	JIMMY McCRACKLIN	THE DRAG	JUST GOT TO KNOW	15.00
61	3006 EP PS	MAURICE WILLIAMS and the ZODIACS	MAURICE WILLIAMS and the ZODIACS	1961 4 track EP with cover	150.00
61	3012 EP PS	SHIRELLES	THE SHIRELLES SOUND	1961 4 track EP with cover	75.00

TOP-TOP

02	007	WILSON, VENICIA	THIS TIME I'M LOVING YOU	same: instrumental	5.00

TORCH

97	001	SPENCER WIGGINS	LET'S TALK IT OVER	same:	20.00

TOUT ENSEMBLE

86	2	CLARENCE CARTER	MESSING WITH MY MIND	I WAS IN THE NEIGHBOURHOOD	40.00
86	2 PS	CLARENCE CARTER	MESSING WITH MY MIND	I WAS IN THE NEIGHBOURHOOD	50.00

TOWERBELL

82	28 PS	JOHNNY MOORE	YOUR BROKEN HEART	SOUL OF LOVE	8.00

TPL

01		JOSIE JAMES	WIN YOUR LOVE	CALL ME (WHEN YOU NEED MY LOVE	40.00

TRACK

In 1970 Polydor release an LP for 99p, it was to influence an army of fledgling soul fans like myself, to search for more of the type of music laid on the 12 tracks. BACKTRACK 6 was the last in a series of cheap LP promoted by Polydor through the Track label. The previous five were rock compilations mainly featuring Jimi Hendrix, The Who, Fairport Convention etc. Imagine the surprise and the delight as a soul LP hit the shops with tracks from Parliaments, Al Kent, Precisions, Debonairs and The Sandpebbles. Although Motown had bought the rights to Ric Tic 4 years earlier, Polydor had retained the contractual right to release Ric-Tic and some of it's subsidiaries until 1970. For Polydor it was the last throw of the dice to cash in on their rights deal. As all the releases as 45's in 1967 and 1968 met with extremely poor sales. Consequently the soul releases on the label are extremely difficult to find.

The sales figures on Backtrack 6 must have raised a few eyebrows at headquarters, as word spread amongst soul devotees that the biggest bargain could be had for less than a £1. Every one of my "soul" mates purchased a copy, with every track being a winner, it was on my turntable almost constantly. Within no time I knew every track off by heart, I was a Detroit junkie without knowning: because Polydor had no cover notes on the LP to give a hint who the Parliaments or any other artist was or where they came from. The only thing I knew at the time was The Parliaments "Don't Be Sore At Me" was the most sensational record I'd ever heard, dragging me even deeper into "rare soul" and the all comsuming search for the next sound.

For some reason that sensational track never saw UK release as a 45. One theory was that they pulled the wrong master and released "I Can Feel The Ice Melting" twice. That theory holds up for me, because why release "Ice Melting" on two occasions within 18 months, it certainly wasn't commercial sense as neither release sold in worthwhile quantities.

An interesting point with Track 45's is that all releases seem to have the factory with solid center and a small hole, also but rarer are the "Die Cut" centers with a small hole and the four pronge spine center.

67	604012 solid	TONY SIMON	GIMME A LITTLE SIGN	NEVER TOO MUCH LOVE	20.00
67	604012 die cut	TONY SIMON	GIMME A LITTLE SIGN	NEVER TOO MUCH LOVE	20.00
67	604013 solid	PARLIAMENTS	I CAN FEEL THE ICE MELTING	I WANNA TESIFY	40.00
67	604013 die cut	PARLIAMENTS	I CAN FEEL THE ICE MELTING	I WANNA TESIFY	45.00
67	604014 solid	PRECISIONS	IF THIS IS LOVE (I'D RATHER BE LONELY)	YOU'LL SOON BE GONE	50.00
67	604014 die cut	PRECISIONS	IF THIS IS LOVE (I'D RATHER BE LONELY)	YOU'LL SOON BE GONE	45.00

67	604015 solid	SAND PEBBLES	LOVE POWER	BECAUSE OF LOVE	25.00
67	604015 die cut	SAND PEBBLES	LOVE POWER	BECAUSE OF LOVE	20.00
67	604016 solid	AL KENT	YOU'VE GOT TO PAY THE PRICE	WHERE DO I GO FROM HERE	75.00
67	604016 die cut	AL KENT	YOU'VE GOT TO PAY THE PRICE	WHERE DO I GO FROM HERE	100.00
68	604028 solid	SAND PEBBLES	LOVE POWER	BECAUSE OF LOVE	20.00
68	604028 die cut	SAND PEBBLES	LOVE POWER	BECAUSE OF LOVE	15.00
68	604032 solid	PARLIAMENTS	I CAN FEEL THE ICE MELTING	(I WANNA) TESTIFY	20.00
68	604032 die cut	PARLIAMENTS	I CAN FEEL THE ICE MELTING	(I WANNA) TESTIFY	15.00
68	604032 test press	PARLIAMENTS	I CAN FEEL THE ICE MELTING	(I WANNA) TESTIFY	25.00
	White label with hand written credits				
68	604035 solid	DEBONAIRES	HEADACHE IN MY HEART	I'M IN LOVE AGAIN	100.00
68	604035 die cut	DEBONAIRES	HEADACHE IN MY HEART	I'M IN LOVE AGAIN	75.00

TRACO
	602	FRANK WILSON	JANICE, DON'T BE SO BLIND TO LOVE	PROMISES TO KEEP	5.00

TRANSATLANTIC
72	503	ERROL DIXON	LET THE LOVE SHINE INTO YOUR HEART	IN A MOMENT OF WEAKNESS	5.00

TANGERINE RECORD COMPANY
69	6121001	RAY CHARLES	BOOTY BOOT	ZIG ZAG	8.00
69	6121002	RAELETTS	BAD WEATHER	WHAT GOES TO SHOW	6.00
69	6121003	RAELETTS	HERE I GO AGAIN	LEAVE MY MAN (WOMAN) ALONE	6.00

TRENTHAM GARDENS
01	1	MR SOUL	WHAT HAPPENED TO YESTERDAY	SWEETEST FEELING	10.00
02	FINAL 1	JACKIE WILSON c/w WALTER JACKSON	BECAUSE OF YOU	LET ME COME BACK	15.00

TRIDENT STUDIOS
	acetate	TOMMY HUNT	ONE FINE MORNING	same: instrumental	10.00

TROJAN
	7806	JIMMY JAMES & THE VAGABONDS	HELP YOURSELF	WHY	30.00
	HOSS 1	JACKIE EDWARDS	I MUST GO BACK	BABY I WANT TO BE NEAR YOU	10.00

TROJAN DISCO PICK
	1	JIMMY JAMES & THE VAGABONDS	HELP YOURSELF	WHY	5.00
	1 blue	JIMMY JAMES & THE VAGABONDS	HELP YOURSELF	WHY	5.00

TWIRL
	1	ROCQ-E HARRELL	MY HEART KEEPS BEATING FAST	same: instrumental	4.00

UK
75	2	DEAN PARRISH	I'M ON MY WAY	WATCH OUT!	8.00
75	2 DJ	DEAN PARRISH	I'M ON MY WAY	WATCH OUT!	15.00
75	4	MOB	I'D LIKE TO SEE MORE OF YOU	GIVE IT TO ME	10.00
75	4 DJ	MOB	I'D LIKE TO SEE MORE OF YOU	GIVE IT TO ME	15.00
75	5	DEVONNES	I'M GONNA PICK UP MY TOYS AND GO	LIMITS	6.00
75	5 DJ	DEVONNES	I'M GONNA PICK UP MY TOYS	LIMITS	10.00
75	6	COURTSHIPS	OOPS IT JUST SLIPPED OUT	LOVE AIN'T LOVE (UNTIL YOU GIVE IT)	10.00
75	6 DJ	COURTSHIPS	OOPS IT JUST SLIPPED OUT	LOVE AIN'T LOVE (UNTIL YOU GIVE IT)	15.00
75	8	BRENDA LEE JONES	YOU'RE THE LOVE OF MY LIFE	THREAD YOUR NEEDLE	10.00
75	8 DJ	BRENDA LEE JONES	YOU'RE THE LOVE OF MY LIFE	THREAD YOUR NEEDLE	15.00
75	9	MUSIC EXPLOSION	LITTLE BIT OF SOUL	I SEE THE LIGHT	5.00
75	9 DJ	MUSIC EXPLOSION	LITTLE BIT OF SOUL	I SEE THE LIGHT	6.00
75	10	VARIATIONS	SAYIN' IT - DOIN' IT	SAYIN' IT - DOIN' IT Part2	10.00
75	10 DJ	VARIATIONS	SAYIN' IT - DOIN' IT	SAYIN' IT - DOIN' IT part 2	15.00
75	11 ink	CLYDIE KING	PUNISH ME	same: instrumental	5.00
75	13 ink	HOAGY LANDS	TRUE LOVE AT LAST	FRIENDS AND LOVERS TOGETHERS	40.00
75	14 ink	HOAGY LANDS	THE NEXT IN LINE	I'M YOURS	15.00
75	19	ROY C	SHOTGUN WEDDING	I'M GONNA MAKE IT	6.00
75	19 ink	ROY C	SHOTGUN WEDDING	I'M GONNA MAKE IT	5.00
76	27	ROY C	THE WEDDING IS OVER	HIGH SCHOOL DROP-OUT	6.00
76	136 ink	ROY C	SHOTGUN WEDDING	I'M GONNA MAKE IT	6.00
76	2012004 ink	BRENDA LEE JONES	YOU'RE THE LOVE OF MY LIFE	THREAD YOUR NEEDLE	8.00

UNDERWORLD
83	1	SKIP MAHONEY	JANICE (DON'T BE SO BLIND TO LOVE)	DON'T STOP ME NOW	50.00
83	1 with press sheet	SKIP MAHONEY	JANICE (DON'T BE SO BLIND TO LOVE)	DON'T STOP ME NOW	75.00

UNI
68	501	MIRETTES	IN THE MIDNIGHT HOUR	TO LOVE SOMEBODY	8.00
68	501 DJ	MIRETTES	IN THE MIDNIGHT HOUR	TO LOVE SOMEBODY	12.00
68	504	HUGH MASEKELA	GRAZING IN THE GRASS	BAJABULA BONKE (THE HEALING SO	10.00
68	504 DJ	HUGH MASEKELA	CRAZING IN THE GRASS	BAJABULA BONKE (THE HEALING SO	12.00
68	505	MIRETTES	THE REAL THING	TAKE ME FOR A LITTLE WHILE	10.00
68	505 DJ	MIRETTES	THE REAL THING	TAKE ME FOR A LITTLE WHILE	12.00
69	510	HUGH MASEKELA	I HAVEN'T SLEPT	WHERE HAS ALL THE GRASS GONE	6.00
69	510 DJ	HUGH MASEKELA	I HAVEN'T SLEPT	WHERE HAS ALL THE GRASS GONE	8.00
70	517	BETTY EVERETT	SUGAR	HOLD ON	8.00
70	517 DJ	BETTY EVERETT	SUGAR	HOLD ON	10.00
70	519	BOB AND EARL	PICKIN' UP LOVE'S VIBRATIONS	UH, UH, NAW NAW NAW	5.00
70	519 DJ	BOB AND EARL	PICKIN' UP LOVE'S VIBRATIONS	UH, UH, NAW NAW NAW	8.00
70	524	3rd. AVENUE BLUES BAND	COME AND GET IT	I NEVER PROMISED YOU A ROSE GARDEN	15.00
70	524 DJ	3rd. AVENUE BLUES BAND	COME AND GET IT	I NEVER PROMISED YOU A ROSE GARDEN	25.00
72	539	LOVE UNLIMITED	WALKIN' IN THE RAIN WITH THE ONE I LOVE	I SHOULD HAVE KNOWN	10.00
72	539 DJ	LOVE UNLIMITED	WALKIN' IN THE RAIN WITH THE ONE I LOVE	I SHOULD HAVE KNOWN	15.00

72	549	LOVE UNLIMITED	I'LL BE YOURS FOREVER MORE	IS IT RTEALLY TRUE BOY	4.00
72	549 DJ	LOVE UNLIMITED	I'LL BE YOURS FOREVER MORE	IS IT REALLY TRUE BOY	5.00

UNIGRAM

77	777	BILL FREDERICKS	TOO BUSY THINKING ABOUT MY BABY	same: long version	5.00

UNITED ARTISTS

76	403 EP PS	GARNET MIMMS	REMEMBER: GARNET MIMMS	70s 4 track EP with pic cover	10.00
76	405 EP DJ	LITTLE ANTHONY & the IMPERIALS	GOIN OUT OF MY HEAD + HURT SO BAD	GONNA FIX YOU GOOD + I'M ON TH	10.00
80	613 PS	JIMMY McGRIFF	I GOT A WOMAN	ALL ABOUT MY GIRL + WATERMELON MAN	6.00
80	615	BRASS CONSTRUCTION	SHAKIT	MUSIC MAKES YOU FEEL LIKE DANC	4.00
80	619	RONNIE LAWS	YOUNG CHILD	TOMORROW	4.00
80	622	DONALD BYRD	DOMINOES	WIND PARADE	10.00
80	626	RONNIE LAWS	EVERY GENERATION	same: instrumental	4.00
81	644	RONNIE LAWS	STAY AWAKE	HEAVY ON EASY	4.00
82	648	RONNIE LAWS	YOUR STUFF	THERE'S A WAY	4.00
65	1004 EP PS	LITTLE ANTHONY & the IMPERIALS	LITTLE ANTHONY & the IMPERIALS	1965 4 track EP with cover	85.00
65	1005 EP PS	ECXCITERS	DO WAH DIDDY DIDDY	1965 4 track EP with cover	85.00
63	1011	EXCITERS	HARD WAY TO GO	TELL HIM	15.00
63	1011 DJ	EXCITERS	HARD WAY TO GO	TELL HIM	30.00
64	1014	EXCITERS	DO WAH DIDDY DIDDY	IF LOVE CAME YOR WAY	15.00
64	1014 DJ	EXCITERS	DO WAH DIDDY DIDDY	IF LOVE CAME YOR WAY	25.00
64	1055	GENE PITNEY	I'M GONNA FIND MYSELF ANOTHER GIRL	LIPS ARE REDDER ON YOU	20.00
64	1055 DJ	GENE PITNEY	I'M GONNA FIND MYSELF ANOTHER GIRL	LIPS ARE REDDER ON YOU	28.00
66	1016 EP PS	BOBBY GOLDSBORO	IT'S TOO LATE	1965 4 track EP with cover	15.00
64	1017	EXCITERS	HE'S GOT THE POWER	DRAMA OF LOVE	15.00
64	1017 DJ	EXCITERS	HE'S GOT THE POWER	DRAMA OF LOVE	22.00
64	1020	WANDERERS	RUN RUN SENORITA	AFTER HE BREAKS YOUR HEART	25.00
64	1020 DJ	WANDERERS	RUN RUN SENORITA	AFTER HE BREAKS YOUR HEART	30.00
64	1026	EXCITERS	GET HIM	IT'S SO EXCITING	10.00
64	1026 DJ	EXCITERS	GET HIM	IT'S SO EXCITING	15.00
64	1033	GARNET MIMMS & the ENCHANTERS	CRY BABY	DON'T CHANGE YOR HEART	25.00
64	1033 DJ	GARNET MIMMS & the ENCHANTERS	CRY BABY	DON'T CHANGE YOR HEART	40.00
64	1034	ISLEY BROTHERS	SHE'S GONE	TANGO	10.00
64	1034 DJ	ISLEY BROTHERS	SHE'S GONE	TANGO	15.00
64	1038	GARNET MIMMS & the ENCHANTERS	BABY DON'T YOU WEEP	FOR YOUR PRECIOUS LOVE	20.00
64	1038 DJ	GARNET MIMMS & the ENCHANTERS	BABY DON'T YOU WEEP	FOR YOUR PRECIOUS LOVE	28.00
64	1048	GARNET MIMMS & the ENCHANTERS	TELL ME BABY	ANYTIME YOU WANT ME	20.00
64	1048 DJ	GARNET MIMMS & the ENCHANTERS	TELL ME BABY	ANYTIME YOU WANT ME	28.00
64	1050	ISLEY BROTHERS	SHAKE IT WITH ME BABY	STAGGER LEE	10.00
64	1050 DJ	ISLEY BROTHERS	SHAKE IT WITH ME BABY	STAGGER LEE	15.00
64	1065	LITTLE ANTHONY & the IMPERIALS	I'M ON THE OUTSIDE LOOKING IN	PLEASE GO	20.00
64	1065 DJ	LITTLE ANTHONY & the IMPERIALS	I'M ON THE OUTSIDE LOOKING IN	PLEASE GO	30.00
64	1073	LITTLE ANTHONY & the IMPERIALS	GOIN' OUT OF MY HEAD	MAKE IT EASY ON YOURSELF	20.00
64	1073 DJ	LITTLE ANTHONY & the IMPERIALS	GOIN' OUT OF MY HEAD	MAKE IT EASY ON YOURSELF	30.00
65	1078	LONG JOHN BALDRY	I'M ON TO YOU BABY	GOODBYE BABY	25.00
65	1078 DJ	LONG JOHN BALDRY	I'M ON TO YOU BABY	GOODBYE BABY	35.00
65	1079	BOBBY GOLDSBORO	LITTLE THINGS	I JUST CAN'T GO ON PRETENDING	8.00
65	1079 DJ	BOBBY GOLDSBORO	LITTLE THINGS	I JUST CAN'T GO ON PRETENDING	15.00
65	1083	LITTLE ANTHONY & the IMPERIALS	HURT SO BAD	REPUTATION	20.00
65	1083 DJ	LITTLE ANTHONY & the IMPERIALS	HURT SO BAD	REPUTATION	30.00
65	1090	GARNET MIMMS	IT WAS EASIER TO HURT HER	SO CLOSE	30.00
65	1090 DJ	GARNET MIMMS	IT WAS EASIER TO HURT HER	SO CLOSE	50.00
65	1098	LITTLE ANTHONY & the IMPERIALS	TAKE ME BACK	OUR SONG	20.00
65	1098 DJ	LITTLE ANTHONY & the IMPERIALS	TAKE ME BACK	OUR SONG	30.00
65	1101	LENA HORNE	THE SAND AND THE SEA	IT HAD BETTER BE TONIGHT	30.00
65	1101 DJ	LENA HORNE	THE SAND AND THE SEA	IT HAD BETTER BE TONIGHT	40.00
65	1104	BOBBY GOLDSBORO	IF YOU WAIT FOR LOVE	IF YOU'VE GOT A HEART	15.00
65	1104 DJ	BOBBY GOLDSBORO	IF YOU WAIT FOR LOVE	IF YOU'VE GOT A HEART	20.00
65	1106	JIVE FIVE	I'M A HAPPY MAN	KISS KISS KISS	30.00
65	1106 DJ	JIVE FIVE	I'M A HAPPY MAN	KISS KISS KISS	45.00
65	1107	LONG JOHN BALDRY	HOUSE NEXT DOOR	HOW LONG WILL IT LAST	30.00
65	1107 DJ	LONG JOHN BALDRY	HOUSE NEXT DOOR	HOW LONG WILL IT LAST	45.00
65	1108	JAY & THE AMERICANS	GIRL	SOME ENCHANTED EVENING	10.00
65	1108 DJ	JAY & THE AMERICANS	GIRL	SOME ENCHANTED EVENING	15.00
65	1110	CRYSTALS	YOU CAN'T TIE A GOOD GIRL DOWN	MY PLACE	75.00
65	1110 DJ	CRYSTALS	YOU CAN'T TIE A GOOD GIRL DOWN	MY PLACE	100.00
65	1111	RAY POLLARD	THE DRIFTER	LET HIM GO	350.00
65	1111 DJ	RAY POLLARD	THE DRIFTER	LET HIM GO	**811.00**
65	1112	LITTLE ANTHONY & the IMPERIALS	GET OUT OF MY LIFE	I MISS YOU SO	20.00
65	1112 DJ	LITTLE ANTHONY & the IMPERIALS	GET OUT OF MY LIFE	I MISS YOU SO	30.00
66	1126	LITTLE ANTHONY & the IMPERIALS	NEVER AGAIN	HURT	30.00
66	1126 DJ	LITTLE ANTHONY & the IMPERIALS	NEVER AGAIN	HURT	40.00
66	1128	BOBBY GOLDSBORO	IT'S TOO LATE	I'M GOIN' HOME	15.00
66	1128 DJ	BOBBY GOLDSBORO	IT'S TOO LATE	I'M GOIN' HOME	50.00
66	1130	GARNET MIMMS	LOOKING FOR YOU	I'LL TAKE GOOD CARE OF YOU	**141.00**
66	1130 DJ	GARNET MIMMS	LOOKING FOR YOU	I'LL TAKE CARE OF YOU	**280.00**
66	1133	RAY POLLARD	IT'S A SAD THING	ALL THE THING YOU ARE	150.00
66	1133 DJ	RAY POLLARD	IT'S A SAD THING	ALL THE THING YOU ARE	**205.00**
66	1136 DJ	LONG JOHN BALDRY	THE DRIFTER	ONLY A FOOL BREAKS HIS OWN HEA	85.00
66	1137	LITTLE ANTHONY & the IMPERIALS	BETTER USE YOUR HEAD	THE WONDER OF IT ALL	100.00
66	1137 DJ	LITTLE ANTHONY & the IMPERIALS	BETTER USE YOUR HEAD	THE WONDER OF IT ALL	200.00
66	1139	SAMANTHA JONES	THAT SPECIAL WAY	SOMEBODY ELE'S BABY	12.00
66	1139 DJ	SAMANTHA JONES	THAT SPECIAL WAY	SOMEBODY ELE'S BABY	20.00
66	1140	JORDAN CHRISTOPHER	HELLO LOVER	WHAT THAT I WAS	50.00
66	1140 DJ	JORDAN CHRISTOPHER	HELLO LOVER	WHAT THAT I WAS	75.00
66	1142	JAY & THE AMERICANS	LIVIN' ABOVE YOUR HEAD	SHE'S THE GIRL (THAT'S MESSING	45.00

66	1142 DJ	JAY & THE AMERICANS	LIVIN' ABOVE YOUR HEAD	SHE'S THE GIRL (THAT'S MESSING	75.00
66	1146	BOBBY GOLDSBORO	LONGER THAN FOREVER	TAKE YOUR LOVE	40.00
66	1146 DJ	BOBBY GOLDSBORO	LONGER THAN FOREVER	TAKE YOUR LOVE	60.00
66	1147	GARNET MIMMS	IT'S BEEN SUCH A LONG WAY HOME	THINKIN'	20.00
66	1147 DJ	GARNET MIMMS	IT'S BEEN SUCH A LONG WAY HOME	THINKIN'	30.00
66	1151	LITTLE ANTHONY & the IMPERIALS	GONNA FIX YOU GOOD	YOU BETTER TAKE IT EASY BABY	50.00
66	1151 DJ	LITTLE ANTHONY & the IMPERIALS	GONNA FIX YOU GOOD	YOU BETTER TAKE IT EASY BABY	120.00
67	1153	GARNET MIMMS	MY BABY	IT WON'T HURT (HALF AS MUCH)	20.00
67	1153 DJ	GARNET MIMMS	MY BABY	IT WON'T HURT (HALF AS MUCH)	30.00
67	1156	BOBBY GOLDSBORO	IT HURTS ME	PITY THE FOOL	8.00
67	1156 DJ	BOBBY GOLDSBORO	IT HURTS ME	PITY THE FOOL	10.00
67	1166	BOBBY GOLDSBORO	HOLD ON	NO FUN AT THE FAIR	10.00
67	1166 DJ	BOBBY GOLDSBORO	HOLD ON	NO FUN AT THE FAIR	20.00
67	1170	JIMMY McGRIFF	SEE SEE RIDER	HALLELUJAH	10.00
67	1170 DJ	JIMMY McGRIFF	SEE SEE RIDER	HALLELUJAH	20.00
67	1172	GARNET MIMMS	ALL ABOUT LOVE	THE TRUTH HURTS	20.00
67	1172 DJ	GARNET MIMMS	ALL ABOUT LOVE	THE TRUTH HURTS	30.00
67	1174	JAY BLACK	WHAT WILL MARY SAY?	RETURN TO ME	8.00
67	1174 DJ	JAY BLACK	WHAT WILL MARY SAY?	RETURN TO ME	10.00
07	1177	BOBBY GOLDSBORO	TOO MANY PEOPLE	GOODBYE TO ALL YOU WOMEN	85.00
67	1177 DJ	BOBBY GOLDSBORO	TOO MANY PEOPLE	GOODBYE TO ALL YOU WOMEN	125.00
67	1179	VINCE EDWARDS	THE LIVELY ONE	I CAN'T TURN BACK TIME	20.00
67	1179 DJ	VINCE EDWARDS	THE LIVELY ONE	I CAN'T TURN BACK TIME	30.00
67	1180	ELLIE GREENWICH	I WANT TO BE MY BABY	GOODNIGHT, GOODNIGHT	20.00
67	1180 DJ	ELLIE GREENWICH	I WANT TO BE MY BABY	GOODNIGHT, GOODNIGHT	40.00
67	1181	GARNET MIMMS	ROLL WITH THE PUNCHES	ONLY YOUR LOVE	20.00
67	1181 DJ	GARNET MIMMS	ROLL WITH THE PUNCHES	ONLY YOUR LOVE	35.00
67	1185	SAMANTHA JONES	SURROUNDED BY A RAY OF SUNSHINE	HOW DO YOU SAY GOODBYE	175.00
67	1185 DJ	SAMANTHA JONES	SURROUNDED BY A RAY OF SUNSHINE	HOW DO YOU SAY GOODBYE	**506.00**
67	1186	GARNET MIMMS	AS LONG AS I HAVE YOU	YESTERDAY	15.00
67	1186 DJ	GARNET MIMMS	AS LONG AS I HAVE YOU	YESTERDAY	25.00
67	1189	ANTHONY & THE IMPERIALS	MY LOVE IS A RAINBOW	YOU ONLY LIVE TWICE	10.00
67	1189 DJ	ANTHONY & THE IMPERIALS	MY LOVE IS A RAINBOW	YOU ONLY LIVE TWICE	15.00
67	1191	JAY & THE AMERICANS	GOT HUNG UP ALONG THE WAY	(WE'LL MEET IN THE) YELLOW FOREST	50.00
67	1191 DJ	JAY & THE AMERICANS	GOT HUNG UP ALONG THE WAY	(WE'LL MEET IN THE) YELLOW FOREST	85.00
68	1204	LONG JOHN BALDRY	LET HIM GO (AND LET ME LOVE YOU)	ONLY A FOOL BREAKS HIS OWN HEART	20.00
68	1204 DJ	LONG JOHN BALDRY	LET HIM GO (AND LET ME LOVE YOU)	ONLY A FOOL BREAKS HIS OWN HEART	30.00
68	1206	CARL DOUGLAS	SERVING THE SENTENCE OF LIFE	NOBODY CRIES	300.00
68	1206 DJ	CARL DOUGLAS	SERVING THE SENTENCE OF LIFE	NOBODY CRIES	**358.00**

United Artists 2000 series, label design changes to blue and silver.

68	2214	ELLIE GREENWICH	A LONG TIME COMING	SUNSHINE AFTER THE RAIN	10.00
68	2214 DJ	ELLIE GREENWICH	A LONG TIME COMING	SUNSHINE AFTER THE RAIN	15.00
68	2223	BOBBY GOLDSBORO	SHE CHASED ME	AUTUMN OF MY LIFE	10.00
68	2223 DJ	BOBBY GOLDSBORO	SHE CHASED ME	AUTUMN OF MY LIFE	20.00
68	2227	CARL DOUGLAS & the BIG STAMPEDE	SELL MY SOUL TO THE DEVIL	GOOD HARD WORKER	15.00
68	2227 DJ	CARL DOUGLAS & the BIG STAMPEDE	SELL MY SOUL TO THE DEVIL	GOOD HARD WORKER	20.00
68	2233	SHORT KUTS feat. EDDIE HARRISON	YOUR EYES MAY SHINE	LET THE TEARS TUMBLE DOWN	30.00
68	2233 DJ	SHORT KUTS feat. EDDIE HARRISON	YOUR EYES MAY SHINE	LET THE TEARS TUMBLE DOWN	50.00
68	2235	SARI & the SHALIMARS	IT'S SO LONELY (BEING TOGETHER)	YOU WALKED OUT ON ME BEFORE	20.00
68	2235 DJ	SARI & the SHALIMARS	IT'S SO LONELY (BEING TOGETHER)	YOU WALKED OUT ON ME BEFORE	30.00
68	2246	SPICE	WHAT ABOUT THE MUSIC	IN LOVE	75.00
68	2246 DJ	SPICE	WHAT ABOUT THE MUSIC	IN LOVE	100.00
68	2247	BABY WASHINGTON	GET A HOLD OF YOURSELF	HURT SO BAD	85.00
68	2247 DJ	BABY WASHINGTON	GET A HOLD OF YOURSELF	HURT SO BAD	100.00
68	2258	SAMANTHA JONES	AND SUDDENLY	GO SAHEAD AND LOVE ME	50.00
68	2258 DJ	SAMANTHA JONES	AND SUDDENLY	GO SAHEAD AND LOVE ME	85.00
69	2260	ANTHONY & THE IMPERIALS	ANTHEM	GOODBYE GOODTIMES	8.00
69	2260 DJ	ANTHONY & THE IMPERIALS	ANTHEM	GOODBYE GOODTIMES	10.00
69	2261	LEE VANDERBILT	SOME GIRLS DO	DARK IN THE CITY	8.00
69	2261 DJ	LEE VANDERBILT	SOME GIRLS DO	DARK IN THE CITY	10.00
69	2264	BOBBY GOLDSBORO	LOVE ARRESTOR	DISSATISFIED MAN	8.00
69	2264 DJ	BOBBY GOLDSBORO	LOVE ARRESTOR	DISSATISFIED MAN	10.00
69	2269	INEZ & CHARLIE FOXX	MOCKINGBIRD	HURT BY LOVE	5.00
69	2269 DJ	INEZ & CHARLIE FOXX	MOCKINGBIRD	HURT BY LOVE	8.00
69	2274	EXCITERS	HARD WAY TO GO	DO-WHA-DIDDY DIDDY	8.00
69	2274 DJ	EXCITERS	HARD WAY TO GO	DO-WHA-DIDDY DIDDY	10.00
71	31592	SHIRELLES	DEDICATED TO THE ONE I LOVE	TAKE ME	5.00
71	31592 DJ	SHIRELLES	DEDICATED TO THE ONE I LOVE	TAKE ME	6.00
69	35010	MARV JOHNSON	I LOVE THE WAY YOU LOVE	YOU GOT WHAT IT TAKES	5.00
69	35010 DJ	MARV JOHNSON	I LOVE THE WAY YOU LOVE	YOU GOT WHAT IT TAKES	6.00
69	35013	INEZ & CHARLIE FOXX	LA DE DA I LOVE YOU	DON'T DO IT NO MORE	8.00
69	35013 DJ	INEZ & CHARLIE FOXX	LA DE DA I LOVE YOU	DON'T DO IT NO MORE	10.00
69	35017	ANTHONY and the IMPERIALS	ANTHEM (GROW, GROW, GROW)	GOODBYE GOODTIMES	6.00
69	35017 DJ	ANTHONY and the IMPERIALS	ANTHEM (GROW, GROW, GROW)	GOODBYE GOODTIMES	8.00
69	35018	PATTI AUSTIN	MAGICAL BOY	THE FAMILY TREE	10.00
69	35018 DJ	PATTI AUSTIN	MAGICAL BOY	THE FAMILY TREE	15.00
69	35025	JIMMY McGRIFF	THE WORM	WHAT'S THAT	25.00
69	35025 DJ	JIMMY McGRIFF	THE WORM	WHAT'S THAT	30.00
69	35029	JACK HAMMER	WHAT GREATER LOVE	THE MASON DIXON LINE	50.00
69	35029 DJ	JACK HAMMER	WHAT GREATER LOVE	THE MASON DIXON LINE	75.00
69	35034	BOBBY GOLDSBORO	MUDDY MISSISSIPPI LINE	RICHER MAN THAN I	6.00
69	35034 DJ	BOBBY GOLDSBORO	MUDDY MISSISSIPPI LINE	RICHER MAN THAN I	8.00
69	35039	ELECTRIC INDIAN	KEEM-O-SABE	BROAD STREET	10.00
69	35039 DJ	ELECTRIC INDIAN	KEEM-O-SABE	BROAD STREET	12.00
70	35097	PATTI AUSTIN	IT'S EASIER TO LAUGH THAN CRY	YOUR LOVE MADE THE DIFFERENCE	10.00
70	35097 DJ	PATTI AUSTIN	IT'S EASIER TO LAUGH THAN CRY	YOUR LOVE MADE THE DIFFERENCE	15.00
70	35103	BOBBI MARTIN	FOR THE LOVE OF HIM	I FALL TO PIECES	20.00

70	35103 DJ	BOBBI MARTIN	FOR THE LOVE OF HIM	I FALL TO PIECES	30.00
71	35151	CASSIDY	LOVE, LOVE, LOVE	PLACE IN MY HEART	8.00
71	35151 DJ	CASSIDY	LOVE, LOVE, LOVE	PLACE IN MY HEART	10.00
71	35218	CORNELIUS BROTHERS & SISTER ROSE	TREAT HER LIKE A LADY	OVER AT MY PLACE	10.00
71	35218 DJ	CORNELIUS BROTHERS & SISTER ROSE	TREAT HER LIKE A LADY	OVER AT MY PLACE	12.00
71	35219	IKE & TINA TURNER	CRAZY 'BOUT YOU BABY	I'VE BEEN LOVING YOU TOO YOU	6.00
71	35219 DJ	IKE & TINA TURNER	CRAZY 'BOUT YOU BABY	I'VE BEEN LOVING YOU TOO YOU	8.00
71	35245	IKE & TINA TURNER	OOH POO PAH DOO	I WANNA JUMP	6.00
71	35245 DJ	IKE & TINA TURNER	OOH POO PAH DOO	I WANNA JUMP	8.00
71	35266	BRENTON WOOD	GIMME A LITTLE SIGN	I THINK YOU'VE GOT YOUR FOOLS	6.00
71	35266 DJ	BRENTON WOOD	GIMME A LITTLE SIGN	I THINK YOU'VE GOT YOUR FOOLS	8.00
71	35273	LOLEATTA HOLLOWAY	RAINBOW "71"	BRING IT ON UP	6.00
71	35273 DJ	LOLEATTA HOLLOWAY	RAINBOW "71"	BRING IT ON UP	8.00
72	35308	POETS	SHE BLEW A GOOD THING	OUT TO LUNCH	15.00
72	35308 DJ	POETS	SHE BLEW A GOOD THING	OUT TO LUNCH	20.00
71	35210	IKE & TINA TURNER	DOIN' IT	I'M YOURS	5.00
71	35210 DJ	IKE & TINA TURNER	DOIN' IT	I'M YOURS	6.00
72	35327	WAR	SLIPPIN' INTO DARKNESS	NAPPY HEAD	5.00
72	35327 DJ	WAR	SLIPPIN' INTO DARKNESS	NAPPY HEAD	6.00
72	35337	O'JAYS	HOLD ON	WORKING ON YOUR CASE	20.00
72	35337 DJ	O'JAYS	HOLD ON	WORKING ON YOUR CASE	25.00
72	35339	BOBBY WOMACK	THAT'S THE WAY I FEEL ABOUT CHA	COME L'AMORE	5.00
72	35339 DJ	BOBBY WOMACK	THAT'S THE WAY I FEEL ABOUT CHA	COME L'AMORE	6.00
72	35345	LITTLE ANTHONY & the IMPERIALS	GONNA FIX YOU GOOD	YOU BETTER TAKE IT EASY BABY	10.00
72	35345 DJ	LITTLE ANTHONY & the IMPERIALS	GONNA FIX YOU GOOD	YOU BETTER TAKE IT EASY BABY	15.00
72	35352	TIMMY WILLIS	MR. SOUL SATISFACTION	I'M WONDERING	10.00
72	35352 DJ	TIMMY WILLIS	MR. SOUL SATISFACTION	I'M WONDERING	15.00
72	35360	HOMER BANKS	HOOKED BY LOVE	LADY OFSTONE	10.00
72	35360 DJ	HOMER BANKS	HOOKED BY LOVE	LADY OFSTONE	15.00
72	35371	JIMMY HOLIDAY & CLYDIE KING	READY WILLING AND ABLE	GIVE ME YOUR LOVE	10.00
72	35371 DJ	JIMMY HOLIDAY & CLYDIE KING	READY WILLING AND ABLE	GIVE ME YOUR LOVE	15.00
72	35373	IKE & TINA TURNER	FEEL GOOD	OUTRAGEOUS	5.00
72	35373 DJ	IKE & TINA TURNER	FEEL GOOD	OUTRAGEOUS	6.00
72	35375	BOBBY WOMACK	WOMAN'S GOTTA HAVE IT	IF YOU DON'T WANT MY LOVE	5.00
72	35375 DJ	BOBBY WOMACK	WOMAN'S GOTTA HAVE IT	IF YOU DON'T WANT MY LOVE	6.00
72	35378	CORNELIUS BROTHERS & SISTER ROSE	TOO LATE TO TURN BACK NOW	LIFT YOUR LOVE HIGHER	20.00
72	35378 DJ	CORNELIUS BROTHERS & SISTER ROSE	TOO LATE TO TURN BACK NOW	LIFT YOUR LOVE HIGHER	28.00
72	35388	SOUL SISTERS	GOOD TIME TONIGHT	SOME SOUL FOOD	10.00
72	35388 DJ	SOUL SISTERS	GOOD TIME TONIGHT	SOME SOUL FOOD	15.00
72	35402	IRMA THOMAS	TIME IS ON MY SIDE	ANYONE WHO KNOWS WHAT LOVE IS	8.00
72	35402 DJ	IRMA THOMAS	TIME IS ON MY SIDE	ANYONE WHO KNOWS WHAT LOVE IS	10.00
72	35403	CANDI STATON	IN THE GHETTO	SURE AS SIN	6.00
72	35403 DJ	CANDI STATON	IN THE GHETTO	SURE AS SIN	8.00
72	35411	IKE TURNER	LAWDY MISS CLAWDY + TACKS IN MY	SOPPIN' MALASSES	5.00
72	35411 DJ	IKE TURNER	LAWDY MISS CLAWDY + TACKS IN MY	SOPPIN' MALASSES	6.00
72	35412	TRAVIS WAMMACK	WHATEVER TURNS YOU ON	SLIP AWAY	5.00
72	35412 DJ	TRAVIS WAMMACK	WHATEVER TURNS YOU ON	SLIP AWAY	6.00
72	35427	CORNELIUS BROTHERS & SISTER ROSE	DON'T EVER BE LONELY	I'M SO GLAD (TO BE LOVED BY YOU)	8.00
72	35427 DJ	CORNELIUS BROTHERS & SISTER ROSE	DON'T EVER BE LONELY	I'M SO GLAD (TO BE LOVED BY YOU)	10.00
72	35431	BOBBY WOMACK	SWEET CAROLINE (GOOD TIMES HAVE NEVER BEEN SO GOOD)	SIMPLE MAN	5.00
72	35431 DJ	BOBBY WOMACK	SWEET CAROLINE (GOOD TIMES HAVE NEVER BEEN SO GOOD)	SIMPLE MAN	6.00
72	35431 PS	BOBBY WOMACK	SWEET CAROLINE (GOOD TIMES HAVE NEVER BEEN SO GOOD)	SIMPLE MAN	6.00
72	35456	BOBBY WOMACK	I CAN UNDERSTAND IT	HARRY HIPPIE	10.00
72	35456 DJ	BOBBY WOMACK	I CAN UNDERSTAND IT	HARRY HIPPIE	15.00
72	35456 PS	BOBBY WOMACK	I CAN UNDERSTAND IT	HARRY HIPPIE	15.00
73	35468	TRAVIS WAMMACK	SO GOOD	DARLING, YOU'RE ALL THAT I NEE	5.00
73	35468 DJ	TRAVIS WAMMACK	SO GOOD	DARLING, YOU'RE ALL THAT I NEE	6.00
73	35469	WAR	THE WORLD IS A GHETTO	FOUR CORNERED ROOM	4.00
73	35469 DJ	WAR	THE WORLD IS A GHETTO	FOUR CORNERED ROOM	5.00
73	35497	IKE & TINA TURNER	WITH A LITTLE HELP FROM MY FRIENDS	EARLY ONE MORNING	4.00
73	35497 DJ	IKE & TINA TURNER	WITH A LITTLE HELP FROM MY FRIENDS	EARLY ONE MORNING	5.00
73	35497 PS	IKE & TINA TURNER	WITH A LITTLE HELP FROM MY FRIENDS	EARLY ONE MORNING	5.00
73	35502	CORNELIUS BROTHERS & SISTER ROSE	I'M NEVR GONNA BE ALONE ANYMORE	LET'S STAY TOGETHER	5.00
73	35502 DJ	CORNELIUS BROTHERS & SISTER ROSE	I'M NEVR GONNA BE ALONE ANYMORE	LET'S STAY TOGETHER	6.00
73	35512	BOBBY WOMACK	ACROSS 110TH. STREET	HANG ON IN THERE	15.00
73	35512 DJ	BOBBY WOMACK	ACROSS 110TH. STREET	HANG ON IN THERE	20.00
73	35517	MARLENA SHAW	LAST TANGO IN PARIS	SAVE THE CHILDREN	4.00
73	35517 DJ	MARLENA SHAW	LAST TANGO IN PARIS	SAVE THE CHILDREN	5.00
73	35521	WAR	THE CISCO KID	BEETLES IN THE BOG	4.00
73	35521 DJ	WAR	THE CISCO KID	BEETLES IN THE BOG	5.00
73	35550	IKE & TINA TURNER	WORK ON ME	BORN FREE	4.00
73	35550 DJ	IKE & TINA TURNER	WORK ON ME	BORN FREE	5.00
73	35552	CLARENCE CARTER	MOTHER-IN-LAW	SIXTY MINUTE MAN	5.00
73	35552 DJ	CLARENCE CARTER	MOTHER-IN-LAW	SIXTY MINUTE MAN	6.00
73	35563	ELECTRIC INDIAN	LAND OF 1,000 DANCES	CERONIMO	8.00
73	35563 DJ	ELECTRIC INDIAN	LAND OF 1,000 DANCES	CERONIMO	10.00
73	35564	DONALD BYRD	BLACK BYRD	STOP JAR BLUES	5.00
73	35564 DJ	DONALD BYRD	BLACK BYRD	STOP JAR BLUES	6.00
73	35565	BOBBY WOMACK	NOBODY WANTS YOU WHEN YOU'RE	I'M THROUGH TRYING TO PROVE MY	5.00
73	35565 DJ	BOBBY WOMACK	NOBODY WANTS YOU WHEN YOU'RE	I'M THROUGH TRYING TO PROVE MY	6.00
73	35576	WAR	GYPSY MAN	DELIVER THE WORD	4.00
73	35576 DJ	WAR	GYPSY MAN	DELIVER THE WORD	5.00
73	35578	SHIRLEY & LEE	LET THE GOOD TIMES ROLL	THAT'S WHAT I WANNA DO	5.00
73	35578 DJ	SHIRLEY & LEE	LET THE GOOD TIMES ROLL	THAT'S WHAT I WANNA DO	6.00
73	35582	IKE & TINA TURNER	NUTBUSH CITY LIMITS	HELP HIM	4.00
73	35582 DJ	IKE & TINA TURNER	NUTBUSH CITY LIMITS	HELP HIM	5.00
73	35595	CORNELIUS BROTHERS & SISTER ROSE	I JUST CAN'T STOP LOVING YOU	THESE LONELY NIGHTS	10.00

73	35595 DJ	CORNELIUS BROTHERS & SISTER ROSE	I JUST CAN'T STOP LOVING YOU	THESE LONELY NIGHTS	15.00
74	35623	WAR	ME AND BABY BROTHER	IN YOUR EYES	4.00
74	35623 DJ	WAR	ME AND BABY BROTHER	IN YOUR EYES	5.00
74	35626	CLARENCE CARTER	I'M THE MIDNIGHT SPECIAL	I GOT ANOTHER WOMAN	4.00
74	35626 DJ	CLARENCE CARTER	I'M THE MIDNIGHT SPECIAL	I GOT ANOTHER WOMAN	5.00
74	35632	IKE & TINA TURNER	RIVER DEEP – MOUNTAIN HIGH	FANCY ANNIE	4.00
74	35632 DJ	IKE & TINA TURNER	RIVER DEEP – MOUNTAIN HIGH	FANCY ANNIE	5.00
74	35644	BOBBY WOMACK	LOOKIN' FOR A LOVE	LET IT HANG OUT	5.00
74	35644 DJ	BOBBY WOMACK	LOOKIN' FOR A LOVE	LET IT HANG OUT	6.00
74	35650	IKE & TINA TURNER	SWEET RHODE ISLAND RED	GET IT OUT OF YOUR MIND	4.00
74	35650 DJ	IKE & TINA TURNER	SWEET RHODE ISLAND RED	GET IT OUT OF YOUR MIND	5.00
74	35657	INEZ & CHARLIE FOXX	MOCKING BIRD	HURT BY LOVE	6.00
74	35657 DJ	INEZ & CHARLIE FOXX	MOCKING BIRD	HURT BY LOVE	8.00
74	35726	IKE & TINA TURNER	SEXY IDA	SEXY IDA part 2	4.00
74	35726 DJ	IKE & TINA TURNER	SEXY IDA	SEXY IDA part 2	5.00
75	35766	IKE & TINA TURNER	BABY GET IT ON	BABY GET IT ON part 2	4.00
75	35766 DJ	IKE & TINA TURNER	BABY GET IT ON	BABY GET IT ON part 2	5.00
75	35727	Z.Z. HILL	I KEEP ON LOVING YOU	WHOEVER'S THRILLING YOU	5.00
75	35727 DJ	Z.Z. HILL	I KEEP ON LOVING YOU	WHOEVER'S THRILLING YOU	6.00
75	35770	STEVE KARMEN	BREAKAWAY PART1	BREAKAWAY PART2	10.00
75	35770 DJ	STEVE KARMEN	BREAKAWAY PART1	BREAKAWAY PART2	15.00
75	35771	GEORGE SOULE	GET INVOLVED	EVERYBODY'S GOT A SONG TO SING	5.00
75	35771 DJ	GEORGE SOULE	GET INVOLVED	EVERYBODY'S GOT A SONG TO SING	6.00
75	35779	ODIA COATES	SHOWDOWN	LEAVE ME IN THE MORNING	5.00
75	35779 DJ	ODIA COATES	SHOWDOWN	LEAVE ME IN THE MORNING	6.00
75	35780	GARY LEWIS & THE PLAYBOYS	MY HEART'S SYMPHONY	I WON'T MAKE THAT MISTAKE AGAI	5.00
75	35780 DJ	GARY LEWIS & THE PLAYBOYS	MY HEART'S SYMPHONY	I WON'T MAKE THAT MISTAKE AGAI	8.00
75	35782	EDDIE & ERNIE	I CAN'T DO IT (I JUST CAN'T LEAVE YOU)	LOST FRIENDS	8.00
75	35782 DJ	EDDIE & ERNIE	I CAN'T DO IT (I JUST CAN'T LEAVE YOU)	LOST FRIENDS	10.00
75	35789	VERNON BURCH	CHANGES	CHANGES part 2	4.00
75	35789 DJ	VERNON BURCH	CHANGES	CHANGES part 2	5.00
75	35804 midnight hour	HOMER BANKS	HOOKED BY LOVE	60 MINUTES OF YOUR LOVE	8.00
75	35804 midnight hour DJ	HOMER BANKS	HOOKED BY LOVE	60 MINUTES OF YOUR LOVE	10.00
75	35822	LEA ROBERTS	ALL RIGHT NOW	ALL OVER AGAIN	5.00
75	35822 DJ	LEA ROBERTS	ALL RIGHT NOW	ALL OVER AGAIN	6.00
75	35823	CANDI STATON	LOVE CHAIN	I'M GONNA HOLD ON	5.00
75	35823 DJ	CANDI STATON	LOVE CHAIN	I'M GONNA HOLD ON	6.00
75	35836	WAR	WHY CAN'T WE BE FRIENDS	IN MAZATLAN	4.00
75	35836 DJ	WAR	WHY CAN'T WE BE FRIENDS	IN MAZATLAN	5.00
75	35838	VERNON BURCH	AIN'T GONNA TELL NOBODY	LOVING YOU GETS BETTER WITH TIME	4.00
75	35838 DJ	VERNON BURCH	AIN'T GONNA TELL NOBODY	LOVING YOU GETS BETTER WITH TIME	5.00
75	35859	BOBBY WOMACK	CHECK IT OUT	INTERLUDE # 2	6.00
75	35859 DJ	BOBBY WOMACK	CHECK IT OUT	INTERLUDE # 2	8.00
75	35898	CHARLIE WHITEHEAD	LOVE BEING YOUR FOOL	NOW THAT I CAN DANCE	4.00
75	35898 DJ	CHARLIE WHITEHEAD	LOVE BEING YOUR FOOL	NOW THAT I CAN DANCE	5.00
75	35951	VENTURES	HAWAII FIVE - 0	HIGHER THAN THOU	5.00
75	35951 DJ	VENTURES	HAWAII FIVE - 0	HIGHER THAN THOU	8.00
75	36008	SAM & DAVE	UNDER THE BOARDWALK	GIVE IT WHAT YOU CAN	5.00
75	36008 DJ	SAM & DAVE	UNDER THE BOARDWALK	GIVE IT WHAT YOU CAN	6.00
75	36015	MAXINE NIGHTINGALE	RIGHT BACK WHERE WE STARTED FROM	BELIEVE IN WHAT YOU DO	5.00
75	36015 DJ	MAXINE NIGHTINGALE	RIGHT BACK WHERE WE STARTED FROM	BELIEVE IN WHAT YOU DO	6.00
75	36028	IKE & TINA TURNER	DELIA'S PURPOSE	THAT'S MY PURPOSE	4.00
75	36028 DJ	IKE & TINA TURNER	DELIA'S PURPOSE	THAT'S MY PURPOSE	5.00
76	36042	BOBBY WOMACK	WHERE THERE'S A WILL THERE'S A WAY	EVERYTHING'S GONNA BE ALRIGHT	5.00
76	36042 DJ	BOBBY WOMACK	WHERE THERE'S A WILL THERE'S A WAY	EVERYTHING'S GONNA BE ALRIGHT	6.00
76	36077	PATTI and the PATETTES	TOO MUCH LOVE	SUMMER HERTBREAK	15.00
76	36077 DJ	PATTI and the PATETTES	TOO MUCH LOVE	SUMMER HERTBREAK	20.00
76	36085	HIDDEN STRENGTH	HUSTLE ON UP	HUSTLE ON UP part 2	5.00
76	36085 DJ	HIDDEN STRENGTH	HUSTLE ON UP	HUSTLE ON UP part 2	6.00
76	36090	BRASS CONSTRUCTION	MOVIN'	TALKIN'	5.00
76	36090 DJ	BRASS CONSTRUCTION	MOVIN'	TALKIN'	6.00
76	36098	BOBBY WOMACK	DAYLIGHT	TRUST ME	15.00
76	36098 DJ	BOBBY WOMACK	DAYLIGHT	TRUST ME	20.00
76	36103	MANDRILL	PANAMA	DISCOLPSO	4.00
76	36103 DJ	MANDRILL	PANAMA	DISCOLPSO	5.00
76	36118	LITTLE ANTHONY & the IMPERIALS	BETTER USE YOUR HEAD	GONNA FIX YOU GOOD	15.00
76	36118 DJ	LITTLE ANTHONY & the IMPERIALS	BETTER USE YOUR HEAD	GONNA FIX YOU GOOD	20.00
76	36134	BRASS CONSTRUCTION	CHANGIN'	DANCE	5.00
76	36134 DJ	BRASS CONSTRUCTION	CHANGIN'	DANCE	6.00
76	36141	LITTLE ANTHONY & the IMPERIALS	BETTER USE YOUR HEAD	GONNA FIX YOU GOOD (EVERYTIME YOU'RE BAD)	10.00
76	36141 DJ	LITTLE ANTHONY & the IMPERIALS	BETTER USE YOUR HEAD	GONNA FIX YOU GOOD (EVERYTIME YOU'RE BAD)	12.00
76	36170	BARBARA PENNINGTON	TWENTY FOUR HOURS A DAY	I CAN'T ERASE THE THOUGHTS OF YOU	8.00
76	36170 DJ	BARBARA PENNINGTON	TWENTY FOUR HOURS A DAY	I CAN'T ERASE THE THOUGHTS OF YOU	10.00
76	36204	ENCHANTMENT	DANCE TO THE MUSIC	GLORIA	4.00
76	36204 DJ	ENCHANTMENT	DANCE TO THE MUSIC	GLORIA	5.00
77	36205	BRASS CONSTRUCTION	HA CHA CHA	SAMBO	5.00
77	36205 DJ	BRASS CONSTRUCTION	HA CHA CHA	SAMBO	6.00
77	36226	FATS DOMINO	IT KEEPS RAINING	I'M WALKIN'	6.00
77	36226 DJ	FATS DOMINO	IT KEEPS RAINING	I'M WALKING	8.00
77	36234	BARBARA PENNINGTON	YOU ARE THE MUSIC WITHIN ME	RUNNING IN ANOTHER DIRECTION	4.00
77	36234 DJ	BARBARA PENNINGTON	YOU ARE THE MUSIC WITHIN ME	RUNNING IN ANOTHER DIRECTION	5.00
77	36250	WALTER JACKSON	BABY, I LOVE YOUR WAY	WHAT WOULD YOU DO	5.00
77	36250 DJ	WALTER JACKSON	BABY, I LOVE YOUR WAY	WHAT WOULD YOU DO	6.00
77	36259	DORIS JONES	NO WAY OUT	same: instrumental	4.00
77	36259 DJ	DORIS JONES	NO WAY OUT	same: instrumental	5.00
77	36268	ENCHANTMENT	SUNSHINE	SEXY LADY	4.00
77	36268 DJ	ENCHANTMENT	SUNSHINE	SEXY LADY	5.00

78	36320	MAXINE NIGHTINGALE	DIDN'T I (BLOW YOUR MIND THIS TIME)	YOU ARE EVERYTHING	5.00
78	36320 DJ	MAXINE NIGHTINGALE	DIDN'T I (BLOW YOUR MIND THIS TIME)	YOU ARE EVERYTHING	6.00
78	36339	DORIS JONES	CAN'T YOU SEE THE SMILE ON MY FACE	TIME ON MY HANDS	4.00
78	36339 DJ	DORIS JONES	CAN'T YOU SEE THE SMILE ON MY FACE	TIME ON MY HANDS	5.00
78	36340	BARBARA PENNINGTON	SPEND A LITTLE TIME WITH ME	CAN'T HELP BEING GUILTY	4.00
78	36340 DJ	BARBARA PENNINGTON	SPEND A LITTLE TIME WITH ME	CAN'T HELP BEING GUILTY	5.00
78	37420	ENCHANTMENT	IF YOU'RE READY	ANGEL IN MY LIFE	5.00
78	37420 DJ	ENCHANTMENT	IF YOU'RE READY	ANGEL IN MY LIFE	6.00
78	36353	ENCHANTMENT	IT'S YOU THAT I NEED	SUNNY SHI NE FEELING	6.00
78	36353 DJ	ENCHANTMENT	IT'S YOU THAT I NEED	SUNNY SHI NE FEELING	8.00
78	36371	TYRONE ASHLEY	LOOKS LIKE LOVE IS HERE TO STAY	SURROUND ME	4.00
78	36371 DJ	TYRONE ASHLEY	LOOKS LIKE LOVE IS HERE TO STAY	SURROUND ME	5.00
78	36374	EARL JORDAN	STRANGE, STRANGE FEELING	NEVER SAID A TRUER WORD	15.00
78	36374 DJ	EARL JORDAN	STRANGE, STRANGE FEELING	NEVER SAID A TRUER WORD	20.00
78	36384	WALTER JACKSON	MANHATTAN SKYLINE	IF I COULD SEE MYSELF	5.00
78	36384 DJ	WALTER JACKSON	MANHATTAN SKYLINE	IF I COULD SEE MYSELF	6.00
78	36389	BRASS CONSTRUCTION	CELEBRATE	TOP OF THE WORLD	4.00
78	36389 DJ	BRASS CONSTRUCTION	CELEBRATE	TOP OF THE WORLD	5.00
78	36400	BETTY EVERETT	TRUE LOVE (YOU TOOK MY HEART)	YOU CAN DO IT	4.00
78	36400 DJ	BETTY EVERETT	TRUE LOVE (YOU TOOK MY HEART)	YOU CAN DO IT	5.00
78	36420	ENCHANTMENT	IF YOU'RE READY (HERE IT COMES)	ANGEL IN MY LIFE	4.00
78	36420 DJ	ENCHANTMENT	IF YOU'RE READY (HERE IT COMES)	ANGEL IN MY LIFE	5.00
78	36427	BARBARA PENNINGTON	ALL TIME LOSER	IT'S SO HARD GETTING OVER	4.00
78	36427 DJ	BARBARA PENNINGTON	ALL TIME LOSER	IT'S SO HARD GETTING OVER	5.00
78	36431	TYRONE ASHLEY	DON'T STOP DANCING	PUT YOUR FINGER ON THE TRIGGER	4.00
78	36431 DJ	TYRONE ASHLEY	DON'T STOP DANCING	PUT YOUR FINGER ON THE TRIGGER	5.00
79	36474	BRASS CONSTRUCTION	HELP YOURSELF	PICK YOURSELF UP	4.00
79	36474 DJ	BRASS CONSTRUCTION	HELP YOURSELF	PICK YOURSELF UP	5.00
79	36481	RONNIE LAWS	ALL FOR YOU	LET'S KEEP IT TOGETHER	5.00
79	36481 DJ	RONNIE LAWS	ALL FOR YOU	LET'S KEEP IT TOGETHER	6.00
79	36495	BOBBY GOLDSBORO	TOO MANY PEOPLE	IT'S TOO LATE + SHE CHASED ME	6.00
79	36495 DJ	BOBBY GOLDSBORO	TOO MANY PEOPLE	IT'S TOO LATE + SHE CHASED ME	8.00
79	36513	TINA TURNER	SOMETIMES WHEN WE TOUCH	EARTHQUAKE AND HURRICANE	3.00
79	36513 DJ	TINA TURNER	SOMETIMES WHEN WE TOUCH	EARTHQUAKE AND HURRICANE	4.00
79	36524	FATS DOMINO	IT KEEPS RAINING	BLUEBERRY HILL	6.00
79	36524 DJ	FATS DOMINO	IT KEEPS RAINING	BLUEBERRY HILL	8.00

UNLIMITED GOLD

81	1496	LOVE UNLIMITED ORCHESTRA	LIFT YOUR VOICE AND SAY (UNITED WE STAND)	MY FANTASIES	4.00
81	1496 DJ	LOVE UNLIMITED ORCHESTRA	LIFT YOUR VOICE AND SAY (UNITED WE STAND)	MY FANTASIES	5.00

UPC

70	102	TIKKI, TAKI, SUZI, LIES	I BELIEVE IN LOVE	WELCOME TO MY HOUSE	6.00
70	109	TIKKI, TAKI, SUZI, LIES	DREAM STEALER	BA-DA-DA-DUM	30.00

UPFRONT

71	1	FREDDIE SCOTT	THE GREAT IF	DEEP IN THE NIGHT	6.00
71	5	JOYCE BOND	WIND OF CHANGE	FIRST IN LINE	6.00

URBAN

87	1 PS	MACEO & THE MACKS	CROSS THE TRACKS (WE BETTER GO	SOUL POWER	8.00
87	4	JACKSON SISTERS	I BELIEVE IN MIRACLES	BOY YOU'RE DYNAMITE	15.00
87	6	ROY AYERS	CAN'T YOU SEE ME	LOVE WILL BRING US BACK TOGETHER	5.00
88	13 PS	JAMES BROWN	SHE'S THE ONE	FUNKY PRESIDENT	5.00
88	14 PS	WALTER BEASLEY	I'M SO HAPPY	JUMP ON IT	5.00
88	15	SWEET CHARLES c/w LYNN COLLINS	YES IT'S YOU	ROCK ME AGAIN AND AGAIN AND AGAIN	5.00
88	17	JAMES BROWN	THE PAYBACK PART1	GIVE IT UP OR TURN IT LOOSE	4.00
88	JSB 1 PS	JAMES BROWN	I'M REAL	KEEP KEEPING	5.00

VANGUARD

76	5003	GROVER MITCHELL	WHAT HURTS	SUPER HEROES	60.00
76	5003 DJ	GROVER MITCHELL	WHAT HURTS	SUPER HEROES	75.00

VERVE

Perhaps the worlds most famous jazz label, formed by jazz enthusiast Norman Granz in 1956 absorbing his earlier two labels Clef Records and Norgran under one logo. Throughout the 50's Verves reputation grew as an important part of jazz vinyl. Granz favoured recording established artists whose career was maybe in decline rather than new talent. MGM bought the Verve label in 1961, from then Creed Taylor (driving force behind the CTI label in the 70s) would be at the production helm. Producing many classic jazz LPs for the label. But as with the parent label MGM, Verve went into slow decline after 1965 to cease pressing vinyl in 1972. The Verve label was revived in the 80's concentrating on repackaging and repromoting classic jazz sessions.

It was in 1965 that Verve first starting to delve in the soul sound, Jerry Ragovoy was to emerge as the labels most important influence for soul. In New York and Philadelphia he wrote, arranged and produced some recordings that were to become eternal classics like Garnet Mimms "Cry Baby," Erma Franklin's "Piece of My Heart," Howard Tate's "Get It While You Can," Irma Thomas "Time Is on My Side" and the immortal Lorraine Ellison's "Stay With Me." Ragovoy also contributed to first-class soul records as a producer and arranger. But for the Verve label it was the Howard Tate and the Garnett Mimms releases that gained the attention of the UK soul collector.

In the UK Verve was distributed by EMI, who were well aware of the black music movement developing with teenagers in the UK. To promote the soul sound a little further they put the silver logo SOUL SUPPLY on many of their labels including Verve, to alert shops, DJ's & music reviewers to the fact that the record they were holding by this obscure artist was Soul music; fast becoming the "in" sound of the mid-sixties. 45's with that SOUL SUPPLY logo on Liberty, Verve etc are considered very desirable, and in the 60's soul collectors would check every EMI distributed black and silver label in the hope of seeing the "Soul Supply" motif.

Howard Tate and Garnett Mimms may have been the main artists on this short-lived UK label. But two artists, who only had one release each on the label, hold the most collectable status. Bessie Banks is famous for her original version of The Moody Blues smash hit "Go Now", issued in the UK on Soul City 105, has one of the most soulful double-sided 45's to be released in the UK on Verve # 563. Cal Tjader, vibes genius and jazzman extraordinaire underlines the diversity of soul collecting with an upbeat Jazz instrumental "Soul Sauce", that is now considered a Northern Soul classic.

Like all EMI labels of the era the promo copies were attractively presented, Verve was extremely eye catching just like the mid-sixties UK MGM's were designed with a bright pink background with a label length silver or white A. These promo copies are rightly considered making Verve an extremely sought after 60's label. Missing numbers are not soul related, some being highly collectable rock & pop 45's like the releases from Mother's Of Invention to name but a few.

65	509	JIMMY SMITH	HOBO FLATS	HOBO FLATS part 2	6.00
65	509 DJ	JIMMY SMITH	HOBO FLATS	HOBO FLATS part 2	8.00

65	512	KAI WINDING	COMIN' HOME BABY	MORE	15.00
65	512 DJ	KAI WINDING	COMIN' HOME BABY	MORE	20.00
65	521	JIMMY SMITH	WHO'S AFRAID OF VIGINIA WOOLF	same: part 2	6.00
65	521 DJ	JIMMY SMITH	WHO'S AFRAID OF VIGINIA WOOLF	same: part 2	8.00
65	523	JIMMY SMITH	THE CAT	BASIN STREET BLUES	40.00
65	523 DJ	JIMMY SMITH	THE CAT	BASIN STREET BLUES	50.00
65	529	CAL TJADER	SOUL SAUCE (GAUCHA GUARO)	NAKED CITY THEME	45.00
65	529 DJ	CAL TJADER	SOUL SAUCE (GAUCHA GUARO)	NAKED CITY THEME	85.00
65	531	JIMMY SMITH	ORGAN GRINDER'S SWING	I'LL CLOSE MY EYES	8.00
65	531 DJ	JIMMY SMITH	ORGAN GRINDER'S SWING	I'LL CLOSE MY EYES	10.00
65	532	DONALD BYRD	BOOM BOOM	SEE SEE RIDER	10.00
65	532 DJ	DONALD BYRD	BOOM BOOM	SEE SEE RIDER	15.00
66	534	JIMMY SMITH	THEME FROM "WHERE THE SPIES ARE"	same: part 2	10.00
66	534 DJ	JIMMY SMITH	THEME FROM "WHERE THE SPIES ARE"	same: part 2	15.00
66	535	RIGHTEOUS BROTHERS	(YOU'RE MY) SOUL AND INSPIRATION	B SIDE BLUES	8.00
66	535 DJ	RIGHTEOUS BROTHERS	(YOU'RE MY) SOUL AND INSPIRATION	B SIDE BLUES	10.00
66	536	JIMMY SMITH	GOT MY MOJO WORKING	same: part II	10.00
66	536 DJ	JIMMY SMITH	GOT MY MOJO WORKING	same: part II	15.00
66	537	RIGHTEOUS BROTHERS	HE WILL BREAK YOUR HEART	HE	10.00
66	637 DJ	RIGHTEOUS BROTHERS	HE WILL BREAK YOUR HEART	HE	15.00
66	538	JIMMY WITHERSPOON	IT'S ALL OVER BUT THE CRYING	IF I COULD HAVE YOU BACK AGAIN	10.00
66	538 DJ	JIMMY WITHERSPOON	IT'S ALL OVER BUT THE CRYING	IF I COULD HAVE YOU BACK AGAIN	15.00
66	540	JIMMY SMITH	I'LL YOUR HOOCHIE-COOCHIE MAN	same: part 2	6.00
66	540 DJ	JIMMY SMITH	I'LL YOUR HOOCHIE-COOCHIE MAN	same: part 2	8.00
66	541	HOWARD TATE	HOW COME MY BULL DOG DON'T BARK	AIN'T NOBODY HOME	22.00
66	541 DJ	HOWARD TATE	HOW COME MY BULL DOG DON'T BARK	AIN'T NOBODY HOME	30.00
66	542	RIGHTEOUS BROTHERS	GO AHEAD AND CRY	THINGS DIDN'T GO YOUR WAY	8.00
66	542 DJ	RIGHTEOUS BROTHERS	GO AHEAD AND CRY	THINGS DIDN'T GO YOUR WAY	10.00
66	547	RIGHTEOUS BROTHERS	ISLAND IN THE SUN	WHAT NOW MY LOVE	6.00
66	547 DJ	RIGHTEOUS BROTHERS	ISLAND IN THE SUN	WHAT NOW MY LOVE	10.00
66	548	WILLIE BOBO	SOCK IT TO ME	SUNSHINE SUPERMAN	15.00
66	548 DJ	WILLIE BOBO	SOCK IT TO ME	SUNSHINE SUPERMAN	22.00
66	549	HOWARD TATE	HALF A MAN	LOOK AT GRANNY RUN RUN	15.00
66	549 DJ	HOWARD TATE	HALF A MAN	LOOK AT GRANNY RUN RUN	25.00
67	550	POINDEXTER BROTHERS	(GIT YOUR) BACKFIELD IN MOTION	GRANDMA GIVE THAT GIRL SOME SLACK	15.00
67	550 DJ	POINDEXTER BROTHERS	(GIT YOUR) BACKFIELD IN MOTION	GRANDMA GIVE THAT GIRL SOME SLACK	22.00
67	551	JIMMY SMITH	CAT IN A TREE	CAT IN A TREE part 2	15.00
67	551 DJ	JIMMY SMITH	CAT IN A TREE	CAT IN A TREE part 2	22.00
67	552	HOWARD TATE	GET IT WHILE YOU CAN	GLAD I KNEW BETTER	15.00
67	552 DJ	HOWARD TATE	GET IT WHILE YOU CAN	GLAD I KNEW BETTER	22.00
67	553	JIMMY WITHERSPOON	MY BABY'S QUIT ME	PAST FORTY YEARS	20.00
67	553 DJ	JIMMY WITHERSPOON	MY BABY'S QUIT ME	PAST FORTY YEARS	25.00
67	554	RIGHTEOUS BROTHERS	DON'T GIVE UP ON ME	MELANCHOLY MUSIC MAN	6.00
67	554 DJ	RIGHTEOUS BROTHERS	DON'T GIVE UP ON ME	MELANCHOLY MUSIC MAN	8.00
67	555	HOWARD TATE	BABY I LOVE YOU	HOW BLUE CAN YOU GET	28.00
67	555 DJ	HOWARD TATE	BABY, I LOVE YOU	HOW BLUE CAN YOU GET	50.00
67	556	HOWARD TATE	I LEARNED IT ALL THE HARD WAY	PART-TIME LOVE	10.00
67	556 DJ	HOWARD TATE	I LEARNED IT ALL THE HARD WAY	PART-TIME LOVE	15.00
67	560	RIGHTEOUS BROTHERS	STRANDED IN THE MIDDLE OF NO PLACE	BEEN SO NICE	10.00
67	560 DJ	RIGHTEOUS BROTHERS	STRANDED IN THE MIDDLE OF NO PLACE	BEEN SO NICE	20.00
67	562	JIMMY SMITH	MICKEY MOUSE	T-BONE STEAK	10.00
67	562 DJ	JIMMY SMITH	MICKEY MOUSE	T-BONE STEAK	15.00
67	563	BESSIE BANKS	I CAN'T MAKE IT	NEED YOU	70.00
67	563 DJ	BESSIE BANKS	I CAN'T MAKE IT	NEED YOU	100.00
67	565	HOWARD TATE	STOP	SHOOT 'EM ALL DOWN	15.00
67	565 DJ	HOWARD TATE	STOP	SHOOT 'EM ALL DOWN	25.00
67	567	AMAZING DANCING BAND	DEEP BLUE TRAIN	SIMON SMITH AND HIS AMAZING DA	50.00
67	567 DJ	AMAZING DANCING BAND	DEEP BLUE TRAIN	SIMON SMITH AND HIS AMAZING DA	75.00
68	569	GARNET MIMMS	STOP AND THINK IT OVER	I CAN HEAR MY BABY CRYING	15.00
68	569 DJ	GARNET MIMMS	STOP AND THINK IT OVER	I CAN HEAR MY BABY CRYING	25.00
68	569 mispress	GARNET MIMMS c/w BILL MEDLEY	I CAN HEAR MY BABY CRYING	THAT LUCKY OLD SUN	8.00
68	570	BOBBY HATFIELD	HANG UPS	SOUL CAFE	8.00
68	570 DJ	BOBBY HATFIELD	HANG UPS	SOUL CAFE	10.00
68	571	HOWARD TATE	NIGHT OWL	EVERYDAY I HAVE THE BLUES	20.00
68	571 DJ	HOWARD TATE	NIGHT OWL	EVERYDAY I HAVE THE BLUES	30.00
68	574	GARNET MIMMS	CAN YOU TOP THIS	WE CAN FIND THAT LOVE	50.00
68	574 DJ	GARNET MIMMS	CAN YOU TOP THIS	WE CAN FIND THAT LOVE	75.00
69	1519	RICHIE HAVENS	INDIAN ROPE MAN	LADY MADONNA	20.00
69	1519 DJ	RICHIE HAVENS	INDIAN ROPE MAN	LADY MADONNA	30.00
65	5008 EP PS	JIMMY SMITH	WALK ON THE WILD SIDE	1965 4 track EP with cover	6.00
65	5016 EP PS	JIMMY SMITH	PLAYS THE BLUES	1965 4 track EP with cover	15.00
65	5021 EP PS	JIMMY SMITH	CREEPER	1965 4 track EP with cover	15.00
65	5022 EP PS	JIMMY SMITH	SWINGING WITH THE INCREDIBLE	1965 4 track EP with cover	15.00
66	5024 EP PS	RIGHTEOUS BROTHERS	SOUL AND INSPIRATION	1966 4 track EP with cover	25.00
66	5025 EP PS	RIGHTEOUS BROTHERS	THE RIGHTEOUS BROTHERS	1966 4 track EP with cover	20.00

VIRGIN

80	103 dbl pack PS	P.P. ARNOLD	EVERYTHING'S GONNA BE ALRIGHT	5 track 2 x 45 double pack with gatefold sleeve	15.00
87	1037 PS	TAMS	MY BABY SURE CAN SHAG	THANK YOU JOHN	4.00
86	859 PS	HEAVEN 17 feat. JIMMY RUFFIN	MY SENSITIVITY (GETS IN THE WAY)	THE FOOLISH THING TO DO	10.00

VOCALION

64	1278 EP PS	JIMMY WITHERSPOON	JIMMY WITHERSPOON	1964 4 track EP with cover	25.00
65	1284 EP PS	JIMMY WITHERSPOON	OUTSKIRTS OF TOWN	1965 4 track EP with cover	25.00
63	9206	JIMMY HOLIDAY	HOW CAN I FORGET	JABET	25.00
63	9206 DJ	JIMMY HOLIDAY	HOW CAN I FORGET	JABET	35.00
64	9222	BOBBY BLAND	HONEY CHILD	AIN'T NOTHING YOU CAN DO	30.00
64	9222 DJ	BOBBY BLAND	HONEY CHILD	AIN'T NOTHING YOU CAN DO	45.00

64	9224	JOE HINTON	FUNNY HOW TIME SLIPS AWAY	YOU GOTTA HAVE LOVE	15.00
64	9224 DJ	JOE HINTON	FUNNY HOW TIME SLIPS AWAY	YOU GOTTA HAVE LOVE	22.00
64	9229	BOBBY BLAND	SHARE YOUR LOVE WITH ME	AFTER IT'S TOO LATE	20.00
64	9229 DJ	BOBBY BLAND	SHARE YOUR LOVE WITH ME	AFTER IT'S TOO LATE	30.00
65	9232	BOBBY BLAND	YIELD NOT TO TEMPTATION	HOW DOES A CHEATING WOMAN FEEL	25.00
65	9232 DJ	BOBBY BLAND	YIELD NOT TO TEMPTATION	HOW DOES A CHEATING WOMAN FEEL	40.00
65	9233	ERNIE K-DOE	MY MOTHER IN LAW (IS IN MY HAIR	LOOKING INTO THE FUTURE	15.00
65	9233 DJ	ERNIE K-DOE	MY MOTHER IN LAW (IS IN MY HAIR	LOOKING INTO THE FUTURE	22.00
65	9234	LITTLE JOHNNY TAYLOR	SOMEWHERE DOWN THE LINE	PART TIME LOVE	50.00
65	9234 DJ	LITTLE JOHNNY TAYLOR	SOMEWHERE DOWN THE LINE	PART TIME LOVE	75.00
65	9236	MISS LAVELL	EVERYBODY'S GOT SOMEBODY	THE BEST PART OF ME	20.00
65	9236 DJ	MISS LAVELL	EVERYBODY'S GOT SOMEBODY	THE BEST PART OF ME	30.00
65	9237	DELANY BRAMLETT	YOU HAVE NO CHOICE	LIVERPOOL LOU	40.00
65	9237 DJ	DELANY BRAMLETT	YOU HAVE NO CHOICE	LIVERPOOL LOU	75.00
65	9239	TONI HARPER	NEVER TRUST A STRANGER	AS TIME GOES BY	20.00
65	9239 DJ	TONI HARPER	NEVER TRUST A STRANGER	AS TIME GOES BY	30.00
65	9244	LISA RICHARDS	MEAN OLD WORLD	TAKE A CHANCE	45.00
65	9244 DJ	LISA RICHARDS	MEAN OLD WORLD	TAKE A CHANCE	70.00
65	9245	ROSCOE GORDON	KEEP ON DOGGIN'	BAD DREAM	30.00
65	9245 DJ	ROSCOE GORDON	KEEP ON DOGGIN'	BAD DREAM	45.00
65	9247	SONNY & CHER	SPRING FEVER	THE LETTER	10.00
65	9247 DJ	SONNY & CHER	SPRING FEVER	THE LETTER	15.00
65	9248	ROY HEAD	TREAT HER RIGHT	SO LONG, MY LOVE	15.00
65	9248 DJ	ROY HEAD	TREAT HER RIGHT	SO LONG, MY LOVE	25.00
65	9249	O.V.WRIGHT	MONKEY DOG	YOU'RE GONNA MAKE ME CRY	22.00
65	9249 DJ	O.V.WRIGHT	MONKEY DOG	YOU'RE GONNA MAKE ME CRY	35.00
65	9251	BOBBY BLAND	THESE HANDS (SMALL BUT MIGHTY)	TODAY	50.00
65	9251 DJ	BOBBY BLAND	THESE HANDS (SMALL BUT MIGHTY)	TODAY	75.00
65	9252	BUD HARPER	MR. SOUL	LET ME LOVE YOU	50.00
65	9252 DJ	BUD HARPER	MR. SOUL	LET ME LOVE YOU	85.00
65	9254	ROY HEAD	APPLE OF MY EYE	I PASS THE DAY	10.00
65	9254 DJ	ROY HEAD	APPLE OF MY EYE	I PASS THE DAY	15.00
66	9255	O.V.WRIGHT	POOR BOY	I'M IN YOUR CORNER	20.00
66	9255 DJ	O.V.WRIGHT	POOR BOY	I'M IN YOUR CORNER	30.00
66	9256	JUNIOR PARKER	THESE KIND OF BLUES	THESE KIND OF BLUES part 2	50.00
66	9256 DJ	JUNIOR PARKER	THESE KIND OF BLUES	THESE KIND OF BLUES part 2	85.00
66	9258	JOE HINTON	PLEDGING MY LOVE	JUST A KID NAMED JOE	15.00
66	9258 DJ	JOE HINTON	PLEDGING MY LOVE	JUST A KID NAMED JOE	22.00
66	9259	BILLY STRANGE	RUN SPY RUN	GET SMART	25.00
66	9259 DJ	BILLY STRANGE	RUN SPY RUN	GET SMART	35.00
66	9260	OTIS RUSH	HOMEWORK	I HAVE TO LAUGH	85.00
66	9260 DJ	OTIS RUSH	HOMEWORK	I HAVE TO LAUGH	100.00
66	9262	BOBBY BLAND	I'M TOO FAR GONE (TO TURN AROUND	IF YOU COULD READ MY MIND	28.00
66	9262 DJ	BOBBY BLAND	I'M TOO FAR GONE (TO TURN AROUND	IF YOU COULD READ MY MIND	45.00
66	9264	LITTLE JOHNNY TAYLOR	ONE LAST CHANCE	LOOKING AT THE FUTURE	25.00
66	9264 DJ	LITTLE JOHNNY TAYLOR	ONE LAST CHANCE	LOOKING AT THE FUTURE	40.00
66	9267	CHAMBERS BROTHERS	LOVE ME LIKE THE RAIN	PRETTY GIRLS EVERYWHERE	10.00
66	9267 DJ	CHAMBERS BROTHERS	LOVE ME LIKE THE RAIN	PRETTY GIRLS EVERYWHERE	15.00
66	9268	LITTLE MR. LEE and the CHEROKEES	YOUNG LOVER	I DON'T WANT TO GO	45.00
66	9268 DJ	LITTLE MR. LEE and the CHEROKEES	YOUNG LOVER	I DON'T WANT TO GO	70.00
66	9269	ROY HEAD	MY BABE	PAIN	15.00
66	9269 DJ	ROY HEAD	MY BABE	PAIN	22.00
66	9271	DON FLETCHER	TWO WRONGS DON'T MAKE A RIGHT	I'M SO GLAD	35.00
66	9271 DJ	DON FLETCHER	TWO WRONGS DON'T MAKE A RIGHT	I'M SO GLAD	50.00
66	9272	O.V.WRIGHT	GONE FOR GOOD	HOW LONG BABY	20.00
66	9272 DJ	O.V.WRIGHT	GONE FOR GOOD	HOW LONG BABY	30.00
66	9273	BOBBY BLAND	GOOD TIME CHARLIE	same: instrumental	45.00
66	9273 DJ	BOBBY BLAND	GOOD TIME CHARLIE	same: instrumental	75.00
66	9274	ROY HEAD	WIGGIN' AND GIGGLIN'	DRIVING WHEEL	15.00
66	9274 DJ	ROY HEAD	WIGGIN' AND GIGGLIN'	DRIVING WHEEL	22.00
66	9275	JUNIOR PARKER	WALKING THE FLOOR OVER YOU	GOODBYE LIITLE GIRL	30.00
66	9275 DJ	JUNIOR PARKER	WALKING THE FLOOR OVER YOU	GOODBYE LIITLE GIRL	45.00
66	9276	CHAMBERS BROTHERS	CALL ME	SEVENTEEN	10.00
66	9276 DJ	CHAMBERS BROTHERS	CALL ME	SEVENTEEN	15.00
66	9277	SEEDS	PUSHIN' TOO HARD	TRY TO UNDERSTAND	40.00
66	9277 DJ	SEEDS	PUSHIN' TOO HARD	TRY TO UNDERSTAND	60.00
66	9278	AL TNT BRAGGS	EARTHQUAKE	HOW LONG (DO YOU HOLD ON)	28.00
66	9278 DJ	AL TNT BRAGGS	EARTHQUAKE	HOW LONG (DO YOU HOLD ON)	45.00
66	9279	BOBBY ADENO	THE HANDS OF TIME	IT'S A SAD WORLD	40.00
66	9279 DJ	BOBBY ADENO	THE HANDS OF TIME	IT'S A SAD WORLD	60.00
66	9280	LEON HAYWOOD	AIN'T NO USE	HEY, HEY, HEY	40.00
66	9280 DJ	LEON HAYWOOD	AIN'T NO USE	HEY, HEY, HEY	70.00
66	9281	KAREN SMALL	THAT'S WHY I CRY	TO GET YOU BACK AGAIN	15.00
66	9281 DJ	KAREN SMALL	THAT'S WHY I CRY	TO GET YOU BACK AGAIN	25.00
67	9285	RODGER COLLINS	SHE'S LOOKING GOOD	I'M SERVING TIME	15.00
67	9285 DJ	RODGER COLLINS	SHE'S LOOKING GOOD	I'M SERVING TIME	50.00
67	9287	SEEDS	CAN'T SEEM TO MAKE YOU MINE	DAISY MAE	30.00
67	9287 DJ	SEEDS	CAN'T SEEM TO MAKE YOU MINE	DAISY MAE	40.00
67	9288	LEON HAYWOOD	SKATE A WHILE	EVER SINCE YOU WERE SWEET SIXTEEN	25.00
67	9288 DJ	LEON HAYWOOD	SKATE A WHILE	EVER SINCE YOU WERE SWEET SIXTEEN	**55.00**
68	9290	TOMMY NEAL	GOIN' TO A HAPPENING	TEE TA	40.00
68	9290 DJ	TOMMY NEAL	GOIN' TO A HAPPENING	TEE TA	**214.00**
64	170153 EP PS	BOBBY BLAND	BOBBY BLAND	1964 4 track EP with cover	60.00
64	170154 EP PS	JAMES BOOKER	GONZO	1964 4 track EP with cover	75.00
64	170155 EP PS	LITTLE RICHARD	MEMPHIS SLIM and LITTLE RICHARD	1964 4 track EP with cover	75.00
66	170158 EP PS	JIMMY WITHERSPOON	FEELING THE SPIRIT	1965 4 track EP with cover	25.00
66	170159 EP PS	JIMMY WITHERSPOON	FEELING THE SPIRIT vol. 2	1966 4 track EP with cover	25.00
65	170160 EP PS	JIMMY McCRACKLIN	JIMMY McCRACKLIN	1965 4 track EP with cover	100.00

65	170162 EP PS	JOHNNY OTIS	JOHNNY OTIS	1965 4 track EP with cover	100.00
65	170163 EP PS	AL TNT BRAGGS	AL "TNT" BRAGGS	1965 4 track EP with cover	75.00
66	170165 EP PS	O.V.WRIGHT	CAN'T FIND TRUE LOVE	1966 4 track EP with cover	150.00

VOGUE

61	1269 EP PS	JIMMY WITHERSPOON	JIMMY WITHERSPOON AT MONTEREY	1961 EP with cover	30.00
61	1270 EP PS	JIMMY WITHERSPOON	JIMMY WITHERSPOON AT MONTEREY # 2	1961 EP with cover	30.00
60	2417	LES McCANN LTD.	FISH THIS WEEK	VAKUSHNA	6.00
62	2420	JIMMY WITHERSPOON	WHEN THE LIGHTS GO OUT	ALL THAT'S GOOD	40.00
61	9175	WALLY COX	I CAN'T HELP IT	THE HEEBIE JEEBEES	20.00
61	9177	JAMES BOOKER	GONZO	COOL TURKEY	40.00
61	9178	BOBBY BLAND	CRY CRY CRY	I'VE BEEN WRONG SO LONG	30.00
61	9179	LITTLE JUNIOR PARKER	I'LL FORGET ABOUT YOU	STAND BY ME	30.00
61	9180	JOHNNY ACE	PLEDGING MY LOVE	ANYMORE	85.00
61	9182	BOBBY BLAND	LEAD ME ON	HOLD ME TENDERLY	30.00
61	9185	MARATHONS	PEANUT BUTTER	TALKIN' TRASH	20.0
61	9188	BOBBY BLAND	DON'T CRY NO MORE	ST. JAMES INFIRMARY	30.0
62	9190	BOBBY BLAND	TURN ON YOUR LOVELIGHT	(YOU'RE THE ONE) THAT I NEED	30.00
62	9192	BOBBY BLAND	BLUE MOON	WHO WILL THE NEXT FOOL BE	40.00
62	9193	LITTLE JUNIOR PARKER	MARY JO	ANNIE GET YOUR YO-YO	30.00

VOGUE CORAL

57	72290	JACKIE WILSON	REET PETITE	BY THE LIGHT OF THE SILVERY MOON	25.00

VOGUE POP

60	9174	OLYMPICS	I WISH I COULD SHIMMY LIKE MY SISTER	WORKIN' HARD	15.00
61	9181	OLYMPICS	DANCE WITH A DOLLY	DIDGE CITY	15.00
61	9184	OLYMPICS c/w CAPPY LEWIS	LITTLE PEDRO	BULL FIGHT	20.00
62	9196	OLYMPICS	EVERYBODY LIKES TO CHA CHA CHA	THE TWIST	15.00
62	9198	OLYMPICS	THE STOMP	MASH THEM 'TATERS	15.00
62	9204	OLYMPICS	BABY IT'S HOT	THE SCOTCH	15.00

VULCAN

75	1005	CIMARONS	WICKY WACKY	TRADITION	30.00

WA RECORDS

88	1 PS	RICK CLARKE	I'LL SEE YOU ALONG THE WAY	same: (dance mix)	6.00

WAND

71	14	KINGSMEN	LOUIE LOUIE	IF I NEEDED SOMEONE	8.00
71	14 DJ	KINGSMEN	LOUIE LOUIE	IF I NEEDED SOMEONE	8.00
71	17	LLOYD PRICE	HJOOKED ON A FEELING	IF YO REALLY LOVE ME	5.00
71	17 DJ	LLOYD PRICE	HJOOKED ON A FEELING	IF YO REALLY LOVE ME	6.00
71	18	BEVERLEY BREMERS	GET SMART GIRL	DON'T SAY YOU DON'T REMEMBER	10.00
71	18 DJ	BEVERLEY BREMERS	GET SMART GIRL	DON'T SAY YOU DON'T REMEMBER	15.00
71	21	LLOYD PRICE	MR. & MRS. UNTRUE	NATURAL SINNER	5.00
71	21 DJ	LLOYD PRICE	MR. & MRS. UNTRUE	NATURAL SINNER	6.00
72	26	RONNIE MILSAP	AIN'T NO SOUL (LEFT IN THESE OLE SHOES)	ANOTHER BRANCH FROM THE OLD TREE	10.00
72	26 DJ	RONNIE MILSAP	AIN'T NO SOUL (LEFT IN THESE OLE SHOES)	ANOTHER BRANCH FROM THE OLD TREE	15.00
72	27	ROSCO ROBINSON	THAT'S ENOUGH	ONE MORE TIME	10.00
72	27 DJ	ROSCO ROBINSON	THAT'S ENOUGH	ONE MORE TIME	20.00
72	29	INDEPENDANTS	JUST AS LONG AS YOU NEED ME	same: part 2	5.00
72	29 DJ	INDEPENDANTS	JUST AS LONG AS YOU NEED ME	same: part 2	5.00
72	31	SHIRELLES	WILL YOU STILL LOVE ME TOMORROW	DEDICATED TO THE ONE I LOVE	4.00
72	31 DJ	SHIRELLES	WILL YOU STILL LOVE ME TOMORROW	DEDICATED TO THE ONE I LOVE	4.00

WANTED

78	101	JIMMY CROSS	I WANT MY BABY BACK	PLAY THE OTHER SIDE	6.00
78	101 PS	JIMMY CROSS	I WANT MY BABY BACK	PLAY THE OTHER SIDE	8.00

WARNER BROS

Up to release #8000, this label was distributed throughout the 60's in the UK by Pye International. As with other Pye associated labels like Hickory, Cameo Parkway, etc the company used the same number as the USA release. Ie: Bill Cosby – "Little Ole Man" - was released on both sides of the Atlantic on Warner Bros 7072, and surprisingly The Enchanters – "We Got Love" - was issued in the USA on LOMA 2054 and released in the UK on Warner Bros 2054. which could cause confusion, if ordering over the internet and it doesn't state the county of origin.

 One of the disappointments about this label, was its lack of interest in soul. When you consider it had the whole of the Loma catalogue to chose from and it only went with ten releases, you can see little or no effort was made to develop the catalogue in the UK. These shores, saw no Apollas releases, only two Linda Jones's and there could have been a Larry Laster, Kell Osbourne, Ben Aiken on UK white demos, the mouth waters at the prospect. So unfortunately Warner Bros failed in its task to introduce the British music fan to it's fair share of sixties USA soul.

But there are highlights along the way: The classy vocal of Johnny Nash's appealing early Warners recordings. Plus obscure groups, such as The Socialites with a solid Northern Soul dancer. Cajun Hart with their pop soul dancer that changes hands, for ever increasing sums. Interesting and collectable label, but for soul collectors it certainly under performed with the releases it put out.

60	21	ED TOWNSEND	STAY WITH ME (A LITTLE WHILE	I LOVE EVERYTHING ABOUT YOU	30.00
60	21 DJ	ED TOWNSEND	STAY WITH ME (A LITTLE WHILE	I LOVE EVERYTHING ABOUT YOU	40.00
61	32	BILL DOGGETT	THE HULLY GULLY	JACKRABBIT	6.00
61	32 DJ	BILL DOGGETT	THE HULLY GULLY	JACKRABBIT	10.00
61	46	BILL DOGGETT	YOU CAN'T SIT DOWN	YOU CAN'T SIT DOWN part 2	10.00
61	46 DJ	BILL DOGGETT	YOU CAN'T SIT DOWN	YOU CAN'T SIT DOWN part 2	15.00
62	63	CONNIE STEVENS	WHY'S YOU WANNA MAKE ME CRY	JUST ONE KISS	15.00
62	63 DJ	CONNIE STEVENS	WHY'S YOU WANNA MAKE ME CRY	JUST ONE KISS	22.00
62	65	JOHNNY NASH	MOMENT OF WEAKNESS	DON'T TAKE AWAY YOUR LOVE	25.00
62	65 DJ	JOHNNY NASH	MOMENT OF WEAKNESS	DON'T TAKE AWAY YOUR LOVE	35.00
62	76	JOHNNY NASH	OLD MAN RIVER	MY DEAR LITTLE SWEETNESS	30.00
62	76 DJ	JOHNNY NASH	OLD MAN RIVER	MY DEAR LITTLE SWEETNESS	45.00
63	93	JOHNNY NASH	I'M MOVING ON	CIGARETTES, WHISKEY AND WILD WOMEN	20.00
63	93 DJ	JOHNNY NASH	I'M MOVING ON	CIGARETTES, WHISKEY AND WILD WOMEN	28.00
64	120	MARKETTS	BELLA DALENA	OUT OF LIMITS	15.00

64	120 DJ	MARKETTS	BELLA DALENA	OUT OF LIMITS	30.00
64	125	RAMONA KING	IT'S IN HISS KISS	IT COULDN'T HAPPEN TO A NICER	20.00
64	125 DJ	RAMONA KING	IT'S IN HISS KISS	IT COULDN'T HAPPEN TO A NICER	30.00
64	130	MARKETTS	VANISHING POINT	BOREALIS	8.00
64	130 DJ	MARKETTS	VANISHING POINT	BOREALIS	10.00
64	148	SOCIALITES	YOU'RE LOSING YOUR TOUCH	JIVE JIMMY	85.00
64	148 DJ	SOCIALITES	YOU'RE LOSING YOUR TOUCH	JIVE JIMMY	100.00
65	153	IKE & TINA TURNER	FINGERPOPIN'	OOH POO PAH DOO	20.00
65	153 DJ	IKE & TINA TURNER	FINGERPOPIN'	OOH POO PAH DOO	30.00
65	157	OLYMPICS	OLYMPIC SHUFFLE	GOOD LOVIN'	20.00
65	157 DJ	OLYMPICS	OLYMPIC SHUFFLE	GOOD LOVIN'	30.00
65	619 EP PS	IKE & TINA TURNER	IKE AND TINA TURNER SHOW	4 track EP with pic cover	45.00
67	620 EP PS	IKE & TINA TURNER	SOMEBODY NEEDS YOU	4 track EP with pic cover	75.00
67	2054	ENCHANTERS	WE GOT LOVE	I'VE LOST ASLL COMMUNICATIONS	25.00
67	2054 DJ	ENCHANTERS	WE GOT LOVE	I'VE LOST ASLL COMMUNICATIONS	40.00
67	2070	LINDA JONES	I CAN'T STOP LOVIN' MY BABY	HYPNOTIZED	75.00
67	2070 DJ	LINDA JONES	I CAN'T STOP LOVIN' MY BABY	HYPNOTIZED	100.00
67	2075	ROY REDMOND	THAT OLD TIME FEELING	GOOD DAY SUNSHINE	20.00
67	2075 DJ	ROY REDMOND	THAT OLD TIME FEELING	GOOD DAY SUNSHINE	30.00
67	2082	J.J.JACKSON	SHO NUFF (GOT A GOOD THING GOING)	HERE WE GO AGAIN	15.00
67	2082 DJ	J.J.JACKSON	SHO NUFF (GOT A GOOD THING GOING)	HERE WE GO AGAIN	30.00
67	2090	J.J.JACKSON	DOWN, BUT NOT OUT	WHY DOES IT TAKES SO LONG	10.00
67	2090 DJ	J.J.JACKSON	DOWN, BUT NOT OUT	WHY DOES IT TAKES SO LONG	20.00
67	2094	LORRAINE ELLISON	IN MY TOMORROW	TRY (JUST A LITTLE BIT HARDER)	8.00
67	2094 DJ	LORRAINE ELLISON	IN MY TOMORROW	TRY (JUST A LITTLE BIT HARDER)	10.00
66	5646	NANCY WAYBURN	THE WORLD GOES ON WITHOUT ME	LISTEN TO MY HEART CRY	20.00
66	5646 DJ	NANCY WAYBURN	THE WORLD GOES ON WITHOUT ME	LISTEN TO MY HEART CRY	30.00
66	5696	MARKETTS	THE BATMAN'S THEME	RICHIE'S THEME	10.00
66	5696 DJ	MARKETTS	THE BATMAN'S THEME	RICHIE'S THEME	15.00
66	5753	IKE & TINA TURNER	FINGER POPPIN'	TELL HER I'M NOT HOME	15.00
66	5753 DJ	IKE & TINA TURNER	FINGER POPPIN'	TELL HER I'M NOT HOME	28.00
66	5766	IKE & TINA TURNER	SOMEBODY (SOMEWHERE) NEEDS YOU	(I'LL DO ANYTHING) JUST TO BE WITH YOU	**110.00**
66	5766 DJ	IKE & TINA TURNER	SOMEBODY (SOMEWHERE) NEEDS YOU	(I'LL DO ANYTHING) JUST TO BE WITH YOU	150.00
66	5847	MARKETTS	STIRRIN' UP SOME SOUL	TARZAN (TARZAN'S MARCH)	50.00
66	5847 DJ	MARKETTS	STIRRIN' UP SOME SOUL	TARZAN (TARZAN'S MARCH)	100.00
66	5850	LORRAINE ELLISON	I'VE GOT MY BABY BACK	STAY WITH ME	10.00
66	5850 DJ	LORRAINE ELLISON	I'VE GOT MY BABY BACK	STAY WITH ME	30.00
66	6029	J.J.JACKSON	COURAGE AIN'T STRENGTH	YOU DID IT CAUSE YOU WANNA	10.00
66	6029 DJ	J.J.JACKSON	COURAGE AIN'T STRENGTH	YOU DID IT CAUSE YOU WANNA	22.00
66	6059	BOB AND EARL	EVERYBODY JERK	HE'S A PLAYBROTHER	10.00
66	6059 DJ	BOB AND EARL	EVERYBODY JERK	HE'S A PLAYBROTHER	20.00
71	6125	EARTH, WIND & FIRE	HELP SOMEBODY	LOVE IS LIFE	5.00
71	6125 DJ	EARTH, WIND & FIRE	HELP SOMEBODY	LOVE IS LIFE	6.00
67	7072	BILL COSBY	LITTLE OLE MAN (UPTIGHT EVERYTHING)	DON'CHA KNOW	50.00
67	7072 PS	BILL COSBY	LITTLE OLE MAN (UPTIGHT EVERYTHING)	DON'CHA KNOW	70.00
67	7072 DJ	BILL COSBY	LITTLE OLE MAN (UPTIGHT EVERYTHING)	DON'CHA KNOW	75.00
68	7096	BILL COSBY	HOORAY FOR THE SALVATION ARMY	URSALENA	5.00
68	7096 DJ	BILL COSBY	HOORAY FOR THE SALVATION ARMY	URSALENA	8.00
68	7190	MASON WILLIAMS	CLASSICAL GAS	LONG TIME BLUES	8.00
68	7190 DJ	MASON WILLIAMS	CLASSICAL GAS	LONG TIME BLUES	15.00
69	7250	CHARLES WRIGHT& WATTS 103	DO YOUR THING	A DANCE, A KISS AND A SONG	10.00
69	7250 DJ	WATTS 103rd. ST. RHYTHM	DO YOUR THING	A DANCE, A KISS AND A SONG	15.00
69	7238	CAJUN HART	GOT TO FIND MY WAY	LOVER'S PRAYER	**251.00**
69	7238 DJ	CAJUN HART	GOT TO FIND MY WAY	LOVER'S PRAYER	**304.00**
05	7258 DJ	LINDA JONES c/w CAJUN HART	A LAST MINUTE MIRACLE	GOT TO FIND MY WAY	15.00

Promo copies only, pressed to promote the 2005 "After Hours vol. 3" CD release.

69	7276	J.J. JACKSON	BUT IT'S ALRIGHT	AIN'T TOO PROUD TO BEG	10.00
69	7276 DJ	J.J. JACKSON	BUT IT'S ALRIGHT	AIN'T TOO PROUD TO BEG	40.00
69	7298	CHARLES WRIGHT& WATTS 103	LIGHT MY FIRE	TILL YOU GET ENOUGH	10.00
69	7298 DJ	CHARLES WRIGHT& WATTS 103	LIGHT MY FIRE	TILL YOU GET ENOUGH	12.00
70	7358	HERBIE HANCOCK	FAT MAMA	WIGGLE-WAGGLE	8.00
70	7358 DJ	HERBIE HANCOCK	FAT MAMA	WIGGLE-WAGGLE	10.00
70	7365	CHARLES WRIGHT& WATTS 103	LOVE LAND	SORRY CHARLIE	10.00
70	7365 DJ	CHARLES WRIGHT& WATTS 103	LOVE LAND	SORRY CHARLIE	15.00
70	7394	LORRAINE ELLISON	YOU'VE EALLY GOT A HOLD ON ME	YOU DON'T KNOW NOTHING ABOUT LOVE	10.00
70	7394 DJ	LORRAINE ELLISON	YOU'VE EALLY GOT A HOLD ON ME	YOU DON'T KNOW NOTHING ABOUT LOVE	18.00
70	7417	CHARLES WRIGHT& WATTS 103	EXPRESS YOURSELF	LIVING ON BORROWED TIME	20.00
70	7417 DJ	CHARLES WRIGHT& WATTS 103	EXPRESS YOURSELF	LIVING ON BORROWED TIME	28.00
70	7434	VAN MORRISON	DOMINO	SWEET JANNIE	20.00
70	7434 DJ	VAN MORRISON	DOMINO	SWEET JANNIE	40.00
70	8000	JOHNNY HARRIS ORCHESTRA	LULU'S THEME	FOOTPRINTS ON THE MOON	10.00
70	8000 DJ	JOHNNY HARRIS ORCHESTRA	LULU'S THEME	FOOTPRINTS ON THE MOON	20.00
85	9014	GEORGE BENSON	BEYOND THE SEA	BREEZIN'	4.00
85	9014 DJ	GEORGE BENSON	BEYOND THE SEA	BREEZIN'	5.00
83	9510	LARRY GRAHAM	I'M SICK AND TIRED	VICTORY	5.00
83	9510 DJ	LARRY GRAHAM	I'M SICK AND TIRED	VICTORY	6.00
83	9551 PS	GEORGE BENSON	FEEL LIKE MAKING LOVE	USE ME	4.00
83	9551 DJ	GEORGE BENSON	FEEL LIKE MAKING LOVE	USE ME	5.00
72	16001	LORRAINE ELLISON	STAY WITH ME	I'VE GOT MY BABY BACK	5.00
72	16001 DJ	LORRAINE ELLISON	STAY WITH ME	I'VE GOT MY BABY BACK	6.00
72	16011	MASON WILLIAMS	CLASSICAL GAS	LONG TIME BLUES	5.00
72	16011 DJ	MASON WILLIAMS	CLASSICAL GAS	LONG TIME BLUES	6.00
72	16190	TOWER OF POWER	DOWN TO THE NIGHTCLUB	YOU GOT TO FUNKIFIZE	5.00
72	16190 DJ	TOWER OF POWER	DOWN TO THE NIGHTCLUB	YOU GOT TO FUNKIFIZE	6.00
72	16211	TOWER OF POWER	YOU'RE STILL A YOUNG MAN	SKATING ON THIN ICE	4.00
72	16211 DJ	TOWER OF POWER	YOU'RE STILL A YOUNG MAN	SKATING ON THIN ICE	6.00
73	16265	MYSTIC MOODS	COSMIC SEA	THE AWAKENING	10.00

73	16265 DJ	MYSTIC MOODS	COSMIC SEA	THE AWAKENING	15.00
73	16278	TOWER OF POWER	SO VERY HARD TO GO	CLEAN SKATE	8.00
73	16278 DJ	TOWER OF POWER	SO VERY HARD TO GO	CLEAN SLATE	15.00
73	16282	PAUL KELLY	COME LAY SOME LOVIN' ON ME	COME BY HERE	4.00
73	16282 DJ	PAUL KELLY	COME LAY SOME LOVIN' ON ME	COME BY HERE	5.00
73	16291	BOBBY BYRD	TRY IT AGAIN	I'M ON THE MOVE	6.00
73	16291 DJ	BOBBY BYRD	TRY IT AGAIN	I'M ON THE MOVE	8.00
73	16312	LOU RAGLAND	SINCE YOU SAID YOU'D BE MINE	I DIDN'T MEAN TO LEAVE YOU	75.00
73	16312 DJ	LOU RAGLAND	SINCE YOU SAID YOU'D BE MINE	I DIDN'T MEAN TO LEAVE YOU	100.00
73	16333	LALO SCHIFRIN	THEME FROM ENTER THE DRAGON	THE BIG BATTLE	6.00
73	16333 DJ	LALO SCHIFRIN	THEME FROM ENTER THE DRAGON	THE BIG BATTLE	8.00
73	16334	MAJOR LANCE	SWEETER	WILD AND FREE	10.00
73	16334 DJ	MAJOR LANCE	SWEETER	WILD AND FREE	15.00
74	16346	BILL COSBY	LITTLE OLE MAN (UPTIGHT EVERYTHING)	DON'CHA KNOW	6.00
74	16346 DJ	BILL COSBY	LITTLE OLE MAN (UPTIGHT EVERYTHING)	DON'CHA KNOW	15.00
74	16373	ASHFORD AND SIMPSON	HAVE YOU EVER TRIED IT	TIME	15.00
74	16373 DJ	ASHFORD AND SIMPSON	HAVE YOU EVER TRIED IT	TIME	20.00
74	16385	MAJOR LANCE	WITHOUT A DOUBT	OPEN THE DOOR TO YOUR HEART	20.00
74	16385 DJ	MAJOR LANCE	WITHOUT A DOUBT	OPEN THE DOOR TO YOUR HEART	25.00
74	16389	TOWER OF POWER	DON'T CHANGE HORSES (IN THE MIDDLE)	TIME WILL TELL	5.00
74	16389 DJ	TOWER OF POWER	DON'T CHANGE HORSES (IN THE MIDDLE)	TIME WILL TELL	6.00
74	16395	JAY DEE	STRANGE FUNKY GAMES AND THINGS	same: instrumental	6.00
74	16395 DJ	JAY DEE	STRANGE FUNKY GAMES AND THINGS	same: instrumental	8.00
74	16426	TERRY COLLINS	I L.O.V.E. Y.O.U.	ACTION SPEAKS LOUDER THAN WORDS	10.00
74	16426 DJ	TERRY COLLINS	I L.O.V.E. Y.O.U.	ACTION SPEAKS LOUDER THAN WORDS	15.00
74	16435	WATTS 103rd. ST. RHYTHM	BROWN SUGAR	THE JOKER (ON A TRIP THRU THE JUNGLE)	6.00
74	16435 DJ	WATTS 103rd. ST. RHYTHM	BROWN SUGAR	THE JOKER (ON A TRIP THRU THE JUNGLE)	10.00
74	16441	ASHFORD & SIMPSON	MAIN LINE	DON'T FIGHT IT	6.00
74	16441 DJ	ASHFORD & SIMPSON	MAIN LINE	DON'T FIGHT IT	10.00
75	16465	ROSALIND CLARK	NIGHTOWL	STUMBLE AND FALL	6.00
75	16465 DJ	ROSALIND CLARK	NIGHTOWL	STUMBLE AND FALL	8.00
75	16506	GRAHAM CENTRAL STATION	FEEL THE NEED ME	WE BE'S GETTIN' DOWN	6.00
75	16506 DJ	GRAHAM CENTRAL STATION	FEEL THE NEED ME	WE BE'S GETTIN' DOWN	8.00
75	16530	DIONNE WARWICKE	TAKE IT FROM ME	SURE THING	10.00
75	16530 DJ	DIONNE WARWICKE	TAKE IT FROM ME	SURE THING	15.00
75	16536	LEROY HUTSON	ALL BECAUSE OF YOU	same: instrumental	10.00
75	16536 DJ	LEROY HUTSON	ALL BECAUSE OF YOU	same: instrumental	15.00
75	16543	TOWER OF POWER	ONLY SO MUCH OIL IN THE GROUND	IT'S NOT THE GRIME	6.00
75	16543 DJ	TOWER OF POWER	ONLY SO MUCH OIL IN THE GROUND	IT'S NOT THE GRIME	8.00
75	16559	DOOBIE BROTHERS	TAKE ME IN YOUR ARMS (ROCK ME A LITLE WHILE	SLAT KEY SOQUEL RAG	4.00
75	16559 DJ	DOOBIE BROTHERS	TAKE ME IN YOUR ARMS (ROCK ME A LITLE WHILE	SLAT KEY SOQUEL RAG	5.00
75	16563	IMPRESSIONS	SOONER OR LATER	MIRACLE WOMAN	10.00
75	16563 DJ	IMPRESSIONS	SOONER OR LATER	MIRACLE WOMAN	15.00
75	16588	MIKE POST COALITION	AFTERNOON OF THE RHINO	BUBBLEGUM BREAKTHROUGH	10.00
75	16588 DJ	MIKE POST COALITION	AFTERNOON OF THE RHINO	BUBBLEGUM BREAKTHROUGH	15.00
75	16619	REALISTICS	PUTTING IT DOWN (TO THE WAY I FEEL	APRIL FOOL CONNECTION	75.00
75	16619 DJ	REALISTICS	PUTTING IT DOWN (TO THE WAY I FEEL	APRIL FOOL CONNECTION	85.00
75	16621	LINDA JONES	I JUST CAN'T LIVE MY LIFE	MY HEART (WILL UNDERSTAND)	30.00
75	16621 DJ	LINDA JONES	I JUST CAN'T LIVE MY LIFE	MY HEART (WILL UNDERSTAND)	45.00
75	16644	WINNERS CIRCLE	BORN A STAR	same: disco version	10.00
75	16644 DJ	WINNERS CIRCLE	BORN A STAR	same: disco version	12.00
75	16677	DIONNE WARWICK	ONCE YOU HIT THE ROAD	WORLD OF MY DREAMS	10.00
75	16677 DJ	DIONNE WARWICK	ONCE YOU HIT THE ROAD	WORLD OF MY DREAMS	15.00
76	16714	QUICKEST WAY OUT	THANK YOU BABY FOR LOVING ME	SAD LOVE SONG	5.00
76	16714 DJ	QUICKEST WAY OUT	THANK YOU BABY FOR LOVING ME	SAD LOVE SONG	6.00
76	16730	CANDI STATON	YOUNG HEARTS RUN FREE	I KNOW	8.00
76	16730 DJ	CANDI STATON	YOUNG HEARTS RUN FREE	I KNOW	10.00
76	16796	GEORGE BENSON	BREEZIN'	LADY	4.00
76	16796 DJ	GEORGE BENSON	BREEZIN'	LADY	5.00
76	16804	UNDISPUTED TRUTH	YOU + ME = LOVE	same: instrumental	6.00
76	16804 DJ	UNDISPUTED TRUTH	YOU + ME = LOVE	same: instrumental	8.00
77	16942	LAMONT DOZIER	GOING BACK TO MY ROOTS	GOING BACK TO MY ROOTS part 2	6.00
77	16942 DJ	LAMONT DOZIER	GOING BACK TO MY ROOTS	GOING BACK TO MY ROOTS part 2	8.00
77	16972	CANDI STATON	NIGHTS ON BROADWAY	YOU ARE	4.00
77	16972 DJ	CANDI STATON	NIGHTS ON BROADWAY	YOU ARE	6.00
78	17070	LAMONT DOZIER	SIGHT FOR SORE EYES	TEAR DOWN THE WALLS	5.00
78	17070 DJ	LAMONT DOZIER	SIGHT FOR SORE EYES	TEAR DOWN THE WALLS	6.00
78	17120	GEORGE BENSON	ON BROADWAY	WE AS LOVE	8.00
78	17120 DJ	GEORGE BENSON	ON BROADWAY	WE AS LOVE	10.00
78	17164	CANDI STATON	HONEST I DO LOVE YOU	SO BLUE	4.00
78	17164 DJ	CANDI STATON	HONEST I DO LOVE YOU	SO BLUE	5.00
78	17173	ETTA JAMES	(TAKE ANOTHER LITTLE) PIECE OF MY HEART	LOVESICK BLUES	4.00
78	17173 DJ	ETTA JAMES	(TAKE ANOTHER LITTLE) PIECE OF MY HEART	LOVESICK BLUES	5.00
78	17196	BOOTSY'S RUBBER BAND	BOOTZILLA	HOLLYWOOD SQUARES	5.00
78	17196 DJ	BOOTSY'S RUBBER BAND	BOOTZILLA	HOLLYWOOD SQUARES	6.00
78	17246	FUNKADELIC	ONE NATION UNDER A GROOVE	ONE NATION UNDER A GROOVE pt 2	5.00
78	17246 DJ	FUNKADELIC	ONE NATION UNDER A GROOVE	ONE NATION UNDER A GROOVE pt 2	6.00
78	17269	CHAKA KHAN	I'M EVERY WOMAN	A WOMAN IN A MAN'S WORLD	4.00
78	17269 DJ	CHAKA KHAN	I'M EVERY WOMAN	A WOMAN IN A MAN'S WORLD	5.00
79	17321	FUNKADELIC	CHOLLY (FUNK GETTING READY TO	INTO YOU	5.00
79	17321 DJ	FUNKADELIC	CHOLLY (FUNK GETTING READY TO	INTO YOU	6.00
79	17345	ASHFORD & SIMPSON	FLASHBACK	GET UP AND DO SOMETHING	4.00
79	17345 DJ	ASHFORD & SIMPSON	FLASHBACK	GET UP AND DO SOMETHING	5.00
79	17345 pic disc	ASHFORD & SIMPSON	FLASHBACK	GET UP AND DO SOMETHING	5.00
79	17494	FUNKADELIC	(NOT JUST) KNEE DEEP	(NOT JUST) KNEE DEEP part 2	4.00
79	17494 DJ	FUNKADELIC	(NOT JUST) KNEE DEEP	(NOT JUST) KNEE DEEP part 2	5.00
80	17550	NICOLETTE LARSON	BACK IN MY ARMS AGAIN	TROUBLE	4.00

80	17550 DJ	NICOLETTE LARSON	BACK IN MY ARMS AGAIN	TROUBLE	5.00
80	17673	GEORGE BENSON	GIVE ME THE NIGHT	DINORAH, DINORAH	4.00
80	17673 DJ	GEORGE BENSON	GIVE ME THE NIGHT	DINORAH, DINORAH	5.00
70	17699	GEORGE BENSON	LOVE X LOVE	OFF BROADWAY	4.00
70	17699 DJ	GEORGE BENSON	LOVE X LOVE	OFF BROADWAY	5.00
81	17786	FUNKADELIC	THE ELECTRIC SPANKING OF THE WAR	same: instrumental	4.00
81	17786 DJ	FUNKADELIC	THE ELECTRIC SPANKING OF THE WAR	same: instrumental	5.00
81	17810	MASON WILLIAMS	CLASSICAL GAS	GREENSLEVES	4.00
81	17810 DJ	MASON WILLIAMS	CLASSICAL GAS	GREENSLEVES	6.00
81	17877	GEORGE BENSON	NEVER GIVE UP ON A GOOD THING	CALIFORNIA PM	4.00
81	17877 DJ	GEORGE BENSON	NEVER GIVE UP ON A GOOD THING	CALIFORNIA PM	5.00
81	17902 PS	GEORGE BENSON	NEVER GIVE UP ON A GOOD THING	CALIFORNIA P.M.	4.00
81	17902 DJ	GEORGE BENSON	NEVER GIVE UP ON A GOOD THING	CALIFORNIA P.M.	5.00
81	17925	LARRY GRAHAM	ONE IN A MILLION YOU	SOONER OR LATER	4.00
81	17925 DJ	LARRY GRAHAM	ONE IN A MILLION YOU	SOONER OR LATER	5.00
81	17935	ATKINS	FEEL IT, DON'T FIGHT IT	LOVE IS GROWING STRONGER	4.00
81	17935 DJ	ATKINS	FEEL IT, DON'T FIGHT IT	LOVE IS GROWING STRONGER	5.00
81	17961	MARC SADANE	ONE MINUTE FROM LOVE	NEVER HAD A LOVE LIKE YOU	10.00
81	17961 DJ	MARC SADANE	ONE MINUTE FROM LOVE	NEVER HAD A LOVE LIKE YOU	12.00
02	49059 DJ	ALICE CLARK c/w HARVEY AVERNE	YOU HIT ME (RIGHT WHERE IT HURT ME)	THINK IT OVER	15.00
03	67855 DJ	BOBBY SHEEN c/w BEN E. KING	SOMETHING NEW TO DO	CAN'T BREAK THE NEWS TO MYSELF	8.00

WARNER SPECTOR

74	19010	CRYSTALS	DA DOO RON RON	AND THEN HE KISSED ME	6.00
74	19010 blue vinyl	CRYSTALS	DA DOO RON RON	THEN HE KISSED ME	8.00
74	19011	DARLENE LOVE	CHRISTMAS (BABY PLEASE COME HOME)	WAIT TILL MY BOBBY COMES HOME	4.00
74	19011 blue vinyl	DARLENE LOVE	CHRISTMAS (BABY PLEASE COME HOME)	WAIT TILL MY BOBBY COMES HOME	6.00

WEA

84	7 PS	CHANGE	SEARCHING	CHANGE OF HEART	3.00
84	14 PS	CHANGE	THE GLOW OF LOVE	YOU ARE MY MELODY	4.00
84	27	JACKIE VERDELL	CAN I GET A WITNESS	WHEN THE SAINTS GO MARCHING IN	5.00
81	18867 PS	DUKES	MYSTERY GIRL	MY SIMPLE HEART	15.00
80	79141	CHANGE	THE GLOW OF LOVE	A LOVER'S HOLIDAY	6.00
80	79156	CHANGE	SEARCHING	ANGEL IN MY POCKET	5.00
80	79156 DJ	CHANGE	SEARCHING	ANGEL IN MY POCKET	6.00
81	79196	CHANGE	PARADISE	YOUR MOVE	4.00
82	79300 PS	CARLY SIMON c/w CHIC	WHY	WHY version	6.00

WESTBOUND

74	6146100	OHIO PLAYERS	FUNKY WORM	PAINT ME	6.00
74	6146102	DENISE LASALLE	DO ME RIGHT	YOUR MAN AND YOUR BEST FRIEND	20.00
74	6146103	DETROIT EMERALDS	YOU WANT IT, YOU GOT IT	WHAT'CHA GONNA WEAR TOMORROW	4.00
74	6146104	DETROIT EMERALDS	I THINK OF YOU	SO LONG	4.00
74	6146105	DENISE LASALLE	TRAPPED BY A THING CALLED LOVE	I'M FOR YOU	5.00
74	6146108	DETROIT EMERALDS	YOU'RE GETTING A LITTLE TOO SMART	LEE	5.00

WHITE LODGE

83	1 PS	DAVID EMMANUEL	GIVING IT UP FOR LOVE	STIR IT AROUND	20.00

WHITFIELD

Innovative Motown producer Norman Whitfield's label which came under the distribution umbrella of Kinney all release numbers are prefixed by a K.

76	16804	UNDISPUTED TRUTH	YOU + ME = LOVE	same: instrumental	6.00
77	16909	UNDISPUTED TRUTH	LET'S GO TO THE DISCO	A HOLE IN THE WALL	4.00
77	17006	ROSE ROYCE	DANCE YOUR DANCE	DANCE YOUR DANCE part 2	4.00
77	17060	ROSE ROYCE	WISHING ON A STAR	FUNK FACTORY	4.00
78	17148	ROSE ROYCE	IT MAKES ME FEEL LIKE DANCING	YOU'RE MY WORLD GIRL	4.00
78	17236	ROSE ROYCE	LOVE DON'T LIVE HERE ANYMORE	DO IT, DO IT	4.00
79	17318	WILLIE HUTCH	COME ON AND DANCE WITH ME	EASY DOES IT	4.00
79	17347	ROSE ROYCE	ANGEL IN THE SKY	HELP	4.00
79	17456	ROSE ROYCE	IS IT LOVE YOU'RE AFTER	YOU CAN'T RUN AWAY FROM YOURSE	4.00
79	17463	ROSE ROYCE	I WONDER WHERE YOU ARE TONIGHT	YOU CAN'T RUN AWAY FROM YOURSELF	4.00
79	17575 PS	ROSE ROYCE	OH BOY	WHAT YOU WAITING FOR	4.00
80	17674	ROSE ROYCE	POP YOUR FINGERS	I WONDER WHERE YOU ARE TONIGHT	4.00
81	17747	ROSE ROYCE	GOLDEN TOUCH	LOVE IS IN THE AIR	4.00

WIGAN CASINO

02	FULL SET	VARIOUS ARTISTS	10 x 45s complete with SPECIAL BOX	ALL SINGLES IN PICTURE SLEEVES	100.00
02	201 PS	PROFFESIONALS c/w SAM WARD	THAT'S WHY I LOVE YOU	SISTER LEE	8.00
02	202 PS	JACKEY BEAVERS c/w JOE MATTHEWS	I NEED MY BABY	SHE'S MY BEAUTY QUEEN	8.00
02	203 PS	LESTER TIPTONc/w AL WILLIAMS	THIS WON'T CHANGE	I AM NOTHING	8.00
02	204 PS	EDDIE HOLMAN c/w FOUR PERFECTIONS HURT		I'M NOT STRONG ENOUGH	8.00
02	205 PS	LEE ANDREWS c/w LARRY CLINTON	I'VE HAD IT	SHE WANTED	8.00
02	206 PS	AGENTS c/w LITTLE JOE COOK	TROUBLE	I'M FALLING IN LOVE WITH YOU BABY	8.00
02	207 PS	MARTHA STAR c/w EMANUEL LASKEY	LOVE IS THE ONLY SOLUTION	I'M A PEACE LOVIN' MAN	8.00
02	208 PS	DEE EDWARDS c/w DONI BURDICK	ALL THE WAY HOME	BARI TRACK	8.00
02	209 PS	GEORGE BLACKWELL c/w THE GROUP	CAN'T LOSE MY HEAD	I DON'T LIKE TO LOSE	8.00
02	210 PS	BETTY BOO c/w BELLES	SAY IT ISN'T SO	DON'T PRETEND	8.00

WMOT

77	10951	FAT LARRY'S BAND	CENTER CITY	NIGHTTIME BOOGIE	5.00

the above was issue on an Kinney distributed Atlantic release #

80	101	PHILLY CREAM	COWBOYS TO GIRLS	NO TIME LIKE NOW	4.00
80	103	BARBARA MASON	YES, I'M READY	ON AND OFF	5.00
80	104	FRANKIE SMITH	DOUBLE DUTCH BUS	DOUBLE DUTCH BUS part 2	4.00
81	479	BRANDI WELLS	WATCH OUT	YOU ARE MY LIFE	5.00
83	632 PS	FAT LARRY'S BAND	DON'T LET IT GO TO YOUR HEAD	NAUGHTY	8.00

YORK

72	513	LOVELACE WATKINS	GET READY	ANGEL SHE WAS LOVE	5.00
72	513 DJ	LOVELACE WATKINS	GET READY	ANGEL SHE WAS LOVE	6.00
73	202	CRYIN' SHAMES	I DON'T BELIEVE IT	I'M GONNA TELL THE WORLD	8.00
73	202 DJ	CRYIN' SHAMES	I DON'T BELIEVE IT	I'M GONNA TELL THE WORLD	10.00

YOUNGBLOOD

69	1005	MAC KISSOON	WEAR IT ON YOUR FACE	IN A DREAM	10.00
69	1005 DJ	MAC KISSOON	WEAR IT ON YOUR FACE	IN A DREAM	15.00
70	1013	PAINTBOX	GET READY FOR LOVE	CAN I GET TO KNOW YOU	8.00
70	1013 DJ	PAINTBOX	GET READY FOR LOVE	CAN I GET TO KNOW YOU	10.00
71	1023	JACK HAMMER	COLOUR COMBINATION	SWIM	15.00
71	1023 DJ	JACK HAMMER	COLOUR COMBINATION	SWIM	15.00
71	1028	MAC KISSOON and KATIE	SHOW ME	PIDGEON	4.00
71	1028 DJ	MAC KISSOON and KATIE	SHOW ME	PIDGEON	6.00
71	1029	PAINTBOX	GET READY FOR LOVE	CAN I GET TO KNOW YOU	6.00
71	1029 DJ	PAINTBOX	GET READY FOR LOVE	CAN I GET TO KNOW YOU	8.00
73	1060	MAC AND KATIE KISSOON	LOVE WILL KEEP US TOGETHER	I'M UP IN HEAVEN	4.00
74	1075	MAC AND KATIE KISSOON	I CARE ABOUT YOU	I FOUND MY FREEDOM	10.00
74	1075 DJ	MAC AND KATIE KISSOON	I CARE ABOUT YOU	I FOUND MY FREEDOM	15.00

ZE RECORDS

| 82 | 6808 PS | SWEET PEA ATKINSON | DON'T WALK AWAY | DANCE OR DIE | 8.00 |

ZELLA RECORDS

| 68 | studio acetate | JON FORD | YOU'VE GOT ME WHERE YOU WANT ME | YOU'RE ALL ALONE TONIGHT | **125.00** |

ZONOPHONE

| 82 | 38 | CARGO feat: DAVE COLLINS | HOLDING ON FOR LOVE | IT'S YOUR LOVE LOVE | 20.00 |

NOTES